THE NEW NATURAL HISTORY OF

MADAGASCAR

VOLUME 2

THE NEW NATURAL HISTORY OF

MADAGASCAR

VOLUME 2

EDITED BY STEVEN M. GOODMAN

SUBJECT EDITORS

Aristide Andrianarimisa, Amanda H. Armstrong, Andrew Cooke, Maarten De Wit, Jörg U. Ganzhorn, Laurent Gautier, Steven M. Goodman, Julia P. G. Jones, William L. Jungers, David W. Krause, Olivier Langrand, Porter Peter Lowry III, Paul A. Racey, Achille P. Raselimanana, Roger J. Safford, John S. Sparks, Melanie L. J. Stiassny, Pablo Tortosa, and Miguel Vences

PRINCETON UNIVERSITY PRESS

PRINCETON AND OXFORD

Published by Princeton University Press
41 William Street, Princeton, New Jersey 08540
6 Oxford Street, Woodstock, Oxfordshire OX20 1TR

press.princeton.edu

Library of Congress Cataloging-in-Publication Data
Names: Goodman, Steven M., editor. | Andrianarimisa, Aristide, editor.
Title: The new natural history of Madagascar / edited by Steven M. Goodman ; subject editors: Aristide Andrianarimisa [and sixteen others].
Description: Princeton : Princeton University Press, 2022. | Includes bibliographical references and index. | Contents: History of Scientific Exploration—Geology—Climate—Forest and Grassland Ecology—Human Ecology—Diversity, Evolutionary History, Transmission of Zoonotic Pathogens, and Other Infectious Microbes—Marine and Coastal Ecosystems—Plants—Invertebrates—Freshwater Fishes—Amphibians—Reptiles—Birds—Mammals—Conservation.
Identifiers: LCCN 2021048337 (print) | LCCN 2021048338 (ebook) | ISBN 9780691222622 (hardback) | ISBN 9780691229409 (ebook)
Subjects: LCSH: Natural history—Madagascar. | Biodiversity—Madagascar. | Biodiversity conservation—Madagascar.
Classification: LCC QH195.M2 N395 2022 (print) | LCC QH195.M2 (ebook) | DDC 508.691–dc23
LC record available at https://lccn.loc.gov/2021048337
LC ebook record available at https://lccn.loc.gov/2021048338

British Library Cataloging-in-Publication Data is available

Editorial: Robert Kirk and Megan Mendonça
Production Editorial: Kathleen Cioffi
Jacket Design: Wanda España
Production: Steven Sears
Publicity: Matthew Taylor and Caitlyn Robinson
Copyeditors: Amy K. Hughes, Laurel Anderton, Frances Cooper, Patricia Fogarty, Judith Hoffman, and Maia Vaswani
Typeset and Design: D & N Publishing, Wiltshire, UK

Jacket images:
Front of jacket: © Harald Schütz
Back of jacket: (Top left) P.-S. Gehring; (top right) H. Schütz; (bottom left) F. Glaw; (bottom right) H. Schütz; (center) C. Chen-Kraus

Publication of this book has been aided by Bioculture (Mauritius) Ltd., Ellis Goodman Family Foundation, Field Museum of Natural History (FMNH), Fondation pour les Aires Protégées et la Biodiversité de Madagascar (FAPBM), and Programme des Nations Unies pour le Développement (PNUD)

This book has been composed in Garamond Premier Pro and Brandon Grotesque
Printed on acid-free paper. ∞

Printed in Italy

10 9 8 7 6 5 4 3 2 1

CONTENTS

11. Amphibians

12. Reptiles

ABBREVIATIONS AND ACRONYMS

Over the years, there has been a remarkable—perhaps *daunting* is the correct word—proliferation of acronyms and abbreviations associated with governmental and nongovernmental organizations, projects and programs, protected areas, technical terms, and so forth, related to the natural history and conservation of the remaining natural habitats of Madagascar. Within each contribution, we have attempted to define these at first usage. To help uninitiated readers navigate through this near Babylon of acronyms and abbreviations, we present below a listing of the terms used in this book, including translations when appropriate from French and Malagasy to English.

ABC approximate Bayesian computation
ABFMP Antongil Bay Fisheries Co-Management Plan
ACAP Amphibian Conservation Action Plan
ACEP African Coelacanth Ecosystem Programme
ACLME Agulhas Current Large Marine Ecosystem
α-CoV *Alphacoronavirus*
ACSAM A Conservation Strategy for the Amphibians of Madagascar
AFD Agence Française de Développement
AFLP amplified fragment-length polymorphism
AFOLU Agriculture, Forestry, and Other Land Use
AFR100 African Forest Landscape Restoration Initiative
AFS allele frequency spectrum
AGERAS Appui à la Gestion Régionalisée et à l'Approche Spatiale (Support to Decentralized Management and the Ecoregional Approach)
ALD abbreviated larval development
ALOs *Arsenophonus*-like organisms
AMNH American Museum of Natural History
APMCs *aires protégées marines et côtières* (protected marine and coastal areas)
AMS accelerator mass spectrometry
AMT annual mean temperature
ANAE Association Nationale pour l'Action Environnementale (National Association for Environmental Action)
ANGAP Association Nationale pour la Gestion des Aires Protégées (National Association for the Management of Protected Areas; now **MNP**)
AOO area of occupancy
APG Angiosperm Phylogeny Group
APN Agents de Protection de la Nature (Nature Protection Agents)
ARDRA amplified ribosomal DNA restriction analysis; see **DNA**
ASCLME Agulhas and Somali Current Large Marine Ecosystems
ASE Association de Sauvegarde de l'Environnement (Association to Save the Environment)
AstVs astroviruses
AVHRR Advanced Very High Resolution Radiometer
AWG Angiosperm Working Group
AZA Association of Zoos and Aquariums
AZE Alliance for Zero Extinction

BCE before the Common Era
BCM Biodiversity Conservation Madagascar
β-CoV *Betacoronavirus*
Bd *Batrachochytrium dendrobatidis*
BIN barcode index number
BIOPAT Patrons for Biodiversity
BMNH British Museum (Natural History); now Natural History Museum, London (**NHMUK**)
BN-CCCREDD+ Bureau National des Changements Climatiques, du Carbone et de la REDD+ (National Office for Climate Change, Carbon, and Reduction of Emissions from Deforestation and Forest Degradation)
BNS basic necessity surveys
BOLD Barcode of Life Data System
BP years before present ("present" is taken to be the year 1950)
bp base pairs
BRD bycatch reduction devices
BS breeding stock
BSP Bayesian skyline plots
Bsal *Batrachochytrium salamandrivorans*

C3 Community Centered Conservation
CABI Centre for Agricultural Bioscience International
CAF Cadre d'Appui Forestier (Forestry Support Units)
CAFF/CORE Comité Ad Hoc pour la Faune et la Flore/Comité Organisationel pour la Recherche Environnementale (Ad Hoc Committee for Fauna and Flora/Organizational Committee for Environmental Research)
cal BP calibrated years before present
CAM crassulacean acid metabolism
CAMP Conservation Assessment and Management Plan (Evaluation et Plans de Gestion pour la Conservation)
CAS California Academy of Sciences
CAZ Corridor Ankeniheny-Zahamena (Ankeniheny-Zahamena Forested Corridor)
CBD Convention on Biological Diversity
CBOL Consortium for the Barcode of Life
CCBA Climate Community and Biodiversity Alliance
CCC Coelacanth Conservation Council (Conseil pour la Conservation du Cœlacanthe)
CCHFV Crimean-Congo Hemorrhagic Fever Virus
CDC Centers for Disease Control (USA)
CE Common Era
CEC Chytrid Emergency Cell (Cellule d'Urgence Chytride)
CEMES Cercle d'Etudes Multidisciplinaires pour l'Environnement et la Santé (Circle of Multidisciplinary Research for Environment and Health)
CEPF Critical Ecosystem Partnership Fund
CF constant frequency

CFM Community Forest Management (Gestion Communautaire des Forêts; see **TGRN**)
CFPF Centre de Formation Professionnelle Forestière (Professional Forestry Training Center; now **CNFEREF**)
CGP Comité de Gestion de la Pêche aux Poulpes (Octopus Fishing Management Committee)
CHIKV Chikungunya Virus
CHIRPS Climate Hazards InfraRed Precipitation with Station
CI Conservation International
CIBIO-InBIO Centro de Investigação em Biodiversidade e Recursos Genéticos (Research Centre in Biodiversity and Genetic Resources)
CIRAD Centre de Coopération Internationale en Recherche Agronomique pour le Développement (Agricultural Research Center for International Development)
CITES Convention on International Trade in Endangered Species of Wild Fauna and Flora (Convention sur le Commerce International des Espèces de Faune et de Flore Sauvages Menacées d'Extinction)
CJB Conservatoire et Jardin botaniques de la Ville de Genève
CM causal modeling
CMR capture-mark-recapture
CMS Convention on Migratory Species
CMU Crocodile Management Unit
CNA Conservation Needs Assessment
CNARP Centre National d'Application des Recherches Pharmaceutiques (National Center for the Application of Pharmaceutical Research)
CNFEREF Centre National de Formation, d'Etudes et de Recherche en Environnement et Foresterie (formerly **CFPF**) (National Center for Training, Studies, and Research in Environment and Forestry)
CNGIM Commission Nationale de Gestion Intégrée des Mangroves (National Integrated Mangrove Management Commission)
CNGIZC Comité National de la Gestion Intégrée des Zones Côtières (National Committee for Integrated Coastal Zone Management)
CNRE Centre National de Recherches sur l'Environnement (National Center for Environmental Research)
CNRO Centre National de Recherches Océanographiques (National Center for Oceanographic Research)
CNRS Centre National de la Recherche Scientifique (National Center for Scientific Research)
COGAP Code de Gestion des Aires Protégées (Protected Areas Management Code)
CoBa *communauté de base* (community-based association)
COFAV Corridor Forestier Fandriana–Ambositra–Vondrozo (Fandriana–Ambositra–Vondrozo Forested Corridor)
COGAP Code de Gestion des Aires Protégées (Protected Areas Management Code)
COI Commission de l'Océan Indien (Indian Ocean Commission)
COI cytochrome oxidase I
COMATSA Nord Corridor Marojejy–Anjanaharibe-Sud–Tsaratanàna Nord (Northern Corridor Marojejy–Anjanaharibe-Sud–Tsaratanàna)
COMATSA Sud Corridor Marojejy–Anjanaharibe-Sud–Tsaratanàna Sud (Southern Corridor Marojejy–Anjanaharibe-Sud–Tsaratanàna)
Copefrito Compagnie de Peche Frigorifique de Toliara
CORDIO Coastal Oceans Research and Development–Indian Ocean
CoVs coronaviruses
CPUE catch per unit of effort
CR Critically Endangered (IUCN Red List status)
CRESICA Consortium for Research, Higher Education, and Innovation in New Caledonia
CRISPR Clustered Regularly Interspaced Short Palindromic Repeat
CSIC Consejo Superior de Investigaciones Científicas (Spanish National Research Council)
CSP Centre de Surveillance des Pêches (Fisheries Monitoring Center)
CSPN Conseil Supérieur pour la Protection de la Nature (High Council for Nature Protection)
CTFT Centre Technique Forestier Tropical (Technical Center for Tropical Forestry)

DAPTF Declining Amphibian Populations Task Force
DBA Département de Biologie Animale, Université d'Antananarivo (**UADBA**) (see also **MZBA**)
DBC/SAP Biodiversity Conservation/Protected Area System Directorate
DBEV Département de Biologie et Ecologie Végétales, Université d'Antananarivo (see also **MBEV**)
dbh diameter at breast height
DBV Dakar Bat Virus
δ-CoV *Deltacoronavirus*
DD Data Deficient (IUCN Red List status)
ddRAD double-digest restriction-site-associated sequencing
DEA *diplôme d'études approfondies*
DEAP Droit d'Entrée dans les Aires Protégées (protected area entry fee)
DEF Département des Eaux et Forêts (Department of Water and Forest)
DELC Development and Environmental Law Center
DENV Dengue Virus
DFN Domaine Forestier National (National Forest Lands)
DGEF Direction Générale des Eaux et Forêts (General Directorate of Water and Forests)
DGF Direction Générale des Forêts (General Directorate of Forests)
DGGE denaturing gradient gel electrophoresis
DIANA Region Diego–Ambilobe–Nosy Be–Ambanja region
DLC Duke Lemur Center
D-loop displacement-loop
DNA deoxyribonucleic acid
DPZ Deutsches Primatenzentrum (German Primate Center)
DREDD Direction Régionale de l'Environnement et du Développement Durable (Regional Department of Environment and Sustainable Development)
DREEF Direction Régionale de l'Environnement, de l'Ecologie et des Forêts (Regional Department of Environment, Ecology, and Forests)
DRFP/FOFIFA Département des Recherches Forestières et Piscicoles (Forestry and Pisciculture Research Department)
DUPC Duke University Primate Center (now **DLC**)
DWCT Durrell Wildlife Conservation Trust
DWFN distant water fishing nation

E herbarium code for Royal Botanic Garden Edinburgh
EAZA European Association of Zoos and Aquaria
EBSA Ecologically or Biologically Significant Area
EBSP Extended Bayesian skyline plots
EC European Community
ECH energy conservation hypothesis
ECMWF European Centre for Medium-Range Weather Forecasts
ED evolutionary distinctiveness
EDEN Ecole Doctorale Ecosystèmes Naturels, Université de Mahajanga
EDGE Evolutionarily Distinct and Globally Endangered
eDNA environmental DNA; see **DNA**
EEP European Endangered Species Programme
EEZ exclusive economic zone
EGP extra-group paternity
EIA environmental impact assessment (*étude d'impact environnemental*)
EL ear (pinna) length
ELD extended larval development
ELISA enzyme-linked immunosorbent assay
EN Endangered (IUCN Red List status)
EOT Eocene–Oligocene transition
EP1, 2, 3 National Environmental Action Plan, first, second, and third phases
ER-PA Emission Reductions Purchase Agreements

ESBL-E extended-spectrum-beta-lactamase-producing Enterobacteriaceae
ESSA-Forêts Etablissement de l'Enseignement Supérieur des Sciences Agronomiques, Département des Eaux et Forêts, Université d'Antananarivo (School of Agronomical Sciences, Department of Water and Forest, University of Antananarivo)
ETP Ecology Training Program
EVI Enhanced Vegetation Index
EX Extinct (IUCN Red List status)

FAO Food and Agriculture Organization of the United Nations
FAPBM Fondation pour les Aires Protégées et la Biodiversité de Madagascar (Madagascar Biodiversity and Protected Areas Fund)
FBM Fikambanana Bongolava Maitso (Association for a Green Bongolava)
FC Forêt Classée (classified forest)
FCPF Forest Carbon Partnership Facility
FFEM Fonds Français pour l'Environnement Mondial (French Funds for Global Environment)
FIPs fishery improvement plans
FLR Forest Landscape Restoration
FM frequency modulated
FMG *franc malgache* (Malagasy franc; now Malagasy ariary, **MGA**)
FMNH Field Museum of Natural History
FMTF Fikambanana Miaro ny Trozona sy Fesotra (Association for the Protection of Whales and Dolphins)
FOFIFA Foibem-pirenena momba ny Fikarohana ampiharina amin'ny Fampandrosoana ny eny Ambanivohitra (Centre National de la Recherche Appliquée au Développement Rural; National Center for Applied Research on Rural Development)
FTM Foiben-Taosarintanin'i Madagasikara (Institut Géographique et Hydrographique de Madagascar, or National Institute of Survey and Cartography)

G herbarium code for the Conservatoire et Jardin botaniques de la Ville de Genève, Switzerland
GAA Global Amphibian Assessment
GAPCM Groupement des Aquaculteurs et Pêcheurs de Crevettes à Madagascar (Association of Aquaculturists and Shrimp Fishers in Madagascar)
GBIF Global Biodiversity Information Facility
GBSSI granule-bound starch synthase
GCF Gestion Contractualisée des Forêts (contractualized forest management)
γ-CoV *Gammacoronavirus*
GDP gross domestic product
GE global endangerment
GEE Google Earth Engine
GEF Global Environment Facility
GELOSE Gestion Locale des Ressources Naturelles Renouvelables, or Gestion Locale Sécurisée (Local Management of Renewable Natural Resources, or Secure Local Management)
GERP Groupe d'Etude et de Recherche sur les Primates de Madagascar (Group for the Study and Research on Madagascar Primates)
GHG greenhouse gas
GHR growth-hormone receptor
GIS geographic information system
GLAD Global Land Analysis and Discovery alerts
GMYC General Mixed Yule-Coalescent
GPL Global Pandemic Lineage
GPP gross primary productivity
GPS global positioning system
GRENE Gestion de Ressources Naturelles et Environnement; now Institut Supérieur de Sciences, Environnement et Développement Durable, Université de Toamasina (see ISSEDD)
GSAF global shark attack files
GTZ Deutsche Gesellschaft für Technische Zusammenarbeit (German Technical Cooperation)

HBL head-and-body length
HCPS hantavirus cardiopulmonary syndrome
HD-CF high duty–constant frequency
HDR *habilitation à diriger des recherches*
HEV Hepatitis E Virus
HF hindfoot length
HFRS hemorrhagic fever with renal syndrome
hPa hectopascal
HPD highest probability density
HWE Hardy-Weinberg equilibrium

IBA Important Bird and Biodiversity Area
IBD isolation by distance
IBE isolation by environment or by ecology
IBR isolation by resistance
ICDP integrated conservation and development project
ICMAA Institut de Civilisations Musée d'Art et d'Archéologie (Institute of Civilizations and Museum of Art and Archeology)
ICTE Institute for the Conservation of Tropical Environments
ICTV International Committee on Taxonomy of Viruses
ICZM integrated coastal zone management
iDNA invertebrate DNA
IEFN Inventaire Ecologique Forestier National (National Ecological Forestry Inventory)
IgG immunoglobulin G
IgM immunoglobulin M
IHSM Institut Halieutique et des Sciences Marines (Institute of Fisheries and Marine Sciences)
IMMA Important Marine Mammal Area
IMRA Institut Malgache de Recherches Appliquées (Malagasy Institute of Applied Research)
INDC intended nationally determined contribution
ind/ha individuals per hectare
ind/km^2 individuals per square kilometer
INR Integrated Nature Reserve (Réserve Spéciale Intégrale)
IOC Indian Ocean Commission
IOTC Indian Ocean Tuna Commission
IPCC Intergovernmental Panel on Climate Change
IPM Institut Pasteur de Madagascar (Institute Pasteur of Madagascar)
IPSIO Insects and People of the Southwest Indian Ocean
IRBP interphotoreceptor retinoid-binding protein
IRD Institut de Recherche pour le Développement (Institute of Research for Development); formerly Office de la Recherche Scientifique et Technique Outre-Mer (**ORSTOM**)
IRSM Institut de Recherche Scientifique de Madagascar (Institute of Scientific Research of Madagascar)
ISAF international shark attack files
ISSEDD Institut Supérieur de Sciences, Environnement et Développement Durable, Université de Toamasina (Higher Institute of Sciences, Environment and Sustainable Development, University of Toamasina)
ISSG Invasive Species Specialist Group
ISTE Institut des Sciences et Techniques de l'Environnement, Université de Fianarantsoa
ITCZ Intertropical Convergence Zone
IUCN International Union for the Conservation of Nature and Natural Resources
IWC International Whaling Commission

JEV Japanese Encephalitis Virus

K herbarium code for Royal Botanic Gardens, Kew
KBA Key Biodiversity Areas
Kbp kilobase pair
KfW Kreditanstalt für Wiederaufbau
kHz kilohertz
K–Pg Cretaceous–Paleogene extinction event
Kya thousand years ago

L liter
LC Least Concern (IUCN Red List status)
LD-CF low-duty cycle, constant frequency
LD-QCF low-duty cycle, quasi-constant
LGM Last Glacial Maximum
LMD *licence-master-doctorat*
LMMA locally managed marine area
LPWG Legume Phylogeny Working Group

LRSAE Laboratoire de Recherche sur les Systèmes Aquatique et Leur Environnement (Research Laboratory on Aquatic Systems and their Environment)

MAB Man and Biosphere Reserve
MAEE Ministère et Affaires Etrangères et Européennes de France (Ministry and Foreign and European Affairs of France)
MAEP Ministère de l'Agriculture, de l'Elevage et de la Pêche (Ministry of Agriculture, Livestock and Fisheries)
MAHERY Madagascar Health and Environmental Research
MAP mean annual temperature
MAT microscopic-agglutination test
MaVoa Madagasikara Voakajy
MBEV Mention de Biologie et Ecologie Végétales, Université d'Antananarivo (formerly Département de Biologie et Ecologie Végétales, Université d'Antananarivo, **DBEV**)
MBG Missouri Botanical Garden
MBP Madagascar Biodiversity Partnership
Mbp megabase pairs (1 million base pairs)
MCCSUP Madagascar Crocodile Conservation and Sustainable Use Program
MCP minimum convex polygon
MCSN Museo Civico di Storia Naturale, Comiso, Italy
MECIE Mise en Compatibilité des Investissements avec l'Environnement (Compatibility of Investments with the Environment)
MEDD Ministère de l'Environnement et du Développement Durable (Ministry of the Environment and Sustainable Development; formerly **MEF**, then **MEEF**)
MEEF Ministère de l'Environnement, de l'Ecologie et des Forêts (Ministry of the Environment, Ecology, and Forests)
MEF Ministère des Eaux et Forêts (Ministry of Waters and Forests)
MERS Middle East respiratory syndrome
MFG Madagascar Fauna and Flora Group
MGA Malagasy ariary (monetary unit)
MHC major histocompatibility complex
MICET Malagasy Institut pour la Conservation des Ecosystèmes Tropicaux (Malagasy Institute for the Conservation of Tropical Environments)
MinSup Ministère de l'Enseignement Supérieur (Ministry of Higher Education)
MISA Miaro Ny Sahona
MLE maximum likelihood estimate
MMPATF Marine Mammal Protected Areas Task Force
MNHN Muséum National d'Histoire Naturelle, Paris
MNHU Museum für Naturkunde Humboldt-Universtät, Berlin
MNP Madagascar National Parks (formerly **ANGAP**)
MO herbarium code for Missouri Botanical Garden
MODIS Moderate Resolution Imaging Spectroradiometer
MoU memorandum of understanding
MPA marine protected area
MPRH Ministère de la Pêche et des Ressources Halieutiques (Ministry of Fisheries and Fishery Resources)
MRCA most recent common ancestor
Ms milliseconds
MSC Marine Stewardship Council
MSY maximum sustainable yield
Mt megaton
mtDNA mitochondrial DNA
MWSP Madagascar Whale Shark Project
Mya million years ago
MZBA Mention Zoologie et Biodiversité Animale, Université d'Antananarivo (formerly Département de Biologie Animale, Université d'Antananarivo, or **UADBA**)

NAP *nouvelle aire protégée* (new protected area)
NASA National Aeronautics and Space Administration, USA
NATO North Atlantic Treaty Organization
NCAR CESM1 National Center for Atmospheric Research Community Earth System Model, USA
NCEP National Centers for Environmental Prediction
NDV Newcastle Disease Virus
NDVI Normalized Difference Vegetation Index
NE nephropathia epidemica
NE Not Evaluated (IUCN Red List status)
NEAP National Environmental Action Plan
NEMC Northern East Madagascar Current
NGO nongovernmental organization (*organisation non-gouvernementale*)
NGS next-generation sequencing
NHMUK Natural History Museum, London
NJ neighbor joining
NMP National Monitoring Plan
NOAA National Oceanic and Atmospheric Administration, USA
NP National Park
NPFWs nonpollinating fig wasps
NRGT natural resource governance tools
NSAP New Sahonagasy Action Plan
NSF National Science Foundation
NTAC National Toad Advisory Committee
NT Near Threatened (IUCN Red List status)

ODK Open Data Kit
OMNIS Office des Mines Nationales et des Industries Stratégiques de Madagascar (Office of National Mines and Strategic Industries of Madagascar)
ONE Office National pour l'Environnement (National Office for the Environment)
ONG SEDIM Sauvegarde de l'Environnement et pour le Développement Intégré de Madagascar (NGO for the Protection of the Environment and for the Integrated Development of Madagascar)
OPJ Officier de Police Judiciaire (Judicial Police Officer)
ORSTOM Office de la Recherche Scientifique et Technique Outre-Mer (Overseas Office of Scientific and Technical Research), now Institut de Recherche pour le Développement (**IRD**) (Research Institute for Development)
OSL optically stimulated luminescence

P herbarium code for Muséum National d'Histoire Naturelle, Paris
PA protected area
PADAP Projet Agriculture Durable par une Approche Paysage (Sustainable Agriculture Project through a Landscape Approach)
PAE Plan d'Action Environnementale (Environmental Action Plan)
PAMELA Passive Margins Exploration Laboratories
PANA Programme d'Action National d'Adaptation au Changement Climatique (National Adaptation Program of Action on Climate Change)
PAP *plan d'aménagement des pêches* (fisheries management plan)
PBI Planetary Biodiversity Inventory
PBZT Parc Botanique et Zoologique de Tsimbazaza (Botanical and Zoological Park of Tsimbazaza)
PC principal component
PCD Pêche Côtière Durable (Sustainable Coastal Fisheries)
PCR polymerase chain reaction
PERR-FH Programme Eco-Régional REDD+ des Forêts Humides (Eco-Regional REDD+ Program for Humid Forests); see **REDD +**
PES payment for ecosystem services
PF peak frequency
PHVA population and habitat viability analysis
PIT passive integrated transponder
PIMIT Processus Infectieux en Milieu Insulaire Tropical
PK *point kilométrique* (kilometer point)
PlanGRAP Plan Stratégique de Gestion du Réseau des Aires Protégées (Protected Area Network Management Plan)
PMVs paramyxoviruses
PN Parc National (National Park)
POWO Plants of the World Online
ppb parts per billion
ppt parts per thousand
PRISM Projet Récif Ile Sainte Marie (Sainte Marie Island Reef Project)
PRU Polyaquaculture Research Unit

PSMC pairwise sequentially Markovian coalescent
PVA population viability analysis

QMM QIT Madagascar Minerals (Rio Tinto)

RABV Rabies Lyssavirus
RAD-seq restriction-site-associated DNA sequencing
RAI relative abundance index
RAP rapid assessment program
RAPD random amplification of polymorphic DNA
RB Réserve de Biosphère (Biosphere Reserve)
RBG or **RBG-Kew** Royal Botanic Gardens, Kew
RCP Recherche Coopérative sur Programme (Cooperative Program Research)
REBIOMA Réseau de la Biodiversité de Madagascar (Madagascar Biodiversity Network)
REDD+ Reducing Emissions from Deforestation and Forest Degradation
RLE Red List of Ecosystems
RLE reference level of emissions
REMMOA Recensement des Mammifères Marins et Autre Mégafaune Pélagique par Observation Aérienne (Census of Marine Mammals and other Pelagic Megafauna by Aerial Observation)
RF Réserve Forestière (Forestry Reserve)
RFLP restriction fragment-length polymorphism
RMCA Royal Museum for Central Africa, Tervuren, Belgium
RMR resting metabolic rate
RNA ribonucleic acid
RNI Réserve Naturelle Intégrale (Strict Nature Reserve)
RoC rate of change
RPP Readiness Preparation Proposal
R/R regurgitation and reingestion
rRNA ribosomal RNA
RS Réserve Spéciale (Special Reserve)
RVF Rift Valley fever
RVFV Rift Valley Fever Virus

SAGE Service d'Appui à la Gestion de l'Environnement (Support Service for Environmental Management)
SANBI South African National Biodiversity Institute
SAP Sahonagasy Action Plan
SAPM Système des Aires Protégées de Madagascar (Madagascar Protected Areas Network/System)
SARS severe acute respiratory syndrome
SAVA Region Sambava–Antalaha–Vohemar–Andapa region
SD standard deviation
SDM species distribution modeling
SEED-Madagascar Sustainable Environment, Education and Development in Madagascar
SEMC Southern East Madagascar Current
SF Station Forestière (Forestry Station)
SFS site frequency spectrum
SMACC Southwest Madagascar Coastal Current
SMART Spatial Monitoring and Reporting Tool
SNP single-nucleotide polymorphism
SODA Simple Ocean Data Assimilation
SOPTOM Station for the Observation and Protection of Tortoises and Their Environment
SPAGeDI Spatial Pattern Analysis of Genetic Diversity
SRI System of Rice Intensification
SROV Station de Recherches Océanographiques de Vangaindrano (Vangaindrano Oceanographic Research Station)
SSC Species Survival Commission
SSP Species Survival Program
SST sea surface temperature
STM seasonal trend model
STs sequence types
SVL snout-to-vent length
SWIO southwest Indian Ocean

t ton
TAMIA Tahosoa Alandriake Mitambatse Ianantsono Andatabo
TAN herbarium code for Parc Botanique et Zoologique de Tsimbazaza
TCI Temperature Condition Index
TEAM Tropical Ecology and Assessment Monitoring
TEDs turtle excluder devices
TEF herbarium code for Foibem-pirenena momba ny Fikarohana ampiharina amin'ny Fampandrosoana ny eny Ambanivohitra (see **FOFIFA**)
TGRH Transfert de Gestion des Ressources Halieutiques (Aquatic Resource Management Transfer)
TGRN Transfert de Gestion des Ressources Naturelles (Natural Resource Management Transfer)
TL tail length
TL total length
TPF The Peregrine Fund

UADBA Département de Biologie Animale, Université d'Antananarivo
UAVS unmanned aerial vehicles
UCE ultraconserved genetic element
UMRVs Unclassified Morbilli-related paramyoxoviruses
UNA Université d'Antananarivo
UNDP United Nations Development Programme
UNEP United Nations Environmental Programme
UNESCO United Nations Educational, Scientific and Cultural Organization (Organisation des Nations unies pour l'Education, la Science et la Culture)
UNFCCC United Nations Framework Convention on Climate Change
URL Unité de Recherche Langoustière (Lobster Research Unit)
USAID United States Agency for International Development
USDA United States Department of Agriculture
USGS United States Geological Survey
USNM United States National Museum; now National Museum of Natural History, Washington, DC
USTA Unité Statistique Thonière d'Antsiranana (Statistical Unit of Antsiranana Tuna Fisheries)

VCI Vegetation Condition Index
VH vegetation health
VHI Vegetation Health Index
VIF Vondrona Ivon'ny Fampandrosoana (Association for Local Development)
VOCs volatile organic compounds
VOI Vondron Olona Ifotony
VSF Vétérinaires Sans Frontières (Veterinarians Without Borders)
VU Vulnerable (IUCN Red List status)

WCMC World Conservation Monitoring Centre
WCS Wildlife Conservation Society
WCSP World Checklist of Selected Plant Families
WFO World Flora Online
WGD whole-genome duplication
WGS whole-genome sequencing
WHO World Health Organization
WIKTROP Weed Identification and Knowledge in the Tropical and Mediterranean Areas
WIKWIO Weed Identification and Knowledge in the Western Indian Ocean
WIOMER Western Indian Ocean Marine Ecoregion
WNV West Nile Virus
WSC World Spider Catalog
WSLV Wesselsbron Virus
WWF World Wide Fund for Nature, or World Wildlife Fund

YFV Yellow Fever Virus

ZICOMA Les Zones d'Importance pour la Conservation des Oiseaux à Madagascar
ZIKAV Zika Virus
ZMUH Zoologisches Institut und Museum der Universität, Hamburg, Germany
ZPC Zone Prioritaire de Conservation (Priority Zone for Conservation)
ZSM Zoologische Staatssammlung München

FORMAT AND PRESENTATION

GENERAL

Although information presented in this book is in the form of discrete chapters, each composed of up to 51 separate contributions, many of the covered subjects are interconnected. In order to guide readers between contributions, we have included, when appropriate, cross-references to link together different portions of the book. In some cases, certain points that are critical for context or detail are repeated between chapters.

As is natural for the diversity of subjects treated herein, not all authors agree on certain points. For example, there are several systems proposed for vegetation types on Madagascar, particularly for the mesic forest formations, and it was considered inappropriate to impose on authors a single system, although we have generally used the vegetation-type terms proposed by Gautier et al. (2018). In order to help navigate the names used for vegetation types between the different published systems, we have included in the introduction to the Plants chapter a summary of terms used in the literature and their equivalent names or synonyms (see Gautier et al., pp. 452–64, Table 8.1). Other points of disagreement include, for example, interpretations of the phylogenetic relationships between certain organisms, the role of human versus natural environmental changes associated with the disappearance of different ecosystems and now-extinct organisms, and points on the geological history of the island.

GEOGRAPHIC NAMES AND DEFINITIONS

For certain localities on Madagascar, two parallel systems of geographic place names exist, one associated with the former colonial system and the other employing more standard Malagasy designations. We have generally followed Malagasy names used on recent maps published by Foiben-Taosarintanin'i Madagasikara (FTM, or National Institute of Survey and Cartography). In many cases, names dating from the colonial era have been added in parentheses at first use within a contribution—e.g., Tolagnaro (Fort Dauphin) ; many of these are more widely employed than the Malagasy names in local daily use on the island. On the other hand, certain authors preferred to use place names from the colonial system, and we decided not to impose a single system but, in such cases, to provide the FTM name in parentheses at first use within a contribution.

All references to elevation in the text are given in meters above sea level. The use of the term "region" also poses some complications. Other than as a reference to a general geographical area, the term has additional specific meanings. One is associated with recognized biogeographical areas, such as Afrotropical region, or a specific vegetational type, such as Sambirano Region. For a definition of the term *Malagasy Region*, see below. Another meaning has an administrative context: formerly, Madagascar was divided into administrative provinces (*faritany* in Malagasy); in October 2009, this system was changed to one of regions (*faritra* in Malagasy), which includes 22 administrative units, such as the Sofia Region.

There have been changes in the past years to categories of Malagasy protected areas; for example, several preexisting reserves have been reclassified as national parks, new categories have been designated, and many protected areas have been named (see Goodman et al., pp. 2091–107). In Table 15.1, we present a listing of the definitive protected areas of the island as of November 2020, including both marine (see Figure 7.10) and terrestrial sites (see Figure 15.1), and the most recent statute governing each site. The spelling of protected-area site names varies in the literature; we have used those from Goodman et al. (2018), which are, for the most part, based on official governmental decrees.

SCIENTIFIC VERSUS VERNACULAR NAMES

With a few exceptions, mostly notably for birds and mammals, we have generally shied away from the use of English vernacular names when referring to a specific organism, which can create a certain level of ambiguity; we prefer the use of scientific names. In many chapters, particularly those for land vertebrates, at first mention of a species in a given contribution, the scientific name is given, followed by the generally accepted English vernacular name with initial capital letters. Further, while we mention them in some cases for a given organism or group, we tend not to use Malagasy common names, which can show considerable regional and dialectal differences.

PUBLISHED VERSUS UNPUBLISHED WORK

Given the diversity of researchers working on Madagascar, as well as many conservation, development, and aid projects, a considerable number of unpublished reports are available. We have generally asked authors, when possible, to refrain from using this "gray literature." However, in certain cases, the citation of this unpublished literature was necessary, and authors have indicated in the associated reference citation where these unpublished documents can be obtained, often with a web addresses where they can be downloaded. In other cases, unpublished data are referred to and the name of the individual(s) or organization are provided. The existence of published literature, gray literature, and unpublished documents (some broadly circulated and others not widely diffused) is problematic with regard to access and quality control via the peer-review process.

OTHER TERMS AND DEFINITIONS

Highland areas: In general, Madagascar is geographically divided into two broad zones, lowland areas and highland areas, the latter often defined as the inland portion of the island situated at 800 or 900 m above sea level, herein referred to as the **Central Highlands** and with a range of alternative terms (e.g., Central Plateau, Hautes Terres Centrales, etc.). Finer analyses, such as in Betsch (2000), have shown that there are northern and southern biogeographic breaks, specifically, to the north of the Mandritsara Valley and another to the south of the Menaharaka Valley, which separates the Central Highlands into two additional zones, the **Northern Highlands** and **Southern Highlands**, respectively. These latter two terms and this biogeographic classification are used herein by certain authors.

IUCN Red List categories: The conservation statutes extracted from the IUCN Red List are widely cited. Those falling in the "threatened" category include Critically Endangered (CR), Endangered (EN), and Vulnerable (VU). Other categories, including Near Threatened (NT), Least Concern (LC), and Data Deficient (DD), indicate lower or poorly known conservation threats. Not Evaluated (NE) indicates that a taxon has not yet been evaluated against the IUCN criteria.

Malagasy language: In the text, words, names, and expressions from the Malagasy are in italics and generally lowercase, with the exception of proper names.

Malagasy Region: We use this term in a biogeographic sense to include Madagascar and neighboring archipelagoes, which comprise the Comoros (Mayotte and the three islands of the Union of the Comoros), the Mascarenes (La Réunion, Mauritius, and Rodrigues), and the Seychelles (over 110 islands and islets that range across a distance of about 1120 km from Aldabra in the west to Coëtivy Island in the east).

Malagasy versus Madagascan: Throughout the book, we use the term Malagasy as a noun and adjective, not Madagascan, to refer to the people, culture, and other animate and inanimate objects of Madagascar. See Voarintsoa et al. (2019) for further details.

Megafauna: This term has been widely used in the literature to denote the large-bodied animals that have gone extinct on the island in the past few millennia. Herein, we generally follow Martin's (1984) use of the term to denote animals of at least an estimated body mass of 44 kg (100 lb.); for those that are smaller, other descriptive terms (e.g., extinct large-bodied mammals) are used.

REFERENCES

Betsch, J.-M. 2000. Types of spéciation chez quelques collemboles Symphypleones Sminthuridae (Aptérygotes) de Madagascar. In *Diversité et endémisme à Madagascar*, eds. W. R. Lourenço and S. M. Goodman, pp. 295–306. Paris: Mémoires de la Société de Biogéographie.

Gautier, L., Tahinarivony, J. A., Ranirison, P., and Wohlhauser, S. 2018. Végétation/Vegetation. In *Les aires protégées terrestres de Madagascar: Leur histoire, description et biote/The Terrestrial Protected Areas of Madagascar: Their History, Description, and Biota*, eds. S. M. Goodman, M. J. Raherilalao, and S. Wohlhauser, pp. 207–242. Antananarivo: Association Vahatra.

Martin, P. S. 1984. Prehistoric overkill: The global model. In *Quaternary Extinctions: A Prehistoric Revolution*, eds. P. S. Martin and R. G. Klein, pp. 354–403. Tucson: University of Arizona Press.

Voarintsoa, N.R.G., Raveloson, A., Barimalala, R., and Razafindratsima, O. H. 2019. "Malagasy" or "Madagascan"? Which English term best reflects the people, the culture, and other things from Madagascar? *Scientific African* 4: e00091.

CHAPTER 10

FRESHWATER FISHES

INTRODUCTION TO THE FRESHWATER FISHES

J. S. Sparks and M. L. J. Stiassny

Since the publication of the introductory contribution to the freshwater fishes chapter in the precursor to this book (Sparks and Stiassny 2003), several ichthyofaunal surveys have taken place across much of Madagascar, resulting in the discovery of numerous new endemic freshwater species, many of which have now been formally described (Table 10.1). The increase in diversity that has been revealed by these surveys is nothing short of remarkable, yet levels of endangerment and threat have continued to escalate. In 2003 we noted that although many of Madagascar's terrestrial vertebrates had been studied in great detail, particularly the lemurs, very little up-to-date information was then available for the highly threatened freshwater fishes native to the island. As a result of significant survey efforts taking place over the past quarter century, specifically in regions that were previously poorly inventoried, we now have a somewhat better understanding of the diversity and conservation status of the island's native freshwater fishes. Despite increased discovery rates, the native ichthyofauna of Madagascar remains highly threatened in the face of continued and accelerating deforestation and habitat degradation, competition from a wide array of introduced species, and overexploitation, among other threats (Ravelomanana et al. 2018).

This introductory contribution provides a much-needed revised summary overview of Madagascar's native freshwater ichthyofauna, as well as an update on current knowledge regarding the origins, composition, biogeography, and phylogenetic relationships of this unique and highly threatened vertebrate fauna. We do not attempt a review of the hydrology, limnology, or conservation status of Madagascar's aquatic resources here, as these have been presented in detail elsewhere (e.g., see references in Benstead et al. 2003; Sparks and Stiassny 2003; Irwin et al. 2010) and are recently summarized in Máiz-Tomé et al. (2018). Herein we focus on patterns of Malagasy freshwater fish diversity and distribution, highlighting many exciting new discoveries, and the historical geological events that have shaped them; details on the coastal marine fish fauna (for which see chapter 7 of this volume) are not discussed in any detail in this chapter.

ORIGIN, COMPOSITION, AND STUDY OF THE MALAGASY FISH FAUNA

Our research team has conducted several extensive ichthyofaunal surveys since the mid-1990s, including surveys of the Masoala Peninsula and the Makira region (1996, 2003), far northern basins (2008, 2011), northwestern basins (1994, 1996, 2008, 2011), southwestern karst habitats (2008), and remote forested regions in the eastern Central Highlands (1994, 1996, 1997, 1998, 2014). In addition, taxonomically comprehensive phylogenetic studies of several endemic Malagasy assemblages, including ehiravin clupeids (Clupeidae, Pellonulinae, tribe Ehiravini), cichlids (Cichlidae), bedotiid rainbowfishes (Bedotiidae), and gobiiforms (Gobiiformes), have dramatically increased our understanding regarding the evolution and diversification of these lineages (e.g., Stiassny 2002; Sparks and Smith 2004a, 2004b; Chakrabarty et al. 2012; Kuang et al. 2018).

To usefully interpret the origin(s) and composition of the ichthyofauna, we need not only knowledge of distributions in space and time but also information on the phylogenetic affinities of the groups present. We summarize both historical and recent survey data collected since the first version of this introductory contribution (Sparks and Stiassny 2003) and attempt to synthesize these and current phylogenetic hypotheses, in order to provide a contextual overview of the island's ichthyofauna. Contrary to a commonly expressed belief that Madagascar's ichthyofauna is fully documented (e.g., Grandidier and Petit 1932), and despite recent survey efforts, the island's fishes are still not comprehensively known, and much survey work remains to be undertaken. However, the phylogenetic relationships of several groups with endemic Malagasy assemblages—for example, cichlids, ehiravin clupeids, bedotiid rainbowfishes, aplocheilid killifishes (Aplocheilidae), pantanodontids (Pantanodontidae), and gobiiform cavefishes—have been investigated in the past two decades.

TABLE 10.1. **Checklist of native Malagasy freshwater fishes with their region(s) of occurrence and most recent IUCN status**

FAMILY	SCIENTIFIC NAME		IUCN STATUS	REGION				
				SOUTHERN BASINS	WESTERN BASINS	NORTHWESTERN BASINS	EASTERN HIGHLANDS	EASTERN LOWLANDS
Elopidae	*Elops*	*machnata*	LC	X	X	X	–	X
Megalopidae	*Megalops*	*cyprinoides*	DD	–	X	X	–	–
Anguillidae	*Anguilla*	*bicolor*	NT	X	X	X	X	X
Anguillidae	*A.*	*marmorata*	LC	X	X	X	X	X
Anguillidae	*A.*	*mossambica*	NT	X	X	X	X	X
Ophichthidae	*Yirrkala*	*tenuis*	LC	X	X	X	–	X
Pristigasteridae	*Pellona*	*ditchela*	LC	–	X	X	–	X
Clupeidae	**Sauvagella**	**madagascariensis**	LC	X	–	–	X	X
Clupeidae	*S.	**robusta**	EN	–	–	X	–	–
Clupeidae	**Spratellomorpha**	**bianalis**	DD	–	X	X	–	–
Ariidae	*Arius*	**madagascariensis**	LC	–	X	X	–	–
Ariidae	*A.	**uncinatus**	CR	–	–	X	–	–
Ariidae	*A.	**festinus**	CR	–	–	X	–	–
Ariidae	*Plicofollis*	*dussumieri*	LC	–	X	X	–	–
Ariidae	*P.*	*polystaphylodon*	NE[1]	–	X	X	–	–
Anchariidae	**Ancharius**	**fuscus**	LC	–	–	–	X	X
Anchariidae	*A.	**griseus**	EN	–	X	–	–	–
Anchariidae	**Gogo**	**brevibarbis**	DD	–	–	–	X	X
Anchariidae	*G.	**arcuatus**	DD	–	–	–	X	–
Anchariidae	*G.	**ornatus**	EN	–	–	–	X	–
Anchariidae	*G.	**atratus**	DD	–	–	–	X	X
Atherinidae	*Atherinomorus*	cf. *duodecimalis*	LC	X	–	–	X	X
Atherinidae	**Teramulus**	**kieneri**	LC	–	–	–	X	X
Atherinidae	**T.**	**waterloti**	EN	–	–	X	–	–
Bedotiidae	**Bedotia**	**geayi**	EN	–	–	–	X	X
Bedotiidae	**B.**	**madagascariensis**	EN	–	–	–	–	X
Bedotiidae	**B.**	**longianalis**	EN	–	–	–	–	X
Bedotiidae	**B.**	**tricolor**	CR	–	–	–	X	X
Bedotiidae	**B.**	**marojejy**	EN	–	–	–	X	–
Bedotiidae	**B.**	**masoala**	VU	–	–	–	X	–
Bedotiidae	*B.	**albomarginata**	EN	–	–	–	X	–
Bedotiidae	*B.	**leucopteron**	EN	–	–	–	X	–
Bedotiidae	*B.	**alveyi**	NT	–	–	–	X	–
Bedotiidae	**B.**	**n. sp. "mangoro"**	NA	–	–	–	–	X
Bedotiidae	**B.**	**n. sp. "nosivolo"**	NA	–	–	–	X	–
Bedotiidae	**B.**	**n. sp. "namorona"**	NA	–	–	–	X	–
Bedotiidae	**B.**	**n. sp. "garassa"**	NA	–	–	–	–	X
Bedotiidae	**B.**	**n. sp. "anosy"**	NA	–	–	–	X	–
Bedotiidae	**B.**	**n. sp. "betampona"**	NA	–	–	–	X	X
Bedotiidae	**B.**	**n. sp. "sambava"**	NA	–	–	–	–	X
Bedotiidae	**B.**	**n. sp. "bemarivo"**	NA	–	–	–	–	X
Bedotiidae	**B.**	**n. sp. "mahanara"**	NA	–	–	–	–	X
Bedotiidae	**B.**	**n. sp. "manombo"**	NA	–	–	–	–	X
Bedotiidae	**B.**	**n. sp. "antalaha"**	NA	–	–	–	–	X
Bedotiidae	**B.**	**n. sp. "mananare"**	NA	–	–	–	–	X
Bedotiidae	**B.**	**n. sp. "manambolo"**	NA	–	–	–	–	X
Bedotiidae	**Rheocles**	**alaotrensis**	EN	–	–	–	X	–

FAMILY	SCIENTIFIC NAME		IUCN STATUS	REGION				
				SOUTHERN BASINS	WESTERN BASINS	NORTHWESTERN BASINS	EASTERN HIGHLANDS	EASTERN LOWLANDS
Bedotiidae	***R.***	***lateralis***	CR	–	–	–	X	–
Bedotiidae	***R.***	***sikorae***	DD	–	–	–	X	–
Bedotiidae	***R.***	***wrightae***	EN	–	–	–	X	–
Bedotiidae	***R.***	**n. sp. “rianila”**	NA	–	–	–	X	–
Bedotiidae	***R.***	**n. sp. “mangoro”**	NA	–	–	–	X	–
Bedotiidae	***“Rheocles”***	***pellegrini***	DD	–	–	–	X	–
Bedotiidae	***“R.”***	***derhami***	CR	–	–	X	–	–
Bedotiidae	*“R.”	***vatosoa***	EN	–	–	–	X	–
Aplocheilidae	*Pachypanchax*	***sakaramyi***	EN	–	–	X	–	–
Aplocheilidae	*P.*	***omalonotus***	EN	–	–	X	–	–
Aplocheilidae	*P.	***arnoulti***	VU	–	X	–	–	–
Aplocheilidae	*P.	***sparksorum***	EN	–	–	X	–	–
Aplocheilidae	*P.	***varatraza***	EN	–	–	–	X	–
Aplocheilidae	*P.	***patriciae***	EN	–	–	X	–	–
Aplocheilidae	*P.*	**n. sp. “sofia”**	NA	–	–	X	–	–
Aplocheilidae	*P.*	**n. sp. “mahamasina”**	NA	–	–	X	–	–
Aplocheilidae	*P.*	**n. sp. “ankarana”**	NA	–	–	X	–	–
Aplocheilidae	*P.*	**n. sp. “maevarano”**	NA	–	–	X	–	–
Aplocheilidae	*P.*	**n. sp. “analalava”**	NA	–	–	X	–	–
Aplocheilidae	*P.*	**n. sp. “doroa”**	NA	–	–	X	–	–
Aplocheilidae	*P.*	**n. sp. “manambaho”**	NA	–	X	–	–	–
Aplocheilidae	*P.*	**n. sp. “manambolo”**	NA	–	X	–	–	–
Aplocheilidae	*P.*	**n. sp. “tsiribihina”**	NA	–	X	–	–	–
Aplocheilidae	*P.*	**n. sp. “makay”**	NA	–	X	–	–	–
Pantanodontidae	*Pantanodon*	***madagascariensis***	EX	–	–	–	–	X
Pantanodontidae	*P.*	**n. sp. “manombo”**	NA [EX][2]	–	–	–	–	X
Syngnathidae	*Microphis*	*leiaspis*	LC	–	–	X	X	X
Syngnathidae	*M.*	*brachyurus*	LC	–	–	–	X	–
Syngnathidae	*M.*	*fluviatilis*	DD	–	X	X	–	X
Syngnathidae	*Hippichthys*	*cyanospilos*	LC	–	X	X	–	X
Syngnathidae	*H.*	*spicifer*	LC	–	X	X	–	X
Ambassidae	*Ambassis*	***fontoynonti***	DD	–	–	–	–	X
Ambassidae	*A.*	*natalensis*	LC	–	X	X	X	X
Ambassidae	*A.*	*ambassis*	LC	–	X	X	X	X
Terapontidae	*Terapon*	*jarbua*	LC	–	X	X	–	X
Terapontidae	***Mesopristes***	***elongatus***	DD	–	–	–	X	X
Kuhliidae	*Kuhlia*	*rupestris*	LC	–	X	X	X	X
Kuhliidae	*K.*	***sauvagii***	VU	–	–	–	–	X
Monodactylidae	*Monodactylus*	*argenteus*	LC	–	X	X	–	X
Monodactylidae	*M.*	*falciformis*	LC	–	X	X	–	X
Scatophagidae	*Scatophagus*	*tetracanthus*	LC	–	X	X	–	X
Chanidae	*Chanos*	*chanos*	LC	–	X	X	–	X
Cichlidae	***Paratilapia***	***polleni***	VU	–	–	X	–	–
Cichlidae	***P.***	***bleekeri***	DD	–	X	–	–	–
Cichlidae	***P.***	***typus***	NE	–	–	–	–	X
Cichlidae	***P.***	**n. sp. “andapa”**	NA	–	–	–	–	X
Cichlidae	***P.***	**n. sp. “onilahy”**	NA	–	X	–	–	–

(continued overleaf)

TABLE 10.1. ***continued***

FAMILY	SCIENTIFIC NAME		IUCN STATUS	REGION				
				SOUTHERN BASINS	WESTERN BASINS	NORTHWESTERN BASINS	EASTERN HIGHLANDS	EASTERN LOWLANDS
Cichlidae	_P._	n. sp. "vondrozo"	NA	–	–	–	X	–
Cichlidae	_P._	n. sp. "fony"	NA	–	–	–	X	X
Cichlidae	_P._	n. sp. "akanga"	NA	–	–	–	X	X
Cichlidae	_P._	n. sp. "fiamanga"	NA	–	X	–	–	–
Cichlidae	_P._	n. sp. "ilempo"	NA	–	X	–	–	–
Cichlidae	_P._	n. sp. "betsiboka"	NA	–	–	X	–	–
Cichlidae	_Ptychochromis_	_oligacanthus_	EN	–	–	X	–	–
Cichlidae	_P._	_grandidieri_	LC	–	–	–	X	X
Cichlidae	*_P._	_inornatus_	EN	–	–	X	–	–
Cichlidae	*_P._	_onilahy_	EX	–	X	–	–	–
Cichlidae	*_P._	_makira_	DD	–	–	–	–	X
Cichlidae	*_P._	_loisellei_	EN	–	–	–	–	X
Cichlidae	*_P._	_curvidens_	DD	–	–	X	–	–
Cichlidae	*_P._	_insolitus_	CR	–	–	X	–	–
Cichlidae	*_P._	_ernestmagnusi_	DD	–	–	–	–	X
Cichlidae	*_P._	_mainty_	DD	–	–	–	X	–
Cichlidae	_Katria_	_katria_	EN	–	–	–	X	–
Cichlidae	_Ptychochromoides_	_betsileanus_	CR	–	X	–	–	–
Cichlidae	_P._	_vondrozo_	EN	–	–	–	X	–
Cichlidae	*_P._	_itasy_	CR	–	X	–	–	–
Cichlidae	_Oxylapia_	_polli_	EN	–	–	–	X	–
Cichlidae	_Paretroplus_	_damii_	VU	–	–	X	–	–
Cichlidae	_P._	_kieneri_	VU	–	–	X	–	–
Cichlidae	_P._	_maculatus_	CR	–	–	X	–	–
Cichlidae	_P._	_petiti_	DD	–	–	X	–	–
Cichlidae	_P._	_polyactis_	LC	–	–	–	X	X
Cichlidae	_P._	_maromandia_	EN	–	–	X	–	–
Cichlidae	_P._	_nourissati_	EN	–	–	X	–	–
Cichlidae	_P._	_menarambo_	CR	–	–	X	–	–
Cichlidae	*_P._	_tsimoly_	EN	–	–	X	–	–
Cichlidae	*_P._	_dambabe_	CR	–	–	X	–	–
Cichlidae	*_P._	_gymnopreopercularis_	CR	–	–	X	–	–
Cichlidae	*_P._	_lamenabe_	EN	–	–	X	–	–
Cichlidae	*_P._	_loisellei_	EN	–	–	–	X	X
Cichlidae	_P._	n. sp. "anjingo"	NA	–	–	X	–	–
Mugilidae	_Agonostomus_	_catalai_	DD	–	–	–	X	–
Mugilidae	_A._	_telfairii_	LC	–	–	–	X	–
Mugilidae	_Chelon_	_melinopterus_	LC	–	X	X	–	X
Mugilidae	_C._	_buchanani_	LC	–	X	X	–	X
Mugilidae	_C._	_crenilabis_	LC	–	X	X	–	X
Mugilidae	_Mugil_	_cephalus_	LC	–	X	X	–	–
Mugilidae	_Osteomugil_	_engeli_	LC	–	X	X	–	X
Mugilidae	_O._	_perusii_	LC	X	X	X	–	X
Mugilidae	_O._	_robustus_	LC	–	X	X	–	–
Mugilidae	_Planiliza_	_macrolepis_	LC	–	X	X	–	X
Mugilidae	_P._	_alata_	LC	–	X	X	–	X
Batrachoididae	_Allenbatrachus_	_meridionalis_	DD	–	–	–	–	X
Sillaginidae	_Sillago_	_sihama_	LC	X	X	X	–	X
Kraemeriidae	_Gobitrichinotus_	_arnoulti_	LC	–	–	–	X	X

				REGION				
FAMILY	SCIENTIFIC NAME		IUCN STATUS	SOUTHERN BASINS	WESTERN BASINS	NORTHWESTERN BASINS	EASTERN HIGHLANDS	EASTERN LOWLANDS
Gobiidae	*Acentrogobius*	*audax*	LC	–	X	X	–	X
Gobiidae	*A.*	***therezieni***	DD	–	X	X	–	–
Gobiidae	*Bathygobius*	*fuscus*	LC	–	–	–	X	–
Gobiidae	*Favonigobius*	*reichei*	NT	–	X	X	–	X
Gobiidae	*Glossogobius*	***ankaranensis***	LC[3]	–	–	X	–	X
Gobiidae	*G.*	*callidus*	LC	–	X	X	–	X
Gobiidae	*G.*	*giuris*	LC	–	X	X	X	X
Gobiidae	*Gobius*	***hypselosoma***	LC	–	–	X	–	X
Gobiidae	*Istigobius*	*ornatus*	LC	–	X	X	–	X
Gobiidae	*Psammogobius*	*biocellatus*	LC	–	X	X	–	–
Gobiidae	*Yongeichthys*	*nebulosus*	LC	–	X	X	–	X
Oxudercidae	*Awaous*	*aeneofuscus*	LC	–	X	X	X	X
Oxudercidae	*A.*	***macrorhynchus***	LC	–	–	X	–	X
Oxudercidae	*Oligolepis*	*acutipennis*	DD	–	X	X	–	X
Oxudercidae	*Redigobius*	*balteatus*	LC	–	–	–	–	X
Oxudercidae	*R.*	*dewaali*	LC	–	–	–	–	X?
Oxudercidae	*R.*	***sambiranoensis***	DD	–	–	X	–	–
Oxudercidae	*Sicyopterus*	***franouxi***	LC	–	–	–	X	X
Oxudercidae	*S.*	***punctissimus***	DD	–	–	–	X	X
Oxudercidae	*Stenogobius*	*polyzona*	LC	–	X	X	–	X
Oxudercidae	*Taenioides*	*gracilis*	LC	–	–	–	–	X
Butidae	*Butis*	*butis*	LC	–	X	X	X	–
Butidae	*Ophiocara*	*porocephala*	LC	–	X	X	–	X
Butidae	*O.*	***macrolepidota***	NE	–	–	–	X	X
Eleotridae	*Eleotris*	*fusca*	LC	–	X	X	X	X
Eleotridae	*E.*	*mauritiana*	LC	–	X	X	–	X
Eleotridae	*E.*	*melanosoma*	LC	–	X	X	–	X
Eleotridae	*E.*	***pellegrini***	LC	–	–	X?	–	X
Eleotridae	*E.*	***vomerodentata***	DD	–	–	–	–	X
Eleotridae	*Giuris*	*margaritaceus*	LC	X	X	X	–	X
Eleotridae	*Hypseleotris*	***tohizonae***	NE	–	–	X	–	X
Eleotridae	***Ratsirakia***	***legendrei***	DD	–	–	–	X	X
Milyeringidae	***Typhleotris***	***madagascariensis***	EN	X	–	–	–	–
Milyeringidae	***T.***	***pauliani***	CR	–	X	–	–	–
Milyeringidae	****T.***	***mararybe***	CR	X	–	–	–	–
Total counts:								
29 families	62 genera	178 total species		12	63	89	59	90
(2 endemic)	(17 endemic)	(122 endemic)						

Notes: Family, genus, and species names in **boldface type** are endemic to Madagascar. Species that have been formally described since Sparks and Stiassny (2003) are indicated with an asterisk (*). Undescribed species are designated by "n. sp." and their names are enclosed in quotation marks. IUCN (2021) Red List conservation assessment status: CR, Critically Endangered; DD, Data Deficient; EN, Endangered; EX, Extinct; LC, Least Concern; NE, Not Evaluated; NT, Near Threatened; VU, Vulnerable. NA (not assessed; not an IUCN assessment category) is used herein to designate currently unnamed species awaiting description and yet to be evaluated. The five major ichthyological ecoregions listed correspond to those discussed in the text. X indicates presence of species in a particular ecoregion; – indicates no presence. Totals for each column are presented at the bottom of the table.

[1] Not assessed by IUCN (2021), but provisional assessment based on survey data indicates a status of LC (see Ng and Sparks, pp. 1263–65).

[2] Not assessed by IUCN (2021) as it has not been formally described; however, the lack of specimens collected on survey efforts over the past two decades indicate that the species is likely extinct.

[3] See the text for clarification of this species' status.

Although such advances have been made, there persists a low level of basic knowledge, and below we discuss several possible reasons for it, as well as how our understanding of this fauna has advanced over the past 20 years and where gaps persist. Finally, in the face of the current rapid rate of aquatic habitat degradation on the island, we present our view regarding the future of the ichthyofauna, as well as the most recent International Union for Conservation of Nature (IUCN) Red List assessments.

In many ways Madagascar is characterized by a typical island ichthyofauna, but it also deviates in certain respects owing to its size and continental (Gondwanan) origin. Like that of many true oceanic islands, Madagascar's fish fauna is relatively depauperate at broad taxonomic levels (Table 10.1) when compared with those of the much larger continental landmasses, such as mainland Africa or South America, which are characterized by far more diverse aquatic habitats (Stiassny et al. 2010). However, based on the updated species totals presented herein, and considering the surface area of the island, the notion of a depauperate fauna at the species level is simply no longer tenable (e.g., Jenkins 1987). At the species level Madagascar's fish fauna is numerically fully in line with those of other continental landmasses and islands of similar size, and the island supports more or less exactly as many species as would be predicted given its surface area of nearly 600,000 km^2 (Figure 10.1a; Sparks and Stiassny 2003: Figure 9.1; MacArthur and Wilson 1967; Brown and Lomolino 1998). This finding is even more dramatic given the large-scale attrition of freshwater habitats across the island and the concomitant rapid decline of native and endemic species (Figures 10.1b and c; Irwin et al. 2010; Kull 2012).

In contrast to many other island systems in the Malagasy Region, including the archipelagoes of the Seychelles, Comoros, and Mascarenes (La Réunion, Mauritius, and Rodrigues), Madagascar, physically isolated since the Cretaceous period (B. C. Storey 1995; Hay et al. 1999), is home to small radiations of freshwater fishes (e.g., cichlids, bedotiid rainbowfishes, aplocheilid killifishes) that do not readily enter marine habitats. Many taxonomic groups with members present on the island exhibit broad Gondwanan distributions and thus rich potential to provide insight into the past connections of the southern continents. Oceanic islands of the region, such as the Comoros and Mascarenes (which are of recent volcanic origin, 15 million years old or less) and the coralline and granitic Seychelles (the latter being ancient Gondwanan fragments isolated since approximately the Late Cretaceous; Plummer and Bell 1995; B. C. Storey 1995) have extremely depauperate fish faunas dominated by marine colonizers or species with life histories dependent on marine habitats, such as anguillid eels (Anguillidae), gray mullets (Mugilidae), ambassids (Ambassidae), and various gobioids (Bleeker and Pollen 1875; Teugels et al. 1985).

An extensive literature on Madagascar's freshwater fishes dates back to the mid-1800s (see Sparks and Stiassny 2003 for a review), and by the early part of the 20th century, most biologists had concluded that the ichthyofauna of Madagascar was more or less well known (e.g., Grandidier and Petit 1932). However, beyond compiling faunal lists of species known at the time, little additional information on the island's fishes was reported in this literature (see Andriamialisoa and Langrand, pp. 1–38, for details on ichthyological research on the island). Notably lacking was information on life history or reproductive biology, or insights into the evolution of

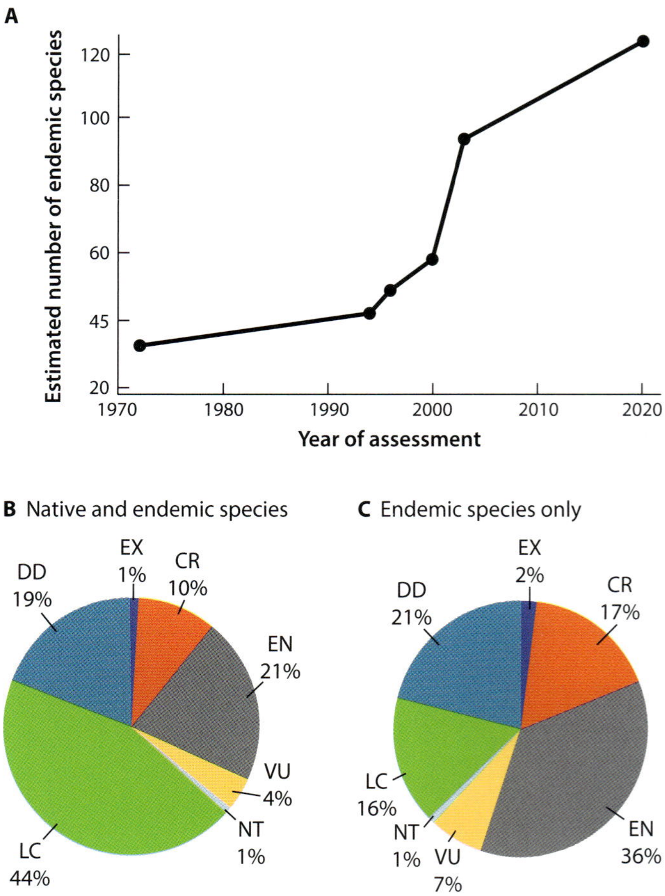

FIGURE 10.1 **A) Plot depicting increase in endemic Malagasy freshwater fish species by study since 1972 (Kiener and Richard-Vindard 1972; Stiassny and Raminosoa 1994; de Rham 1996; Benstead et al. 2000; Sparks and Stiassny 2003; this study; see text for additional details on specific studies). Charts showing most recent IUCN Red List (2021) assessment categories for native Malagasy freshwater fishes with percentage of species in each category: B) IUCN totals for both native and endemic species. C) IUCN totals for endemic species only. Note high percentage (60%) of threatened endemic species and additional 2% of endemic species that are classified as Extinct. IUCN categories: CR: Critically Endangered; DD: Data Deficient; EN: Endangered; EX: Extinct; LC: Least Concern: NT: Near Threatened; VU: Vulnerable.**

the native fishes and their patterns of distribution both within Madagascar and regionally. In fact, despite a rich literature dating back 150 years, it is remarkable how little we still know about the basic biology of a majority of Madagascar's fishes. Much of this lack of knowledge is a result of the difficulty of studying this fauna, given the rarity and poorly known ranges of many species. Perhaps as a result of this lack of knowledge, and a failure to comprehend how severely threatened Madagascar's freshwater fauna currently is, the island's fishes have not been a mainstream focus for recent efforts of conservation organizations or government agencies, and in the design and implementation of protected areas, native fishes have tended to be neglected or ignored (for more details, see Conservation section, below).

It has been well over a decade since a comprehensive, updated faunal list for Madagascar's freshwater fishes has been published, and previous summary works on Malagasy freshwater fishes are now quite outdated (see references in Sparks and Stiassny 2003, 2005, 2008). Unfortunately, many edited compilations purportedly dealing with entire Malagasy faunas have failed to include consideration of fishes or aquatic systems in general. Fortunately, there are recent indications of change (see, e.g., Sparks and Stiassny 2005, 2008; Irwin et al. 2010), and herein we feel it timely to again reevaluate the status of Madagascar's freshwater fishes in light of recent ichthyofaunal surveys and the discovery and formal description of numerous new species from across the island (Table 10.1). The results presented below represent many decades of surveys conducted across the island, as well as phylogenetic and revisional studies of several native and endemic Malagasy fish groups.

SPECIES INVENTORY

Thanks to numerous survey efforts in recent years, we now have accumulated a reasonably comprehensive overview of the island's current fish diversity throughout its major river basins and hydrological regions. These more recent surveys have included far northern basins, including those draining Montagne d'Ambre, the Masoala Peninsula, and the Makira region; western and southwestern karst habitats; and remote forested regions in the eastern highlands (e.g., Vevembe-Vondrozo forests, upper Mangoro basin) (Figures 10.2 and 10.3). Nevertheless, a few critical areas remain in urgent need of exploration. In particular, we still lack comprehensive data for much of western Madagascar to the south and west of the Mahavavy du Sud basin, the remote forested expanses of the eastern region extending from Mandritsara south to Lake Alaotra (including headwaters of both eastern and western drainages encompassed by this region, containing the Sofia, Mahajamba, Kamoro, Betsiboka, Rantabe, and Marimbona Rivers), the headwaters of the Tsaratanàna Massif in the north, and the remaining forested regions of the southeastern Central Highlands (especially south of the Mananara drainage basin) (Sparks and Stiassny 2003: Figure 9.3a shaded regions; Figure 10.3). This deficit unfortunately mostly persists to this day, despite increased, albeit limited, sampling since Sparks and Stiassny (2003) of major eastern rivers to the south of the Masoala Peninsula, basins draining the Tsaratanàna Massif, rivers in the far north including those draining Montagne d'Ambre, and far southwestern basins, including the coastal karst formations of the Mahafaly Plateau. Despite increased geographical coverage in other regions, critically missing are repeat surveys to previously sampled areas to assess change of native fish assemblages and species over time. With a small team of in-country ichthyologists working in collaboration with equally sparse teams of international researchers, and increasingly limited funding sources for baseline surveys, it has rarely been feasible to accomplish this critical goal of monitoring freshwater habitats (see Andrianandrasana et al. 2005 for a recent exception).

Species listed in Table 10.1 not collected personally by the authors or by research collaborators (i.e., those listed in recent global compendiums such as Fricke et al. 2020) have been verified by examination of existing museum collections that house significant holdings of Malagasy fishes. A primary objective of this review is to compile an accurate, up-to-date list of the native fishes inhabiting fresh waters of Madagascar. Several species have not been collected in recent years, and for these we relied on museum records and specimens to verify their occurrence (e.g., *Pantanodon madagascariensis*, known only from the type series). This approach has resulted in the exclusion of certain historically reported species, such as *Arius africanus* and *Galeichthys feliceps*, for which we were unable to verify a record of occurrence on the island (Ng and Sparks 2003; see Ng and Sparks, pp. 1263–65). The attributions of these species to Malagasy inland waters are due to either taxonomic misidentification or incorrectly reported locality data.

Further, in this revised update we have rectified several taxonomic and species misidentifications that had persisted in the literature and have verified that all species names are valid by consulting summary sources for current ichthyological taxonomy (Froese and Pauly 2019; Fricke et al. 2020). In cases where there is disagreement, or a lack of consensus regarding current validity of a species name, we utilized the one most commonly used in recent studies of Malagasy freshwater fishes.

Several undescribed species are included in Table 10.1. Inclusion of these novel, yet currently undescribed, taxa is not only justified but necessary for an accurate representation of what is known about Malagasy ichthyofaunal diversity. The large number of undescribed species results in part from intensive collecting efforts during the past two and a half decades, often focused on remote areas that previously had not been comprehensively surveyed, including the upper and middle reaches of northwestern basins; eastern-, southeastern-, and western-draining basins of the southern Central Highlands; and northeastern drainages. The great majority of undescribed species are members of Aplocheilidae (*Pachypanchax*), Bedotiidae (*Bedotia* and *Rheocles*), and Cichlidae (*Paratilapia* and *Paretroplus*), reflecting in part a greater taxonomic discrimination as these assemblages of Malagasy freshwater fishes have been subjected to recent revisional and/or phylogenetic study (see the Systematic Accounts section for these genera). As can be seen by comparing Table 10.1 to Sparks and Stiassny (2003) Table 9.1, 30 new endemic species have been described over the intervening two decades.

As in 2003, we consider a taxon to be a freshwater fish if it is generally collected in fresh water, is commonly found well inland, or is restricted to completely freshwater habitats. Following this definition, we also include species whose life histories are poorly known but that appear to spend a significant portion of their life in fresh waters, as opposed to entering fresh water for the sole purpose of reproduction. Our interpretation errs on the conservative side and may underestimate the true diversity of native Malagasy freshwater fish species. Again, we have not included numerous species of Carangidae (jacks), Lutjanidae (snappers), Gerreidae (mojarras), Leiognathidae (ponyfishes), Sparidae (porgies), and Haemulidae (grunts), in addition to a number of species belonging to other marine families that are frequently collected well inland on Madagascar (Fricke et al. 2018). We note that among ichthyologists there are differences in the definition of a freshwater species, and lists will necessarily vary somewhat in terms of the inclusion and exclusion of these peripheral, primarily marine taxa.

In Table 10.1 we list 178 native freshwater species, belonging to 29 families and 62 genera, representing an increase of about 25%

FIGURE 10.2 **Comparative photos of a variety of typical freshwater fish habitats throughout Madagascar that are discussed in text, including pristine to moderately disturbed eastern and western basins. A) Andranomaloto River, a typical large, shallow sandy river in the northwest, which is home to *Paretroplus damii* and *Ptychochromis oligacanthus*; B) a deep, lower tidally influenced section of the Maintsomalaza River, near Maromandia in the northwest, type locality of *Paretroplus maromandia*; C) typical shallow floodplain lake in the Betsiboka River basin, central west, habitat of *P. maculatus*; D) noodling for *P. nourissati* near Mandritsara, in the shallow, rocky, swift-flowing Amboaboa River (a tributary of the much larger Sofia River), which is also home to *Ptychochromis insolitus* and "*Rheocles*" *derhami*; E) forested headwaters of the Mahavoua River, a tributary of the upper Mangoro River, in the east, home to an undescribed species of *Rheocles*; F) upper reaches of a typical rocky east coast river near the Anjanaharibe-Sud protected area in the northeast, habitat of *Bedotia marojejy*; and G) lower reaches of the Maloutrondro River, amid rare intact coastal forest, in the east.** (PHOTOS A, B, and C by J. S. Sparks, D by C. B. Braun, E and G by P. V. Loiselle, and F by O. Lucanus.)

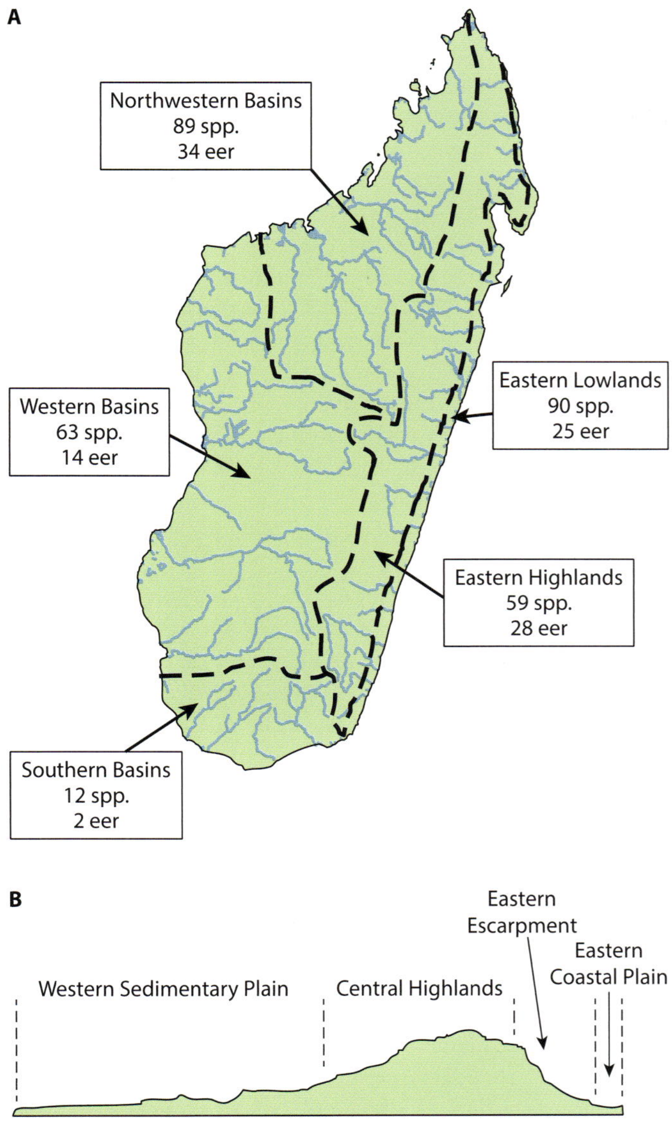

FIGURE 10.3 **A) Five major hydrographic ecoregions of Madagascar recognized in this study (outlined by dashed lines), comprising the eastern highlands, eastern lowlands, western basins, the rivers and lakes of the northwest, and southern basins. Figures in boxes indicate the total number of native freshwater species (spp.) recorded from the particular ecoregion and the number of those species that are endemic (eer) to that particular ecoregion. B) Cross-sectional relief map of Madagascar, illustrating the wide western plain; narrow, steep eastern escarpment; and other features.**

over our previous total of 143 native species (Sparks and Stiassny 2003: Table 9.1). Of these 178 native freshwater species, 122 (69%) are endemic to Madagascar, whereas 127 species (71%) are endemic to the Malagasy Region (as defined above) but excluding mainland Africa. In our prior summary (Sparks and Stiassny 2003: Table 9.1), we reported that Malagasy freshwater fish endemism had increased dramatically over the preceding years and was 60–90% greater than that reported in the then most recent faunal studies (Figure 10.1a). Here, we report an increase of 30 endemic Malagasy freshwater species (indicated with an asterisk [*] in Table 10.1) formally described since our 2003 total of 93 (which included undescribed species), representing an additional increase of over 32% in species diversity.

Considering only the 50 formally described endemic freshwater species recognized in our 2003 total, this increase of 30 new described species in less than two decades represents a remarkable 60% increase in described species diversity (Figure 10.1a), however, this must be tempered with the high number of endemic species that are now considered threatened (IUCN 2021; Figures 10.1b and c). Please note that species totals for various categories may not add up exactly when comparing the old and new tables, as several undescribed species listed in Sparks and Stiassny (2003) are no longer considered valid, some previously synonymized endemic Malagasy species have been removed from synonymy of more widely distributed taxa (e.g., *Kuhlia sauvagii*, Kuhliidae), and some revisions have been made as to whether certain previously listed species are endemic to Madagascar (e.g., *Spratellomorpha bianalis*). This steady increase in the number of native freshwater fishes underscores the importance of continued ichthyofaunal surveys in regions of the island that have yet to be comprehensively sampled and/or are under continued threat of habitat destruction and resource exploitation. Despite the high level of endemism at the species rank, we reiterate that at higher taxonomic ranks endemism is distinctly decreased, consistent with island ichthyofaunas, and just two endemic families (~6.9%) and 17 endemic genera (~27.4%) are currently recorded from the island.

Details for recent new species descriptions since Sparks and Stiassny (2003) are presented in the Systematic Accounts section of this chapter. Among newly described taxa are two endemic genera, *Gogo* (Anchariidae [Ng and Sparks 2005]) and *Katria* (Cichlidae [Stiassny and Sparks 2006]). Newly described species include six new endemic catfishes (of the genera *Arius* [Ng and Sparks 2003], *Ancharius*, and *Gogo* [Ng and Sparks 2005; Ng et al. 2008]), a new clupeid (*Sauvagella* [Stiassny 2002]), four new killifishes (*Pachypanchax* [Loiselle 2006]), four new bedotiids (*Bedotia* [Sparks and Rush 2005; Loiselle and Rodriguez 2007; Jones et al. 2010] and "*Rheocles*" [Stiassny et al. 2002]), 14 new cichlids (*Paretroplus* [Stiassny et al. 2001; Sparks 2002a, 2008; Sparks and Schelly 2011], *Ptychochromis* [Sparks 2002b; Stiassny and Sparks 2006; Sparks and Stiassny 2010; Martinez et al. 2015], and *Ptychochromoides* [Sparks 2004a]), and a new cavefish (*Typhleotris* [Sparks and Chakrabarty 2012]). In addition, as can be seen by the undescribed taxa identified by the designation "n. sp." in Table 10.1, numerous new endemic freshwater species recently discovered await formal description, including many new species of *Pachypanchax*, *Bedotia*, *Rheocles*, and *Paratilapia*. These findings strongly suggest that important portions of the island's ichthyofaunal diversity likely await discovery by fish biologists.

HYDROLOGY AND FISH COMMUNITIES

Aldegheri (1972: 261) divided Madagascar into five major hydrographic regions: 1) the slopes of Montagne d'Ambre in the far north; 2) drainages of the Tsaratanàna Massif in the north; 3) eastern drainages; 4) western and northwestern basins; and 5) southern basins. Although endemic freshwater fish species are found in each, as in Sparks and Stiassny (2003) we restrict our discussion to regions with the highest ichthyofaunal diversity. These regions with strong local ichthyofaunal endemism are the eastern Central Highlands and lowlands, the western basins, and the rivers and lakes of the northwest (Sparks and Stiassny 2003: Figure 9.3a; Figure 10.3, Table 10.1).

Traditionally, two major ichthyofaunal regions on the island have been recognized: the east coast drainages, with the highest diversity of freshwater fishes (Kiener and Richard-Vindard 1972), and the much drier and supposedly species-poor western basins, which are subject to large fluctuations in seasonal flow rate. East coast drainages emptying into the Indian Ocean are characteristically steep, with many rapids and cascades, particularly in their upper reaches (Figures 10.2e and f). These rivers are short, generally clear-watered, and terminate on a narrow coastal plain over a limited continental shelf (Figure 10.2g). The steep eastern slopes, constituting approximately 25% of the total surface area of the island (Aldegheri 1972; Sparks and Stiassny 2003; Figure 10.3b), are subjected to high average annual rainfall. The headwaters of eastern rivers have depauperate fish assemblages, frequently comprising only a few gobiiform species; and anguillid eels (*Anguilla* spp.) are also present in some of these headwater regions where there are no significant barriers to upstream passage, although several landlocked populations are known. According to Kiener (1963), only gobiiforms, eels, and members of the cichlid genera *Paratilapia* and *Ptychochromoides* have distributions extending above 1000 m elevation, but none of our recent ichthyofaunal surveys have found either of these cichlid genera above 1000 m.

In contrast, western Madagascar is considerably drier (average annual rainfall is only about 25% that of the eastern slopes) and characterized by longer, generally slow-flowing rivers subjected to much seasonal fluctuation in water level and flow rate, and shallow, extremely turbid, oligotrophic floodplain lakes (Figures 10.2a–c). Many of the smaller western river basins are dry from April to November. The rivers, and to a lesser extent also the lakes, of the western and northwestern coastal regions contain numerous marine species, many of which are frequently collected far inland (Kiener 1965), as well as large numbers of introduced species. This is largely due to an expansive continental shelf extending along most of the west coast, and the presence of numerous coral reefs in the region with large fish populations, as well as the high salinity tolerance of many introduced species. Western rivers exhibit significant tidal influence in their lower reaches, facilitating colonization and recolonization by marine forms after periods of drought may have extirpated native freshwater species from these regions (Figure 10.3a).

A significant result of our long-term fieldwork on the island is the recognition that in addition to east coast drainages, the rivers and floodplain lakes of the northwest are a major locus of ichthyofaunal diversity (Table 10.1, Figures 10.2a–d and 10.3). Accordingly, we consider the rivers and floodplain lakes of the northwest, the eastern lowlands, and the eastern Central Highlands (a subdivision of the eastern region based on a clear elevational disjunction in species distribution), as distinct ichthyofaunal zones, each characterized by more or less unique fish faunas (see also Sparks and Stiassny 2005, 2008). Eighty-nine native freshwater species are recorded from northwestern rivers and lakes, 90 species from the eastern lowlands, and 59 species from the eastern Central Highlands, making the eastern lowlands and northwestern basins the most species-rich eco-hydrological zones.

Seventy-one native species have distributions restricted to eastern drainages, occurring in either or both the eastern lowlands and eastern Central Highlands but nowhere else on the island, whereas 53 native species are entirely restricted to western drainages. Considered in their entirety, the eastern drainages therefore represent the most species-rich region of the island. However, if the upper and lower basins are considered separately, as seems appropriate given an elevational divide and substantial differences in the fish assemblages present in each, then the northwestern basins (89 species) are nearly as species rich as the eastern lowlands (90 species). We emphasize that species diversity in the northwest and the eastern lowlands and eastern Central Highlands is likely underestimated, as a majority of the basins draining the Tsaratanàna Massif, as well as a number of other basins in the northwest, extreme north, and east (particularly to the south of the Masoala Peninsula and the southeast Central Highlands), remain essentially unsurveyed for freshwater fishes (Sparks and Stiassny 2003: Figure 9.3a shaded regions; Figure 10.3).

In addition to these three primary regions of ichthyofaunal diversity, several localized areas with unique and interesting endemic fish assemblages are found throughout the island. These include the *tsingy* formations of the north, where *Glossogobius ankaranensis* (see Chakrabarty et al., pp. 1295–98) is endemic to caves within the Ankarana Massif, and western regions of the island, and the numerous karstic caves and sinkholes of the southwest that are home to a small radiation of blind cavefishes of the family Milyeringidae (*Typhleotris* spp.) (see Sparks and Chakrabarty, pp. 1298–300). The Central Highlands and eastern coastal Madagascar also contain both lowland and highland *Pandanus* swamps (see Callmander et al., pp. 551–59), where a number of rare and highly stenotopic fish species occur (or have occurred), including members of *Pantanodon* (both Malagasy species are likely extinct; see Sparks and Smith, pp. 1270–71) and numerous species of *Bedotia* (see Stiassny et al., pp. 1273–76). The larger rivers in the southwest, near the Isalo Massif, are (or were formerly) home to extremely rare and localized freshwater fish assemblages, including members of the cichlid genera *Ptychochromoides* (see Sparks and Loiselle, pp. 1293–95), *Ptychochromis* (now presumed extinct in this region; see Sparks and Stiassny, pp. 1289–93), and *Paratilapia* (see Loiselle and Ravelomanana, pp. 1282–84), as well as the endemic catfish genus *Ancharius*, whose closest relatives are restricted to eastern and southeastern drainages (see Ng and Sparks, pp. 1260–62). The composition and relationships of the ichthyofauna of the Isalo Massif are suggestive of a recent connection with southeastern drainages, where closely related species occur (Sparks and Reinthal 2001; Ng and Sparks 2005). The largest islands, Nosy Be and Ile Sainte Marie, separated from Madagascar by shallow water and connected during different periods in recent geological history, share most elements with the main island. The small crater lakes on Nosy Be are currently free of introduced predators (P. V. Loiselle, unpublished data) and are home to *Ptychochromis oligacanthus*, *Paratilapia polleni*, and *Paretroplus damii*; however, the lattermost species has not been found in recent surveys and may have been extirpated from the island, its type locality.

Riseng (1997) compiled baseline data for most of the island's major drainage basins and compared disturbed and pristine sites for several water-quality parameters. On average, western rivers were found to be warmer than eastern rivers, lower in conductivity, slightly higher in pH (nearly neutral vs slightly acidic for eastern rivers), and much higher in dissolved carbonates (i.e., alkalinity). Oxygen content was found to be similar for waters in both eastern and western drainages. The shallow oligotrophic floodplain lakes of the northwest were found to be warmer than eastern lakes, with higher conductivity, higher pH (7.3 vs. 5.6), and higher levels of dissolved carbonates. Again, dissolved oxygen content was found to be similar regardless of hydrological region.

OVERVIEW OF THE FRESHWATER FISH FAUNA

Small radiations of cichlids (six genera, all endemic), bedotiids (endemic family; three genera, including the currently undescribed "*Rheocles*"; see Stiassny et al., pp. 1277–79), aplocheilids (one genus, endemic to Madagascar and granitic Seychelles), and anchariids (endemic family; two genera) characterize the island's insular rivers, streams, wetlands, and lakes (see Stiassny et al. 2010 for a detailed characterization of aquatic habitat types). However, most families represented on Madagascar, including Ambassidae, Anguillidae, Ariidae, Butidae, Eleotridae, Gobiidae, Kuhliidae, Milyeringidae, Mugilidae, Oxudercidae, and Syngnathidae, are primarily marine and are frequent colonizers of fresh waters on oceanic islands. Interestingly, other than native eels of the genus *Anguilla*, the island lacks large predatory species; however, *Channa maculata* (Asian Snakehead) was introduced in the 1960s, has since become widespread, and continues to devastate native fish populations over much of the island. Predation by *Channa* on both juveniles and adults has contributed to the disappearance of both *Ptychochromoides itasy* and *Paratilapia bleekeri* from the Central Highlands and has impacted *Bedotia* species throughout much of their historical range.

Madagascar's ichthyofauna is noteworthy also for a lack of families generally considered "primary" freshwater fishes (*sensu* Myers 1938: those families whose members are very strictly confined to fresh water based on their perceived physiological intolerance to salinity and their present and presumed historical distributions) and for the presence of representatives of only two "secondary" freshwater families (those that are generally restricted to fresh water but in some cases enter the sea voluntarily for short periods), Aplocheilidae and Cichlidae (Stiassny and Raminosoa 1994; but see Sparks and Smith 2005 for a discussion on these non-phylogenetic classifications). Most other families with members present on Madagascar have generally been considered to represent either marine or "peripheral" families (but see below). The term *peripheral* is used to refer to primarily marine families with members that are permanent residents of freshwater habitats or that require freshwater habitats to complete their life cycles. Most surprising perhaps is the absence of a diverse otophysan fauna (catfishes [Siluriformes], characins and allies [Characiformes], minnows and allies [Cypriniformes]) on the island, as this group comprises the vast majority of so-called primary freshwater fishes worldwide and is well represented on other Gondwanan landmasses (i.e., South America, Africa, and India). However, such physiological distributional generalizations are restrictive and arbitrary, and we believe that it is not only more informative but necessary to adopt a phylogenetic approach. As stressed by Lundberg (1993), it is important to recognize the phylogenetic level at which subgroups within a clade show strictly freshwater distributions, and both Bedotiidae and Anchariidae must therefore be considered to represent freshwater families. Clearly, the traditional "primary" and "secondary" distinctions of Myers (1938) are holdovers from a dispersalist perspective, and as such they ignore much recent phylogenetic evidence that brings into question and contradicts the restrictions implied by these terms (see Sparks and Smith 2005).

Madagascar is home to a surprisingly diverse gobiiform fauna, comprising at least six families (Butidae, Eleotridae, Gobiidae, Kraemeriidae, Milyeringidae, and Oxudercidae), 22 genera, and 36 species, and including two endemic genera and 16 endemic species (Table 10.1). Gobiiformes are common throughout Madagascar and are frequently the only fishes encountered in the headwaters of many of the steep and cascading rivers draining the eastern escarpment. This is particularly true of *Awaous* and *Sicyopterus* species, often referred to as "rock-climbing gobies." These and related genera are commonly found above waterfalls and have been reported elsewhere in the tropics even to penetrate beyond sheer drops of 130 m (Fitzsimons and Nishimoto 1990). Two distinct genera of troglodytic gobiiforms are also present on Madagascar; a blind cave *Glossogobius* is found within the karst formations of Ankarana in the north (see Chakrabarty et al., pp. 1295–98), and a small radiation of blind *Typhleotris* species is restricted to limestone karst formations in the southwest (see Sparks and Chakrabarty, pp. 1298–300).

As noted previously, Madagascar is home to two endemic freshwater fish families: Bedotiidae, the Malagasy rainbowfishes, with three genera (*Bedotia* and *Rheocles* and "*Rheocles*"; see Stiassny et al., pp. 1273–76, and pp. 1277–79, respectively); and a poorly known catfish family, Anchariidae, comprising two genera (*Ancharius* and *Gogo*; see Ng and Sparks, pp. 1260–62). The phylogenetic relationships of both families have historically been viewed as controversial and problematic to resolve. For example, Taylor (1986) placed *Ancharius* within Ariidae, whereas de Pinna (1993) recovered it as its sister group. In contrast, Mo (1991) proposed that *Ancharius* is most closely related to the African freshwater family Mochokidae. More recently, however, strong morphological (Diogo 2005) and molecular (Sullivan et al. 2006) evidence corroborate de Pinna (1993) in resolving Anchariidae as sister to Ariidae. Similarly, although the phylogenetic placement of Bedotiidae has also proved problematic (e.g., Dyer and Chernoff 1996; Campanella et al. 2015), Sparks and Smith (2004b), combining morphological and molecular evidence, recover Bedotiidae as sister to the Australian–New Guinean Melanotaeniidae. The Australasian Telmatherinidae and Pseudomugilidae, in turn, compose a clade that is recovered as the sister to the Melanotaeniidae-Bedotiidae clade (Melanotaenioidei). Until recently, both of Madagascar's endemic families were considered to be restricted entirely to eastern drainages on the island; however, surveys conducted within the past two decades have discovered species belonging to both families in western basins (Table 10.1; Stiassny and Rodriguez 2001: "*Rheocles*" *derhami*; Ng and Sparks 2005: *Ancharius griseus*).

Finally, Madagascar is home to several extremely rare endemic and stenotopic freshwater species, including the Atherinidae genus *Teramulus* (see Sparks, pp. 1272–73), which is known only from isolated, generally forested, stream habitats in northern and northwestern Madagascar. The clupeid *Spratellomorpha bianalis*, now considered a Malagasy endemic (see Stiassny, pp. 1267–68), is currently known from scattered localities in floodplain lakes in the northwest. Similarly, the enigmatic genus *Pantanodon*, currently placed in its own family, Pantanodontidae (see Bragança et al. 2018), was rediscovered in the mid-1990s in a single small *Pandanus* swamp (approximately 10 × 50 m) along the southeastern coast within the Manombo protected area. This population, which represented an undescribed species, has not been collected since the late 1990s, despite repeated attempts, and is presumed extinct (see Sparks and Smith, pp. 1270–71). Two described species currently compose the genus, *Pantanodon stuhlmanni*, from Kenya and Tanzania, and *P. madagascariensis*, formerly endemic to swamps in eastern Madagascar but now classified as Extinct (IUCN 2021). *Pantanodon* represents the first fish genus to go extinct on Madagascar.

ORIGINS, RELATIONSHIPS, AND BIOGEOGRAPHY

For students of Gondwanan biogeography, the perplexing origin(s) and composition of Madagascar's extant freshwater fish fauna have led to many, often conflicting, hypotheses. Missing in both the contemporary and the fossil records are several major groups found in, but not necessarily restricted to, the African mainland. These include cyprinids (Cypriniformes), alestids (Characiformes), numerous catfish families (Siluriformes), polypterids (Polypteriformes), and osteoglossomorphs (Osteoglossomorpha) among others (Kiener and Richard-Vindard 1972; Stiassny and Raminosoa 1994; Sparks and Stiassny 2003). Madagascar lacks representatives of families present not only in Africa but also in India (often with ranges extending into Southeast Asia). These include Anabantidae, Bagridae, Schilbeidae, Clariidae, Latidae, Channidae, Cyprinidae, Nastacembelidae, and Notopteridae. Further, many families present in South America, Africa, and India–Southeast Asia are also conspicuously absent from Madagascar. Examples include the families Nandidae and Synbranchidae (Berra 2007; Nelson et al. 2016). (See Stiassny and Raminosoa 1994: Table II, for a list of families present on various Gondwanan landmasses.)

Before discussing the origins and affinities of Madagascar's extant ichthyofauna, it is helpful to summarize paleogeographic data bearing on the Mesozoic fragmentation of Gondwanan landmasses (also see Krause et al., pp. 59–68; Collins et al., pp. 45–51). Current data suggest that Madagascar and India, or the Indo-Madagascar block, separated from Africa ~165 million years ago (Mya), and that Madagascar attained its current position with respect to Africa ~130 Mya (B. C. Storey 1995; M. Storey et al. 1995). Although motion between the Indian subcontinent and Madagascar began as early as ~135 Mya, at about the same time that India began to rift from Antarctica, Madagascar and India remained in close proximity until the Late Cretaceous, ~88 Mya (Rabinowitz et al. 1983; M. Storey et al. 1995; Hay et al. 1999). As the Indian landmass continued to migrate rapidly northward during the Late Cretaceous, rifting between the granitic Seychelles and India occurred ~64 Mya (Plummer and Bell 1995; B. C. Storey 1995). Western Gondwanan rifting, between South America and Africa, began ~130 Mya, and the two landmasses were subaerially isolated (with no exposed, abovewater connection) by the Middle Cretaceous (~120–100 Mya) (B. C. Storey 1995; Hay et al. 1999).

Interestingly, studies have also hypothesized that the Indo-Madagascar landmass and eastern Antarctica were in contact until ~120 Mya (B. C. Storey 1995; Krause et al. 1997a) and possibly even well into the Late Cretaceous (~80 Mya) (Hay et al. 1999). Thus, at the end of the Cretaceous, under the revised reconstruction of Hay et al. (1999), it is hypothesized that subaerial connections remained between all Gondwanan landmasses except for Africa (Sampson et al. 1998; Hay et al. 1999). Potentially, at least, freshwater corridors remained between Madagascar–India–granitic Seychelles, and possibly all Gondwanan landmasses, minus Africa, until very late in the Cretaceous.

Whether the absence of many widespread Gondwanan fishes from Madagascar's extant freshwater fauna is attributable to major extinctions on the island (for which there is currently no evidence), or to the fact that these groups were never present, will continue to be a focus of both paleontological and historical biogeographic studies (e.g., Samonds et al. 2012, 2013). What we do know is that representatives of Madagascar's extant freshwater fish groups are conspicuously absent from Cretaceous deposits on the island (Gottfried and Krause 1994, 1998; Krause et al. 1997b; see Krause et al., pp. 59–68), but prior to the Late Pleistocene, the island's Cenozoic fossil record is dominated by marine deposits (Krause et al. 1997b). Further, only a few families with extant endemic species on Madagascar, for example, Ariidae, have a fossil record that currently extends back to the Cretaceous (Patterson 1993a, 1993b; Gottfried and Krause 1998). Ariid fossils are known from the Late Campanian–Early Maastrichtian in North and South America, and although there are Maastrichtian otoliths from the Old World attributed to Ariidae, the earliest identifiable ariid bony elements are from the lowermost Eocene of Africa, Asia, and Europe (Gayet and Meunier 2003; Betancur-R 2009). This lack of fossil evidence has led paleontologists to conclude that extant and recently extinct vertebrate taxa did not colonize the island until the Cenozoic (Krause et al. 1997a; Gottfried and Krause 1998; Gottfried et al. 1998), well after Madagascar was isolated by the Mesozoic breakup of Gondwana (M. Storey et al. 1995; Hay et al. 1999; also see Samonds et al., pp. 73–78). Thus, paleontologists have hypothesized that the island's extant fishes are descended from post-Mesozoic (intercontinental marine) colonizers and not from freshwater taxa isolated on Madagascar by the fragmentation of Gondwana.

However, as Maisey (1993) has pointed out, "absence of evidence is not evidence of absence," and despite a lack of fossil corroboration, our current understanding of the phylogenetic relationships of many Malagasy freshwater fish clades presents a compelling argument in support of vicariance as an explanation of their present distribution. Groups with broadly Gondwanan distributions and currently present on Madagascar include Cichlidae, Bedotiidae, Aplocheilidae, Pantanodontidae, ehiravin Clupeidae, and Milyeringidae. Transoceanic sister-group relationships congruent with prevailing hypotheses of Gondwanan fragmentation (i.e., congruent with the temporal sequence of Gondwanan breakup) have been hypothesized for the cichlid genera *Etroplus* (India–Sri Lanka) and *Paretroplus* (Madagascar) (Stiassny et al. 2001; Sparks 2004b; Sparks and Smith 2004a); the family Cichlidae in general (congruent with the revised paleogeographic reconstruction of Hay et al. 1999) (Sparks 2004b; Sparks and Smith 2004a); the atheriniform families Bedotiidae (Madagascar) and Melanotaeniidae (Australia–New Guinea), forming Melanoteanoidei (Dyer and Chernoff 1996; Aarn and Ivantsoff 1997; Sparks and Smith 2004b); the aplocheilid genera *Pachypanchax* (Madagascar and Seychelles) and *Aplocheilus* (India–Asia) (Costa 1998; J. S. Sparks and W. L. Smith, unpublished data); and the obligate cavefish genera *Milyeringa* (Western Australia) and *Typhleotris* (Madagascar), which represents the first record of a transoceanic sister-group relationship between obligate vertebrate troglobites (Chakrabarty et al. 2012).

Recovered patterns for these groups suggest that Madagascar's freshwater fishes owe their origin to the Mesozoic breakup of Gondwana and not to Cenozoic transoceanic dispersal. The closest relatives to the Malagasy members of Cichlidae, Bedotiidae, Aplocheilidae, and Milyeringidae are found on distant landmasses of Gondwanan origin (e.g., Australia, India–Sri Lanka, Seychelles). Although separated from Madagascar by thousands of kilometers of open ocean throughout the Cenozoic, India, the Seychelles, and Australia share more recent direct or indirect connections with Madagascar than Madagascar does with the geographically proximate continent of Africa. For freshwater fishes, only two sister-group relationships have been recovered between mainland African and Malagasy members. These are *Pantanodon* (see Sparks and Smith, pp. 1270–71) and *Spratellomorpha* (see Stiassny, pp. 1267–68), both of which have a congener on the African continent.

Among the freshwater (i.e., continentally restricted) pellonuline (Pellonulinae) clupeid genera, an ehiravin (tribe Ehiravini) clade comprising *Sauvagella* (Madagascar), *Spratellomorpha* (Madagascar and East Africa), *Ehirava* (southern India–Sri Lanka), *Dayella* (southwestern India), *Clupeichthys* (Southeast Asia), *Corica* (India and Southeast Asia), and *Gilchristella* (southern Africa) has been hypothesized by Grande (1985) and Stiassny (2002; see Stiassny, pp. 1266–67). Although relationships within the ehiravin clade remain to be resolved, monophyly of this widespread, essentially Gondwanan freshwater clade is not incongruent with a vicariance explanation for its current distribution.

Novel phylogenetic studies of Madagascar's other freshwater and nearshore marine fish groups are likely to reveal additional biogeographic patterns congruent with Gondwanan fragmentation (J. S. Sparks and W. L. Smith, unpublished data). For example, a sister-group relationship between the Mascarene and Indian–South Asian Oxudercidae (rock-climbing) gobies of the genus *Sicyopterus* is hypothesized (Sparks and Nelson 2004) but requires additional phylogenetic study to corroborate. Such historical biogeographic patterns elucidated by phylogeny provide insight into evolutionary processes, which can in turn be used to analyze and explain present distributions (Lundberg 1993).

The sister-group relationships presented here are consistent with current hypotheses regarding the sequence of Gondwanan fragmentation, and it seems improbable that such congruence would have resulted from multiple, independent, intercontinental dispersals. Moreover, we feel it inadvisable *a priori* to dismiss vicariance in intercontinental faunal comparisons, even in the absence of fossil data, unless it can be shown for the organisms in question that their closest relatives are marine taxa (Lundberg 1993; Stiassny and Raminosoa 1994; Sparks and Smith 2005). Based on our current phylogenetic understanding of Madagascar's endemic freshwater fish assemblages, we do not find this to be the case for members of Aplocheilidae, Bedotiidae, Cichlidae, Milyeringidae, or the ehiravin clupeid genera discussed above.

Finally, we note that paleichthyological studies of Madagascar are few, and the fossil record for many of the families in question is surprisingly poor, not only on the island but worldwide. It was only a few decades ago that fossil gars, large and rather conspicuous animals, were identified from Cretaceous deposits on Madagascar (Gottfried and Krause 1998), a discovery supporting our contention that the current absence of fossil evidence for the early presence of Madagascar's extant freshwater fish lineages does not rule out the possibility that their fossils will someday be discovered on the island.

DISTRIBUTIONAL PATTERNS

In the Malagasy fish fauna, regional endemism is notably high (Table 10.1, Figure 10.3), especially in the northwestern and eastern regions of the island. For example, Sparks (2008) provides an updated distribution map for species of *Paretroplus*, illustrating their extremely localized distributions in the northwest; Stiassny and Sparks (2006) show the same for species of *Ptychochromis* in northern and northwestern basins; and Stiassny and Rodriguez (2001) and Sparks and Smith (2004b) depict similarly restricted distributions for "*Rheocles*," *Rheocles*, and *Bedotia* species in eastern drainages. Other examples include the highly stenotopic species *Ptychochromoides itasy*, *P. vondrozo*, *Ptychochromis insolitus*, *Oxylapia polli*, *Katria katria*, *Pantanodon* n. sp. "manombo," *Glossogobius ankaranensis*, and the three species of *Typhleotris* restricted to limestone karst formations in the southwest. Interest in the biogeography of Madagascar's flora and fauna has been high at a global scale, as Raxworthy and Nussbaum (1997) underscore, but relatively muted regarding within-island biogeographic patterns for vertebrates. Although several regions with highly endemic fish communities have been identified, within-island biogeographic patterns of fish distributions have yet to be rigorously investigated.

CONSERVATION

Current and Future Threats

Our prognosis a few decades ago (Sparks and Stiassny 2003) for the future of Madagascar's extraordinary freshwater fish fauna was extremely bleak, and while research undertaken in the intervening years has uncovered considerable additional diversity, the levels of threat, endangerment, and extinction have continued to escalate. Human-mediated disturbance continues to play an increasingly significant role in aquatic habitat degradation and attrition of native species, and Madagascar continues to have one of the highest population growth rates in the world (World Bank 2020). Between 1993 and 2008, hundreds of millions of dollars were invested in over 500 environmental and development projects, and the island's protected areas network subsequently expanded threefold, yet deforestation continues today virtually unchecked, biodiversity is in a tailspin of decline, and efforts to reduce poverty or improve the livelihoods of the country's rural poor have failed (Waeber et al. 2016). Continued poverty, resulting in heavy reliance on natural resources, and most recently the devastation associated with the SARS Covid-19 pandemic will undoubtedly exacerbate this truly grim predicament. For the past quarter century, deforestation has continued unabated: 0.9% of remaining forest was lost annually from 1990 to 2000 (Irwin et al. 2010), and Harper et al. (2007) determined that over 80% of remaining forest area was <1 km from an edge. More recently, Vieilledent et al. (2018) estimated that from 1953 to 2014, Madagascar lost 44% of its original forest cover, 37% of it from 1973 to 2014. Disturbingly, Vieilledent et al. (2018) also showed that the annual deforestation rate has progressively increased on Madagascar since 2005 to 99,000 ha per year during the period 2010–2014, a rate that corresponds to 1.1% annually, and that 46% of remaining forest is now within 100 m from an edge.

To the litany of impacts to aquatic habitats that follow deforestation should be added the profound effects of sedimentation from agricultural land clearance and pollution from mining, as well as overexploitation and the increasing use of destructive fishing techniques (Máiz-Tomé et al. 2018). Compounding these deleterious impacts on native fish communities is the dismal observation that introduced species appear able to thrive in, and dominate, such highly degraded habitats. Some 23 non-native species have been deliberately introduced into the island's freshwater systems dating back to the mid-1800s (Reinthal and Stiassny 1991; Benstead et al. 2000, 2003; Irwin et al. 2010). Several tilapia species, introduced for (failed) aquaculture purposes decades ago (see Reinthal and Stiassny 1991: Table 4, for a complete list of introductions), are now fully established and compete for resources with nearly all native species. Perhaps even more impactful has been the introduction and rapid spread of the predatory *Channa maculata* (Asian Snakehead), which preys extensively on juvenile and smaller-bodied native fishes. Currently, all of Madagascar's large lakes are infested with tilapias, *C. maculata*, and a range of other introduced species, resulting in precipitously declining native fish catches, which will likely lead to the collapse of many artisanal fisheries in the near future. Despite the designation of Lakes Kinkony and Mandrozo and surrounding wetlands in 2012 as Ramsar sites (Wetlands of International Importance under the terms of the international Ramsar Convention of 1971), as well as the integration of these areas into the protected area system, our survey efforts indicate that many species of *Paretroplus* that are highly valued for local consumption have suffered dramatic declines in recent years. *Paretroplus menarambo* from Lake Sarodrano and *P. dambabe* from Lake Kinkony, both in the northwest, are now verging on extinction, apparently as a direct result of heavy predation by *C. maculata*, competition with introduced tilapias, and overexploitation from the use of unregulated fishing techniques. *Paretroplus maculatus*, once quite common in Lake Ravelobe and the surrounding region, including the lower reaches of the Betsiboka and Ikopa drainages southeast of Mahajanga, was not found in a 2011 survey in either Lake Ravelobe or the surrounding area (J. S. Sparks, unpublished data). In addition, several ptychochromine (Ptychochrominae) cichlid species, including *Ptychochromoides itasy* (Sparks 2004a; Sparks et al. 2012) and *Ptychochromis insolitus* (Stiassny and Sparks 2006), are now extremely rare and likely verging on extinction.

Some species appear already to have succumbed to the combined pressures on their aquatic habitats described above and are now presumed extinct (Harrison and Stiassny 1999; Sparks and Stiassny 2003, 2005; IUCN 2021; Ravelomanana et al. 2018; Figures 10.1b and c). Survey efforts over the past quarter century have failed to locate individuals of *Ptychochromis onilahy*, apparently once abundant in the Onilahy River basin in the southwest (Stiassny and Sparks 2006; see Sparks and Stiassny, pp. 1289–93), or *Pantanodon madagascariensis*, formerly endemic to eastern coastal swamps (see Sparks and Smith, pp. 1270–71). Sadly, an undescribed species of *Pantanodon*, first collected in 1994 by our team from a single, small lowland *Pandanus* swamp within the Manombo protected area, south of Farafangana, its only known locality, became extinct in the late 1990s, not long after it was first discovered. Unfortunately, introduced *Gambusia holbrooki*, erroneously named "mosquitofish," which appears to prefer fish larvae and eggs to mosquito larvae, is prevalent at this locality. Thus, the genus *Pantanodon* is now considered extinct on the island.

Actions

Species inhabiting islands may be more susceptible to extinction due to a high degree of specialization and low resilience to competition with other species (MacArthur and Wilson 1967; D'Antonio and Dudley 1995), a devastating combination in the face of burgeoning populations of introduced competitors and predators, and this appears to hold particularly true for the Malagasy ichthyofauna. Further, the vulnerability of the island's freshwater ichthyofauna is exacerbated by the extreme stenotopy of numerous native species. Many endemic cichlids, aplocheilids, clupeids, atherinids, and bedotiids, as well as the island's two genera of gobiiform cavefishes, *Glossogobius* and *Typhleotris*, have restricted geographic distributions, and many are known only from their type localities or at most a very localized area, frequently a single body of water or isolated drainage basin (see Chakrabarty et al., pp. 1295–98; Sparks and Chakrabarty, pp. 1298–300).

In many of the world's top biodiversity hotspots, freshwater systems are frequently overlooked, and this has had tragic consequences not only for Madagascar's unique and fragile aquatic communities but also for the terrestrial systems that depend upon them (Mittermeier et al. 2011). Madagascar's river systems are commonly excluded from protection, even if surrounded by protected land, as riparian areas with their proximity to water are the most desirable for swidden agriculture and paddy rice production (de Laulanié 2011). This is not to say that conservation efforts are always futile. An ichthyofaunal survey of the Masoala Peninsula was instrumental in ensuring the inclusion of river basins into the design of the Masoala National Park (Kremen et al. 1999), and in recent years a number of important aquatic habitats for freshwater fishes have been afforded some degree of protection. Another example is the Nosivolo River, a notable hotspot of endemic diversity, which was designated as Madagascar's seventh Wetland of International Importance in 2010, becoming the country's first riverine Ramsar site.

Larger rivers frequently are chosen to serve as protected area boundaries, and as a result the included reserves do little to protect the integrity of the river and excluded watershed. Exemplary exceptions, besides the protection of the Nosivolo River in the upper Mangoro basin, as noted above, include the designation of Masoala National Park (Kremen et al. 1999; Rübel et al. 2003), which was designed to include river basins within its borders specifically to protect native fish communities. The decision to incorporate river basins was based directly on the results of ichthyofaunal surveys we conducted, which highlighted the unique local freshwater fish fauna (J. S. Sparks and K. Riseng, unpublished data).

Another possible reason for a persistent terrestrial bias is the woeful fact that today there remain few areas of the island where intact native fish communities persist. An array of introduced species, especially tilapiine cichlids introduced for aquaculture purposes, is ubiquitous in all but the most remote and undisturbed regions (Reinthal and Stiassny 1991; J. S. Sparks and K. Riseng, unpublished data), and continued habitat degradation and destruction on Madagascar has been, and continues to be, severe (Irwin et al. 2010; Máiz-Tomé et al. 2018; Vieilledent et al. 2018).

The paucity of information on Madagascar's freshwater fishes, and the lack of consideration they have received from conservationists, are certainly also attributable to the difficulty associated with conducting research in remote regions of Madagascar, as well as the problems related to the conservation of river systems in general, particularly in areas where strongly agrarian populations live (Boon et al. 2000; Sparks and Stiassny 2005; Darwall et al. 2011). Additionally, as Andriamialisoa and Langrand (pp. 1–38) note, for example, only one scientist from the Université d'Antananarivo, now retired, Noromalala Raminosoa, worked in the field of ichthyology, and not one of the few active international ichthyologists working on Malagasy fishes is permanently based on the island—and these factors have limited progress. Most of Madagascar's terrestrial protected areas are small, frequently consisting of a forest fragment surrounded by an expansive deforested region and degraded watersheds (Goodman et al. 2018). Under such circumstances, at very best, only a few headwater streams can be afforded any protection. Unfortunately, these headwaters do not harbor diverse fish assemblages and as such are not the habitats most in need of protection from the perspective of maintaining freshwater vertebrate diversity. On the contrary, the habitats that continue to support the most diverse native freshwater fish assemblages are the middle to lower reaches of river basins and associated floodplain lakes, particularly in eastern and northwestern portions of the island (Table 10.1).

Conservation Status and Programs

It has long been recognized that Madagascar is characterized by a highly endemic freshwater ichthyofauna (omitting marine taxa that are frequently encountered in the lower reaches of rivers; Fricke et al. 2018). The species totals presented here (Table 10.1), and discussed in detail below, bring Malagasy freshwater fish species diversity completely into line with that of other continental landmasses and islands of comparable size (Sparks and Stiassny 2003: Figure 9.1), and while these findings are satisfying from a theoretical standpoint, they are disheartening from one of preservation. The combined pressures of human encroachment, deforestation, overfishing, and the introduction of a wide variety of non-native species, including various tilapias and predatory species such as *Channa maculata* (Asian Snakehead) and *Gambusia holbrooki* (Mosquitofish), continue to exert a significant negative impact on native fish populations (Irwin et al. 2010; Ravelomanana et al. 2018).

A full 60% of Madagascar's described endemic freshwater fish species are currently considered threatened by IUCN, and 2% are classified as Extinct (Figures 10.1b and c). Within the IUCN threatened categories, 7% are classified as Vulnerable, 36% as Endangered, and 17% as Critically Endangered (Table 10.1; Máiz-Tomé et al. 2018; Ravelomanana et al. 2018). Even this extraordinary level of endangerment is likely a significant underestimate, given that the assessment protocols used by IUCN tend to overestimate ranges by including entire basins in calculations, whereas many species inhabit only a small portion of any given basin. Furthermore, a vast majority of recently discovered, yet undescribed species were not assessed in the most recent IUCN Red List update (Table 10.1) but, based on recent survey data, are highly threatened. Concomitant with the discovery of new taxa, recent surveys have documented a rapid decline in both the abundance and range of numerous native species, particularly the island's endemic radiation of cichlids (Sparks 2008; J. S. Sparks et al., unpublished data). Although infrequently reported in the conservation literature, Madagascar's endemic freshwater fishes likely represent some of the most, if not the most, endangered groups of vertebrates on the island.

Globally, freshwater systems have often been overlooked in the drafting and implementation of conservation protocols, and Madagascar's freshwater systems have proved no exception to this bias. This is a remarkable oversight when one considers that freshwater fishes alone account for an astounding 20–25% of the world's vertebrate diversity (Lundberg et al. 2000; Dudgeon et al. 2007). There have been few papers dealing specifically with the conservation of Madagascar's freshwater fishes, yet the entire freshwater ichthyofauna and aquatic systems of the island in general continue to face serious threats, as has been well documented over the past decades (Riseng 1997; Máiz-Tomé et al. 2018). Few freshwater habitats remain that are not highly disturbed, degraded, and dominated by introduced species, and these remaining few are disappearing at an alarming rate (Ravelomanana et al. 2018).

While the need for protection of Madagascar's freshwater fish fauna, and particularly its aquatic habitats, is increasingly being considered in the island's protected area system, all too often, sadly, such protection lacks enforcement. When you are hungry, a tilapia or a snakehead may not taste as good as the *Paretroplus* or *Ptychochromis* that you ate as a child, but it is food, just as a pristine wetland ecosystem may not appear to offer the immediate return of a rice paddy. Of course, we understand and empathize with the predicament of the Malagasy people but nonetheless hope they will find a way to preserve at least some remnant of a true treasure of the island, its unique endemic freshwater fishes, as a globally recognized hotspot of ichthyofaunal diversity.

CONCLUSION

We noted nearly two decades ago, after conducting research in many tropical regions of the world, that neither of us had witnessed anything surpassing the degree and extent of environmental degradation as that on Madagascar (Sparks and Stiassny 2003); that general observation remains every bit as true today. Since 2003, each new field survey, although uncovering increased diversity, has at the same time revealed ongoing and widespread degradation of aquatic habitats and an overall decline of the native fish fauna.

While a number of small forested regions have been afforded protection, and forest restoration projects have been initiated (e.g., Manjaribe et al. 2013; Favretto et al. 2020; see Jones et al., pp. 2130–40), these efforts do little to offer protection to entire river basins, given that aquatic systems are so vulnerable to removal of riparian cover and upstream influences, which lead to increased sedimentation and the degradation of downstream habitats. Many of Madagascar's current reserves are simply too small to maintain viable populations of native fish species, especially those that must migrate during reproduction or that require expansive and/or diverse habitats to complete their life cycle. At least for the time being, in certain isolated parts of the island, including the protected areas of Makira and Masoala, as well as other remote regions in the east and northwest, forested basins remain, and every effort must be made to save them.

Although it may already be too late to save all but remnants of Madagascar's unique freshwater ichthyofauna, it is our hope that this tragic story will serve as a warning and underscore the importance of early protection of vulnerable island freshwater ecosystems and their fragile ichthyofaunas elsewhere in the world.

ACKNOWLEDGMENTS

We are again extremely grateful to numerous colleagues around the globe for their help with the ongoing work, done by us and our colleagues, on the freshwater fishes of Madagascar. In particular, we thank Paul Loiselle, who has been a resource of inestimable value throughout the study. Thanks also to Karen Riseng, Tsilavina Ravelomanana, Steve Goodman, Franco Andreone, Jean Claude Nourissat (1942–2003), Patrick de Rham, Alex Saunders, Oliver Lucanus, and John Barnes for providing us with data and specimens from their fieldwork. We are grateful to the curators and collection staffs at different natural history museums for the loan of specimens and/or hospitality during visits to their collections.

Subject editor: Steven M. Goodman

SYSTEMATIC ACCOUNTS

ANCHARIIDAE: *ANCHARIUS*, *GOGO*, CATFISH, *FIAVOALAVO*, *GOGO*, *VAHO*, *VAONA*, *VAHONA*

H. H. Ng and J. S. Sparks

Anchariidae is a small family of medium-size riverine catfishes (maximum size 300 mm standard length, usually much smaller) that occurs exclusively in fresh water and is endemic to Madagascar. Two genera and six species are currently recognized within the family: *Ancharius*, with two valid species, and *Gogo*, with four valid species (Table 10.2).

SYSTEMATICS AND IDENTIFICATION

There is strong morphological (Diogo 2005) and molecular (Sullivan et al. 2006) phylogenetic evidence that Anchariidae is the sister group of Ariidae. Members of Anchariidae are distinguished from other Malagasy catfishes by the following combination of features: three pairs of barbels (maxillary, inner, and outer mandibular); widely separated anterior and posterior nostrils; moderately long adipose fin that is as long as, or longer than, the anal-fin base; reduced maxilla (relative to palatine); lack of vomerine teeth; and bicuspid premaxillary and dentary teeth. *Ancharius* differs from *Gogo* in having 9–11 (vs. 7 or 8) branched anal-fin rays, the snout not strongly (vs. strongly) produced, a subterminal (vs. inferior) mouth, and longer maxillary (to middle of pectoral-fin base vs. not reaching base of pectoral spine) and outer mandibular (beyond vs. to vertical through posterior orbital margin) barbels (Ng and Sparks 2005) (Figure 10.4).

DISTRIBUTION

The two described species of *Ancharius* are *A. fuscus*, restricted to the Central Highlands sections of several eastern drainages extending from the Tohizona to the Mananara Rivers; and *A. griseus* (Figure 10.4a), known only from upland forested habitats and clear water in southwestern Madagascar, specifically the Ihazofotsy River near Isalo and the Ilanana River south of Ranohira. Four species of *Gogo* are currently recognized: *G. arcuatus*, *G. atratus* (Figure 10.4b), *G. brevibarbis*, and *G. ornatus*. Both *G. arcuatus* and *G. brevibarbis* are known from the southeastern Central

TABLE 10.2. **Species of *Ancharius* and *Gogo* with range information and most recent IUCN status**

SCIENTIFIC NAME	DISTRIBUTION	IUCN STATUS
A. fuscus Steindachner, 1880	Eastern highlands and lowlands: Restricted to upland to middle sections of several eastern drainages extending from the Tohizona to the Mananara Rivers	LC
A. griseus Ng & Sparks, 2005	Western basins: Known only from upland forested habitats and clear water in southwestern Madagascar, specifically the Ihazofotsy River near Isalo and the Ilanana River south of Ranohira	EN
G. brevibarbis (Boulenger, 1911)	Eastern highlands and lowlands: Restricted to the upper to middle reaches of the Mananjary River drainage system, southeastern uplands	DD
G. arcuatus Ng & Sparks, 2005	Eastern highlands: Known only from the middle reaches of the Sandrananta River drainage, southeastern uplands	DD
G. ornatus Ng & Sparks, 2005	Eastern highlands: Known only from the Mangoro and Nosivolo Rivers within the upper Mangoro River drainage system in the east	EN
G. atratus Ng, Sparks & Loiselle, 2008	Eastern highlands and lowlands: Restricted to the lower reaches of the Mananara du Nord River drainage in the northeastern uplands	DD

Note: IUCN Red List conservation assessment status from IUCN (2021); for abbreviations, see Table 10.1.

FIGURE 10.4 **A) Holotype of *Ancharius griseus*, a recently described species collected in the Ihazofotsy River near Isalo, south-central Madagascar. B) *Gogo atratus* specimen (~190 mm standard length), illustrating live adult coloration, collected in main channel of Mananara River, northeastern Madagascar.** (PHOTO A by H. H. Ng and J. S. Sparks, and B by P. V. Loiselle.)

Highlands: *G. arcuatus* from the middle reaches of the Sandrananta River drainage, and *G. brevibarbis* from the upper to middle reaches of the Mananjary River drainage system. *Gogo atratus* is known from the lower reaches of the Mananara du Nord River drainage in northeastern Madagascar. *Gogo ornatus* is known only from the Mangoro and Nosivolo Rivers within the upper Mangoro River drainage system in the east. There is considerable regional endemism within the family, and additional species may be discovered with increased sampling of the upper reaches of drainages, especially those in the west.

HABITAT AND NATURAL HISTORY

Anchariids are found exclusively in clear, rocky, and silt-free upland freshwater habitats in both eastern and southwestern drainages

FIGURE 10.5 **Type locality and typical riverine habitat of *Gogo atratus*, Mananara du Nord River, northeastern Madagascar.** (PHOTO by P. V. Loiselle.)

(Figure 10.5). They appear to be intolerant of brackish conditions and are much more local in distribution than Malagasy catfishes of the family Ariidae, which are also known locally as *gogo*. Anchariids feed on smaller fishes and aquatic invertebrates. Nothing is currently known about their reproductive behavior.

CONSERVATION STATUS

All species of anchariids are rare and local throughout their respective ranges. After nearly three decades of intense collecting throughout Madagascar by our research group, nowhere were members of the genus found to be even remotely common, despite reports to the contrary by fishers regarding the local abundance of certain species (Ng et al. 2008). Museum collections hold at most only a few specimens per species, generally from a single locality (Ng and Sparks 2005; Ng et al. 2008). It should, however, be noted that anchariids are primarily nocturnal, and that may at least partly explain why they are so infrequently encountered. Of the six described anchariid species, two species, *A. griseus* and *G. ornatus*, were listed in the most recent Red List assessment (IUCN 2021) as Endangered; *A. fuscus* was assessed as Least Concern; and three species, *G. arcuatus*, *G. atratus*, and *G. brevibarbis* were categorized as Data Deficient—simply because so little is currently known regarding the distributions and population sizes of these three species. All three are extremely rare and represented by very few specimens in museum collections: *G. brevibarbis* is known only from the holotype; *G. arcuatus* is known only from the holotype and a single paratype; and *G. atratus* is known only from the holotype and three paratypes.

Small-scale artisanal fisheries for anchariids exist, but the most serious threat to long-term survival comes from continued deforestation, habitat degradation, and predation by the introduced *Channa maculata* (Asian Snakehead) (see Sparks and Stiassny, pp. 1245–60). Anchariids are likely the rarest and most poorly studied catfishes in the world, and the continued destruction of headwater habitats and the spread of introduced predators will certainly have a negative impact on population numbers and ranges of all species.

Subject editors: John S. Sparks and Melanie L. J. Stiassny

ARIIDAE: *ARIUS*, *PLICOFOLLIS*, CATFISH, *FIAVOALAVO*, *GOGO*, *VAHO*, *VAONA*, *VAHONA*

H. H. Ng and J. S. Sparks

Ariidae is a species-rich family (>150 species in 30 genera) of medium-size to large catfishes (maximum size about 150 cm standard length) found across the world and predominantly in coastal waters, but a portion of ariid diversity occurs in freshwater habitats. Two genera of ariid catfishes have been recorded from the coastal and inland waters of Madagascar: *Arius*, with three species, and *Plicofollis*, with two species (Table 10.3). A third genus, *Galeichthys*, has been reported in the literature to occur on Madagascar, but this awaits verification (see Distribution, below).

SYSTEMATICS AND IDENTIFICATION

Despite a number of higher-level phylogenetic studies of catfishes in recent years, the relationships of the ariids to the other catfishes remain unresolved. Based on morphological evidence, Ariidae has been hypothesized to be the sister group either to a clade consisting of the African mochokids and South American auchenipterids and doradids (de Pinna 1998) or to the African claroteids (Diogo 2005). Molecular phylogenetic evidence for the relationships of ariids to other catfishes is equivocal, with the ariids being recovered in an unresolved polytomy with many other catfish clades (Sullivan et al. 2006).

Arius is distinguished from other Malagasy catfishes by the following combination of characters: three pairs of barbels (maxillary, inner, and outer mandibular); closely situated anterior and posterior nostrils (usually separated by only a flap of skin); adipose fin of moderate length, about half the length of the anal-fin base; autopalatine highly compressed at the articulation face with lateral ethmoid; lateral line bifurcated at the caudal region; a single patch of teeth on each side of the palate; and unicuspid premaxillary and dentary teeth.

Plicofollis is distinguished from other Malagasy catfishes by the following combination of characters: three pairs of barbels (maxillary, inner and outer mandibular); closely situated anterior and posterior nostrils (usually separated by only a flap of skin); adipose fin short, less than half the length of the anal-fin base; elongate posterior median fontanel, reduced in size with growth; lateral line bifurcated at the caudal region; two pairs of tooth plates longitudinally arranged on the palate; and unicuspid premaxillary and dentary teeth.

DISTRIBUTION

Eighteen species of the predominantly marine genus *Arius* are found from eastern Africa eastward through Madagascar to southern and southeastern Asia (Marceniuk et al. 2012); of these, three species have been recorded from Malagasy freshwater habitats (Ng and Sparks 2003; Table 10.3). *Arius madagascariensis* is widespread in the middle to lower reaches of rivers and floodplain lakes in western and northwestern Madagascar. *Arius festinus* (Figure 10.6) is an insular freshwater species restricted to the Amboaboa River within the upper Sofia River drainage, a westward-flowing basin in the northeastern part of the island. *Arius uncinatus* (Figure 10.7) is similarly restricted to Lake Andrapongy within the middle reaches of the Ankofia River drainage basin in the northwest.

Nine species of the almost exclusively marine *Plicofollis* are found in the Red Sea, eastern Africa, and Madagascar eastward through southern and southeastern Asia to the Philippines and southward

TABLE 10.3. **Species of *Arius* and *Plicofollis* with range information and most recent IUCN status**

SCIENTIFIC NAME	DISTRIBUTION	IUCN STATUS
A. madagascariensis Vaillant, 1894	Northwestern basins: Widespread in the middle to lower reaches of rivers and floodplain lakes in the west and northwest	LC
A. uncinatus Ng & Sparks, 2003	Northwestern basins: Restricted to Lake Andrapongy within the middle reaches of the Ankofia River drainage basin in the northwest	CR
A. festinus Ng & Sparks, 2003	Northwestern basins: Restricted to the Amboaboa River within the upper Sofia River drainage, a westward-flowing basin in the northeast	CR
P. dussumieri (Valenciennes in Cuvier & Valenciennes, 1840)	Northwestern and western basins: Recorded from the northern and western coasts	LC
P. polystaphylodon (Bleeker, 1846)	Northwestern and western basins: Recorded from the western coast	NA[1]

Note: IUCN Red List conservation assessment status from IUCN (2021); for abbreviations, see Table 10.1.

[1] Not assessed by IUCN (2021), but provisional assessment based on survey data indicates a status of LC (see Ng and Sparks, pp. 1263–65).

FIGURE 10.6 **A) *Arius festinus*, recently described from the headwaters of the Sofia River drainage, northeastern Madagascar. B) Type locality and typical rheophilic habitat of *A. festinus*, Amboaboa River near Mandritsara.** (PHOTO A by H. H. Ng and J. S. Sparks, and B by J. S. Sparks.)

to New Guinea and Australia; of these, two species have been recorded from the coastal waters of Madagascar (Marceniuk et al. 2017; Table 10.3): *P. dussumieri*, which has been recorded from the northern and western coasts (Ng and Sparks 2003; Marceniuk and Menezes 2007), and *P. polystaphylodon*, which has been found along the western coast (Marceniuk and Menezes 2007). Given the biology of both species, it is very likely that they are found in coastal habitats around the island. A third, possibly unnamed, species of *Plicofollis*, known from material collected from the northern coast of Madagascar, was reported by Marceniuk et al. (2017).

Galeichthys feliceps, a species known from coastal and estuarine habitats along the southern tip of Africa (from Walvis Bay in Namibia to East London in South Africa; Kulongowski 2010), has been reported from Madagascar by various authors (Fricke et al. 2018); however, we are unaware of any confirmed specimens from the island to support its presence there.

HABITAT AND NATURAL HISTORY

On Madagascar, ariids are found along all coasts, in most of the major river drainages, and in the large, shallow floodplain lakes in the northwest, including Lake Kinkony and Lake Andrapongy. They occur predominantly in silty, turbid coastal waters and estuaries. The three endemic freshwater species, *A. madagascariensis* and two recently described species, *A. festinus* (Figure 10.6a) and *A. uncinatus* (Figure 10.7a), are restricted to insular freshwater habitats (floodplain lakes and middle to upper reaches of rivers), although *A. madagascariensis* is also reported to occur in estuarine habitats (but see Ng and Sparks 2003 for a discussion of the distributions for all Malagasy species of *Arius*). Although these freshwater ariid species are generally found in turbid rivers and shallow floodplain lakes (*A. madagascariensis* and *A. uncinatus*) (Figure 10.7b), *A. festinus* appears to be restricted to clear, shallow, swift-flowing riverine habitats (Figure 10.6b). Interestingly, the endemic freshwater Malagasy ariids are rarely found in the upper reaches or headwaters of these systems (Ng and Sparks 2003).

Plicofollis dussumieri is known from coastal habitats with a sand or sand-mud substrate (Marceniuk et al. 2017). Although the habitat type of *P. polystaphylodon* has not been documented, it is expected to be similar. Members of *Arius* and *Plicofollis* are benthic carnivores that feed on smaller fishes and aquatic invertebrates (predominantly crustaceans). Ariids are paternal mouth brooders. The females manipulate the eggs using their greatly enlarged pelvic fins, which the males then brood in their mouth.

FIGURE 10.7 A) *Arius uncinatus*, recently described from Lake Andrapongy, a large floodplain lake in the Ankofia River drainage, northwestern Madagascar. B) Typical lacustrine habitat and type locality of *A. uncinatus*, Lake Andrapongy. (PHOTO A by H. H. Ng and J. S. Sparks, and B by J. S. Sparks.)

CONSERVATION STATUS

Ariids are the subject of both commercial and artisanal fisheries throughout their ranges on Madagascar, especially in coastal areas. The endemic insular freshwater species *A. festinus* and *A. uncinatus* are threatened by widespread habitat loss and predation by introduced piscivorous fishes across their ranges. Based on comprehensive survey efforts throughout their respective distributions, these insular freshwater forms do not appear to be abundant or even very common within their limited geographic ranges. In the most recent Red List assessment, both *A. festinus* and *A. uncinatus* are listed as Critically Endangered (IUCN 2021). Although the more widespread *A. madagascariensis* was recently classified as Least Concern (IUCN 2021), this assessment was based primarily on historical survey records dating back to the 1990s, and new surveys throughout the species' range are needed to accurately assess its current status.

Both species of *Plicofollis* are widespread and abundant throughout their ranges. With a lack of any known major widespread threats, *P. dussumieri* has been assessed as Least Concern (IUCN 2021). Although the conservation status of *P. polystaphylodon* has not been assessed, it is almost certainly also a species of Least Concern, given its abundance and lack of major threats throughout its range.

As observed for many other Malagasy freshwater fishes, including cichlids, there appears to be a degree of regional endemism in northwestern Madagascar for ariid catfishes. Given the highly restricted distributions observed for the two recently described insular freshwater species, *A. festinus* and *A. uncinatus*, there is cause for concern, as very little of these unique habitats is currently afforded any protection.

Subject editors: John S. Sparks and Melanie L. J. Stiassny

CLUPEIDAE, PELLONULINAE: *SAUVAGELLA*, MALAGASY ROUND HERRING, *VARILAVA*, *VILVARI*, *VILIMENA*

M. L. J. Stiassny

Sauvagella species are small herring-like fishes (maximum size 6.6 cm standard length, usually smaller) belonging to the pellonuline tribe Ehiravini and are among the least-known components of Madagascar's endemic fishes.

SYSTEMATICS AND IDENTIFICATION

Scales are large, cycloid, and easily shed. The body is elongate and rounded, lacking pre- and post-pelvic scutes on the belly. Jaws have a single row of tiny conical teeth. A single supramaxilla is present on the upper jaw. Gill rakers are well developed, numbering 15–20 on the outer face of the first arch. A short row of rakers is present on the posterior face of the third epibranchial. The anal fin is continuous and lacking the separate anal finlet present in *Spratellomorpha* (see Stiassny, pp. 1267–68).

The genus currently comprises two described species (Table 10.4). Little is known of the precise relationships of either of the Malagasy ehiravin genera (*Sauvagella* and *Spratellomorpha*), but morphological data suggest a sister-group relationship between them and that this generic pair is the sister group of the Indian–Sri Lankan genus *Ehirava* (Stiassny 2002).

DISTRIBUTION

Sauvagella madagascariensis is widely distributed in fresh and brackish habitats in middle and lower reaches of eastern coastal rivers and throughout the interconnecting Pangalanes Canal, and *S. robusta* is restricted to a single westward-flowing drainage (Sofia) in the northeastern part of the island (Figure 10.8).

TABLE 10.4. **Species of *Sauvagella* with range information and most recent IUCN status**

SCIENTIFIC NAME	DISTRIBUTION	IUCN STATUS
S. madagascariensis (Sauvage, 1883)	Eastern highlands and lowlands: Fresh and brackish habitats in middle and lower reaches of eastern coastal rivers and throughout the interconnecting Pangalanes Canal	LC
S. robusta Stiassny, 2002	Northwestern basins: Middle and upper reaches of the Amboaboa, Mangarahara, and Anjombony Rivers and in a few small lakes in the Sofia River drainage	EN

Note: IUCN Red List conservation assessment status from IUCN (2021); for abbreviations, see Table 10.1.

HABITAT AND NATURAL HISTORY

Very little is known of the biology or ecology of either *Sauvagella* species, but anatomy suggests they are planktivores. Further, no data are available on reproductive behavior, but in life, two color forms (yellow and red or orange) have been noted in *S. madagascariensis*. Live coloration in *S. robusta* is a muted pale, creamy yellow with some silvery iridescence on the chest and ventrum.

FIGURE 10.8 **Distributional ranges of *Sauvagella madagascariensis* (light blue) and *S. robusta* (dark blue), modified after the most recent Red List assessment (IUCN 2021). Specimen of *S. robusta* (upper left; AMNH 211130) and of *S. madagascariensis* (lower right; AMNH 232463).**

CONSERVATION STATUS

Despite widespread deforestation within its range and some small-scale fishing for local consumption, *S. madagascariensis* is classified as a species of Least Concern (IUCN 2021) mainly because of its broad distribution throughout many eastern coastal drainages and the moderate salt tolerance of the species. *Sauvagella robusta* has a far more restricted distribution and faces severe threats from ongoing habitat degradation throughout its range. Historically, the species was known to occur in the middle and upper reaches of the Amboaboa, Mangarahara, and Anjombony Rivers and in a few small lakes in the Sofia drainage. However, populations are threatened by ongoing deforestation and erosional siltation, and much of the Amboaboa River has ceased to flow downstream of a dam on the Mangarahara River. Commercial overfishing of the Lake Tseny population of *S. robusta* has been reported (Andriafidison et al. 2011). *Sauvagella robusta* is classified as Endangered (IUCN 2021), and it is unlikely that the species is currently extant over much of its historical range.

Subject editors: Melanie L. J. Stiassny and John S. Sparks

CLUPEIDAE, PELLONULINAE: *SPRATELLOMORPHA*, TWO-FINNED ROUND HERRING, *VARILAVA*, *VILVARI*

M. L. J. Stiassny

Spratellomorpha is a genus of small herring-like fishes (maximum size 5.5 mm standard length, usually smaller) belonging to the pellonuline tribe Ehiravini. As currently recognized, the genus is considered monotypic, represented by *S. bianalis*; however, it remains unclear whether there are additional congeners present on Madagascar or in coastal Kenyan waters.

FIGURE 10.9 **Distributional range (in dark blue) of *Spratellomorpha bianalis*, modified after the most recent Red List assessment (IUCN 2021); specimen of *S. bianalis* (AMNH 211129); and inset (upper left) of anal fin, with arrow indicating finlet.**

SYSTEMATICS AND IDENTIFICATION

Despite past confusion, *S. bianalis* is considered here to be endemic to northwestern Madagascar. The type locality of the species was given as "Madagascar" by Bertin (1940), but Whitehead (1985) considered the species also to occur in coastal waters of Kenya (Port Tudor, Mombasa Market). Stiassny (2002) questioned that assessment, and further morphological examination of Kenyan specimens suggests that, while congeneric, they are likely not conspecific with *S. bianalis* and instead represent an undescribed species.

Members of *Spratellomorpha* are gracile, torpedo-shaped ehiravins, lacking pre- and post-pelvic scutes on the belly, and are extremely similar in overall appearance to closely related *Sauvagella*, particularly to *S. madagascariensis* (see Stiassny, pp. 1266–67). Externally, they differ from both *Sauvagella* species in having a discontinuous anal fin with a distinct anal finlet well separated from the main body of the fin (Figure 10.9).

DISTRIBUTION

The geographic range of *S. bianalis* on Madagascar appears to be restricted entirely to fully freshwater habitats of inland floodplain lakes in the former Mahajanga Province in the northwest, but its full distribution is currently unknown.

HABITAT AND NATURAL HISTORY

As with *Sauvagella*, very little is known of the biology or ecology of *Spratellomorpha*, but anatomy suggests that these fishes are planktivores.

CONSERVATION STATUS

Because of the general lack of available information on *Spratellomorpha bianalis*, it is listed as Data Deficient (IUCN 2021). However, major threats persist across its range, including almost complete deforestation of riparian habitats and resultant sedimentation, overfishing, and competition from introduced non-native species.

Subject editors: Melanie L. J. Stiassny and John S. Sparks

APLOCHEILIDAE: *PACHYPANCHAX*, MALAGASY KILLIFISH, *MORORA*, *KOMORORA*, *ZOTO*

P. V. Loiselle and P. de Rham

Pachypanchax species are small fishes (maximum size 10 cm standard length, usually smaller) of the order Cyprinodontiformes endemic to Madagascar and the granitic Seychelles (Figure 10.10). The genus comprises seven described species, six of which are endemic to Madagascar, and an estimated 10 undescribed species (Table 10.5).

FIGURE 10.10 **A) Male *Pachypanchax sakaramyi*, a species that is classified as Endangered and is now restricted to streams draining the eastern slopes of Montagne d'Ambre. B) Male of the red form of *P. omalonotus*, native to Nosy Be and the Sambirano River system; this highly polymorphic species was the first Malagasy freshwater fish to be formally described.** (PHOTOS by P. V. Loiselle.)

SYSTEMATICS AND IDENTIFICATION

The phylogenetic relationships of *Pachypanchax* remain unresolved. Two competing morphology-based hypotheses suggest that this genus is 1) either sister to a clade composed of the southern Asian genus *Aplocheilus* and the western and central African *Epiplatys* (Parenti 1981), or 2) that *Pachypanchax* is the sister group to *Aplocheilus* (Costa 1998). A more recent molecular study supports the latter hypothesis, resolving *Pachypanchax* as sister to *Aplocheilus*, with the two together composing the Aplocheiliidae, which in turn is sister to the African Nothobranchiidae (Pohl et al. 2015).

The combination of a single, spineless dorsal fin originating posterior to the anal-fin origin, a rounded caudal fin with its basal two-thirds covered with fine scales, and the lack of pored scales in the lateral line distinguishes *Pachypanchax* from all other Malagasy freshwater fishes. The mouth is superior, the lower jaw longer than the upper, and jaws have a single row of large conical teeth. The gill rakers are short, numbering fewer than 12 on the outer face of the first arch. The scales are ctenoid (toothed or comb-edged). Members of the genus exhibit marked sexual dimorphism and dichromatism.

DISTRIBUTION

Pachypanchax is widespread throughout the western versant of Madagascar. *Pachypanchax sakaramyi* is native to the northern and eastern versant of Montagne d'Ambre (Figure 10.10a). It has often been confused with *P. playfairi*, a species endemic to the granitic Seychelles. *Pachypanchax omalonotus* was described from Nosy Be but also occurs on the adjacent mainland, including the Sambirano

TABLE 10.5. **Species of *Pachypanchax* with range information and most recent IUCN status**

SCIENTIFIC NAME	DISTRIBUTION	IUCN STATUS
P. sakaramyi (Holly, 1928)	Northwestern basins: Northern (expirated) and eastern versant of Montagne d'Ambre	EN
P. omalonotus (Dumeril, 1861)	Northwestern basins: Nosy Be and adjacent mainland, including the Sambirano River and streams draining the Ankify Peninsula	EN
P. arnoulti Loiselle, 2006	Western basins: Betsiboka and Kamoro Rivers, and Lake Kinkony basin	VU
P. sparksorum Loiselle, 2006	Northwestern basins: Tributaries of the Ankofia River draining the Bora protected area	EN
P. varatraza Loiselle, 2006	Eastern highlands: Upper reaches of the eastward-draining Manambery, Fanambana, and Ampanobe Rivers	EN
P. patriciae Loiselle, 2006	Northwestern basins: Northwestern rivers from the Manajena River south to the Manehoko River	EN
Pachypanchax n. sp. "sofia"	Northwestern basins: Middle and upper reaches of the Sofia River	NA
P. n. sp. "mahamasina"	Northwestern basins: Ambodimadiro-Ampomdrabe River	NA
P. n. sp. "ankarana"	Northwestern basins: Endorheic streams associated with Ankarana Massif	NA
P. n. sp. "maevarano"	Northwestern basins: Maevarano River	NA
P. n. sp. "analalava"	Northwestern basins: Ampasikely Creek, which flows into the Loza River, near the town of Analalava	NA
P. n. sp. "doroa"	Northwestern basins: Ankaranobe Creek, a tributary of the Doroa River, at the village of Ambodibonara	NA
P. n. sp. "manambaho"	Western basins: Manambaho River	NA
P. n. sp. "manambolo"	Western basins: Manambolo River	NA
P. n. sp. "tsiribihina"	Western basins: Tsiribihina River	NA
P. n. sp. "makay"	Western basins: Headwaters of the Mangoky River on Makay Massif	NA

Notes: The names of species that have been identified as new to science and remain to be formally described are designated as "n. sp." (new species) and enclosed in quotation marks. IUCN Red List conservation assessment status from IUCN (2021); for abbreviations, see Table 10.1.

River drainage and the streams draining the Ankify Peninsula. Topotypical populations and most mainland populations ascribed to *P. omalonotus* are characterized by male color polymorphism. Body coloration can be gold, blue, or red, and fins red, yellow orange, or blue. *Pachypanchax varatraza* inhabits the upper reaches of the eastward-draining Manambery, Fanambana, and Ampanobe Rivers. *Pachypanchax patriciae* is native to rivers of northwestern Madagascar from the Manajena southward to the Manehoko. *Pachypanchax sparksorum* is restricted to tributaries of the Ankofia River draining the Bora protected area. *Pachypanchax arnoulti* occurs in the Betsiboka and Kamoro River drainages, as well as in the Lake Kinkony basin. The 10 undescribed species are all native to the western versant of Madagascar (see Table 10.5).

HABITAT AND NATURAL HISTORY

Members of *Pachypanchax* are found exclusively in freshwater habitats from near sea level to about 900 m, in small streams and shallow peripheral waters of lakes and marshes. They are carnivores, feeding on stranded terrestrial insects and aquatic invertebrates, particularly mosquito larvae.

Pachypanchax species are egg-scatterers with a consort-type mating system. Males attempt to monopolize access to a ripe female as she searches for a spawning site. Patches of coarse gravel, the roots of floating aquatic plants, or the exposed roots of terrestrial plants growing along the water's edge are preferred spawning sites. After a vigorous courtship, pairs assume a side-by-side position, curve their bodies into an S shape, and quiver intensely for a few moments. The female then breaks free, and the pair repeats the performance. One or two eggs are deposited with each spawning bout. Eggs of *P. sparksorum* may remain attached via numerous fibers to the female's vent after oviposition, the resulting cluster dropping off several hours later. Ripe females have been collected in October and November; spawning proceeds throughout the austral summer. Eggs hatch in 10–14 days depending upon the water temperature. Growth rates in nature are unknown, but in captivity, sexual maturity is attained four to six months after hatching, although it may take an additional year or two for fish to attain adult size.

CONSERVATION STATUS

No commercial fishery targets this genus, whose members are considered too small to warrant the effort, although some are caught for local consumption. All six described Malagasy species were included in the most recent IUCN Red List assessment (IUCN 2021). With the exception of *P. arnoulti*, which was classified as Vulnerable, all were assessed as Endangered.

Although there is evidence that the geographic ranges of most *Pachypanchax* species have contracted in the face of habitat degradation and introduced competitors (see Sparks and Stiassny, pp. 1245–60), the widespread distribution and the ability to persist in the face of serious environmental degradation afford a degree of security to *P. arnoulti*. The restricted distributions of *P. sparksorum* and all the undescribed species of the genus (Table 10.5) render them vulnerable to the deleterious effects of anthropogenic habitat modification, which will be exacerbated by the effects of climate change on rainfall patterns.

The survival of the only known Manambery drainage population of *P. varatraza* is clearly dependent upon the relict Sambirano-type forest that remains in its severely degraded watershed, although the Fanambana and Ampanobe populations appear secure for the moment. *Pachypanchax sakaramyi* is now restricted to high-gradient headwaters of streams draining the eastern versant of Montagne d'Ambre, having been eliminated from their lower reaches and from the northern versant by introduced competitors and predators. Because of the extremely seasonal character of rainfall in northern Madagascar, the persistence of such habitats and their associated aquatic communities is contingent upon fully forested watersheds. Although the forests of the Montagne d'Ambre have statutory protection, illicit cutting threatens both their survival and that of *P. sakaramyi*. The illicit diversion of the headwaters of the Sakaramy River for domestic human consumption represents the latest threat to the survival of this species.

Subject editors: Melanie L. J. Stiassny and John S. Sparks

PANTANODONTIDAE: *PANTANODON*

J. S. Sparks and W. L. Smith

Members of *Pantanodon* are small, oviparous cyprinodontiform fishes (maximum size about 30 mm standard length, usually much smaller) occurring, or formerly occurring, in eastern Africa and eastern Madagascar. The genus currently comprises two described species, *P. stuhlmanni*, found from Kenya to Tanzania, and *P. madagascariensis*, which is now classified as Extinct (IUCN 2021) but was endemic to forested swamps in eastern coastal Madagascar. A third species, awaiting formal description, was discovered in 1994 and is also presumed to be extinct (Figure 10.11).

FIGURE 10.11 **Live adult male *Pantanodon* sp. nov. "manombo," photographed shortly after capture in 1994.** (PHOTO by P. Reinthal and J. S. Sparks.)

SYSTEMATICS AND IDENTIFICATION

The genus *Pantanodon* was described by Myers (1955) to encompass *P. podoxys*, which was subsequently determined to be a junior synonym of *Haplochilichthys stuhlmanni* (Seegers 1996). Whitehead (1962) commented on the great similarity of these two genera, but retained *Pantanodon* as a valid taxon for the African species *P. podoxys*.

The immediate relationships of *Pantanodon* remain somewhat unresolved. In his description of *P. podoxys*, Myers (1955) created the subfamily Pantanodontinae to include his morphologically distinct new species. This was supported by Whitehead (1962), who treated *Pantanodon* as a subfamily of Cyprinodontidae. Rosen (1965) then assigned the Malagasy form, which had previously been placed within *Oryzias* (Arnoult 1963), to *Pantanodon* and suggested classifying the genus in its own family, Pantanodontidae, because its relationships were unclear. Clausen (1967) suggested that *Pantanodon* may be closely related to modern aplocheilichthyine poeciliids. In the first phylogenetic analysis of the Cyprinodontiformes, Parenti (1981) presented a much revised phylogeny and classification of the order based on morphological characters, corroborating Clausen's hypothesis, and placed *Pantanodon* in the Poeciliidae, subfamily Aplocheilichthyinae, which was later supported by Ghedotti (2000). J. S. Sparks et al. (unpublished data) have revised the phylogenetic relationships of *Pantanodon* based on a reexamination of these data and in light of both new evidence and additional specimens (i.e., the undescribed new species).

In contrast to explicit morphological studies, recent multi-gene molecular studies have recovered *Pantanodon* (represented only by the African species, *P. stuhlmanni*) in its own family that is sister to the Cyprinodontoidei and distantly related to the Poeciliidae and Aplocheilichthyinae (Pohl et al. 2015; Bragança et al. 2018). Preliminary genomic analyses using ultraconserved elements that included *P. stuhlmanni* and the novel undescribed Malagasy species corroborate the monophyly of transcontinental *Pantanodon*, the recognition of Pantanodontidae as a distinct family, and the placement of Pantanodontidae as sister to all other cyprinodontoids (J. S. Sparks and W. L. Smith, unpublished data).

Members of *Pantanodon* are distinguished from all other cyprinodontiforms by the presence of greatly enlarged second pharyngobranchial tooth plates, the first three or four pelvic-fin rays in males being thickened and with well-developed hooks at the tips, and the lack of hypobranchial ossifications. The pelvic fins of males are united. The dorsal and anal fins of males are produced, with long trailing margins, but the anal fin of males is not modified into a gonopodium (a modification of the anterior part of the anal fin in male poeciliids that permits internal fertilization) (Figure 10.11). The only other fish species found on Madagascar that could potentially be confused with *Pantanodon* is an introduced species of *Gambusia*. However, in the latter taxon, the anal fin of males is modified into a gonopodium, the dorsal and anal fins are not produced, and the pelvic fins lack hooks at the tips.

The mainland African *Pantanodon* species, *P. stuhlmanni*; the endemic Malagasy species, *P. madagascariensis*; and the undescribed species of *Pantanodon* differ anatomically, the most notable feature being the lack of jaw teeth in *P. stuhlmanni*, whereas the two Malagasy species possess well-toothed jaws. A number of morphological dissimilarities easily differentiate *P. madagascariensis* and the undescribed Malagasy species of *Pantanodon* (J. S. Sparks et al., unpublished data).

DISTRIBUTION

The genus currently comprises two described species: *Pantanodon stuhlmanni*, endemic to coastal regions (fresh- and brackish-water habitats) from Kenya to Tanzania, and *P. madagascariensis*, which is now classified as Extinct (IUCN 2021) but was endemic to forested swamps in eastern coastal Madagascar. A third species, awaiting formal description, was discovered in 1994 by our research team and is also presumed to be extinct, as subsequent collecting efforts in the region have failed to locate additional specimens or populations (Figure 10.11).

HABITAT AND NATURAL HISTORY

Both species of Malagasy *Pantanodon* were historically found exclusively in freshwater forested (*Pandanus*) swamps in eastern coastal Madagascar. Members of *Pantanodon* are omnivorous. In aquaria, the new undescribed species of Malagasy *Pantanodon* fed on algae, zooplankton, and chironomid larvae. These fishes are oviparous, and fertilization is external. We were able to keep them for several years in aquaria but were unfortunately unable to get them to reproduce. Little else is known regarding reproductive behavior of the Malagasy forms.

CONSERVATION STATUS

Based on the most recent Red List assessment (IUCN 2021), *Pantanodon madagascariensis* is classified as Extinct. Although the new undescribed species from southeastern coastal Madagascar, informally referred to as *Pantanodon* n. sp. "manombo," was not assessed by IUCN in 2016, which is limited to formally described species, and subsequent and extensive collecting efforts by our research team and others have failed to locate additional individuals, it can be presumed that this undescribed species is also extinct. Both of the known Malagasy species of *Pantanodon* exhibited extremely restricted ranges in eastern coastal Madagascar. *Pantanodon madagascariensis* was known only from forested areas in the region of Mahambo, about 80 km north of Toamasina. No specimens have been recovered from the region since collection of the type series in 1963. *Pantanodon* sp. nov. "manombo" was first collected in 1994 from a single, small lowland *Pandanus* swamp within the Manombo Special Reserve, south of Farafangana, its only known locality. Unfortunately, introduced *Gambusia* is prevalent at this locality, and specimens of the new species of *Pantanodon* have not been collected at the site since 1997. The region upstream of the only known site of this species is outside of the Manombo protected area, is afforded no protection, and has experienced rapid deforestation. It is likely that this species became extinct in the late 1990s, not long after it was first discovered.

Subject editors: John S. Sparks and Melanie L. J. Stiassny

ATHERINIDAE, ATHERINOMORINAE: *TERAMULUS*, SILVERSIDE, *ZONO*

J. S. Sparks

Teramulus is a genus of small silverside (atherinid) fishes (maximum size generally less than 60 mm standard length) that are endemic to fresh- and brackish-water habitats in northern and eastern Madagascar. Two described species, *T. kieneri* and *T. waterloti*, compose this very poorly known genus (Figure 10.12a).

SYSTEMATICS AND IDENTIFICATION

Based on survey efforts spanning the years 1994–2020, the status of *T. kieneri* as distinct from species in the genus *Atherinomorus* is questioned. Aside from the type specimens, which are in very poor condition, no additional material attributable to *T. kieneri* has been subsequently collected. As noted in the most recent Red List assessment (IUCN 2021), although *T. kieneri* is reported to be largely distributed along the eastern coast of Madagascar, in reality its range is poorly known, as this taxon is difficult to identify and regularly confused with other species. *Teramulus waterloti*, however, is determined to be valid on the basis of recently collected material that conforms to the original description by Pellegrin (1932), and as a result, the genus is likely monotypic. Interestingly, the type series of both species were obtained from material originally identified as *A.* (*Atherina*) *duodecimalis*.

Teramulus has never been adequately diagnosed on the basis of broad phylogenetic comparisons, and the genus is in need of revision. The type series for both named species are in extremely poor condition, and a paucity of suitable study material has precluded revisional studies to date. Until recently, nothing was known regarding the precise relationships of *Teramulus* within the family Atherinidae. For example, *Teramulus* incertae sedis was placed within Atherinomorinae based on anatomical features listed in the original description (Smith 1965) but not on the examination of preserved specimens (Dyer and Chernoff 1996). More recently, additional material of *T. waterloti* has been collected from multiple localities in northern and northwestern Madagascar, and as a result, *Teramulus* was included in a taxonomically comprehensive phylogenetic study of atherinoid relationships by Sparks and Smith (2004b). In this study, based on a combination of morphological and molecular evidence, *Teramulus* was recovered within the family Atherinidae, in a clade with members of the genera *Hypoatherina* and *Atherinomorus* (Sparks and Smith 2004b: Figure 2).

Specimens of *T. waterloti* can be differentiated from all other atherinids (including species of *Atherinomorus*, to which this taxon is closely related) occurring on Madagascar by a number of unique dental and osteological characters, an elongate dorsolateral process of the pelvic girdle, and the dorsal-most two ceratobranchial gill rakers markedly reduced in length. The body is elongate and laterally compressed. The eyes are large, the snout short and blunt, and the mouth upturned. Oral jaw teeth are numerous, short and robust, and mildly to strongly hooked, and cover the premaxilla internally as well as externally. The ceratobranchial gill rakers are numerous, closely set, and elongate (less the dorsal-most two). The vomer may or may not bear teeth; the palatine is edentulous. The second dorsal fin and anal fin are well developed (and approaching the produced condition observed in *Rheocles*; see Stiassny et al., pp. 1277–79). In life, *T. waterloti* is translucent and bluish overall, and rust-colored on the ventral flank, with a prominent iridescent mid-lateral band (Figure 10.12a). The first dorsal fin is black. *Teramulus waterloti* is sexually dimorphic, with males markedly more colorful overall and exhibiting more elongate and well-developed second dorsal and anal fins. Adults of both sexes develop elaborate urogenital tassels (soft-tissue structures associated with the urogenital opening). Live coloration of *T. kieneri* is not known.

FIGURE 10.12 **A) Live *Teramulus waterloti* in aquarium. B) Typical forested, small stream habitat of *T. waterloti*, Ankaze Creek, Sambirano River, northwestern Madagascar.** (PHOTOS by P. V. Loiselle.)

DISTRIBUTION

Teramulus kieneri is currently known only from the type series, which was apparently collected in brackish water near Toamasina.

As mentioned above, the status of this taxon is questionable, and these east coast specimens appear to be indistinguishable from *A. duodecimalis*, an extremely widespread Indo–West Pacific coastal species that is found in both marine and brackish habitats. *Atherinomorus duodecimalis* is a problematic taxon itself and likely comprises more than a single species throughout its extensive range. Smith (1965) lists a dubious specimen of *T. kieneri* that was collected from a western drainage in northern Madagascar, from Antikotazo near Ambilobe, with the type series of *T. waterloti*. The identity of this specimen has not been confirmed. Although Smith (1965) listed a wider range in northwestern Madagascar for *T. waterloti* in his original description, until recently our research team collected the species only from a single small forested stream, a tributary of the Anjingo River drainage, within the Bora protected area in the northwest. More recently (2011), we found the species to be more widespread in the north, present in a number of small streams in the region of Ankarana (J. S. Sparks, unpublished data) as well as the Sambirano River basin (Figure 10.12b). Thus, the range of *T. waterloti* likely extends from the Mananjeba River southward to the Anjingo River drainage.

HABITAT AND NATURAL HISTORY

Based on our survey efforts, it appears that *T. waterloti* is restricted to forested or semi-forested freshwater streams where habitat degradation is minimal (Figure 10.12b). We did not find the species in highly degraded habitats or habitats with an abundance of introduced species. Although locality data for the type series of *T. kieneri* indicate that this taxon, if valid, inhabits brackish water, this has yet to be confirmed. Nothing is known regarding the diet of *Teramulus*; however, oral dentition and internal anatomy—the gut is short and simple—suggest that it is likely an insectivore. Further, no information is available on the reproductive behavior of these fishes. Males and females have a single, greatly enlarged, ventrally situated gonad. The oocytes are very large and, not surprisingly, low in number.

CONSERVATION STATUS

In the most recent Red List assessment (IUCN 2021), *T. kieneri* was treated as a valid species and classified as Least Concern, and *T. waterloti* was listed as Endangered. There is no commercial or artisanal fishery for this genus, which is not only too small for consumption but also too rare or sparsely distributed to support a fishery. The restricted range of *T. waterloti* emphasizes the precarious position of the genus, especially as the putatively more widespread *T. kieneri*, which is reported to occur along much of the eastern coast of Madagascar, may not be a valid taxon. Within its limited range, *T. waterloti* was not found to be common at any locality where it was collected. There is definitely cause for concern, particularly since the species does not seem to tolerate either substantial habitat degradation or the presence of introduced species.

Subject editors: John S. Sparks and Melanie L. J. Stiassny

BEDOTIIDAE: *BEDOTIA*, MALAGASY RAINBOWFISH, *ZONO*, *GARASSA*, *VILY*

M. L. J. Stiassny, P. V. Loiselle, and J. S. Sparks

Bedotia is a radiation of small (maximum size 8.8 cm standard length, usually smaller), colorful rainbowfishes endemic to freshwater habitats on Madagascar. They are readily distinguished from members of the closely related *Rheocles* and "*Rheocles*" (see Stiassny et al., pp. 1277–79) in the possession of a conspicuous indentation on the dentigerous face of the premaxilla, forming a diagnostic "*Bedotia* notch" in the jaw.

Bedotia species are typically found in small to medium-size clear-water rivers and streams and, to a lesser extent, also in fringing wetlands where riparian cover persists. Different species have been collected from coastal and inland drainages from along the entire eastern versant of the island, within an elevational range extending from sea level to over 700 m. *Bedotia* is generally considered to be a good indicator of instream ecosystem health, as it typically undergoes rapid population decline, or may disappear entirely, in areas where riparian cover is lost and aquatic habitats become degraded due to erosional siltation.

SYSTEMATICS AND IDENTIFICATION

Delimitation of species within the genus *Bedotia* has proved to be highly problematic. Qualitative morphological variation between putative species and populations is muted, and consequently, differentiating features has tended to focus almost exclusively on a combination of coloration and pigmentation patterning as well as some morphometric comparisons. Jones et al. (2010) correctly note that significant work will be required to resolve the species composition and taxonomy of the genus, an observation that is especially cogent given that almost every newly explored eastern drainage appears to

TABLE 10.6. **Species of *Bedotia* organized by geographic clade with range information and most recent IUCN status**

CLADE	SPECIES SCIENTIFIC NAME	DISTRIBUTION	IUCN STATUS
madagascariensis clade	*B. geayi* Pellegrin, 1907	Eastern highlands and lowlands: Upper reaches of the Mananjary River	EN
	B. madagascariensis Regan, 1903	Eastern lowlands: Lower reaches of coastal rivers from the Ivoloina to Manambolo Creek, inclusive of the lower Rianila	EN
	B. tricolor Pellegrin 1932	Eastern highlands and lowlands: Upper reaches of the Faraony and Sandrananta Rivers	CR
	B. albomarginata Sparks & Rush, 2005	Eastern highlands: Upper and middle Mananara and Rienana Rivers	EN
	B. leucopteron Loiselle & Rodriguez, 2007	Eastern highlands: Middle reaches of the Iaroka-Rianila basin	EN
	B. n. sp. "mangoro"	Eastern lowlands: Coastal rivers from the Sakanila southward to the Sakaleona, inclusive of the lower Mangoro	NA
	B. n. sp. "nosivolo"	Eastern highlands: Nosivolo River (Mangoro basin)	NA
	B. n. sp. "namorona"	Eastern highlands: Upper and middle reaches of the Namorona River	NA
	B. n. sp. "garassa"	Eastern lowlands: Masihanaka and Mananara Rivers	NA
	B. n. sp. "anosy"	Eastern highlands: Small streams draining the Anosyenne Mountains north of Tolagnaro	NA
	B. n. sp. "manombo"	Eastern lowlands: Lower Tokahandra River	NA
marojejy clade	*B. marojejy* Stiassny & Harrison, 2000	Eastern highlands: Manantenina River (Lokoho basin)	EN
	B. n. sp. "sambava"	Eastern lowlands: Sambava River	NA
	B. n. sp. "bemarivo"	Eastern lowlands: Bemarivo River	NA
	B. n. sp. "mahanara"	Eastern lowlands: Mahanara River	NA
longianalis clade	*B. longianalis* Pellegrin, 1914	Eastern lowlands: Lower reaches of rivers from the Ifontsy northward to the Marimbona and Nosy Boraha	EN
	B. masoala Sparks, 2001	Eastern highlands: Ankavanana du Sud River and tributaries	VU
	B. alveyi Jones, Smith & Sparks, 2010	Eastern highlands: Vohimaro and Antainambalana Rivers	NT
	B. n. sp. "betampona"	Eastern highlands and lowlands: Middle and upper reaches of the Ivoloina River	NA
	B. n. sp. "antalaha"	Eastern lowlands: Ankavanana du Nord and Ankavia Rivers	NA
	B. n. sp. "mananare"	Eastern lowlands: Mananara River	NA
	B. n. sp. "manambolo"	Eastern lowlands: Manambola and Ivoloina Rivers	NA

Source: Clades after Sparks and Smith (2004b).
Notes: The names of species that have been identified as new to science and remain to be formally described are designated as "n. sp." (new species) and enclosed in quotation marks. IUCN Red List conservation assessment status from IUCN (2021); for IUCN status abbreviations, see Table 10.1.

harbor distinctively colored *Bedotia* species/population. Currently nine species have been formally described, and upwards of 10 more are awaiting taxonomic description (Table 10.6). The high incidence of single-basin or within-basin endemism (Figures 10.13 and 10.14) suggests that further investigation of unsampled regions is likely to result in the discovery of additional putative species, many of which will likely be driven to extinction before they can be formally described.

In the first comprehensive analysis of the genus, based on a combination of molecular and morphological data, Sparks and Smith (2004b) provide a well-supported phylogenetic framework for *Bedotia*. In that study, all nominal species were validated, and geographical populations previously hypothesized to represent undescribed species were confirmed to represent discrete lineages, several of which have since been formally described (e.g., *B. masoala*, *B. albomarginata*, *B. leucopteron*, *B. alveyi*).

DISTRIBUTION

The analysis of Sparks and Smith (2004b) resolved *Bedotia* into three more-or-less geographically discrete clades (B, C, and D clades): the B clade (herein the *madagascariensis* clade, Figures 10.13a and b), with distributions ranging from mid-eastern to southeastern regions of the island; the C clade (herein the *marojejy* clade, Figure 10.14b), with distributions restricted to eastern drainages north of the Masoala Peninsula; and the D clade (herein the *longianalis* clade, Figure 10.14a), extending from the Masoala Peninsula southward to the Ivoloina River, in mid-eastern portions of the island (see Sparks and Smith 2004b).

HABITAT AND NATURAL HISTORY

Bedotia species are strongly sexually dimorphic, with males usually attaining larger adult sizes, more enhanced coloration/pigmentation patterning, and enlarged unpaired fins. The genus exhibits male fin-color polymorphism and geographic variation in this feature. The abundance of each morph in a given population varies from one year to the next, suggesting the polymorphism is maintained by the operation of the "rare male" effect. As far as is known, all members of the genus are egg-scatterers. Patches of coarse gravel, fine-leafed aquatic plants, or the exposed roots of terrestrial plants growing along the water's edge are preferred spawning sites. Ripe females have been collected in October and November, and spawning occurs throughout the austral summer. The clear beige eggs hatch in 10–14 days, depending on water temperature. Growth rates in nature are unknown, but in captivity, sexual maturity is attained six to eight months post hatching.

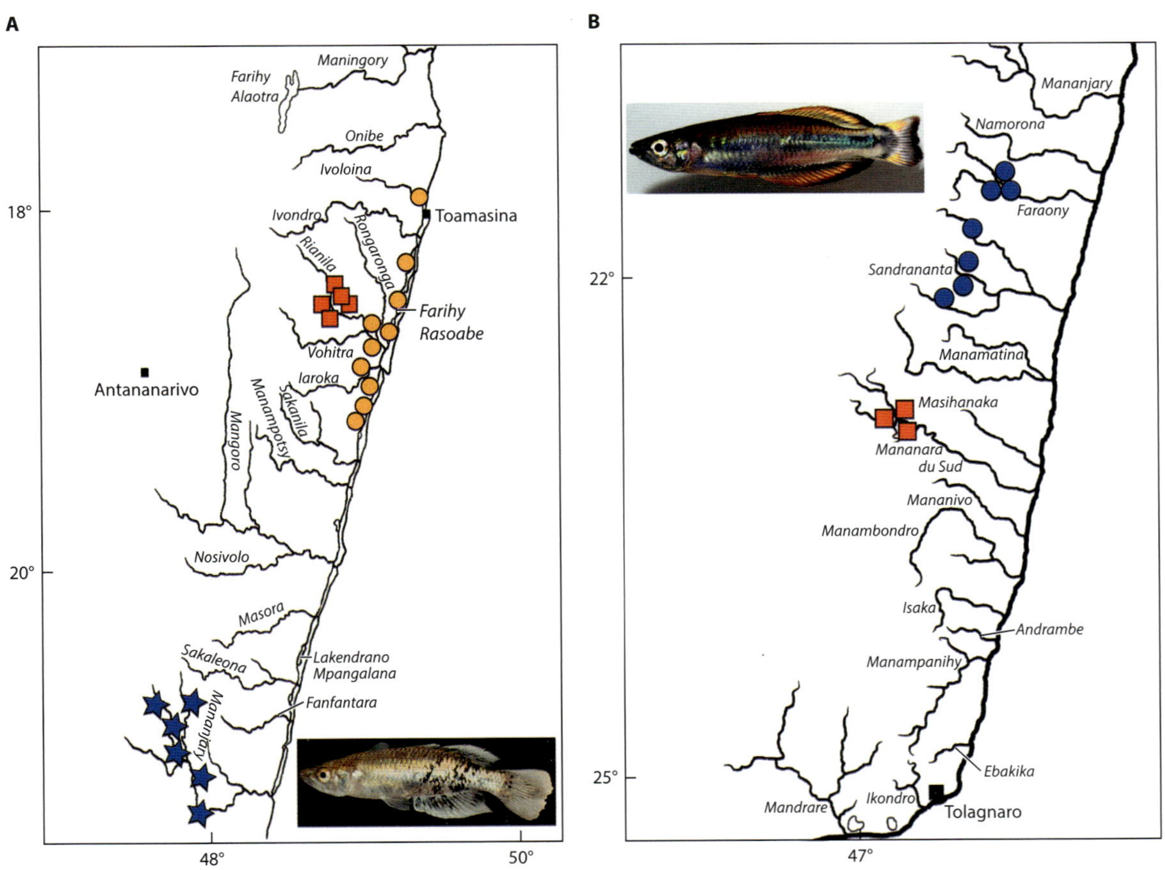

FIGURE 10.13 **A) Distribution of described members of the "northern" *madagascariensis* clade: yellow circles, *Bedotia madagascariensis*; red squares, *B. leucopteron*; blue stars, *B. geayi*. Inset image, *B. leucopteron*. B) Distribution of described members of the "southern" *madagascariensis* clade: blue circles, *B. tricolor*; red squares, *B. albomarginata*. Inset image, *B. tricolor*.** (PHOTOS by P. V. Loiselle.)

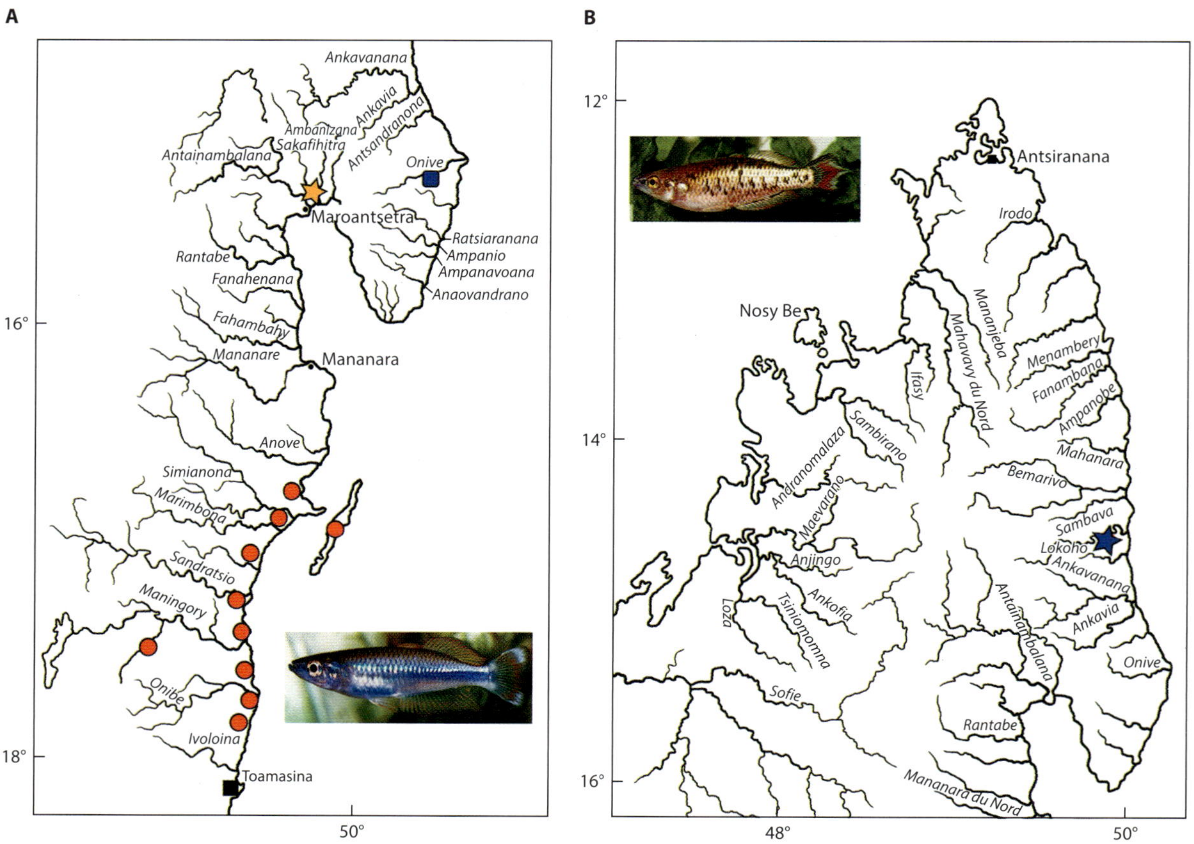

FIGURE 10.14 **A) Distribution of described members of the *longianalis* clade: red circles, *Bedotia longianalis*; blue square, *B. masoala*; yellow star, *B. alveyi*. Inset image, *B. longianalis*. B) Distribution of described member of the *marojejy* clade: blue star, *B. marojejy*. Inset image, *B. marojejy*.** (PHOTOS by P. V. Loiselle.)

As far as is known, all species are carnivores feeding primarily on stranded terrestrial insects taken from the water surface and to a lesser extent upon aquatic invertebrates. *Bedotia* populations are therefore particularly susceptible to loss of the riparian cover that is the primary source of allochthonous inputs into their aquatic habitats.

CONSERVATION STATUS

Although *Bedotia* is not subject to commercial fisheries, small-scale artisanal fishing using woven baskets (*tandroho*) is widespread, and these fishes are frequently dried and sold in markets. This constitutes a significant source of predation pressure on exploited populations. The replacement of the traditional baskets with mosquito nets has led to the extirpation of many local *Bedotia* populations.

Given their often highly limited distributional ranges, frequently encompassing a single basin, susceptibility to population decline owing to loss of riparian cover and habitat degradation, and increasing impacts from predation by and competition with numerous introduced species, members of *Bedotia* are among the most threatened of Madagascar's endemic fishes. Detailed assessment of the conservation status of each described *Bedotia* species was provided by IUCN, and the resultant assessment category is provided in Table 10.6. The most recent assessments (IUCN 2021) highlight significant endangerment, with one species assessed as Critically Endangered, six as Endangered, one as Vulnerable, and one as Near Threatened.

Subject editors: Melanie L. J. Stiassny and John S. Sparks

BEDOTIIDAE: *RHEOCLES*, MALAGASY RAINBOWFISH, *KATRANA*, *ZONA*, *ZONOBE*

M. L. J. Stiassny, P. V. Loiselle, and J. S. Sparks

Rheocles is a small radiation of rainbowfishes endemic to freshwater habitats in eastern Madagascar. Most are small (maximum size 10 cm standard length, usually much smaller), somewhat nondescript, silverside-like fishes. They are similar in general appearance to *Bedotia* species (see Stiassny et al., pp. 1273–76) but tend to be less colorful, and they lack the characteristic "*Bedotia* notch" on the upper jaw.

SYSTEMATICS AND IDENTIFICATION

Morphological diagnosis of the genus has proved problematic, and in the first comprehensive analysis based on a combination of molecular and morphological data, Sparks and Smith (2004b) provide support for a monophyletic grouping of *Rheocles* species but with the exclusion of two species, "*Rheocles*" *derhami* and "*Rheocles*" *vatosoa* (Figures 10.15 and 10.16b), which were recovered as sister taxa and resolved to be more closely related to *Bedotia* than to *Rheocles sensu stricto*. In a revised classification of melanotaenioid rainbowfishes, Sparks and Smith (2004b) recognize *Rheocles* and a new genus, tentatively referred to as "*Rheocles*" pending formal taxonomic description. While bedotiid relationships remain far from resolved (Campanella et al. 2015), in the following account, *Rheocles sensu stricto* is recognized to comprise the following four described species: *R. sikorae* (type species), *R. alaotrensis*, *R. lateralis*, and *R. wrightae* (Figure 10.16a), and two currently undescribed taxa, *R.* sp. "mangoro" and *R.* sp. "rianila."

DISTRIBUTION

Distributions range from central-eastern to northeastern regions of the island, where these fishes are found mainly in isolated upland habitats (Table 10.7, Figure 10.15). "*Rheocles*" is considered to include "*R.*" *derhami* and "*R.*" *vatosoa*, which are found in the northeast. Based on preliminary studies, the enigmatic species originally described as *Rheocloides pellegrini* and reassigned to *Rheocles* by Stiassny (1990) is included here within "*Rheocles*." "*Rheocles*" *pellegrini* was originally described from four specimens collected in 1930 at a locality "one day west of Andapa." In 2012, additional specimens were collected from a small mountain stream near the confluence the Manandriana and Amparihy Rivers, some 70 km south of Andapa. Although the precise extent of occurrence of "*R.*" *pellegrini* remains unclear, its generic assignment in "*Rheocles*," if further corroborated, would suggest a biogeographic disjunction between the two assemblages, similar to that observed among clades of *Bedotia* (see Stiassny et al., pp. 1273–76). "*Rheocles*" *derhami*, which is known only from the Mangarahara and Amboaboa Rivers, mid-reach tributaries of the Sofia River, is the only species of either *Rheocles* or "*Rheocles*" that occurs in a westward-flowing basin. All other species are restricted to eastern drainages (Figure 10.15).

HABITAT AND NATURAL HISTORY

Members of both genera are generally found in clear, silt-free, well-oxygenated, often rapidly flowing fresh waters, over gravel or coarse sand bottoms (Figure 10.16). Specimens have been collected from near sea level to about 1000 m elevation, mostly in smaller rivers and streams flowing where some riparian forest cover persists. And like *Bedotia*, *Rheocles* and "*Rheocles*" are considered good indicators of aquatic ecosystem health. They are also carnivorous, feeding in equal measure upon stranded terrestrial insects taken from the surface and aquatic invertebrates taken from the bottom, and are therefore vulnerable to both loss of riparian cover, the primary source of allochthonous inputs into their habitats, and to a reduction of benthic invertebrate communities due to erosional siltation.

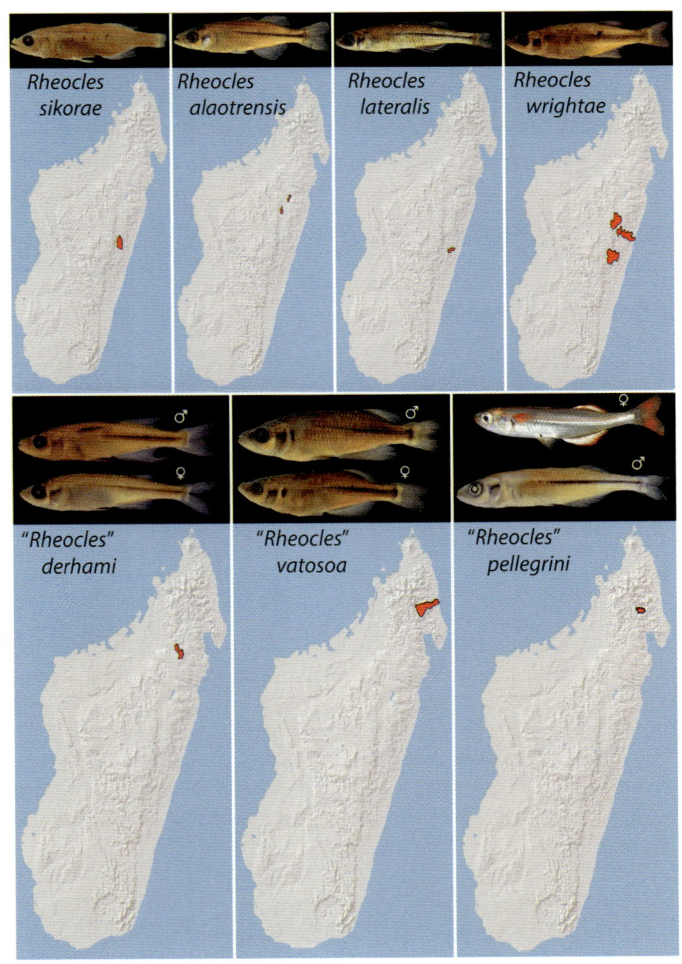

FIGURE 10.15 **Species of *Rheocles* and "*Rheocles*" with their respective distributions, based on most recent Red List assessment (IUCN 2021).**

FIGURE 10.16 **Composite figure of typical habitats for members of *Rheocles* and "*Rheocles*." A) *Rheocles wrightae*, Mamavou River, km 42, Anosibe An'ala Road; and B) "*Rheocles*" *vatosoa*, upper Lokoho River.** (PHOTOS by P. V. Loiselle.)

TABLE 10.7. **Species of *Rheocles and* "*Rheocles*" organized by clade with range information and most recent IUCN status**

SCIENTIFIC NAME	DISTRIBUTION	IUCN STATUS
R. alaotrensis (Pellegrin, 1914)	Eastern highlands: Lake Alaotra and headwaters of the Maningory and upper Rianila Rivers	EN
R. lateralis Stiassny & Reinthal, 1992	Eastern highlands: Nosivolo River, a mid-reach tributary of the Mangoro River	CR
R. sikorae (Sauvage, 1891)	Eastern highlands: Manambola River, a mid-reach tributary of the Mangoro River	DD
R. wrightae Stiassny, 1990	Eastern highlands: Sandrangato River, a mid-reach tributary of the Mangoro River	EN
R. n. sp. "rianila"	Eastern highlands: Middle reaches of the Rianila River basin	NA
R. n. sp. "mangoro"	Eastern highlands: Upper reaches of the Mangoro River basin	NA
"*Rheocles*" *pellegrini* (Nichols & LaMonte, 1931)	Eastern highlands: Upper reaches of the Antainambalana River	DD
"*R.*" *derhami* Stiassny & Rodriguez, 2001	Northwestern basins: Mangarahara and Amboaboa Rivers, mid-reach tributaries of the Sofia River	CR
"*R.*" *vatosoa* Stiassny, Rodriguez & Loiselle, 2002	Eastern highlands: Upper reaches of the Lokoho and Bemarivo Rivers	EN

Source: Clades after Sparks and Smith (2004b).
Notes: The names of species that have been identified as new to science and remain to be formally described are designated as "n. sp." (new species) and enclosed in quotation marks. "*Rheocles*" refers to a potentially distinct genus (see text). IUCN Red List conservation assessment status from IUCN (2021); for IUCN status abbreviations, see Table 10.1.

As far as is known, all are egg-scatterers, and under aquarium conditions, *R. alaotrensis* and "*R.*" *vatosoa*—to date, the only two species bred in captivity—exhibit a consort-type mating system in which males seek to monopolize access to ripe females rather than defend breeding territories. Patches of coarse gravel, fine-leafed aquatic plants, or the exposed roots of terrestrial plants growing along the water's edge are preferred spawning sites. Females of both *R. alaotrensis* and "*R.*" *vatosoa* collected in October and November did not contain ripe eggs, but specimens taken into captivity began spawning in late December and early January. The clear beige eggs hatch in 10–14 days, depending upon water temperature. Growth rates in nature are unknown. In captivity, sexual maturity is attained 10–12 months post hatching.

In the phylogenetic analysis of Sparks and Smith (2004b), a clade comprising "*R.*" *derhami* and "*R.*" *vatosoa* was recovered as the sister taxon to *Bedotia*. While *Rheocles* species are not discernibly sexually dimorphic, "*R.*" *pellegrini*, "*R.*" *derhami*, and "*R.*" *vatosoa* are markedly so (Stiassny and Rodriguez 2001; Stiassny et al. 2002) and in this regard are similar to *Bedotia*.

CONSERVATION STATUS

Small-scale artisanal fishing of *Rheocles* and "*Rheocles*" is widespread throughout their ranges, and in the case of *R. alaotrensis*, there is an important commercial fishery in Lake Alaotra for regional markets. While the distribution of *R. alaotrensis* has previously been considered to include both lake and numerous regional riverine populations, recent studies suggest that subpopulations from the Rianila and Mangoro Rivers are not conspecific with *R. alaotrensis* and represent two undescribed taxa; *R.* n. sp. "mangoro" and *R.* n. sp. "rianila." *Rheocles alaotrensis* is therefore likely restricted to Lake Alaotra and parts of the Maningory basin.

As for other bedotiid rainbowfishes, the combination of highly restricted distributional ranges, susceptibility to population decline owing to loss of riparian cover and habitat degradation, and increasing impacts from predation by and competition with numerous introduced species, places members of *Rheocles* among the most threatened of Madagascar's endemic fishes. Assessment of the conservation status of *Rheocles sensu lato* is provided by IUCN (2021). Of the four described *Rheocles* species, *R. lateralis* is listed as Critically Endangered, *R. alaotrensis* and *R. wrightae* as Endangered, and *R. sikorae* as Data Deficient. *Rheocles sikorae* has no designated type locality, as the species was recorded by Sauvage (1891) as inhabiting "rivières du versant est du grand massif centrale," and the few museum specimens are from a short stretch of the Manambola River (Mangoro drainage). No specimens have been collected since the mid-1960s, and some taxonomic confusion persists as to the distinction of *R. wrightae* from this species (IUCN 2021; but see Stiassny 1990). Of the three "*Rheocles*" species, "*R.*" *derhami* is listed as Critically Endangered, "*R.*" *vatosoa* as Endangered, and "*R.*" *pellegrini* as Data Deficient.

Subject editors: Melanie L. J. Stiassny and John S. Sparks

CICHLIDAE, PTYCHOCHROMINAE: *KATRIA*, CICHLID, *KATRIA*

M. L. J. Stiassny

Katria is a monotypic genus of relatively deep-bodied, small to medium-size ptychochromine cichlids (maximum size 12.7 cm standard length). The genus is represented by a single species, *K. katria*. Its distribution is restricted to a single river basin in central-eastern Madagascar (Figure 10.17).

SYSTEMATICS AND IDENTIFICATION

Katria is a ptychochromine cichlid readily identified by a pigmentation pattern consisting of two prominent dark vertical bars on the body, which in life are contrasted against a striking, iridescent golden background coloration, particularly prominent in large males, which may also exhibit a large nuchal hump (Figure 10.17b). While *K. katria* was originally placed within the genus *Ptychochromoides* (see Sparks and Loiselle, pp. 1293–95), molecular (Sparks and Smith 2004b) and morphological (Stiassny and Sparks 2006) studies provide strong support for the placement of the species as sister to *Ptychochromis* (see Sparks and Stiassny, pp. 1289–93). Because *K. katria* lacks several derived morphological features diagnostic of *Ptychochromis*, Stiassny and Sparks (2006) erected and diagnosed the genus *Katria* to accommodate this morphologically distinctive ptychochromine lineage.

DISTRIBUTION

Katria appears to have a relatively restricted distribution in the middle and lower reaches of a single drainage, the Nosivolo River, a small southern tributary of the Mangoro system in the eastern portion of the island (Figures 10.17a and c). With regard to the genus *Oxylapia* (see Ravelomanana et al., pp. 1281–82), anecdotal reports of the occurrence of *Katria* in the Namorona River drainage to the south of the Mangoro system have not been confirmed.

HABITAT AND NATURAL HISTORY

Within its known distributional range, the species is abundant, although restricted to rocky, still-water stretches of the river above and around the settlement of Marolambo and at sites some 26 km downstream of that locale. Collections below that point, despite targeted efforts, have failed to catch this species. *Katria katria* occurs exclusively in clear, well-oxygenated, relatively still water and is particularly abundant in large boulder-strewn pools and rocky side-channels. The species is heavily targeted by artisanal fisheries during certain seasons, and in visits to Marolambo in late September

FIGURE 10.17 **A) Distributional range of *Katria katria* modified after most recent Red List assessment (IUCN 2021); B) *K. katria* holotype (AMNH 217739), male; C) type locality, Nosivolo River, upstream of Marolambo.** (PHOTOS B and C by M. L. J. Stiassny.)

1996, when the species was first collected, *K. katria* was the dominant species for sale at regional fish markets. Because of local population increase, poverty, and food insecurity throughout the region, fishing pressures on this species will undoubtedly continue to climb.

No information is available on its diet in nature, but based on examination of gut contents of preserved specimens, *K. katria* feeds primarily on plant material, and filamentous algae scraped from rocks appear to be the major component of its diet. Like most cichlids, however, *Katria* is an opportunistic feeder, and guts also contained considerable amounts of detritus, as well as macerated insect remains and numerous sand grains, presumably ingested incidentally while scraping rock surfaces to harvest the dense periphyton mats (*aufwachs* in German, or "overgrowth") that cover rocks in still, clear-water habitats.

Katria katria is a biparental substrate spawner (both parents participate in care of the eggs after they have been deposited) and has been observed breeding during late October over territories clustered along rocky ridges. Nests are constructed by both parents and consist of series of small pits, but once the eggs hatch, the pits are consolidated, and by the time the larvae are free-swimming, the nests consist of single pits of about 20 cm in diameter with a flat rock on the bottom. Males tend to be larger than females, are more brightly colored, and typically develop a large and distinctive nuchal hump, very similar to that of *Ptychochromoides* species.

CONSERVATION STATUS

Katria is listed as Endangered in the latest Red List assessment (IUCN 2021), primarily owing to its restricted distribution and considerable habitat degradation throughout its limited range in the Nosivolo River system (see Ravelomanana et al., pp. 1281–82). In addition to deforestation, agricultural encroachment, and artisanal gold mining, the catchment is threatened by pollution from mercury mining. Additionally, a number of introduced species are established in the Marolambo region (Reinthal and Stiassny 1997), including two tilapiine cichlids, *Oreochromis niloticus* and *O. mossambicus*, potential competitors posing possible threats to *Katria* populations, particularly in the lentic lower reaches of the Nosivolo River system.

Subject editors: Melanie L. J. Stiassny and John S. Sparks

CICHLIDAE, PTYCHOCHROMINAE: *OXYLAPIA*, CICHLID, *SONGATANA*

T. Ravelomanana, J. S. Sparks, and M. L. J. Stiassny

Members of *Oxylapia* are small to medium-size ptychochromine cichlids (maximum size 15 cm standard length, usually considerably smaller) with an elongate body and somewhat goby-like appearance. The genus is known from one species, *O. polli*, endemic to a single river basin in central-eastern Madagascar (Figure 10.18).

SYSTEMATICS AND IDENTIFICATION

Morphologically, *Oxylapia polli* is characterized by pelvic fins that are fleshy and seemingly modified for adhering to the substrate (Figure 10.18b). Lips are large and notably fleshy. Outer-row teeth are prominent unicuspids with brown, chisel-shaped cusps. Three anal-fin spines are present, gradually increasing in length. Body scales are strongly ctenoid; chest scales are very small and deeply embedded. Median sensory canal pores (NLF0) on the frontal bones of the neurocranium are widely separated, and fourth ceratobranchial tooth plates (forming part of the branchial basket) are separate from the outer gill rakers of that element.

Oxylapia is recovered as the sister taxon to *Ptychochromoides* (see Sparks and Loiselle, pp. 1293–95), also endemic to Madagascar, on the basis of both morphological and molecular evidence (Sparks 2004b, 2008; Sparks and Smith 2004a). Morphological features uniting *Oxylapia* and *Ptychochromoides* include chest scales that are markedly reduced in size and embedded, moderately to extremely fleshy lips, and a blotchy, mottled, and speckled grayish-black or brownish overall pigmentation pattern (Sparks 2008; Sparks et al. 2012). The clade comprising *Oxylapia* and *Ptychochromoides* is in turn recovered as the sister group to a clade comprising *Katria* and *Ptychochromis* (Sparks 2004b; Sparks and Smith 2004a; Stiassny and Sparks 2006; see Stiassny, pp. 1279–80; see Sparks and Stiassny, pp. 1289–93).

DISTRIBUTION

Oxylapia polli has a restricted distribution limited to the Nosivolo River basin, a small tributary of the Mangoro system (Figures 10.18a and c). Prior to 2000, this species was known only from the vicinity of the town of Marolambo, but subsequently it was found to be widely distributed in the Nosivolo River and its major tributaries, occurring in the upper and middle reaches from the headwaters at Ambodivoara (790 m), where it is particularly abundant, to its middle reaches at Ambatomasina, a village a few kilometers downstream of Marolambo (at 380 m). The species is absent from the lower reaches of the river, likely because downstream habitats are more lentic and subjected to increased habitat degradation. Whereas some fishermen living in the neighboring Namorona and Mananara River basins recognize images of this species and claim it is present in those watersheds, this remains unconfirmed, despite targeted sampling efforts in both of those rivers.

FIGURE 10.18 **A) Distributional range of *Oxylapia polli*, modified after the most recent Red List assessment (IUCN 2021); B) preserved specimen of *O. polli*; and C) Nosivolo River near the town of Ankazomasina, where *O. polli* is notably abundant.** (PHOTOS B and C by T. Ravelomanana.)

HABITAT AND NATURAL HISTORY

Oxylapia polli is an elusive fish, found exclusively in fast-flowing waters, especially in rocky habitat with rapids and riffles, where it is generally caught at water depths of between 50 and 100 cm (Figure 10.18c). It is occasionally harvested by local fishers using both cast nets and a traditional dip net attached to the end of a long pole. Fishers position themselves on rocks above and within the rapids and scoop the fish from beneath rocks, where it seems to accumulate.

Little information is available on the diet of this fish in nature; however, anatomical structures are suggestive of a specialized insectivore. Examination of gut contents indicates that *O. polli* is highly opportunistic, feeding on insects, detritus, and aquatic plants as available. The species is a biparental substrate spawner that practices long-term care of mobile fry. Eggs are placed beneath rocks and tended by one parent while the other defends the perimeter of the territory. Parental fish have been observed in late October, and according to local residents, breeding continues through early December.

CONSERVATION STATUS

Oxylapia polli is currently classified as Endangered in the Red List (IUCN 2021), primarily owing to its greatly restricted distribution and considerable habitat degradation throughout its range. The Nosivolo River is the zone of intensive artisanal mining activities. Gold extraction occurs in the headwaters of tributaries such as the Sandranamby, which, as a result, is now highly turbid throughout the year. There is also mining activity around Ambodivoara and along almost the entire length of the main channel of the Nosivolo River, especially during low water. Despite these impacts, much of the Nosivolo River continues to support a diverse ichthyofauna dominated by native species, and *O. polli* remains abundant in isolated, restricted rocky, fast-flowing reaches.

There currently exists no commercial fishery for *Oxylapia*, owing to the difficulties entailed in exploiting rapids; however, as noted above, it is taken opportunistically by artisanal fishermen. The absence of intensive fishing pressures, combined with the apparent competitive disadvantage experienced by introduced species in remaining fast-flowing habitats on Madagascar, have thus far preserved this species from the fate of many other native Malagasy cichlids. The Nosivolo River is currently protected by the Malagasy government as Paysage Harmonieux Protégé de la Rivière Nosivolo (a category V protected area), and it is also a Ramsar site. The site is co-managed by Cercle d'Etudes Multidisciplinaires pour l'Environnement et la Santé (CEMES) and the local population. However, owing to increases in the local human population and poverty, fishing pressures in the region are continuing to climb.

Subject editors: Melanie L. J. Stiassny and John S. Sparks

CICHLIDAE, PTYCHOCHROMINAE: *PARATILAPIA*, CICHLID, *MARAKELY*, *FONY*, *FIAMANGA*, *TRONDRO MAINTY*

P. V. Loiselle and T. Ravelomanana

Members of *Paratilapia* are large (maximum size 30 cm standard length, usually smaller) cichlids endemic to Madagascar. The genus comprises three described and at least eight undescribed species (Table 10.8). *Paratilapia* species can be found on both versants of the island, and while known to occur in the quieter stretches of large rivers, these cichlids have a marked preference for smaller streams and standing bodies of water.

SYSTEMATICS AND IDENTIFICATION

The relationships of *Paratilapia* are not fully resolved. Some anatomical data suggest that the genus is sister to a large clade composed of the etropline cichlids (subfamily Etroplinae), *Heterochromis*, and all other Neotropical and African cichlids, or that *Paratilapia* is the sister taxon to the remainder of the Malagasy cichlids and the south Asian cichlids. However, relationships reconstructed using nucleotide characters indicate that *Paratilapia* is either the sister taxon of a clade comprising all other Malagasy cichlids and *Etroplus* (Sparks 2001), or a member of Ptychochrominae, which also includes the endemic Malgasy genera *Katria*, *Oxylapia*, *Ptychochromis*, and *Ptychochromoides* (Sparks 2004b; Sparks and Smith 2004a).

Members of *Paratilapia* are robust, moderately deep-bodied fishes with relatively acute snouts. Jaw teeth are numerous and uniformly conical. Scales are ctenoid. Species of *Paratilapia* are distinguished from all other Malagasy cichlids by the presence of conical jaw teeth and the absence of tooth plates on the fourth ceratobranchial of the branchial basket. Median sensory canal pores (NLF0) on the frontal bones are more or less coalesced in the midline. The caudal fin is rounded, and the anal fin has three spines increasing gradually in length. A "*Tilapia* spot" is present basally in the soft dorsal fin of juveniles, and adult coloration generally features discrete metallic blue or gold spots against a dark background. Based on the size of these spots, *Paratilapia* species can be

TABLE 10.8. **Species of *Paratilapia* with range information and most recent IUCN status**

SCIENTIFIC NAME	DISTRIBUTION	IUCN STATUS
P. polleni Bleeker, 1868	Northwestern basins: Range extending from the Sofia north to streams draining Montagne d'Ambre, and crater lakes on Nosy Be	VU
P. bleekeri Sauvage, 1882	Western basins: Upper reaches of the Betsiboka-Ikopa basin in the vicinity of Antananarivo	DD
P. typus (Bleeker, 1879)	Eastern lowlands: Mananara River	NA
P. n. sp. "andapa"	Eastern lowlands: Lokoho and Bemarivo Rivers	NA
P. n. sp. "onilahy"	Western basins: Lower Onilahy River and Lake Ihotry basin	NA
P. n. sp. "vondrozo"	Eastern highlands: Upper reaches of the Mananara du Sud River	NA
P. n. sp. "fony"	Eastern highlands and lowlands: Maningory River and Lake Alaotra basin south to the Mananara du Sud and Masihanaka Rivers inclusive of Nosy Boraha	NA
P. n. sp. "akanga"	Eastern highlands and lowlands: Manampanihy River south to Lake Anjanaborona, Mananara River watershed, and rivers draining the Anosyenne Mountains	NA
P. n. sp. "fiamanga"	Western basins: Upper Mangoky River	NA
P. n. sp. "ilempo"	Western basins: Lake Ilempo and formerly Lake Itasy	NA
P. n. sp. "betsiboka"	Northwestern basins: Lower Betsiboka and Ikopa Rivers and Lake Kinkony satellite lakes	NA

Notes: The names of species that have been identified as new to science and remain to be formally described are designated as "n. sp." (new species) and enclosed in quotation marks. IUCN Red List conservation assessment status from IUCN (2021); for IUCN status abbreviations, see Table 10.1.

designated as either a "large spot" or "small spot" phenotype, but whether spot size indicates relationship is currently unknown.

The taxonomy of the genus has a long and confused history; however, recent genetic studies have confirmed the validity of *P. typus* and *P. bleekeri*, both long treated as junior synonyms of *P. polleni*. Accordingly, the name *P. polleni* appends only to the "large spot" fish (Figure 10.19a) present in northwestern basins, from the Sofia River basin north to streams draining Montagne d'Ambre, and in crater lakes on Nosy Be. *Paratilapia typus*, *P. bleekeri* and *P.* n. sp. "andapa" are also representatives of the "large spot" phenotype. *Paratilapia* n. sp. "fony" (Figure 10.19b) and the remaining undescribed species are of the "small spot" phenotype.

FIGURE 10.19 **A) Male of the topotypical population of *Paratilapia polleni*, a "large spot" species. B) Female of an undescribed "small spot" species, the widely distributed *Paratilapia* n. sp. "fony."** (PHOTOS by P. V. Loiselle.)

DISTRIBUTION

Paratilapia was formerly widespread throughout eastern, northwestern, and western Madagascar. See Table 10.8 for distribution data for each putative species of the genus. Although *Paratilapia* remains relatively common in eastern Madagascar and on Nosy Be, it has become rare and localized throughout the remainder of the island.

HABITAT AND NATURAL HISTORY

Paratilapia species are found in a wide variety of habitats, including small to medium-size rivers, lakes, and the brackish-water lagoons of the Pangalanes Canal along the eastern coast of the island. Members of the genus are opportunistic carnivores, feeding on aquatic invertebrates, stranded terrestrial insects, and small fishes.

Males grow larger than females, and all species are monogamous substrate spawners that practice long-term biparental defense of mobile fry. Eggs are rosy beige in color, each with a long adhesive filament that intertwines with the others, binding the eggs together in a compact mass, a mode of egg attachment unique among the Cichlidae (Stiassny and Gerstner 1992; Stiassny and Mezey 1993). Spawns are large, numbering several thousand eggs. Sexual maturity is attained about 12 months after spawning, at a standard length of about 10.5 cm for males, slightly shorter for females. Several years of additional growth are required before any *Paratilapia* species attains its maximum size.

CONSERVATION STATUS

All recognized *Paratilapia* species were formerly widespread and abundant enough to support targeted artisanal fisheries. However, ranges of most members of the genus have contracted dramatically during the past century, and many local populations have disappeared in the face of habitat degradation, introduced competitors and predators, and overfishing.

Two described species of *Paratilapia* were included in the latest IUCN Red List assessment, with *P. polleni* listed as Vulnerable, due to deforestation and water extraction throughout most of its restricted range, and *P. bleekeri* as Data Deficient (IUCN 2021), although more recent observations suggest a designation of Critically Endangered may be appropriate for the latter, as surviving populations are sparse and continuing to decline. Although not formally assessed in 2016, *P. typus* maintains relatively robust populations in the forested Mananara River basin. If formally assessed, *Paratilapia* n. spp. "fiamanga," "vondrozo," "onilahy," "ilempo," and "betsiboka" would likely satisfy the classification of Critically Endangered. The consequences of anthropogenic habitat degradation are exacerbated by the presence of the introduced and invasive *Channa maculata* (Asian Snakehead), which preys upon *Paratilapia* juveniles and competes with adults wherever the two occur syntopically. The relatively robust populations of *P. typus* and *P.* n. sp. "akanga" owe their existence to both the relatively well-forested watersheds of the Mananara River and the Anosy basin and the absence of the snakehead in both regions. The extensive range and moderate salt tolerance of *P.* n. sp. "fony" afford populations of this species a degree of protection from this invasive species. Nonetheless, all *Paratilapia* populations remain vulnerable to habitat degradation that climate change can be anticipated to accelerate, and the extirpation of isolated local populations seems only a matter of time.

Subject editors: Melanie L. J. Stiassny and John S. Sparks

CICHLIDAE, ETROPLINAE: *PARETROPLUS*, CICHLID, *DAMBA* AND MANY OTHER MALAGASY NAMES

J. S. Sparks

Members of *Paretroplus* are medium-size to large (maximum size about 200 mm standard length in large lake species, riverine/rheophilic species usually smaller), moderate- to deep-bodied and laterally compressed cichlid fishes that are endemic to fresh- and brackish-water habitats on Madagascar (Figures 10.20–10.22). Since the assessment of Loiselle and de Rham (2003), three new species of *Paretroplus* have been formally described, and the genus was revised (Sparks 2008; Sparks and Schelly 2011). *Paretroplus* currently comprises 13 valid species (Table 10.9). An undescribed species within the *P. damii* species group from northwestern Madagascar is currently being formally described (J. S. Sparks, unpublished data) (Figure 10.20b).

For local vernacular names of *Paretroplus* species (in addition to *damba*), see Table 10.9.

SYSTEMATICS AND IDENTIFICATION

Paretroplus is an etroplin genus readily diagnosed by numerous unique anatomical features, including the following: spatulate, unicuspid dentition is present in a single row in both upper and lower jaws (Sparks 2008: Figures 3B, 4D, and 5A); greatly enlarged, elongate teeth are present on either side of the premaxillary symphysis, with correspondingly small lower jaw symphyseal teeth; oral dentition is restricted anteriorly on the premaxilla and dentary; very few teeth occur in both the upper (18 or fewer) and lower (14 or fewer) oral jaws; the dorsal (i.e., primordial) process of the angulo-articular is closely apposed to the posterior margin (i.e., coronoid process) of the dentary; the first pharyngobranchial articulates only with the parasphenoid, or at the parasphenoid-prootic margin; the maxillary process of the palatine is elongate and tapered rostrally (Sparks 2008: Figure 15B); the lacrimal is expanded anteroventrally, elongate, and paddle-shaped (Sparks 2008: Figure 16D); the entopterygoid bears a flange or "calyx" along its anterodorsal margin that partially overlies the dorsomedial surface of the ectopterygoid and forms a slot into which the median palato-prevomerine ligament inserts (Sparks 2008: Figure 15B); a substantial gap is present between the symplectic and the preopercle in lateral view, with no overlap between these two bones; the paired anterior gas-bladder bullae are structurally complex and polyp-like (i.e., teardrop-shaped), with

FIGURE 10.20 **A) *Paretroplus maromandia*, a rarely encountered species, imaged in the field immediately after capture. B) A new species of *Paretroplus*, collected in Lake Andrapongy in 2011 and in the process of being formally described.** (PHOTOS A and B by J. S. Sparks.)

FIGURE 10.21 **A) *Paretroplus maculatus*, once common in Lake Ravelobe at Ankarafantsika. B) The highly degraded state of Lake Ravelobe in 2011, covered completely in water hyacinth, *Eichhornia crassipes*, an introduced and invasive plant.** (PHOTO A by P. V. Loiselle and B by J. S. Sparks.)

markedly narrow connections to the main gas-bladder chamber (Sparks 2008: Figures 18D and 20B–C); and the anterior gas-bladder bullae exhibit a thickened, tough, and rigid tunica externa.

Other features useful for identification, but that are not unique to *Paretroplus* within Cichlidae (also shared with the South Asian genera *Etroplus* and *Pseudetroplus*), include: well-developed, scaled sheaths along the dorsal- and anal-fin bases into which these fins can partly retract; an elevated anal-fin spine count of 7–11 (rarely 6); and an adult pigmentation pattern that features a prominent vertical barring pattern on the flanks (number and intensity of vertical bars varies among species).

Paretroplus is recovered as the sister group to a clade comprising the endemic South Asian genera *Etroplus* and *Pseudetroplus* (Sparks 2004b, 2008; Sparks and Smith 2004a), representing a well-corroborated, Gondwanan transoceanic sister-group pair. The cichlid subfamily Etroplinae comprises the genera *Etroplus*, *Pseudetroplus*, and *Paretroplus* (Sparks and Smith 2004a). Etroplinae is recovered as the sister group to the remaining members of Cichlidae, including the subfamilies Ptychochrominae (Madagascar), Cichlinae (Neotropics), and Pseudocrenilabrinae (Africa) (Sparks 2004b; Sparks and Smith 2004a; McMahan et al. 2013).

Etroplinae is morphologically quite distinct from the remainder of the Cichlidae and is diagnosed by numerous unique anatomical features (see Sparks 2008, for a full list of apomorphic features; the figure references in this paragraph are from that work). The following characters can most easily be used to identify members of the subfamily: a second premaxillary-maxillary ligament originates from the anterior portion of the articulating head of the maxilla (Figure 3B); the median frontal canals and median frontal pores of the neurocranium are coalesced, forming a continuous median canal with a single dorsal pore (Figure 6C); the exoccipital foramina are greatly enlarged, such that much of the lateral faces of these bones are lost, creating a dorsally projecting exoccipital chamber (Figures 7C and 8A–B); there is excavation of the posterior margin of the supraoccipital bone (Figures 10B and 19C); molariform teeth are present on the third pharyngobranchial tooth plates (Figure 11D) and on the fifth ceratobranchial tooth plates (Figure 14B); the anterior hemal spines bear anteroposteriorly oriented laminar extensions, which may connect or "interlock" (Figure 19C); the anterior anal-fin pterygiophores (internal bony-fin support element) insert into slots formed by laminar expansion of the anterior hemal spines (Figure 19C); broad caudal extensions of the gas bladder are present, with corresponding compression of the anterior hemal spines and anal-fin pterygiophores (Figure 19C); and well-developed lateral ridges of scales (i.e., scale sheathing) occur along the bases of the dorsal and anal fins (Figure 22).

In the phylogenetic analyses of Sparks and Smith (2004a) and Sparks (2008), two major clades within *Paretroplus* were recovered

FIGURE 10.22 **A) *Paretroplus menarambo*, freshly captured from Lake Tseny. B) Lake Tseny habitat, which remains in relatively good condition and still supports a diverse assemblage of native cichlids. C) By comparison, Lake Sarodrano, the type locality of *P. menarambo*, is now highly degraded, and no individuals of this species have been captured in the lake since the mid-1990s. All images from 2011 survey.** (PHOTOS A and B by R. Schelly and C by J. S. Sparks.)

with strong support, one comprising deep-bodied lacustrine forms and the other more elongate and shallow-bodied, primarily lotic species (see Sparks 2008: Figure 1B; Sparks and Schelly 2011: Figure 1). These two assemblages can be easily separated on the basis of anatomical features. The deep-bodied clade, comprising *P. dambabe*, *P. gymnopreopercularis*, *P. kieneri*, *P. maculatus*, *P. maromandia*, *P. menarambo*, *P. petiti*, and *P. polyactis*, is characterized by the presence of a large, wide, and rounded excavation (i.e., in-cut) on the posterior margin of the supraoccipital bone (Sparks 2008: Figures 10b and 19c). Likewise, the elongate-bodied clade, comprising *P. damii*, *P. loisellei*, *P. nourissati*, *P. tsimoly*, *P. lamenabe*, and *P.* n. sp. "anjingo," can be identified by several unique morphological features: the posterior field of the lateral body scales is thin and not ossified; multiple discrete rows of scales extend onto both the soft dorsal and anal fins; the chest scales are markedly reduced in size and highly embedded; multiple rows of scales that are markedly reduced in size extend laterally on the flanks dorsal to the pelvic fins and anus; and a triangular, black or dark gray pectoral-axil patch is present (Sparks and Schelly 2011).

DISTRIBUTION

Paretroplus currently comprises 13 valid species (Sparks and Schelly 2011; Table 10.9). All but a single described species, *P. polyactis*, which is widespread in fresh- and brackish-water habitats along nearly the entire eastern coast, are restricted to freshwater basins in the northwestern and northern regions of the island (*P. maromandia* is reported to enter brackish water; however, we have encountered the species only in strictly freshwater habitats; Sparks and Reinthal 1999; Figure 10.20a). Aside from *P. damii* and *P. kieneri*, which exhibit comparatively widespread distributions and occur across multiple drainage basins, the remaining northern and northwestern species of *Paretroplus* are restricted to single basins or to only portions of a single drainage basin. Members of the genus are conspicuously absent from the Central Highlands as well as drainages in the central west, the southwest, and the extreme south.

HABITAT AND NATURAL HISTORY

Paretroplus have strong pharyngeal tooth plates specialized for crushing and feed almost exclusively upon gastropods. However, to a much lesser degree, they will also consume aquatic invertebrates and plant material (Martinez and Sparks 2017). Members of this genus are monogamous substrate spawners that exhibit long-term care of mobile fry. Lotic, rheophilic species, including *P. nourissati*, *P. tsimoly*, and *P. loisellei*, spawn on the underside of rocks or in holes, whereas lentic species, such as *P. dambabe*, *P. menarambo*, and *P. maculatus*, spawn in the open, utilizing submerged wood and stumps, rocks, or large excavated pits as spawning sites (Loiselle and de Rham 2003). Eggs are deposited in a condensed, circular plaque on a cleaned solid substratum. Based on observations in aquaria, it takes at least three to five years for any species of *Paretroplus* to attain its maximum size.

CONSERVATION STATUS

Members of *Paretroplus* are highly sought after for human consumption and have been extirpated from much of their original range owing to a combination of overfishing, habitat degradation, and competition from introduced species (Sparks 2008; Irwin et al.

TABLE 10.9. **Species of *Paretroplus* with range information, local names, and most recent IUCN status**

SCIENTIFIC NAME	DISTRIBUTION	VERNACULAR NAMES	IUCN STATUS
P. damii Bleeker, 1868	Northwestern basins: Lake Ampombilava-Djabala system on Nosy Be (type locality) and westward draining rivers from the Mananjeba to the Sambirano	*Damba, damba mena, filaopisaka, dridri mena, lamena, loakapisaka*	VU
P. kieneri Arnoult, 1960	Northwestern basins: From southwest to northeast, the Mahavavy du Sud basin and Lake Kinkony (where presumed extinct); the lower Betsiboka basin, including Lake Ravelobe, Ankalimilotrabe (Kalamilotra) River, Lake Parinandrina, the Ikopa basin lakes, upper Kamoro River, Mahajamba River; and the Bemarivo basin and Lakes Sarodrano and Tseny, within the Sofia River drainage system	*Kotsovato*	VU
P. maculatus Kiener & Maugé, 1966	Northwestern basins: Endemic to turbid, shallow floodplain lakes in the lower reaches of the Betsiboka and Ikopa drainage basins, extending in the north from Lake Ravelobe and surrounding small rivers in the vicinity of Ampijoroa Forestry Station, southeast of Mahajanga, southward to a number of small lakes in the vicinity of Maevatanana, including lakes in the region of Ambato-Boeny	*Damba, damba mipentina*	CR
P. petiti Pellegrin, 1929	Northwestern basins: Maintimaso River, tributary of the westward-flowing Betsiboka River, near town of Maintimaso, situated roughly 69 km southeast of Mahajanga	Unknown	DD
P. polyactis Bleeker, 1878	Eastern highlands and lowlands: Extensive latitudinal range spanning nearly the entire eastern coast, extending from the Manambato River, north of Vohémar, southward to the Manampanihy River, near Tolagnaro	*Masovoatoaka*	LC
P. maromandia Sparks & Reinthal, 1999	Northwestern basins: Endemic to the lower reaches of the Andranomalaza River, including the Maintsomalaza River just downstream from the confluence of the Manongarivo and Andranomalaza Rivers (type locality), near the town of Maromandia	*Damba mena*	EN
P. nourissati (Allgayer, 1998)	Northwestern basins: Endemic to the Amboaboa and Mangarahara Rivers, tributaries of the middle Sofia River, at their confluence near the town of Mandritsara. Range may extend into lower reaches of the Bemarivo River, including Lake Tseny.	*Lamena*	EN
P. menarambo Allgayer, 1996	Northwestern basins: Lower reaches of the Bemarivo River floodplain, including Lake Sarodrano (type locality, now extinct) and Lake Tseny (extant). The Bemarivo is a tributary of the extensive Sofia River drainage system, but the species is not known from the Sofia River	*Damba, menarambo*	CR
P. tsimoly Stiassny, Chakrabarty & Loiselle, 2001	Northwestern basins: Middle reaches of the Betsiboka River, including the Ankalimilotrabe (Kalamilotra or Kamilotra) River, a tributary of the Betsiboka River, near the town of Ankalimilotrabe, and upper reaches of the Kamoro River near the village of Antsalahina	*Tsimoly*	EN
P. dambabe Sparks, 2002	Northwestern basins: Endemic to lower Mahavavy du Sud basin; preserved specimens available only from Lake Kinkony (type locality, likely extinct), and also reported to occur in two smaller satellite lakes near the village of Antongomena and in the Mahavavy du Sud River proper	*Kotso, damba*	CR

(*continued overleaf*)

TABLE 10.9. ***continued***

SCIENTIFIC NAME	DISTRIBUTION	VERNACULAR NAMES	IUCN STATUS
P. gymnopreopercularis Sparks, 2008	Northwestern basins: Endemic to the Mangarahara River and its tributary the Amboaboa River, tributaries of the Sofia River, at their confluence near the town of Mandritsara	*Melemshishka*	CR
P. lamenabe Sparks, 2008	Northwestern basins: Known from the lower reaches of the Mahajamba River, near the town of Androka, but may have a wider distribution encompassing the lower reaches of the Bemarivo River floodplain, including Lake Tseny	*Lamena, tsimoly, damba*	EN
P. loisellei Sparks & Schelly, 2011	Eastern highlands and lowlands: Middle reaches of the eastward-draining Mahanara River, north of Sambava near the town of Antsirabe-Nord	*Ventitry*	EN
Paretroplus n. sp. "anjingo"	Northwestern basins: Endemic to the Anjingo and Ankofia River drainages, including Lake Andrapongy	*Damba, lamena*	NA

Notes: The name of a species that has been identified as new to science and remains to be formally described is designated as "n. sp." (new species) and enclosed in quotation marks. IUCN Red List conservation assessment status from IUCN (2021); for IUCN status abbreviations, see Table 10.1.

2010; J. S. Sparks, unpublished data). *Paretroplus petiti* is known only from the holotype, and efforts to collect additional specimens over the past two and a half decades have proved unsuccessful. It is listed as Data Deficient in the most recent Red List assessment (IUCN 2021) only because nothing is known regarding its range or current status. *Paretroplus dambabe* is considered extirpated in Lake Kinkony, its type locality, and although it may be extant in smaller satellite lakes in the region and/or the lower Mahavavy du Sud basin, no specimens have been collected in recent years, and the species is listed as Critically Endangered (IUCN 2021). *Paretroplus maculatus*, which used to be quite common in rivers and streams draining and surrounding Lake Ravelobe, and the lower reaches of the Betsiboka and Ikopa drainages southeast of Mahajanga, was not found on a 2011 survey in either Lake Ravelobe or the surrounding area and is listed as Critically Endangered (IUCN 2021) (Figure 10.21b). Lake Ravelobe was subsequently largely drained (Goodman et al. 2018), which does not bode well for the once plentiful population of *P. maculatus* (and to a lesser extent *P. kieneri*) that formerly inhabited the artificially constructed lake. All three of these species, if not extinct already, are certainly on the verge of extinction. *Paretroplus menarambo* was considered extinct in its only known habitat, Lake Sarodrano, in the lower reaches of the Bemarivo River basin; however, in recent years an extant population was located in Lake Tseny, not far away (Sparks 2008; J. S. Sparks, unpublished data) (Figure 10.22).

As Loiselle and de Rham (2003) noted for *Paretroplus* nearly 20 years ago, the conservation status varies markedly among the species. Those that inhabit multiple basins, and that occur in both rivers and lakes, appear to be the most stable (e.g., *P. damii*, *P. kieneri*, *P. polyactis*), whereas species found primarily in floodplain lakes are by far the most threatened (e.g., *P. dambabe*, *P. maculatus*, *P. menarambo*) (Ravelomanana et al. 2018) (Figures 10.21a and 10.22a). Loiselle and de Rham stressed that this difference may reflect the fact that lakes are generally the sites of important commercial fisheries on the island, whereas riverine habitats are only sporadically fished.

In the most recent IUCN Red List assessment (IUCN 2021), *P. dambabe*, *P. maculatus*, and *P. menarambo* are listed as Critically Endangered, however, the former two species have not been collected in recent years and are very likely extinct. *Paretroplus gymnopreopercularis*, which has an extremely restricted range and is known only from the Mangarahara River and its tributary the Amboaboa River near their confluence in the northwest, has experienced a serious decline in population size in recent years and also was assessed as Critically Endangered. Of the remaining species, *P. loisellei*, *P. lamenabe*, *P. nourissati*, *P. tsimoly*, and *P. maromandia* were listed as Endangered (Figure 10.20a). Among the more widespread species, *P. kieneri* and *P. damii*, which inhabit both rivers and lakes and occur in multiple basins, were assessed as Vulnerable, and only the very widespread *P. polyactis*, which occurs in both fresh and brackish water along nearly the entire eastern coast, was listed as Least Concern.

Since our research group began extensive survey work on Madagascar in 1994, apart from *P. polyactis*, all remaining members of the genus have undergone extensive range contractions and significant declines in population numbers, and at least three species are now likely extinct in the wild (J. S. Sparks, unpublished data). Given the continued rapid pace of habitat degradation, overfishing, and competition with introduced species, in addition to being highly sought after as food, all species of *Paretroplus* are at significant risk.

Subject editors: John S. Sparks and Melanie L. J. Stiassny

CICHLIDAE, PTYCHOCHROMINAE: *PTYCHOCHROMIS*, CICHLID, *SAROY* AND MANY OTHER MALAGASY NAMES

J. S. Sparks and M. L. J. Stiassny

Members of *Ptychochromis* are medium-size (maximum size about 200 mm standard length, usually considerably smaller), laterally compressed, and deep-bodied cichlid fishes that are endemic to Madagascar. Since the assessment of Sparks (2003a), eight new species of *Ptychochromis* have been described, based on extensive survey efforts throughout Madagascar, and the genus has been formally revised (Sparks 2002b; Stiassny and Sparks 2006; Sparks and Stiassny 2010; Martinez et al. 2015). *Ptychochromis* currently comprises 10 valid species (Table 10.10, Figure 10.23).

For local vernacular names of *Ptychochromis* species (in addition to *saroy*), see Table 10.10.

SYSTEMATICS AND IDENTIFICATION

Ptychochromis is recovered as the sister group to *Katria*, based on the analysis of both morphological and molecular data (Sparks 2004b; Sparks and Smith 2004a; Stiassny and Sparks 2006). *Ptychochromis* and *Katria* are united by the following unique morphological features: the fourth ceratobranchial bone bears a characteristically elongate process and deeply rounded indentation on its inner margin; the laterosensory canal system of the neurocranium, preopercle, and mandible is hypertrophied, with markedly enlarged laterosensory canals and expanded pores; the two supraneural elements are located anterior to the first neural spine; and the palatine bone bears a well-developed, expansive, and dorsally elevated lateral ethmoid process on the dorsal margin of the palatine head, with a broad articulation surface on the medial face (Stiassny and Sparks 2006). The clade comprising *Katria* and *Ptychochromis* is recovered as the sister taxon to a clade comprising *Ptychochromoides* and *Oxylapia* (see Sparks and Loiselle, pp. 1293–95; Ravelomanana et al., pp. 1281–82) (Sparks 2004b; Sparks and Smith 2004a; Stiassny and Sparks 2006). This assemblage, including the genera *Katria*, *Ptychochromis*, *Ptychochromoides*, and *Oxylapia*, along with *Paratilapia* (see Loiselle and Ravelomanana, pp. 1282–84), composes the endemic Malagasy cichlid subfamily Ptychochrominae (Sparks 2004b; Stiassny and Sparks 2006).

Due to relatively muted intrageneric anatomical variation, resolution of phylogenetic relationships among *Ptychochromis* species has proved problematical. However, Stiassny and Sparks (2006) tentatively recognized a grouping of species (*P. oligacanthus*, *P. onilahy*, *P. insolitus*, and *P. inornatus*) restricted in geographical distribution to western drainages of Madagascar (Figure 10.23) and characterized by a derived palatine morphology, but were unable to resolve relationships among the taxa *P. grandidieri*, *P. makira*, *P. loisellei*, and *P. curvidens*. It is noteworthy that, with the exception of *P. curvidens*, all the species in this unresolved group are restricted in distribution to eastern-flowing drainages. Martinez et al. (2015) provide additional molecular support for the monophyly of the "western clade" and recognize as an "east coast clade" *P. makira*, *P. loisellei*, *P. grandidieri*, and *P. mainty*, albeit with weak support for the inclusion of *P. makira*. Martinez et al. (2015) were unable to include *P. ernestmagnusi* or *P. curvidens* in their molecular analysis because of a lack of suitable material, and final resolution of intrageneric relationships and phylogeography of *Ptychochromis* remains an important task.

Ptychochromis is a ptychochromine genus that was diagnosed in Stiassny and Sparks (2006; figures cited in this paragraph are from that work) by the presence of a free second epibranchial tooth plate associated with, but not fused to, the second epibranchial bone (an ossified upper gill arch element) (Figure 7A); exclusion of the second infraorbital bone (IO2) from the orbit by IO3 (Figure 8F); a prominent palatine groove (Figure 6F–G); ventrally displaced insertion of the palatine-palatine ligament compared to other ptychochromine genera (Figure 6F–G); a horizontally oriented palatine bone with an elongate palatine prong and weakly elevated lateral ethmoid process (Figure 6G; modified in members of the "western clade"); and anterior displacement of the supraneural bones such that the anterior element comes to overlie the dorsoposterior margin of the supraoccipital crest (Figure 3A–C; lacking in members of the "western clade") (Stiassny and Sparks 2006; Sparks and Stiassny 2010).

Other features useful for identification include: fourth ceratobranchial tooth plates that are well developed and confluent with the outer gill rakers of that element (shared only with *Katria* [see Stiassny, pp. 1279–80] and *Ptychochromoides* [see Sparks and Loiselle, pp. 1293–95] within Cichlidae); oral dentition that comprises bilaterally symmetrical, bicuspid teeth, both inner and outer rows of a similar morphology (shared with *Ptychochromoides*); and three anal-fin spines, the first much shorter than the following two (shared with *Ptychochromoides*). Members of *Ptychochromis* are further characterized by hypertrophied (overdeveloped) laterosensory canals and pores on the head. Body scales are large and ctenoid (toothed); scales are reduced in size and embedded on the chest. Species of *Ptychochromis* exhibit a pigmentation pattern that generally features a series of large dark spots on a lighter background, characteristic of both *Ptychochromis* and its sister taxon *Katria* (Stiassny and Sparks 2006).

DISTRIBUTION

Members of the genus *Ptychochromis* are widespread throughout eastern and northwestern coastal areas and less widely distributed in insular and upland habitats within these regions (Figures 10.23 and 10.24). The genus was formerly distributed in the southwest, in the Onilahy basin, although the species found there, *P. onilahy*, is presumed to be extinct (Stiassny and Sparks 2006).

TABLE 10.10. **Species of *Ptychochromis* with range information, local names, and most recent IUCN status**

SCIENTIFIC NAME	DISTRIBUTION	VERNACULAR NAMES	IUCN STATUS
P. oligacanthus (Bleeker, 1868)	Northwestern basins: Restricted to freshwater habitats from the Sambirano River northward to the Mananjeba drainage (Andranomaloto River), and including the crater lakes of Nosy Be	*Tsipoy*	EN
P. grandidieri Sauvage, 1882	Eastern highlands and lowlands: Restricted to eastern drainages and most commonly found at low elevations in coastal regions, however, occasionally also collected in the submontane forest zone (up to 100 km upstream from the sea). Uniquely among *Ptychochromis*, species is somewhat salt tolerant and occurs in brackish, as well as fresh, waters along much of eastern coast (except far north and extreme southern coastal areas).	*Saroy*	LC
P. inornatus Sparks, 2002	Northwestern basins: Known only from the Ankofia drainage basin and its tributaries, including the Anjingo River and Lake Andrapongy	*Joba, juba*	EN
P. onilahy Stiassny & Sparks, 2006	Western basins: Currently known only from the type series collected in the Onilahy River. No additional specimens have been collected from the Onilahy River or surrounding basins in recent decades, and the species in considered to be extinct.[1]	*Boramany, kotro*	EX
P. makira Stiassny & Sparks, 2006	Eastern lowlands: Known only from the type series collected in the Antainambalana River just north of Maroantsetra	*Saroy*	DD
P. loisellei Stiassny & Sparks, 2006	Eastern lowlands: Currently known only from the Mahanara River and its tributaries in the northeastern coastal region near the town of Antsirabe-Nord	*Garaka*	EN
P. curvidens Stiassny & Sparks, 2006	Northwestern basins: Known only from rivers draining the western flank of Montagne d'Ambre; most specimens from the Andranofanjava-Sandriapiana River system, located southwest of Antsiranana	*Garaka*	DD
P. insolitus Stiassny & Sparks, 2006	Northwestern basins: Known only from the Mangarahara and Amboaboa Rivers, tributaries of the westward-flowing Sofia River, near the town of Mandritsara	*Joba, juba*	CR
P. ernestmagnusi Sparks & Stiassny, 2010	Eastern lowlands: Known only from the middle to lower reaches of the Mananara du Nord River	*Saroy*	DD
P. mainty Martinez, Arroyave & Sparks, 2015	Eastern highlands: Known only from forested habitats in the upper reaches of rivers and streams in the Tolagnaro region	*Saroy*	DD

Notes: The names of species that have been identified as new to science and remain to be formally described are designated as "n. sp." (new species) and enclosed in quotation marks. IUCN Red List conservation assessment status from IUCN (2021); for IUCN status abbreviations, see Table 10.1.
[1] See Stiassny and Sparks (2006: 19) for additional historical range information.

Ptychochromis oligacanthus is restricted to freshwater habitats of the northwest, from the Sambirano River northward to the Mananjeba drainage (i.e., Andranomaloto River), including the crater lakes of Nosy Be; Bleeker (1868) referred to these latter populations as *P. oligacanthus* var. *nossibeënsis*. *Ptychochromis grandidieri* occurs in eastern drainages and is most commonly found at low elevations, in coastal regions; however, it is occasionally also collected in the submontane forest zone, where it may be encountered up to 100 km upstream from the sea (de Rham and Nourissat 2004). Uniquely among *Ptychochromis*, *P. grandidieri* is somewhat salt tolerant and occurs in brackish as well as fresh waters along eastern coastal regions. *Ptychochromis inornatus* is known only from the Ankofia drainage basin and its tributaries, including the Anjingo River and Lake Andrapongy, in northwestern Madagascar. Despite extensive survey efforts in southwestern Madagascar, no additional specimens of *P. onilahy* have been captured from the Onilahy River or surrounding basins since the type series was collected in 1962 by Kiener, and the species is listed as Extinct (IUCN 2021). *Ptychochromis makira* also is known only from the type series, collected in the Antainambalana River just north of Maroantsetra in the

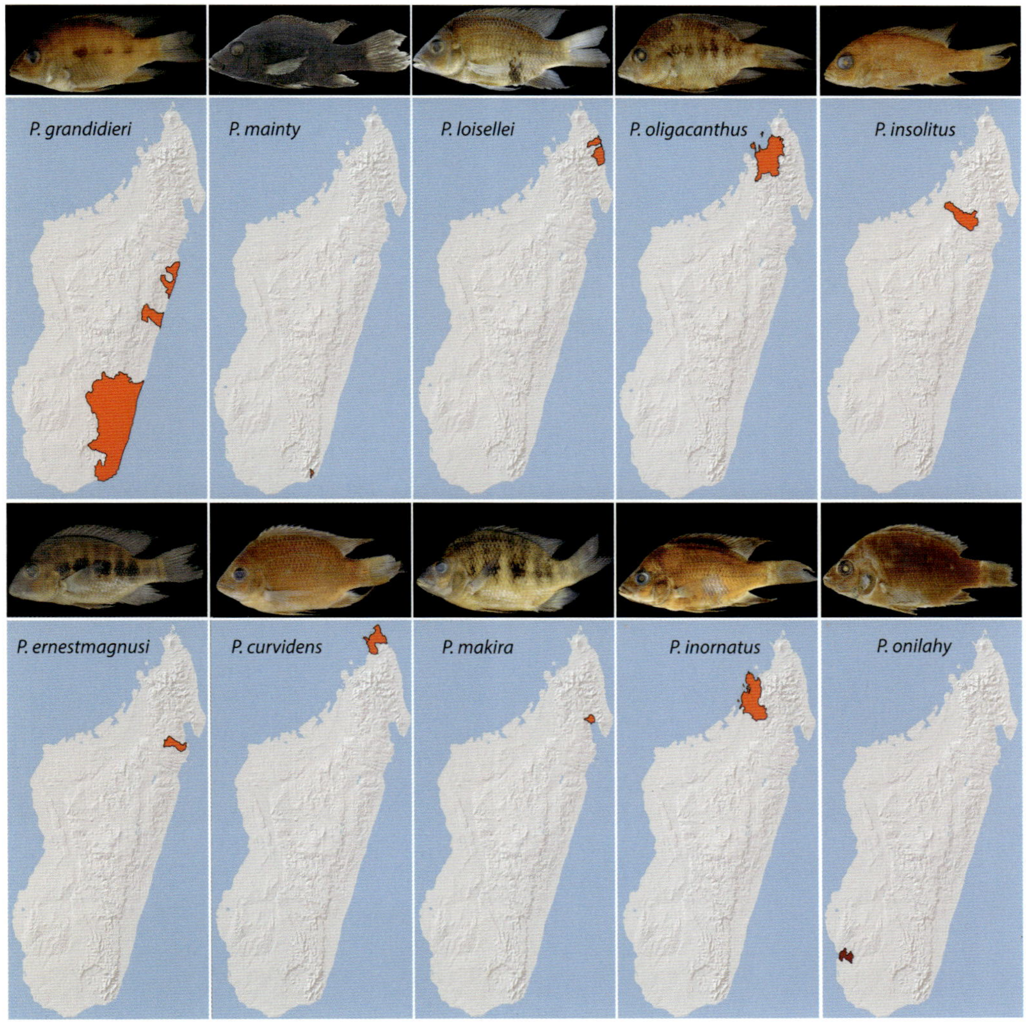

FIGURE 10.23 Species of *Ptychochromis* with their associated distributions based on the most recent Red List assessment (IUCN 2021).

northeast. *Ptychochromis loisellei* is currently known only from the Mahanara River and its tributaries in northeastern coastal areas and near the town of Antsirabe-Nord. *Ptychochromis curvidens* is recorded only from rivers draining the western flank of Montagne d'Ambre in the extreme north, and most specimens are from the Andranofanjava-Sandriapiana River system, located southwest of the town of Antsiranana. *Ptychochromis insolitus* is known only from the Mangarahara and Amboaboa Rivers, tributaries of the westward-flowing Sofia River, near the town of Mandritsara in the northeast. *Ptychochromis ernestmagnusi* is currently documented only from the middle to lower reaches of the Mananara du Nord River in the northeast. *Ptychochromis mainty* is known only from the upper reaches of rivers and streams in forested habitats in the Tolagnaro region in the extreme southeast (Figure 10.25).

HABITAT AND NATURAL HISTORY

Species of *Ptychochromis* are generally found in the middle to lower reaches of small to medium-size rivers, and some populations can tolerate brackish conditions, especially along the eastern coast, where *P. grandidieri* exhibits a widespread distribution in both fresh and brackish water habitats. Habitats range from slow-flowing turbid rivers to clear, swift, and rocky conditions. A number of populations are found to inhabit the crater lakes on Nosy Be, and occasionally specimens are collected from the shallow, floodplain lakes of the northwest.

Ptychochromis species are omnivorous and highly opportunistic feeders, consuming a wide variety of aquatic insects and invertebrates and also a considerable amount of plant material. Members of the genus are biparental custodial substrate spawners that practice long-term care of mobile fry. Breeding is thought to occur from October through December, when water levels are comparatively low.

CONSERVATION STATUS

Ptychochromis supplies an artisanal fishery along the east coast of the island and is sought by local fishers in the floodplain lakes of the northwest. It is frequently encountered in markets in eastern Madagascar. The moderate salt tolerance of *P. grandidieri* along the east coast affords the Pangalanes Canal populations some protection from the introduced *Channa maculata* (Asian Snakehead) (see Sparks and Stiassny, pp. 1245–60). Whereas populations along eastern coastal Madagascar appear more or less stable, those in northern, northeastern, and western Madagascar are becoming increasingly

FIGURE 10.24 **Images of typical collection localities for members of *Ptychochromis* in northwestern Madagascar, highlighting the wide variety of habitats they occupy. A) Mananjeba River, a shallow sandy river that is habitat for *P. oligacanthus*. B) Fisher using a *doboka* tool at Lake Andrapongy, a shallow, turbid floodplain lake where *P. inornatus* occurs. C) Amboaboa River, fast-flowing rocky habitat where the rare species *P. insolitus* has been collected.** (PHOTOS A, B, and C by J. S. Sparks.)

FIGURE 10.25 **Image of a live individual of the recently described *Ptychochromis mainty*, collected from near Tolagnaro in the extreme southeast, highlighting how colorful some species become as adults.** (PHOTO by A. Saunders.)

rare, especially insular forms from the Sofia and Ankofia-Anjingo basins. In the face of continued habitat destruction, competition with introduced species, and predation by the Asian Snakehead, populations of *Ptychochromis* throughout Madagascar should be considered highly vulnerable.

Of the 10 valid species of *Ptychochromis*, three are currently listed in the Red List as Endangered (*P. oligacanthus*, *P. inornatus*, and *P. loisellei*), one as Critically Endangered (*P. insolitus*), and one as Extinct (*P. onilahy*) (IUCN 2021; Table 10.10). Of the remaining five species, although four are listed as Data Deficient (*P. makira*, *P. curvidens*, *P. ernestmagnusi*, and *P. mainty*), not one of these species is either widely distributed or common within its respective limited geographic range. Additional survey efforts are needed to assess their populations and status. Only the widely distributed *P. grandidieri* was listed as Least Concern, although it should be noted that recent survey efforts have not focused on this species, which is highly sought as a food fish.

Subject editors: John S. Sparks and Melanie L. J. Stiassny

CICHLIDAE, PTYCHOCHROMINAE: *PTYCHOCHROMOIDES*, CICHLID, *FIAPOTSY* AND MANY OTHER MALAGASY NAMES

J. S. Sparks and P. V. Loiselle

Endemic to Madagascar, the genus *Ptychochromoides* comprises three described species (Table 10.11). A population of uncertain status, but closely related to *P. betsileanus*, is reported from the Manantantana River near Ambalavao (de Rham and Nourissat 2004). A fourth species previously assigned to *Ptychochromoides*, as *P. katria*, has subsequently been placed in its own genus, *Katria* (Stiassny and Sparks 2006; see Stiassny, pp. 1279–80).

For local vernacular names of *Ptychochromoides* species (in addition to *fiapotsy*), see Table 10.11.

SYSTEMATICS AND IDENTIFICATION

Members of *Ptychochromoides* are medium-size to large cichlid fishes (frequently exceeding 300 mm standard length). They are laterally compressed fishes, ranging from robust and deep-bodied (*P. betsileanus* and *P. itasy*) (Figure 10.26a) to somewhat shallow-bodied and elongate in form (*P. vondrozo*) (Figure 10.26b). The genus is diagnosed by the following apomorphic morphological features (see Sparks 2008 for full character descriptions): a single row of dentition on the second pharyngobranchial tooth plate; chest scales that are reduced in size and embedded; and a blotchy, mottled white-and-gray, blotchy grayish-black, or nearly jet-black pigmentation pattern. Mature, sexually active individuals of both *P. betsileanus* and *P. itasy* develop a moderate to very dramatic nuchal hump (Sparks and Reinthal 2001; Sparks et al. 2012; Figure 10.26a).

Other features useful for identifying *Ptychochromoides*, and that are shared by but not necessarily restricted to closely related taxa, include: median sensory canal pores (NLF0) on the frontal bones of the neurocranium that are widely separated; predorsal bones in the shape of inverted Ls; and a procurrent (anteriorly oriented bony process) process present on the first dorsal fin pterygiophore (internal bony-fin support element). Body scales are large and ctenoid, and reduced in size and embedded on the chest.

Both morphological and molecular evidence place *Ptychochromoides* as the sister group to *Oxylapia* (Sparks 2004b; Sparks and Smith 2004a; Stiassny and Sparks 2006), a monotypic genus endemic to eastern Madagascar. Anatomical features uniting *Ptychochromoides* and *Oxylapia* include a blotchy, mottled, and speckled grayish-black or brownish overall pigmentation pattern, chest scales that are markedly reduced in size and highly embedded, and moderately to extremely fleshy lips (Sparks 2008; Sparks et al. 2012). This clade is in turn the sister taxon to a clade comprising *Katria* and *Ptychochromis* (Sparks and Smith 2004a). Along with *Paratilapia*, this assemblage of the genera *Katria*, *Ptychochromis*, *Ptychochromoides*, and *Oxylapia* composes the endemic Malagasy cichlid subfamily Ptychochrominae (Sparks 2004b).

TABLE 10.11. **Species of *Ptychochromoides* with range information, local names, and most recent IUCN status**

SCIENTIFIC NAME	DISTRIBUTION	VERNACULAR NAMES	IUCN STATUS
P. betsileanus (Boulenger, 1899)	Western basins: Restricted to the upper to middle reaches of western drainages in the south central and southwest	*Fiapotsy, fiafotsy, fiampotsy, marakely à bosse, trondro mainty*	CR
P. vondrozo Sparks & Reinthal, 2001	Eastern highlands: Restricted to the extreme upper reaches of the Mananara drainage in the Vevembe and Vondrozo region	*Fiandahy, fiapotsy*	EN
P. itasy Sparks, 2004	Western basins: Extirpated from Lake Itasy, type locality, and currently restricted to the upper reaches of the westward-draining Tsiribihina River and its tributaries	*Marakely à bosse, trondro mainty*	CR

Notes: The names of species that have been identified as new to science and remain to be formally described are designated as "n. sp." (new species) and enclosed in quotation marks. IUCN Red List conservation assessment status from IUCN (2021); for IUCN status abbreviations, see Table 10.1.

FIGURE 10.26 **A) Live specimen (small adult, approximately 165 mm standard length), immediately after capture, of recently rediscovered *Ptychochromoides itasy*, collected in the Sakay River, a tributary of the Tsiribihina River, in the Central Highlands. B) *Ptychochromoides vondrozo* holotype (adult female, 182 mm standard length), collected in the Ramanara River, southeastern Madagascar. C) Ilanana River in southwestern Madagascar, typical habitat of *P. betsileanus*.** (PHOTO A by P. Loiselle, B by J. S. Sparks, and C by O. Lucanus.)

DISTRIBUTION

All members of the genus are restricted to the upper and middle reaches of eastern, western, and southwestern drainages, and they are never encountered in lowland, coastal habitats or in brackish conditions. All species appear to require clear (nonturbid), cool, well-oxygenated waters with a rocky and sandy substrate. All known species of *Ptychochromoides* are found only in highland habitats (headwaters and middle reaches of rivers) except for *P. betsileanus*, which is restricted to the upper to middle reaches of western drainages in the south-central and southwestern portions of the island but occurs at lower elevations (Figure 10.26c). *Ptychochromoides itasy*, extirpated from Lake Itasy, its type locality, is currently restricted to the upper reaches of the westward-draining Tsiribihina River and its tributaries in the Central Highlands (Sparks 2004a; Sparks et al. 2012), whereas *P. vondrozo* occurs in the extreme upper reaches of the Mananara River drainage in the southeast (Sparks and Reinthal 2001).

HABITAT AND NATURAL HISTORY

Members of *Ptychochromoides* are omnivorous and highly opportunistic, feeding on a variety of aquatic insects and invertebrates, aquatic macrophytes, and algae. All species appear to consume a large proportion of plant material. *Ptychochromoides* are biparental custodial substrate spawners that practice long-term care of mobile fry. Breeding is thought to occur from October through December, when water levels are comparatively low.

CONSERVATION STATUS

Because of their restricted ranges and very small populations, all members of *Ptychochromoides* are assessed in the Red List (IUCN 2021) as either Critically Endangered (*P. betsileanus* and *P. itasy*) or Endangered (*P. vondrozo*). All species of the genus are especially vulnerable as deforestation continues to encroach farther into the upper reaches of river basins within their respective ranges. *Ptychochromoides betsileanus* was only recently rediscovered in remote localities in south-central and southwestern Madagascar, where it is extremely local and rare (Figure 10.26c). *Ptychochromoides itasy* was removed from the roster of extinct Malagasy fishes with the recent discovery of a relict population in the upper reaches of the Tsiribihina River (Sparks et al. 2012; Figure 10.26a). The decline of this taxon, which was once highly abundant in Lake Itasy, is likely in large measure a result of overfishing and the introduction of non-native species. *Ptychochromoides vondrozo* is rare and local within its extremely restricted range, and the survival of this taxon depends in large part on protection of forests in the Vevembe and Vondrozo region (Sparks and Reinthal 2001).

Subject editors: John S. Sparks and Melanie L. J. Stiassny

GOBIIDAE: *GLOSSOGOBIUS*, CAVEFISH, *TOHO*

P. Chakrabarty, M. Byrnes, and J. S. Sparks

Glossogobius is a widely distributed genus of gobies found throughout the Indo–West Pacific in both freshwater and marine habitats. Three species of *Glossogobius* have been recorded from freshwater habitats on Madagascar (Table 10.12). Both *G. giuris* and *G. callidus* are widespread, with the former species occurring in coastal regions throughout the Indo–West Pacific, and the latter ranging from Mozambique south to the Swartvlei region of the Western Cape, South Africa, in addition to Madagascar (IUCN 2021). One remarkable species, *G. ankaranensis* is a troglomorphic form endemic to subterranean freshwater streams and pools within the Ankarana protected area in far northern Madagascar (Figure 10.27). The Ankarana Plateau (or Massif) is a limestone karst formation with a vast subterranean network of caverns, sinkholes, rivers, and pools.

SYSTEMATICS AND IDENTIFICATION

Glossogobius ankaranensis is distantly related to Madagascar's other endemic cavefishes, the three described species of *Typhleotris*, which are restricted to freshwater eroded karst habitats in the southwest lowlands (Sparks and Chakrabarty 2012; see Sparks and Chakrabarty, pp. 1298–300). Members of *Typhleotris* also belong to the suborder Gobioidei but are placed in a distinct family, Milyeringidae. Interestingly, the sister group to *Typhleotris* is *Milyeringa*, which is endemic to similar karstic habitats in northwestern Australia (Chakrabarty et al. 2012; Kuang et al. 2018).

Fully blind and pigment-free *G. ankaranensis* can be found in the waters of Ankarana more or less side by side with sighted, pigmented fishes that closely resemble it, possibly *G. callidus* individuals that have entered the cave habitat (Wilson 1996; P. Chakrabarty and J. S. Sparks, unpublished data); it is not clear whether there is any interbreeding between fully blind individuals and those with functional eyes. *Glossogobius* cf. *callidus* and *G. ankaranensis* were recovered as sister taxa in the phylogenetic analysis of Chakrabarty et al. (2012). Our recent collections of specimens in the Ankarana area clearly indicate that there is a cline, ranging from fully pigmented, sighted forms outside the cave entrance (Figure 10.28a), to faintly pigmented and partially blind forms near and just inside the

TABLE 10.12. **Species of *Glossogobius* occurring in Malagasy waters with range information and most recent IUCN status**

SCIENTIFIC NAME	DISTRIBUTION	IUCN STATUS
G. ankaranensis Banister, 1994	Northwestern basins: Endemic to subterranean freshwater streams and pools within the Ankarana protected area	LC[1]
G. callidus (Smith, 1937)	Western and northwestern basins, eastern lowlands: Ranging from Mozambique south to the Swartvlei region of the Western Cape, South Africa, in addition to Madagascar	LC
G. giuris (Hamilton, 1822)	Western and northwestern basins, eastern highlands and lowlands: Widespread in coastal regions throughout the Indo–West Pacific	LC

Note: IUCN Red List conservation assessment status from IUCN (2021); for IUCN status abbreviations, see Table 10.1.
[1] See text for clarification.

FIGURE 10.27 **A) The western side of the Ankarana Massif *tsingy* formation, with heavily eroded karst, viewed from a distance. B) Capturing *Glossogobius ankaranensis* in its typical subterranean habitat within the Ankarana protected area.** (PHOTOS by R. Schelly.)

cave entrance, to fully blind and pigment-free forms well within the cave system proper (Figure 10.28b) (P. Chakrabarty and J. S. Sparks, unpublished data). Whether these different morphological forms represent distinct species is currently unclear. In the original description of *G. ankaranensis*, Banister (1994) presumed that its closest relative was *G. giuris*. Notably, *G. ankaranensis* lacks head pores, similar to members of the *G. flavipinnis* complex from Sulawesi (Hoese et al. 2015), the only other members of the genus with a complete absence of head pores. Many details on the evolutionary history of *Glossogobius* are unknown, as it has not yet been the subject of thorough phylogenetic review.

Glossogobius ankaranensis adults (no juveniles or young have been observed) range from about 40 to 70 mm standard length. For individuals captured within the Ankarana cave system, body coloration is a pale yellowish white to white in life, with pinkish gills and blood vessels visible through the skin (Figure 10.28b). The only dark, pigmented areas are the spherical lenses, which are all that remains visible externally of the eyes. Rows of sensory papillae can be found along the head, as illustrated in the original description (Banister 1994).

The relationships among species of *Glossogobius* found on Madagascar are somewhat difficult to untangle, given variation in all three species and a lack of a thorough molecular phylogenetic analysis that includes multiple individuals of each species. Morphological descriptions are also largely insufficient for more than basic comparisons and the genus will require a detailed systematic study in the future. At present, the distinction between two species can be noted as: *G. ankaranensis* is depigmented and lacks eyes, and *G. giuris* is reported to have a shorter interorbital crest, more scales in the lateral line, and more rays in the pectoral fin (Bannister 1994). However, all these features will require additional comparisons for verification. Greenwood (1994) compares *G. giuris* and *G. callidus* specimens from South Africa, but notes their uncertain nomenclature and taxonomy. In that work he notes that *G. giuris* has a rounded caudal fin (vs. pointed), a scaled nape (vs. asquamate), a larger adult body total length (40 cm vs. about 12 cm), and body coloration that is more unevenly (diffusely) pigmented (vs. a clearer mid-body pigmentation, nearing a distinct stripe, in *G. callidus*). *Glossogobius ankaranensis* has a rounded caudal fin, as in *G. giuris*, but is otherwise, again, easily distinguished by a lack of pigment and eyes.

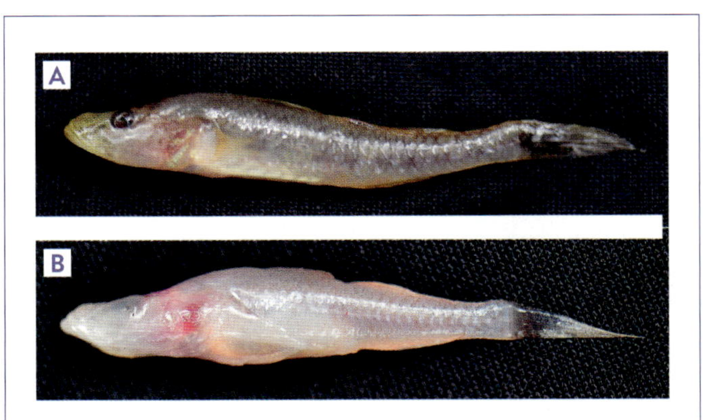

FIGURE 10.28 **Comparison of *Glossogobius ankaranensis* specimens from different collection locations. A) Faintly pigmented form collected near and just inside the cave entrance, which is also sometimes referred to as *G.* cf. *callidus*. B) Fully blind and pigment-free troglobitic form collected deep within the Ankarana cave system.** (PHOTOS by J. S. Sparks and R. Schelly.)

DISTRIBUTION

Glossogobius ankaranensis is known from only a single subterranean river system, although the full extent of its distribution, both inside and outside of the Ankarana cave system, has not been fully explored. The species can be found in shallow and deeper pools of Napoleon Cave within the Second River (or Second Canyon) Cave system, which is located in the Ankarana protected area (Figure 10.27a). The number of individuals observed at a particular site (i.e., cave or pool) can range up to dozens on a given visit and likely varies between the dry and wet seasons. *Glossogobius callidus* has notably been collected in similar small pools in South Africa (Greenwood 1994) and may avoid the more turbid areas for foraging (Parkinson and Booth 2011).

HABITAT AND NATURAL HISTORY

Glossogobius callidus is reported to spawn in early summer (Greenwood 1994) and consume aquatic invertebrates (Parkinson and Booth 2011). *Glossogobius giuris* is known to consume a varied diet that includes a range of invertebrates, fishes, and algae (Rao and Rao 2002), at least in India. Widespread on Madagascar, *G. giuris* is relatively common throughout its range and occurs in a variety of habitats, ranging from estuaries to rivers and streams, to shallow floodplain lakes.

The diet of *G. ankaranensis* is unclear, but the invertebrate fauna of the cave or detritus seem most likely (Wilson et al. 1988; Wilson 1996). Nothing is known about its reproductive biology and natural history.

CONSERVATION STATUS

There is no commercial or artisanal fishery for *Glossogobius ankaranensis*. The only measure of protection is afforded by its occurrence in the Ankarana protected area. Deforestation and other anthropogenic pressures outside of the cave system and within the protected area (Goodman et al. 2018) may have consequences within the limited habitat of this species.

In the most recent Red List assessment (IUCN 2021), all three *Glossogobius* species found in freshwater habitats on Madagascar were listed as Least Concern. Both *G. giuris* and *G. callidus* are widespread species, and populations appear stable throughout much of their range. The justification for categorizing *G. ankaranensis* as a species of Least Concern requires some explanation. Although the very restricted range of this cave-dwelling species falls entirely within the boundaries of Ankarana, its subterranean habitat is not subjected to anthropogenic degradation. In addition, local *fady* (taboo) protects the species from exploitation by local people. Moreover, *G. ankaranensis* has no known introduced competitors or predators, and the species is rarely encountered or collected, given its isolated habitat. Surveys by our group in recent years (2008, 2011) indicate that populations are relatively stable (J. S. Sparks and P. Chakrabarty, unpublished data). Under the IUCN Red List criteria, *G. ankaranensis* was accordingly assessed as Least Concern; however, we stress that the population needs to be monitored on a regular basis, and this assessment could drastically change if there is a sign of decline.

Subject editors: John S. Sparks and Melanie L. J. Stiassny

MILYERINGIDAE: *TYPHLEOTRIS*, MALAGASY CAVEFISH, *TOHO*

J. S. Sparks and P. Chakrabarty

Typhleotris is a genus of small, blind, pigment-free troglobitic gobioids endemic to Madagascar. Members of the genus are restricted to a vast network of freshwater subterranean limestone (karst) habitats in remote arid regions of the coastal southwest (Kiener 1964; Sparks and Chakrabarty 2012). Since the publication of Sparks (2003b), a novel, fully pigmented *Typhleotris* species has been discovered and formally described, and there are currently three valid species in the genus (Figure 10.29, Table 10.13).

SYSTEMATICS AND IDENTIFICATION

Members of *Typhleotris* are small gobioids, reaching approximately 70 mm standard length, usually much smaller. Molecular phylogenetic analyses indicate that the genus *Typhleotris* is the sister group to *Milyeringa*, endemic to similar subterranean karstic habitats near the Exmouth and Cape Range National Park region of Western Australia (Chakrabarty et al. 2012; Kuang et al. 2018). This extraordinary result is the only known transoceanic sister-group relationship between cavefishes or any vertebrate troglobites (Chakrabarty et al. 2012). These two genera constitute the family Milyeringidae, members of which superficially resemble sleepers (Eleotridae) but can be distinguished from non-stygobitic eleotrids by the complete absence of eyes; an elongate, shovel-like snout; a well-developed network of sensory papillae on the head; and the loss of pigment across the body (except for *T. mararybe*, which has uniform dark brown pigmentation on the body and dorsal fins, with the distal portion of the other fins white) (Chakrabarty 2010; Sparks and Chakrabarty 2012). Members of *Typhleotris* are easily distinguished from the only other member of Milyeringidae, the Australian genus *Milyeringa*, by the presence of scales extending onto the head, ctenoid scales on the body, and a fully scaled ventrum, including laterally below the pectoral fin (Figure 10.29).

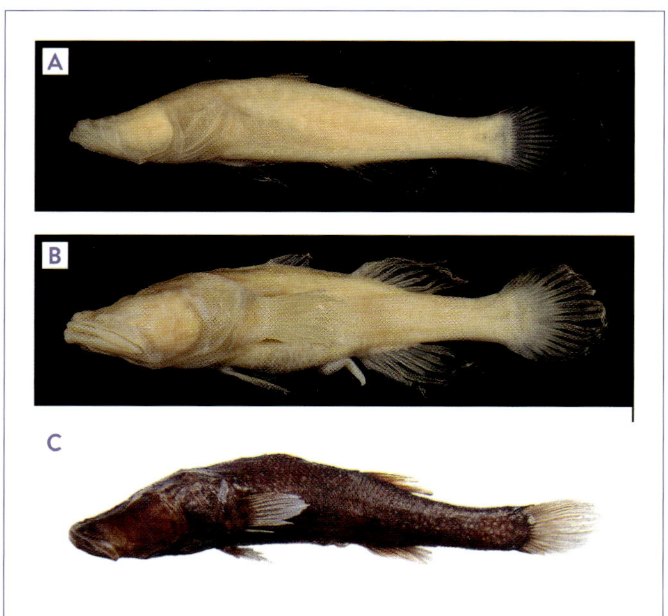

FIGURE 10.29 Comparison of the external morphology and pigmentation of the three species of *Typhleotris*. A) *Typhleotris madagascariensis*, B) *T. pauliani*, and C) *T. mararybe*. (PHOTOS by J. S. Sparks.)

Stygobitic species of Eleotridae are currently known from Papua New Guinea, Indonesia, and Mexico, and these taxa can readily be distinguished from *Typhleotris* by different fin counts, squamation patterns, arrangement of head pores, and other morphological features (Walsh and Chakrabarty 2016). However, despite their superficial resemblance, the families Eleotridae and Milyeringidae are not sister taxa; Milyeringidae is recovered as the sister group to the remaining families of Gobioidei, except for Odontobutidae and Ryacichthyidae (Kuang et al. 2018).

Members of *Typhleotris* are characterized by the presence of numerous, well-developed free neuromasts (neurosensory structures that open to the water via pores and, when displaced by sound waves, allow fish to detect disturbances in the environment) on the head that are arranged into regular transverse and longitudinal rows. The mouth and snout are elongate and shovel-like, and the head is broad and dorsoventrally compressed. Teeth in the oral jaws are numerous, small, conical, and slightly to moderately recurved; these teeth are arrayed in numerous closely set and irregular rows in the anterior region of the mouth, tapering to fewer rows posteriorly. Scales are large, and both ctenoid (toothed) and cycloid (nontoothed) scales are present.

In the molecular phylogenetic analysis of Chakrabarty et al. (2012), *T. madagascariensis* and *T. mararybe* were recovered as sister taxa, and *T. pauliani* was the sister taxon to a clade comprising *T. madagascariensis* and *T. mararybe*. *Typhleotris madagascariensis*

TABLE 10.13. **Species of *Typhleotris* with range information and most recent IUCN status**

SCIENTIFIC NAME	DISTRIBUTION	IUCN STATUS
T. madagascariensis Petit, 1933	Southern basins: Known from several isolated localities (caves and sinkholes) south of the Onilahy River and near Lake Tsimanampesotse, from just north of the town of Efoetse southward to Itampolo	EN
T. pauliani Arnoult, 1959	Western basins: Restricted to subterranean habitats located south of Morombe, in the vicinity of Andalambezo, north of the Onilahy River	CR
T. mararybe Sparks & Chakrabarty, 2012	Southern basins: Type locality Grotte de Vitane, sinkhole within the extremely restricted range of the species, which is limited to the immediate area around the town of Itampolo	CR

Source: IUCN Red List conservation assessment status from IUCN (2021); for IUCN status abbreviations, see Table 10.1.

is distinguished from congeners by the presence of scales extending fully onto the head (Figure 10.29a). *Typhleotris pauliani* is distinguished from congeners by the lack of scales on the head, less the operculum (i.e., a scaled operculum is common to all species of *Typhleotris*); the presence of single feeble leading spines in both the second dorsal and anal fins (vs. soft rays); an enlarged, bony operculum; a pelvic formula of I, 4 (vs. I, 5); and a more robust and heavier body, particularly in adults (Figure 10.29b). *Typhleotris mararybe* is unique among congeners in possessing a uniformly dark brown pigmentation throughout the body and extending onto the fins for one-third their length, apart from the dorsal fins, which are uniformly dark brown (vs. all white body and fins in congeners) (Figure 10.29c). In addition, *T. mararybe* can be distinguished from congeners by the presence of prominent and protruding anterior

FIGURE 10.30 **Variety of habitats in southwestern Madagascar from which *Typhleotris* species are known. A) Collecting at entrance of Mitoho Cave, type locality of *T. madagascariensis*, Tsimanampesotse. B) Collecting *T. madagascariensis* in a small well near Mitoho Cave. C) Grotte de Vitane (Vitany), open sinkhole habitat (type locality) of *T. mararybe*, near Itampolo. D) Collecting the type series of the recently described species *T. mararybe* in Grotte de Vitane.** (PHOTO A by P. Willink, B and C by J. S. Sparks, and D by P. Chakrabarty.)

skeletal elements that lend the head a sculpted, angled, bony appearance (vs. relatively smooth and more or less fleshy in congeners); a shorter pectoral fin not reaching a vertical through the anus when adpressed (vs. pectoral fin extending to anus in congeners); and an elevated vertebral count (26 vs. 25 or fewer in congeners). This new species is further distinguished from *T. madagascariensis* by the absence of scales fully covering the head (vs. head fully scaled) and a longer second predorsal length, and from *T. pauliani* by a shorter prepelvic length, a pelvic formula of I, 5 (vs. I, 4), and the absence of a single leading spine in both the second dorsal and anal fins (vs. leading spines present).

DISTRIBUTION

All three recognized species of *Typhleotris* are troglobitic forms, typically blind and pigment-free obligate cave-dwelling lineages, and are restricted to freshwater habitats within the coastal karst formations of the Mahafaly Plateau in southwestern Madagascar (Sparks and Chakrabarty 2012). *Typhleotris madagascariensis* is known from several isolated localities (caves and sinkholes), all south of the Onilahy River and near Lake Tsimanampesotse, ranging from just north of the town of Efoetse southward to Itampolo (Figures 10.30a and b). *Typhleotris pauliani* is restricted to subterranean habitats located to the south of Morombe in the vicinity of Andalambezo, to the north of the Onilahy River. *Typhleotris mararybe* was described from Grotte de Vitane (Vitany), a sinkhole within the extremely restricted range of the species, which is limited to the area around the town of Itampolo, on the coastal plain below and immediately to the west of the extensive Mahafaly Plateau (Figures 10.30c and d) (Rasoloariniaina et al. 2016).

Populations of the three species of *Typhleotris* vary considerably in abundance, from only a few individuals to hundreds, but all exhibit markedly restricted ranges. The northern limit for the genus is at Andalambezo (*T. pauliani*), the southern limit near Itampolo (both *T. madagascariensis* and *T. mararybe*), spanning approximately 250 km along the southwestern coast of the island. Based on the results of recent survey efforts, we believe that it is highly likely that additional novel species will be discovered with continued exploration of previously unsurveyed caves in the region (Sparks and Chakrabarty 2012).

HABITAT AND NATURAL HISTORY

Members of the genus *Typhleotris* are omnivorous, feeding on a variety of crustaceans, plankton, and both epigeal and troglodytic aquatic insects. No data are available on their reproductive ecology, and their behavior is in need of study. Recent studies have provided information on habitat water quality, as well as the distribution and population sizes, of both *T. madagascariensis* and *T. mararybe* (Rasoloariniaina et al. 2016).

CONSERVATION STATUS

In the most recent Red List assessment (IUCN 2021), *T. madagascariensis*, which exhibits the most widespread geographic distribution in the genus, is assessed as Endangered, whereas both *T. pauliani* and *T. mararybe*, which have extremely localized distributions, are listed as Critically Endangered. There is no commercial or artisanal fishery for members of this genus, which is likely due to the small size and low abundance of these fishes throughout their ranges. The very restricted ranges of all species of *Typhleotris* emphasize the precarious conservation status, although local *fady* (taboo) limits exploitation, and the Tsimanampesotse protected area, encompassing part of the range of *T. madagascariensis*, affords protection to some of the habitats where *Typhleotris* occurs (Figure 10.30). Although the extremely localized distributions for all members of the genus and poorly known population numbers are certainly reasons for concern, the region inhabited by these fishes is remote and has a sparse human population, and their habitats are difficult to access.

Subject editors: John S. Sparks and Melanie L. J. Stiassny

REFERENCES

Aarn, and Ivantsoff, W. 1997. Descriptive anatomy of *Cairnsichthys rhombosomoides* and *Iriatherina werneri* (Teleostei: Atheriniformes), and a phylogenetic analysis of Melanotaeniidae. *Ichthyological Exploration of Freshwaters* 8: 107–150.

Aldegheri, M. 1972. Rivers and streams on Madagascar. In *Biogeography and Ecology in Madagascar*, eds. R. Battistini and G. Richard-Vindard, pp. 261–310. The Hague: W. Junk.

Andriafidison, D., Jenkins, R.K.B., Loiselle, P. V., McCaskie, T., Rakotoarivelo, A. A., Rahalambomanana, J., Ravelomanana, T., Raminosoa, N., and Saunder, A. 2011. Preliminary fish survey of Lac Tseny in north-western Madagascar. *Madagascar Conservation and Development* 6(2): 83–87.

Andrianandrasana, H. T., Randriamahefasoa, J., Durbin, J., Lewis, R. E., and Ratsimbazafy, J. H. 2005. Participatory ecological monitoring of the Alaotra wetlands in Madagascar. *Biodiversity and Conservation* 14: 2757–2774.

Arnoult, J. 1963. Un oryziiné (Pisces, Cyprinodontidae) nouveau de l'est de Madagascar. *Bulletin Muséum National d'Histoire Naturelle*, Paris, série 2, 35(3): 235–237.

Banister, K. E. 1994. *Glossogobius ankaranensis*, a new species of blind cave goby from Madagascar (Pisces: Gobiodei: Gobiidae). *Aqua: Journal of Ichthyology and Aquatic Biology* 1: 25–28.

Benstead, J. P., Stiassny, M.L.J., Loiselle, P. V., Riseng, K. J., and Raminosoa, N. 2000. River conservation in Madagascar. In *Global Perspectives on River Conservation: Science, Policy, and Practice*, eds. P. J. Boon, B. R. Davies, and G. E. Petts, pp. 205–231. Chichester: Wiley.

Benstead, J. P., de Rham, P. H., Gattolliat, J.-L., Gibon, F.-M., Loiselle, P. V., Sartori, M., Sparks, J. S., and Stiassny, M.L.J. 2003. Conserving Madagascar's freshwater biodiversity. *Bioscience* 53: 1101–1111.

Berra, T. M. 2007. *Freshwater Fish Distribution*. Chicago: University of Chicago Press.

Bertin, L. 1940. Catalogue des types de poisons du Muséum national d'Histoire naturelle. *Bulletin du Muséum National d'Histoire Naturelle*, Paris, 12: 300.

Betancur-R, R. 2009. Molecular phylogenetics and evolutionary history of ariid catfishes revisited: A comprehensive sampling. *BMC Evolutionary Biology* 9: 175. doi:10.1186/1471-2148-9-175.

Bleeker, P. 1868. Description de trois espèces inédites de Chromidoides de Madagascar. *Verslagen en Medeedelingen der Koninklijke, Akademie van Wetenschappen, Afdeeling Naturukunde*, Amsterdam, 2(11): 307–314.

Bleeker, P., and Pollen, F. 1875. *Poissons de Madagascar et de l'ile de la Réunion*. Leiden: J. K. Steenhoff.

Boon, P. J., Davies, K. J., and Petts, G. E., eds. 2000. *Global Perspectives on River Conservation: Science, Policy and Practice*. Chichester: Wiley.

Bragança, P.H.N., Amorim, P. F., and Costa, W.J.E.M. 2018. Pantanodontidae (Teleostei, Cyprinodontiformes), the sister group to all other cyprinodontoid killifishes as inferred by molecular data. *Zoosystematics and Evolution* 94: 137–145.

Brown, J. H., and Lomolino, M. V. 1998. *Biogeography*. 2nd ed. Sunderland: Sinauer.

Campanella, D., Hughes, L., Unmack, P., Bloom, D., Piller, K., and Orti, G. 2015. Multi-locus fossil-calibrated phylogeny of Atheriniformes (Teleostei, Ovalentaria). *Molecular Phylogenetics and Evolution* 86: 8–23.

Chakrabarty, P. 2010. Status and phylogeny of Milyeringidae, with the description of a new blind cave fish from Australia, *Milyeringa brooksi*, n. sp. *Zootaxa* 2557: 19–28.

Chakrabarty, P., Davis, M. P, and Sparks, J. S. 2012. The first record of a trans-oceanic sister-group relationship between obligate vertebrate troglobites. *PLoS One* 7: e44083.

Clausen, H. S. 1967. *Tropical Old World Cyprinodonts*. Copenhagen: Akademisk Forlag.

Costa, W.J.E.M. 1998. Phylogeny and classification of Rivulidae revisited: Origin and evolution of annualism and miniaturization in rivulid fishes (Cyprinodontiformes: Aplocheiloidei). *Journal of Comparative Biology* 3: 33–92.

D'Antonio, C. M., and Dudley, T. L. 1995. Biological invasions as agents of change on island versus mainland. In *Islands: Biological Diversity and Ecosystem Function*, eds. P. M. Vitousek, L. L. Loope, and H. Andersen, pp. 103–121. Berlin: Springer-Verlag.

Darwall, W.R.T., Holland, R. A., Smith, K. G., Allen, D., Wright, E., et al. 2011. Implications of bias in conservation research and investment for freshwater species. *Conservation Letters* 4: 474–482.

de Laulanié, H. 2011. Intensive rice farming in Madagascar. *Tropicultura* 29(3): 183–187.

de Pinna, M.C.C. 1993. Higher-level phylogeny of Siluriformes, with a new classification of the Order (Teleostei, Ostariophysi). PhD thesis, City University, New York.

———. 1998. Phylogenetic relationships of Neotropical Siluriformes: Historical overview and synthesis of hypotheses. In *Phylogeny and Classification of Neotropical Fishes*, eds. L. R. Malabarba, R. E. Reis, R. P. Vari, Z.M.S. Lucena, and C.A.S. Lucena, pp. 49–68. Porto Alegre: EDIPUCRS.

de Rham, P. H. 1996. Poissons des eaux intérieures de Madagascar. In *Biogéographie de Madagascar*, ed. W. R. Lourenço, pp. 423–440. Paris: Editions ORSTOM.

de Rham, P., and Nourissat, J.-C. 2004. *The Endemic Cichlids of Madagascar*. English trans. St. Lucia: French Cichlid Association.

Diogo, R. 2005. *Morphological Evolution, Aptations, Homoplasies, Constraints and Evolutionary Trends: Catfishes as a Case Study on General Phylogeny and Macroevolution*. Enfield: Science Publishers.

Dudgeon, D., Arthington, A. H., Gessner, M. O., Kawabata, Z.-I., Knowler, D. J., et al. 2007. Freshwater biodiversity: Importance, threats, status and conservation challenges. *Biological Reviews* 81(2): 163–182. https://doi.org/10.1017/S1464793105006950.

Dyer, B. S., and Chernoff, B. 1996. Phylogenetic relationships among atheriniform fishes (Teleostei: Atherinomorpha). *Zoological Journal of the Linnean Society* 117: 1–69.

Favretto, N. Afionis, S., Stringer, L. C., Dougill, A. J., Quinn, C. H., and Ranarijaona, H.L.T. 2020. Delivering climate-development co-benefits through multi-stakeholder forestry projects in Madagascar: Opportunities and challenges. *Land* 9(5): 157.

Fitzsimons, J. M., and Nishimoto, R. T. 1990. Territories and site tenacity in males of the Hawaiian stream goby *Lentipes concolor* (Pisces: Gobiidae). *Ichthyological Exploration of Freshwaters* 1: 185–189.

Fricke, R., Mahafina, J., Behivoke, F., Jaonalison, H., Léopold, M., and Ponton, D. 2018. Annotated checklist of the fishes of Madagascar, southwestern Indian Ocean, with 158 new records. *FishTaxa* 3(1): 1–432.

Fricke, R., Eschmeyer, W. N., and van der Laan, R., eds. 2020. Eschmeyer's catalog of fishes: Genera, species, references. Electronic version. Accessed 22 July 2020. http://researcharchive.calacademy.org/research/ichthyology/catalog/fishcatmain.asp.

Froese, R. and Pauly, D., eds. 2019. FishBase. Version 12/2019. www.fishbase.org.

Gayet, M., and Meunier, F. J. 2003. Paleontology and palaeobiogeography of catfishes. In *Catfishes*, vol. 2, eds. G. Arratia, B. G. Kapoor, M. Chardon, and R. Diogo, pp. 491–522. Enfield: Science Publishers.

Ghedotti, M. J. 2000. Phylogenetic analysis and taxonomy of the poecilioid fishes (Cyprinodontiformes: Teleostei). *Zoological Journal of the Linnean Society* 130(1): 1–53.

Goodman, S. M., Raherilalao, M. J., and Wohlhauser, S., eds. 2018. *Les aires protégées terrestres de Madagascar: Leur histoire, description et biote / The Terrestrial Protected Areas of Madagascar: Their History, Description, and Biota*. Antananarivo: Association Vahatra.

Gottfried, M. D., and Krause, D. W. 1994. Late Cretaceous fishes from Madagascar: A first look. *Journal of Vertebrate Paleontology* 14 (supplement): 26A.

———. 1998. First record of gars (Lepisosteidae, Actinopterygii) on Madagascar: Late Cretaceous remains from the Mahajunga basin. *Journal of Vertebrate Paleontology* 18: 275–279.

Gottfried, M. D., Randriamiarimanana, L. L., Rabarison, J. A., and Krause, D. W. 1998. Late Cretaceous fish from Madagascar: Implications for Gondwanan biogeography. *Journal of African Earth Sciences*, Special Abstracts issue, Gondwana 10: Event Stratigraphy of Gondwana, 27, no. 1A, published abstract.

Grande, L. 1985. Recent and fossil clupeomorph fishes with materials for revision of the subgroups of clupeoids. *Bulletin of the American Museum of Natural History* 181: 235–372.

Grandidier, G., and Petit, G. 1932. Les poissons d'eau douce. In *Zoologie de Madagascar*, pp. 184–188. Paris: Société d'Editions Géographiques, Maritimes et Coloniales.

Greenwood, P. H. 1994. Gobiid fishes of the genus *Glossogobius* in the Limpopo system: A first record and a range extension of *G. callidus* (Smith, 1937). *Southern African Journal of Aquatic Science* 20(1–2): 88–92.

Harper, G. J., Steininger, M. K., Tucker, C. J., Juhn, D., and Hawkins, F. 2007. Fifty years of deforestation and forest fragmentation in Madagascar. *Environmental Conservation* 34: 325–333.

Harrison, I. J., and Stiassny, M.L.J. 1999. The quiet crisis: A preliminary listing of freshwater fishes of the world that are either extinct or "missing in action." In *Extinctions in Near Time: Causes, Contexts, and Consequences*, ed. R.D.E. MacPhee, pp. 271–331. New York: Kluwer Academic / Plenum Press.

Hay, W. W., DeConto, R. M., Wold, C. N., Wilson, K. M., Voight, S., et al. 1999. Alternative global Cretaceous paleogeography. In *Evolution of the Cretaceous Ocean-Climate System*, eds. E. Barrera and C. C. Johnson, pp. 1–47. Special paper 332. Boulder: Geological Society of America.

Hoese, D. F., Hadiaty, R. K., and Herder, F. 2015. Review of the dwarf *Glossogobius* lacking head pores from the Malili lakes, Sulawesi, with a discussion of the definition of the genus. *Raffles Bulletin of Zoology* 63: 14–26.

Irwin, M. T., Wright, P. C., Birkinshaw C., Fisher, B. L., Gardner, C. J., et al. 2010. Patterns of species change in anthropogenically disturbed forests of Madagascar. *Biological Conservation* 143: 2351–2362.

IUCN. 2021. The IUCN Red List of Threatened Species. Version 2021-1. Accessed 15 August 2021. https://www.iucnredlist.org.

Jenkins, M. D. 1987. *Madagascar: An Environmental Profile*. Gland: IUCN.

Jones, C. C., Smith, W. L., and Sparks, J. S. 2010. A new species of rainbowfish (Teleostei: Melanotaenioidei: Bedotiidae) from the Makira region of northeastern Madagascar. *Copeia* 2010(2): 284–291.

Kiener, A. 1963. Poissons, pêche et pisciculture à Madagascar. *Centre Technique Forestier Tropical* 24: 1–244.

———. 1964. De la présence de certaines populations ichtyologiques dans les eaux souterraines des formations karstiques de la côte ouest de Madagascar. *Bulletin de Madagascar* 218: 573–592.

———. 1965. Contribution à l'étude écologique et biologique des eaux saumâtres malgaches. *Vie et Millieu*, C, 16(2): 1013–1149.

Kiener, A., and Richard-Vindard, G. 1972. Fishes of the continental waters of Madagascar. In *Biogeography and Ecology in Madagascar*, eds. R. Battistini and G. Richard-Vindard, pp. 477–499. The Hague: W. Junk.

Krause, D. W., Prasad, G.V.R., von Koenigswald, W., Sahni, A., and Grine, F. E. 1997a. Cosmopolitanism among Gondwanan Late Cretaceous mammals. *Nature* 390: 504–507.

Krause, D. W., Hartman, J. H., and Wells, N. A. 1997b. Late Cretaceous vertebrates from Madagascar: Implications for biotic change in deep time. In *Natural Change and Human Impact in Madagascar*, eds. S. M. Goodman and B. D. Patterson, pp. 3–43. Washington, DC: Smithsonian Institution Press.

Kremen, C., Razafimahatratra, V., Guillery, R. P., Rakotomalala, J., Weiss, A., and Ratsisompatrarivo, J.-S. 1999. Designing the Masoala National Park in Madagascar based on biological and socioeconomic data. *Conservation Biology* 13: 1055–1068.

Kuang, T., Tornabene, L., Li, J., Jiang, J., Chakrabarty, P., Sparks, J. S., Naylor, G.J.P., and Li, C. 2018. Phylogenomic analysis on the exceptionally diverse fish clade Gobioidei (Actinopterygii: Gobiiformes) and data-filtering based on molecular clocklikeness. *Molecular Phylogenetics and Evolution* 128: 192–202.

Kull, C. A. 2012. Air photo evidence of land cover change in the highlands: Wetlands and grasslands give way to crops and woodlots. *Madagascar Conservation and Development* 7(3): 144–152.

Kulongowski, C. 2010. Revision of the ariid catfish genus *Galeichthys* Valenciennes (subfamily Galeichthyinae), with description of a new species from South Africa and designation of a neotype for *G. ater* Castelnau. *Smithiana: Publications in Aquatic Biodiversity*, Bulletin 12: 9–23.

Loiselle, P. V. 2006. A review of the Malagasy *Pachypanchax* (Teleostei: Cyprinodontiformes, Aplocheilidae), with descriptions of four new species. *Zootaxa* 1366: 1–44.

Loiselle, P. V., and de Rham, P. 2003. *Paretroplus, damba*. In *The Natural History of Madagascar*, eds. S. M. Goodman and J. P. Benstead, pp. 877–878. Chicago: University of Chicago Press.

Loiselle, P. V., and Rodriguez, D. 2007. A new species of *Bedotia* (Teleostei: Atherinomorpha: Bedotiidae) from the Rianila drainage of eastern Madagascar, with redescriptions of *Bedotia madagascariensis* and *Bedotia geayi*. *Zootaxa* 1520: 1–18.

Lundberg, J. G. 1993. African-South American freshwater fish clades and continental drift: Problems with a paradigm. In *Biological Relationships between Africa and South America*, ed. P. Goldblatt, pp. 156–199. New Haven: Yale University Press.

Lundberg, J. G., Kottelat, M., Smith, G. R., Stiassny, M.L.J., and Gill, A. C. 2000. So many fishes, so little time: An overview of recent ichthyological discovery in continental waters. *Annals, Missouri Botanical Garden* 87: 26–62.

MacArthur, R. H., and Wilson, E. O. 1967. *The Theory of Island Biogeography*. Monographs in Population Biology 1. Princeton: Princeton University Press.

Maisey, J. G. 1993. Tectonics, the Santana lagerstätten, and the implications for late Gondwanan biogeography. In *Biological Relationships between Africa and South America*, ed. P. Goldblatt, pp. 435–454. New Haven: Yale University Press.

Máiz-Tomé, L., Sayer, C., and Darwall, W., eds. 2018. *The Status and Distribution of Freshwater Biodiversity in Madagascar and the Indian Ocean Islands Hotspot*. Cambridge, UK, and Gland: IUCN Freshwater Biodiversity Unit.

Manjaribe, C., Frasier, C. L., Rakouth, B., and Louis, E. E. 2013. Ecological restoration and reforestation of fragmented forests in Kianjavato, Madagascar. *International Journal of Ecology* 2013(2): 1–12.

Marceniuk, A. P., and Menezes, N. A. 2007. Systematics of the family Ariidae (Ostariophysi, Siluriformes), with a redefinition of the genera. *Zootaxa* 1416: 1–126.

Marceniuk, A. P., Menezes, N. A., and Britto, M. R. 2012. Phylogenetic analysis of the family Ariidae (Ostariophysi: Siluriformes), with a hypothesis on the monophyly and relationships of genera. *Zoological Journal of the Linnean Society* 165: 534–669.

Marceniuk, A. P., Bogorodsky, S. V., Mal, A. O., and Alpermann, T. J. 2017. Redescription of the blacktip sea catfish *Plicofollis dussumieri* (Valenciennes) (Siluriformes: Ariidae), with a new record from the Red Sea and notes on the diversity and distribution of *Plicofollis* spp. *Marine Biodiversity* 47(4): 1239–1250.

Martinez, C. M., and Sparks, J. S. 2017. Malagasy cichlids differentially limit impacts of body shape evolution on oral jaw functional morphology. *Evolution* 71(9): 2219–2229.

Martinez, C. M., Arroyave, J., and Sparks, J. S. 2015. A new species of *Ptychochromis* from southeastern Madagascar (Teleostei: Cichlidae). *Zootaxa* 4044(1): 79–92.

McMahan, C. D., Chakrabarty, P., Sparks, J. S., Smith, W. L., and Davis, M. P. 2013. Temporal patterns of diversification across global cichlid biodiversity (Acanthomorpha: Cichlidae). *PLoS One* 8(8): e71162.

Mittermeier, R. A., Turner, W. R., Larsen, F. W., Brooks, T. M., and Gascon, C. 2011. Global biodiversity conservation: The critical role of hotspots. In *Biodiversity Hotspots: Distribution and Protection of Conservation Priority Areas*, eds. F. Zachos and J. Habel, pp. 3–22. Berlin: Springer.

Mo, T. 1991. Anatomy, relationships and systematics of the Bagridae (Teleostei, Siluroidei) with a hypothesis of siluroid phylogeny. *Thesis Zoologicae* 17: 1–216.

Myers, G. S. 1938. Fresh-water fishes and West Indian zoogeography. *Annual Report of the Smithsonian Institution* 1937: 339–364.

———. 1955. Notes on the classification and names of cyprinodont fishes. *Tropical Fish Magazine*, Mar.: 1–7.

Nelson, J. S., Grande, T. C., and Wilson, M.V.H. 2016. *Fishes of the World*. 5th ed. Hoboken: John Wiley and Sons.

Ng, H. H., and Sparks, J. S. 2003. The ariid catfishes (Teleostei: Siluriformes: Ariidae) of Madagascar, with the description of two new species. *Occasional Papers, Museum of Zoology, University of Michigan* 735: 1–21.

———. 2005. Revision of the endemic Malagasy catfish family Anchariidae (Teleostei: Siluriformes), with descriptions of a new genus and three new species. *Ichthyological Exploration of Freshwaters* 16: 303–323.

Ng, H. H., Sparks, J. S., and Loiselle, P. V. 2008. A new species of catfish of the genus *Gogo* from northeastern Madagascar (Siluriformes: Anchariidae). *Copeia* 2008(2): 395–400.

Parenti, L. R. 1981. A phylogenetic and biogeographic analysis of cyprinodontiform fishes (Teleostei: Atherinomorpha). *Bulletin of the American Museum of Natural History* 168: 335–557.

Parkinson, M. C., and Booth, A. J. 2011. Effect of turbidity on the foraging success of *Glossogobius callidus* (Teleostei: Gobiidae). *African Journal of Aquatic Science* 36(2): 213–216.

Patterson, C. 1993a. An overview of the early fossil record of acanthomorphs. *Bulletin of Marine Science* 52: 29–59.

———. 1993b. Osteichthyes, Teleostei. In *The Fossil Record 2*, ed. M. Benton, pp. 621–656. London: Chapman and Hall.

Pellegrin, J. 1932. Poissons de Madagascar recueillis par M. Waterlot. Description d'une variété nouvelle. *Bulletin de la Société Zoologique de France* 57: 225–228.

Plummer, P. S., and Belle, E. R. 1995. Mesozoic tectono-stratigraphic evolution of the Seychelles microcontinent. *Sedimentary Geology* 96: 73–91.

Pohl, M., Milvertz, F. C., Meyer, A., and Vences, M. 2015. Multigene phylogeny of cyprinodontiform fishes suggests continental radiations and a rogue taxon position of *Pantanodon*. *Vertebrate Zoology* 65: 37–44.

Rabinowitz, P. D., Coffin, M. F., and Falvey, D. 1983. The separation of Madagascar and Africa. *Science* 220: 67–69.

Rao, L. M., and Rao, P. S. 2002. Food and feeding habits of *Glossogobius giuris* from Gosthani estuary. *Indian Journal of Fisheries* 49(1): 35–40.

Rasoloariniaina, J. R., Ganzhorn, J. U., Riemann, J. C., and Raminosoa, N. 2016. Water quality and biotic interaction of two cavefish species: *Typhleotris madagascariensis* Petit, 1933 and *Typhleotris mararybe* Sparks & Chakrabarty, 2012, in the Mahafaly Plateau groundwater system, Madagascar. *Subterranean Biology* 18: 1–16.

Ravelomanana, T., Máiz-Tomé, L., Darwall, W., Sayer, C., and Sparks, J. S. 2018. The status and distribution of freshwater fishes. In *The Status and Distribution of Freshwater Biodiversity in Madagascar and the Indian Ocean Islands Hotspot*, eds. L. Máiz-Tomé, C. Sayer, and W. Darwall, pp. 13–28. Cambridge, UK, and Gland: IUCN Freshwater Biodiversity Unit.

Raxworthy, C. J., and Nussbaum, R. A. 1997. Biogeographic patterns of reptiles in eastern Madagascar. In *Natural Change and Human Impact in Madagascar*, eds. S. M. Goodman and B. D. Patterson, pp. 124–141. Washington, DC: Smithsonian Institution Press.

Reinthal, P. N., and Stiassny, M.L.J. 1991. The freshwater fishes of Madagascar: A study of an endangered fauna with recommendations for a conservation strategy. *Conservation Biology* 5: 231–243.

———. 1997. Revision of the Madagascan genus *Ptychochromoides* (Teleostei: Cichlidae), with a description of a new species. *Ichthyological Exploration of Freshwaters* 7: 353–368.

Riseng, K. J. 1997. The distribution of fishes and the conservation of aquatic resources in Madagascar. MS thesis, University of Michigan, Ann Arbor.

Rosen, D. E. 1965. *Oryzias madagascariensis* Arnoult redescribed and assigned to the East African fish genus *Pantanodon* (Atherinformes, Cyprinodontoidei). *American Museum Novitates* 2240: 1–10.

Rübel, A., Hatchwell, M., MacKinnon, J., and Ketterer, P. 2003. *Masoala—The Eye of the Forest: A New Strategy for Rainforest Conservation in Madagascar*. Zurich: Zoo Zurich.

Samonds, K. E., Godfrey, L. R., Ali, J. R., Goodman, S. M., Vences, M., Sutherland, M. R., Irwin, M. T., and Krause, D. W. 2012. Spatial and temporal arrival patterns of Madagascar's vertebrate fauna explained by distance, ocean currents, and ancestor type. *Proceedings of the National Academy of Sciences of the USA* 109: 5352–5357.

———. 2013. Imperfect isolation: Factors and filters shaping Madagascar's extant vertebrate fauna. *PLoS One* 8: e62086.

Sampson, S. D., Witmer, L. M., Forster, C., Krause, D. W., O'Connor, P. M., Dodson, P., and Ravoavy, F. 1998. Predatory dinosaur remains from Madagascar: Implications for the Cretaceous biogeography of Gondwana. *Science* 280: 1048–1051.

Sauvage, H. 1891. *Histoire naturelle des poissons*. Collection Histoire Physique, Naturelle, Politique de Madagascar. Paris: Imprimerie Nationale.

Seegers, L. 1996. The fishes of the Lake Rukwa drainage. *Annales de la Société Zoologique de Belgique* 278: 1–407.

Smith, J.L.B. 1965. Fishes of the family Atherinidae of the Red Sea and the Western Indian Ocean with a new freshwater genus and species from Madagascar. *Ichthyological Bulletin, Rhodes University* 31: 601–632.

Sparks, J. S. 2001. Phylogeny and biogeography of the Malagasy and south Asian cichlid fishes (Teleostei: Perciformes: Cichlidae), including a survey of freshwater fishes of Madagascar. PhD thesis, University of Michigan, Ann Arbor.

———. 2002a. *Paretroplus dambabe*, a new cichlid fish (Teleostei: Cichlidae) from northwestern Madagascar, with a discussion on the status of *P. petiti*. *Proceedings of the Biological Society of Washington* 115: 546–563.

———. 2002b. *Ptychochromis inornatus*, a new cichlid (Teleostei: Cichlidae) from northwestern Madagascar, with a discussion of intrageneric variation in *Ptychochromis*. *Copeia* 2002(1): 120–130.

———. 2003a. *Ptychochromis*. In *The Natural History of Madagascar*, eds. S. M. Goodman and J. P. Benstead, pp. 873–874. Chicago: University of Chicago Press.

———. *Typhleotris*. In *The Natural History of Madagascar*, eds. S. M. Goodman and J. P. Benstead, pp. 878–879. Chicago: University of Chicago Press

———. 2004a. A new and presumably extinct species of *Ptychochromoides* (Teleostei: Perciformes: Cichlidae) from central Madagascar. *Zootaxa* 524: 1–15.

———. 2004b. Molecular phylogeny and biogeography of the Malagasy and South Asian cichlid fishes (Teleostei: Perciformes: Cichlidae). *Molecular Phylogenetics and Evolution* 30: 599–614.

———. 2008. Phylogeny of the cichlid subfamily Etroplinae and taxonomic revision of the Malagasy cichlid genus *Paretroplus* (Teleostei: Cichlidae). *Bulletin of the American Museum of Natural History* 314: 1–151.

Sparks, J. S., and Chakrabarty, P. 2012. Revision of the endemic Malagasy cavefish genus *Typhleotris* (Teleostei: Gobiiformes: Milyeringidae), with discussion of its phylogenetic placement and description of a new species. *American Museum Novitates* 3764: 1–28.

Sparks, J. S., and Nelson, D. W. 2004. Review of the Malagasy sicydiine gobies (Teleostei: Gobiidae), with description of a new species and comments on the taxonomic status of *Gobius lagocephalus* Pallas, 1770. *American Museum Novitates* 3440: 1–20.

Sparks, J. S., and Reinthal, P. N. 1999. *Paretroplus maromandia*, a new cichlid fish from the northwest of Madagascar. *Occasional Papers, Museum of Zoology, University of Michigan* 727: 1–18.

———. 2001. A new species of *Ptychochromoides* from southeastern Madagascar (Teleostei: Cichlidae), with comments on the monophyly and relationships of the ptychochromine cichlids. *Ichthyological Exploration of Freshwaters* 12: 115–132.

Sparks, J. S., and Rush, L.M.R. 2005. A new rainbowfish (Teleostei: Melanotaenioidei: Bedotiidae) from the southeastern highlands of Madagascar, with comments on the biogeography of *Bedotia*. *Zootaxa* 1051: 39–54.

Sparks, J. S., and Schelly, R. C. 2011. A new species of *Paretroplus* (Teleostei: Cichlidae: Etroplinae) from northeastern Madagascar, with a phylogeny and revised diagnosis for the *P. damii* clade. *Zootaxa* 2768: 55–68.

Sparks, J. S., and Smith, W. L. 2004a. Phylogeny and biogeography of cichlid fishes (Teleostei: Perciformes: Cichlidae). *Cladistics* 20: 501–517.

———. 2004b. Phylogeny and biogeography of the Malagasy and Australasian rainbowfishes (Teleostei: Melanotaenioidei): Gondwanan vicariance and evolution in freshwater. *Molecular Phylogenetics and Evolution* 33: 719–734.

———. 2005. Freshwater fishes, dispersal ability, and non-evidence: "Gondwana life rafts" to the rescue. *Systematic Biology* 54: 158–165.

Sparks, J. S., and Stiassny, M.L.J. 2003. Introduction to the freshwater fishes of Madagascar. In *The Natural History of Madagascar*, eds. S. M. Goodman and J. P. Benstead, pp. 849–863. Chicago: University of Chicago Press.

———. 2005. Madagascar's freshwater fishes, an imperiled treasure. In *Freshwater Ecoregions of Africa and Madagascar: A Conservation Assessment*, eds. M. L. Thieme, R. Abell, M.L.J. Stiassny, B. Lehner, P. Skelton, G. Teugals, E. Dinerstein, A. Kamdem Toham, N. Burgess, and D. Olson, pp. 62–70. Washington, DC: Island Press.

———. 2008. Les poissons d'eau douce. In *Paysages naturels et biodiversité de Madagascar*, ed. S. M. Goodman, pp. 283–309. Paris: Publications Scientifiques Muséum national d'Histoire naturelle.

———. 2010. A new species of *Ptychochromis* from northeastern Madagascar (Teleostei: Cichlidae), with an updated phylogeny and revised diagnosis for the genus. *Zootaxa* 2341: 33–51.

Sparks, J. S., Loiselle, P. V., and Baldwin, Z. H. 2012. Rediscovery and phylogenetic placement of the endemic Malagasy cichlid *Ptychochromoides itasy* (Teleostei: Cichlidae: Ptychochrominae). *Zootaxa* 3352: 17–24.

Stiassny, M.L.J. 1990. Notes on the anatomy and relationships of the bedotiid fishes of Madagascar, with a taxonomic revision of the genus *Rheocles* (Atherinomorpha: Bedotiidae). *American Museum Novitates* 2979: 1–33.

———. 2002. Revision of *Sauvagella* Bertin (Clupeidae; Pellonulinae; Ehiravini) with a description of a new species from the freshwaters of Madagascar and diagnosis of the Ehiravini. *Copeia* 2002 (1): 67–76.

Stiassny, M.L.J., and Gerstner, C. L. 1992. The parental care behaviour of *Paratilapia polleni* Bleeker, 1868 (Perciformes, Labroidei) a phylogenetically primitive cichlid from Madagascar, with a discussion of the evolution of maternal care in the family Cichlidae. *Environmental Biology of Fishes* 34: 219–233.

Stiassny, M.L.J., and Mezey, J. 1993. Egg attachment systems in the family Cichlidae (Perciformes: Labroidei), with some comment on their significance for phylogenetic studies. *American Museum Novitates* 3058: 1–11.

Stiassny, M.L.J., and Raminosoa, N. 1994. The fishes of the inland waters of Madagascar. In *Biological Diversity in African Fresh- and Brackish Water Fishes*, eds. G. G. Teugels, J. F. Guegan, and J. J. Albaret. Geographical overviews, Symposium PARADI. *Annales Muséum Royal de l'Afrique Centrale, Sciences Zoologiques* 275: 133–149.

Stiassny, M.L.J., and Rodriguez, D. M. 2001. *Rheocles derhami*, a new species of freshwater rainbowfish (Atherinomorpha: Bedotiidae) from the Ambomboa River in northeastern Madagascar. *Ichthyological Exploration of Freshwaters* 12: 97–104.

Stiassny, M.L.J., and Sparks, J. S. 2006. Phylogeny and taxonomic revision of the endemic Malagasy cichlid genus *Ptychochromis* (Teleostei: Cichlidae), with the description of five new species and a diagnosis for *Katria*, new genus. *American Museum Novitates* 3535: 1–55.

Stiassny, M.L.J., Chakrabarty, P., and Loiselle, P. V. 2001. Relationships of the Madagascan cichlid genus *Paretroplus*, with description of a new species from the Betsiboka River drainage of northwestern Madagascar. *Ichthyological Exploration of Freshwaters* 12: 29–40.

Stiassny, M.L.J., Rodriguez, D. M., and Loiselle, P. V. 2002. *Rheocles vatosoa*, a new species of freshwater rainbowfish (Atherinomorpha: Bedotiidae) from the Lokoho River basin in northeastern Madagascar. *Cybium* 26(1): 71–77.

Stiassny, M.L.J., Revenga, C., and Comer, P. 2010. Aquatic ecosystems: Diversity and dynamism. In *Fresh Water: The Essence of Life*, eds. R. A. Mittermeier, T. Farrell, I. Harrison, T. M. Brooks, and A. Upgren, pp. 93–116. Arlington: CEMEX/ILCP.

Storey, B. C. 1995. The role of mantle plumes in continental breakup: Case histories from Gondwanaland. *Nature* 377: 301–308.

Storey, M., Mahoney, J. J., Saunders, A. D., Duncan, R. A., Kelly, S. P., and Coffin, M. F. 1995. Timing of hot spot–related volcanism and the breakup of Madagascar and India. *Science* 267: 852–855.

Sullivan, J. P., Lundberg, J. G., and Hardman, M. 2006. A phylogenetic analysis of the major groups of catfishes (Teleostei: Siluriformes) using *rag1* and *rag2* nuclear gene sequences. *Molecular Phylogenetics and Evolution* 41(3): 636–662.

Taylor, W. R. 1986. Ariidae. In *Checklist of the Freshwater Fishes of Africa*, vol. 2, eds. J. Daget, J.-P. Gosse, and D.F.E. Thys van den Audenaerde, pp. 153–159. Brussels: ISNB; Tervuren: MRAC; Paris: ORSTOM.

Teugels, G. G., Janssens, L.J.M., Bogaert, J., and Dumalin, M. 1985. Sur une collection de poissons de rivière des Comores. *Cybium* 9: 41–56.

Vieilledent, G., Grinand, C., Rakotomalala, F. A., Ranaivosoa, R., Rakotoarijaona, J.-R., Allnutt, T. F., and Achard, F. 2018. Combining global tree cover loss data with historical national forest cover maps to look at six decades of deforestation and forest fragmentation in Madagascar. *Biological Conservation* 222: 189–197.

Waeber, P. O., Wilmé, L., Mercier, J.-R., Camara, C., and Lowry, P. P., II. 2016. How effective have thirty years of internationally driven conservation and development efforts been in Madagascar? *PLoS One* 11(8): e0161115.

Walsh, S. J., and Chakrabarty, P. 2016. A new genus and species of blind sleeper (Teleostei: Eleotridae) from Oaxaca, Mexico: First obligate cave gobiiform in the Western Hemisphere. *Copeia* 104: 506–517.

Whitehead, P.J.P. 1962. The Pantanodontinae, edentulous toothcarps from East Africa. *Bulletin of the British Museum Natural History, Zoology* 9: 105–137.

———. 1985. *FAO Species Catalogue*. Vol. 7. *Clupeoid Fishes of the World. An Annotated and Illustrated Catalogue of the Herring, Sardine, Pilchards, Sprats, Anchovies and Wolf-herrings*. Pt. 1, Chirocentridae, Clupeidae and Pristigasteridae, pp. 1–303. Rome: Food and Agriculture Organization of the United Nations.

Wilson, J. M. 1996. Conservation and ecology of a new blind fish *Glossogobius ankaranensis* from the Ankárana Caves, Madagascar. *Oryx* 30: 218–221.

Wilson, J. M., Stewart, P. D., and Fowler, S. V. 1988. Conservation and ecology of a new blind fish *Glossogobius ankaranensis* from the Ankárana Caves, Madagascar. *Oryx* 22: 163–171.

World Bank. 2020. Population growth (annual %): Madagascar. https://data.worldbank.org/indicator/SP.POP.GROW?locations=MG.

CHAPTER 11

AMPHIBIANS

DIVERSITY AND EXPLORATION OF THE MALAGASY AMPHIBIAN FAUNA

F. Glaw, A. Crottini, A. Rakotoarison, M. D. Scherz, and M. Vences

The amphibian fauna of Madagascar is exceptional, with all its native species being endemic to this "micro-continent" and its nearshore islands. In the past three decades, there have been substantial increases in the amount of information available on the Malagasy herpetofauna, and species numbers have almost tripled since the monograph of Blommers-Schlösser and Blanc (1991). Currently, more than 365 Malagasy amphibian species are recognized (AmphibiaWeb 2021; Table 11.1), but this number will certainly increase in the future, with 100–150 candidate species already identified but not yet assessed and scientifically named (Vieites et al. 2009; Perl et al. 2014). It is very likely that more than 500 amphibian species occur on Madagascar. Considering scientifically named species only, about 4.5% of the world's amphibian fauna occurs on and is restricted to Madagascar. Few countries in the world, such as Brazil and Colombia, have more endemic amphibian species. The amphibian fauna therefore confirms Madagascar's rank as one of the most important biodiversity hotspots on the planet (Myers et al. 2000).

HISTORY OF EXPLORATION

The first amphibian species scientifically named from Madagascar was *Boophis goudotii* by Johann Jakob von Tschudi (1838). The first major increase in species discoveries then took place in the second half of the 19th century, when mainly George Albert Boulenger (London) (e.g., Figure 11.1) and Oskar Boettger (Frankfurt) named many species. In the 1970s, field expeditions by French researchers led to a second increase in discoveries, including numerous remarkable frogs described by Jean Guibé from poorly accessible areas such as Marojejy, Andohahela, and Tsaratanàna. The research of Rose Blommers-Schlösser in the 1970s was the first to integrate observations of behavior, bioacoustic traits, and karyotypes with morphological data, and this led to a much better understanding of the evolutionary relationships and biological diversity of Madagascar's frog fauna (e.g., Blommers-Schlösser 1979a, 1979b). The monographs of Blommers-Schlösser and Blanc (1991, 1993) were the starting point for a dramatic increase in studies of Malagasy amphibians. These authors recognized 133 species from the island, but this number nearly doubled to 244 species in less than 20 years (Vieites et al. 2009) and further increased to 292 over the following five years (Perl et al. 2014). This increase was accompanied by a higher-level classification better in line with the evolutionary relationships at the subgenus, genus, and subfamily levels (Glaw and Vences 2006; Scherz et al. 2016b).

FIGURE 11.1 **The tree frog *Boophis luteus* was described by George Albert Boulenger in 1882 and is one of the most charismatic frogs of Madagascar. Multiple other green *Boophis* species have been described in the past decades, but the bright red outer iris and the police-siren-like vocalizations provide the needed characters to distinguish *B. luteus* from other members of the genus.** (PHOTO by J. Köhler.)

TABLE 11.1. **The modern amphibian fauna of Madagascar as of 15 June 2021**

FAMILY (SUBFAMILY) GENUS (SUBGENUS) SPECIES	DISTRIBUTION	IUCN STATUS
HYPEROLIIDAE		
Heterixalus alboguttatus	Southeast	LC
H. andrakata	Northeast	LC
H. betsileo	Central Highlands	LC
H. boettgeri	Extreme southeast	LC
H. carbonei	Central west and extreme north	LC
H. luteostriatus	West and central south	LC
H. madagascariensis	Eastern coast and northeast	LC
H. punctatus	Eastern coast and northeast	LC
H. rutenbergi	Central Highlands	LC
H. tricolor	Central west and northwest	LC
H. variabilis	Northwest	LC
MANTELLIDAE (BOOPHINAE)		
Boophis (Boophis) albilabris	East, northeast, central east, and northeast	LC
B. (B.) albipunctatus	East and central east	LC
B. (B.) andohahela	Southeast	VU
B. (B.) andrangoloaka	Central Highlands	EN
B. (B.) andreonei	Northwest	VU
B. (B.) anjanaharibeensis	Northeast	EN
B. (B.) ankarafensis	Northwest	CR
B. (B.) ankaratra	Central Highlands	LC
B. (B.) arcanus	Central southeast	EN
B. (B.) axelmeyeri	Northeast and northwest	LC
B. (B.) baetkei	Extreme north	CR
B. (B.) blommersae	North and northwest	VU
B. (B.) boehmei	Central Highlands and central east	EN
B. (B.) boppa	Central southeast	EN
B. (B.) bottae	Central east and central southeast	LC
B. (B.) brachychir	North and northwest	VU
B. (B.) burgeri	Central east	DD
B. (B.) elenae	Central east and central southeast	NT
B. (B.) englaenderi	Northeast	VU
B. (B.) entingae	Northwest, north, and northeast	LC
B. (B.) erythrodactylus	Central Highlands and central east	LC
B. (B.) fayi	Northeast and central east	VU
B. (B.) feonnyala	Central east	EN

FAMILY (SUBFAMILY) GENUS (SUBGENUS) SPECIES	DISTRIBUTION	IUCN STATUS
B. (*B.*) *goudotii*	Central Highlands	LC
B. (*B.*) *haematopus*	Extreme southeast	EN
B. (*B.*) *haingana*	Extreme southeast	EN
B. (*B.*) *jaegeri*	Northwest	EN
B. (*B.*) *laurenti*	Central south and Central Highlands	EN
B. (*B.*) *liami*	Central east	CR
B. (*B.*) *lilianae*	Central southeast	DD
B. (*B.*) *luciae*	East and southeast	LC
B. (*B.*) *luteus*	Central Highlands, east, and southeast	LC
B. (*B.*) *madagascariensis*	Central Highlands, east, and southeast	LC
B. (*B.*) *majori*	Central southeast	VU
B. (*B.*) *mandraka*	Central east	DD
B. (*B.*) *marojezensis*	East and northeast	LC
B. (*B.*) *masoala*	Northeast	NE
B. (*B.*) *miadana*	Extreme southeast	EN
B. (*B.*) *microtympanum*	Central Highlands	LC
B. (*B.*) *miniatus*	Extreme southeast	VU
B. (*B.*) *narinsi*	Southeast and central southeast	EN
B. (*B.*) *obscurus*	Southeast and south of Central Highlands	NT
B. (*B.*) *occidentalis*	West and south of Central Highlands	LC
B. (*B.*) *periegetes*	Southeast	NT
B. (*B.*) *picturatus*	Central east and central southeast	LC
B. (*B.*) *piperatus*	Central southeast	EN
B. (*B.*) *popi*	South of Central Highlands and central southeast	VU
B. (*B.*) *praedictus*	Southeast	LC
B. (*B.*) *pyrrhus*	East and central east	LC
B. (*B.*) *quasiboehmei*	Central southeast	NT
B. (*B.*) *rappiodes*	Central southeast and extreme southeast	LC
B. (*B.*) *reticulatus*	Central east and Central Highlands	LC
B. (*B.*) *rhodoscelis*	Central east and central southeast	EN
B. (*B.*) *roseipalmatus*	North and northeast	LC
B. (*B.*) *rufioculis*	Central east	NT
B. (*B.*) *sambirano*	Northwest	EN
B. (*B.*) *sandrae*	Central east and southeast	EN
B. (*B.*) *schuboeae*	Central southeast	EN
B. (*B.*) *septentrionalis*	North and northeast	LC

(*continued overleaf*)

TABLE 11.1. ***continued***

FAMILY (SUBFAMILY) GENUS (SUBGENUS) SPECIES	DISTRIBUTION	IUCN STATUS
B. (B.) sibilans	Central east and northeast	LC
B. (B.) solomaso	Central east	EN
B. (B.) spinophis	Central Highlands and central southeast	VU
B. (B.) tampoka	West and northwest	LC
B. (B.) tasymena	East	LC
B. (B.) tsilomaro	Northwest	CR
B. (B.) ulftunni	Northeast	VU
B. (B.) viridis	East	LC
B. (B.) vittatus	Northwest and northeast	VU
B. (B.) williamsi	Central Highlands	CR
Boophis (Sahona) calcaratus	Central east and east	LC
B. (S.) doulioti	West and southeast	LC
B. (S.) guibei	Central east and central southeast	LC
B. (S.) idae	Central east and central southeast	LC
B. (S.) lichenoides	East and northeast	LC
B. (S.) opisthodon	East coast	LC
B. (S.) pauliani	Central southeast and extreme southeast	LC
B. (S.) tephraeomystax	Northwest and east	LC
B. (S.) xerophilus	West and extreme southeast	LC
MANTELLIDAE (LALIOSTOMINAE)		
Aglyptodactylus australis	Extreme southeast	EN
A. chorus	Northeast	NT
A. inguinalis	Central southeast and extreme southeast	LC
A. laticeps	West	VU
A. madagascariensis	Central east and north	LC
A. securifer	West and northwest	LC
Laliostoma labrosum	West, north, southwest, and south of Central Highlands	LC
MANTELLIDAE (MANTELLINAE)		
Blommersia angolafa	Northeast and central east	LC
B. blommersae	Central east, east coast, and extreme southeast	LC
B. dejongi	Central east	LC
B. domerguei	Central east and central southeast	LC
B. galani	Central east	LC
B. grandisonae	Central east, southeast, and northeast	LC
B. kely	Central east	LC

FAMILY (SUBFAMILY) GENUS (SUBGENUS) SPECIES	DISTRIBUTION	IUCN STATUS
B. sarotra	Central east	LC
B. variabilis	Northeast	LC
B. wittei	Northwest and north	LC
Boehmantis microtympanum	Extreme southeast	VU
Gephyromantis (Asperomantis) ambohitra	North and northwest	VU
G. (A.) angano	Sambirano Region	NE
G. (A.) asper	Central east	LC
G. (A.) ceratophrys	South central east	NE
G. (A.) spinifer	Extreme southeast	VU
G. (A.) tahotra	Northeast	VU
Gephyromantis (Duboimantis) cornutus	Central and central east	VU
G. (D.) granulatus	Northwest, north, and northeast	LC
G. (D.) grosjeani	Northeast	NE
G. (D.) leucomaculatus	Northeast and central east	LC
G. (D.) luteus	East, northeast, and southeast	LC
G. (D.) moseri	Central east and northeast	LC
G. (D.) plicifer	Central southeast and southeast	LC
G. (D.) redimitus	Central east, east, and northeast	LC
G. (D.) salegy	Northeast	VU
G. (D.) saturnini	Sambirano Region	NE
G. (D.) schilfi	Northeast	VU
G. (D.) sculpturatus	Central east and central southeast	LC
G. (D.) tandroka	Northeast	VU
G. (D.) tohatra	Northeast	NE
G. (D.) tschenki	Central southeast and southeast	LC
G. (D.) zavona	Northwest	EN
Gephyromantis (Gephyromantis) blanci	Central southeast	NT
G. (G.) boulengeri	Northeast, central east, and central southeast	LC
G. (G.) decaryi	Central southeast and southeast	LC
G. (G.) eiselti	Central east	EN
G. (G.) enki	Central southeast	VU
G. (G.) hintelmannae	Central southeast	EN
G. (G.) leucocephalus	Extreme southeast	NT
G. (G.) mafy	Central east	CR
G. (G.) runewsweeki	Central southeast	VU
G. (G.) thelenae	Central east	EN

(continued overleaf)

TABLE 11.1. ***continued***

FAMILY (SUBFAMILY) GENUS (SUBGENUS) SPECIES	DISTRIBUTION	IUCN STATUS
G. (G.) verrucosus	Central southeast	LC
Gephyromantis (Laurentomantis incert. sed.) klemmeri	Northeast	EN
G. (L.) horridus	Northwest	VU
G. (L.) malagasius	Central east and northeast	LC
G. (L.) ranjomavo	Northeast	EN
G. (L.) striatus	Northeast	VU
G. (L.) ventrimaculatus	Central east, central southeast, and southeast	LC
Gephyromantis (Phylacomantis) atsingy	West	EN
G. (P.) corvus	South of Central Highlands	EN
G. (P.) kintana	South of Central Highlands	NE
G. (P.) pseudoasper	Northwest, north, and northeast	LC
Gephyromantis (Vatomantis) lomorina	Northeast	NE
G. (V.) rivicola	Northeast	VU
G. (V.) silvanus	Northeast	VU
G. (V.) webbi	Northeast	EN
Guibemantis (Guibemantis) depressiceps	Central east and central southeast	LC
G. (G.) diphonus	Southeast	CR
G. (G.) kathrinae	Northeast and central east	VU
G. (G.) timidus	East, northeast, and central southeast	LC
G. (G.) tornieri	Central east, central southeast, and southeast	LC
Guibemantis (Pandanusicola) albolineatus	Extreme southeast	LC
G. (P.) albomaculatus	Sambirano Region and north	NE
G. (P.) annulatus	Extreme southeast	EN
G. (P.) bicalcaratus	Northeast	LC
G. (P.) flavobrunneus	Central east	LC
G. (P.) liber	North, northeast, central east, east, and southeast	LC
G. (P.) methueni	Central east	LC
G. (P.) milingilingy	Northeast	NE
G. (P.) pulcher	East, southeast, and northeast	LC
G. (P.) punctatus	Central Highlands and southeast	CR
G. (P.) tasifotsy	Southeast	VU
G. (P.) wattersoni	Extreme southeast	EN
G. (P.) woosteri	Northeast	NE
Mantella aurantiaca	Central east	EN
M. baroni	Central east, east, and central southeast	LC

FAMILY (SUBFAMILY) GENUS (SUBGENUS) SPECIES	DISTRIBUTION	IUCN STATUS
M. bernhardi	Extreme southeast	VU
M. betsileo	West and south of Central Highlands	LC
M. cowanii	Central Highlands	EN
M. crocea	Central east and Central Highlands	VU
M. ebenaui	Northwest and northeast	LC
M. expectata	Southern Central Highlands	EN
M. haraldmeieri	Extreme southeast	EN
M. laevigata	Northeast and central east	LC
M. madagascariensis	Central southeast	VU
M. manery	Northeast	VU
M. milotympanum	Central east	CR
M. nigricans	Northwest and northeast	LC
M. pulchra	Central east and northeast	NT
M. viridis	Extreme north	EN
Mantidactylus (Brygoomantis) alutus	Central Highlands	LC
M. (B.) ambohimitombi	Central Highlands	DD
M. (B.) bellyi	Northeast	LC
M. (B.) betsileanus	Central east	LC
M. (B.) biporus	Central east	LC
M. (B.) bourgati	Southeastern Central Highlands	EN
M. (B.) curtus	Central Highlands	LC
M. (B.) madecassus	Southeastern Central Highlands	EN
M. (B.) noralottae	Southeastern Central Highlands	DD
M. (B.) pauliani	Central Highlands	CR
M. (B.) schulzi	Sambirano Region	NE
M. (B.) tricinctus	Extreme southeast	VU
M. (B.) ulcerosus	Central west and northwest	LC
Mantidactylus (Chonomantis) aerumnalis	East, central east, central southwest, and southeast	LC
M. (C.) albofrenatus	Central east	EN
M. (C.) brevipalmatus	Central Highlands	LC
M. (C.) charlotteae	Central east and northeast	LC
M. (C.) delormei	South of Central Highlands and central southeast	EN
M. (C.) melanopleura	East coast, northeast, and southeast	LC
M. (C.) opiparis	Central Highlands, central east, north, and northeast	LC
M. (C.) paidroa	Central southeast	EN
M. (C.) zipperi	Central east	LC

(continued overleaf)

TABLE 11.1. ***continued***

FAMILY (SUBFAMILY) GENUS (SUBGENUS) SPECIES	DISTRIBUTION	IUCN STATUS
Mantidactylus (Hylobatrachus) atsimo	Southeast	NE
M. (H.) cowanii	Central Highlands and central east	NT
M. (H.) lugubris	Central east	LC
M. (H.) petakorona	Northeast	NE
Mantidactylus (Maitsomantis) argenteus	East coast and central east	LC
Mantidactylus (Mantidactylus) grandidieri	Central east to northeast, Central Highlands, and east coast	LC[1]
M. (M.) guttulatus	Central east, east coast, and southeast	LC[1]
M. (M.) radaka	Northwest	NE
Mantidactylus (Ochthomantis) ambony	North	NE
M. (O.) ambreensis	Northwest and north	LC
M. (O.) femoralis	Central Highlands and east	LC
M. (O.) majori	Central southeast and southeast	LC
M. (O.) mocquardi	Central east	LC
M. (O.) zolitschka	Central east	CR
Spinomantis aglavei	East coast and extreme southeast	LC
S. beckei	Extreme southeast	NE
S. bertini	Southern Central Highlands and extreme southeast	NT
S. brunae	Extreme southeast	EN
S. elegans	Southern Central Highlands and extreme southeast	NT
S. fimbriatus	Northeast, central east, and southeast	LC
S. guibei	Extreme southeast	VU
S. massi	Northwest	VU
S. microtis	Central southeast and extreme southeast	EN
S. mirus	Southeast	NE
S. nussbaumi	Central northwest	CR
S. peraccae	Central east and east coast	LC
S. phantasticus	Northeast and central east	LC
S. tavaratra	North and northwest	VU
Wakea madinika	Northwest	DD
MANTELLIDAE (TSINGYMANTINAE)		
Tsingymantis antitra	North	EN
PTYCHADENIDAE		
Ptychadena mascareniensis	Across island	LC
MICROHYLIDAE (COPHYLINAE)		
Anilany helenae	Central Highlands	CR

FAMILY (SUBFAMILY) GENUS (SUBGENUS) SPECIES	DISTRIBUTION	IUCN STATUS
Anodonthyla boulengeri	Central east and east coast	NT
A. emilei	Central southeast	EN
A. eximia	Southern central east	NE
A. hutchisoni	Northeast	EN
A. jeanbai	Extreme southeast	EN
A. montana	Southern Central Highlands and extreme southeast	VU
A. moramora	Central southeast	EN
A. nigrigularis	Extreme southeast	EN
A. pollicaris	Central east	DD
A. rouxae	Extreme southeast	EN
A. theoi	Southeast	CR
A. vallani	Central Highlands	CR
Cophyla berara	Northwest	EN
C. fortuna	Northeast	NE
C. maharipeo	North	CR
C. noromalalae	North	EN
C. occultans	Northwest and northeast	VU
C. phyllodactyla	Northwest	LC
C. puellarum	North	CR
Madecassophryne truebae	Extreme southeast	EN
Mini ature	Southeast	NE
M. mum	Southeast	NE
M. scule	Southeast	NE
Platypelis alticola	Northwest	EN
P. ando	Northeast	NE
P. barbouri	Northeast and central southeast	LC
P. cowanii	Northeast	DD
P. grandis	Central east, east coast, northeast, and southeast	LC
P. karenae	Central east	CR
P. laetus	Northeast	NE
P. mavomavo	Northeast	EN
P. milloti	Northwest	EN
P. olgae	Northwest	EN
P. pollicaris	Central east and central southeast	LC
P. ranjomena	Northeast	NE
P. ravus	Northeast	EN

(continued overleaf)

TABLE 11.1. ***continued***

FAMILY (SUBFAMILY) GENUS (SUBGENUS) SPECIES	DISTRIBUTION	IUCN STATUS
P. tetra	Northeast	EN
P. tsaratananaensis	Northwest and northeast	EN
P. tuberifera	East coast, southeast, central east, and northeast	LC
Plethodontohyla alluaudi	East, central east, northeast to extreme southeast	LC
P. bipunctata	East coast, central east, southeast, and extreme southeast	LC
P. brevipes	Central southeast	VU
P. fonetana	West	EN
P. guentheri	Northeast	EN
P. inguinalis	East coast, central southeast, and extreme southeast	LC
P. laevis	Southeast	NE
P. mihanika	Central east and central southeast	LC
P. notosticta	Central east, east coast, northeast to extreme southeast	LC
P. ocellata	East coast and northeast	LC
P. tuberata	Central Highlands and southeast	NT
Rhombophryne botabota	Northeast	EN
R. coronata	Central east	LC
R. coudreaui	Central east and northeast	NT
R. diadema	North	NE
R. ellae	North	NE
R. guentherpetersi	Northwest	EN
R. laevipes	North and northwest	LC
R. longicrus	North	EN
R. mangabensis	Northeast	VU
R. matavy	North	CR
R. minuta	North	EN
R. nilevina	Central east	NE
R. ornata	Northeast	EN
R. proportionalis	North	NE
R. regalis	Northeast	NE
R. savaka	Northeast	EN
R. serratopalpebrosa	Northeast	EN
R. tany	Northeast	EN
R. testudo	Northwest and northeast	EN
R. vaventy	Northeast	EN
Stumpffia achillei	Northeast	NE

FAMILY (SUBFAMILY) GENUS (SUBGENUS) SPECIES	DISTRIBUTION	IUCN STATUS
S. analamaina	Northwest	CR
S. analanjirofo	Northeast coast and central east	NE
S. angeluci	North	NE
S. be	North	EN
S. betampona	Central east coast	NE
S. contumelia	Northeast	NE
S. davidattenboroughi	Central east coast	NE
S. diutissima	Northeast	NE
S. dolchi	Northeast	NE
S. edmondsi	Central east	NE
S. froschaueri	Northwest	NE
S. fusca	Northeast	NE
S. garraffoi	Central east	NE
S. gimmeli	Northwest	LC
S. grandis	Northeast	LC
S. hara	North	CR
S. huwei	Northwest	NE
S. iharana	Northeast	NE
S. jeannoeli	Central east coast	NE
S. kibomena	Central east	EN
S. larinki	North	NE
S. madagascariensis	North	EN
S. makira	Northeast	NE
S. maledicta	North	NE
S. mamitika	North and northeast	NE
S. megsoni	North	DD
S. meikeae	Sambirano Region	NE
S. miery	Southeast	EN
S. miovaova	Northeast	NE
S. nigrorubra	South central east	NE
S. obscoena	Central east	NE
S. pardus	Central to northeast	NE
S. psologlossa	Northwest	EN
S. pygmaea	Northwest	EN
S. roseifemoralis	Northeast	EN
S. sorata	Northeast	NE

(continued overleaf)

TABLE 11.1. ***continued***

FAMILY (SUBFAMILY) GENUS (SUBGENUS) SPECIES	DISTRIBUTION	IUCN STATUS
S. spandei	Central east	NE
S. staffordi	North	VU
S. tetradactyla	Northeast	DD
S. tridactyla	Northeast	DD
S. yanniki	Northwest	NE
MICROHYLIDAE (DYSCOPHINAE)		
Dyscophus antongilii	Northeast and central east	LC
D. guineti	Southeast, central east, and northeast	LC
D. insularis	Southwest, west, and northwest	LC
MICROHYLIDAE (SCAPHIOPHRYNINAE)		
Paradoxophyla palmata	Central east, east, and southeast	LC
P. tiarano	Northeast	DD
Scaphiophryne (Pseudohemisus) brevis	Southwest and south	LC
S. (P.) calcarata	Southwest and south)	LC[2]
S. (P.) obscura	West	NE[2]
Scaphiophryne (Scaphiophryne) boribory	Central east and north of Central Highlands	VU
S. (S.) gottlebei	South of Central Highlands	EN
S. (S.) madagascariensis	South of Central Highlands	NT
S. (S.) marmorata	Central east	VU
S. (S.) matsoko	Northeast	NT
S. (S.) menabensis	West	LC
S. (S.) spinosa	Northeast, central east, and southeast	LC
DICROGLOSSIDAE		
Hoplobatrachus tigerinus	Northwest, north, northeast, and east	LC (introduced)
BUFONIDAE		
Duttaphrynus melanostictus	East coast near Toamasina	LC (introduced)

Notes: All species are endemic to Madagascar, except for two introduced species (*Hoplobatrachus tigerinus* and *Duttaphrynus melanostictus*) and one native Malagasy species (*Ptychadena mascareniensis*) that was introduced to the Mascarenes and probably to the Seychelles. Candidate species that have already been characterized but not provided with formal scientific names are not listed. The IUCN status is after the IUCN Red List of Threatened Species (IUCN 2019); species described since 2017 have not yet been officially assessed for their Red List status. CR, Critically Endangered; DD, Data Deficient; EN, Endangered; LC, Least Concern; NE, Not Evaluated; NT, Near Threatened; VU, Vulnerable. Species names for some genera are given with subgenus name in parentheses.

[1] *Mantidactylus (Mantidactylus) guttulatus* and *M. (M.) grandidieri* have recently been revised and redefined by Rancilhac et al. (2020).

[2] *Scaphiophryne (Pseudohemisus) calcarata* and *S. (P.) obscura* have recently been revised and redefined by Scherz et al. (2021).

The steep and ongoing increase in the number of recognized anuran species is directly related to the large-scale intensification of biological exploration efforts by numerous researchers in remote areas of the island, and the integration of bioacoustic and molecular characters in species delimitation (Köhler et al. 2005). The remarkable amount of unnamed and cryptic diversity discovered via these techniques led Vieites et al. (2009) to employ the concept of confirmed and unconfirmed candidate species. This system of proposing provisionary unique references to undescribed deep genetic lineages enables reference to these organisms in ecological and evolutionary studies, and in conservation assessments. Paradoxically, we have on the one hand an enormous gap in taxonomic knowledge of Madagascar's batrachofauna, with many candidate species in need of taxonomic study (Perl et al. 2014), and on the other hand, a comparatively good knowledge of their phylogeny (Wollenberg et al. 2007, 2008b, 2011; Scherz et al. 2016b; Hutter et al. 2018b), biogeography (Brown et al. 2014, 2016), conservation status (Andreone et al. 2005c, 2008a, 2008b; Kremen et al. 2008), and larval morphology and ecology (Strauß et al. 2010, 2013, 2016; Grosjean et al. 2011a, 2011b; Randrianiaina et al. 2011a, 2011b, 2011c, 2012).

SYSTEMATICS AND AFFINITIES

Living amphibians are classified in three major groups: frogs and toads (order Anura, with about 7,370 known species), salamanders and newts (order Urodela, with about 765 species), and the wormlike caecilians (order Gymnophiona, with about 215 species) (AmphibiaWeb 2021). Of these three groups, only anurans are represented on Madagascar. Urodeles occur mainly north of the equator and are lacking in Africa south of the Sahara. Their absence on Madagascar is therefore not surprising. In contrast, gymnophiones occur mainly on southern landmasses and are distributed in Africa, India, and even on the granitic Seychelles (Duellman and Trueb 1986). Their absence on Madagascar is therefore unexpected. Anurans are widely distributed on most major landmasses of the world, being absent only in extremely cold regions (e.g., Greenland, Antarctica) and on most oceanic islands.

The origin of the extant Malagasy amphibian fauna is incompletely known. It seems likely that the current native amphibians of Madagascar all descend from ancestors that reached the island in the Late Cretaceous period or Early Cenozoic era, and at least some probably rafted to Madagascar over the sea (Crottini et al. 2012b; Feng et al. 2017; Yuan et al. 2019). However, virtually no fossils have been discovered that would help us understand their evolutionary history (Asher and Krause 1998), and the available Mesozoic amphibian fossils from the island probably bear no direct relationships to the extant taxa. For instance, the early (Triassic) history of frogs has been based largely on one famous fossil from northern Madagascar representing a clade considered to be ancestors of living frogs. This unique species, *Triadobatrachus massinoti*, is about 250 million years old, and although frog-like, it still has a short tail (Rage and Rocek 1989). A further extraordinary extinct frog from Madagascar is the giant frog *Beelzebufo ampinga* from the Late Cretaceous (Evans et al. 2008, 2014). This large, hyperossified frog apparently bears no relationships to living Malagasy anurans. It has been hypothesized that it belongs to the South American family Ceratophryidae (Evans et al. 2008), but this hypothesis has been disputed (Ruane et al. 2011), and a relationship with ancient australobatrachian frogs, today represented for instance by *Calyptocephalella* from southern South America, has been suggested (Agnolin 2012). In this context it is also relevant that calyptocephalellid fossils have recently been recovered from Antarctica (Mörs et al. 2020).

Madagascar's native extant amphibians belong to five major clades, each of which represents an independent colonization event (Vences et al. 2003d; Crottini et al. 2012b; Samonds et al. 2012, 2013; see Samonds et al., pp. 73–78): 1) The largest of these clades is the family Mantellidae, with currently about 230 species on Madagascar and three species on Mayotte in the Comoro archipelago (Vences et al. 2003d; Glaw et al. 2019; Vieites et al. 2020). Mantellids are morphologically and ecologically highly diverse, with arboreal, scansorial, riparian, and aquatic species ranging in body length from 11 to 120 mm. They are the sister group of the Asian tree frogs of the family Rhacophoridae. 2) Microhylid frogs (a highly diverse and old family of pantropical distribution) are represented by three subfamilies endemic to Madagascar; two of these, the Cophylinae and Scaphiophryninae, form a species-rich and morphologically diverse clade. According to comprehensive molecular phylogenies, this clade includes at least 113 species, but their sister group remains unclear (e.g., Van der Meijden et al. 2007; Kurabayashi et al. 2011; Peloso et al. 2016; Scherz et al. 2016b, 2017b; Feng et al. 2017; Streicher et al. 2020). 3) The Dyscophinae, another subfamily of Malagasy microhylids, contains a single genus with three species and appears to be related to Asian microhylids (Van Bocxlaer et al. 2006; Van der Meijden et al. 2007; Kurabayashi et al. 2011; de Sá et al. 2012; Peloso et al. 2016; Streicher et al. 2020). 4) The genus *Heterixalus*, endemic to Madagascar, contains 11 species and is deeply nested in the family Hyperoliidae, a diverse group occurring mainly in sub-Saharan Africa. This family also includes one genus and species occurring in the Seychelles archipelago (*Tachycnemis*) that is the sister group of *Heterixalus* (Vences et al. 2003a, 2003d; Frost et al. 2006; Wollenberg et al. 2007). 5) The otherwise African genus *Ptychadena* (family Ptychadenidae) contains one species on Madagascar that, according to current molecular data, is endemic to the Malagasy Region and contains various deep mitochondrial lineages (Vences et al. 2004b; Measey et al. 2007; Zimkus et al. 2017). In addition, two introduced species of anurans occur on Madagascar: a frog, *Hoplobatrachus tigerinus*, probably from India (Kosuch et al. 2001; see Vences et al., pp. 1402–3), and a toad, *Duttaphrynus melanostictus*, from Southeast Asia (Moore et al. 2015; Vences et al. 2017a; see Freeman et al., pp. 1404–10).

ECOLOGY AND BEHAVIOR

Nutrition

All amphibians are largely carnivorous as adults, although occasionally other food types are ingested. They either use their tongue to catch prey or subdue larger items with their jaws. Many frogs appear to be quite generalized feeders, whereas others are highly specialized. Generalized feeders, which prey on moderately sized arthropods, are apparently common in the genera *Mantidactylus* and *Boophis* (Vences et al. 1999b). Only a few large frogs are known to feed on rather big prey. The stomach of a *Plethodontohyla inguinalis* specimen contained two scorpions, fragments of leaves (almost certainly from the forest floor), beetles, and a stick insect (Lourenço et al. 1997). Myriapods, sometimes of considerable size, are commonly found in the gut contents of cophyline microhylids (e.g., *Rhombophryne vaventy*, see Scherz et al. 2014; *P. laevis*, see Bellati et al. 2018). The gut contents of a *B. goudotii* specimen consisted of three *B. idae* adults, the remains of a large grasshopper, and a eucalyptus fruit (Glaw and Vences 1997a), and the gut of a *M. femoralis* specimen contained a chameleon hatchling (Vences et al. 1999b). A *Rhombophryne ornata* individual had also eaten a smaller frog (Scherz et al. 2015b). A large *M. radaka* individual was found preying on a crab (Raselimanana 2018; species identity following Rancilhac et al. 2020). Feeding on ants seems to be widespread in cophyline and scaphiophrynine microhylids (Blommers-Schlösser 1975b). Ants or other small arthropods are the main prey of the genus *Mantella* (Woodhead et al. 2007; Moskowitz et al. 2018).

The trophic niche of tadpoles is very different from that of their metamorphosed adult form and varies from endotrophic (nonfeeding) to exotrophic (feeding) larvae. Most exotrophic tadpoles do not actively search for living prey but are rather omnivorous suspension feeders (Altig et al. 2007). They consume small particles, including plant material, and typically use a horny beak and labial teeth to rasp this material from surfaces underwater. The mantellids, however, include lineages with unusual and unique feeding ecology, in particular in the genera *Gephyromantis* and *Mantidactylus*.

Predation and Antipredator Strategies

Predation is an important factor in ecology, and frogs are regularly fed on by a considerable variety of predators, both diurnal (e.g., birds, snakes, spiders, lizards) and nocturnal (e.g., birds, snakes, invertebrates, mammals; Figure 11.2). An important strategy to prevent predation by diurnal predators is cryptic coloration to blend in with the surroundings. For this purpose, the coloration of most diurnal frogs resembles that of their habitat, with the notable exception of *Mantella* species, which show a bright aposematic warning coloration (Vences et al. 1998a) and contain toxins in their skin (Daly et al. 1996).

Tree frogs are most often brown or green. Although little is known about the "day shelters" of nocturnal frogs, we assume that the green species rest on green leaves, whereas the brown species may prefer a woody background. It is therefore not surprising that brown species like *Boophis reticulatus* or *B. burgeri* have reticulations on the back similar to tree bark. Sometimes, unusual spots occur on the back of certain species, and only a closer look reveals that these spots may function as lichen imitations; an extreme example is *B. lichenoides* (Figure 11.3). When this frog sits on a branch covered with lichens, it becomes very difficult to spot. To support the concealing effect of this coloration, this frog can bend its body and flatten itself against the substrate (Vallan et al. 1998).

The structure of the dorsal skin is also quite bizarre in several arboreal *Spinomantis* species. *Spinomantis aglavei* has strange fringes on the lateral parts of the body. The function of these structures is almost certainly associated with camouflage, as this species spends the day appressed against the bark of a tree. In the closely related but shiny green *S. phantasticus*, the whole back is covered with soft dermal spines. These frogs live in moist evergreen mossy forests and become nearly invisible when sitting on a branch with moss or lichen. A similar, although less expressed skin structure with short dermal spines is found in the microhylid *Scaphiophryne spinosa*. Dermal spines above the eyelids occur in several *Gephyromantis* species (e.g., *G. cornutus*) and some terrestrial cophylines (e.g., *Rhombophryne serratopalpebrosa* and related species), whereas tree frogs of the *B. madagascariensis* group have a distinct spine-shaped skin flap on the heel and elbow. These structures may also be involved with camouflage, but their function is not obvious. Several semiarboreal (e.g., *Plethodontohyla notosticta*, *P. guentheri*, *P. mihanika*) and leaf-litter frogs (e.g., species of the genus *Mantidactylus* subgenus *Chonomantis*, some *Mantella* species) possess a distinct lateral coloration that differs from the dorsal coloration and is likely associated with camouflage. Similarly, many *Gephyromantis* species show dorsal ridges and spines or a very granular skin (e.g., species of the subgenus *Laurentomantis*), which helps camouflage them. Some terrestrial frogs, such as *P. ocellata*, have dark inguinal marks, which can be interpreted as "eyespots" (see Duellman and Trueb 1986: 254), with the suggestion that the broad pelvic region with elevated "eyes" gives the impression of a much larger organism. The very colorful eyes of many *Boophis* species (Figure 11.1) possibly also act as an antipredator mechanism: the

FIGURE 11.2 ***Ptychadena mascareniensis*, one of the most common frogs on Madagascar, being preyed on by the snake *Thamnosophis lateralis*. Snakes are among the most important predators of Malagasy frogs.** (PHOTO by P.-S. Gehring.)

FIGURE 11.3 **Both the color pattern and the dermal flaps on limbs and mouth provide a very efficient lichen-like crypsis in *Boophis lichenoides* (individual photographed at Betampona).**
(PHOTO by G. M. Rosa.)

conspicuous color is hidden in animals resting during the day but becomes suddenly visible when the frog is disturbed and opens its eyes (Glaw and Vences 1997b; Amat et al. 2013). Finally, several species have striking colors like bright or very dark red, orange, or purple on hidden surfaces of their limbs that can be exposed when the frog is threatened (e.g., several *Mantella* and *Boophis* species, *Platypelis ranjomena*, *P. barbouri*, and *Rhombophryne ellae*), presumably likewise serving an antipredator function.

When caught, some frogs emit very loud vocalizations, so-called distress calls (Hödl and Gollmann 1986). These calls, which are known from several *Mantidactylus* and a few *Plethodontohyla* and *Boophis* species, have a very characteristic acoustic structure (Vences et al. 2006). They can be emitted by males, females, and even juveniles. Distress calling may briefly frighten a predator, or it may attract further enemies that compete with or threaten the original predator—in either case giving the frog a chance to escape.

Activity Patterns

Most Malagasy frogs call during several months of the rainy season, which coincides with the reproduction of most species. Only a few Malagasy frog species in the genera *Scaphiophryne*, *Paradoxophyla*, *Aglyptodactylus*, some species of the *Boophis albilabris* group, and the *Boophis* subgenus *Sahona* seem to be explosive breeders, laying their eggs only after the first heavy rains, while only a single known species (*B. burgeri*) apparently does not call or reproduce during the rainy season. Although little is known about amphibian activity in the dry season (Blommers-Schlösser 1979b; Andreone 1994; Andreone et al. 2000), several species in lowland moist evergreen forests (e.g., *Heterixalus madagascariensis*, *B. madagascariensis*, *B. luteus*, *B. tephraeomystax*, *Dyscophus antongilii*) seem to call and reproduce more or less the whole year (Segev et al. 2012), and some species such as *B. viridis* appear to have a peak of reproductive activity in the months before the start of the wet season (Heinermann et al. 2015).

An amphibian survey conducted over nine years in the Betampona protected area revealed that several species are active across the entire year, whereas other species are preferentially active during the dry or wet season (Dubos et al. 2020). This study also revealed that beta diversity and abundance patterns were more variable between years than within years, with temporal variation in beta diversity best explained by temperature, and species abundance best explained by temperature, monthly humidity, and monthly rainfall.

Most moist evergreen forest species are partly diurnal and terrestrial (e.g., *Stumpffia*, *Mantella*, *Mantidactylus* subgenera *Chonomantis*, *Hylobatrachus*, *Brygoomantis*), or alternatively, arboreal and nocturnal (e.g., *Platypelis*, *Cophyla*, *Anodonthyla*, most *Boophis* species, *Guibemantis*, *Spinomantis*). Some *Gephyromantis* species, such as *G. granulatus* and *G. boulengeri*, call from near the ground during the day and from higher positions after sunset. Some semi-fossorial species are apparently neither strictly diurnal nor nocturnal. *Plethodontohyla* and especially *Rhombophryne* species call during both day and night, but almost exclusively during or after heavy rain. Some terrestrial species have a high degree of nocturnal activity (e.g., *Gephyromantis*, *Mantidactylus* subgenera *Mantidactylus*, *Ochthomantis*), and very few are both diurnal and arboreal; these often live in habitats that provide protection from predation by birds, for example many *Guibemantis* species in leaf axils of *Pandanus* plants. The greenish *M. argenteus* is strictly arboreal and diurnal. Males call along streams from mossy branches and leaves between 0.5 and 3 m above the ground and are apparently not protected by the way they position themselves or by poisonous skin. However, in this and several other diurnal-calling frogs, the vocal sacs are not strongly inflated during emission of the call and are inconspicuously colored.

In general, anurans of arid western Madagascar show a different activity pattern. Because of the dry climate, terrestrial and diurnal frogs or those that are nocturnal and arboreal are rare. After heavy rain at the beginning of the wet season, most western frog species aggregate around water bodies for explosive breeding at night and often call from positions on the ground or directly from the water. However, this nocturnal terrestrial activity is restricted to a rather short period, and density of individual frogs is high.

On several of the highest mountains of the island, the upper limit of the forest falls between about 1900 and 2000 m; above this zone the natural vegetation is a low montane ericoid thicket, and the nights can be very cold. This may force most amphibian species to become largely diurnal. The high mountain species of the normally arboreal genera *Boophis*, such as *B. microtympanum*, *B. williamsi*, and *B. laurenti*, and *Anodonthyla*, such as *A. montana*, are partially diurnal and terrestrial in these habitats.

Calls

Frogs communicate largely acoustically. Their calls are the main component of the nocturnal background noise of Malagasy moist evergreen forests. By far the most common category of anuran vocalizations is the advertisement call of males, used to attract females for mating and to indicate the delimitation of a territory to conspecific males. Usually, call emission is aided by conspicuous vocal sacs, present only in males, which can take various shapes and colors and probably often also function as visual signals (Figure 11.4). To avoid mis-matings between closely related species with similar habits and reproductive modes, these animals need to have distinct differences in their advertisement calls when occurring in sympatry. In contrast, geographically separated species may have similar calls. As a systematic character, reproduction calls are an excellent taxonomic attribute: two frogs strongly differing in their advertisement call (and excluding other factors) almost certainly belong to different species; on the other hand, two species with very similar calls may or may not belong to the same species (Köhler et al. 2017).

Advertisement calls are also influenced by other factors. For instance, smaller frogs call at higher spectral frequencies, and this relation is also obvious in Malagasy species (Köhler et al. 2017). Also, temperature might affect the temporal parameters of frog calls (not their structure) to a certain extent, with the general rule that the repetition rates of calls and notes are lower at lower temperatures.

Reproductive Diversity

The diversity of Malagasy frogs is also reflected by the large variety of reproductive modes. This is especially evident in the subfamily Mantellinae (family Mantellidae). As far as is known, all mantellines lay their relatively large eggs outside of water, sometimes just above the water surface, and usually in smaller clutches than other mantellids (Vences et al. 1999c). This life history trait seems to have been an important step for the evolution of the great diversity of reproductive modes found in this subfamily, which include egg deposition near the water on the ground or close to the ground, for example in most *Mantella* and *Mantidactylus*, and some *Blommersia* species; on rocks (*Mantella expectata*, some species of *Mantidactylus* subgenus *Ochthomantis*, and some species of *Gephyromantis* subgenus *Phylacomantis*); on leaves above stagnant or slowly running water (many *Guibemantis*, *Blommersia*, *Spinomantis*, some *Mantidactylus* species; Figure 11.5); in phytotelms (many *Guibemantis* species); in fallen palm leaves (*B. angolafa*); or in tree holes (*Mantella laevigata*). In some manteline species (e.g., *Mantidactylus argenteus* and some species of *Mantidactylus* subgenus *Ochthomantis*), the male or female guards the eggs after deposition, and *Mantella laevigata* shows a complex nursing behavior (Fischer et al. 2019).

Species of the subfamilies Boophinae and Laliostominae deposit their eggs directly in the water; foam nests, common in Asian rhacophorids, have not been found in the otherwise very similar Malagasy genus *Boophis*. The high diversity of reproductive modes among mantellids is paralleled only by their amazing larval diversity, including generalized, suctorial, funnel-mouthed, carnivorous, and nonfeeding tadpoles, as well as several other specialized larval morphologies whose function is not completely understood (Altig and McDiarmid 2006; Grosjean et al. 2011a; Randrianiaina et al. 2011b, 2011c, 2012; Reeve et al. 2011). In fact, Wollenberg Valero et al. (2017) found evidence for the evolution of tadpole

FIGURE 11.4 **Calling males of two species of Malagasy frogs. A) *Boophis luteus* from Isalo emitting its characteristic advertisement call; the inflated vocal sac has a bilobate subgular morphology. B) *Gephyromantis tandroka* from Marojejy, with a blackish paired subgular vocal sac at its maximum inflation.** (PHOTOS by M. Vences.)

FIGURE 11.5 **Pair of *Guibemantis tornieri* displaying the typical mating behavior of mantellid frogs in the subfamily Mantellinae. Instead of amplexus (the male clasping the female), here the male (on top) touches the female with the underside of his thigh, probably releasing pheromones from his femoral glands, while the female lays the greenish-brown eggs on a leaf overhanging a pond. Tadpoles will later drop into water, where they will complete their development.**
(PHOTO by J. Köhler.)

ecomorphology being decoupled from that of adult morphology in mantellids, and likely being influential in driving the adaptive radiation of these frogs.

Microhylids also have a substantial diversity of reproductive modes. *Dyscophus* and *Paradoxophyla* deposit small eggs on the surface of stagnant water bodies. The tadpoles are typical microhylid filter feeders, whereas the tadpoles of *Scaphiophryne*, which also lay small eggs on the water surface, are intermediate between the microhylid and the ranoid type (Blommers-Schlösser 1975b; Grosjean et al. 2007). Among cophylines, the arboreal species (*Anodonthyla*, *Cophyla*, *Platypelis*, and a few *Plethodontohyla*) deposit large unpigmented eggs in water-filled tree holes, or phytotelms, where they hatch into nonfeeding tadpoles that live exclusively from the yolk provided by the egg and develop into small froglets. Sometimes the eggs are not singletons but are connected to form an egg string (e.g., in *P. mihanika*). This may explain the observation of C. Blanc, who found a frog on the Tsaratanàna Massif carrying eggs on its hind legs (Blommers-Schlösser and Blanc 1993). Unfortunately, this Tsaratanàna specimen was lost. It is quite curious that Boettger (1913) also described a frog from Madagascar with eggs on the limbs, the specimen of which also cannot be located in a museum collection. The terrestrial cophylines reproduce in water-filled holes in rocks (*Anodonthyla montana*), in water-filled cavities such as snail shells (some *Stumpffia* species), with liquefied jelly in cavities (probably many *Plethodontohyla* and *Rhombophryne* species), with jelly in leaf litter (*S. davidattenboroughi*), or in foam nests (in at least one clade of *Stumpffia*) that serve for development of eggs and nonfeeding tadpoles.

A summary of the reproductive modes of Malagasy anurans is given below (numbering follows Haddad and Prado 2005, modified after Duellman and Trueb 1986; see also Crump 2015; missing numbers refer to modes that are not known to occur in Malagasy frogs). Note that the list of species in the following is incomplete; only taxa with known mode are listed.

Aquatic eggs

- Eggs deposited in water

Mode 1. Eggs and feeding (exotrophic) tadpoles in lentic water (*Ptychadena, Heterixalus, Hoplobatrachus, Laliostoma, Dyscophus, Scaphiophryne, Paradoxophyla, Aglyptodactylus*, and subgenus *Sahona* in *Boophis*).

2. Eggs and feeding (exotrophic) tadpoles in lotic water (other species of *Boophis*).

8. Eggs and nonfeeding (endotrophic) tadpoles in water in tree holes or aerial plants (*Anodonthyla, Cophyla, Platypelis*, several *Plethodontohyla* species including *P. notosticta, P. inguinalis*, and *P. mihanika*), or in cavities such as snail shells (some *Stumpffia*).

Eggs terrestrial or arboreal (not in water)

- Eggs on ground, on rocks, or in burrows

17. Eggs and early tadpoles in excavated nest; subsequent to flooding (e.g., after heavy rains), feeding (exotrophic) tadpoles live in ponds or streams (*Mantella* except *M. laevigata* and *M. expectata*, *Mantidactylus* subgenera *Brygoomantis, Chonomantis, Ochthomantis*, and perhaps *Hylobatrachus* and *Mantidactylus*).

21. Eggs hatch into nonfeeding tadpoles that complete their development in the nest (*Plethodontohyla tuberata*, probably *Rhombophryne testudo*, and *Gephyromantis* subgenera *Gephyromantis, Duboimantis*, and probably *Laurentomantis*; note that in *Duboimantis* and *Laurentomantis*, exceptionally or regularly, the endotrophic tadpoles complete development in small streams, which may represent a novel reproductive mode).

- Eggs arboreal

24. Eggs hatch into feeding (exotrophic) tadpoles that drop into lentic water (i.e., ponds) and complete their development there (many *Blommersia*, some *Spinomantis* and *Guibemantis* species). A modification of this mode is the reproductive mode of *B. angolafa*, whose tadpoles fall into fallen water-filled curved palm leaves on the ground, a habitat that cannot really be considered phytotelmic.

25. Eggs hatch into feeding (exotrophic) tadpoles that drop into lotic water (i.e., streams) and complete their development there (many *Spinomantis*, some *Ochthomantis* species, *Mantidactylus argenteus, Blommersia* sp. [currently considered *B. grandisonae*]).

26. Eggs hatch into feeding (exotrophic) tadpoles that develop in water-filled cavities in trees (in tree holes: *Mantella laevigata*; in phytotelmic leaf axils: *Guibemantis* subgenus *Pandanusicola*).

- Eggs in foam nest

32. Nest in burrows; nonfeeding tadpoles (endotrophic) complete development in nest (*Stumpffia pygmaea, S. maledicta*).

THREATS, CONSERVATION, AND FUTURE RESEARCH

Madagascar's amphibians are threatened by a variety of factors, above all by destruction of original habitat (e.g., deforestation). Habitat fragmentation, diseases, environmental pollution, invasive species, international trade, and bushmeat consumption represent additional threats. Occasional exploitation of amphibians includes the use of common species (e.g., *Ptychadena mascareniensis*) to feed pigs or ducks as additional protein. Further, local people of the Central Highlands prepare a soup with skinned *Boophis goudotii* to treat nutritional rickets in children.

For several species evaluated as Critically Endangered in the context of the IUCN Red list (IUCN 2019), a number of detailed studies on distribution, habitat, habits, and life history have been carried out. However, for a large proportion of Madagascar's amphibians, almost nothing is known about these aspects, and their conservation status assessment relies almost entirely on their poorly known distribution (extent of occurrence), their tolerance of habitat degradation, and the disappearance of natural habitat within their range. Furthermore, we are already aware that many species as currently defined are complexes of closely related but genetically and ecologically distinct species, but this is usually not considered in their conservation assessment (Scherz et al. 2019a). Despite the enormous efforts invested in species survey work in remote areas of Madagascar, many of the records obtained for amphibians remain in need of confirmation because diagnosing closely related species of Malagasy frogs based only on morphology is seldom easy and is sometimes impossible.

How can the scientific basis for conservation assessments, and for an overall understanding of the biology of Madagascar's amphibians, be improved? Continued survey work is important, and it is imperative that voucher specimens continue to be collected during field inventories. To make identifications verifiable, these specimens should be integrated into scientific collections, and their museum catalog numbers listed in associated reports or publications. The optimal voucher for taxonomic study of frogs is a male with associated recorded vocalizations and a color photograph of the live individual to document its coloration. In addition, taking separate tissue samples of all species and specimens and making these available for molecular study (DNA barcoding) will allow a greater and more reliable understanding of how species and intraspecific genetic lineages are distributed geographically.

We furthermore encourage descriptive groundwork on the biology, behavior, ecology, and physiology of Madagascar's amphibians. Such data can be gathered without sophisticated technical equipment or complex statistical analysis and will provide valuable and sound scientific contributions. To give only a few examples, observing the mating behavior, daily and yearly activity patterns, mate choice, field body temperature, morphological and chromatic variation, or microhabitat choice all require only simple experiments or field observations and will lead to substantially improved understanding of the astonishing diversity of Madagascar's amphibians.

Subject editors: Miguel Vences and Achille P. Raselimanana

SPECIES INVENTORIES, BIOGEOGRAPHY, PHYLOGEOGRAPHY, AND SPECIES FORMATION OF AMPHIBIANS ON MADAGASCAR

M. Vences, F. Andreone, J. L. Brown, A. Crottini, N. D'Cruze, C. J. Gardner,
A. P. Raselimanana, C. J. Raxworthy, D. R. Vieites, and K. C. Wollenberg Valero

As elaborated in the previous contribution, Madagascar is famous for its hyperdiverse and unique assemblage of frog species (Glaw and Vences 2007) and is currently home to more than 365 named amphibian species (AmphibiaWeb 2021; Table 11.1), rivaled by only a few other amphibian diversity hotspots in the Neotropics (Pyron and Wiens 2011). The first comprehensive foray into the biogeography of Madagascar's amphibian fauna was made by Blommers-Schlösser and Blanc (1993). Since this pioneering work, scientists have dramatically expanded the exploration and sampling of Malagasy amphibians, which has led to a steady increase in the number of described species and a better understanding of their distributions. These field-based efforts resulted in the publication of several broadly disseminated field guides and considerably increased the number of available museum specimens. The data assembled from these field campaigns were used in conjunction with scientific advances in evolutionary genetics, geospatial modeling methods, and DNA sequencing (e.g., the first reference database for DNA barcoding) (Vieites et al. 2009; Perl et al. 2014), which have substantially improved our understanding of the island's amphibian diversification patterns and the processes driving these radiations.

In the past few decades, the large-scale biogeographic patterns of Madagascar's amphibians have become apparent, and scientists have begun understanding the fine-scale processes that led to their astonishing diversity. Native Malagasy frogs belong to five endemic radiations, the Mantellidae (the largest portion of species, which have very diverse morphologies and ecological specializations), the Microhylidae (present on the island with two independent lineages, the Cophylinae + Scaphiophryninae and the Dyscophinae), the Hyperoliidae (only one genus—*Heterixalus*—with 11 species; Glaw and Vences 2007), and *Ptychadena mascareniensis*, a species that is closely related to African frogs and can be found in rice fields and other secondary habitats (Zimkus et al. 2017).

SPECIES INVENTORIES AND BIOGEOGRAPHY

The past three decades have seen enormous efforts to improve our understanding of the geographic occurrence of Madagascar's herpetofauna via intensive inventories of these animals, particularly in protected areas (Raxworthy and Nussbaum 1994, 1996a; Raxworthy et al. 1994, 1998; Raselimanana 1998; Nussbaum et al. 1999; Raselimanana et al. 2000; Andreone et. al. 2003b; D'Cruze et al. 2009; Rosa et al. 2012; Brown et al. 2016; Goodman et al. 2018). In addition to the routine application of the techniques used to survey herpetological diversity (e.g., direct observations, refuge searching, and pitfall traps), amphibian inventories have also benefited from the application of bioacoustic survey methods (Vences et al. 2008; Köhler et al. 2017). Although the presence of a large number of morphologically cryptic frog species on Madagascar prevents an uncritical use of inventory lists in biogeographic assessments, it is evident from the records of easily diagnosable species that many of Madagascar's frog species are distinctly microendemic—that is, they have very restricted geographic distributions. Whether this prevalent pattern of microendemism is a characteristic feature of Madagascar or also characterizes other tropical amphibian faunas remains poorly studied (Vences et al. 2009).

Several biogeographic patterns are apparent in Madagascar's amphibians. As could be expected in a group of organisms that depend heavily on moisture, the species richness of the island's amphibians peaks in the moist evergreen forests, with only a few species occurring in the drier western and southwestern biomes (Andreone et al. 2005a). However, within the moist evergreen forests, endemism and richness are unevenly distributed. Several species-rich genera such as *Gephyromantis*, *Rhombophryne*, and *Stumpffia* have their centers of diversity and endemism in northern Madagascar, in an area roughly delimited to the south by a diagonal spanning from 15.5°S on the east coast to about 15.0°S on the west coast (Wollenberg et al. 2008b; Kaffenberger et al. 2012; Brown et al. 2016; Rakotoarison et al. 2017a). Other groups, most of which have fewer species, are instead centered in southeastern Madagascar, such as *Anodonthyla* and *Mini*. The massifs of northern and southeastern Madagascar also harbor several unique deep phylogenetic lineages, such as the monospecific *Boehmantis* and *Madecassophryne* (southeast) and *Tsingymantis* (north). This concentration of locally and regionally endemic taxa in southeastern and northern Madagascar also leads to a concentration of threatened species in these areas (Andreone et al. 2005a).

A curious biogeographic pattern called the "mid-domain effect" was first detected on Madagascar by Lees (1996) for butterflies and frogs and was later found in many other Malagasy animals by Colwell and Lees (2000) and Lees and Colwell (2007). They observed a concentration of species richness in the center of Madagascar, in particular around the village of Andasibe, named the "Périnet" effect (Andasibe is a synonym of Périnet, which at least historically was the best biologically studied site on the island). This pattern may be observed when species ranges are randomly organized within a defined area: the center of the area will, just by chance, receive a high number of overlapping species ranges and thus have higher biodiversity. In Malagasy amphibians, such a pattern can be observed in tree frogs of the genus *Boophis*, and it is also apparent but less clear in other mantellid frogs (Brown et al. 2016).

Elevationally, diversity of Madagascar's amphibians peaks around 800–1000 m (Raxworthy and Nussbaum 1994, 1996a; Raxworthy et al. 1998; Nussbaum et al. 1999; Raselimanana et al. 2000; Brown et al. 2016), with the richest communities in medium-altitude moist evergreen forests (representing the mid-elevation species richness bulge that has been frequently reported in the tropics). However, recent inventories of small and isolated lowland moist evergreen forest fragments are also revealing remarkably high species richness at some sites such as Betampona (Rosa et al. 2012).

Species turnover of Malagasy amphibians, which describes the pattern of how communities change across the landscape, largely reflects the differences among major biomes (Brown et al. 2014, 2016), with a clear distinction between western versus eastern/highland areas (Ferrier et al. 2007), and differences between major massifs (Raxworthy and Nussbaum 1996b). Furthermore, several small areas harboring distinct frog communities occur in northern Madagascar, highlighting the importance of this region as a cradle of species diversification driven by rugged elevational gradients (Raxworthy and Nussbaum 1995, 1996c; Rabibisoa et al. 2008; Wollenberg et al. 2008b).

PHYLOGEOGRAPHY

Globally, amphibians are generally considered poor dispersers, and consequently, they usually have a strong phylogeographic structure—that is, spatially separated populations are genetically sharply differentiated (Vences and Wake 2007; Zeisset and Beebee 2007). Several Malagasy frog species, in particular those of high conservation concern, have been the subject of phylogeographic studies and match this pattern (Chiari et al. 2005, 2006; Vieites et al. 2006; Rabemananjara et al. 2007a, 2007b; Crottini et al. 2008, 2012a, 2019; Orozco-terWengel et al. 2013; Pabijan et al. 2015; Klonoski et al. 2019). In general, forest-dwelling species such as *Mantella bernhardi* have highly divergent populations, even in forest fragments that are only a few kilometers apart (Vieites et al. 2006). Also, some species living in open, nonforested landscapes without apparent barriers to gene flow such as *Heterixalus betsileo* have a pronounced phylogeographic structure (Gehring et al. 2012)—perhaps the populations of these species were separated by forests acting as barriers before the arrival of humans and human-caused deforestation on the island (also see Lehmann et al., pp. 152–68). Conspecific populations of frogs occurring on nearby massifs such as Marojejy and Sorata often differ genetically, but the degree of genetic divergence differs among species, suggesting variation in their phylogeographic histories (Scherz et al. 2018a).

The phylogeographic histories for other species appear to be more complicated and less uniform among taxa. Several widespread species that occur in the drier biomes, such as *Laliostoma labrosum*, also show genetic differentiation, but different genetic (mitochondrial) clusters can occur in the same location, which suggests repeated events of population separation and confluence (Pabijan et al. 2015). Other Malagasy taxa show unexpected genetic uniformity, even across broad geographic distances in moist evergreen forest. Perhaps most striking is the situation in the poison frogs of the *Mantella cowanii* group, where populations that according to current classification belong to two distinct species (*M. baroni* and *M. nigricans*), spanning more than 1000 km over most of eastern Madagascar, share identical DNA sequences in the mitochondrial cytochrome b gene.

This observation may alternatively mean that mitochondrial DNA sequences alone do not provide enough evidence to determine the unique genetic structure of all of Madagascar's frog species. For species studied in detail, evidence for historic hybridization and mitochondrial introgression (the exchange of mitochondrial DNA between closely related species), as well as inconsistency between mitochondrial phylogeographic patterns and morphological characters, has frequently been encountered (Orozco-terWengel et al. 2013; Crottini et al. 2019; Klonoski et al. 2019). For instance, in one population of *M. aurantiaca*, some individuals—clearly diagnosable as *M. aurantiaca* by morphology and microsatellites—bear a mitochondrial genome of *M. crocea*, which is probably a relic of a past introgression event between ancestors of these species (Crottini et al. 2019). The tomato frogs *Dyscophus antongilii* and *D. guineti* present another complicated case (Orozco-terWengel et al. 2013). These morphologically similar species can typically be identified by high-resolution nuclear genetic markers (microsatellites). However, geographically close populations at the margins of both species' distributions possess indistinguishable mitochondrial DNA, suggesting the historic or recent exchange of mitochondrial DNA through hybridization and subsequent introgression of mtDNA. However, the southernmost population of *D. guineti* has a highly different mitochondrial genome, suggesting that introgression with *D. antongilii* has affected only the northern populations of this species. These examples indicate the need to increase genome-level sequence data to better understand past and ongoing differentiation in many of Madagascar's amphibian species. Such future studies should focus on zones of contact of genetically different lineages (i.e., the deep conspecific lineages as defined in Vieites et al. 2009) and known areas of hybridization, potentially leading to another surge in species discovery and descriptions from the island.

SPECIES FORMATION

Malagasy amphibians have served as a model group for a series of studies relevant to understanding general mechanisms of diversification and formation of new species. As mentioned above, analysis of their spatial distribution patterns, for instance in cophyline frogs, has revealed that species richness is associated with the rugged landscape of mountainous regions, which means that such landscape features could have promoted species formation (Wollenberg et al. 2008b). Often, several related species occurring on the same massif are segregated into elevational bands, for instance the three species of *Cophyla* occurring on Montagne d'Ambre (Rakotoarison et al. 2015a). This observation is in line with the results of a study across continents, including many species from Madagascar, where the authors found that frog species specialized in forest habitat and/or from topographically complex regions show higher phylogeographic structure (Rodríguez et al. 2015)

Phylogeographic structure is generally high in amphibians (Vences and Wake 2007; Zeisset and Beebee 2008), suggesting that allopatric processes (the formation of species in geographic isolation) are the dominant factors in amphibian speciation. This is supported by distribution patterns of sister species. For instance, sister species of mantellids largely do not overlap in their geographic ranges (Wollenberg et al. 2011). However, in this general trend, it is also observed that younger sister species pairs of mantellids have more proximate distribution areas, suggesting that the event leading to their separation occurred in spatial proximity, while older species' distribution ranges might have moved farther apart. The analysis of distribution patterns in mantellids also suggests that range sizes increase with evolutionary age, as do range size differences between sister species, which makes it unlikely that peripatric speciation (species formation through isolation of peripheral populations that "bud" into new species) plays a major role in this group. Because of this large body of evidence for allopatric speciation, the possibility of sympatric speciation (speciation without clear geographic isolation) has, in general, been little considered in amphibians but merits future attention in specific cases.

Several recently divergent sister species of frogs on Madagascar occur in full sympatry (with identical distribution areas) and even in syntopy (in the same patch of habitat). These sister species pairs typically have very different advertisement calls, for example *Boophis majori / B. narinsi*, and *Gephyromantis eiselti / G. thelenae* (Wollenberg et al. 2011; Vences et al. 2012). Call playback studies on *G. thelenae* males with conspecific calls demonstrate that male frogs emit a special "aggressive call" combined with approach behavior toward the speaker; however, they do not react similarly to calls of *G. eiselti*, confirming that the two species are reproductively isolated (Wollenberg and Harvey 2010).

As previously mentioned, local adaptation across montane habitats remains a major potential mechanism for facilitating sympatric or parapatric speciation. Allopatric divergence in montane refugia across massifs has certainly played a significant role in generating the current amphibian diversity of Madagascar (Raxworthy and Nussbaum 1996b; Rabibisoa et al. 2008; Raxworthy et al. 2008). In addition, there is growing evidence for differentiation occurring on a given massif across elevation gradients. For example, species of *Stumpffia* occurring across a wide elevational range at Marojejy show genetic differences between high and low elevations (Rakotoarison et al. 2019b). One potential mechanism for speciation is divergent selection separating populations into different environments or ecological niches, which may lead to species divergence even in sympatry, yet knowledge about ecological niches at both larval and adult life stages is limited for Malagasy frogs.

Examination of fine-scale phylogeographic structure has also suggested that rivers, even small ones, can act as barriers to gene flow for Malagasy frogs (Gehring et al. 2012; Wollenberg Valero 2015). It remains uncertain whether rivers represent the *primary* barriers that initially disrupted gene flow, or whether they act as *secondary* barriers where lineages that diverged allopatrically in more distant refugia meet upon range extension. Speciation can also be influenced by intrinsic species-specific factors. One trait that merits particular attention and has been intensively studied on Madagascar is body size. The smaller a frog is, the lower its dispersal potential. Smaller frogs are also at higher desiccation risk, which further confounds dispersal capacity. Therefore, it is not surprising that body size is negatively correlated with distribution range size, as shown by Wollenberg et al. (2011) across mantellids and by Brown et al. (2016) across the entirety of Madagascar's amphibian species. Further, Pabijan et al. (2012) found that body size also influences within-species gene flow: comparing conspecific populations at two moist evergreen forest sites, Andasibe and Ranomafana, their study demonstrated that small frogs had higher between-population genetic divergence than large frogs. Further, Wollenberg Valero (2015) showed that a smaller species of *Gephyromantis*, *G. enki*, showed larger genetic differentiation across the same area in Ranomafana than its larger relative *G. boulengeri*.

OUTLOOK

As suggested by Vences et al. (2009), Madagascar offers a unique system to study a variety of biogeographic patterns and processes. In fact, Brown et al. (2014) concluded that the observed patterns are influenced by a combination of diversification processes rather than by a single predominant mechanism, and a "one-size-fits-all" model therefore does not exist. Although the knowledge of amphibian distributions on the island is incomplete, we now have a much better understanding of amphibian biogeographic patterns, and it is time to move toward studying fine-scale processes of divergence and adaptation at the population level. Genomic tools will soon enable the identification of genes involved in adaptation and will aid understanding the processes of adaptation acting on both adult frogs and tadpoles, the latter of which may actually be the life stage that has been driving the radiation of some of Madagascar's amphibian clades (Wollenberg Valero et al. 2017).

Future studies should aim to incorporate carefully vetted taxonomies to make sure the individuals and populations being compared indeed belong to the same species. As such, routine taxonomic assessment and species inventories should include, where possible, molecular and bioacoustic tools. Unfortunately, though understandably, some field biologists conducting inventories have not collected these data sets. However, almost all the larger-scale inventories include good series of museum voucher specimens with associated DNA samples (often flash-frozen in liquid nitrogen in the field), which allow for future updating and verification of taxonomic identification.

New inventories accompanied by comprehensive DNA barcoding efforts, and collection of diverse field data to document all aspects of species morphology, behavior, and ecology, will be needed to fully address taxonomic and sampling issues in the different regions of the island. This is especially important concerning the current rapid advances that are being made associated with species delimitation, and the desire to identify more recent speciation events and cryptic biodiversity, which are easily overlooked by applying simple genetic divergence thresholds (such as >3% 16S mtDNA). Further, novel techniques such as bait capture now enable DNA sequencing of collection-based voucher specimens, even from formalin-fixed specimens that were previously not usable because of the high degree of DNA fragmentation caused by the preservative (e.g., Rancilhac et al. 2020; Scherz et al. 2020). This approach, although still quite expensive, will be extremely useful in ascertaining the identity of a limited number of important voucher specimens such as name-bearing types, together with other novel techniques such as micro-CT scans to assess osteological and other anatomical characters. Outstanding taxonomic conundrums may therefore soon become solvable, particularly in zones of the island that are now deforested and where the collection of fresh material is impossible.

Species distribution modeling (SDM) tools have been of great utility in outlining the distribution ranges and spatial biodiversity patterns for amphibians (Brown et al. 2016) and will also be useful in detecting ecological niche divergence in species complexes (Raxworthy et al. 2007), but their full application remains limited because of the scarcity of reliable species occurrence records and the incredible extent of natural habitat loss, particularly in the moist evergreen forests. Indeed, a big challenge for the future will be to understand the distribution patterns and genetic variation of Malagasy amphibians and assess whether the observed high rate of anthropogenic habitat loss that is fragmenting the original patterns is currently eroding this diversity. In the future, field expeditions may be guided by SDM, as the information contained in these models can be used to identify habitat remnants that may harbor amphibian populations from part of the original species pool. Sadly, even if species do not go extinct altogether, the recent declines of local populations and the accompanying reduction of local genetic variation will need to be considered for future biogeographic and phylogeographic studies on Madagascar.

Subject editors: Miguel Vences and Achille P. Raselimanana

AMPHIBIAN CONSERVATION THROUGH THE IMPLEMENTATION OF "A CONSERVATION STRATEGY FOR THE AMPHIBIANS OF MADAGASCAR—ACSAM"

A. Crottini, S. H. Ndriantsoa, A. Rakotoarison, T. F. Rakotonanahary, G. García, N. H. C. Rabibisoa, and F. Andreone

Amphibians are one of the most threatened terrestrial vertebrate classes on earth (Stuart et al. 2004), with about 40% of recognized species worldwide currently threatened with extinction (IUCN 2019). The native amphibian fauna of Madagascar also shares this worrying situation, with a similar percentage of threatened species. Malagasy amphibians belong to five independent anuran lineages (Crottini et al. 2012b; see Glaw et al., pp. 1305–22), with more than 365 currently described species and at least 100–150 candidate species that are awaiting assessment and formal description (Glaw and Vences 2007; Vieites et al. 2009; Perl et al. 2014). All the native species and 88% of the genera are endemic to Madagascar and its nearshore islands (AmphibiaWeb 2021). Given the impressive amphibian richness, endemism rates, and fragile situation of the pristine or semi-pristine habitats of Madagascar, it is worth summarizing the conservation activities carried out in recent years to promote the preservation of this extraordinary anuran fauna. Although no recent extinctions have been documented (Glaw and Vences 2007), the most recent update by the IUCN lists 144 threatened species over the 309 currently assessed species, of which 21 species have been classified as Critically Endangered, 79 as Endangered, and 44 as Vulnerable (IUCN 2019).

Habitat loss and degradation are the primary threats affecting Madagascar's amphibians, with pollution and climate change also likely to have an impact on particular species (Andreone and Randrianirina 2003). Further, collection for the international pet trade and human consumption may also have relevant effects on at least some species and in certain geographic areas (Andreone et al. 2006b, 2008b; Jenkins et al. 2009). In addition, the recent detection of the amphibian chytrid fungus highlights a potentially new relevant threat to the country's amphibian fauna (Bletz et al. 2015a, 2015b; see Bletz et al., pp. 1342–49). Similarly, the introduction and invasion of the Black-spined Toad, *Duttaphrynus melanostictus* (Crottini et al. 2014a; Licata et al. 2019; see Freeman et al., pp. 1404–10), and the impact of several other introduced species (Kull et al. 2015; Goodman et al. 2017) are now posing new challenges not only to amphibians but to many different facets of Madagascar's biota.

EARLIER CONSERVATION ACTIVITIES

The conservation of Malagasy amphibians has long been considered a priority, and the need for a collaborative and coordinated approach across all stakeholders and local communities has been repeatedly highlighted as one of the main targets (Andreone and Randriamahazo 2008; Andreone et al. 2015, 2016). Since Madagascar is an extremely poor country (with a current gross domestic product per capita of around US$460 according to International Money Fund 2019), it is commonly stated that nature, specifically via ecotourism, should be transformed into a crucial economic resource for the country. With the aim of raising awareness and achieving long-term conservation, several actions have been pursued over the past 15 years. This effort was driven mainly by the conviction that the management of amphibian populations and species conservation can represent a good development opportunity for local communities.

To summarize the different actions over the past decades, we should commence with the first conservation-driven approaches promoting the preservation of amphibians (Behra 1991). At the end of the 1980s and beginning of the 1990s, there was a partial shift in research activities from appreciation and validation of biodiversity richness to a more comprehensive understanding of the Malagasy amphibian fauna. One of the first exchanges of ideas on the conservation of Malagasy herpetofauna took place during the Evaluation et Plans de Gestion pour la Conservation (CAMP) meeting, held in 2001 at Mantasoa (Andreone et al. 2001).

The transformation of earlier conservation activities into an organized plan for amphibian conservation became a reality during the launch of the world Amphibian Conservation Action Plan (ACAP) and the Global Amphibian Assessment (GAA), both resulting from a conference held in Washington, DC (Gascon et al. 2007). During this meeting the conservationists Russell A. Mittermeier and Claude Gascon proposed to boost amphibian conservation on Madagascar. This was soon followed by the establishment of the Declining Amphibian Populations Task Force (DAPTF) seed grants, aimed at supporting pioneering projects on the conservation of *Mantella cowanii*, one of the most threatened amphibians on the island. The transformation of the Madagascar Working Group of the DAPTF into the IUCN SSC Amphibian Specialist Group Madagascar provided the opportunity to organize a first international meeting in Gland, Switzerland, where researchers joined to brainstorm on conservation programs to safeguard Malagasy amphibians. In line with the GAA assessment, this also resulted in the release of the first evaluation of the extinction risks of Malagasy amphibians (Andreone et al. 2005a).

LAUNCH OF "A CONSERVATION STRATEGY FOR THE AMPHIBIANS OF MADAGASCAR—ACSAM"

These first actions were followed by the launch of the ACSAM program, which officially took place during an international workshop held in Antananarivo in 2006 (Andreone 2008) (Figure 11.6a). This meeting resulted in the release of the first national action plan, the so-called Sahonagasy Action Plan (SAP) (Andreone and Randriamahazo 2008). Malagasy authorities officially supported the implementation of the SAP, making Madagascar one of the first countries in the world to identify a specific strategy for the conservation of its amphibians. With the release of the SAP came the first attempt to provide researchers, conservation practitioners, institutions, and stakeholders with a consensual road map to promote amphibian conservation actions over a five-year period. This document identified eight priority strategic axes, as follows:

1. Coordinating research and conservation activities
2. Monitoring Madagascar's amphibians
3. Managing emerging amphibian disease
4. Assessing the impact of climate change on amphibians
5. Managing focal amphibian sites for conservation
6. Harvesting and trading amphibians
7. Engaging in captive breeding and zoo actions;
8. Developing a national herpetological collection

The full implementation of the SAP was estimated to cost about 1.8 million Euros over a five-year period (Andreone et al. 2012).

There followed an evaluation of progress toward achieving these targets, also assessing whether progress was consistent with realistic expectations (Andreone et al. 2012). When each conservation action was examined in detail, the highest proportion of implemented activities was found to be associated with theme 3 (managing emerging amphibian disease) and theme 6 (harvesting and trading amphibians), and all priority activities set for theme 5 (managing focal amphibian sites for conservation) were in progress at the end of this four-year period. On the other hand, only limited progress was made toward achieving the goals set for theme 4 (assessing the impact of climate change on amphibians) and theme 8 (developing a national herpetological collection).

Despite the potential to connect with foreign and local institutions, limited progress was obtained for theme 7 (engaging in captive breeding and zoo actions), with the notable exception of the development of the first in-country facility at Andasibe, managed by the community-run Association Mitsinjo in collaboration with the Direction Générale des Forêts (DGF) and Amphibian Specialist Group Madagascar (Edmonds et al. 2015). This captive-breeding facility was launched in 2010 and conducted husbandry research to determine the captive requirements of species from various ecological guilds (Andreone et al. 2012; Edmonds et al. 2012; Rakotonanahary et al. 2017). This project also encompassed the maintenance of a genetically viable population of the Endangered *Mantella aurantiaca* from the founder stock collected at natural breeding sites in the Ambatovy mining area (see Edmonds et al., pp. 1331–36, for more details).

Andreone et al. (2012) estimated that it was possible to secure only around 40% of the required total funds for the SAP; this may have been the result of the difficult political situation in Madagascar during this four-year period (Randriamalala and Liu 2010). Beside the numerous challenges, the years following the official launch of the SAP saw the development of a multitude of conservation studies and increased interest in some iconic species. Those were 1) *Mantella cowanii* (Figure 11.7a)—especially the population near Antoetra—with the launch of an action plan focused on this species (Rabibisoa 2008) and the implementation of monitoring activities across its whole geographic range. This species had been intensively collected for the pet trade since the late 1980s, until its inclusion in Appendix II of CITES. In 2003 and following the alert launched by Andreone and Randrianirina (2003), the species was taken off the international market by governmental authorities and was put in a "zero quota" category that forbid its collection and exportation. Thanks to this action, the largest remaining population also received some protection (Rabibisoa 2008; Rabibisoa et al. 2013). 2) *Mantella aurantiaca* (Figure 11.7b), restricted to a few severely fragmented breeding sites in the Moramanga District (Alaotra-Mangoro Region) (Vences and Raxworthy 2008; Crottini et al. 2019). Since 1995, the species has been listed in Appendix II of CITES, and its export for the international trade is based on an annual quota system sanctioned by this Convention. Since 2008 the Madagasikara Voakajy organization has carried out several research and conservation activities on this endangered species in collaboration with various stakeholders to ensure its sustainable management. This species has also been subject to a specific program to establish captive-bred colonies. 3–5) *Mantella viridis* (Figure 11.7c), limited to the northern tip

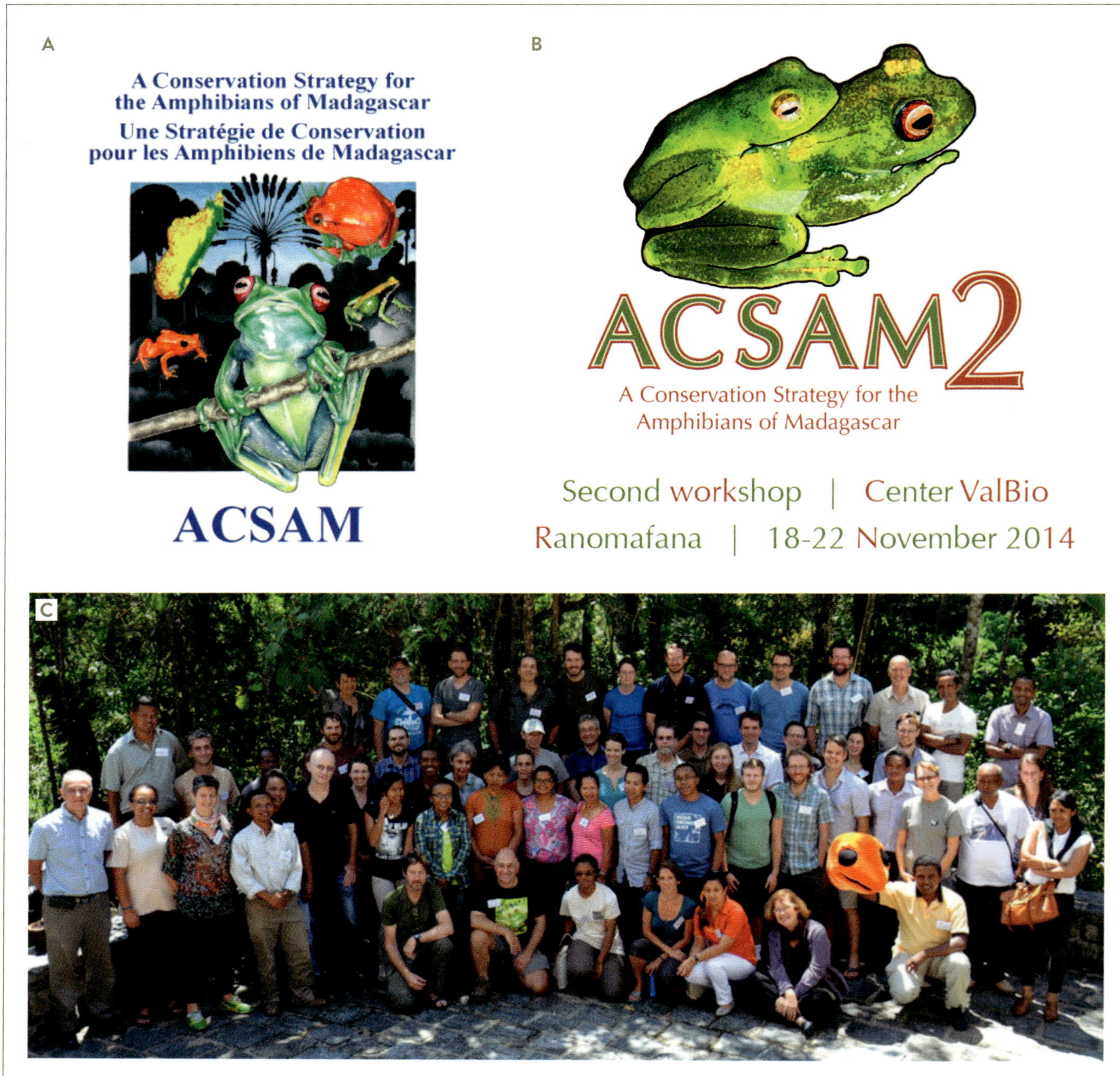

FIGURE 11.6 **A) Logo of the ACSAM (A Conservation Strategy for the Amphibians of Madagascar) workshop held in Antananarivo in 2006, drawn by C. Girard; B) logo of the ACSAM2 workshop held in Ranomafana in 2014, drawn by S. Newman; and C) group photo of the participants in the ACSAM2 workshop.** (PHOTO C by M. Fisher.)

of Madagascar (Crottini et al. 2012a), and *Scaphiophryne gottlebei* (Figure 11.7d) and *M. expectata* (Figures 11.7e and f), both microendemics of the Isalo Massif (Crottini et al. 2008). It has been possible to characterize the distribution and genetic diversity of all these species, as well as investigate numerous aspects of their biology. 6–7) Long-term monitoring of the microendemic frogs *Boophis williamsi* (Figure 11.7g) and *Mantidactylus pauliani* (Figure 11.7h) of the Ankaratra Massif enabled the assessment of their abundance and fine-scale distribution. 8) The Tomato Frog, *Dyscophus antongilii* (Figure 11.7i), is one of the few species that has an important urban nucleus, Maroantsetra, allowing for the unique possibility to develop research and education activities with schools and other institutions. Thanks to support from the Zurich Zoo and the European Association of Zoos and Aquaria, field research was intensified, and a patch of land was purchased using funds obtained through the German foundation BIOPAT Patenschaften für biologische Vielfalt (Andreone et al. 2012). Research on and conservation of *D. antongilii*, including the "Tomato Frog Festival" held in Maroantsetra in 2009 (Andreone et al. 2013), led to better knowledge of the species and to a subsequent downgrading in 2016 of this species from CITES Appendix I to Appendix II.

FIGURE 11.7 **Species subjected to targeted conservation studies in the years following the launch of the Sahonagasy Action Plan: A) *Mantella cowanii* (Antoetra); B) *M. aurantiaca* (Torotorofotsy); C) *M. viridis* (captive specimen); D) *Scaphiophryne gottlebei* (Isalo); E) *M. expectata* (Isalo, Zahavola); F) *M. expectata*, yellow/red back morphotype (Isalo, Antambonoa); G) *Boophis williamsi* (Ankaratra); H) *Mantidactylus pauliani* (Ankaratra); and I) *Dyscophus antongilii* (Maroantsetra).** (PHOTOS A, B, C, D, G, and I by F. Andreone; E and F by V. Mercurio; and H by A. Crottini.)

Another important result from this period was the organization of the workshop "Disease Screening in Amphibians," held at Parc Ivoloina, just north of Toamasina. This meeting resulted in the constitution of the Chytridiomycosis Working Group, later transformed into the Chytrid Emergency Cell (CEC), a group of national and international researchers aimed at facilitating studies on one of the most widespread and feared pathogens affecting wild amphibian populations globally, the chytrid fungus (*Batrachochytrium dendrobatidis*, *Bd*) (Weldon et al. 2013; see Bletz et al., pp. 1342–49). The CEC aimed to develop a program to promptly detect the arrival of *Bd* on Madagascar. As such, this meeting set the basis for the launch of the National Monitoring Program for the early detection of *Bd* on the island, a plan to survey eight selected sites across the island biannually for the occurrence of this pathogen (Weldon et al. 2013). Similarly relevant, a workshop led in 2012 by Chester Zoo and Durrell Wildlife Conservation set the ground to develop a second in-country husbandry facility on Madagascar (at Parc Ivoloina), with the training of local keepers in captive-breeding techniques (Rakotonanahary et al. 2017), and to develop husbandry training capacities at the Association Mitsinjo (see Edmonds et al., pp. 1331–36).

THE NEW SAHONAGASY ACTION PLAN (NSAP)

The continued and severe loss of amphibian habitat, together with the identification of the chytrid fungus in several wild amphibian populations (Bletz et al. 2015a, 2015b; see Bletz et al., pp. 1342–49) and the invasion of the central east coast by *Duttaphrynus melanostictus* (see Freeman et al., pp. 1404–10), prompted the conservation community to organize a new ACSAM meeting, so that an updated version of the SAP could be prepared (Figures 11.6b and c). The ACSAM2 meeting took place in November 2014 at Centre Valbio in Ranomafana National Park and brought together numerous researchers, conservationists, and politicians eight years after the first meeting (Andreone et al. 2015). Participants, based on the analysis available in Andreone et al. (2012), reviewed the progress made against the actions identified in the first SAP and proposed a new set of strategies and revised actions (Andreone et al. 2015, 2016). One of the main comments presented during the meeting was that it was difficult to ascertain whether an action was fully achieved, as many actions were too broad in finality and were not measurable or time bound (Andreone et al. 2016). Participants felt this needed to be addressed when developing the New Sahonagasy Action Plan.

This new five-year action plan included six broad themes. "Coordinating research and conservation activities" (theme 1) covered actions related to the overall delivery of the action plan, including coordination, communication (i.e., raising amphibian conservation awareness), and fund-raising. "Monitoring Madagascar's amphibians and their environment" (theme 2) centered on the need to improve understanding of amphibian diversity, their environment, and distribution and included the development of long-term studies to create baseline data for future climate change research. "Emerging infectious diseases" (theme 3) included population screening, strategic planning to mitigate potential future disease outbreaks, and disease-specific education and communication. "Managing sites for the conservation of amphibians" (theme 4) covered actions related to improving protected area coverage for amphibians on Madagascar. "Harvesting and trading amphibians" (theme 5) related to the research and monitoring of amphibian species within the international and domestic trade. "Captive breeding and zoo actions" (theme 6) was dedicated to developing the captive breeding of Malagasy amphibians both in the country and overseas.

After the ACSAM2 meeting, and through the support of the Critical Ecosystem Partnership Fund, it was possible to recruit an in-country professional program team in charge of overseeing the implementation of the NSAP through an open partnership approach. The ACSAM2 meeting was also the ideal background to update the IUCN Red List, which was released in 2017. In this manner, it was possible to revise the species extinction risk assessments and identify which species deserved the highest conservation priority, focusing on the specific conservation actions that could be developed.

Other important achievements since the ACSAM2 meeting include 1) the use of the Amphibian Ark Conservation Needs Assessment tool for the amphibians of Madagascar, which enabled the assessment of over 200 species and prioritized the species most in need of ex situ conservation initiatives (Rakotonanahary et al. 2017); 2) the organization of a meeting held in Antoetra (December 2018) aimed at updating the *Mantella cowanii* action plan and ensuring the conservation of this species in its natural habitat; 3) the creation of social media pages aimed at sharing information on conservation activities and the results of conservation campaigns, and promoting awareness of the rich Malagasy amphibian community; 4) the maintenance of the National Monitoring Program to continue monitoring for *Bd* occurrence and prevalence across six wild amphibian populations; 5) formal protection of the home of the Critically Endangered *Boophis williamsi* and *Mantidactylus pauliani* (with the creation of the new protected area Manjakatompo Ankaratra, designated in April 2015), thanks to funding from the MacArthur Foundation, Global Wildlife Conservation, Critical Ecosystem Partnership Fund, and the continuous commitment of the local association Vondrona Ivon'ny Fampandrosoana (VIF); 6) the creation in April 2015 of the Mangabe-Ranomena-Sahasarotra protected area, with a total area of 27,346 ha, started by Madagasikara Voakajy, to ensure the protection of key habitats for *Mantella aurantiaca*.

The summary of the main outcomes of the amphibian conservation activities during the past 15 years on Madagascar is encouraging, although this is only the beginning and many more actions and education initiatives need to be implemented. We believe that the role of the IUCN SSC Amphibian Specialist Group Madagascar and of the main conservation stakeholders has been relevant to achieving all this, and we hope that the recent constitution of the local association MISA (Miaro Ny Sahona, "protect the frogs") will provide opportunities for many more young Malagasy herpetologists to become more closely involved in amphibian conservation.

Subject editors: Angelica Crottini, Miguel Vences, and Achille P. Raselimanana

EX SITU CONSERVATION EFFORTS FOR THE AMPHIBIANS OF MADAGASCAR

D. Edmonds, K. Johnson, J. C. Rakotoarisoa, R. Dolch, and C. Randrianantoandro

Given the range and severity of threats facing Madagascar's frogs, in situ conservation efforts alone appear inadequate to ensure a future for many of the most highly threatened species. Globally, more than one-third of described amphibian species are threatened with extinction, but on Madagascar the situation is worse, with nearly half of the more than 365 species facing a high risk of extinction (IUCN 2019). Habitat loss continues to be the main threat, with emerging infectious diseases, climate change, overexploitation, and introduced species also of great concern (Andreone et al. 2005a, 2008a; Bletz et al. 2015a, 2015b). Ex situ conservation programs are increasingly being considered as an additional option to ensure a future for Madagascar's threatened amphibian species.

Compared to other animals, amphibians are especially well suited for ex situ conservation programs because of their small space requirements, relatively inexpensive maintenance costs, and lack of behavioral aspects that can complicate reintroduction efforts (Griffiths and Pavajeau 2008). Here, we define ex situ conservation as involving captive populations but not necessarily outside a species' native range. This form of conservation is needed when threats are too severe or develop too rapidly to be mitigated in time to prevent loss of a species or population. In addition to safeguarding against extinction, ex situ programs can provide stock for reintroductions—that is, establishing or reestablishing new wild populations—as well as for augmenting declining populations. Such programs require careful planning and long-term financial commitment to succeed, which can be challenging to secure in the case of Madagascar.

BUILDING CAPACITY ON MADAGASCAR

It was not until recently that organized efforts were made to develop amphibian breeding capacity on the island. As described by Crottini et al. (see pp. 1326–30), different steps and actions were taken to establish an amphibian breeding center, and the critical Sahonagasy Action Plan (SAP) (Andreone and Randriamahazo 2008) identified objectives for the ex situ conservation community to work toward.

The first recommendation of the SAP was to develop husbandry expertise for several Malagasy frog species that had not previously been kept in captivity. A review of zoo programs by García et al. (2008) found that nearly 100 zoological institutions worldwide were working with Malagasy amphibians in captivity; that the Malagasy amphibians in their collections were limited to only 23 species, mostly of the genera *Dyscophus* and *Mantella*; and that reproduction in captivity had been achieved in fewer than two-thirds of these species. This study illustrated that nearly nothing is known about the husbandry requirements of most Malagasy amphibian species, hindering ex situ conservation.

A second objective of the SAP was to build capacity in Malagasy institutions for improved captive-breeding efforts by developing husbandry expertise with common frog species from varied ecological guilds prior to participating in ex situ conservation efforts for threatened species. Recognized zoological institutions abroad would then support these programs through training courses and workshops. Several Malagasy institutions expressed interest in developing capacity to manage captive amphibian populations, including the Université d'Antananarivo and the Parc Botanique et Zoologique de Tsimbazaza (PBZT). In the end, while programs were piloted at these institutions, Madagascar's first breeding center for amphibians was developed by a local community-run group, Association Mitsinjo.

MITSINJO CAPTIVE-BREEDING FACILITY

Launched collaboratively with the Direction Générale des Eaux et Forêts (DGEF) and the IUCN SSC Amphibian Specialist Group Madagascar, Mitsinjo's captive-breeding facility is the only center on Madagascar dedicated to the ex situ conservation of amphibians. It was installed in late 2010 near the village of Andasibe. Initial support for the project was provided by the Association of Zoos and Aquariums as well as by Amphibian Ark. The building was constructed from the remnant foundations of a historic forest station measuring 185 m^2 and containing three main rooms (Figure 11.8). Nearly half the building is dedicated to producing live food; the other half houses captive frogs. A separate quarantine room provides space for habituating new individuals to captivity and isolating animals if there is a threat of disease.

Constructed before the detection of the chytrid fungus (*Batrachochytrium dendrobatidis*, *Bd*) on Madagascar (Bletz et al. 2015a, 2015b), the facility was developed proactively with the threat of foreign infectious diseases arriving on Madagascar in mind. The project was intended to support local species from the Alaotra-Mangoro Region rather than across Madagascar. As a result, the risk of introducing or spreading infectious diseases to or from other parts of the island was reduced. Separate entrances were designed to allow staff working at the facility to change into dedicated footwear and clothing before entering. Most importantly, a biosecurity protocol for personnel was developed during facility construction, outlining what materials could be brought into the facility, how to treat waste leaving the building, and the norms and expectations for staff and visitors to the center.

Three objectives were defined at the onset of the project to guide activities. The first was to build in-country capacity for enacting ex situ amphibian conservation programs, involving both infrastructure installation (constructing the facility, establishing live food colonies, designing terraria, etc.) and the development of local

FIGURE 11.8 **The main room of the Mitsinjo amphibian captive-breeding facility near Andasibe. Terraria in the photo house *Mantella aurantiaca*.** (PHOTO by D. Edmonds.)

amphibian husbandry expertise. The second objective was to carry out husbandry research on poorly known species to learn how to maintain them in captivity. Importantly, Mitsinjo and collaborators worked to design hypothesis-driven studies to test questions about frog care, for example the best diet to feed tadpoles (see Soamiarimampionona et al. 2015). Third, for threatened species already in need of ex situ assistance, Mitsinjo would establish captive populations to safeguard against extinction and facilitate reintroductions or population augmentation programs if or when needed.

To avoid introducing insects or potential pests to Madagascar, Mitsinjo established cultures of locally collected arthropods for food, including fruit flies, springtails, and six species of crickets (Edmonds et al. 2012). Cockroaches and isopods were also attempted but reproduced too slowly to serve as a regular food source for captive frogs. Earthworms are offered to larger frog species, namely *Mantidactylus betsileanus*, and are collected from outside, but otherwise all foods are produced at the center. Powdered vitamin and mineral supplements designed for amphibians are brought from abroad and used on food items prior to feeding frogs to help prevent nutritional deficiencies and related health issues.

To train staff in amphibian husbandry, Mitsinjo's technicians first worked to culture fruit flies and crickets. Over six months during facility construction and before keeping any frogs, staff worked to maintain live food cultures and develop guidelines for their care. A more advanced training course focusing on live food production was carried out in Andasibe by the Durrell Wildlife Conservation Trust. Further training workshops on amphibian husbandry were led by staff from Woodland Park Zoo, Chester Zoo, Amphibian Ark, and several private amphibian breeders. Later, in 2013 and 2015, Mitsinjo's amphibian technicians studied abroad at both Toledo Zoo and Jersey Zoo. Training workshops helped local staff develop amphibian husbandry expertise and learn a variety of skills related to ex situ conservation.

As of December 2019, Mitsinjo's breeding facility housed 12 species of amphibians (Table 11.2). Most species have reproduced, and two species (*Mantidactylus betsileanus* and *Mantella aurantiaca*) have bred beyond the second generation. Reports on the captive husbandry of *Boophis pyrrhus* (Edmonds et al. 2016) and *M. aurantiaca* (Edmonds et al. 2015) provide an overview of conditions needed to maintain these species. Mitsinjo technicians have also collected basic life history data and made behavioral observations on poorly known local frog species, such as clutch size for nine species of Malagasy amphibians (Table 11.3). Such information can be used to calculate fecundity and predict population persistence.

TABLE 11.2. **Amphibian species maintained at Mitsinjo's amphibian captive-breeding facility since 2011**

SPECIES	BRED TO F1	BRED TO F2
Anodonthyla pollicaris	X	–
Blommersia blommersae	X	–
Boophis bottae	X	–
B. pyrrhus	X	–
Dyscophus guineti	–	–
Gephyromantis boulengeri	X	–
Guibemantis aff. *albolineatus*	X	–
G. pulcher	–	–
Heterixalus betsileo	X	–
H. punctatus[1]	–	–
Mantella aurantiaca	X	X
Mantidactylus betsileanus	X	X
Platypelis barbouri	X	–
Plethodontohyla mihanika	X	–
Stumpffia sp.[1]	–	–

Notes: F1 indicates the species has been bred to the first generation. F2 indicates the species has been bred to the second generation. *Dyscophus guineti* was received from a local confiscation and is maintained only at a public environmental education center near the breeding facility.

[1] These species are no longer in the collection as of December 2019.

TABLE 11.3. **Mean clutch size for amphibian species that successfully bred at the Mitsinjo facility near Andasibe and for which quantitative details were recorded**

SPECIES	MEAN CLUTCH SIZE	95% CI	*n*
Anodonthyla pollicaris	28.5	17.5–39.5	13
Blommersia blommersae	74.6	58.0–91.2	37
Boophis pyrrhus	82.6	61.1–104.1	18
Gephyromantis boulengeri	8.2	5.1–11.3	28
Guibemantis aff. *albolineatus*	17.3	12.4–22.2	17
Mantella aurantiaca	69.4	68.3–70.5	1894
Mantidactylus betsileanus	67.2	65.4–69.0	1010
Platypelis barbouri	26.2	17.5–34.9	6
Plethodontohyla mihanika	52.0	40.1–63.9	6

Note: CI is confidence interval; *n* is number of clutches counted.

MANTELLA AURANTIACA CAPTIVE BREEDING AND REINTRODUCTION

Although initially developed to prepare for the threat of introduced infectious diseases, soon after launching, Mitsinjo's breeding facility was contacted by the nearby Ambatovy nickel and cobalt mine to establish a survival assurance colony of *Mantella aurantiaca* displaced by its activities. Specifically, four *M. aurantiaca* breeding ponds were scheduled to be cleared, and along with translocation efforts, Ambatovy suggested creating a genetically viable captive assurance population to supply stock for future reintroductions. Mitsinjo received 162 *M. aurantiaca* individuals from the breeding ponds in February 2012. The frogs were acclimated to captivity in the facility's quarantine room and moved to permanent terraria in May 2012. Annual health assessments were performed by an amphibian pathologist from the Institute for Conservation Research at the San Diego Zoo, who also trained a Malagasy veterinarian in basic amphibian medicine and diagnostic procedures.

In June 2012, the first *M. aurantiaca* captive breeding was recorded. Mitsinjo initially culled eggs to prevent the captive population from growing beyond the capacity of the breeding facility. Miscommunications between Mitsinjo and Ambatovy resulted in several hundred tadpoles being saved for a pilot reintroduction program in 2013, but release sites were not ready to receive animals at the intended time. Consequently, the captive *M. aurantiaca* population at Mitsinjo grew to more than 600 frogs, over half of which were surplus stock originally intended for reintroductions, which did not occur.

In 2016, project partners began planning a trial reintroduction using captive-bred stock from Mitsinjo's facility. This time, Ambatovy identified potential breeding ponds ("receptor sites") in protected habitat adjacent to the mine footprint. Initial meetings about trial reintroductions involved personnel from governmental and nongovernmental sectors. The effort was framed as a trial program, with a primary goal of determining reintroduction methodology for the species.

Careful consideration was given to receptor site selection. Project partners developed a set of criteria for candidate receptor sites based on habitat characteristics of existing *M. aurantiaca* breeding ponds. Sites had to have 1) a potential breeding pond, 2) a sloped forested hillside, and 3) nearby flowing water. The breeding pond component needed to be at least 700 m^2. Surrounding habitat required at least 30% native forest and a hillside of between 15° and 25°. Sites could not have extant populations of *M. aurantiaca* and were surveyed at least three times during the breeding season to verify the absence of this species before captive-raised animals were released. Receptor sites also had to be legally protected and within the historical distribution of *M. aurantiaca*. Other species that might compete with *M. aurantiaca* could not be present, for example the closely related *M. crocea* or *M. milotympanum*. Finally, disease screening needed to be carried out on the local amphibian community at receptor sites, with no infectious diseases detected.

In principle, suitable habitat for *M. aurantiaca* should already support the species, so attention was given to the aspects of receptor sites that might not be appropriate and how habitat could be modified to improve its quality. Put another way, why would this species be absent at breeding ponds if the habitat was within its native range and wild populations were close enough for colonization? The main factor identified at potential receptor sites that differed from occupied *M. aurantiaca* breeding ponds was water level during the breeding season. Surveys determined that the substrate of breeding ponds should be at least 15% clay, with sand not exceeding 70%, in order to retain water. Where these soil conditions were not met, Ambatovy would modify the receptor site accordingly, improving the likelihood of establishing a population through reintroduction.

In the end, four receptor sites were selected for trial reintroductions. Of these, three were within the Corridor Forestier Analamay-Mantadia, and one was in the Ambatovy conservation zone. Two sites were modified by adding clay to better retain water during the rainy season, and by planting the fern *Osmunda regalis*, which is a non-native but dominant species at many *M. aurantiaca* breeding sites (Rakotondrasoa et al. 2017). Additionally, moss, leaf litter, and wood were added to receptor sites from breeding habitat scheduled to be cleared. Two sites also required small canals to be built to drain water during the breeding season so that the water depth remained below 25 cm. Sites were modified in late 2016 and early 2017.

After disease screening, *M. aurantiaca* individuals were released at receptor sites in April 2017. Two sites received tadpoles (439 tadpoles at one, 196 at another), one site received 649 juvenile frogs, and one site received 238 adult frogs. Juvenile and adult frogs were marked with visual implant elastomers specific to each receptor site. Initially, frogs and tadpoles were confined within screen enclosures set around the ponds for monitoring. Students from the universities of Antananarivo, Mahajanga, and Fianarantsoa monitored ponds and screen enclosures, collecting data for their undergraduate and master's theses. Released males were heard calling from December 2017 to February 2018 and from October 2018 to February 2019 at three of the four sites, but no eggs or tadpoles were found. Long-term monitoring is needed to determine the success of trial reintroductions, a process that can take a decade or more and requires sustained funding (Griffiths and Pavajeau 2008).

MADAGASCAR PRIORITY SPECIES FOR EX SITU PROGRAMS

Although the *Mantella aurantiaca* captive-breeding and trial reintroduction program is encouraging, there are still many other Malagasy amphibian species in need of conservation. In most cases, ex situ efforts are likely not warranted. Whether or not to establish a captive population depends on what measures are needed to conserve wild populations (Canessa 2017). With limited resources, assessing species for their conservation needs is a vital first step in identifying and prioritizing species for both ex situ and in situ conservation actions.

To this end, a Conservation Needs Assessment (CNA) facilitated by the Amphibian Ark was carried out in 2015. The IUCN Red List process provides information and analyses on species status, trends, and threats to measure the relative risk of extinction; however, it is not the aim of Red List assessments to suggest conservation actions (Collen et al. 2016). A CNA combines the risk of extinction with other vital data to provide practitioners with more concise priorities for a range of actions, based on current expert knowledge of each species. Using a series of weighted questions, a CNA both prioritizes species for conservation action and indicates broadly which types of conservation actions are needed (K. Johnson et al. 2020). These high-level actions, along with extensive notes recorded during the assessment, can subsequently be used by national or regional amphibian conservation groups. The process can be used to update existing amphibian action plans within a country or region, or to provide a prioritized guide to inform future program development.

Within each species assessment, some responses are assigned a numeric value and summed to provide a score. Higher scores indicate species with a higher priority for conservation action. Responses not including a numeric value provide additional data to help determine appropriate conservation actions. Using the responses, the program recommends one or more conservation actions for each species automatically, to minimize the risk of assessors introducing a bias toward preferred species or conservation actions.

Since 2007, the CNA process has been used to create over 3400 assessments for about 2900 (34%) of the world's amphibian species through 32 national or regional workshops or through the online assessment program, covering 42 countries (Amphibian Ark 2019). The assessments for Malagasy species were not produced during a workshop but rather were completed online over approximately 12 months by 16 assessors who worked individually or in small groups. The reliability of assessments, and therefore the recommendations generated from them, rely on assembling a broad range of assessor expertise.

CONSERVATION NEEDS ASSESSMENT RESULTS

Of 365 currently described amphibian species on Madagascar, 332 species (90%) were assessed. Of those, 19 species were considered to be facing imminent extinction without ex situ intervention (Table 11.4). Rescue species occur either in unprotected habitat (e.g., *Gephyromantis mafy* known from a single forest fragment northeast of Lake Alaotra) or in legally protected areas that are not effectively protected (e.g., *Stumpffia hara* on Nosy Hara where tourism continues to threaten its karstic habitat). The species of highest ex situ conservation priority, *Mantella aurantiaca*, is actively involved in an ex situ program within its native range. *Mantella milotympanum* was also ranked high and is the only other rescue species successfully maintained in captivity, though not on Madagascar. Other rescue species have never been kept in captivity and their biology is poorly known. Notably, for most species, assessors were uncertain whether founders were available to establish captive populations. Only *Boophis jaegeri*, *Cophyla maharipeo*, and the two *Mantella* species were identified as having sufficient founders available. The other 15 rescue species are either so poorly known or thought to occur at such low densities that assessors were not certain it would be possible to collect founders.

In addition to identifying species in need of rescue, assessors also suggested six analogue species for husbandry research (Table 11.5), which would be used to develop captive husbandry requirements of rescue species prior to establishing ex situ programs. An additional 70 species were also noted as needing husbandry research, but in most cases, they were identified as analogues for species not suggested for rescue. Recommendations were made to prioritize husbandry research on analogue species before resources are used for others.

While using analogues to develop husbandry requirements for highly threatened species is one important form of ex situ research, the assessment also identified species for which in situ conservation efforts depend on research most easily carried out in captivity. Reproductive biology was a common theme in this research category. Learning basic life history traits such as clutch size and breeding frequency, and identifying reproductive strategies requiring specific microhabitats, may be most easily accomplished through ex situ research. For example, *Mantidactylus grandidieri* and *M. guttulatus* are heavily commercialized for food trade because of their large size and ease of collection (Jenkins et al. 2009; Rancilhac et al. 2020). Although they are regularly encountered in the field, their breeding biology remains almost entirely unknown. Understanding impacts of trade on these species requires estimates of fecundity and

TABLE 11.4. **Species recommended for ex situ rescue by the Conservation Needs Assessment**

SPECIES	TAXONOMY	HABITAT	FOUNDERS
Anodonthyla emilei	X	–	–
A. jeanbai	X	–	–
A. theoi	X	–	–
Boophis baetkei	X	X	–
B. jaegeri	X	–	X
B. williamsi	X	–	–
Cophyla maharipeo	X	–	X
Gephyromantis hintelmannae	X	–	–
G. mafy	X	–	–
Mantella aurantiaca	X	X	X
M. milotympanum	–	X	X
Mantidactylus pauliani	X	–	–
Platypelis alticola	X	X	–
P. mavomavo	–	–	–
P. olgae	X	–	–
Rhombophryne longicrus	X	–	–
Spinomantis brunae	X	X	–
Stumpffia hara	X	X	–
S. staffordi	X	–	–

Notes: The "Taxonomy" column indicates species that have been taxonomically revised and whose species status and delimitation are unambiguous. "Habitat" indicates there is enough reliably protected habitat for possible reintroduction, translocation, or population supplementation. "Founders" indicates enough individuals could likely be sourced to establish an ex situ program.

TABLE 11.5. **Analogue species recommended for ex situ husbandry research by the Conservation Needs Assessment and associated rescue species**

ANALOGUE SPECIES	RESCUE SPECIES
Boophis microtympanum	*B. williamsi*
Cophyla phyllodactyla	*C. maharipeo*
Gephyromantis boulengeri	*G. mafy*
Platypelis barbouri	*P. mavomavo, P. olgae*
Rhombophryne laevipes	*R. longicrus*

Note: Analogue species are used for developing husbandry protocols and breeding techniques for species in need of ex situ assistance before establishing a breeding program.

identification of breeding habitat, which may be most easily determined under captive conditions.

Finally, an important resulting message from the assessment was the need for continued taxonomic research. The IUCN Red List underestimates threats to Madagascar's amphibians because species complexes are treated as single conservation units (Scherz et al. 2019a), and only 73% of 332 assessed taxa were considered to have a clear taxonomic status with determined species limits.

RECOMMENDATIONS FOR FUTURE EX SITU PROGRAMS

Considerable progress has been made over the past decade toward building capacity to enact ex situ efforts as part of an integrated conservation strategy for Madagascar's amphibians. While such progress is encouraging, there is still a gap between the need for ex situ conservation programs and the ability to enact them. Rakotonanahary et al. (2017) noted several steps to take to fill this gap, including identifying priority species for ex situ programs, incorporating field data to improve captive husbandry, and partnering with reintroduction specialists outside Madagascar to better plan and execute ex situ programs. They suggested increasing participation of zoological institutions abroad that already maintain Malagasy amphibians as one way to help meet some of these needs.

Zoological institutions outside Madagascar have eagerly shared captive husbandry expertise through training workshops and keeper exchanges, but there is also room to improve other aspects of amphibian ex situ conservation programs. Notably, project management skills are still lacking, with the need to improve the ability of Malagasy institutions to plan and implement projects to achieve goals and meet objectives. We encourage the international conservation community to support efforts to improve the ability of Malagasy institutions to manage their ex situ programs more effectively and not focus solely on the specialized knowledge related to amphibian captive care and husbandry.

A second area requiring attention is funding, both to maintain current ex situ activities and to launch new conservation plans for target species. Support from zoological institutions outside Madagascar was influential in launching Mitsinjo's breeding facility, but grants are typically project based and have a finite duration. Considering the great need, international institutions that govern biodiversity conservation and that typically finance in situ efforts are called on to support integrated efforts that include ex situ components (Pritchard et al. 2011).

Given that conservation resources are limited, novel approaches to funding ex situ conservation on Madagascar may be needed. One example of an alternative funding strategy can be seen at Centro Jambatu in Ecuador, where amphibian conservation efforts are supported through the sale of captive-bred offspring to the international pet trade through its partner company Wikiri (Yeager and Zarling 2020). Such an approach could potentially work on Madagascar given the demand for the country's amphibians from private breeders and terrarium hobbyists abroad. Funding ex situ conservation through tourism also has potential. As a start in this direction, Mitsinjo recently developed a public amphibian exhibit near its breeding facility (Wolf 2018; Rakotoarisoa 2019). The exhibit is used both for local environmental education and for generation of revenue to support amphibian conservation.

Finally, we recommend working rapidly to support conservation programs for rescue species listed in Table 11.4. A decision about the role of ex situ conservation in their recovery should be made by following the IUCN ex situ management guidelines (McGowan et al. 2017). To start, stakeholders must carry out a status review and threat analysis, requiring participation of the scientific community. Improving knowledge of distribution, effects of habitat degradation, impacts of emerging infectious diseases, and estimates of abundance to monitor population trends will be a valuable scientific contribution that will help inform the process. Researchers and the scientific community can contribute to efforts by focusing on these areas.

Subject editors: Devin Edmonds, Miguel Vences, and Achille P. Raselimanana

CONSEQUENCES OF FOREST FRAGMENTATION AND HABITAT ALTERATIONS FOR AMPHIBIANS

J. C. Riemann, A. Crottini, R. M. Lehtinen, S. H. Ndriantsoa, M.-O. Rödel, D. Vallan, and J. Glos

Madagascar's natural ecosystems are highly threatened by ongoing deforestation, habitat degradation, and human land-use intensification. With 44% of the remaining primary vegetation lost between 1953 and 2014 (Vieilledent et al. 2018), the remaining forest habitats are now severely fragmented. This results in landscapes that provide fewer natural forest habitats, and these are split into an increasing number of smaller, isolated forest fragments with an increasing ratio of edge to interior habitat. Habitat loss and alteration are known to be the most severe causes of the global amphibian decline (Chanson et al. 2008; Sodhi et al. 2008). Building knowledge about the effects of habitat alteration and fragmentation on amphibians on Madagascar is essential because of the high rates of microendemism observed in this group (Vences et al. 2009; Brown et al. 2016), with species distributed across small and sometimes extremely limited geographic areas (e.g., *Scaphiophryne gottlebei* and *Mantella expectata*, both restricted to the Isalo Massif, Crottini et al. 2008; or *Mantidactylus pauliani* and *Boophis williamsi*, found only on the Ankaratra Massif, Andreone et al. 2014a). Here we summarize the results of 15 studies that analyzed the effects of fragmentation on amphibian species richness and composition, species-area relationships, functional diversity, fragmentation sensitivity and extinction proneness, logging, edge effects, and the influence of matrix habitat; the studies also surveyed amphibian diversity in fragmented landscapes over the island and a range of forest types.

THE CENTRAL HIGHLANDS

One of the first studies investigating fragmentation effects on Malagasy amphibians was conducted by Vallan (2000) in the Ambohitantely Special Reserve. This protected area occurring between 1300 and 1650 m above sea level has an area of 5600 ha and contains some of the last remnant medium-altitude moist evergreen forest fragments of the Central Highlands. It forms a mosaic of native and anthropogenic habitats (Langrand 2003). At least in the recent past, the zone contained more than 500 fragments that were sharply demarcated from the surrounding grassland (Figure 11.9), but the number of fragments is now greatly reduced (M. Rakotondratsimba and S. M. Goodman, unpublished data). In the Vallan study, amphibian diversity of seven fragments that contained running water and ranged in size from 0.16 to 1250 ha was compared, using the largest fragment as the control site. Vallan (2000) explored the effects of patch size on species richness, composition, and density and assessed the fragmentation sensitivity of the detected amphibian species. A total of 32 amphibian species were present in Ambohitantely, of which 26 were recorded exclusively in the forest fragments (including all microhylids), two species (*Boophis goudotii* and *Mantidactylus betsileanus*) occurred in and outside the forest fragments, and four species were found only outside the forest (*Heterixalus rutenbergi*, *M. alutus*, *Blommersia domerguei*, and *Ptychadena mascareniensis*). Species numbers in the surveyed fragments ranged between nine (in the smallest) and 26 (in the control site) and were positively correlated with fragment area. Amphibian assemblages within the fragments formed clear nested subsets (*sensu* Atmar and Patterson 1995), and thus the reduction of species richness as a function of forest size was not stochastic. In contrast, the relative individual density was negatively correlated with fragment size. Vallan (2000) explained that the density of streams was higher in small fragments, and thus they harbored a larger proportion of stream-dwelling amphibian species than larger fragments. Species with reproduction strategies independent of running water or ponds, such as certain microhylids, were detected only in fragments larger than 30 ha, probably because larger fragments contain more distinct microhabitats. This study revealed that microhylids and certain mantelline frogs were most sensitive to microclimate changes and concluded that they represent good bioindicators. Vallan (2000) further highlighted that forest fragments of 1250 ha seem to be large enough to contain a large part of the original amphibian fauna, given that suitable microhabitats are present.

Crottini et al. (2011a) surveyed amphibian diversity in the Atsirakambiaty relict, a small remaining medium-altitude moist evergreen forest fragment (<5 ha) on the Itremo-Ambatofinandrahana Massif (around 1550 m), embedded in a deforested area. They recorded 12 amphibian species, representing a typical assemblage of Madagascar's Central Highlands, including *Mantidactylus* sp. Ca20, which seems to be microendemic to Itremo, and the Endangered *Mantella cowanii*, thus confirming this forest fragment as an important refuge for these species.

A recent study by S. Rosa et al. (unpublished data) assessed the effects of structural landscape modifications during the past 30 years on amphibian diversity on the Ankaratra Massif, based on amphibian occurrence and abundance data collected at six sites over two years. This extinct volcanic formation includes the third highest peak on Madagascar (2643 m) and is characterized by a remnant medium-altitude moist evergreen forest (between 1500 and 2200 m), large areas of introduced trees, montane grassland, and montane ericoid thicket above tree line (Vences et al. 2002b). The area suffers from severe deforestation, illegal logging, and charcoal exploitation pressures, with the few remaining native forest elements embedded in a matrix of highly degraded landscapes (Goodman et al. 2018). These fragments harbor 15 amphibian species, including three microendemic species, *Boophis williamsi*, *Mantidactylus pauliani*, and *Mantidactylus* sp. Ca19 (Glaw and Vences 2007), two of which are classified as Critically Endangered (IUCN 2019). Analyzing how this amphibian community is responding to changes in structural (habitat loss) and functional processes (primary productivity and thermal condition), the authors found a negative relation between the Normalized Difference Vegetation Index (NDVI), used as a proxy for primary productivity and vegetation functional attributes, and species richness, with more species found in areas of lower NDVI (i.e., less productive

FIGURE 11.9 **A forest fragment surrounded by grassland, near Ambohitantely, Central Highlands. Note the abrupt ecotone between forest and grassland.** (PHOTO by M. Vences.)

areas), whereas habitat loss was the variable that best explained the observed patterns of abundance and microendemism (S. Rosa et al., unpublished data). In accordance with the results obtained by Vallan et al. (2004) in analyzing another amphibian community, this study found that the high-elevation amphibian community of the Ankaratra Massif was responding to forest alteration, with fewer amphibians and decreased microendemism rates at sites where recent forest clearing was evident. However, the situation on Ankaratra is special, as there have not been any areas of native forest on the massif for close to a century (Goodman et al. 1996, 2018), and it is therefore difficult to establish what the native amphibian fauna would have been before habitat modification.

MOIST EVERGREEN FOREST OF THE EASTERN ESCARPMENT

Two studies investigating anthropogenic habitat alteration effects on amphibian diversity are available from the Andasibe area (Vallan 2002; Vallan et al. 2004). Andasibe (about 900 m) is on the border between the Central Highlands and the eastern region, and the original forest type was lowland moist evergreen. Like the Central Highlands, this area was severely deforested as a result of intense swidden agriculture, conversion to rice fields or *Eucalyptus* plantations, and firewood harvesting.

Vallan (2002) compared amphibian species richness and composition between intact lowland moist evergreen forest, secondary vegetation, *Eucalyptus* plantations, and rice fields. Species richness in secondary forests, *Eucalyptus* plantations, and rice fields decreased to 54%, 46%, and 12%, respectively, of the species found in relatively intact forest. The number of species detected and individual density augmented with increasing structural complexity of the habitat and the presence of local water bodies. The study also showed that the reproductive mode best predicted the occurrence of species in a habitat, with more species spawning in water (most Malagasy amphibians, members of the family Mantellidae, lay eggs outside of water) in areas with increasing degradation. Hyperoliidae and Ptychadenidae were characteristic of degraded habitats, whereas Microhylidae and Mantellinae were representative of natural habitats.

In another study, Vallan et al. (2004) assessed the effects of low-level logging on amphibian diversity. Data were collected prior to and after selective logging at An'Ala, a 600 ha forest fragment in the Andasibe area at an elevation of about 850 m. Generally, amphibian abundance and diversity were not affected by low-level selective logging, although the abundance of individual species differed. The abundance of Mantellinae decreased by 16%, whereas abundance of Boophinae and Microhylidae increased by 12% and 4%, respectively, suggesting that mantellines were most sensitive to logging effects. This study revealed that in the short term, amphibians were relatively resilient to low-level forest logging. However, species composition was affected, with typical intact lowland moist evergreen forest species being replaced by species adapted to secondary habitats.

Three more-recent studies addressing fragmentation and matrix effects on different components of amphibian diversity are available for the Ranomafana National Park region (Riemann et al. 2015, 2017; Ndriantsoa et al. 2017). Ranomafana comprises 41,601 ha of continuous lowland to medium-altitude moist evergreen forest (500–1300 m) and represents most of the remaining forest habitat in the region. The few remaining forest fragments outside the park are embedded in a matrix of highly degraded (clear-cut and secondary bush and shrub vegetation) and cultivated (swidden agriculture) land (Figure 11.10). About 110 frog species are known from the Ranomafana area, including several candidate species (Glaw and Vences 2007; Vieites et al. 2009; see Vences et al., pp. 1442–45). The researchers collected amphibian diversity and trait data along stream and terrestrial transects in the eastern part of the park (used as the control site), nine adjacent forest fragments that ranged in size between 2 and 16.5 ha, and in the matrix (secondary vegetation). The authors targeted forest fragments that had been separated from continuous forest for at least 50 years. Additionally, banana plantations and rice fields were considered.

Riemann et al. (2015) compared amphibian species richness and assemblage composition between continuous forest and forest fragments to assess the conservation value of forest fragments for maintaining amphibian diversity. They found no fragmentation effects on species richness, demonstrating that the same habitat amount (transect area) in forest fragments maintained the same number of species as continuous forest. The most important factor for high species richness was the presence of streams, which may act as a buffer against microclimatic changes in forest fragments. Thus, they concluded that all remaining forest fragments (independent of patch size but crossed by streams) provided suitable habitat and could be important for maintaining Malagasy amphibian diversity. At the same time, these authors found that forest fragmentation affected species composition, with 30% of detected amphibian species restricted to continuous forest, 46% occurring in both forest types, and 25% only in fragments. Large and medium-size microhylids of the genera *Platypelis* and *Plethodontohyla* seemed the most sensitive to fragmentation, as they were detected only in continuous forest. In contrast, small microhylid species of the genera *Anodonthyla* and *Stumpffia* occurred in both forest types or only in fragments. No clear pattern was observed in the species-rich mantellid genera *Boophis*, *Gephyromantis*, and *Mantidactylus*; however, the largest mantellid species occurred in both forest types. Independent of their different habitat preferences, many mantellid species seemed to tolerate fragmentation. However, some species were not detected in forest fragments (e.g., *B. picturatus*, *G.* "*asper*" [now *G. ceratophrys*, see Vences et al. 2017c], *M. alutus*). This study showed that forest fragments cannot substitute for large continuous forest blocks but are important refuges for maintaining a large part of amphibian diversity, particularly when streams are present.

Ndriantsoa et al. (2017) investigated the effects of the quality of the matrix (the habitat outside the forest) on amphibian species richness, abundance, and assemblage composition. They compared amphibian diversity along streams in the matrix (with a narrow band of gallery forest), secondary bush and shrub vegetation, banana plantations, and rice fields, with amphibian diversity in continuous forest and forest fragments. Overall, Riemann et al. (2015) and Ndriantsoa et al. (2017) detected 62 amphibian species on standardized transects and found that the total number of species in all matrix habitats combined (43) was comparable to total species richness on transects in continuous forest (42) and forest

FIGURE 11.10 **A) and B) Deforested and fragmented landscape around Ranomafana National Park; C) an area recently cleared as a result of traditional swidden agriculture; and D) banana plantation adjacent to continuous forest.** (PHOTOS by J. C. Riemann.)

fragments (40). Total species richness within the matrix was highest along streams (35), followed by banana plantations (18), and declined severely in secondary vegetation (7) and rice fields (8). Likewise, local (per transect) species richness, relative abundance, and composition differed significantly between matrix habitats. Although amphibian diversity was affected in all matrix habitats compared to forest, matrix quality was found to be an important factor, with species richness and abundance along streams in matrix, fragments, and continuous forest being similar, thus confirming their high conservation value. However, assemblage composition changed within the habitat alteration gradient, with matrix streams most probably serving as corridors and valuable habitat. Banana plantations might act as buffer zones if they contain some trees typical of the native forest, along with understory vegetation and a layer of leaf litter. In contrast, secondary vegetation and rice fields were found to be unsuitable and acted as a barrier for most species, except for a few tolerant species and open-habitat specialists (e.g., *Heterixalus alboguttatus*, *Ptychadena mascareniensis* in rice fields). Therefore, Ndriantsoa et al. (2017) concluded that the implementation and maintenance of corridors along streams connecting forest habitats would be an important contribution to amphibian conservation on Madagascar.

Finally, Riemann et al. (2017) assessed the effects of forest fragmentation and conversion (i.e., matrix quality) on functional diversity. Functional diversity was measured in the form of functional richness and functional beta diversity based on traits associated with resource use, considering that the major ecosystem functions of amphibians are ecosystem productivity, nutrient cycling, and energy flows (Hocking and Babbitt 2014). This study revealed distinct changes in the functional structure of frog assemblages (i.e., resource-use trait composition) and complex patterns in the relationship between species richness and functional richness. Disturbed habitats were found to provide different, rather than fewer, functions compared to intact forest, and the observed changes in functional beta diversity reflected the anthropogenic disturbance gradient (from continuous forest to forest fragments to matrix) and water availability. Streams were the functionally richest habitats in all land-use categories and were considered important for ecosystem functioning. Species richness was found to be a relevant driver of functional richness, but not the only one. Functional clustering (i.e., the sharing of similar traits by many species in a community) in matrix habitats indicated a direct negative effect of human habitat alterations on functional diversity, potentially because of the dependence of environmental filters on resource availability, but such clustering was also caused by natural drivers in undisturbed terrestrial habitats. Riemann et al. (2017) showed that in systems where fragmented landscapes maintain high taxonomic diversity, functional diversity can be altered by forest fragmentation and conversion. Consequently, ecosystem processes like productivity, nutrient cycling, and energy flows could be affected, suggesting that functional aspects should be considered and addressed to a greater extent in conservation planning and future research.

LOWLAND MOIST EVERGREEN FOREST IN EASTERN MADAGASCAR

Rosa et al. (2012) conducted a survey of amphibian diversity in the Betampona protected area, a 2228 ha remnant lowland moist evergreen forest fragment in the central east. They confirmed the occurrence of 76 amphibian species, a strikingly high species number in relation to the relatively small area and narrow elevational range (275–650 m). Of these species, 36 were classified as candidate species, with 24 taxa known exclusively from there. Betampona is surrounded by a highly degraded landscape, which could lead to impoverishment of its amphibian fauna in the future. The authors suggested that a forest corridor connecting Betampona with Zahamena, the nearest protected site (40 km), via the restoration and management of the last remaining forest patches between these two sites could prevent potential amphibian species loss.

LITTORAL FOREST IN SOUTHEASTERN MADAGASCAR

Four studies investigated different aspects of forest fragmentation effects on amphibians on the coastal plain of the Anosy Region, including the oldest available data set covering fragmentation effects on Malagasy amphibians (Ramanamanjato 2000, 2008; Lehtinen et al. 2003; Lehtinen and Ramanamanjato 2006). This area is made up of littoral forest (0–20 m) growing on coastal sand, a forest type that has suffered from severe deforestation. The remaining forest habitat is severely fragmented and embedded in an extremely degraded anthropogenic sand-scrub matrix. Between six and 11 forest fragments located at Mandena (six) and Sainte Luce (five), ranging in size between 10 and 457 ha, most of which have been isolated for at least 50 years, were considered in these studies.

Ramanamanjato (2000, 2008) evaluated patch size effects on amphibian species richness and composition in all 11 fragments. He recorded 23 amphibian species and found that species richness declined monotonically with decreasing fragment size. The amphibian assemblages within the fragments showed clear nested patterns (*sensu* Atmar and Patterson 1995), with nonrandom species loss with declining fragment size. Microhylids were detected only in fragments larger than 40 ha. Forest size and degradation were correlated, and thus degradation might also have contributed to the decline of amphibian species in fragments. These studies revealed that minimum patch sizes of 200–300 ha are needed to maintain a substantial proportion of the original amphibian diversity in littoral forest fragments.

Lehtinen et al. (2003) investigated edge effects on amphibian diversity in six littoral forest fragments at Mandena and Sainte Luce. Only "hard" edges (areas with an abrupt transition between forest and the sand-scrub matrix) were studied. Six amphibian species were detected during the dry season and nine species during the wet season. All three types of edge responses were observed: edge-avoiders, interior-avoiders, and omnipresent species, but with considerable differences between seasons. During the dry season, all species present were edge-avoiders, with *Gephyromantis leucocephalus* (originally identified as *G. boulengeri*) being an edge-avoider in both seasons. All other species either showed no significant response to edge proximity (e.g., *Guibemantis annulatus*, *G. diphonus*, *G. wattersoni*) or were interior-avoiders (*Heterixalus boettgeri*) during the wet season. The authors detected microclimatic changes near edges, including higher temperatures and dew point temperatures, and higher wind speed and lower relative humidity. The reaction of species to microclimatic changes was linked to season. Finally, they suggested that edge sensitivity may be a predictor of extinction proneness.

Lehtinen and Ramanamanjato (2006) assessed rates of species loss and extinction proneness in the same littoral forest fragments. These authors found a total of 17 amphibian species in the six surveyed fragments, and amphibian assemblages in small fragments were subsets of those found in larger fragments. Their study revealed high species loss rates that steadily increased with decreasing fragment size. Compared with the largest fragment included in this study (457 ha), species loss rates ranged from 18% in the next largest fragment to 88% in the smallest fragment (10 ha). They found edge-avoidance (and not body size) to be a good predictor of extinction proneness and detected a significant negative relationship between abundance and extinction proneness. Generally, rare habitat specialists, and species that were intolerant of the matrix habitat, were particularly prone to local extinction, and species loss was likely a consequence of persistent isolation in their study system.

DRY DECIDUOUS FORESTS IN WESTERN AND NORTHERN MADAGASCAR

One study surveyed amphibian assemblages in forest fragments in northern Madagascar (Durkin et al. 2011); three fragments of dry deciduous forest in the Tsarakibany area (between Montagne d'Ambre National Park and Ankarana Special Reserve) were embedded in a matrix of grasslands and rice fields. The fragments ranged in size between 9 and 29.8 ha and were all degraded to some degree (e.g., selectively harvested for timber and partly containing banana plantations). They recorded 15 amphibian species in total, and species richness per fragment ranged between three and 11 species, being highest in the smallest fragment. These authors concluded that these forest fragments likely act as refuges for much of the remaining local amphibian diversity occurring between the two protected areas.

Another study examined species richness of amphibian communities in fragmented forests of central Menabe in western

Madagascar (Glos et al. 2008). There, smaller forest fragments contained fewer species than larger forest blocks (five and seven species versus 10 and 13 species). However, the habitat was also more disturbed (e.g., by selective logging), and amphibian breeding sites were less heterogeneous in smaller forest fragments than in larger forests, making it difficult to disentangle the effects of area size, fragmentation, and general habitat quality on amphibians.

CONCLUSIONS

Several studies addressing fragmentation and habitat alteration effects on amphibian diversity are available from different moist evergreen forest habitats of the Central Highlands and the eastern escarpment and lowlands, and only a few from the dry deciduous forests of western and northern Madagascar. Studies investigating patch size effects revealed that species–area relationships follow a linear pattern, with amphibian species richness declining with decreasing patch size. However, a study from the eastern escarpment showed that forest fragments harbor comparable numbers of frog species to continuous forest, as long as they provide suitable habitats. Such fragments are therefore contributing sensibly to the maintenance of amphibian diversity. Nevertheless, amphibian species loss occurred in all fragmented and altered habitats. In the Central Highlands and in the eastern littoral forest, amphibian assemblages in smaller fragments were subsets of those observed in larger ones. In eastern montane rainforests, habitat fragmentation and conversion and low-level logging caused species turnover (i.e., a change in species composition between frog communities), and it seems that amphibian species loss in altered habitats is rather deterministic.

Microhylids seem to be particularly sensitive to forest fragmentation. This applies especially to larger species. However, in contrast to global patterns (Sodhi et al. 2008), body size alone is not a good predictor of fragmentation sensitivity and extinction proneness for Malagasy amphibians (Lehtinen et al. 2003). Reproductive mode and sensitivity to microclimate changes best explain species' reactions to forest fragmentation and alteration, and at least in littoral forest, edge effects seem to depend on season.

In many regions of Madagascar, forest fragments are crucial for amphibian conservation, with some species known only from these fragments, and with the persistence of biodiversity in altered landscapes also depending on matrix quality. Matrix streams were found to be of high value for amphibian diversity, similar to some plantations (e.g., banana plantations that contain some native forest trees, understory vegetation, and leaf litter) that act as a buffer (Ndriantsoa et al. 2017). In contrast, rice fields and secondary grassland and bushland tend to act as strong environmental filters for most forest-dwelling species. However, if forest fragments in a hostile matrix contain all necessary habitat structures and are large enough to sustain viable populations, they can have high conservation value.

Habitat suitability and overall habitat size, as well as the structure and permeability of matrix habitats, may be of higher relevance than patch size for the persistence of amphibian diversity in human-modified landscapes. Riparian habitats are generally important for the maintenance of amphibian diversity in human-altered landscapes; thus, protecting, restoring, and reforesting riparian habitats should be a key target for conservation actions in Madagascar.

Only one study addressed functional aspects of amphibian diversity in the context of forest fragmentation and habitat alterations (i.e., matrix quality). This study revealed a distinct turnover in trait composition following an anthropogenic habitat alteration gradient (continuous forests to forest fragments to matrix habitats), and water availability. Even in systems where fragmented landscapes maintain high species diversity, the functional diversity of frog communities can be altered by habitat fragmentation and alteration, likely affecting ecosystem functioning.

Unfortunately, our knowledge of the life history and ecological traits of Malagasy amphibian species is still largely incomplete. Notably, information on reproductive and developmental biology is missing, particularly for traits known to be important in predicting sensitivity to habitat fragmentation and alteration (Henle et al. 2004). Thus, future research should focus on collecting comprehensive amphibian life history data. Furthermore, no studies are available on the effect of fragmentation on amphibian genetic diversity, and nothing is known about the minimum viable population size. This information is essential to predict the effects of fragmentation and habitat alteration on amphibian diversity. Nevertheless, ongoing deforestation and the resulting fragmentation constitute a major threat to biodiversity (Harper et al. 2007; Allnutt et al. 2008). Human populations depend on natural forest resources and ecosystem services that natural ecosystems provide (Kari and Korhonen-Kurki 2013). Thus, strategies for the sustainable use of these natural resources are urgently needed to protect amphibian diversity and maintain ecosystem services in human-altered landscapes.

The protection of continuously forested areas is of highest priority. However, considering the current level of deforestation and forest fragmentation on Madagascar, including forest fragments and suitable matrix habitats in protection programs is likely a key component to ensuring long-term amphibian conservation. Forest fragments are a vital complement to the network of larger protected areas on the island, and there should be an effort to both protect and connect remaining forest patches by corridors along matrix streams (lined with at least some riparian forest) and suitable human-modified habitats (e.g., structurally rich plantations).

Subject editors: Julian Glos, Miguel Vences, and Achille P. Raselimanana

AMPHIBIAN DISEASES AND PARASITES

M. Bletz, A. Crottini, C. Weldon, M. Vences, F. C. E. Rabemananjara, M. Fisher, and L. Du Preez

Numerous macro- and microscopic pathogens and parasites are known to infect amphibians. These include viral, bacterial, alveolate, water mold and other fungal, and metazoan agents, many of which have the potential to cause infectious disease in amphibians (e.g., chytrid fungi, ranavirus, severe *Perkinsea* infections). To most people the word *parasite* invokes a negative response, as they generally associate parasites with diseases and pathology. This is not surprising because parasites that cause malaria, such as *Plasmodium*, are responsible for the death of hundreds of thousands of people on an annual basis, and pets are often infected with fleas and other parasites, leading to veterinarian-prescribed medication. The life history of most amphibian parasites is highly efficient and in many cases does not lead to significant ill effects or disease pathologies in the amphibian host. Some pathogen-induced diseases, however—most notably chytridiomycosis (caused by the fungi *Batrachochytrium dendrobatidis*, *Bd*, and *B. salamandrivorans*, *Bsal*) and ranaviral disease—have been implicated as a major factor in amphibian population declines worldwide, making amphibians one of the most threatened animal groups on the planet.

INFECTIOUS PATHOGENS

The emergence of infectious diseases is playing a crucial role in the global amphibian decline, including on Madagascar, and a considerable portion of the efforts of the 2008 Sahonagasy Action Plan (see Crottini et al., pp. 1326–30) have been invested in addressing this threat. In 2010, Madagascar was one of the few places in the world where *Bd* had not yet been reported (Weldon and Du Preez 2008; Weldon et al. 2008, 2013), despite its nearly worldwide distribution and a large portion of the island having been reported to be highly suitable for *Bd* occurrence (Lötters et al. 2008). By that time, several surveys had already been conducted (in 2005–2010; Weldon et al. 2008; Crottini et al. 2011a, 2014b; Vredenburg et al. 2012), and all failed to report its occurrence. This made Madagascar a perfect place for preemptive measures against chytrid to be put in place.

It was under this premise that during the first ACSAM meeting the IUCN SSC Amphibian Specialist Group Madagascar started to develop a national strategy to coordinate studies on *Bd* in the hope of enabling its prompt detection. Coordinated activities to address the potential threat of *Bd* began proactively in October 2010 with the organization of a workshop on chytrid prevention held in Parc Ivoloina, and the publication of specific guidelines (Weldon et al. 2013). This course brought together around 30 national and international researchers, representative of several Malagasy nongovernmental organizations and institutions, Malagasy authorities, and conservation practitioners, and had two main outputs: 1) the establishment of the Chytrid Working Group (later transformed into the Cellule d'Urgence Chytride, or Chytrid Emergency Cell, CEC), which aimed to facilitate chytrid-related research on Madagascar; and 2) the launch of the preemptive National Monitoring Plan (NMP) for the early detection of *Bd* at prioritized sites (Weldon et al. 2013). Malagasy government support was needed to implement these plans, and this was obtained with the formal establishment of the CEC, and clear definition of its role and functions (ministerial decree no. 283/2011/MEF/SG/DGF/DVRN/SGFF), which included: 1) the coordination of the NMP and of the response actions related to *Bd* on Madagascar, 2) the development of specific protocols to prevent the arrival of *Bd*, 3) the organization of training opportunities for students, researchers, and decision-makers, and 4) the development of a fund-raising strategy to launch and maintain the NMP. The NMP for the early detection of *Bd* aimed to biannually screen (covering both the dry and wet seasons) eight selected sites across the island (Weldon et al. 2013) and to be operational from 2011 to 2015. In 2016, two sites (Mandena and Farankaraina) were removed from the monitoring program, where *Bd* had not been identified and where maintaining regular sampling proved to be particularly difficult. Furthermore, monitoring was reduced from twice per year to once. After the detection of *Bd*, different priorities were identified in the New Sahonagasy Action Plan (Andreone et al. 2016). These included the implementation and dissemination of biosafety protocols among researchers and authorities, the development of an emergency response strategy, the establishment of a national protocol to streamline permitting issues, the enhancement of mitigation research and ex situ conservation capacity, the identification of the *Bd* lineage(s), and the characterization of the associated virulence.

Biannual meetings are held by the CEC to provide updates on the findings about *Bd* and all research related to its mitigation and to provide new perspectives on preemptively mitigating the presence of *Bd* on the island. The group encourages protected area managers and all stakeholders working on biodiversity to communicate any abnormalities concerning the health of Malagasy amphibians at their respective sites to the CEC.

Bd surveys through the framework of the NMP, as well as other research projects conducted between 2005 and 2014, showed the first detection of *Bd* on Madagascar in samples collected in 2010 on the Makay Massif. Low levels of *Bd* were also detected in frogs exported from Madagascar for the pet trade in 2012 (Kolby 2014). *Bd* was subsequently detected in multiple areas, including Ranomafana and Ankaratra, in 2013 and 2014. Detection of *Bd* occurred mainly at mid- to high-elevation sites and was greater during the dry season, with low to no detection in the wet season (Bletz et al. 2015a, 2015b; Kolby et al. 2015).

While *Bd*-positive samples were detected in multiple specialized laboratories, as well as in collected samples amplified with a probe specific for the Global Pandemic Lineage (GPL) of *Bd* (Bletz et al. 2015b), it remains unclear what genotype, if any, has been detected on the island, and it is possible that the detected chytrid is not a lethal *Bd* form, or that it may even represent cross-amplification of DNA from another genus of chytrid. Detection of *Bd* in samples collected on Madagascar since 2014 as part of the NMP has been limited, and the most recent samples exhibited no trace of *Bd*, suggesting it may no longer be present at the positive collection sites.

Despite the absence of *Bd* positives among the most recently sampled frogs, continued monitoring remains imperative for early detection and effective rapid response if a lethal strain should become established in Malagasy amphibian communities. Furthermore, studies have been done on the bacterial microbiome of Madagascar's amphibians, to understand the interaction of these cutaneous bacteria with *Bd* and as part of a strategy to possibly develop probiotic *Bd* mitigation strategies (Bletz et al. 2017a, 2017b).

Ranavirus, another potentially deadly amphibian pathogen, has been surveyed for on Madagascar only once, in 2014. This viral pathogen was detected in only a small number of frogs, including one adult *Mantidactylus cowanii* and three tadpoles in Ranomafana National Park, and one adult *M. mocquardi* from Ankaratra, but it was also detected in water samples collected from two commercial amphibian export facilities in the Toamasina area (Kolby et al. 2015).

PARASITES

Although amphibians are usually small bodied, their parasites are diverse and include all major parasitic groups: protozoans, hemoparasites, ciliates, nematodes, acanthocephalans, monogenic flukes, digenic flukes, cestodes, mites, and leeches. A single amphibian host may harbor several different parasite taxa. Because of their amphibious lifestyle and their association with water or damp environments to reproduce, they are prone to parasitic infections. These characteristics all favor parasite transmission, which in turn enables the diversification of numerous taxonomic forms of parasites as well as their associated life history strategies. An extreme example of parasite abundance in a single anuran species is the African Clawed Frog *Xenopus laevis*, which hosts 25 different parasite genera (Tinsley 1996).

While studies on amphibians have increased over the past two decades, amphibians represent one of the most poorly studied vertebrate groups in terms of their parasite diversity. In this respect, Madagascar is no exception; parasites from the diverse group of Malagasy frogs have been poorly studied. However, a few isolated studies revealed that the island's frogs host a rich diversity of parasites, as either definitive or intermediate hosts (Table 11.6).

Frog hemoparasites are usually abundant in African amphibian hosts (Netherlands et al. 2015). With the diversity and abundance of anuran species and potential vectors in the form of mosquitoes, leeches, and biting flies, it can be expected that an enormous and yet undiscovered diversity remains to be found. Anuran gut ciliates have only rarely been studied on Madagascar (Maeder et al. 2019). Undescribed *Trichodina* spp. have been collected from the urinary bladder of *Blommersia blommersae*, *Heterixalus alboguttatus*, *H. punctatus*, *H. tricolor*, and *Mantidactylus curtus* (Table 11.6), and a large number of placidozoans (Opalinidae) have been described from cloacal samples of various Malagasy frog hosts (Delvinquier et al. 1998). Overall, at least 19 described species of protozoan parasites are known from Malagasy frogs.

Nematodes are typically the most abundant and species rich of all parasitic taxa. At least 14 species of nematodes are currently known from Malagasy anurans, with undescribed forms being collected from another 12 host species (Table 11.6), and possible additional species for *Ptychadena mascareniensis* (see Blommers-Schlösser and Blanc 1993: 257). In southern Africa, for example, *Amietia delalandii* (family Pyxicephalidae), hosts seven nematode species (Halajian et al. 2013; Svitin and Du Preez 2017). Many more nematodes remain to be discovered in Malagasy frogs.

For monogeneans, apart from the 12 known species, 11 undescribed morphotypes were collected from different hosts (Table 11.6). For most of these unnamed candidate species of polystomes, more parasite material is needed to enable accurate descriptions. All Malagasy polystomes have their closest relatives on the African continent, with *Metapolystoma* (Figure 11.11e) known only from Madagascar and Africa, and *Kankana* being endemic to Madagascar and having its closest relative in *Eupolystoma* from Africa and India (Héritier et al. 2015). *Madapolystoma* (Figure 11.11d) is unique among all polystomes in that it is the only viviparous form known (Landman et al. 2018). On one occasion a juvenile polystome was observed on the egg mass of a *Mantidactylus* sp. (L. Du Preez, unpublished data), and the possibility that transfer could happen to another host individual that might visit the egg mass cannot be excluded.

In contrast to monogeneans, digeneans have complex life cycles involving at least one but often more intermediate hosts. Because most amphibians spend time in or around wetlands, they are often infected with metacercariae of trematodes. The definitive host is often a bird or reptile. Only two trematodes are currently known from Madagascar, yet undescribed forms from *Heterixalus betsileo*, *Mantidactylus grandidieri*, and *Guibemantis tornieri*, and additional species from *Ptychadena mascareniensis* have been identified (L. Du Preez, unpublished data; see also Blommers-Schlösser and Blanc 1993). Although abundant in some vertebrates, cestodes are not abundant in amphibians globally, and only a single cestode has been described from Malagasy frogs. A few undescribed forms have been collected in *Guibemantis liber* and *Ptychadena mascareniensis* (L. Du Preez, unpublished data).

Four species of leeches in the genus *Malagabdella* are known from Malagasy frogs (Table 11.6). Some leeches not only feed on amphibians (Figure 11.11a) but may act as an intermediate host in the transmission of various hemoparasites (Netherlands et al. 2015). In an extensive molecular analysis of blood meals from leeches collected at Analamazaotra and Ranomafana, both mantellid and microhylid frogs were identified among their hosts (Schnell et al. 2018).

The mite *Endotrombicula madagascariensis* is known from *Aglyptodactylus madagascariensis*, *Gephyromantis luteus*, and *Mantidactylus brevipalmatus*, and a second, apparently host-specific species of the same genus, *E. ptychadenae*, from *Ptychadena mascareniensis* (Wohltmann et al. 2007). These mites penetrate the skin, primarily on the ventral side of the frog host, to form a small blister-like structure (Figure 11.11c).

TABLE 11.6. **Parasites collected from Malagasy frogs**

PARASITE GROUP	PARASITE SPECIES	HOST SPECIES	SITE IN HOST	REFERENCE
"Protozoa"	*Cepedea lemuriae*	*Boophis rhodoscelis*	Collected from host cloaca	Metcalf (1940)
	C. madagascariensis	*Heterixalus madagascariensis*	Collected from host cloaca	Metcalf (1923)
	Cepedea sp.	*Heterixalus*	Collected from host cloaca	Delvinquier et al. (1998)
	Hepatozoon neireti	*Ptychadena mascareniensis*	Blood	Laveran (1905)
	Opalina mantellae	*Mantella baroni*	Collected from host cloaca	Metcalf (1940)
	Opalina sp.	*Boophis, Mantidactylus*	Collected from host cloaca	Delvinquier et al. (1998)
	Protoopalina devinckae	*Ptychadena mascareniensis*	Collected from host cloaca	Delvinquier et al. (1998)
	P. primordialis	*P. mascareniensis*	Collected from host cloaca	Delvinquier et al. (1998)
	P. drachi	*P. mascareniensis*	Collected from host cloaca	Delvinquier et al. (1998)
	P. legeardi	*Mantidactylus lugubris, M. grandidieri*	Collected from host cloaca	Delvinquier et al. (1998)
	P. grolleaudi	*Scaphiophryne marmorata*	Collected from host cloaca	Delvinquier et al. (1998)
	P. charvisi	*S. calcarata*	Collected from host cloaca	Delvinquier et al. (1998)
	P. perantonii	*Aglyptodactylus madagascariensis*	Collected from host cloaca	Delvinquier et al. (1998)
	Trichodina sp.	*Blommersia blommersae*	Urinary bladder	L. Du Preez (unpublished data)
	Trichodina sp.	*Heterixalus alboguttatus*	Urinary bladder	L. Du Preez (unpublished data)
	Trichodina sp.	*Heterixalus punctatus*	Urinary bladder	L. Du Preez (unpublished data)
	Trichodina sp.	*Heterixalus tricolor*	Urinary bladder	L. Du Preez (unpublished data)
	Trichodina sp.	*Mantidactylus curtus*	Urinary bladder	L. Du Preez (unpublished data)
	Zelleriella madagascariensis	*Dyscophus insularis*	Collected from host cloaca	Delvinquier et al. (1998)
Nematoda	*Acanthocephalus domerguei*	*Anodonthyla montana*	Intestine	Golvan et al. (1972)
	Aplectana brygooi	*Mantella betsileo, Mantidactylus lugubris, Mantidactylus* sp., *Boophis luteus*	Intestine	Baker (1980)

PARASITE GROUP	PARASITE SPECIES	HOST SPECIES	SITE IN HOST	REFERENCE
	A. courdurieri	*Ptychadena mascareniensis*	Intestine	Chabaud and Brygoo (1958)
	Falcaustra golvani	*Boophis goudotii* or *B. madagascariensis*	Intestine	Chabaud and Brygoo (1957)
	Harentinema ambocatca	*Boophis goudotii* or *B. madagascariensis*	Intestine	Chabaud and Brygoo (1957)
	Madochotera alata	Reported as "*Rhacophorus* sp." (probably referring to a *Boophis*)	Intestine	Bain and Brunhes (1968)
	M. landauae	Reported as "*Rhacophorus* sp." (probably referring to a *Boophis*)	Intestine	Prod'hon and Bain (1974)
	M. pichoni	Reported as "*Rhacophorus* sp." (probably referring to a *Boophis*)	Intestine	Bain and Brunhes (1968)
	Paramadochotera guibei	*Gephyromantis redimitus*	Intestine	Prod'hon and Bain (1974)
	Raillietnema parapetterae	*Dyscophus antongili*	–	Prod'hon (1969)
	R. petterae	*Dyscophus antongili*	–	Prod'hon (1969)
	Rhabdias blommersiae	*Blommersia domerguei*	Lung	Kuzmin et al. (2013)
	R. madagascariensis	*Ptychadena mascareniensis*	Lung	Chabaud et al. (1961)
	R. vencesi	*Boophis madagascariensis*	Lung	Junker et al. (2010)
	Unidentified / Undescribed	*Aglyptodactylus laticeps*	Between dermis and musculature	Glaw et al. (1998)
	Unidentified / Undescribed	*Blommersia wittei*	–	L. Du Preez (unpublished data)
	Unidentified / Undescribed	*Boophis luteus*	–	L. Du Preez (unpublished data)
	Unidentified / Undescribed	*B. rufioculis*	–	L. Du Preez (unpublished data)
	Unidentified / Undescribed	*Heterixalus luteostriatus*	–	L. Du Preez (unpublished data)
	Unidentified / Undescribed	*Mantella baroni*	–	L. Du Preez (unpublished data)
	Unidentified / Undescribed	*M. expectata*	–	L. Du Preez (unpublished data)
	Unidentified / Undescribed	*M. laevigata*	–	L. Du Preez (unpublished data)
	Unidentified / Undescribed	*Mantidactylus betsileanus*	–	L. Du Preez (unpublished data)
	Unidentified / Undescribed	*M. curtus*	–	L. Du Preez (unpublished data)
	Unidentified / Undescribed	*M. majori*	–	L. Du Preez (unpublished data)

(continued overleaf)

TABLE 11.6. ***continued***

PARASITE GROUP	PARASITE SPECIES	HOST SPECIES	SITE IN HOST	REFERENCE
	Unidentified / Undescribed	*Plethodontohyla notosticta*	–	L. Du Preez (unpublished data)
	Unidentified / Undescribed	*Ptychadena mascareniensis*	–	L. Du Preez (unpublished data)
Acanthocephala	Unidentified / Undescribed	*Boophis elenae*	–	L. Du Preez (unpublished data)
	Unidentified / Undescribed	*B. madagascariensis*	–	L. Du Preez (unpublished data)
	Unidentified / Undescribed	*B. rappiodes*	–	L. Du Preez (unpublished data)
	Unidentified / Undescribed	*Ptychadena mascareniensis*	–	L. Du Preez (unpublished data)
Monogenea	*Kankana manampoka*	*Platypelis pollicaris*	Urinary bladder	Raharivololoniaina et al. (2011)
	Madapolystoma biritika	*Mantella madagascariensis*, *M. baroni*	Urinary bladder	Du Preez et al. (2010)
	M. cryptica	*Guibemantis liber*	Urinary bladder	Berthier et al. (2014)
	M. isaloensis	*Mantella expectata*	Urinary bladder	Landman et al. (2018)
	M. magnahami	*Blommersia domerguei*	Urinary bladder	Landman et al. (2018)
	M. ramilijaonae	*Guibemantis liber*	Urinary bladder	Berthier et al. (2014)
	Madapolystoma sp.	*Blommersia blommersae*	Urinary bladder	L. Du Preez (unpublished data)
	Madapolystoma sp.	*B. wittei*	Urinary bladder	L. Du Preez (unpublished data)
	Madapolystoma sp.	*Gephyromantis luteus*	Urinary bladder	L. Du Preez (unpublished data)
	Madapolystoma sp.	*G. sculpturatus*	Urinary bladder	L. Du Preez (unpublished data)
	Madapolystoma sp.	*Guibemantis tornieri*	Urinary bladder	L. Du Preez (unpublished data)
	Madapolystoma sp.	*Mantella betsileo*	Urinary bladder	L. Du Preez (unpublished data)
	Madapolystoma sp.	*M. cowanii*	Urinary bladder	L. Du Preez (unpublished data)
	Madapolystoma sp.	*M. laevigata*	Urinary bladder	L. Du Preez (unpublished data)
	Madapolystoma sp.	*M. pulchra*	Urinary bladder	L. Du Preez (unpublished data)
	Madapolystoma sp.	*Mantidactylus femoralis*	Urinary bladder	L. Du Preez (unpublished data)
	Metapolystoma ansuanum	*Boophis luteus*	Urinary bladder	Landman et al. (2021)

PARASITE GROUP	PARASITE SPECIES	HOST SPECIES	SITE IN HOST	REFERENCE
	M. brygoonis	*Ptychadena mascareniensis*	Urinary bladder	Euzet and Combes (1964)
	M. falcatum	*Boophis doulioti*	Urinary bladder	Landman et al. (2021)
	M. multiova	*B. occidentalis*	Urinary bladder	Landman et al. (2021)
	M. theroni	*B. madagascariensis*	Urinary bladder	Landman et al. (2021)
	M. vencesi	*Boophis albilabris*	Urinary bladder	Landman et al. (2021)
	Metapolystoma sp.	*Aglyptodactylus madagascariensis*	Urinary bladder	L. Du Preez (unpublished data)
Digenea	*Diplodiscus brevicoeca*	*Ptychadena mascareniensis*	Intestine	Richard et al. (1968)
	Unidentified / Undescribed	*Guibemantis tornieri*	Intestine	L. Du Preez (unpublished data)
	Unidentified / Undescribed	*Heterixalus betsileo*	Intestine	L. Du Preez (unpublished data)
	Unidentified / Undescribed	*Mantidactylus grandidieri*	Intestine	L. Du Preez (unpublished data)
	Unidentified / Undescribed	*Ptychadena mascareniensis*	Intestine	L. Du Preez (unpublished data)
Cestoda	*Nematotaenia dispar*	*Aglyptodactylus madagascariensis*	Intestine	Lühe (1910)
	Unidentified / Undescribed	*Guibemantis liber*	Intestine	L. Du Preez (unpublished data)
	Unidentified / Undescribed	*Ptychadena mascareniensis*	Intestine	L. Du Preez (unpublished data)
Hirudinea	*Malagabdella fallax*	*Boophis roseipalmatus*	Skin surface	Rocha et al. (2012)
	M. niarchosorum	*B. madagascariensis*	Skin surface	Rocha et al. (2012)
	M. vagans	*Mantidactylus* sp. aff. *grandidieri*	Skin surface	Rocha et al. (2012)
	Malagabdella sp.	*Gephyromantis luteus*	Skin surface	Rocha et al. (2012)
Acari	*Endotrombicula madagascareniensis*	*Aglyptodactylus madagascariensis*, *Gephyromantis luteus*, *Mantidactylus brevipalmatus*	Skin	Wohltmann et al. (2007)
	E. ptychadenae	*Ptychadena mascareniensis*	Skin	Wohltmann et al. (2007)

Very little is known about insects, in particular dipterans, parasitizing Malagasy amphibians. It is certain that many mosquitoes and midges suck blood from amphibians (Figure 11.11b), but no detailed assessment has yet been done. A worldwide group of dipterans that specialize on amphibians are the frog-biting midges (Corethrellidae) (Borkent 2008; see Borkent and Robert, pp. 1132–34), and species of this family have also recently been found on Madagascar (Robert and Borkent 2014).

If one takes the frog diversity of Madagascar into account, then the few parasite taxa currently known (Table 11.6) from Malagasy frogs are certainly not a true reflection of the parasite diversity present, but rather the result of limited study. To date, more than 12 different parasite species including four protozoans, three nematodes, one acanthocephalan, one monogenean, two digeneans, and one cestode have been detected from *Ptychadena mascareniensis* (Table 11.6; additional records in Blommers-Schlösser and Blanc 1993). Overall, little is known about the parasite diversity of the island's amphibians, and it remains a vastly unexplored field of study. The few specimens for which full parasite accounts exist reveal a rich parasite diversity, and with 365 frog species known from Madagascar (AmphibiaWeb 2021), we can expect that many more parasites await discovery.

FIGURE 11.11 **Selected images of parasites on Malagasy frogs. A) A leech, *Malagabdella* sp., on the eye of *Boophis madagascariensis*; B) mosquito feeding on a calling *Gephyromantis asper* male (photographed at Mandraka); C) *Endotrombicula* mites embedded in the skin of the vocal sac, upper surfaces of the toes, and thigh of a specimen of *Cophyla fortuna* (photographed at Marojejy); D) *Madapolystoma biritika* from *Mantella madagascariensis*; and E) *Metapolystoma brygoonis* from *Ptychadena mascareniensis*.** (PHOTOS A, D, and E by L. Du Preez; B and C by M. Vences.)

CONSERVATION IMPLICATIONS

Parasites survive by using resources provided by a host without offering any direct benefits to the host, possibly with costs to the host. But when do parasites become a conservation issue? Because parasite extinction is related to the probability of host extinction, a general assumption is that parasites are unlikely to threaten biodiversity without compromising their own survival (Garner et al. 2012). Traditionally, ecologists have overlooked the role that parasites play as partakers in the maintenance of healthy functioning ecosystems. However, there is growing interest in the field of conservation ecology to consider parasites in biodiversity conservation programs because of their importance to ecosystem structure and function (Christe et al. 2006). The threat imposed to the conservation of biodiversity by organisms that cause disease in their hosts is more widely recognized.

In few taxonomic groups have the consequences of disease been expressed more severely than for the amphibian chytridiomycosis pandemic. A meta-analysis of the evidence for adverse conservation consequences of chytridiomycosis indicated its role in the decline of 501 amphibian species, including presumed extinction in a staggering 90 species (Scheele et al. 2019). Yet entire communities or regions exist with infection without any apparent evidence of host declines, indicating that the mere presence of a known pathogen on its own does not necessarily constitute a conservation threat. A risk assessment that aims to identify traits of the host, parasite, and environment that render a species susceptible to disease is one approach to increase accuracy of predicting risk in populations and species. For example, one assessment of chytridiomycosis-related extinction risk indicated that host life history traits, such as low fecundity and aquatic habits, as well as restricted geographic distribution and occurrence at higher elevations, were associated with disease-driven declines (Bielby et al. 2008).

Such disease-related traits can then be used to model the most likely distribution of suspected diseases, even in geographic areas that lack disease data. Indeed, Lötters et al. (2008) identified that areas most suitable for *Bd* largely overlap with areas of highest amphibian species richness, and importantly with areas identified as in situ conservation priorities for amphibians. Spatial and temporal data should then be used to advance new priority directions of existing conservation initiatives, such as the Sahonagasy Action Plans (Andreone and Randriamahazo 2008; Andreone et al. 2016). Surveillance by conservation medicine practitioners will have to determine whether disease occurrences fit endemic, cyclical, or novel patterns of disease dynamics if threats to hosts are to be identified accurately (Garner et al. 2012).

In the case of parasites adversely affecting populations and species, scientists should be thinking about how ecosystems on Madagascar will function differently with low amphibian biodiversity. Investment in research into the understanding of ecosystem services rendered by a range of organisms may serve as a catalyst to motivate conservation. The ecological unit of a community of hosts plays a part in regulating transmission potential of parasites to other hosts, including humans. Calculating transmission risk will require a basic knowledge of which hosts are infected, the range of infection loads, and estimates of population densities for each host (Keesing et al. 2009). Once the role of a given host in a community is known, one can start predicting what would happen with parasite diversity and transmission if host species were to be lost to an infectious disease such as chytridiomycosis. The health and conservation of each individual species is therefore inadvertently linked to how other species that make up a community cope with infection. Evidence of how host species diversity reduces infection was demonstrated for the New World trematode parasite *Ribeiroia ondatrae*, responsible for limb deformities and mortality in amphibians (P. Johnson et al. 2008). In an experiment involving *R. ondatrae* infection in a single species and multi-host community, the presence of multiple hosts significantly reduced infection, resulted in fewer malformations, and increased survival.

Disease dynamics are often complex to untangle because they depend on countless intrinsic and ecological factors and become even more unpredictable in the face of environmental perturbations such as climate change. Amphibian population structures and aggregation structures will certainly respond to these changes as they adapt to new conditions and alter host-parasite relationships. Life-cycle dependency on water, for example, will likely result in concentration of amphibians at persistent water bodies in response to a drying climate. But unsustainable resources and competitive exclusion will reduce biodiversity in the long run. These and similar changes in amphibian distribution and density patterns will inevitably affect parasite transmission rates and persistence. For diseases in which transmission is host density dependent, such as chytridiomycosis, crowding in the remaining suitable habitat may increase transmission rates and threaten community-level disease outbreaks (Rachowicz and Briggs 2007).

Another driver of changes in disease dynamics that is particularly pronounced on Madagascar and can threaten amphibian populations is habitat fragmentation. Ecological theory of disease dynamics suggests that habitat patches that have suffered a reduction in size and increased isolation are more prone to introduced species and infectious disease than intact habitat (Suzán et al. 2008). The consequent change in community composition and ecosystem function will disrupt disease resilience provided by pathogen dilution by resistant hosts and regulated transmission rates.

Africa boasts eight biodiversity hotspots, regions of global importance for biodiversity conservation, of which Madagascar and the western Indian Ocean islands form one, owing to the diverse terrestrial, freshwater, and marine ecoregions (Mittermeier et al. 2004). Interestingly, biodiversity hotspots are often densely populated regions housing almost one-third of the global human population. This statistic considerably influences the way in which we should approach biodiversity conservation on Madagascar, since human occupation of these regions is a major influence on conservation practice and management. A loss of biodiversity, especially in a rich fauna such as the amphibians of Madagascar, will not only result in a thinning out of unique species but will also impose risks to human health.

Nature has, since the dawn of humanity, been a source of medicinal remedies. Amphibian skin secretions are well known for the myriad compounds they contain, including biogenic amines, and steroids such as bufotoxins, alkaloids, and peptides, many of which display biomedical potential (Clarke 1997). Although not widespread in amphibians, alkaloids are common among New World poison dart frogs (family Dendrobatidae), as well as among the mantelline frogs of Madagascar (genus *Mantella*) and in a few other groups (Daly et al. 1996). One field of biomedical research on alkaloids that has received considerable attention is their use as an antibacterial agent and their ability to enhance antibiotic activity, as summarized in Cushnie et al. (2014). Amphibians have long been a model group for scientific research that has led to breakthrough discoveries in human medicine, and an unquantifiable number of further potential discoveries will be at stake in the wake of species extinction.

Addressing the issue of disease risk to the amphibians of Madagascar will require innovative ways to document parasite diversity, abundance, and distribution if it is to effectively deal with parasites as a conservation threat. The acknowledgment that health, whether of individuals or communities, is linked through all levels of hierarchical organization to ecosystems and the landscape has led to the research discipline of conservation medicine. It is founded on the notion that a disruption in this web of connectivity will affect the well-being of all species, even humans. Conservation medicine is therefore concerned with the health component of conserving biodiversity by considering disease maintenance and transmission in endangered species, as well as ecosystem functioning (Aguirre et al. 2012). Much will depend on how effectively the gaps between traditional medical science and environmental science can be bridged by multidisciplinary teams to synthesize new approaches to monitoring, reporting, and responding to parasitemia and disease.

Subject editors: Molly Bletz, Miguel Vences, and Achille P. Raselimanana

TADPOLE COMMUNITIES AND TADPOLE DIVERSITY

J. Glos, S. H. Ndriantsoa, and A. Strauß

Tadpole assemblages in the moist evergreen forests of Madagascar stand out for (at least) two reasons: 1) as a result of the mountainous topography of this region, certain families of frogs are restricted largely to streams (not ponds), which is the major habitat for their breeding (Figure 11.12); and 2) the tadpole assemblages in these Malagasy forest streams are among the most species rich in the world. They are therefore not only impressive but also offer data to gain insight into forces shaping tadpole communities. Tadpoles of up to 22 species were detected in stream sections of only 30 m in Ranomafana National Park (Strauß et al. 2013), and a maximum of 28 species were reported in a 50 m stream section in the An'Ala moist evergreen forest in central eastern Madagascar (Vences et al. 2008). These assemblages are dominated by tadpoles of only one family, the Mantellidae, while other anuran families (Microhylidae, Hyperoliidae, and Ptychadenidae) that are known to also occur in these regions (in ponds within and outside the forest, or in environments independent of open water) are virtually absent from forest streams. Moreover, abundance of tadpoles in Malagasy streams can be impressively high, with up to 1100 individual tadpoles per 30 m of stream (Strauß et al. 2010). These numbers demonstrate the importance of tadpoles for Malagasy stream ecosystems, such as being significant grazers or food resources for other species.

This high diversity and abundance of tadpoles begs for an explanation. The total number of frog species in many of Madagascar's

FIGURE 11.12 **Common types of streams in Ranomafana National Park. Streams represent the most frequent aquatic habitat in the Malagasy moist evergreen forest. Current speed, substrate, and water depth of these streams influences the composition of tadpole communities, whereas the surrounding vegetation does not.** (PHOTOS by A. Strauß.)

moist evergreen forest habitats is around 100, which is very high but not markedly different from the number in other tropical amphibian hotspots (Vieites et al. 2009). In contrast to other tropical amphibian assemblages, however, Malagasy moist evergreen forest assemblages show a higher proportion of stream-breeding frog species in relation to pond-breeding species, likely because Malagasy forests along the topographically steep eastern escarpment simply do not offer many pond habitats. Some species breed in water-filled cavities in terrestrial plants (phytotelmata), such as leaf axils (many *Guibemantis*) or tree holes (some microhylids and *Mantella laevigata*), or nest on the forest floor (*Gephyromantis* subgenus *Gephyromantis*) (Glaw and Vences 2007), but robust data on their relative frequency and population density are lacking. Many of the small Malagasy moist evergreen forest streams are exceptional among tropical forest streams in their remarkably low density and diversity of fish (see Sparks and Stiassny, pp. 1245–60). In most of the small streams in Ranomafana National Park, for example, only eels (*Anguilla*) occur, and in low numbers.

ECOMORPHOLOGY IN TADPOLE COMMUNITIES

The high diversity of tadpoles continues from the taxonomic to the morphological and finally the functional level. Tadpole communities in moist evergreen forest streams contain a variety of morphotypes, and some are truly exceptional (Figure 11.13). However, most species have generalized tadpoles, with a moderately sized anteroventrally oriented oral disc and a partially keratinized jaw sheath, a moderate number of tooth rows and oral papillae, and a body shape adapted to a lotic and benthic habitat (e.g., relatively low fins and high caudal muscles, depressed body; Altig and Johnston 1989). This morphotype can be found in species of different genera or subgenera (e.g., *Boophis*, *Spinomantis*, *Gephyromantis*; Raharivololoniaina et al. 2006; Vejarano et al. 2006c; Randrianiaina et al. 2007, 2009; Rasolonjatovo Hiobiarilanto et al. 2010; Ndriantsoa et al. 2012), which occur in high individual numbers in all stream types. The generalized tadpoles of *Boophis* tree frogs are by far the most common in Ranomafana streams. For example, *Boophis* sp. Ca16 can be found in >90% of streams in the park, with an average abundance of >70 individuals in 30 m stream sections. There is a continuum from several almost omnipresent species to some that are rarely encountered.

A high incidence rate has also been found for tadpoles of leaf-litter frogs of the subgenus *Chonomantis* (genus *Mantidactylus*). Two of the species (*M. melanopleura* and *M. opiparis*) were each found in 60–70% of the streams in Ranomafana, though their abundance was relatively low, with fewer than 20 individuals per 30 m stream section on average (Strauß et al. 2013). *Chonomantis* tadpoles, in contrast to the previous groups, are characterized by very specialized, umbelliform oral discs ("funnel-mouthed tadpoles") and the absence of well-developed keratodonts (Grosjean et al. 2011b), indicating that these tadpoles might feed on particles from the water surface. Despite their relatively high species diversity, with up to five *Chonomantis* species co-occurring in the same stream, they are remarkably similar in their larval morphology and ecology (Grosjean et al. 2011b; Vences et al. 2016).

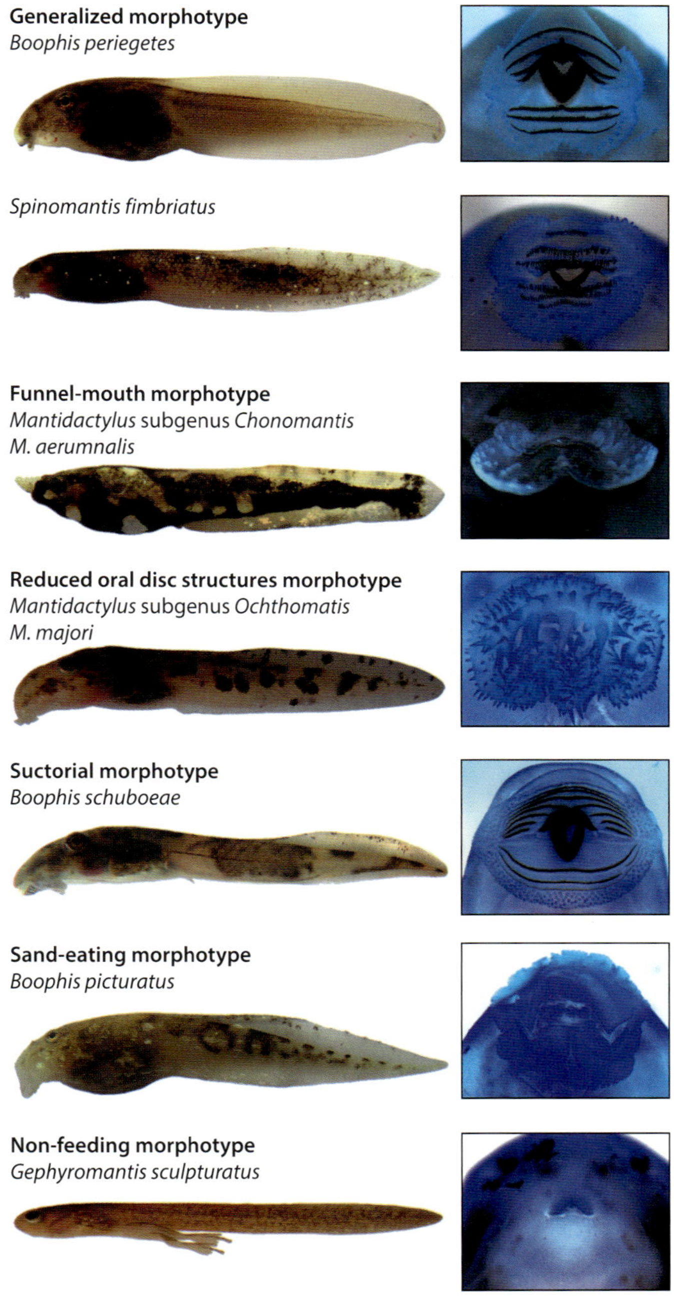

FIGURE 11.13 **Morphotype diversity of a selection of Malagasy stream-living tadpoles from Ranomafana National Park. Morphotypes are characterized by an oral disc (i.e., structure, size, and orientation) and general body shape (i.e., proportions of body, tail, and fin; eye position). Oral disc soft structures such as papillae and labia are stained with methylene blue. Black structures are keratinized structures such as labial teeth and jaw sheaths. Note that the assignment of *Mantidactylus majori* to the subgenus *Ochthomantis* needs revision (see Scherz et al., pp. 1365–68).** (PHOTOS by R.-D. Randrianiaina.)

Tadpoles of riverbank frogs (subgenera *Ochthomantis* and *Maitsomantis*, genus *Mantidactylus*) are, in terms of incidence, relatively common, with single species appearing in 20–40% of streams. Abundance is rather low, with mostly far fewer than 20 individuals per 30 m stream section. They show different degrees of reduction of their oral disc, from moderately developed to reduced oral discs and only poorly keratinized jaw sheaths and teeth, to a further reduction of oral disc structures that includes a complete lack of labial teeth (e.g., *M. mocquardi*; Randrianiaina et al. 2011b). *Mantidactylus majori*, the most derived species in this group, is characterized by the transformation of the upper jaw sheath into three thorn-shaped projections. Ecological data suggest that the tadpoles of the three most abundant species of this group at Ranomafana (*M. femoralis*, *M. majori*, and *M.* sp. 47) do not obviously differ in their choice of microhabitat. They all show a preference for stream areas with slow current and leaf-litter substrate, although the differences in their oral structures indicate that they might use different food resources.

Some species of tree frogs in the genus *Boophis* have tadpoles that are highly adapted to fast-flowing streams (Raharivololoniaina et al. 2006; Glos et al. 2007c). Single species of this group are each found in up to 35% of the streams at Ranomafana, with abundance being low for most species (fewer than 5–10 individuals per 30 m stream section) to medium (25 individuals per 30 m stream section) for *B. andohahela*. They have very large oral discs with multiple rows of both marginal papillae and labial teeth. These suctorial tadpoles seem to graze on substrate growing on submerged rocks in stream sections with strong current. Indeed, this morphotype might be a case of convergent evolution, as it may have evolved separately in the *B. albipunctatus* group, the *B. mandraka* group, and the *B. blommersae* group (Raharivololoniaina et al. 2006; Randrianiaina et al. 2012).

The most remarkable tadpole in the Malagasy moist evergreen forest stream communities belongs to the tree frog *B. picturatus*, which has an extremely derived oral disc without any keratodonts and with completely reduced jaw sheaths (Grosjean et al. 2011a). It is known to ingest sand particles, supposedly by sucking the sand through its tube-shaped mouth like a vacuum cleaner sucking dust from the floor. Sand particles mixed with organic matter were found in the anterior but not in the posterior part of the gut, suggesting that the organic matter is largely digested during its passage through the intestine. At Ranomafana, *B. picturatus* tadpoles occur in about 40% of the streams, with an average abundance of about 20 individuals per 30 m stream section.

While it is assumed that most tadpole species are general feeders—that is, they graze on organic substrate and filter small food particles out of the water—some species of *Gephyromantis* have developed a carnivorous morphology (*G. corvus*, *G. pseudoasper*, and *G. kintana*). They have been observed to actively prey on invertebrates, and on heterospecific and conspecific tadpoles (Randrianiaina et al. 2007; Reeve et al. 2011). Among them, at least one species, *G. corvus*, is exceptional, as it communicates acoustically underwater while attacking its prey (Reeve et al. 2011; observations reported under the name *G. azzurrae*). It has been assumed that the spectral frequency of the tadpole calls carries some information about tadpole size, which might be important during competitive feeding to assess the size and strength of competitors.

The nidicolous tadpoles of the forest-dwelling species of the subgenus *Duboimantis* (genus *Gephyromantis*) can rarely be observed in streams. These tadpoles have only tiny oral discs, and whether they ingest any food is unknown at this stage but they are typically considered non-feeding, so-called exotrophic larvae. Their bodies are very long and without prominent fins. Whether they need to develop in streams at some stage or are only washed accidentally into these habitats by heavy rain is unclear (Randrianiaina et al. 2011c).

COMMUNITY STRUCTURE AND ASSEMBLY IN MALAGASY TADPOLES

Different studies from Ranomafana have assessed the community structure of tadpoles, and how species are assembled in these communities. Strauß et al. (2010, 2013) showed that species richness is determined largely by the characteristics of the larval habitat (e.g., stream structure), and much less by the habitat of the adult frogs (e.g., structure of the forest surrounding the stream). In particular, a higher number of tadpole species and of tadpole morphotypes were found in wide and relatively slow-moving streams. Both rare and common species are represented in these morphotype groups of tadpoles. Studies to date suggest that the assembly of these species-rich communities is influenced mostly by environmental filtering—that is, the characteristics of specific stream types influence which tadpole species can colonize the stream. In contrast, direct competition between tadpole species does not seem to be a major structuring force in these communities.

Biodiversity is often understood mostly as the diversity of species, but there are other ways to measure diversity that may be equally important in understanding ecosystems. One such important but often neglected variable is functional diversity, which illustrates the range of ecological functions in a community. The analysis of functional diversity may disclose functional redundancy in communities and in processes of community assembly. Functional redundancy illustrates the overlap in ecological functions of community members, which may be an indicator of community resilience. At Ranomafana, with increasing species richness in stream tadpole communities, there is also an increase in the functional diversity of communities. However, the more species that co-occur, the more they overlap in their function—that is, there is a decrease in functional diversity, which is known as functional redundancy. Also, in species-rich communities, functional diversity is less than that predicted by random sampling models, also described as low functional diversity (Strauß et al. 2010, 2016). Therefore, many species within these communities are very similar with respect to their morphology, and thus probably also with respect to their ecological role in the ecosystem.

Season also plays an important role in periods of reproduction, and in associated diversity and assemblage composition, as well as in different diversity measures (Strauß et al. 2016). From the warm-wet to the cool-dry season, species richness of tadpole assemblages decreased. Functional diversity and phylogenetic diversity also decreased, but functional diversity less so and phylogenetic diversity more so than expected by chance. During the dry season, despite high functional diversity, where only species that were less similar to each other remained, tadpole assemblages were characterized by functional redundancy, as more species assembled and they overlapped more in their function. Also, communities showed relatively low phylogenetic diversity (i.e., species were more closely related to each other than expected) and phylogenetic clustering. This indicates that different assembly processes are important in different seasons of the year in this system. Accordingly, although competition between tadpole species may not be the driving force in community assembly during the wet season (Strauß et al. 2010), it might well be important during the limiting cool-dry season. The different patterns observed for functional and phylogenetic diversity indicate that functional similarity does not reflect relatedness in these tadpole communities.

POND TADPOLE COMMUNITIES IN THE EASTERN LOWLANDS AND WESTERN DRY DECIDUOUS FORESTS

In low-elevation areas, such as the eastern lowlands and in particular the dry areas of western and northern Madagascar, pond systems ranging from small puddles to lakes are the predominant breeding habitats for frogs. One crucial difference between the seasonally dry areas and the mostly permanent stream habitat of the moist evergreen forests is that these lentic systems have an often short and unpredictable period containing surface water, independent of whether they are part of a natural (e.g., dry deciduous forest) or anthropogenic ecosystem (e.g., rice paddy). As an adaptation to their temporally unpredictable habitat, many pond-breeding species have a very short embryonic (<24 hours) and larval development (e.g., only 10 days in *Aglyptodactylus laticeps*, *Scaphiophryne brevis*, *S. obscura*, published as *S. calcarata* Glos 2003), which is among the fastest known for amphibians anywhere in the world. Also, many species in this system are explosive breeders that reproduce only after very heavy rains, when ponds are full of water and when water will be present the longest.

The smaller tadpole diversity of pond communities reflects the overall smaller amphibian diversity of these systems. In the dry deciduous forests, such as Kirindy Forest CNFEREF (Glos 2006), for example, a maximum of eight species within one pond community was found. However, most communities consist of fewer species, with only a couple in very anthropogenically affected habitats, such as grassland ponds and rice paddies (mostly *Heterixalus* and *Ptychadena*).

Most tadpole species in pond systems have a generalized morphology. These generalized tadpoles belong to different genera, for example *Aglyptodactylus* (Glos and Linsenmair 2004), *Laliostoma* (Glos and Linsenmair 2004; Glaw and Vences 2007), *Heterixalus* (Raharivololoniaina et al. 2003), *Blommersia* and *Ptychadena* (Glaw and Vences 2007), and the lentic clade of *Boophis* (Glos and Linsenmair 2005; Glaw and Vences 2007). Microhylid species of the genera *Dyscophus* and *Scaphiophryne* complement these generalized species and expand the functional roles of tadpoles in these systems. *Dyscophus* tadpoles are purely filter-feeding species with no external mouthparts (Grosjean et al. 2007). Tadpoles of *Scaphiophryne*, however, are intermediate between the filter-feeding larval type typical for most microhylids and the generalized tadpole of most ranoid and hyloid frogs (Wassersug 1984). They are referred to as the psammonektonic ecomorphological guild (Glos et al. 2005; Mercurio and Andreone 2006; Grosjean et al. 2007; Grosjean and Vences 2009), as they lack keratodonts but have papillae that they use as instruments to wipe particles off the substrate or to churn up particles from the ground (Glos 2009).

The most derived lentic tadpole is *Tsingymantis antitra*, which is a microendemic in the karstic limestone of Ankarana. Tadpoles of *Tsingymantis* have strongly enlarged and keratinized jaw sheaths with strong serrations in the upper and lower jaw that are otherwise typical for oophagous tadpoles (Randrianiaina et al. 2011a). This in combination with small rock pools as larval habitat could indicate oophagy or a predatory feeding mode in *Tsingymantis* tadpoles.

Local conditions and within-site habitat diversity are important factors in community assembly. In the dry deciduous Kirindy Forest CNFEREF, the species composition of tadpole communities depends on physical properties of the breeding ponds, such as size and depth, and on their vegetation characteristics. In contrast, the communities of the nearby rock pools found in riverbeds are composed randomly (Glos 2006).

A conspicuous feature of pond tadpole communities is the frequent observation of large schools of up to several thousand tadpoles. These schools are composed of up to four different species, with *Dyscophus insularis* and *Aglyptodactylus securifer* as the most abundant species in these aggregations in dry deciduous forests (Glos et al. 2007a). The formation of tadpole schools is a reaction to predators and is induced either by the direct presence of predators or by indirect chemical cues indicating a predation risk (Glos et al. 2007b).

The species-rich tadpole communities of Madagascar have proven to represent a valuable model system to understand ecological patterns and processes. Yet their thermophysiology and physiological plasticity remain unstudied despite the crucial influence of these variables on a species' susceptibility or resilience to global warming. It also is poorly understood how tadpole communities react to introduced predators (e.g., fish or crayfish) or to pesticides, and how tadpole ecomorphological adaptations have driven evolutionary radiation (Wollenberg Valero et al. 2017). Clearly, the importance of tadpoles in understanding the ecology, evolution, and conservation of Madagascar's amphibians is paramount, and these fascinating organisms require additional study.

Subject editors: Julian Glos, Miguel Vences, and Achille P. Raselimanana

SYSTEMATIC ACCOUNTS

MANTELLIDAE, LALIOSTOMINAE: *AGLYPTODACTYLUS*

J. Köhler and F. Glaw

The genus *Aglyptodactylus* is composed of a group of six robust terrestrial frog species endemic to Madagascar that are *Mantidactylus*-like in general appearance and terrestrial in habit. *Aglyptodactylus* differs from all other mantellids except *Laliostoma* in having the first finger longer than the second, and in having digital terminal expansions that are not completely grooved (*A-glypto-dactylus* means "non-grooved finger"). With a maximum snout-to-vent length of 92 mm, females of *Aglyptodactylus* (*A. australis*) are among the largest native Malagasy frogs. Males are much smaller than females. Dorsal coloration is predominantly light beige to brown, but at the peak of breeding activity males may even become mostly yellow. A black triangle-like spot between nostril and eye is common to all species but is sometimes absent or indistinct in *A. chorus*.

Laliostoma labrosum from western Madagascar shares many general ecological and morphological features with *Aglyptodactylus*. Traditionally these genera were placed in different families, but genetic data confirmed that they are closely related, and currently they form the subfamily Laliostominae in the family Mantellidae (Vences and Glaw 2001; see Vences et al., pp. 1355–56).

SYSTEMATICS AND DISTRIBUTION

Aglyptodactylus is widespread in the forested areas of Madagascar, with two species occurring exclusively in the dry and strongly seasonal regions—*A. laticeps* is known from only three localities in the west and northwest (Kirindy Forest CNFEREF, Tsingy de Bemaraha, and Mitsinjo close to Mahajanga; Glaw et al. 1998; Rakotoarison et al. 2015b), and *A. securifer* occurs from Kirindy Forest CNFEREF in the central west to the far north of the island. Intensive searching during the rainy season may reveal that members of this genus are more widespread in the poorly explored west. Populations from the moist evergreen forests of the east and northeast of the island were formerly considered to represent the single widespread species *A. madagascariensis*. Taxonomic revision of these eastern populations revealed the existence of four distinct species (*A. australis*, *A. chorus*, *A. inguinalis*, and *A. madagascariensis*) differentiated by morphology, molecular genetics, and calls (Köhler et al. 2015). This new taxonomy restricts the distribution of *A. madagascariensis* to higher elevations (650–1510 m) of eastern and northern moist evergreen forests. Furthermore, molecular genetics revealed considerable differentiation among populations of *A. inguinalis* from eastern lowland moist evergreen forests.

ECOLOGY AND REPRODUCTION

Aglyptodactylus frogs are active during the day and night. They are frequently encountered in the leaf litter of moist evergreen forests during all seasons or in the western and northwestern dry deciduous forests after heavy rains (*A. laticeps* and *A. securifer*).

FIGURE 11.14 **Many anurans of arid western Madagascar are explosive breeders. After heavy rain at the beginning of the rainy season, certain frog species aggregate around water bodies and often call from positions on the ground or directly from the water, such as these *Aglyptodactylus securifer* individuals at Kirindy Forest CNFEREF.** (PHOTO by H. Schütz.)

Stomach content analyses indicate that eastern species of *Aglyptodactylus* feed on a variety of arthropods like spiders, orthopterans, hemipterans, ants, and beetles (Vences et al. 1999b). *Aglyptodactylus laticeps* may also be a generalized feeder, but its robust head and remains of large arthropods in its intestine indicate that it may prefer larger prey (Glaw et al. 1998).

Aglyptodactylus species have aquatic egg deposition, axillary amplexus during mating (the coupling of male and female frogs during egg laying and fertilization), and no femoral glands (Blommers-Schlösser 1979a). Males have black keratinized nuptial pads on the inner fingers during the breeding season, and males with numerous keratinized spicules on throat and belly have also been documented (Köhler et al. 2015). The reproduction of western *Aglyptodactylus* species is typical for amphibians inhabiting strongly seasonal environments. Breeding activity is more or less explosive in all species, with mating and egg deposition taking place at the beginning of the rainy season (mainly December or January). At that time, large aggregations of calling males and amplectant couples have been observed (Glos 2003; Köhler at al. 2015; Figure 11.14). The eggs are laid in lentic (still), often temporary water bodies. In this genus, egg numbers are very high and egg size is very small: the clutch size of a single *A. laticeps* female was up to 4130 eggs of about 1 mm diameter, the largest clutch size known for any Malagasy frog (Glaw et al. 1998). Tadpoles develop quickly into froglets (Glos and Linsenmair 2004). This reproductive mode is used by the great majority of amphibians occurring in arid regions of the island, but by only a small portion of species in the moist evergreen forests (Glaw and Vences 1997c). The presence of explosive breeding and high numbers of eggs, even in *Aglyptodactylus* species in moist evergreen forests, led to the hypothesis that the genus might have its origin in the dry west (Vences et al. 2000b).

The advertisement calls of all known species of *Aglyptodactylus* are emitted at night, or sometimes the day during or after very heavy rains, and consist of multiple rather loud and strongly pulsed notes. Although similar in general structure and characteristics, calls among the species all differ distinctly in temporal parameters. This is important to note, as cases of sympatry of two *Aglyptodactylus* species were reported for the dry west (*A. securifer* and *A. laticeps*; Glaw et al. 1998), and at several localities in medium-altitude moist evergreen forest, more than one species might occur locally (Köhler et al. 2015).

Subject editors: Jörn Köhler, Miguel Vences, and Achille P. Raselimanana

MANTELLIDAE, LALIOSTOMINAE: *LALIOSTOMA*

M. Vences, F. Glaw, and M. Pabijan

The Malagasy bullfrog *Laliostoma labrosum* is the only species in its genus and belongs to the subfamily Laliostominae. It is part of the Malagasy-Comorian family Mantellidae but differs from all other mantellids by the absence of an intercalary element between the ultimate and penultimate phalanges of the fingers and toes. Because of this character, it was historically not recognized as a member of the mantellid clade and was instead incorrectly assigned to the non-Malagasy genus *Tomopterna*, based on superficial morphological resemblance caused by convergent adaptations (see Vences et al. 2000b).

MORPHOLOGY

Laliostoma labrosum is a rather stout, terrestrial, and mostly nocturnal frog (sometimes diurnal during rains) with a large inner metatarsal tubercle, typical for burrowing frogs (Figure 11.15). Females reach up to 80 mm snout-to-vent length, as compared to the smaller males at 42–48 mm. The dorsal coloration is brown with variable, rather symmetric light or dark, sometimes greenish markings. A median light stripe can be present. A characteristic (sometimes interrupted) light vertical bar runs from the anterior edge of the eye to the upper lip, forming a "face" pattern typical of the species. The feet are moderately webbed, the terminal tips of fingers and toes are not expanded into discs, and the feet have a well-developed external metatarsal tubercle used for burrowing. When hind limbs are appressed forward along the body, the tibiotarsal articulation reaches the eye.

DISTRIBUTION AND GENETIC DIFFERENTIATION

Laliostoma labrosum is distributed mainly in arid western Madagascar (Blommers-Schlösser and Blanc 1991). It approaches the moist evergreen forests both in the Central Highlands (in the drier areas of Ambalavao and Itremo) and in the southeast close to Tolagnaro. Exceptionally, it has also been found within moist evergreen forest, for example near Benavony in the Sambirano Region (Glaw and Vences 1994). The species also occurs in Madagascar's far north at Montagne des Français (Vences and Glaw 2000), although old records from this area were considered unreliable (Blommers-Schlösser and Blanc 1991).

This species is not strongly differentiated across its range. Bioacoustic data from three localities in southern and western Madagascar (Tolagnaro, Toliara, and Kirindy Forest CNFEREF) did not reveal differences between these populations. Genetically, Pabijan et al. (2015) demonstrated the existence of several mitochondrial

FIGURE 11.15 ***Laliostoma labrosum* individual from near Bealanana.** (PHOTO by M. Vences.)

phylogroups with shallow divergence of up to 1.1% in the 16S rRNA gene, often co-occurring in contact zones. This implies differentiation in five potential refugia in northern, western, and southwestern Madagascar, perhaps as a consequence of Pleistocene range fragmentation during drier and cooler climates, with subsequent expansion and secondary contact. The deepest phylogroups were found in the south, indicating a possible origin of the species in this region, with ensuing stepwise dispersal northward. Multi-locus analysis demonstrated relatively high levels of regional population connectivity in *Laliostoma*, suggesting a mobile species with low breeding site fidelity. Given the vast areas that flood in western Madagascar during heavy rains, gene flow may also occur via tadpoles dispersing in these large, interconnected temporary water bodies. Interestingly, gene flow among populations north and south of the Sambirano River seemed strongly restricted, suggesting that the coastal Sambirano forest may act as a barrier to this species, which is adapted to open and arid areas.

ECOLOGY AND REPRODUCTION

As far as is known, *Laliostoma labrosum* is an explosive breeder that reproduces in stagnant water bodies following heavy rains (e.g., Mori et al. 2015). It often occurs sympatrically with other pond-breeding anurans such as *Scaphiophryne calcarata*, *S. obscura*, *Ptychadena mascareniensis*, *Boophis tephraeomystax*, *B. doulioti*, and species of *Heterixalus*. Beetles, spiders, orthopterans, and small frogs have been recorded among the prey items taken by *L. labrosum* (Vences et al. 1999b).

Laliostoma labrosum males have a single subgular vocal sac and call at night from the ground and close to breeding ponds. The vocal sac is laterally blackish, and males in breeding condition have distinct black nuptial pads on the first finger. The advertisement call is a loud and fast series of up to 46 short notes, with a note duration of 15–22 ms, intervals of 30–44 ms, and a note repetition rate of 17–19 per sec. Up to more than 1500 blackish eggs of 1–2 mm diameter were found in preserved females (Vences et al. 1999c). Tadpoles form large schools in temporary ponds and puddles and co-occur with those of *P. mascareniensis*. The tadpoles of *L. labrosum* are of generalized morphology, uniformly silvery gray with a silvery belly. Maximum total length of tadpoles is about 45 mm. They have one continuous and five interrupted rows of keratodonts (labial teeth) on the upper lip, and three continuous rows on the lower lip (keratodont formula 1:5+5/3) (Schmidt et al. 2009a). Metamorphosing young measure 16–19 mm snout-to-vent length.

CONSERVATION

The species is widely distributed and often occurs in open habitats of little agricultural value, as well as in urban areas (Gardner and Jasper 2009), and is able to breed in temporary ponds and puddles. It is therefore not considered threatened.

Subject editors: Miguel Vences and Achille P. Raselimanana

MANTELLIDAE, BOOPHINAE: *BOOPHIS*

C. R. Hutter, M. Vences, and J. E. Cadle

The bright-eyed tree frogs of the genus *Boophis* are among the most recognizable and species-rich frog genera on Madagascar (with one species present on the nearby Comoro archipelago). As of June 2021, there were 79 accepted species (one of which is endemic to Mayotte) and at least two dozen candidate species (Vieites et al. 2009; Hutter et al. 2018b; AmphibiaWeb 2021), many of which were identified only by highly divergent DNA sequences from tadpole samples. *Boophis* tree frogs have experienced a recent increase in recognized diversity because of the integration of DNA barcoding with bioacoustic analyses that have aided in distinguishing the large amount of cryptic diversity; this has led to the description of 36 new species since 2001 (e.g., Glaw et al. 2001, 2010, 2018, 2019; Vences and Glaw 2002; Köhler et al. 2007, 2008; Wollenberg et al. 2008a; Vences et al. 2012; Penny et al. 2014; Hutter et al. 2015).

FIGURE 11.16 **Representative species of all *Boophis* species groups. The *B. tephraeomystax* group corresponds to the subgenus *Sahona*; all other species groups are in the subgenus *Boophis*.** (PHOTOS by C. R. Hutter.)

SYSTEMATICS

Historically, Guibé (1978) placed most Malagasy tree frogs into the Asian genus *Rhacophorus* based on morphological similarity. Later, Blommers-Schlösser (1979b) recognized *Boophis* as distinct because of the absence of the foam egg nests that *Rhacophorus* uses for reproduction, but *Boophis* was still included in the family Rhacophoridae. With the first molecular phylogenetic evidence, *Boophis* was placed in the family Mantellidae alongside other endemic Malagasy lineages (*Aglyptodactylus*, *Laliostoma*, *Mantella*, and *Mantidactylus*; Richards and Moore 1998; Richards et al. 2000; Vences and Glaw 2001), and it became clear that rhacophorids (the sister group of mantellids) do not occur on the island.

Boophis has been divided into two monophyletic subgenera: *Boophis* and *Sahona*, based on molecular evidence with support from different aspects of their natural history (Glaw and Vences 2006). Species in the subgenus *Boophis* are generally found in moist evergreen forests, including more montane habitats, in eastern and northern Madagascar and are mostly stream-breeding specialists (Glaw and Vences 2006). Species in the subgenus *Sahona* are distributed mainly in the lowland moist evergreen forests and also in the arid regions of western and southern Madagascar, and they breed predominantly in ponds and other standing-water habitats (Glaw and Vences 2006; Glaw et al. 2019). The subgenus *Boophis* has a greater species richness than *Sahona* (69 versus 10 species) and as a result has been divided into nine named species groups (Figure 11.16) to aid in understanding this species-rich subgenus: *B. albilabris* group, *B. albipunctatus* group, *B. blommersae* group, *B. goudotii* group, *B. luteus* group, *B. majori* group, *B. mandraka* group, *B. microtympanum* group, and *B. rappiodes* group (Glaw and Vences 2006; Hutter et al. 2018b).

Blommers-Schlösser (1979b) initially diagnosed seven species groups within the genus based on morphology and bioacoustics. Several of these groups (*B. opisthodon* group, *B. pauliani* group, and *B. rhodoscelis* group) were later abandoned based on morphology (Blommers-Schlösser and Blanc 1991) or molecular phylogenetic evidence (Glaw and Vences 2006). Glaw and Vences (2006) defined the *B. mandraka* group and the *B. albipunctatus* group and transferred the *B. tephraeomystax* group to the subgenus *Sahona* using molecular phylogenetic evidence. Some species were recently placed in a newly created *B. ulftunni* group (Köhler et al. 2008; Wollenberg et al. 2008a), but this group was later dissolved and the species included in the *B. majori* group based on molecular evidence (Hutter et al. 2018b). This latter study also created the new *B. blommersae* group to accommodate lineages that were previously considered *B. majori* group frogs but were not closely related to those or convergent in morphology. Finally, Hutter et al. (2018b) estimated a first comprehensive multi-locus molecular phylogeny for *Boophis* and supported many of the previous systematic results, while providing strong statistical support for these relationships. Despite this, some affiliations among species groups remain unclear, and future systematic work should address these questions.

MORPHOLOGY

Boophis can be distinguished from other mantellid frogs (and other arboreal frogs of Madagascar) by a combination of morphological characters. All *Boophis* species share the following morphological traits: presence of an intercalary element between the ultimate and penultimate phalanges of fingers and toes; presence of nuptial pads and absence of femoral glands in males; absence of gular glands in males; enlarged terminal discs of fingers and toes; lateral metatarsalia separated by webbing; and absence of an outer metatarsal tubercle. Apart from being distinct from other mantellids (except some large arboreal *Guibemantis* species that much resemble *Boophis* at first glance: *G. depressiceps*, *G. kathrinae*, *G. diphonus*, *G. timidus*, and *G. tornieri*), *Boophis* species generally have a markedly conserved external adult morphology (Wollenberg Valero et al. 2017). Important to *Boophis*, however, is the coloration of the body and eyes (Figure 11.17); eye coloration is often used as a diagnostic character (Glaw et al. 2010, 2018).

Generally, males are smaller than females. Apart from this conserved external morphology, body size varies strongly among *Boophis* species, where different body sizes have evolved independently throughout the radiation. Species groups (Wollenberg et al. 2008a; Glaw et al. 2010; Hutter et al. 2018b) in some cases contain species of similar sizes, but in other cases (*B. goudotii* and *B. majori* groups) they contain species with a rather wide range of body sizes (Glaw and Vences 2007; Hutter et al. 2018b).

The tadpoles of *Boophis* have evolved a remarkable ecomorphological diversity and are the most well known among Malagasy frogs (see Glos et al., pp. 1350–53). Generally, tadpoles that inhabit fast-flowing streams have enlarged suctorial mouthparts and are collected while adhering to a rocky substrate. In fact, such suctorial tadpoles are found only in fast-flowing streams (Strauß et al. 2013). They differ from the slow-flowing stream and pond species, which have reduced suctorial mouthparts and sometimes other adaptations. One striking example is the greatly reduced keratinized mouthparts of *B. picturatus*, where the gut contents suggest that the tadpole ingests sand particles, unique among anuran tadpoles (Grosjean et al. 2011a).

REPRODUCTION

Boophis species are nocturnal tree frogs that communicate acoustically mostly during the rainy season and aggregate around water bodies, often in high abundance (Glaw and Vences 2007). Species in the subgenus *Boophis* reproduce mainly near streams, while those in the subgenus *Sahona* reproduce near standing water such as ponds (Andreone et al. 2002; Vences et al. 2002a). Despite the rapid increase in recognized diversity and bioacoustic studies, the reproductive behavior of *Boophis* is not well known. It seems clear, however, that in contrast to the mantellines, which deposit their eggs outside the water, all *Boophis* species lay eggs directly into the water while the couple is in axillary amplexus (i.e., the male clasps the female behind the forelimbs; Figure 11.18). For a discussion of other sexually dimorphic characters of *Boophis*, see Cadle (1995).

At least some species in the *B. albilabris* group show a remarkable scramble-competition mating behavior, described in detail for *B. tsilomaro* (under the name *B. occidentalis*; Andreone et al. 2002). After heavy rains, males form dense aggregations. They remain half-submerged in shallow lentic pools in slow-flowing streams (and several on surrounding trees), while vocalizing in choruses to attract females. Only a single record of a *B. tsilomaro* female in amplexus has been reported, where several males within an aggregation of about 90 individuals attempted amplexus of the female already engaged in this activity. Egg deposition by the pair was observed, whereby the female attached a considerable clutch of large, pigmented eggs to stones while submerged in the water. In this species, sexual size dimorphism seems to be limited, and males may even be larger on average than females, as is often the case in anurans where fighting between males occurs (Shine 1979; Kupfer 2007).

Linsenmair and Glos (2005) described the reproductive ecology of *B. doulioti* and *B. xerophilus* of the subgenus *Sahona*. These species are distributed in western and southern Madagascar, where

FIGURE 11.17 **Two *Boophis viridis* individuals from Andasibe. The function of the bright, species-specific iris coloration in Malagasy tree frogs is unknown but may be related to intraspecific communication.**
(PHOTO by M. Vences.)

FIGURE 11.18 **Reproduction in *Boophis*. A) Males of *B. tsilomaro* (from Anabohazo) form dense aggregations after heavy rains, with scramble competition for females. B) A mating pair of *B. luciae* from Anosibe An'Ala. Species of the Boophinae and Laliostominae show axillary amplexus (female clasped by the male in the axillary region), unlike the Mantellinae, in which no strong mating amplexus exists.** (PHOTOS by G. M. Rosa and J. Köhler.)

ponds and isolated lentic pools in streams are described as the breeding habitat, with the two species differing in the size of these pools. Clutch sizes were also reported from these species, with about 1000–4800 eggs within each clutch.

Advertisement calls of *Boophis* tree frogs are often loud and distinct, with clear differences between closely related species, and their bioacoustics have been critical in triggering the accelerated rate of species discovery in this genus (Köhler et al. 2007, 2008; Glaw et al. 2010; Hutter et al. 2015). As a result, the advertisement calls of most species are well known. *Boophis* can have several different call types, with type 1 being the most commonly described advertisement call, and type 2 a lesser-known type that could be related to territoriality (Glaw and Vences 2007; Glaw et al. 2010). The calls within *Boophis* are variable and can range from high-pitched ringing calls to lower-frequency groans (Vences et al. 2006). Advertisement calls between closely related species typically vary in note duration or note repetition rate (e.g., Vences et al. 2012; Hutter et al. 2015). In many cases the call structure is quite stereotyped, but in a few species, especially in the *B. goudotii* group, a highly variable repertoire of call variants is known (Narins et al. 2000).

ECOLOGY

The life span of *Boophis* species is characterized by mid-longevity, where individuals reach sexual maturity in 1–3 years and live 3–9 years (Tessa et al. 2017). The duration of embryonic development in species of the subgenus *Sahona*, reproducing in often temporary ponds, was about 24 hours, where hatchlings remained attached to the jelly mass for about 12 hours before freely swimming (Linsenmair and Glos 2005). Time to metamorphosis appears to vary; reports range from one to six months (Linsenmair and Glos 2005; Edmonds et al. 2016), but a larval period of one year or more is possible for the montane species *B. laurenti*, *B. microtympanum*, and *B. williamsi* (Blommers-Schlösser 1979b; Thomas et al. 2005).

The diet of *Boophis* frogs is known for only a few species, but adults are all likely to be opportunistic feeders, preying mostly on arthropods. The best-known species is the large-bodied *B. goudotii*, where the literature reports insects being found in its stomach contents (Arnoult and Razarihelisoa 1966). In addition, *B. goudotii* has been reported to feed on other species of frogs, including other *Boophis* species (Glaw and Vences 1997a; Ndriantsoa et al. 2014).

Boophis frogs are also a component of the diet of other organisms. Snakes in particular have been reported to feed on them (Hutter et al. 2018a), and certainly they are consumed by numerous birds, as has been found for *Tyto alba* (Barn Owls) (Goodman et al. 1993b). In addition, the tadpoles of *Boophis* have been known to be components of the diet of other organisms, such as crustaceans (Rosa et al. 2014b).

DISTRIBUTION AND BIOGEOGRAPHY

Boophis is a widespread genus throughout Madagascar; however, species from the subgenus *Boophis* are found predominantly in the moist evergreen forests, while the subgenus *Sahona* is widespread throughout the lowlands and also found in the more arid regions (Glaw and Vences 2007; Hutter et al. 2018b). The lowland and medium-altitude moist evergreen forests have the highest species richness of *Boophis* (Brown et al. 2014, 2016).

According to phylogeny-based reconstructions, these Malagasy tree frogs (or at least the subgenus *Boophis*) may have initially diversified in forested regions of eastern Madagascar above 700 m (Hutter et al. 2018b). It has been hypothesized that after this initial diversification, ancestral subgenus *Boophis* species then dispersed to the lowlands. Further, the absence of tadpole predators in montane streams may have been a key factor leading to a rapid radiation and high species richness of *Boophis* in eastern Madagascar (see Glos et al., pp. 1350–53).

CONSERVATION

The dominant threat to *Boophis*, as with the vast majority of Malagasy forest-dwelling frogs, is natural habitat loss. Most species of *Boophis* (except most species in the subgenus *Sahona* and other generalist species) depend on relatively intact forest and the associated stream environments. Among species that have been assessed by the

IUCN, five have been listed as Critically Endangered and 18 as Endangered, with only three species remaining Data Deficient (IUCN 2019). The dominant trend for these 23 threatened species is habitat loss. Exacerbating this threat is that many *Boophis* species are microendemic and have very small ranges, so habitat loss strongly impacts these taxa. Even more problematic is that many of these microendemic species may represent species complexes, which would further fragment known distributions as new species are described (Perl et al. 2014; Hutter et al. 2018b; Scherz et al. 2019a). Therefore, further taxonomic research is needed for these candidate species, which will likely result in the further splitting of current species ranges and reveal that many more species are more threatened than currently understood. Finally, captive-breeding programs have been successful with *B. pyrrhus* (Dawson et al. 2014; Edmonds et al. 2016).

Subject editors: Carl R. Hutter, Miguel Vences, and Achille P. Raselimanana

MANTELLIDAE, MANTELLINAE: *MANTELLA* AND *WAKEA*

M. Vences, A. Crottini, F. C. E. Rabemananjara, C. Randrianantoandro, and G. A. Tsiorisoa

Malagasy poison frogs, genus *Mantella*, are part of the family Mantellidae and certainly qualify as the most prominent amphibians of Madagascar. They merit this title for numerous reasons. The spectacular aposematic or warning coloration of several species is one aspect of their attractiveness. They are also diurnal and move on the ground in relatively exposed places, making them more likely to be observed than most other frogs. Furthermore, the dietary skin toxins, color polymorphism of some species, and fascinating breeding biology of *M. laevigata* qualify them as a rewarding subject of pharmacological and evolutionary studies and make them attractive for the pet trade.

The second genus that is briefly treated here contains very different frogs at first glance: *Wakea* frogs are small, inconspicuous, probably nocturnal, and poorly known. However, they are phylogenetically the sister clade of *Mantella* and therefore can provide important hints toward understanding the evolutionary origins of the remarkable features observed in *Mantella*.

HISTORY OF RESEARCH ON *MANTELLA*

The first species of *Mantella* were described in 1872 by A. Grandidier, *M. madagascariensis* and *M. betsileo*. On the basis of their coloration and external morphology, he considered them members of the otherwise Neotropical genus *Dendrobates*—an understandable error, considering the remarkable similarity of some *Mantella* species to certain species of poison dart frogs in the genera *Dendrobates* and *Phyllobates* (family Dendrobatidae). Boulenger (1882) first noted the distinctiveness of the Malagasy taxa and erected the genus *Mantella*. A few additional species were described in the following decades, based mainly on differences in coloration. However, 100 years after Boulenger's description of the genus, most herpetologists recognized only four or five species, and data on their biology and ecology remain almost nonexistent (Guibé 1978; Busse 1981).

Andreone (1992) provided field data from An'Ala in central eastern Madagascar. In this study he described the sympatric occurrence of similar *Mantella* forms, indicating that our working knowledge of species limits was still far from complete. Daly et al. (1996) provided detailed information on skin toxins of this genus and on distribution and habitat of several species. Vences et al. (1998b, 1998c) used allozyme and osteological data to assess the relationships among *Mantella* species, followed by a comprehensive taxonomic revision (Vences et al. 1999a). Since then, research on *Mantella* species has exploded, with numerous studies on their molecular phylogenetics, phylogeography and population genetics, skin toxins, distribution, behavior, and natural history.

TOXICITY AND APOSEMATISM

One of the most interesting aspects of *Mantella* evolution is the origin of their bright coloration, which in at least some species is certainly not cryptic. Similar to several other, unrelated groups of frogs, including the South and Central American dendrobatids, *Mantella* species sequester alkaloids into their skin and are therefore unpalatable or even toxic to potential predators (Daly et al. 1996). Recent evidence indicates that these alkaloids are not synthesized by the frogs themselves but rather are accumulated from alkaloid-containing food. Therefore, the alkaloid cocktail of each *Mantella* population, and indeed of each single individual, will differ. Careful handling of a *Mantella* frog with bare hands is typically not harmful to humans—however, we once suffered a very strong, painful burning sensation on our skin after taking measurements of *M. crocea*, probably caused by a particularly bioactive alkaloid compound in the skin of the handled frogs. The alkaloid compounds in *Mantella* are varied and include allopumiliotoxins, pumiliotoxins, dehydrodesmethylpumiliotoxins, 5,8-disubstituted- and 5,6,8-trisubstituted-indolizidines, dehydro-5,8-disubstituted indolizidines, 3,5-disubstituted pyrrolizidines, spiropyrrolizidines, and tricyclic alkaloids (Daly et al. 1996, 2008; Clark et al. 2005, 2006; Andriamaharavo et al. 2015). *Mantella* skin has also been found to contain an endogenous bile acid and dietary sucrose (Clark et al. 2012). Species, populations, and individuals of *Mantella* differ in their alkaloid profiles (Daly et al. 2008; Andriamaharavo et al. 2015), and seasonal differences are apparent as well (Moskowitz et al. 2018), probably dependent on the nature and availability of alkaloid-containing prey items, which in turn depend on geographic location and microhabitat. *Mantella* frogs, similar to dendrobatids and other alkaloid-accumulating frogs, prey mostly on small arthropods, including ants and mites taxa that are known to contain alkaloids (Saporito et al. 2004; Clark et al. 2005).

They are relatively small frogs, with adult body sizes of 18–30 mm from snout to vent. A detailed study of *M. aurantiaca* (Woodhead et al. 2007) suggested that at least this species may not specialize on preying on alkaloid-containing prey items but instead consumes ants and mites simply because these arthropods are abundant in the leaf litter inhabited by the frogs. Available data suggest that oribatid mites—rather than ants—may be the primary source of alkaloids in *Mantella*, especially in species living in swamp forest (Andriamaharavo et al. 2015).

Several of the unique characteristics of *Mantella* are intricately related to each other, forming a fascinating complex of coevolving traits (Vences et al. 1998a). One can, for example, speculate that increasing uptake of alkaloid-containing prey required a strategy to dispose of these toxic compounds, which was achieved partly by sequestering them via the skin. Increased metabolic activity caused by consumed alkaloids required higher feeding intensity and favored more active feeding behavior and a shift to diurnality, and in turn, evolution of aposematic coloration to alert and discourage potential predators. Connected to this, morphological transformations such as reduction of maxillary teeth and evolution of a narrow tongue took place to achieve a more efficient uptake of small, alkaloid-containing prey. How these events were causally and temporally related to each other makes a fascinating field for future research. For dendrobatid frogs, the analysis of Santos and Cannatella (2011) suggested two scenarios: either chemical defense and conspicuousness preceded greater aerobic capacity, which in turn favored the gathering of small prey; or diet specialization and greater aerobic capacity evolved in tandem, and both traits subsequently facilitated the evolution of aposematism. Very little is known about potential predators of *Mantella*; Jovanovic et al. (2009b) report on a *Zonosaurus* lizard and a *Thamnosophis* snake preying on *M. aurantiaca*.

A common feature in several *Mantella* species groups is polymorphism of color and pattern, at both the intra- and interspecific level. There are several instances of species, often not closely related to each other and occurring in sympatry, that are chromatically extremely similar: *M. manery* and *M. laevigata* at Marojejy, and *M. madagascariensis* and *M. baroni* at Ranomafana (Figure 11.19) and in the Mangabe area. Also, *M. milotympanum* and *M. aurantiaca* are strikingly similar to each other and occur in close geographic proximity, and *M. pulchra* and *M. nigricans* can easily be confused at first glance and are both found in the north-central east of the island, even if they have not yet been recorded from exactly the same sites. It is appealing to speculate that these chromatic similarities may have originated by Müllerian mimicry, in which two noxious species evolve a similar aposematic pattern that reinforces the signal to predators (Schaefer et al. 2002). However, at the same time, other populations of *Mantella* show a confusing diversity in pattern, which is especially striking in the *M. crocea-milotympanum* complex (Chiari et al. 2004; Crottini et al. 2019; Klonoski et al. 2019), but also in some populations assigned to *M. baroni*, for example from the Andringitra Massif (Rabemananjara et al. 2007a), and in *M. expectata* and *M. betsileo* from the Isalo Massif (Cocca et al. 2018), as well as in some populations of *M. viridis* in northern Madagascar (Crottini et al. 2012a). It is likely that a combination of predator-induced natural selection, sexual selection (mate choice), and hybridization led to this overall very complex pattern, and detailed genomic studies are needed to elucidate the causes and consequences of chromatic variation in these frogs.

FIGURE 11.19 **Two *Mantella* species that are very similar in color pattern but belong to different species groups, probably suggesting mimicry. The left image shows *M. baroni* and the right image *M. madagascariensis*. Both individuals were found in close syntopy at Ranomafanakely (Ranomafana National Park).** (PHOTOS by M. Vences.)

LIFE HISTORY AND REPRODUCTION

A further fascinating pattern in *Mantella* is the reproductive behavior of one species, *M. laevigata* (Glaw and Vences 1992b; Glaw et al. 2000b; Heying 2001; Oetter et al. 2001; Fischer et al. 2019). All *Mantella* species deposit unpigmented eggs outside the water, and in most species clutches of mostly up to 130 eggs are deposited in leaf litter or on rocks; the tadpoles, of rather generalized morphology (Jovanovic et al. 2009a), are flushed by rain into swamps or streams. Tessa et al. (2009) observed lower egg numbers in clutches of moist evergreen forest–specialized *Mantella* groups compared to those living in more open areas, with the lowest number in *M. cowanii* (37 ± 15 eggs per clutch) and the highest number in *M. viridis* (115 ± 21). The semiarboreal, moist evergreen forest–dwelling *M. laevigata* does not fit this pattern. Instead, this species repeatedly lays single eggs just above the water level of water-filled tree holes or water-filled bamboo nodes (Figure 11.20). Development takes place in these cavities, but food for the tadpoles in these microhabitats is limited. The tadpoles are omnivorous and readily eat eggs and embryos of the same species. Strikingly, their mother often actively feeds them by depositing unfertilized eggs into the tree cavities, but in general the social behavior of *M. laevigata* is rather flexible, and in captivity, not all females feed eggs to their tadpoles. Fischer et al. (2019) found that mothers of *M. laevigata* provision tadpoles not only with nutrients but also with defensive alkaloids by egg feeding; this nursing behavior was associated with activity in similar brain regions as in Neotropical poison frogs.

Overall, *Mantella* frogs are relatively short-lived animals, reaching four years of age in the wild and attaining sexual maturity in their first or second year (Jovanovic and Vences 2010; Andreone et al. 2011). Based on preliminary mark-recapture studies, local population sizes of *Mantella* have been estimated to consist of around 50–200 individuals (Rabemananjara et al. 2008a), but these data refer to individuals at particular reproduction sites in swamps or along streams, and in some cases they are heavily biased toward males. However, these values illustrate that at particular sites and times of year, *Mantella* can occur in high densities.

SYSTEMATICS

The genus *Mantella* is divided into several species groups, which were first defined by Vences et al. (1999a) and subsequently refined based on molecular phylogenetic analyses (Schaefer et al. 2002; Chiari et al. 2004; Crottini et al. 2019). Some of these groups consist of very closely related species, and in some cases their species status will require additional scrutiny. In other cases, the species are well defined and genetically highly divergent from each other, despite their chromatic similarities (e.g., *M. madagascariensis*, *M. baroni*).

Molecular data from nuclear and mitochondrial genes (Crottini et al. 2019) agree in placing the *M. bernhardi* group (with a single species, *M. bernhardi*) as the most divergent species of Malagasy poison frog and sister to the clade containing all other *Mantella* species. This enigmatic species is rather small, with a snout-to-vent length of 19–22 mm, and differs from all other species of the genus by its cricket-like trilling call. The species was described from a forest close to Tolongoina, and at the time it was unknown outside this region (Raxworthy and Nussbaum 2000) and was considered one of the most endangered *Mantella* species. In the meantime, populations have been found in low-elevation portions of Ranomafana National Park, as well as in Manombo Special Reserve and Vevembe Forest. Populations from the southern localities (Manombo, Vevembe) turned out to be highly differentiated in mitochondrial DNA, revealing strong phylogeographic structure despite chromatic similarities (Vieites et al. 2006), in contrast to the pattern observed in many other *Mantella* species (e.g., Crottini et al. 2012a).

FIGURE 11.20 **Two *Mantella laevigata* individuals on a bamboo trunk, next to a water-filled hole typical of those used for reproduction by this species.** (PHOTO by P.-S. Gehring.)

The *M. laevigata* group contains two species, *M. laevigata* and *M. manery*. These two species bear some superficial similarities in color pattern—a greenish or yellowish dorsal patch, usually black flanks and venter, and black venter with bluish markings—yet they are highly distinct genetically, in several morphological characters, and especially in their behavior. Mitochondrial data clearly support the monophyly of the *M. laevigata* group, but the limited number of nuclear DNA sequences available to date have failed to clearly define this clade (Crottini et al. 2019). *Mantella manery* is a poorly known species described from Marojejy National Park (Figure 11.21). Individuals probably belonging to this species have recently also been recorded from Daraina (Edmonds 2009). At Marojejy, the species lives along streams in moist evergreen forest. It can be distinguished from *M. laevigata* by its frenal stripe (a white stripe along the upper lip) and a horseshoe-shaped patch on the throat. Both the frenal stripe and horseshoe-shaped throat marking are absent in the second species of the group, *M. laevigata*, which is also characterized by its widely enlarged terminal discs on fingers and toes. This partly arboreal species lives in lowland and medium-altitude moist evergreen forests, including areas with dense bamboo, in the northeast and north-central east of the island. At Marojejy it occurs syntopically with its likely sister species, *M. manery*, and is characterized by its unique and complex reproductive behavior described above.

The *M. betsileo* group is a genetically well-defined assemblage of rather closely related species. These share with *M. laevigata* a call composed of a series of double click notes, and analysis of DNA sequences from nuclear genes suggests possible relationships between the *M. betsileo* and *M. laevigata* groups (Crottini et al. 2019). Species in the *M. betsileo* group, similar to *M. manery*, are characterized by a light frenal stripe along the upper lip, and, especially in males, a light (generally blue-white) horseshoe-shaped marking on the throat, which becomes apparent during vocal sac inflation and almost certainly has relevance for intraspecific signaling. The group contains *M. viridis* from a small area in the north, *M. expectata* from Isalo, *M. betsileo* from a wide distribution in the west and southwest, *M. ebenaui* along the eastern lowland areas from Betampona Strict Nature Reserve northward and in the Sambirano Region, and one undescribed species close to *M. betsileo* that occurs in the southeast, Isalo, and Bemaraha (Rabemananjara et al. 2007b; Cocca et al. 2018).

Several of these species are poorly defined and probably not fully isolated reproductively. For instance, *M. ebenaui* (small, with brown dorsum and black flanks) and *M. viridis* (larger, with greenish dorsal color extending widely onto flanks) are very similar in their mitochondrial DNA. Individuals in the western part of the distribution area of *M. viridis* are less clearly green, and in the Ankarana limestone massif, specimens with an *M. ebenaui* phenotype occur that are larger and bear mitochondrial DNA of *M. viridis*, suggesting past or ongoing hybridization and bringing into question the taxonomic validity of *M. viridis* (Crottini et al. 2012a). It is likely that a more comprehensive data set for *M. ebenaui* across the entire distributional range will help shed light on the distinctiveness of these taxa.

Similarly, mitochondrial introgression may have confounded the true phylogeny among *M. betsileo*, *M. expectata*, and the morphologically similar lineage mentioned above from the southeast, Isalo, and from Bemaraha. The spectacularly colored *M. expectata*, with a yellow dorsum and bright blue limbs, is microendemic to a small area around the Isalo Massif, where it shows substantial genetic diversity (Crottini et al. 2008), but the overall genetic evidence suggests it might occasionally hybridize with *M. betsileo*. While *M. betsileo* and *M. expectata* live in dry areas and may be vulnerable to habitat destruction, *M. ebenaui* and *M. viridis* are often common in disturbed areas such as plantations, along small brooks, and in swamps (Mercurio and Andreone 2008; Crottini et al. 2012a).

The *M. cowanii* group contains several species that appear to live mainly along moist evergreen forest streams, except for *M. cowanii*, which inhabits streams in the highlands. *Mantella baroni*, *M. nigricans*, and *M. cowanii* have large to medium-size yellow-green or orange blotches on the flanks, while the remaining portions of the

FIGURE 11.21 **A *Mantella manery* individual from Marojejy. This species resembles its sympatric relative, *M. laevigata*, in color pattern.** (PHOTO by M. Vences.)

flanks and dorsum are black or brown; in *M. baroni* and *M. cowanii* the dorsum is also completely black. In contrast to these species with conspicuous, aposematic coloration, *M. haraldmeieri* is more cryptic, with only small beige flank blotches. None of the species in the group have horseshoe-shaped markings on the throat. This is an especially important character for *M. baroni*, which otherwise can be very difficult to distinguish from the sometimes syntopically occurring *M. madagascariensis* (with a horseshoe-shaped marking). The various members of the *M. cowanii* species group are mostly allopatrically distributed in eastern Madagascar (mainly at mid-elevations): *M. nigricans* between Tsaratanàna, Marojejy, and Betampona; *M. baroni* from Mantadia to Ranomafana; *M.* cf. *baroni* from Andringitra to Pic d'Ivohibe; and *M. haraldmeieri* in Andohahela and sites in the Vohimena Mountains. *Mantella cowanii* is a species of higher elevations, occurring in several fragmented populations in the central east from Itremo, Antakasina, and Betafo to the Antoetra area. Based on mitochondrial DNA, *M. haraldmeieri* and *M. cowanii* are well differentiated, whereas *M. baroni* and *M. nigricans* share the same haplotype over a vast area of Madagascar, despite their rather distinct differences in color pattern (Rabemananjara et al. 2007a). This, along with hybridization observed between *M. baroni* and *M. cowanii* in the only place where these species occur sympatrically (Farimazava) (Chiari et al. 2005), suggests that reproductive isolation among the species of the *M. cowanii* group is not complete, and genomic data will be needed to fully understand their evolutionary history. Of the species in this group, *M. cowanii* is specialized to a small area of highly fragmented highland habitat in the central east, and several conservation initiatives have focused on saving this Endangered species.

The *M. madagascariensis* group contains several species that are probably more specialized to swamp areas than the *M. cowanii* group. They have a stouter general appearance, although some species bear a close resemblance to members of the *M. cowanii* group, which in at least one case (*M. madagascariensis* compared to *M. baroni*) may be the result of Müllerian mimicry. The *M. madagascariensis* group contains what is perhaps the most distinctive species of the genus, *M. aurantiaca*. Despite many genetic studies targeting the population genetic and phylogeographic relationships among the different species and color morphs of this group (Chiari et al. 2004; Vences et al. 2004a; Crottini et al. 2019; Klonoski et al. 2019), we are still far from fully understanding this variation and drawing taxonomic conclusions. It is, however, obvious that this group contains numerous genetically distinct clusters, many of which are probably uniquely adapted to local conditions and merit conservation. Especially the swamp-specialized species *M. aurantiaca* and *M. milotympanum* are geographically very restricted and are a conservation priority (e.g., Randrianavelona et al. 2010; Piludu et al. 2015). *Mantella aurantiaca* is distributed across two main areas; one to the southwest of Moramanga town, included in the Mangabe-Ranomena-Sahasarotra Protected Area, which includes 133 ponds; and the second to the northeast of Moramanga, an area that includes three sites: Analamay-Ambatovy (82 ponds), Analamay-Mantadia Forest Corridor (17 ponds), and Torotorofotsy Protected Area (seven ponds) (Piludu et al. 2015; Rakotondrasoa et al. 2017). Of the 239 ponds in which *M. aurantiaca* has been recorded in the Moramanga District, 79% are included in protected areas or other conservation zones, and 17 ponds are in the mining footprint zone.

The closest relative of *Mantella*, surprisingly, is *Wakea madinika*, the sole representative of this genus. This tiny frog, 11–16 mm from snout to vent, has been found in the lowlands along the Sambirano River, near Antsirasira in an area of secondary forest. It has cryptic coloration and externally is more reminiscent of a species of the genus *Blommersia* than of the conspicuous genus *Mantella*. It shares several characters with *Mantella*, however: its tongue is only slightly notched, vomerine teeth are absent, maxillary teeth are largely reduced, and oocytes are unpigmented. Individuals have been found on the ground in the leaf litter of a plantation, close to a small artificial temporary pond. Almost nothing is known about the species' natural history (one dissected female contained 28 oocytes), and it would be of high interest to gather more comprehensive data on this enigmatic amphibian.

CONSERVATION

Because of their striking color and behavior, Malagasy poison frogs are also attractive for the pet trade. For instance, more than 10,000 *Mantella* frogs were exported from Madagascar in the first half of 1990 (Behra 1993), and over 30,000 individuals in 1998 alone (Rabemananjara et al. 2008b). Despite the quota system now in place and the current limits on *Mantella* exports, some species may be vulnerable to over-collecting and have been identified as priority targets for in situ and ex situ conservation (Rakotonanahary et al. 2017; Edmonds et al., pp. 1331–36). Currently, a maximum of 3000 individuals of the widespread species (e.g., *M. baroni*, *M. betsileo*) can be exported, while 110 individuals of the vulnerable species (e.g., *M. madagascariensis*) can be exported annually. *Mantella cowanii* has been collected unsustainably for the pet trade since the late 1980s, and since 2001 there has been a total suspension of the export of live wild specimens (Rabibisoa 2008); another *Mantella* species currently subject to a zero export quota is *M. viridis*. These conservation concerns have helped trigger several research programs on *Mantella* in the past two decades.

Ten of the 16 species of *Mantella* are currently listed in the highest threatened categories of the IUCN Red List (IUCN 2019): one is classified as Critically Endangered (*M. milotympanum*); five as Endangered (*M. aurantiaca*, *M. cowanii*, *M. expectata*, *M. haraldmeieri*, and *M. viridis*); and four as Vulnerable (*M. madagascariensis*, *M. manery*, *M. crocea*, and *M. bernhardi*). *Mantella pulchra* is classified as Near Threatened, and all the remaining species (*M. baroni*, *M. betsileo*, *M. ebenaui*, *M. laevigata*, and *M. nigricans*) are Least Concern. The most critical factors leading to the threatened status of these species are habitat destruction and habitat loss. *Wakea madinika* is classified as Data Deficient. Some species, like *M. ebenaui*, *M. viridis*, *M. aurantiaca*, and *M. crocea*, live in disturbed areas such as plantations, and mine and quarry areas. All *Mantella* species are currently included in Appendix II of CITES, and their trade and export are strictly regulated. All but one species (*M. madagascariensis*) occur in at least one protected area, yet habitat protection and management represents the main required conservation action needed for all species. Because of their attractiveness for the pet trade, the feasibility and associated regulations of continued collection of each species in the wild should be updated regularly.

National Conservation Action Plans exist for two species: *M. aurantiaca* and *M. cowanii*. The first *M. aurantiaca* Action Plan identified a set of priority measures to be put in place from 2010 to 2015 (Randrianavelona et al. 2010). The second five-year *M. aurantiaca* Action Plan was published in 2017 (Rakotondrasoa et al. 2017). Since 2012, *M. aurantiaca* has been bred in captivity, and this program helped put in place the first in-country husbandry center (see Edmonds et al., pp. 1331–36). *Mantella aurantiaca* has also been subject to a first reintroduction program in 2016–2019 (Rabemananjara et al. 2018), and detailed studies on habitat preferences revealed that the species prefers microhabitat with about 30% canopy, 30% herbaceous cover, 70% leaf-litter coverage, and relatively low numbers of tree roots (Edwards et al. 2019). *Mantella aurantiaca* has been listed since 1995 in Appendix II of CITES, and its trade was revised in 2011 with an annual export quota of 550 individuals until 2013. In 2014, this quota was changed to 280, and it is now under a quota determination system that monitors the collecting sites for their sustainable use.

Rabibisoa (2008) proposed the first *M. cowanii* Action Plan, which collected all available information on this amphibian and identified the most important actions to be implemented in the field to ensure the survival of this peculiar species. Subsequently, a second *M. cowanii* Action Plan was released in 2020 (Andreone et al. 2020). The trade of *M. cowanii* was recently suspended, but because a similar species, *M. baroni*, co-occurs sympatrically at one locality, the trade of this latter species should be strictly regulated, and collection at the site where the two species occur should be prohibited.

Subject editors: Miguel Vences and Achille P. Raselimanana

MANTELLIDAE, MANTELLINAE: *MANTIDACTYLUS* AND *BOEHMANTIS*

M. D. Scherz, M. Vences, N. H. C. Rabibisoa, and F. Andreone

Mantidactylus is a diverse genus of moist evergreen forest frogs that is widespread across Madagascar. It is divided into six subgenera that are ecologically distinct as both adults and juveniles, making it a fitting group for evolutionary research. At present, 36 species are described, but over 50 species are awaiting formal description. Body size and geography (especially topology and river barriers) seem to play important roles in the speciation of these frogs. Several species in the genus are local endemics and are threatened with extinction due to habitat destruction. Together with *Mantidactylus*, we also discuss in this contribution the monotypic genus *Boehmantis*, from southeastern Madagascar, about which very little is known but which bears a superficial similarity to large-bodied *Mantidactylus* species.

TAXONOMY AND EVOLUTION

Until 2006, *Mantidactylus* was a large genus containing 90 species of highly diverse morphology. When it became clear that 1) the genus *Mantidactylus* was paraphyletic with respect to *Mantella*, and 2) it contained numerous large clades defined by relatively conserved morphology, the taxonomy of *Mantidactylus* was overhauled, and several subgenera were raised to genus level (Glaw and Vences 2006). Thus, the subgenera *Blommersia*, *Boehmantis*, *Gephyromantis*, *Guibemantis*, and *Spinomantis* were elevated to genus level, and *Mantidactylus* was confined to a subset of its former species. In turn, some species groups of *Mantidactylus* became new subgenera within the new genus-level taxonomy.

Herein, *Mantidactylus* is divided into six subgenera: *Brygoomantis*, *Chonomantis*, *Hylobatrachus*, *Maitsomantis*, *Mantidactylus*, and *Ochthomantis* (Figure 11.22). The genus is sister to *Gephyromantis* (Wollenberg et al. 2011). Subgenera of *Mantidactylus* are generally monophyletic in phylogenetic reconstructions, but no detailed multi-gene phylogeny has yet been produced for the genus as a whole. The single species in the genus *Boehmantis*, *B. microtympanum*, is sister to the *Mantidactylus-Gephyromantis* clade.

In the following, we provide brief accounts of the six subgenera of *Mantidactylus* and the genus *Boehmantis*:

Subgenus *Mantidactylus* (*Mantidactylus*)

Three species from eastern and northern Madagascar (recent taxonomic revision: Rancilhac et al. 2020). Maximum male size up to 120 mm from snout to vent (largest frogs on Madagascar), same size as females. Male and female tympana of similar size. Generalized stream-dwelling tadpole. Generally pronounced oval or round femoral glands in males of type 4 *sensu* Glaw et al. (2000a). Weakly distensible single subgular vocal sac. Rough to smooth skin. Generally brown, often with yellowish elements. Feet strongly webbed. Guttural, pulsed call, repeated at regular intervals at night (recorded for only one species so far).

Subgenus *Mantidactylus* (*Brygoomantis*)

Twelve species mostly from eastern and northern Madagascar (few in western Madagascar), but a taxonomic revision will likely yield

FIGURE 11.22 **Representatives of the six subgenera of *Mantidactylus*, plus *M. majori* and *Boehmantis microtympanum*.** (PHOTOS by M. D. Scherz and M. Vences.)

many more. Maximum male size 19–41 mm, smaller than females. Males with larger tympana than females. Generalized stream-dwelling tadpole. Pronounced femoral glands in males of type 3 *sensu* Glaw et al. (2000a). Weakly distensible single subgular vocal sac. Often with ridges or bumps on the dorsum. Always brown, but highly variable in coloration, even within species. Feet partly webbed. Mostly with subtle, creaking calls, repeated regularly, day or night.

Subgenus *Mantidactylus* (*Chonomantis*)

Nine species from eastern and northern Madagascar. Maximum male size 23–40 mm, smaller than females. Males with much larger tympana than females. Specialized funnel-mouthed tadpole. Pronounced femoral glands in males of type 3 *sensu* Glaw et al. (2000a). Weakly distensible single subgular vocal sac. Smooth-skinned with ridges along the dorsolateral body. Distinct dorsolateral color border. Presence and shape of a white frenal stripe is diagnostic at species level. Feet weakly webbed. Rasping calls, repeated regularly during the day.

Subgenus *Mantidactylus* (*Ochthomantis*)

Six species in the Central Highlands and in eastern, southeastern, northwestern, and northern Madagascar. The assignment of *Mantidactylus majori* to this subgenus needs revision because of differences in reproductive behavior, tadpole characters, and molecular relationships (N. Rabibisoa et al., unpublished data); it may need to be assigned to a separate subgenus. Maximum male size 30–62 mm, smaller than females (34–66 mm). Males with larger tympana than females. Throat coloration variable but often with two parallel markings. Specialized tadpoles with reduced jaw sheaths and reduced rows of labial teeth. Pronounced femoral glands in males of type 3 *sensu* Glaw et al. (2000a). Weakly distensible single subgular vocal sac. Skin generally bumpy, often with black spots. Often yellowish color in the inguinal region. Highly variable. Feet slightly to fully webbed. Subtle quacking calls, repeated irregularly.

Subgenus *Mantidactylus* (*Maitsomantis*)

Monotypic but widespread in eastern Madagascar. Maximum male size 27 mm. Males with much larger tympana than females. Generalized stream-dwelling tadpole with reduced number of labial teeth. Distinct femoral glands in some males probably of type 3 *sensu* Glaw et al. (2000a). Weakly distensible single subgular vocal sac. Smooth, slightly granular skin. Distinct greenish color (similar to some *Guibemantis* species). Feet weakly webbed. Call of 6–15 short melodious notes, repeated regularly.

Subgenus *Mantidactylus* (*Hylobatrachus*)

Four species in eastern and northern Madagascar. Maximum male size 31–41 mm, marginally smaller than females. Male and female tympana of similar size. Highly specialized, slender tadpoles with netlike mouth structures. Distinct femoral glands in some males of type 3 *sensu* Glaw et al. (2000a). Weakly distensible single subgular vocal sac. Smooth to bumpy skin. Variable in coloration, often including dark and light brown bands and greenish color in the inguinal region. Feet completely webbed. Rapid pulsed calls (somewhat trill-like), repeated irregularly.

Genus *Boehmantis*

A single species from southeastern Madagascar. Maximum size of males up to 64 mm snout to vent, females up to 96 mm snout to vent (Andreone and Nussbaum 2006). Male and female tympana of approximately similar size. Enlarged discs on fingers and toes. Females with tubular cloaca, turned downward. Probably generalized stream-dwelling tadpole. Femoral glands as far as known absent. Finely granular to smooth skin. Generally brownish gray, with greenish shades. Feet fully webbed. Advertisement call unknown.

Among the subgenera of *Mantidactylus*, the nominal subgenus *Mantidactylus* is the earliest diverging in phylogenetic reconstructions (Wollenberg et al. 2011). *Brygoomantis* and *Chonomantis* are sister clades, as are *Ochthomantis* and *Maitsomantis*, whereas the relationship between *Hylobatrachus* and the other subgenera remains unclear. The relationships of *Mantidactylus majori* are doubtful; relationships of this species with other *Ochthomantis* were assumed after Blommers-Schlösser and Blanc (1991) and Dubois (1992) but were not recovered in phylogenetic analyses (e.g., Wollenberg et al. 2011). This is confirmed by new information from N. Rabibisoa et al. (unpublished data), as well as by phylogenomic data from C. R. Hutter (unpublished data); it is likely that this species will require inclusion in a separate subgenus in the future.

Species taxonomy within *Mantidactylus* has recently experienced dramatic advancement. This is partly because DNA barcoding studies have revealed numerous genetically highly distinct lineages (Vieites et al. 2009; Perl et al. 2014), and partly because field research has increased in intensity. Between 2003 and 2020, 10 species were described and one revalidated, and about 40 species are now recognized in the genus.

A great deal more taxonomic work on this genus is still needed. Vieites et al. (2009) identified 58 candidate species of *Mantidactylus* (numbered Ca1–7, Ca9–50, and Ca52–60); four further candidates were identified by Randrianiaina et al. (2011b) (Ca61–64); one by Cocca et al. (2018) (Ca65); and two by Rancilhac et al. (2020) (Ca66 and Ca67). Three more candidates were identified by Rosa et al. (2012) under a different numbering scheme (Ca HM364741, Ca HM364642, and Ca HM364733). Meanwhile, only five of these candidate species have been described or assigned to existing names: Ca49 as *M.* (*Hylobatrachus*) *atsimo* and Ca52 as *M.* (*H.*) *petakorona* (Scherz et al. 2019a); Ca32 as *M.* (*Brygoomantis*) *schulzi* (Vences et al. 2018); Ca57 as *M.* (*M.*) *grandidieri* (Rancilhac et al. 2020); and Ca59 as *M.* (*Chonomantis*) *paidroa* (Bora et al. 2011). Furthermore, Poth et al. (2012) used, in a preliminary way, the name *M.* (*B.*) *multiplicatus* (previously a junior synonym of *M. betsileanus*) to refer to Ca28, although this assignment was probably wrong (M. Vences, unpublished genetic data from the type of *multiplicatus*). Thus, at present, there are over 50 recognized candidate species of *Mantidactylus* awaiting revision and—if their species status is confirmed—description. Some new species will be described, and other species assigned available names. An ongoing revision of the subgenus *Ochthomantis* is expected to recognize six more species (N. Rabibisoa et al., unpublished data). Another ongoing revision (Scherz et al., unpublished data) is likely to substantially increase the number of species in the subgenus *Brygoomantis*.

REPRODUCTION AND ECOLOGY

The degree of variation in larval morphology of *Mantidactylus* is similar to that of *Gephyromantis*, although endotrophic (nonfeeding) tadpoles, common in *Gephyromantis*, seem to be absent in *Mantidactylus*. Two subgenera have generalized tadpoles (*Brygoomantis* and *Mantidactylus*). The tadpoles of many *Brygoomantis* species have been described (Knoll et al. 2007; Schmidt et al. 2009b), with particular detail available on *M.* (*B.*) *betsileanus* (Thomas et al. 2005; Scheld et al. 2013; Soariarimampionona et al. 2015). The tadpole of *Mantidactylus* (*M.*) *radaka* was described by Schulze et al. (2016) after decades of searching for tadpoles of this subgenus in various parts of Madagascar. It exhibits no pronounced adaptations and may suggest a rather unremarkable origin of the tadpoles of the genus *Mantidactylus* as a whole.

In *Ochthomantis* tadpoles, labial teeth have been partly or completely lost (Blommers-Schlösser 1979a; Randrianiaina et al. 2011b). The tadpoles of *Maitsomantis* are similar to but slightly less specialized than those of *Ochthomantis* (Vejarano et al. 2006a). The tadpoles of *Hylobatrachus* are also highly specialized, with jaws that may act like a sieve to gather particulates from the water (Altig and McDiarmid 2006). Interestingly, although *Chonomantis* has highly specialized funnel-mouthed tadpoles, these tadpoles are largely morphologically homogeneous among species (Grosjean et al. 2011b).

Boehmantis microtympanum deposits its eggs on rocks at the edges of small rock pools; eggs are 2 mm in diameter, with a jelly capsule of 6.5 mm (Andreone and Nussbaum 2006). Tadpoles assigned to this species are generalized benthic feeders; their oral disc remains to be described in detail.

Parental care is apparently widespread in *Mantidactylus*, although it has not been studied in detail. It is pronounced in *Maitsomantis*, in *Mantidactylus majori* (Figure 11.23), in *Ochthomantis* (Wolf 2013), and probably in some *Brygoomantis* species, and it may be more widespread than previously thought (Glaw and Vences 1994).

Advertisement calls of *Mantidactylus* species differ considerably among subgenera, and generally also at species level, but particular expertise is often required to use calls to identify species. Calls of many species were published by Vences et al. (2006) and Rosa et al. (2011a). In general, the calls of *Mantidactylus* are relatively inconspicuous—for example, *Brygoomantis* species emit calls of rather low intensity, often from a hidden position, and sometimes also diurnally, with only slightly inflatable vocal sacs. Other subgenera such as *Hylobatrachus*, *Ochthomantis*, and *Mantidactylus* are rarely heard at all, and the calls of *Boehmantis* are altogether unknown.

The longevity of one species each of *Brygoomantis*, *Chonomantis*, *Mantidactylus*, and *Ochthomantis* was studied by Tessa et al. (2017). Sexual maturity was reached in one to three years, with the shortest

FIGURE 11.23 **A *Mantidactylus majori* male guarding a clutch of eggs.** (PHOTO by C. R. Hutter.)

maturation time in *Chonomantis* and the longest in *Mantidactylus*. Males took less time to mature than females in all subgenera. Guarino et al. (2019) used skeletochronology to show that *M.* (*Mantidactylus*) sp. Ca67 (from Vevembe), reaches a maximum age of six years, with most males not living beyond four years. In *Boehmantis microtympanum*, a longevity of up to seven years was found by Guarino et al. (1998) based on skeletochronological analysis.

CHEMICAL COMMUNICATION

As is typical for mantellines, *Mantidactylus* species have femoral glands, and unlike other genera, these are also visible as rudimentary structures in females of many species. It is almost certain that these glands play a role during mating, which in *Mantidactylus* has not yet been observed in detail; but very probably, as for instance in *Guibemantis*, it does not involve amplexus (clasping of the female by the male). Instead, the male probably places its femoral glands over the back of the female, releasing compounds that act as chemical signals. Usually, such pheromones in amphibians consist of peptides, but *Mantidactylus* was the first genus in which volatile compounds were identified (Poth et al. 2012): a species related to *M. betsileanus* (*M.* sp. Ca28, named *M. multiplicatus* in that paper) was found to contain two such compounds in male femoral glands, one of which (phoracantholide J) had previously been isolated from a species of beetle. After synthesis, these compounds proved to have the potential to alter the behavior of conspecific males and probably also of females, suggesting they probably act as signals in chemical communication (pheromones). Poth et al. (2013) isolated further compounds from the femoral glands of species in the subgenus *Ochthomantis*, one of which they named mantidactolid. Finally, Junk et al. (2014), Nowack and Vences (2016), and Nowack et al. (2017) correlated the anatomy of the olfactory organ of mantellines, in particular of *Mantidactylus*, with the secretion of volatile compounds from their femoral glands (which was also demonstrated for most other mantelline genera). They found a specialized anatomical configuration of the olfactory organ especially in mantellines, the group characterized by femoral glands and associated reproductive behavior including putative communication by volatiles. Whether this chemical communication can take place over long distances remains untested; the most probable hypothesis is that *Mantidactylus* frogs, like others, communicate acoustically over long distances; once females have been attracted, pheromonal communication may play a role at short distances, or possibly only upon physical contact of the male's femoral gland with the female's body.

BIOGEOGRAPHY

Very little is known on the biogeography of *Mantidactylus*, in part because the taxonomy of the genus is so poorly resolved. Brown et al. (2016) showed that the genus has its center of species richness in the central east of the island, while *Ochthomantis* appears to be the most diverse in the north (Rabibisoa et al. 2008). The genus as a whole appears not to have a true center of endemism; rather, there are several places with locally very high levels of endemism (Isalo, Masoala, Ranomafana, Andringitra, Ankaratra, and Tsaratanàna), and one larger area (Andasibe and surroundings) with elevated endemism. The genus is much less concentrated in the east than *Gephyromantis*.

CONSERVATION

As of June 2021, 31 species of *Mantidactylus* had been assessed by the IUCN Red List (the recently described *M.* [*Brygoomantis*] *schulzi*, *M.* [*Hylobatrachus*] *atsimo*, and *M.* [*H.*] *petakorona* were not assessed). Of these, 20 are Least Concern, one is Near Threatened, one is Vulnerable, five are Endangered, two are Critically Endangered, and two are Data Deficient. All threatened species are assessed under Criterion B (distribution and habitat decline). *Mantidactylus* (*Ochthomantis*) *zolitschka* is the only assessed species not known to occur in any protected areas. The greatest threat to *Mantidactylus* is habitat loss and fragmentation.

Subject editors: Mark D. Scherz, Miguel Vences, and Achille P. Raselimanana

MANTELLIDAE, MANTELLINAE: *BLOMMERSIA*

M. Vences, J. Köhler, and A. P. Raselimanana

The genus *Blommersia* contains a series of inconspicuous, small frogs, with a size range of 14–26 mm from snout to vent in adults of Malagasy species. They are semiarboreal and occur over a wide variety of environments on Madagascar. Often, *Blommersia* species are found on the ground next to water bodies or in grasses in swamps. During the reproductive season, they usually call from low vegetation next to water, often day and night, especially after rainy evenings. Almost all *Blommersia* species reproduce in lentic (still) water bodies such as puddles, swamps, and ponds, but one species, currently considered *B. grandisonae*, is usually found along streams, where it reproduces in side puddles with or without weak current.

REPRODUCTION

Blommersia is one of the few mantellid clades in which mating behavior has been observed; like many *Guibemantis* species, most *Blommersia* frogs deposit their eggs on leaves overhanging water. The male and female position themselves vertically on a leaf, the male astride the female's head (Figure 11.24), and the male's sperm supposedly runs down the female's back onto the eggs (or fertilization may take place when the male moves down and comes in contact with the freshly laid eggs, although this behavior has never been observed in sufficient detail). In a few species, egg deposition takes place in the leaf litter instead. Upon hatching, the tadpoles are washed by rains into the ponds. The tadpoles are of generalized morphology and complete their development in the water. An exceptional reproductive mode characterizes *B. angolafa*, which reproduces in fallen palm leaves (Andreone et al. 2010).

SYSTEMATICS AND SPECIES ACCOUNTS

Overall, the genus *Blommersia* at present contains 12 named species, including two species from Mayotte, but their taxonomy is incompletely known. Despite the recent descriptions of various new species identified by a combination of morphological, genetic, and bioacoustical characters (Andreone et al. 2010; Vences et al. 2010b; Pabijan et al. 2011; Glaw et al. 2019), there are still around five additional candidate species and numerous additional deep mitochondrial lineages (Vieites et al. 2009) that require taxonomic revision.

Perhaps the most striking *Blommersia* species is *B. angolafa*, known from Ambatovaky, Betampona, Masoala, and Zahamena. This rather small frog (snout-to-vent length 17–21 mm) is yellow to olive brownish, with conspicuous bluish-white spots on the flanks and on the tips of fingers and toes. Individuals live and reproduce in fallen prophylls and fallen leaf sheaths of some *Dypsis* palms, where egg laying and complete larval development occur. This habitat specialization may constitute a threat to the species because these palms are exploited by humans (Andreone et al. 2010; see Rakotoarinivo et al., pp. 567–80). It will be worth examining whether this species displays some degree of parental care, similar to other phytotelmic species. Furthermore, it seems that *B. angolafa* is quite localized in nature; during our last two visits to Masoala in 2015 and 2018, and to Betampona in 2016, we did not record this species despite active searching through a large number of fallen leaves (A. P. Raselimanana, unpublished data).

FIGURE 11.24 **A mating pair of *Blommersia blommersae* from Andasibe. The male is loosely sitting on top of the egg-laying female (some of the slightly greenish eggs are visible close to the female's cloaca) and wiping his thighs over the back of the female, probably releasing pheromones from his femoral glands.** (PHOTO by F. Glaw and M. Vences.)

FIGURE 11.25 **A specimen of a moist evergreen forest species usually assigned to *Blommersia grandisonae* but possibly representing a new species, according to ongoing taxonomic revisions.** (PHOTO by M. D. Scherz.)

Another conspicuously colored *Blommersia* species, currently considered *B. grandisonae*, has a distinct black lateral stripe along the entire flank, bordered ventrally by white, and the male is sometimes even more colorful than female (Figure 11.25). This species is widespread along moist evergreen forest streams at mid-elevations in the east. However, since no recent collections have been made at the type locality of *B. grandisonae* in the southeastern Anosyenne Mountains, it remains to be clarified whether this name is correctly assigned to the laterally striped species. Current work in progress (M. Vences, unpublished data) suggests that *B. grandisonae* instead corresponds to another species, which was not observed in the wild again after its original description.

The Central Highlands, particularly the massifs of Ankaratra and Andringitra, host two very small species: *B. domerguei* (16–17 mm), characterized by a typical coloration of dark brown bands on a copper-brown dorsum, and *B. kely* (14–16 mm), with granular dorsal skin. These two species, which are not closely related to each other, are found in low vegetation, often grasses, next to ponds in montane habitat, in open areas, or at the forest edge.

A widespread species in the east is *B. blommersae*, which occurs mostly in swamps next to medium-altitude moist evergreen forest and is one of the representatives of the genus that deposit eggs openly on leaves overhanging water bodies. It reproduces rather explosively, and at the peak of the breeding season its loud chirping call choruses can be very conspicuous during the day and night. This species, as currently understood, contains multiple deep genetic lineages, which may in the future be distinguished as separate species; a detailed analysis of their contact or hybrid zones will likely be necessary for final conclusions. In some forest sites, such as near Andasibe, *B. blommersae* occurs syntopically with the morphologically extremely similar *B. sarotra*, which, however, differs by its advertisement calls, very secretive behavior, and egg deposition in the leaf litter.

Three species of *Blommersia* have rather restricted ranges at low elevations along the east coast: *B. dejongi*, *B. galani*, and *B. variabilis*. These recently described species (Vences et al. 2010b; Pabijan et al. 2011) are probably closely related to each other but have genetic, bioacoustic, and subtle morphological differences. Similar to many other lowland species, they tolerate a substantial amount of habitat degradation and occur in ponds and swamps in degraded forests or plantations, even very close to or within villages. This tolerance of degraded and open habitats is also observed in *B. wittei*, a species occurring in the northeast, northwest, north, and Sambirano Region and characterized by larger body size (22–26 mm snout-to-vent length) than most other members of the genus. In western Madagascar, a candidate species related to *B. wittei* occurs in open swamp habitat in dry areas.

Besides the Malagasy species, *Blommersia* also contains two representatives on Mayotte: *B. transmarina* and *B. nataliae*, which are two of only three mantellid species occurring outside Madagascar (Glaw et al. 2019; Vieites et al. 2020). The other is *Boophis nauticus*, also endemic to Mayotte (Glaw et al. 2019). *Blommersia nataliae* and *B. transmarina* are sister species and related to *B. wittei;* the latter species is characterized by a moderate form of island gigantism, with snout-to-vent length up to 34.5 mm, and several derived osteological features (Santos-Santos et al. 2020).

Subject editors: Miguel Vences and Achille P. Raselimanana

MANTELLIDAE, MANTELLINAE: *GEPHYROMANTIS*

M. D. Scherz, A. Crottini, and A. Rakotoarison

Gephyromantis is a diverse genus of predominantly moist evergreen forest–dwelling frogs that are widespread across Madagascar. Most species can be found along the eastern forest belt and in the north, although one clade (subgenus *Phylacomantis*) occurs in the transitional and moist semi-deciduous forests of central and western Madagascar. The genus *Gephyromantis* is divided into six subgenera: *Gephyromantis*, *Phylacomantis*, *Duboimantis*, *Asperomantis*, *Laurentomantis*, and *Vatomantis*. These subgenera are ecologically distinct as both adults and larvae and are a good model for evolutionary research. As of June 2021, 47 species had been described, but at least 24 species are awaiting description. Body size, ecology, and geography (especially topology and river barriers) seem to play important roles in the speciation of these frogs. Several species are known to be microendemics, and several of those are severely threatened with extinction by habitat loss and fragmentation.

FIGURE 11.26 **Representatives of the six subgenera of *Gephyromantis*, and the uncertain *G. klemmeri*.** (PHOTOS by M. D. Scherz and Carl R. Hutter.)

TAXONOMY AND EVOLUTION

Until 2006, *Gephyromantis* was one of several subgenera of *Mantidactylus*, which at that time contained some 90 species of highly diverse morphology (see Scherz et al., pp. 1365–68). When the taxonomy of *Mantidactylus* was overhauled because of its paraphyly with respect to *Mantella* (Glaw and Vences 2006), *Gephyromantis* was among the subgenera raised to genus level. In turn, some species groups and subgenera of *Mantidactylus* became new subgenera within the new genus-level taxonomy. *Gephyromantis*, as a genus, was organized into five subgenera: *Gephyromantis*, *Phylacomantis*, and *Laurentomantis* (already recognized as subgenera within *Mantidactylus sensu lato*), and two that were newly described (*Vatomantis* and *Duboimantis*). In 2017, a monophyletic subgroup of *Duboimantis* was proposed to be named *Asperomantis*, with the rest of the species remaining *Duboimantis* (Vences et al. 2017c).

Gephyromantis is a diverse genus, with each of its six subgenera displaying distinctive morphology and ecological attributes. Indeed, Wollenberg Valero et al. (2017) showed that clades within *Gephyromantis* have a high rate of phenotypic evolution, in both adult and larval morphology. Kaffenberger et al. (2012) produced the most detailed phylogenetic analysis of the genus to date. This study showed that subgenera within *Gephyromantis* are genetically highly distinct, and it identified paraphyly of *Duboimantis* that was later reconciled by the description of *Asperomantis* (Vences et al. 2017c). In the following, we provide brief accounts of the six subgenera of *Gephyromantis* (Figure 11.26).

Subgenus *Gephyromantis*

Eleven species from eastern Madagascar. Maximum male size 20–29 mm. Endotrophic larvae develop in terrestrial nests in leaf litter. Oblong, granular femoral glands. Paired or bilobate subgular vocal sacs. Weakly enlarged fingertips. Generally with a light-colored stripe along part of the upper lip. Feet with only rudimentary webbing. Generally chirping calls, except in some species such as *G.* (*Gephyromantis*) *thelenae* and *G.* (*G.*) *mafy*, which have extended, rasping calls.

Subgenus *Phylacomantis*

Four species from western and northern Madagascar. Maximum male size 37–44 mm. Carnivorous, exotrophic tadpoles develop in streams. Oblong, granular femoral glands. Paired, round subgular vocal sacs. Enlarged triangular fingertips. Generally with a few rugosities and ridges on the dorsum. Feet moderately webbed. Loud, sometimes scream-like calls.

Subgenus *Duboimantis*

Sixteen species from eastern and northern Madagascar. Maximum male size 30–53 mm. Endotrophic larvae develop in slow-moving water. Oblong, granular femoral glands. Paired or single (e.g., *G.* (*D.*) *redimitus*) subgular vocal sacs. Enlarged triangular fingertips. With distinct inner and outer dorsolateral ridges, sometimes with spines above and between the eyes. Foot webbing variable but always present, with different degrees of development: highly developed in *G.* (*D.*) *luteus*, *G.* (*D.*) *sculpturatus*, and *G.* (*D.*) *plicifer*. Calls vary widely but in most species are pulsed. Exceptions are the rather tonal calls of *G.* (*D.*) *luteus* and *G.* (*D.*) *plicifer*.

Subgenus *Asperomantis*

Six species from eastern and northern Madagascar. Maximum male size 30–41 mm. Generalized, exotrophic tadpoles. Oblong, granular femoral glands. Paired subgular vocal sacs, often black. Enlarged triangular fingertips. Almost always with a white dot in the center of the tympanum, inner and outer dorsolateral ridges, spines above the eye. Foot webbing quite pronounced. Calls jarring and pulsed.

Subgenus *Laurentomantis*

Five species from eastern and northern Madagascar. Maximum male size 23–28 mm. Endotrophic larvae develop in slow-moving water. Bulbous femoral glands with few, large granules. Single subgular vocal sac. Enlarged triangular or rounded fingertips. Highly rugose dorsal skin. Some species have large tibial glands. Often with bright color patches on lateral or ventral side. Foot webbing rudimentary. Calls quiet and creaking or rasping.

Subgenus *Vatomantis*

Four species in northeastern Madagascar. Maximum male size 24–31 mm. Larvae unknown, but eggs are laid on rocks above water, so the larvae are presumably free swimming. Bulbous femoral glands with few, large granules. Paired, whitish or greenish subgular vocal sacs. Enlarged triangular fingertips. Typically granular skin (rugose in *G.* (*V.*) *lomorina*), generally green. Foot webbing rudimentary. Calls are a series of clicks or rasping chirps.

The subgenera *Laurentomantis* (Figure 11.27) and *Vatomantis* are genetically closely related, and their taxonomy needs a systematic reassessment (Kaffenberger et al. 2012; Scherz et al. 2018a), first because *Gephyromantis* (*Vatomantis*) *lomorina* appears to have somewhat intermediate characters between the two genera and is phylogenetically sister to all other *Vatomantis* species (Scherz et al. 2018a). Second, *G. klemmeri* has been considered a member of the subgenus *Gephyromantis* (Glaw and Vences 2007), but genetically it has closer affinities with *Laurentomantis* and *Vatomantis* (Kaffenberger et al. 2012; Scherz et al. 2018a); these authors found low support for the resolution of the position of *G. klemmeri* and have suggested that a broader circumscription of *Laurentomantis* (with synonymy of *Vatomantis*) may be the best way to reconcile current uncertainties. At present, they are still recognized as distinct, and *G. klemmeri* is essentially *incertae sedis* within the genus.

Numerous new species of *Gephyromantis* have been described recently. This is partly a result of the increased intensity of field research, the use of DNA barcoding, and the availability of a reliable database of genetic sequences enabling the identification of numerous genetically highly distinct lineages (Vieites et al. 2009; Perl et al. 2014). Since 2003, 14 species have been described, two have been revalidated, and one was synonymized (Cocca et al. 2020), and there are now 47 nominal species in this genus. However, taxonomic work is far from finished; Vieites et al. (2009) identified 25 candidate species of *Gephyromantis* (numbered Ca1 and Ca4–27); further candidate species were identified by Perl et al. (2014) (Ca28) and Scherz et al. (2017a) (Ca29–31), and two more candidate new species were identified by Rosa et al. (2012) under a different numbering scheme (Ca HM364637 and Ca HM364619). Meanwhile, seven of these mitochondrial lineages have been described or assigned to existing names: Ca1 as *G.* (*Asperomantis*) *tahotra* (Glaw et al. 2011); Ca8 as *G.* (*Gephyromantis*) *hintelmannae* (Wollenberg et al. 2012); Ca10 as

FIGURE 11.27 ***Laurentomantis* comprises several species with bizarre morphology, here exemplified by an individual currently considered as *L. ventrimaculatus* from Vohiparara in Ranomafana National Park.** (PHOTO by F. Glaw.)

G. (*Phylacomantis*) *atsingy* (Crottini et al. 2011b); Ca11 as *G.* (*Laurentomantis*) *ranjomavo* (Glaw and Vences 2011); Ca26 as *G.* (*G.*) *mafy* (Vieites et al. 2012); Ca28 as *G.* (*A.*) *angano* (Scherz et al. 2017a); Ca9 as *G.* (*G.*) *decaryi* (Wollenberg et al. 2012); and specimens formerly attributed to *G.* (*G.*) *decaryi* from Manombo and Vondrozo as *G.* (*G.*) *verrucosus* (Wollenberg et al. 2012). Thus, at present there are still 24 recognized candidate species awaiting assessment and possibly description.

REPRODUCTION AND ECOLOGY

Larval ecomorphology within the genus remains one of its most intriguing hallmarks (Kaffenberger et al. 2012). Previously, it was suggested that at least some *Gephyromantis* species may be direct developers (i.e., the embryo develops into a froglet within the egg) (Blommers-Schlösser 1979a; Glaw and Vences 1994), and the evolution of this trait was discussed by Randrianiaina et al. (2007). However, all species to date for which metamorphosis is documented in detail have a tadpole phase. These species were therefore classified as "nidicolous," calling into question the occurrence of direct development in the genus (Randrianiaina et al. 2011c). However, reproductive habits are currently known for only 13 species (Kaffenberger et al. 2012), and it is still possible that this development strategy could be found for other species.

Randrianiaina et al. (2011c) considerably expanded our knowledge of tadpole diversity within *Gephyromantis*, describing the tadpoles of *G.* (*Duboimantis*) *granulatus*, *G.* (*D.*) *sculpturatus*, *G.* (*D.*) *tschenki*, and *G.* (*Laurentomantis*) *ventrimaculatus* and providing a detailed account of larval development in *G.* (*Gephyromantis*) *blanci* (as "sp. aff. *blanci*," but see Wollenberg et al. 2012). They also illustrated the mouthparts of *G.* (*Asperomantis*) *ambohitra*, *G.* (*A.*) *asper*, *G.* (*Phylacomantis*) *kintana*, *G.* (*P.*) *corvus*, and *G.* (*P.*) *pseudoasper*. The tadpoles of the endotrophic species in this genus have been much less commonly found than those of the exotrophic species and may in fact normally develop terrestrially, but occasionally get washed into streams by heavy rains (Randrianiaina et al. 2011c; Strauß et al. 2013). Similarly, it is remarkable to note that within this genus we also find facultative carnivorous tadpoles. Reeve et al. (2011) showed that *G.* (*P.*) *corvus* larvae emit clicking sounds when attacking prey, especially conspecifics, a very rare behavior otherwise known only from *Ceratophrys cranwelli* and *C. ornata* (family Ceratophryidae) of the New World (Salgado Costa et al. 2014).

Calls of many species of *Gephyromantis* were published by Vences et al. (2006). Advertisement calls of *Gephyromantis* adults are highly distinctive, and bioacoustics is one of the most diagnostic characters for species in the genus, often yielding much more obvious differences than morphology. Several closely related species differ substantially in their calls (Wollenberg and Harvey 2010; Scherz et al. 2017a, 2017b). Behavioral syndromes associated with particular call types have been studied in *G.* (*Gephyromantis*) *thelenae* (Wollenberg and Harvey 2010). This species has both an advertisement call and an aggressive call; the latter was elicited by stimulation with playbacks of conspecific calls. In response to playbacks of the syntopic sister species *G.* (*G.*) *eiselti*, *G.* (*G.*) *thelenae* males reduced calling frequency, avoiding signal overlap. Similar patterns have been observed in *G.* (*G.*) sp. Ca25 in Betampona by Lam et al. (2020), who reported an agonistic encounter (interpreted as territorial behavior) between two males: the advertisement call of the resident male became more aggressive (shorter inter-note duration and higher intensity), and after this change in call structure the two males engaged in a physical altercation.

Snakes are the only known predators of *Gephyromantis* adults (Hutter et al. 2018a), but they are probably also preyed on by birds, specifically raptors, and likely opportunistically by other carnivorans and omnivorans. Tadpoles are preyed on by carnivorous tadpoles that occur at some sites on Madagascar (Reeve et al. 2011), and they are probably an important food resource for crustaceans, fish, snakes, and other aquatic and semiaquatic predators.

BIOGEOGRAPHY

Brown et al. (2016) showed that *Gephyromantis* does not have the same pattern of species richness and endemism in central Madagascar as seen in *Mantidactylus* and *Boophis* but is instead concentrated in the north of the island. This is probably tied to the origin of this genus, which, based on ancestral state reconstruction of the distribution of the genus, seems to be located in the northeast (Kaffenberger et al. 2012), with subsequent radiation into the southeast and central east in *Asperomantis*, *Duboimantis*, and two different lineages of *Gephyromantis*. *Phylacomantis* seems to have reached western Madagascar from the northwest, while *Asperomantis*, *Laurentomantis*, and *Vatomantis* diversified in the north.

Several species pairs of *Gephyromantis* may have diverged in sympatry (Mercurio and Andreone 2007; Wollenberg et al. 2011), making these frogs an excellent system for the study of speciation (Wollenberg Valero 2015). As in other mantellid frogs, genetic divergence of *Gephyromantis* populations is negatively correlated with body size, yet without leading to increased speciation rates, possibly because it is acted against by decreased colonization of new areas (Pabijan et al. 2012). Wollenberg Valero (2015) investigated the biogeography of *G.* (*Gephyromantis*) *enki* and *G.* (*G.*) *boulengeri* in considerable detail in Ranomafana National Park. The smaller *G.* (*G.*) *enki* showed greater genetic differentiation, which cannot be explained by the landscape alone, and both topographic and riverine barriers played an important role in driving intraspecific genetic diversification. Topography apparently has a particularly significant role in limiting or facilitating the spread and diversification of *Gephyromantis* species in northern Madagascar (Scherz et al. 2017a, 2017d, 2018a, 2018b) because of the generally narrow elevational bands in which these species occur. Montane species assemblages along the northern escarpment (between Anjanaharibe-Sud, COMATSA Nord and Sud, Marojejy, Tsaratanàna, Mahimborondro, Bemanevika, and Manongarivo) show greatest species sharing around or slightly above 1400 m, which is above the highest elevation at which there is continuous connection between these massifs (Scherz et al. 2018a, 2018b). At that elevation, river barriers are less substantial, and the physical distance between areas is reduced to its minimum. At higher elevations, microendemism becomes enforced (Scherz et al. 2017d). Lowland species, on the other hand, are often very widespread; *G.* (*Duboimantis*) *granulatus*, for example, is found from Nosy Be to Montagne d'Ambre to Marojejy. It remains to be seen whether large rivers act as a barrier to such species.

CONSERVATION

As of June 2021, 41 species of *Gephyromantis* have been assessed by the IUCN Red List, whereas *G.* (*Vatomantis*) *lomorina*, *G.* (*Asperomantis*) *angano*, *G.* (*A.*) *ceratophrys*, *G.* (*Phylacomantis*) *kintana*, *G.* (*Duboimantis*) *tohatra*, *G.* (*D.*) *saturnini*, and *G.* (*D.*) *grosjeani* are Not Evaluated. Of the assessed species, 15 are classified as Least Concern, three as Near Threatened, 13 as Vulnerable, nine as Endangered, and one as Critically Endangered (*G.* [*Gephyromantis*] *mafy*). All threatened species are assessed under Criterion B (distribution and habitat decline), except *G.* (*G.*) *runewsweeki*, which is assessed under Criterion D2 (also related to distribution). *Gephyromantis* (*G.*) *hintelmannae* and *G.* (*G.*) *mafy* are the only species not known to occur in any protected areas.

The greatest threat to *Gephyromantis* is habitat loss and fragmentation. Species differ in their resilience to habitat modification, with some species even preferring secondary forest and forest edges (Ramamonjisoa et al. 2013). However, all species rely on at least some forest presence since, with few exceptions (some *Phylacomantis* species), they are typically forest dwellers. Certain candidate species awaiting description are probably Critically Endangered, as they are restricted to small forest fragments that are undergoing active deforestation (Scherz et al. 2017a).

Subject editors: Mark D. Scherz, Miguel Vences, and Achille P. Raselimanana

MANTELLIDAE, MANTELLINAE: *GUIBEMANTIS*

R. M. Lehtinen, M. D. Scherz, and M. Vences

Currently, the genus *Guibemantis* is composed of 18 species in two subgenera: *Guibemantis* with five species and *Pandanusicola* with 13 species. The genus was named after Jean Guibé, a 20th-century French herpetologist. These are small to moderately large arboreal frogs that lay eggs over still water. Species in the subgenus *Guibemantis* are moderately large and breed in ponds or swamps. Species in the genus *Pandanusicola* are much smaller, and most species breed in water-filled leaf axils of *Pandanus* ("screw pine") plants (see Callmander et al., pp. 551–59). *Guibemantis* species were formerly placed in the genus *Mantidactylus* (Blommers-Schlösser and Blanc 1991), and much of the older literature uses that generic name.

SYSTEMATICS

Important early contributions to the systematics of *Guibemantis* were made by Blommers-Schlösser (1979a), Blommers-Schlösser and Blanc (1991), and Glaw and Vences (1994) prior to the availability of genetic data for these frogs. Glaw and Vences (1994) erected *Pandanusicola* as a subgenus of *Mantidactylus* for the group of species that breed predominantly in *Pandanus* (see "Ecology" section below), and the nominate subgenus *Guibemantis* contained species in the *G. depressiceps* group, which breed in larger bodies of stagnant water. These two groups were for the most part confirmed by genetic data: Glaw and Vences (2006) raised *Guibemantis* to genus level, consisting of these two subgenera, although *G. liber*, which had formerly been placed in the subgenus *Guibemantis*, was found to be best placed in *Pandanusicola*. Later phylogenetic information dramatically improved our systematic understanding of the genus (Vences et al. 2007; Wollenberg et al. 2011), but resolution at species level is still largely lacking (Bletz et al. 2018; Lehtinen et al. 2018). Numerous candidate species of *Guibemantis* have been identified based on DNA barcoding (Lehtinen et al. 2007; Vieites et al. 2009; Rosa et al. 2012).

MORPHOLOGY

Early contributions to our knowledge of the morphology of *Guibemantis* were made by Guibé (1978), Blommers-Schlösser (1979a), Blommers-Schlösser and Blanc (1991), and Glaw and Vences (1994), and much of what is known today was summarized by Glaw and Vences (2007). Species in the subgenus *Guibemantis* tend to be medium- to large-bodied species (32–59 mm snout-to-vent length) that (as far as is known) breed in ponds, swamps, and other lentic water bodies. They have relatively large hands with large toe and finger discs. Femoral glands in males are diffuse and cover much of the ventral surface of the upper leg. Vocal sacs are single subgular.

Species in the genus *Pandanusicola* are much smaller on average (21–38 mm snout-to-vent length), and all but two species are thought to be specialized *Pandanus* breeders (see below). Most of them also have relatively smaller hands. Most *Pandanusicola* species have much more distinct femoral glands in males (*G. liber* and *G. tasifotsy* are exceptions). Some species have highly variable color patterns, and vocalizations are often not conspicuous, making determination a challenge. The overall color, the contrast with adjacent skin color, and the number of granules in the femoral glands of males are important in species identification. Other diagnostic features of *Pandanusicola* include the presence or absence of rostral

FIGURE 11.28 **A calling *Guibemantis liber* male, illustrating the white vocal sac that certainly acts as a visual signal to conspecifics.** (PHOTO by C. R. Hutter.)

stripes, dorsolateral lines, banding on the arms and/or legs, and "rings" associated with the finger or toe pads.

Males are smaller than females on average in some species (e.g., about 10% smaller in *G. wattersoni*). However, in *G. annulatus* the body sizes of males and females are not significantly different (Lehtinen 2009). Sexual size dimorphism in other species in the genus has not been assessed in detail. Most species apparently have a single, subgular vocal sac, but in several species (e.g., *G. wattersoni*) it is paired and subgular. In *G. liber*, the coloration of the throat is strongly sexually dichromatic, being bright white in males because of the white vocal sac (Figure 11.28), and indistinctly colored in females (Blommers-Schlösser and Blanc 1991).

REPRODUCTION

Like all mantellines, *Guibemantis* frogs do not engage in amplexus but instead have an unusual form of reproduction in which the male and female sit vertically or obliquely on a leaf or branch, the male astride the female's head, and the male's sperm possibly runs down the female's back onto the eggs (or the male may ejaculate it onto the eggs when he shifts downward for short periods; Figure 11.29). This behavior was first observed in *G. liber* by Blommers-Schlösser (1975a) and was later also reported from other *Guibemantis* species (Blommers-Schlösser 1979a). More data on the mating ecology of *Guibemantis* were provided by Blommers-Schlösser and Blanc (1993).

All known members of the subgenus *Guibemantis* are pond breeders. They lay their eggs arboreally on vegetation overhanging standing water and have exotrophic tadpoles. *Guibemantis tornieri* has also been reported to deposit eggs on tree trunks or rocks overhanging water (Glaw and Vences 2007). There are no reports of parental care in the subgenus *Guibemantis*; however, one photograph of *G. tornieri* on AmphibiaWeb suggests possible post-ovipositional care. In this same photograph, three egg clutches are visible,

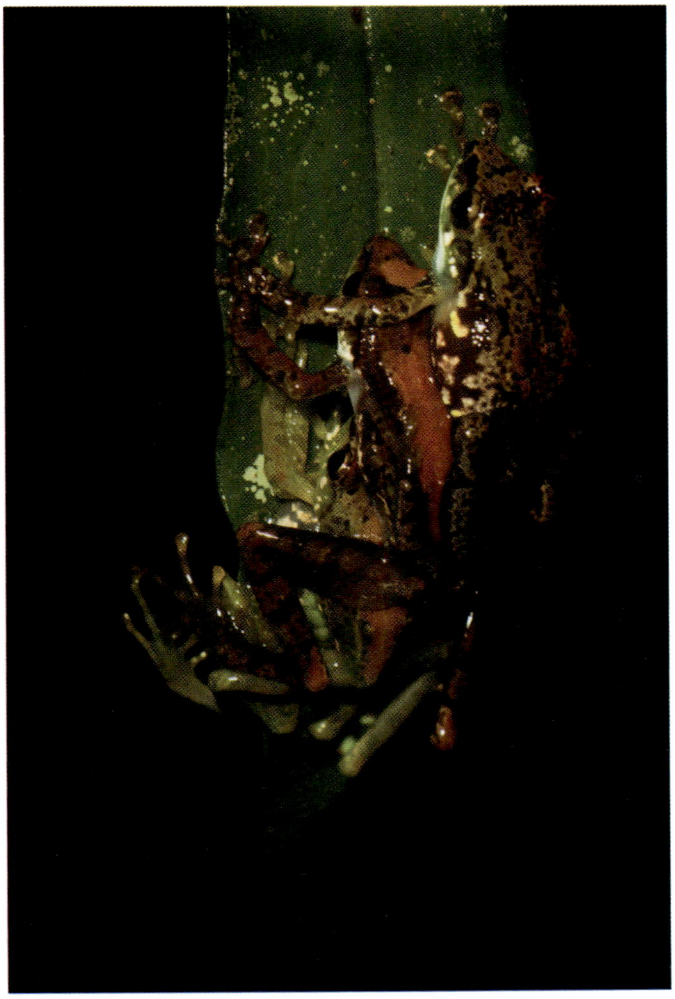

FIGURE 11.29 **Group mating in *Guibemantis liber*, with one egg-laying female and two males. This previously undocumented behavior may lead to multiple paternity in clutches.** (PHOTO by C. R. Hutter.)

TABLE 11.7. **Clutch size in *Guibemantis* species**

SPECIES	CLUTCH SIZE	REFERENCE
G. depressiceps	60–100	Blommers-Schlösser (1979a)
G. timidus	40–100	Blommers-Schlösser (1979a)
G. annulatus	mean = 26	Lehtinen (2003)
G. bicalcaratus	20–30	Blommers-Schlösser and Blanc (1991)
G. liber	30–90 (but one individual had ~240 eggs)	Blommers-Schlösser (1975a); R. M. Lehtinen (unpublished data)
G. milingilingy	10	Bletz et al. (2018)
G. pulcher	58	R. M. Lehtinen (unpublished data)
G. punctatus	10	Lehtinen et al. (2011)
G. wattersoni	mean = 45	Lehtinen (2003)
G. woosteri	4–6	Lehtinen et al. (2018)

indicating that multiple egg clutches from different females (and possibly from different male-female pairs) are sometimes laid on the same leaf. Clutch sizes for members of the genus are given in Table 11.7. Vocalizations of some species are conspicuous, while others are more muted. In *G. timidus*, the male vocalization is often a single "qwok!" Males call at night from vegetation directly overhanging ponds.

Pandanusicola species also lay eggs arboreally, but most species are associated with *Pandanus* plants (Figure 11.30) and breed only in the water-filled leaf axils of these plants. Three species of *Pandanusicola* have been studied in some detail in the field—*G. annulatus* and *G. wattersoni* by Lehtinen et al. (2011), and *G. liber* by Blommers-Schlösser (1975a); other species are assumed to have a similar ecology. *Guibemantis annulatus* and *G. wattersoni* have parental care of embryos (female and/or male egg attendance) that lasts in some cases until hatching (up to eight days). Clutch size is probably much smaller in *Pandanusicola* than in the subgenus *Guibemantis*, perhaps owing to the physical constraints of the small quantities of water in *Pandanus* leaf axils. Known clutch sizes are given in Table 11.7.

Guibemantis tadpoles are exotrophic and feed on detritus and associated organisms. Tadpoles of *G. depressiceps* and *G. timidus* (under the name *Mantidactylus tornieri*) were described by Blommers-Schlösser (1975a) and Glaw and Vences (1994) and

FIGURE 11.30 **A specimen of *Guibemantis pulcher*, a *Pandanus*-dwelling species, on a spiny *Pandanus* leaf.** (PHOTO by C. R. Hutter.)

revisited by Vejarano et al. (2006b); those of *G. kathrinae* and *G. tornieri* were described by Vejarano et al. (2006b). Among *Pandanusicola* species, tadpoles of *G. liber* were first described by Blommers-Schlösser (1975a) and redescribed by Vejarano et al. (2006b); those of *G. pulcher* were briefly described and illustrated by Blommers-Schlösser (1975a) and Glaw and Vences (1994); larvae assigned to *G. bicalcaratus* were briefly described and illustrated by Blommers-Schlösser and Blanc (1991) and Glaw and Vences (1994); and those of *G. punctatus* were described by Blommers-Schlösser (1975a).

The larval development of *G. annulatus* and *G. wattersoni* are the best known (Lehtinen 2009). Once tadpoles hatch from the eggs, they develop in the water-filled leaf axils of *Pandanus*, sometimes moving from one axil to another along the outer leaf surface. The larval period is approximately two to three months (Lehtinen 2004). Size at metamorphosis in both species is approximately 9 mm snout-to-vent length. The appearance of secondary sexual characteristics happens at approximately 16 mm snout-to-vent length for *G. wattersoni* and at 18 mm snout-to-vent length for *G. annulatus* (Lehtinen et al. 2011).

Reported predators of *G. annulatus* and *G. wattersoni* include an unidentified heteropodid spider and the snake *Ithycyphus oursi* (Lehtinen 2002), and *G. pulcher* was eaten by the snake *Liopholidophis grandidieri* (Cadle 2014). Clutches of eggs are predated by wasps (Safarek et al. 2010) and the snake *Compsophis laphystius* (Cadle 1996; Glaw and Vences 2007).

Calls have been described from several species by Vences et al. (2006, 2011). For species that have been studied, calling is typically most active in the early morning and late afternoon, and particularly during rainfall. The calls of *G. annulatus* and *G. wattersoni* are inconspicuous "click" sounds given in ones, twos, or threes (Lehtinen et al. 2011). Males of most *Pandanusicola* species are not known to call at night, although species in the subgenus *Guibemantis* are known to do so. *Guibemantis tasifotsy* calls most actively at dusk (Lehtinen et al. 2012), and *G. liber* calls predominantly at night.

Interestingly, *G. liber* and *G. tasifotsy* (which from molecular markers are strongly supported as relatively derived members of *Pandanusicola*) are pond breeders, similar to species in the subgenus *Guibemantis*. This suggests a reversal from the derived condition of *Pandanus* breeding back to the ancestral condition (Lehtinen et al. 2012). These two species also have diffuse femoral glands and larger clutch sizes (Table 11.7), more characteristic of the subgenus *Guibemantis* than of their closer *Pandanusicola* relatives.

ECOLOGY

Adults are short-lived, with a maximum life span of less than 12 months (including the larval period) in *G. wattersoni* and 12–14 months in *G. annulatus* (Lehtinen 2009). A strongly female-biased sex ratio (~3:1 females to males) was also reported for these two species. Over 20 individuals of several different species have been found in large *Pandanus* plants in some locations. *Pandanus* is used both on the forest floor and in the forest canopy. Asymmetric interspecific competition between syntopic species has been demonstrated for larvae of two species (Lehtinen 2004), and niche partitioning and life history trade-offs (between dispersal ability and/or larval period length and competitive ability) have been hypothesized as coexistence mechanisms (Lehtinen 2005; Lehtinen and Carfagno 2011). Other species of *Pandanusicola* have not been studied in detail ecologically and there remain many opportunities to further our knowledge of the natural history of these frogs. Fighting among male *Guibemantis* (*Pandanusicola*) sp. aff. *bicalcaratus* has been described in detail by Rosa and Andreone (2012), and cursorily for subgenus *Guibemantis* species by Blommers-Schlösser (1979a).

The diet of *Guibemantis* is very poorly known, but Vences et al. (1999b) reported that *G. liber* feeds mostly on hymenopterans and a few coleopterans and larvae. Monogenean parasites of *G. liber* have also been studied and were found to constitute two new species, suggesting possible cryptic diversity within *G. liber*, as these parasites are generally host specific (Berthier et al. 2014; see Bletz et al., pp. 1342–49).

DISTRIBUTION AND BIOGEOGRAPHY

Guibemantis is a widespread genus, occurring throughout the moist evergreen forests of Madagascar, especially in the east and north of the island. At least one species also occurs in a localized population on the Makay Massif in western Madagascar (Rakotondravony and Goodman 2011). The subgenus *Guibemantis* is localized to eastern Madagascar, whereas *Pandanusicola* is far more widespread.

Some species of *Guibemantis* are presumably widespread on the island (e.g., *G. pulcher*, *G. liber*), while others appear to be narrow endemics. For example, *G. albomaculatus*, *G. milingilingy*, and *G. woosteri* are found only in the northern mountains (Marojejy, Montagne d'Ambre, Manongarivo, and Tsaratanàna). Even widespread species show significant population structure and may consist of multiple cryptic species (Rodríguez et al. 2015). There are also several endemics from the southeast of the island (*G. albolineatus*, *G. annulatus*, and *G. wattersoni*). However, cryptic diversity may obscure the true distributional patterns, and the distribution of many species is very incompletely known. In any case, the phylogeny of *Guibemantis* remains too poorly understood to draw clear conclusions about the biogeographic history of the genus.

CONSERVATION

Habitat loss is assumed to be the largest threat to the survival of *Guibemantis* frogs, as most (especially the *Pandanus* breeders) are forest dependent. Even when some habitat remains, however, extinction risk can still be elevated if the forest is fragmented. In a study examining the effects of habitat fragmentation on *G. annulatus* and *G. wattersoni*, Lehtinen et al. (2003) and Lehtinen and Ramanamanjato (2006) showed that these species avoided habitat edges and were more extinction prone than most other frog species at the sites studied. They were found only in the largest habitat fragments.

In some areas of Madagascar, portions of *Pandanus* are used for making baskets and other handicrafts (see Callmander et al., pp. 551–59). Since the life cycle of *Pandanus*-breeding *Guibemantis* is so intimately tied to these plants, this could also be an area of concern. Many other animal species also utilize these unique micro-aquatic environments (e.g., Lehtinen 2002). For members of the subgenus *Guibemantis*, tolerance of fragmentation may be higher, but it remains a threat to their survival (Riemann et al. 2015).

Nine of the 15 (60%) *Guibemantis* species that have been assessed by the IUCN are currently classified as Least Concern. The recently described *G. albomaculatus*, *G. milingilingy*, and *G. woosteri* have not yet been assigned a conservation status. Several species are apparently limited to a small geographic area (e.g., *G. annulatus*, *G. diphonus*, *G. punctatus*, *G. wattersoni*). With a relatively high proportion of Least Concern species, many *Guibemantis* species might not seem especially vulnerable to extinction at the present time. However, some of these species currently classified as Least Concern may actually be composed of morphologically similar, but evolutionarily independent, lineages. Indeed, previous work has documented numerous additional candidate species that are currently lumped into widespread forms (Lehtinen et al. 2007; Vieites et al. 2009). Therefore, as with many groups of Malagasy frogs, taxonomic research is urgently needed to assess species boundaries before it is too late to apply conservation measures. The captive breeding of *G. pulcher* has been established by Association Mitsinjo (Dawson et al. 2014).

Subject editors: Mark D. Scherz, Miguel Vences, and Achille P. Raselimanana

MANTELLIDAE, MANTELLINAE: *SPINOMANTIS*

C. R. Hutter and M. Vences

The genus *Spinomantis* includes some of the most distinctive frog species on Madagascar, as well as a series of the most poorly known species. *Spinomantis* frogs are well known for their characteristic morphological features of dermal spines and fringes on their limbs, but not all species in the genus share these traits. There are 14 described species and at least 10 candidate species in the genus (Vieites et al. 2009; Perl et al. 2014; Vences et al. 2017b; AmphibiaWeb 2021). Despite a fast pace of species description in other groups such as *Boophis*, only four new species have been described for *Spinomantis* in the past 10 years (*S. nussbaumi* and *S. tavaratra*: Cramer et al. 2008; *S. beckei*: Vences et al. 2017b; and *S. mirus*: Sabino-Pinto et al. 2019). As a result, *Spinomantis* remains poorly known relative to other Malagasy frog genera.

SYSTEMATICS

The genus *Spinomantis* has had an unstable taxonomic history. Different species currently placed in this genus have been previously classified in different species groups, subgenera, genera, and even families (Ahl 1931; Blommers-Schlösser and Blanc 1991; Dubois 1992; Glaw and Vences 2006). This systematic instability has resulted from their impressive ecomorphological diversity, with different species appearing most similar to species in the genera *Boophis*, *Blommersia*, *Gephyromantis*, *Mantidactylus*, and even *Rhacophorus* (a genus of the Asian family Rhacophoridae). The species *S. aglavei*, *S. microtis*, and *S. peraccae* were considered to be *Rhacophorus*; *S. aglavei* and *S. microtis* were classified as *Boophis* (Methuen and Hewitt 1913; Guibé 1947; Glaw and Vences 1994); and *S. peraccae* was placed in *Mantidactylus* (Blommers-Schlösser 1978, 1979a) and later in the subgenus *Guibemantis* (Dubois 1992). Furthermore, *S. bertini* was thought to be a *Gephyromantis* and had previously also been classified with species of the subgenus *Blommersia* in *Mantidactylus* (Guibé 1978; Blommers-Schlösser and Blanc 1991; Dubois 1992). *Spinomantis* was originally erected as a subgenus of *Mantidactylus* (Dubois 1992).

The evolutionary relationships among these dissimilar species became clear when molecular data revealed that these morphologically different species were a monophyletic group, and they were considered as a separate genus, *Spinomantis* (Glaw and Vences 2006). These results have also been confirmed by other molecular phylogenetic studies (Pyron and Wiens 2011; Wollenberg et al. 2011). Additionally, some morphologically similar species within *Spinomantis* remain closely related to each other, such as the arboreal tree frogs with fringes (*S. aglavei*, *S. fimbriatus*, and *S. phantasticus*), the fringe- and spine-lacking smooth tree frogs (*S. peraccae* and *S. tavaratra*; Glaw and Vences 2007; Cramer et al. 2008), and the saxicolous, small and smooth, slender-bodied species from the *S. bertini* complex (*S. bertini*, *S. beckei*, and *S. mirus*: Vences et al. 2017b; Sabino-Pinto et al. 2019). Relationships of the other genera in Mantellidae with *Spinomantis* remain somewhat unclear; however, *Spinomantis* is included in the subfamily Mantellinae, and thus related to *Boehmantis*, *Blommersia*, *Guibemantis*, *Gephyromantis*, *Mantidactylus*, *Mantella*, and *Wakea*. Glaw and Vences (2006) found *Spinomantis* to be sister to a clade composed of *Boehmantis*, *Gephyromantis*, and *Mantidactylus*. Conversely, Wollenberg et al. (2011) recovered a sister relationship with *Blommersia*, *Guibemantis*, *Mantella*, and *Wakea*. Future work should clarify the relationships among these genera.

MORPHOLOGY

Spinomantis is among the most morphologically diverse genera of Malagasy frogs, most likely associated with the diversity of habitats its species occupy. Consequently, there is no single derived morphological character that can be used to assign species to this genus. Generally, all *Spinomantis* species share a combination of some morphological characters, but this combination is not exclusive to them: intercalary elements between the ultimate and penultimate phalanges of fingers and toes; distinct type 2 femoral glands in males (Glaw et al. 2000a); paired-bilobed or single subgular vocal sacs; an outer metatarsal tubercle; and maxillary teeth.

The most charismatic among *Spinomantis* species are the arboreal tree frog ecomorphs that have prominent dermal spines and fringes on their limbs (*S. aglavei*, *S. fimbriatus*, *S. phantasticus*, and *S. tavaratra*; Glaw and Vences 2007). In addition, there are more generalized tree frog species that lack the spines and fringes and occur in similar habitats (*S. massi*, *S. nussbaumi*, and *S. peraccae*). More different are the saxicolous species: *S. brunae* and *S. elegans* (Figure 11.31), *S. microtis*, and a candidate species similar to *S. bertini* in Ranomafana National Park. Additionally, some rock-dwelling species are found near streams: *S. guibei* and *S. bertini* (Glaw and Vences 2007; Cramer et al. 2008; Vences et al. 2017b). There is at least one undescribed candidate species from Ranomafana National Park that lives in *Pandanus* plants and morphologically resembles *Pandanus*-dwelling species of *Guibemantis* (Glaw and Vences 2007), but no details are available on where or how it reproduces.

Spinomantis tadpoles display a conserved morphology in those described thus far (*S.* cf. *aglavei*, *S. elegans*, *S.* cf. *fimbriatus*, *S.* aff. *peraccae*, and *S. tavaratra*), with an ecomorphology that is typical for lotic and benthic stream habitats (Thomas et al. 2005; Vejarano et al. 2006c; Ndriantsoa et al. 2012). However, it is unclear whether tadpole morphology remains conserved throughout the rest of the genus; for example, the larvae of most species from saxicolous habitats are not known.

REPRODUCTION AND ECOLOGY

The arboreal *Spinomantis* species are nocturnal tree frogs that communicate acoustically through a short breeding period during the rainy season, specifically in habitats with streams (Glaw and Vences 2007; Figure 11.32). Other species call during the day from alongside rocky streams near the ground or on rocks (Glaw and Vences 2007; Cramer et al. 2008), which may overhang the water (Andreone and Nussbaum 2006). Finally, rock-dwelling species call from the surfaces of rocks, but their tadpoles are also found in streams (Glaw and Vences 2007). The arboreal species (e.g., *S. aglavei*, *S. peraccae*) lay clutches of around 35 eggs (Figure 11.33), which are deposited on the surface of leaves as in some *Blommersia* and *Guibemantis* species (Glaw and Vences 1994, 2007; Hutter et al. 2018a).

The advertisement calls of *Spinomantis* are diverse (Vences et al. 2006), much like the ecomorphology of the genus. The arboreal tree frog ecomorphs that reproduce along streams typically have loud calls that can be heard some distance away and sound like a loud, often metallic "dink" with varying repetition rates and number of notes (e.g., *S. aglavei*, *S. peraccae*). The saxicolous species have quieter calls, which in some species sound like rapid clicks (e.g., *S. bertini* and related species). Even more remarkably, *S. elegans*, which lives in cave-like habitats, has a call that sounds like a droplet falling into a pool of water.

The life span and diet of *Spinomantis* are unknown. *Spinomantis* species have been found to be a component of the diet of other organisms. Snakes in particular are reported to feed on *Spinomantis* frogs and their eggs (Cadle 1996; Hutter et al. 2018a).

Arboreal *Spinomantis* species are found on leaves and tree trunks and call at night to attract mates. Conversely, the saxicolous species call during the day and are found closer to the ground on rocks and other surfaces (Glaw and Vences 2007; Cramer et al. 2008).

FIGURE 11.31 ***Spinomantis elegans*, a species that lives on and between rocks and whose taxonomic assignment has long been uncertain. Photographed at Ranomafana.** (PHOTO by C. R. Hutter.)

FIGURE 11.32 **Calling males of *Spinomantis aglavei* emit very loud, metallic "dink" sounds.** (PHOTO by C. R. Hutter.)

FIGURE 11.33 **A *Spinomantis peraccae* female guarding its eggs shortly after egg deposition.** (PHOTO by C. R. Hutter.)

DISTRIBUTION AND BIOGEOGRAPHY

Spinomantis species are restricted to the moist evergreen forests of Madagascar, and the highest species richness, especially of the large arboreal species, is in the central and northern areas, with fewer species in the southeastern portion of this formation (Glaw and Vences 2007; Brown et al. 2014, 2016). However, the saxicolous and stream-dwelling species seem to have their center of richness and endemism in the southeast. Most species are found in montane forests at elevations between 600 and 1200 m (Glaw and Vences 2007). Apart from these details, not much else is known about the biogeography of the genus, as many species remain undescribed.

CONSERVATION

As with most Malagasy frogs, the major risk for *Spinomantis* is habitat loss. All species of *Spinomantis* depend on intact forest and their specialized habitats within these forests, more so than species of many other mantellid genera. Among species that have been assessed by the IUCN, one is listed as Critically Endangered (*S. nussbaumi*), two as Endangered (*S. brunae* and *S. microtis*), and three as Vulnerable (*S. guibei*, *S. massi*, and *S. tavaratra*) (IUCN 2019). The dominant threats for *Spinomantis* are habitat loss and modification (IUCN 2019). At least 10 candidate species of *Spinomantis* remain undescribed (Vieites et al. 2009; Perl et al. 2014). One important challenge in this group is taxonomically characterizing these distinct lineages so that their conservation status can be adequately assessed and their ecomorphological evolution studied in greater detail.

Subject editors: Carl R. Hutter, Miguel Vences, and Achille P. Raselimanana

MANTELLIDAE, TSINGYMANTINAE: *TSINGYMANTIS*

F. Glaw, A. Rakotoarison, and M. D. Scherz

The enigmatic genus *Tsingymantis*, with a single species, *T. antitra* (Figure 11.34), was described only in 2006, and although it clearly belongs to the Mantellidae, its position within the family is still insufficiently known, as it has a number of intermediate morphological characters compared to other members of the family (Glaw and Vences 2006; Glaw et al. 2006; Raselimanana et al. 2007). It is evidently a very ancient relict lineage; Wollenberg et al. (2011) found it to have diverged from other mantellids over 40 million years ago, and it was recently placed in a new subfamily, Tsingymantinae, without any new data provided (Dubois et al. 2021). According to current knowledge, *Tsingymantis* is endemic to the karstic limestone Ankarana Massif in the north.

The phylogenetic position of *Tsingymantis* remains uncertain; Glaw et al. (2006) and Wollenberg et al. (2011) found it to be sister to Mantellinae, whereas Kurabayashi et al. (2008) found it to be sister to Laliostominae + Boophinae. These different studies recovered relationships with only weak support, and phylogenomic analyses to resolve this problem are ongoing.

MORPHOLOGY

Tsingymantis antitra is a moderately large frog, with males reaching 56 mm and females up to 67 mm snout-to-vent length. It has very enlarged and flattened discs on its fingers, probably an ecological adaptation to climbing rocks (as also found in *Spinomantis microtis*), and moderately enlarged but also flattened discs on its toes. The tympanum is large and highly distinct, and a thick supra-tympanic fold runs over it. The species has a brown ground coloration with mint- to khaki-green mottling over the whole body. This coloration is even more pronounced in juveniles (Glaw and Vences 2007). There are almost no secondary sexual traits in *T. antitra* (Raselimanana et al. 2007), but males do possess nuptial pads (Rakotoarison et al. 2013).

REPRODUCTION

The vocalizations of *T. antitra* were described by Rakotoarison et al. (2013). Males were found calling only during heavy precipitation at the beginning of the rainy season, sitting on rocks near pools of water in the limestone karst. The call is a rather inconspicuous trill of short, unpulsed notes that are repeated at regular intervals and made without distending the vocal sac.

Reproduction of *Tsingymantis* occurs in pools in the limestone karst (Randrianiaina et al. 2011a; Rakotoarison et al. 2013; Figure 11.34). Neither the mode of amplexus nor the eggs are known, but the tadpole was described and depicted by Randrianiaina et al. (2011a). The tadpole is generalized and largely similar to *Aglyptodactylus* and *Laliostoma* but has exceptionally large, serrated jaw sheaths, suggesting possible oophagy or a predatory diet.

CONSERVATION

In 2008, *T. antitra* was assessed by the IUCN Red List as Vulnerable based on incomplete knowledge of the species. This status was updated to Endangered in 2016 in a thorough reassessment of many Malagasy frogs (IUCN SSC Amphibian Specialist Group 2016b). Currently there is no trade in *Tsingymantis*, and the genus is afforded some natural protection by its karstic habitat, as well as by its cryptic habits.

Subject editors: Mark D. Scherz, Miguel Vences, and Achille P. Raselimanana

FIGURE 11.34 ***Tsingymantis antitra* in its habitat in Ankarana National Park.** (PHOTO by M. D. Scherz.)

MICROHYLIDAE: COPHYLINAE, MICROHYLID FROGS

M. D. Scherz, A. Crottini, and A. Rakotoarison

Cophylinae is a large and diverse subfamily of the family Microhylidae (commonly known as microhylid or narrow-mouthed frogs). Currently the subfamily consists of 113 species, with several species described only recently and many candidate species awaiting assessment and description. The Cophylinae is divided into nine genera (*Anilany*, *Anodonthyla*, *Cophyla*, *Madecassophryne*, *Mini*, *Platypelis*, *Plethodontohyla*, *Rhombophryne*, and *Stumpffia*). Lineages in this subfamily have undergone repeated niche shifts, and their ecomorphological evolution is currently the object of multiple studies. As far as is known, all species have nidicolous and endotrophic larvae and exhibit some extent of parental care, which can be quite prolonged in some species. Many species are microendemics (especially the small to miniaturized species), and topography, body size, and ecology are implicated in the diversification of this subfamily. Because of their high rates of microendemism, several species are severely threatened with extinction, mostly from habitat loss.

TAXONOMY

The taxonomic history of the Cophylinae is extremely complex. All studies based on morphology alone (i.e., all work prior to 2003) were misled by convergence in morphological characters and proposed what we now know based on genetics to be polyphyletic or paraphyletic genera. A full recounting of that history is beyond the scope of this contribution, but some aspects can be summarized. The first members of this subfamily were originally described at the end of the 19th century, in such diverse anuran families as the Dendrobatidae, Dyscophidae, Engystomatidae, and Brevicipitidae. It was not until the 1920s that it was realized that these frogs all belonged in one subfamily (Noble and Parker 1926). The most important early works on the evolution of this group were those by Noble (1922), Noble and Parker (1926), and especially Parker (1934)—these provided important information on the skeletons of the cophylines and their putative interrelationships. Further significant contributions to the genus- and species-level classification were made by Guibé (1974, 1978) and Blommers-Schlösser and Blanc (1991).

Blommers-Schlösser and Blanc (1991) recognized 29 species of cophyline microhylids. Subsequently, Vences and Glaw (1991) revised the taxonomy of *Stumpffia*, describing two new species, and when the first edition of their *Field Guide to the Amphibians and Reptiles of Madagascar* (Glaw and Vences 1992a) was released, they described one more species each of *Stumpffia*, *Anodonthyla*, and *Platypelis* (the latter subsequently moved to *Cophyla*). In the second edition of their field guide (Glaw and Vences 1994), they provided the first list of undescribed species, but no new species were described until 2003. Between 2003 and 2005, seven new species were named (Andreone et al. 2003a; Vences and Glaw 2003; Vences et al. 2003c, 2005; Glaw and Vences 2005).

From 2005 to 2009, genetic data overturned much of what was thought about the genus-level taxonomy of the Cophylinae and revealed that a great deal of species diversity remained undescribed. Andreone et al. (2005c) showed that *Plethodontohyla* was polyphyletic, with one clade clustering with *Rhombophryne testudo* (until this point always considered a monotypic genus because of its bizarre, specialized burrowing morphology; Figure 11.35), and the other being the sister clade of *Platypelis* + *Cophyla*. Frost et al. (2006) translated this into a taxonomic change and moved three *Plethodontohyla* species that clustered with *R. testudo* to the genus *Rhombophryne*. In the third edition of their field guide, Glaw and Vences (2007) transferred additional *Plethodontohyla* species to the genus *Rhombophryne*, anticipating the genetic results that would later become available from Wollenberg et al. (2008b), where 26 recognized species and some 23 species-level mitochondrial lineages across five genera were analyzed. In this latter contribution, species of the genus *Stumpffia* were found to be polyphyletic, with "*Stumpffia*" *helenae* retrieved as the sister group of *Rhombophryne* rather than *Stumpffia*, and with a clade of two undescribed and miniaturized species from the southeast of the island recovered as the sister group of *Plethodontohyla*. Vieites et al. (2009) then showed that the 23 undescribed lineages of Wollenberg et al. (2008b) were only a fraction of the undescribed diversity; they recognized 57 candidate species within the subfamily. Eight more candidates were later added by Perl et al. (2014).

De Sá et al. (2012), found strong support for *Rhombophryne* (as recircumscribed by Andreone et al. 2005c; Frost et al. 2006; Glaw and Vences 2007; Wollenberg et al. 2008b) as the sister clade of *Stumpffia*, with *Anodonthyla*, *Platypelis*, and *Plethodontohyla* forming a (poorly supported) clade, a topology recovered also based on karyotype data by Aprea et al. (2007). In the context of a phylogenomic study on the whole family Microhylidae (see below), Peloso et al. (2016) implemented species- and genus-level taxonomic changes in several cases, the most important of which was the synonymization of *Stumpffia* with *Rhombophryne*, and of *Platypelis* with *Cophyla*. These conclusions were challenged by the publication of a new phylogenetic hypothesis (Scherz et al. 2016b), where "*Stumpffia*" *helenae* was moved to a new genus (*Anilany*) to circumvent the paraphyly identified among the *Stumpffia* species (as already shown by Wollenberg et al. 2008b), rendering *Stumpffia* and *Rhombophryne* monophyletic again. Despite further argument about the best course of taxonomic action (Peloso et al. 2017; Scherz et al. 2017b), the conclusions of Scherz et al. (2016b) were supported by the next major phylogenetic reconstruction of the microhylids by Tu et al. (2018), where the recently rediscovered genus *Madecassophryne* (Rakotoarison et al. 2017b) was also analyzed and confirmed as the earliest-diverging member of the Cophylinae subfamily.

The clade of *Stumpffia*-like frogs (with small body size and reduced fingers) first identified in the phylogeny of Wollenberg et al.

FIGURE 11.35 ***Rhombophryne testudo* from Nosy Be, a representative of the fossorial ecomorph within the Cophylinae.** (PHOTO by M. D. Scherz.)

(2008b) was consistently recovered as sister to *Plethodontohyla* in all phylogenies that included these undescribed lineages (e.g., Scherz et al. 2016b). They were assigned to a new genus, *Mini*, by Scherz et al. (2019b). Further phylogenomic analyses by Scherz and colleagues are currently ongoing, and preliminary results suggest that genus-level taxonomy of the Cophylinae is now nearly stable, although the relationship of *Cophyla* and *Platypelis* is not yet resolved.

The publication of DNA barcode reference data sets for the amphibians of Madagascar (Vieites et al. 2009; Perl et al. 2014) enabled the identification of 65 candidate species among the Cophylinae. This laid the foundation for a dramatic increase in the rate of species description in the subfamily, with 61 species subsequently described. Most of these were published in single-species papers, but a few multi-species description papers and monographs are particularly noteworthy, pertaining to *Anodonthyla* (Vences et al. 2010a); *Rhombophryne* (Scherz et al. 2017c); *Cophyla* (Rakotoarison et al. 2015a); and *Platypelis* (Rakotoarison et al. 2012). The recently published systematic revision of *Stumpffia* (Rakotoarison et al. 2017a) deserves special remark, as it resulted in the description of 26 new species. So, too, does the work of Scherz et al. (2019b), which resulted in the formal description of the genus *Mini* with three nominal species, as well as the description of one extremely miniaturized species each of *Rhombophryne* and *Anodonthyla*.

RELATIONSHIPS WITHIN MICROHYLIDAE

The phylogenetic position of the Cophylinae within the Microhylidae has only recently started to become clear from phylogenomic analyses. Van der Meijden et al. (2007) published the first extensive phylogenetic hypothesis and proposed that the Cophylinae was a sister group of the Scaphiophryninae, only distantly related to the Dyscophinae. These results were supported by Kurabayashi et al. (2011). Pyron and Wiens (2011) found the Cophylinae to fall sister to the African Hoplophryninae and recovered extensive paraphyly of genera, while de Sá et al. (2012) recovered the Cophylinae as a sister group of the Phrynomerinae + Kalophryninae + Otophryninae, without close affinity to the Scaphiophryninae.

Peloso et al. (2016) were the first to use phylogenomic methods (target enrichment) and consistently recovered the sister relationship between the Cophylinae and Scaphiophryninae (although with low support). This clade was found to fall in various places, most frequently sister to Gastrophryninae + Otophryninae + *Adelastes*. Tu et al. (2018) also found Scaphiophryninae and Cophylinae to be sister clades with high support, together falling beside a large clade containing, among others, Kalophryninae, Dyscophinae, Microhylinae, and Asterophryinae, but without strong support. The most recent analysis by Streicher et al. (2020) again uses genomic methods but a broader sampling of taxa and finds Cophylinae and Scaphiophryninae sister to one another with rather low support, and this clade sister to a clade of Asterophryinae + Dyscophinae + Microhylinae, but again without high support. In summary, a consensus seems to be emerging that Cophylinae and Scaphiophryninae are sister subfamilies, but their relationships within the Microhylidae are still uncertain.

EVOLUTION

As there are extremely limited fossil records available of Malagasy microhylids (MacPhee et al. 1985), dating their origins has proven challenging. Crottini et al. (2012b) placed the divergence of the Cophylinae + Scaphiophryninae clade from the other microhylids at around 77 million years ago (Mya) and recovered this and the Mantellidae clade as the oldest anuran colonizers. In the most recent dated reconstructions by Moen et al. (2016) and Feng et al. (2017), based on a much larger molecular data set, the origin of the Microhylidae was recovered at around 66 Mya, and the divergence of the Cophylinae + Scaphiophryninae clade was inferred to be more recent, around 59.9–60.5 Mya. This estimate would place the divergence and diversification of these frogs in the early

Paleogene, coinciding with the burst in lineage diversification of neobatrachian anurans following the K-Pg mass extinction (Feng et al. 2017).

The ecomorphological evolution of the Cophylinae was first highlighted by Andreone et al. (2005c) when the first molecular phylogeny of the subfamily was published. As phylogenetic resolution has increased, the picture has become only more interesting. Ecomorphological transitions have occurred several times within the subfamily, with the most basally divergent lineage, *Madecassophryne*, specialized to live in cracks between rocks where water flows constantly (Rakotoarison et al. 2017b)—to the best of our knowledge a unique lifestyle among Malagasy microhylids. Arboreal species occur in the genera *Anodonthyla*, *Plethodontohyla*, *Platypelis*, and *Cophyla*; terrestrial species in *Anodonthyla*, *Plethodontohyla*, *Rhombophryne*, *Mini*, and *Stumpffia*; fossorial species in *Plethodontohyla* and *Rhombophryne* (Figure 11.35); scansorial and rupicolous species in *Anodonthyla*, *Stumpffia*, and *Anilany*. In parallel, miniaturization has also occurred multiple times and can be found in the genera *Mini*, *Anodonthyla*, *Platypelis*, *Rhombophryne*, and *Stumpffia*, while dramatic size increase has occurred in members of at least two genera, *Plethodontohyla* and *Platypelis*.

Scherz et al. (2019b) discussed the evolution of miniaturized body size within the Cophylinae, showing that the smallest cophylines have convergently evolved a paedomorphic (adults retain juvenile-like characters) phenotype, typified by a narrow skull, anteriorly displaced upper jaw, and especially reduced digits. Furthermore, they suggest that miniaturization may give rise to terrestriality, as suggested by *Anodonthyla eximia*, though this remains speculative; *Platypelis karenae* and *P. tetra* are also diminutive species but have not become terrestrial. These same authors suggested that phytotelmic ecology may provide alternatives to being terrestrial. This study also illustrated that, although paedomorphic traits are generally expected to accompany miniaturization, they are not inevitable; *Rhombophryne proportionalis* exhibits hallmarks of proportional dwarfism, rather than paedomorphism, showing features and proportions similar to those of larger frogs, especially in its less reduced hands and feet, short head, and plump body.

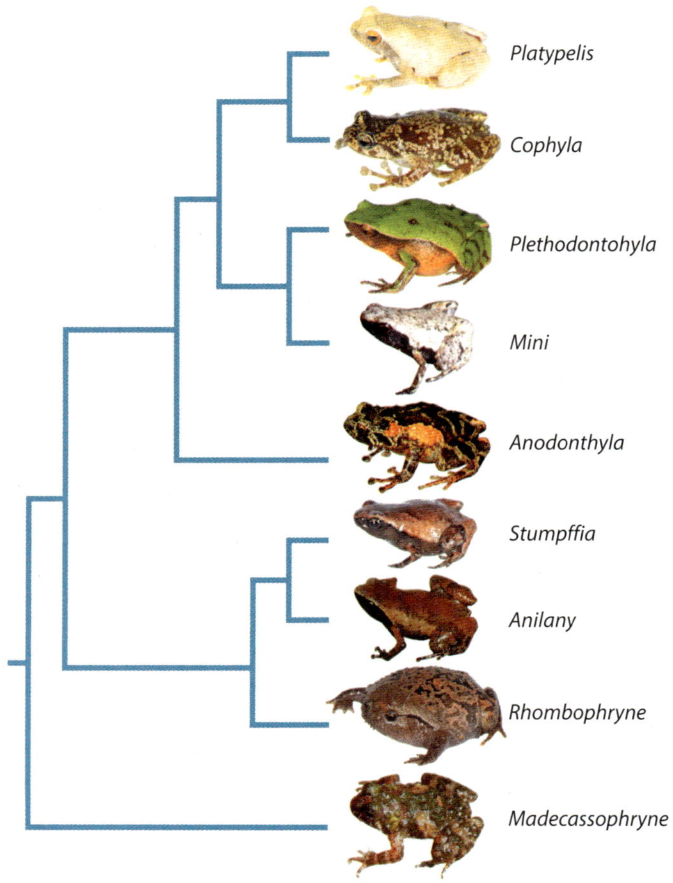

FIGURE 11.36 **A schematic tree summarizing evolutionary relationships among genera in the Cophylinae based on the phylogenetic reconstructions of Scherz et al. (2016b) and Rakotoarison et al. (2017b).** (PHOTOS at branch tips by F. Glaw, A. Rakotoarison, M. D. Scherz, and M. Vences.)

DIVERSITY

In the following, we summarize the nine genera in Cophylinae (Figures 11.36 and 11.37), including the number of nominal species and candidate species, their distribution, external morphological characters, and osteological features. Osteological summaries are based largely on newly collected data.

Anilany

Monotypic: *Anilany helenae*. One numbered candidate species: *Anilany* sp. Ca14 (formerly *Stumpffia* sp. Ca14). From central and western Madagascar (Ambohitantely and Bemaraha). Unique hand morphology, with fingers 3 and 4 with discs and 1 and 2 without, and lateral head color border. Prevomer divided into pre- and post-choanal portion, the latter replacing the neopalatine (which is absent or not ossified), but not in contact with the exceptionally short cultriform process of the parasphenoid. Clavicles curved, starting at the glenoid. Males with expanded humeral crests and prepollex almost as long as first finger. Terminal phalanges of fingers and toes T shaped. Maxillary and vomerine teeth absent.

Anodonthyla

Twelve nominal species. No numbered candidate species, but two candidates are listed in the literature and remain to be assessed, namely *A.* sp. aff. *boulengeri* from Betampona (Rosa et al. 2012) and *A.* sp. aff. *boulengeri* "Ranomafana" (Vences et al. 2010a) (also called *Anodonthyla* CaNew Ranomafana by Scherz et al. 2016b). From central eastern and southeastern Madagascar. All species except *A. eximia* and *A. montana* have distinctly expanded finger discs. Males have an elongated, pointed prepollex that is very obvious. Palate remarkably similar to *Anilany* but the neopalatine/post-choanal vomer element is more lateral and less broad (absent in *A. eximia*). Clavicles strongly curved, starting at the glenoid. Males with expanded humeral crests and prepollex almost as long as first finger. Terminal phalanges of fingers Y shaped, of toes T or Y

FIGURE 11.37 **Representatives of the genera of the subfamily Cophylinae to scale.** (PHOTOS by F. Glaw, A. Rakotoarison, M. D. Scherz, and M. Vences.)

shaped except in *A. eximia*. Maxillary teeth usually but not always present. Vomerine teeth absent.

Cophyla

Seven nominal species. Two numbered candidate species: *Cophyla* sp. Ca5 from Andrafainkona and *Cophyla* sp. Ca6 from Sorata (Rakotoarison et al. 2019a). From northern Madagascar. All species have expanded finger discs and rather smooth skin. Prevomer divided into pre- and post-choanal portion, the latter forming a medial element that sometimes also has ventral denticles and always lacks lateral extensions (absent in *C. berara*), neopalatine long and slender. Clavicles absent in all species except *C. puellarum*, where they start at the midpoint of the coracoid. Terminal phalanges of fingers and toes Y shaped. Maxillary teeth present. Vomerine teeth sometimes present.

Madecassophryne

Monotypic: *Madecassophryne truebae*. No candidate species currently outstanding, but the identity of specimens analyzed by Rakotoarison et al. (2017b) needs to be confirmed, as they are considerably smaller than all known specimens of *M. truebae* from the original type series collected in southeastern Madagascar. Nonexpanded fingertips, round bulbous texture to the dorsal skin, and very long fingers similar to those of *Scaphiophryne*. Prevomer possibly undivided and horseshoe shaped, neopalatine reaching the cultriform process of the parasphenoid. Clavicles absent. Terminal phalanges of fingers and toes long and distally knobbed. Maxillary and vomerine teeth absent.

Mini

Three species. No candidate species currently outstanding. From southeastern Madagascar. Fingers and toes reduced, in some species very strongly, and usually with a lateral head color border. Prevomer divided into pre- and post-choanal portion, post-choanal portion flattened and spatulate, attached to the cultriform process of the parasphenoid, laterally overlapped by the neopalatine. Clavicles present, narrow and curved, starting at the glenoid. Terminal phalanges of fingers and toes distally knobbed or reduced to round elements. Maxillary teeth present or absent, vomerine teeth absent.

Platypelis

Sixteen nominal species. Nine numbered candidate species outstanding: *Platypelis* sp. Ca01 from Sahavontsira and Betampona, *Platypelis* sp. Ca03 from Ambolokopatrika, *Platypelis* sp. Ca06 from Ranomafana, *Platypelis* sp. Ca08 from Manarikoba, *Platypelis* sp. Ca09 from Betampona, *Platypelis* sp. Ca10 from Andranomanga, *Platypelis* sp. Ca11 from Marojejy and elsewhere, *Platypelis* sp. Ca12 from Sorata, and *Platypelis* sp. Ca13 from Andravory. One further candidate species was identified by Rosa et al. (2012) (*P.* sp. aff. *grandis*) and redubbed "*P.* sp. CaBetampona1" by Scherz et al. (2016b). From eastern and northern Madagascar. All species have expanded finger discs. Skin can be smooth or rough. Most members of the *P. grandis* species complex are exceptionally large. Prevomer divided into pre- and post-choanal portion, the latter separated from its contralateral by a small gap and bearing teeth, overlapped laterally by the narrow neopalatine. Clavicles present, starting at the midpoint of the coracoid. Terminal phalanges of fingers and toes Y shaped. Maxillary and vomerine teeth present.

Plethodontohyla

Eleven nominal species. Two numbered candidate species outstanding: *Plethodontohyla* sp. Ca01 from Ambatolahy (possibly conspecific with *P. alluaudi*; see Bellati et al. 2018) and *Plethodontohyla* sp. Ca02 from Tsaratanàna. From extreme southeastern to northern Madagascar, with at least one species in the west. Can be divided into two main phenetic groups, one consisting of arboreal and scansorial species (*P. inguinalis*, *P. guentheri*, *P. notosticta*, *P. mihanika*, and *P. fonetana*), all of which have finger discs broadened to some extent and most of which have a distinct lateral color border; and the other of terrestrial and fossorial species (*P. ocellata*, *P. bipunctata*, *P. alluaudi*, *P. tuberata*, *P. brevipes*, and *P. laevis*), all of which have nonexpanded finger discs and lack a distinct lateral color border, but several of which can have distinct coloration on the lateral head, and/or a characteristic pair of dorsal ridges. Prevomer divided into pre- and post-choanal portion, the latter separated from its contralateral by a small gap and bearing teeth, overlapped laterally by the neopalatine. Clavicles present or absent. When present, clavicles are curved or straight and begin at the glenoid. Terminal phalanges of fingers and toes knobbed or T shaped in the terrestrial and fossorial species, and T or Y shaped in the arboreal and scansorial species. Maxillary and vomerine teeth present.

Rhombophryne

Twenty nominal species. Five numbered candidate species outstanding: *Rhombophryne* sp. Ca01 and *Rhombophryne* sp. Ca10 from Ilampy, *Rhombophryne* sp. Ca03 and *Rhombophryne* sp. Ca07 from Tsaratanàna, and *Rhombophryne* sp. Ca09 from Masoala. A further undescribed species that has long been referred to in the literature as "*R. alluaudi*" (revised by Bellati et al. 2018) is not numbered. It is also unclear whether *R. vaventy*-like specimens from Sorata are distinct from that species (Scherz et al. 2016b, 2017c; S. Lambert et al. 2017). From central eastern and northern Madagascar. Records from the west (Andreone and Randrianirina 2008) have recently been questioned and are considered unverified (A. Crottini, unpublished data). *Rhombophryne* species are terrestrial to fossorial frogs without expanded finger or toe discs. The genus can be divided into five to six species groups with at least some genetic support:

- R. serratopalpebrosa species group—*R. serratopalpebrosa*, *R. guentherpetersi*, *R. coronata*, *R. vaventy*, *R. tany*, *R. ornata*, *R. regalis*, and *R. diadema*—all possess superciliary spines;
- R. minuta species group—*R. minuta* and *R. longicrus*—both have rather long, slender legs;
- R. testudo species group—*R. testudo*, *R. coudreaui*, *R. matavy*, *R. mangabensis,* and *R. savaka*—moderately to extremely specialized burrowing frogs;
- R. ellae species group—*R. ellae*—a moderately small frog with red on its posterior thighs and black inguinal spots; and
- R. laevipes species group—*R. laevipes*, *R. nilevina*, and *R. botabota*—all moderately large frogs, often with white spots on posterior thighs and inguinal region.

The miniaturized *R. proportionalis* may be best placed in its own species group.

Prevomer divided into pre- and post-choanal portion, the latter separated from its contralateral by a small gap and bearing teeth. Clavicles present or absent. When present, clavicles are curved or straight and begin at the glenoid. Terminal phalanges of fingers and toes knobbed or slightly T shaped. Maxillary and vomerine teeth present.

Stumpffia

Forty-two nominal species. About 10 numbered candidate species outstanding: *Stumpffia* sp. Ca02 from Tsaratanàna, *Stumpffia* sp. Ca11 from Ambolokopatrika and Marojejy, *Stumpffia* sp. Ca25 from Montagne des Français, *Stumpffia* sp. Ca29 from Tsaratanàna, *Stumpffia* sp. Ca30 from Angorony, *Stumpffia* sp. Ca34 from Ranomena (Ranomafana National Park), *Stumpffia* sp. Ca42 from Fierenana, and *Stumpffia* sp. Ca57 from Ambodivoangy. Two further candidate species were identified by Peloso et al. (2016): *Stumpffia* "sp1 Tsaratanàna" and *Stumpffia* "sp2 Andapa" (see Scherz et al. 2016b). From central eastern to northern Madagascar, with several members also in northwestern areas such as Ankarafantsika.

Fingers range from possessing discs to being extremely reduced, digital reduction having occurred repeatedly across the group. Generally characterized by a small body size, but some species are larger (Köhler et al. 2010). The genus is currently not divided into species groups, as the genetic clades are highly heterogeneous in morphology, but four main clades have been proposed (clades A–D; see Rakotoarison et al. 2017a), though without clear apomorphies among them. In most species, the prevomer is divided into pre- and post-choanal portions, the latter being slender and slightly broadened medially, usually contacting the cultriform process of the parasphenoid, never bearing teeth, and laterally contacting the equally slender neopalatine. In the diminutive species *S. tridactyla*, *S. contumelia*, and *S. obscoena* (which do not form a clade), the vomer seems to be undivided and is nearly fully looped, and the neopalatine is absent. Clavicles can be present or absent, curved or straight. Terminal phalanges of fingers and toes knobbed or slightly T shaped. Maxillary teeth can be present or absent. Vomerine teeth are always absent.

BIOGEOGRAPHY

Given its relatively ancient origins, it is perhaps no surprise that the biogeographic patterns of species richness and endemism of the Cophylinae are complex. This topic was first investigated by Wollenberg et al. (2008b) and revisited by Brown et al. (2016). Additional contributions were made on specific groups (e.g., by Rakotoarison et al. 2019b for *Stumpffia* and by Scherz et al. 2017c for *Rhombophryne*).

A hallmark of most Cophylinae species is a small to very small geographic distribution. Some species are known only from the summit zones of a single mountain (e.g., *Platypelis olgae* from Tsaratanàna, *R. minuta* from Marojejy), but microendemism is apparently not always associated with elevational restriction; *Mini mum*, for example, occurs at low elevations in Manombo, and several species are seemingly microendemic to Betampona (although in these cases, the extensive deforestation of similar habitat at low elevation is likely a major contributor to currently restricted ranges). Most Cophylinae species are also limited to narrow elevational ranges, often of just a few hundred meters (Wollenberg et al. 2008b; Rakotoarison et al. 2019b, 2020). The combination of these two factors (small distribution areas and narrow elevational ranges) results in strong turnovers in the whole cophyline fauna over short geographic distances and suggests that mountains played an important role in the diversification of these frogs (Wollenberg et al. 2008b).

The cophyline frogs show a center of endemism and species richness in northern Madagascar (Wollenberg et al. 2008b; Brown et al. 2016), especially along the escarpment that connects Makira, Anjanaharibe-Sud, Ambolokopatrika, Marojejy, Tsaratanàna, Bemanevika, Manongarivo, Sorata, and Andravory, and on the separate massif of Montagne d'Ambre—roughly 40% of all known cophyline species are endemic to these mountains. Three genera have their centers of endemism in the north-central east to south-central east: *Plethodontohyla*, *Anodonthyla*, and *Mini*. However, the basally divergent *Madecassophryne* is currently known only from the southeast, except for an unconfirmed record from the north-central east. Finally, a few Cophylinae species are also known from the dry deciduous areas of the west, for example *P. fonetana* (Glaw et al. 2007). Although the subfamily might have diversified in the north, it is likely that the Cophylinae may have originated in the south-central east, but this question remains to be further investigated.

REPRODUCTION

Observations of cophyline reproduction are particularly challenging, and our current knowledge originates from a handful of species (summarized in Table 11.8; representative photographs in Figure 11.38). Amplexus has never been reported but is presumably axillary as in other microhylids (Duellman and Trueb 1986). The absence of such observations is probably a consequence of the male of most cophylines finding or making a nest, to which he then attracts a female by vocalizing. These vocalizations may be given from within the nest itself (especially in phytotelm breeders), or, in at least one *Stumpffia* species (*S. maledicta*), at some distance from the nest, with the female then following the male to his foam nest (M. D. Scherz and A. Rakotoarison, unpublished data). Cophyline nests can be terrestrial in burrows, or among leaf litter and composed of jelly or foam, or in small pools of rainwater, usually in plants (e.g., bamboo or other tree holes, or other plant cavities—phytotelmata), but occasionally also in snail shells or other vessels. Most species are probably seasonally monogamous by virtue of female selection of single males and their nest sites, but in a few cases it seems that multiple females may lay their eggs in the nest of a single male (*S. achillei*, *Platypelis laetus*, *P. tsaratananaensis*, and *P. alticola*), and the mating system may thus be polygynous (Rakotoarison et al. 2012, 2017a, 2020).

Nest building/selection and defense is just part of the parental care present in the Cophylinae. Nest guarding is known from at least 12 species so far (Table 11.8), and in at least two phytotelm-breeding species (*Platypelis grandis* and *Plethodontohyla notosticta*) it is a prerequisite for healthy clutch development, with mold killing a large proportion of eggs when males are removed (Blommers-Schlösser 1975b). In most species, males care for the clutches, but in *P. tuberata* a female was reported guarding a clutch (Guibé 1952), and some species are known to have dual-parental care (Köhler et al. 1997; Rakotoarison et al. 2012; Glaw et al. 2020). In phytotelm-breeding *Plethodontohyla* and *Platypelis* species, care by the male is known to last from oviposition to metamorphosis (Blommers-Schlösser 1975b) (Figure 11.38d).

As reproductive mode is known from so few Cophylinae species, more unusual modes of development potentially remain to be discovered. Clutches have never been observed for *Rhombophryne*, *Anilany*, or *Mini*. At present, the incompleteness of this picture means that it is not possible to draw conclusions about the evolution of reproductive strategies and parental care, but this clearly represents a promising area of future research.

TABLE 11.8. **Summary of available data on reproduction in Malagasy Cophylinae**

SPECIES	EGG NUMBER	OVIPOSITION SITE	PARENTAL CARE	EGG MASS	METAMORPHOSIS DURATION	METAMORPH SVL	SOURCE
Anodonthyla boulengeri	23–30	Tree hole	Male	Nonconnected in water	16–20 days	3.5 mm	BS75
A. emilei	–	Tree hole	Male	–	–	–	Vea10
A. montana	–	Under moss and lichen above puddles	Male	Semi-dispersed	–	–	BSB91
A. nigrigularis	–	Tree hole	Male	–	–	–	GV94
A. rouxae	13–50	Phytotelm	Male	Nonconnected in water	–	–	BSB91
Cophyla maharipeo	–	Tree hole	Male	–	–	–	AR
C. phyllodactyla	50?	Bamboo	Male	Nonconnected in water	–	5 mm	GV94
C. puellarum	21	Tree hole or phytotelm	–	–	–	–	Rea15, AC
Madecassophryne truebae	18	–	Male and female?	–	–	–	BSB91
Platypelis alticola	16	Bamboo	Male	Nonconnected in water	–	–	AeaSub, AR
P. barbouri	–	Tree hole, bamboo or other phytotelm	Male and female	Nonconnected in water	–	~6–7 mm	BSB91, AC
P. grandis	90–100	Phytotelm	Male	Nonconnected in water	5 weeks	7–8 mm	BS75

(continued overleaf)

TABLE 11.8. ***continued***

SPECIES	EGG NUMBER	OVIPOSITION SITE	PARENTAL CARE	EGG MASS	METAMORPHOSIS DURATION	METAMORPH SVL	SOURCE
P. karenae	2–3	Phytotelm	Male	Gelatinous in water	–	–	Roea17
P. laetus	35	Bamboo	Male	Nonconnected in water	–	–	AeaSub
P. pollicaris	–	Bamboo	Male	Nonconnected in water	–	–	MG51, AR
P. ranjomena	–	Phytotelm	Male and female?	–	–	–	GeaSub
P. tsaratananaensis[1]	≤27	Bamboo	Male and/or female	Nonconnected in water	–	–	Rea12
P. tuberifera	–	*Pandanus*	–	–	–	6 mm	BS75
Plethodontohyla fonetana	–	Tree hole	Yes, sex unknown	–	–	–	APR
P. inguinalis	–	Tree hole	Yes, sex unknown	–	–	–	AC
P. mihanika	111	Leaf litter or tree hole	Male	Connected	–	–	GV94, MDS, APR
P. notosticta[2]	43–120	Tree hole or phytotelm	Male	Nonconnected in water	~4 weeks	6 mm	BS75, GV94
P. ocellata	≥100	–	–	–	–	–	BS75
P. tuberata	9–45	Burrow	Female?	Gelatinous	–	–	G52, GV94
Rhombophryne testudo	18	Burrow	Male and female?	–	–	9–11 mm	Kea97
Stumpffia achillei[1]	11–75	Snail shells	Yes, sex unknown	Gelatinous in water	–	–	Rea17
S. analamaina	–	Leaf litter	–	Foam	–	–	Kea13
S. davidattenboroughi	16	Between leaves in litter	Male	Jelly	–	–	Rea17
S. grandis	20	–	–	–	–	–	VG91
S. maledicta[1]		Burrow	–	Foam	–	–	MDS
S. pygmaea	4–8	Leaf litter	–	Foam	–	3 mm	GV94
S. sp. aff. *kibomena*	15	Bamboo	Male	Jelly	–	–	Rea21

Sources: AC, A. Crottini, unpublished data; AeaSub, Rakotoarison et al. (2020); APR, A. P. Raselimanana, unpublished data; AR, A. Rakotoarison, unpublished data; BS75, Blommers-Schlösser (1975b); BSB91, Blommers-Schlösser and Blanc (1991); G52, Guibé (1952); GeaSub, Glaw et al. (2020); GV94, Glaw and Vences (1994); Kea13, Klages et al. (2013); Kea97, Köhler et al. (1997); MDS, M. D. Scherz, unpublished data, MG51, Millot and Guibé (1951); Rea12, Rakotoarison et al. (2012); Rea15, Rakotoarison et al. (2015a); Rea17, Rakotoarison et al. (2017a); Rea21, Razafindraibe et al. (2021); Roea17, Rosa et al. (2014a); Vea10, Vences et al. (2010a); and VG91, Vences and Glaw (1991).

Note: SVL, snout-to-vent length

[1] Eggs probably from multiple females with one male in one site.

[2] Blommers-Schlösser (1975b) stated that the parents' dorsal coloration was olive green, suggesting that these observations may have been from *Plethodontohyla guentheri*.

FIGURE 11.38 **Reproductive modes in the Cophylinae. A) Foam nest of *Stumpffia pygmaea*, B) jelly nest in leaves of *S. davidattenboroughi*, C) jelly nest in water-filled snail shell of an unknown *Stumpffia* species, D) nest-guarding *Plethodontohyla notosticta* adult with froglets in a water-filled tree hole, E) jelly nest and guarding parents of *Platypelis ranjomena* in a leaf axil.** (PHOTOS by A. Crottini, F. Glaw, J. Köhler, G. M. Rosa, and M. D. Scherz.)

CALLS

Cophylines are heard far more often than they are seen. Male advertisement calls are generally loud and have a whistling quality, and the uninitiated often mistake them for birds or insects. Each call generally consists of a single note (although a few species have multi-note calls), and they are emitted in long call series. Although calls have not yet been recorded from all species, it is assumed that all do indeed call, and where advertisement calls are known, they are almost invariably diagnostic by at least one numerical parameter (e.g., dominant frequency, call duration, inter-call duration) (see especially Rakotoarison et al. 2017a).

Cophyline advertisement calls are emitted from a variety of positions. Most terrestrial species call from within the leaf litter or under rotten logs (some *Rhombophryne* and *Plethodontohyla* species call from within burrows), such that a great deal of time can be spent carefully removing one leaf at a time to find a calling specimen. *Stumpffia tridactyla* is known for calling from beneath mats of grass in the summit zone of Marojejy, and finding calling individuals in this habitat is nearly impossible. Arboreal species may call from leaves or tree trunks (e.g., *Cophyla fortuna*), or from inside water-filled tree holes (e.g., *P. grandis*), or at the bottom of leaf axils (e.g., *Platypelis karenae*) (Rosa et al. 2014a; Rakotoarison et al. 2019a; M. D. Scherz, unpublished data). *Madecassophryne* is unusual in calling from between gaps in water-soaked rocks (Rakotoarison et al. 2017b).

Advertisement calls make up the dominant proportion of calls emitted by cophylines, but other calls are known. Territorial calls can be made by males competing for access to tree holes (e.g., *P. grandis*; Blommers-Schlösser 1975b). The male of at least one *Stumpffia* species (*S. maledicta*) emits quiet, creaking calls, which we here term "follow-me" calls, to solicit females to accompany it to its burrow, where lies its foam nest (M. D. Scherz and A. Rakotoarison, unpublished data). Distress calls are known from *Plethodontohyla notosticta* from Betampona (A. Crottini, unpublished data), and release calls are not known. However, the available data on cophyline vocalizations are still limited, and more fieldwork is likely to yield interesting insights into bioacoustic communication in these frogs.

DIET AND PREDATORS

As with many other microhylids, the diet of most cophylines is composed predominantly of various invertebrates, especially hymenopterans (ants) and, in small species, mites and springtails. However, they are also opportunistic predators and will eat anything that fits in their mouths. Known food items include other frogs (Scherz et al. 2015b), snails (Scherz et al. 2016a), scorpions and stick insects (Lourenço et al. 1997), millipedes (Scherz et al. 2014; Bellati et al. 2018), and various other arthropods such as spiders and beetles (Glaw et al. 2007; Scherz et al. 2015a). The diminutive species of *Stumpffia* and *Mini* are also known to eat oribatid mites (Scherz et al. 2019b).

Very few predation records exist for cophylines, most by snakes and owls. Eudeline et al. (2015) described the predation of *Rhombophryne laevipes* by *Compsophis albiventris*, and Hutter et al. (2018a) reported predation of *Platypelis grandis* by *C.* sp. aff. *laphystius*, and of *S.* cf. *sorata* by *Alluaudina bellyi*. Goodman et al. (1993a) found the diet of *Asio madagascariensis* (Madagascar Long-eared Owl) to include *P. grandis*, and small cophylines may be consumed by *Tyto soumagnei* (Red Owl) (Cardiff and Goodman 2008).

CONSERVATION

Among the 113 described cophyline species, 72 (63.7%) are currently assessed under the IUCN Red List criteria. Of these, 20.8% are classified as Least Concern, 4.2% as Near Threatened, 6.9% as Vulnerable, 48.6% as Endangered, and 12.5% as Critically Endangered—a further 6.9% are considered Data Deficient. The dominant threat faced by these species is habitat loss; few cophylines can persist in heavily degraded forest (Vallan 2000), and none are able to survive outside the forest. Because of the high levels of microendemism, these threats are often acute and direct. All threatened cophylines are assessed under either Criterion B or D2 (IUCN 2012), both of which are concerned solely with the distribution area of the species. Given the intrinsically microendemic nature of cophylines as a whole, it remains unclear whether distribution area is an informative measure of their extinction risk.

Subject editors: Mark D. Scherz, Miguel Vences, and Achille P. Raselimanana

MICROHYLIDAE, SCAPHIOPHRYNINAE: *SCAPHIOPHRYNE* AND *PARADOXOPHYLA*

A. Crottini, J. Rabearivony, A. Rakotoarison, M. D. Scherz, and G. M. Rosa

Belonging to the family Microhylidae, the subfamily Scaphiophryninae is entirely endemic to Madagascar. Originally considered allied to ranids by Noble (1931) and Parker (1934), Scaphiophryninae was only later included in the family Microhylidae (Guibé 1956). *Scaphiophryne* adults exhibit a combination of ancestral and derived characters within microhylids, but based on tadpole morphological studies (Wassersug 1984), most authors (Duellman and Trueb 1986; Ford and Cannatella 1993) have traditionally considered this genus part of the microhylids, as was later confirmed by many molecular studies. *Scaphiophryne* tadpoles seem to represent an "intermediate" condition between the filter-feeding larval type typical of most microhylids (type 2) and the generalized tadpole of most ranoid and hyloid frogs (type 4).

TAXONOMY AND EVOLUTION

The phylogenetic position of the subfamily Scaphiophryninae is still debated, although most recent systematic studies place it as the sister clade of the Cophylinae (see Scherz et al., pp. 1382–90). Nevertheless, some authors have suggested a sister relationship with the African Hoplophryninae (Pyron and Wiens 2011), or with all Microhylidae except Hoplophryninae (de Sá et al. 2012).

The subfamily Scaphiophryninae contains two currently recognized genera (Figure 11.39): *Scaphiophryne* and *Paradoxophyla*, where *Scaphiophryne* is the type genus (Laurent 1946). *Paradoxophyla* was assigned to this subfamily by Blommers-Schlösser and Blanc (1991). The precise relationships among these two genera have been somewhat uncertain (see Frost et al. 2006), but the position of *Paradoxophyla* was later confirmed by Van der Meijden et al. (2007) as well as multiple other studies (Kurabayashi et al. 2011; Peloso et al. 2016; Feng et al. 2017; Tu et al. 2018) based on DNA sequence data.

Karyological data are available for almost all Scaphiophryninae species (although some karyotypes are not published). The two species of the genus *Paradoxophyla* have a karyotype of 2n = 26 chromosomes, composed of all biarmed chromosomes, where the first 5 pairs are much larger than the remaining 6–13 pairs (Andreone et al. 2006a). Overall, *Scaphiophryne* shares the plesiomorphic ranoid karyotype of 2n = 26. The exception is *S. gottlebei* with a tetraploid karyotype, a trait that makes the species also unique among all other known Malagasy amphibians (Vences et al. 2002c). Different techniques suggest that the species acquired this state through a process of allopolyploidy, which probably occurred early in the Scaphiophryninae radiation. It is likely that the ecology and behavior of the species belonging to the genus *Scaphiophryne* favored interspecific gene flow and hybridization, which then may have led to slow molecular substitution rates, and to allopolyploid chromosome speciation in *S. gottlebei*.

TAXONOMIC ACCOUNT

Two *Paradoxophyla* and 10 *Scaphiophryne* species are currently considered valid (Glaw and Vences 2007; Scherz et al. 2021). Several uncertain species names were recently clarified, resulting in the resurrection of *S. obscura* (Scherz et al. 2021). A key character of the subfamily Scaphiophryninae is the diplasiocoelous vertebrae (biconcave centra), in contrast to the procoelous vertebrae of Cophylinae (Dyscophinae species also have diplasiocoelous vertebrae).

Paradoxophyla

Two nominal species: *Paradoxophyla palmata* and *P. tiarano*. No numbered candidate species. From eastern and northeastern Madagascar. Pointed snout, flattened body, small eyes. Inner metatarsal tubercle small, no outer metatarsal tubercle. Hand without webbing, foot webbed (only slightly in *P. tiarano*). Maxillary and vomerine teeth absent. Single subgular vocal sac.

Amplexus axillary. Reproduce in stagnant water bodies. Aquatic eggs. Suspension filter-feeding tadpoles. Explosive breeding.

Scaphiophryne

Ten nominal species divided into two subgenera: *Scaphiophryne* (*Scaphiophryne*) *boribory, S.* (*S.*) *gottlebei, S.* (*S.*) *madagascariensis, S.* (*S.*) *marmorata, S.* (*S.*) *menabensis, S.* (*S.*) *matsoko, S.* (*S.*) *spinosa, S.* (*Pseudohemisus*) *brevis, S.* (*P.*) *calcarata,* and *S.* (*P.*) *obscura.* As of 2021, there are no known candidate species of *Scaphiophryne* that remain to be described; the former candidate numbers *Scaphioprhyne* sp. Ca1 (or *S.* sp. aff. *calcarata* B) from Tolagnaro, Isalo, and Berenty, *Scaphiophryne* sp. Ca2 (or *S.* sp. aff. *calcarata* A) from Kirindy Forest CNFEREF, Isalo, and Menabe (terminology following Vieites et al. 2009 and Perl et al. 2014, respectively), and *S.* sp. aff. *calcarata* from Ankarafantsika and Bongolava Plateau near Borziny (Perl et al. 2014; Rakotoarison et al. 2015b) were revised by Scherz et al. (2021). *Scaphiophryne* sp. Ca1 was assigned to *S. calcarata*, and *S.* sp. Ca2 (including *S.* sp. aff. *calcarata* from Ankarafantsika and Bongolava Plateau) was assigned to *S. obscura*. The subgenus *Pseudohemisus* is distributed in western Madagascar; the subgenus *Scaphiophryne* is distributed mostly in central and eastern Madagascar (with *S. gottlebei* being microendemic to the Isalo Massif, *S. menabensis* in the west, and *S. matsoko* in the northeast). Rounded or pointed snout, plump body. Long fingers and toes. Large inner metatarsal tubercle, small or absent outer metatarsal tubercle. Hand without webbing, foot with rudimentary webbing. Maxillary and vomerine teeth absent. Single subgular vocal sac. Amplexus axillary. Reproduction in stagnant water bodies. Aquatic eggs float on the surface. Psammonektonic tadpoles. Explosive breeding.

FIGURE 11.39 **Species diversity within the subfamily Scaphiophryninae: A) *Paradoxophyla palmata* (Betampona), B) *P. tiarano* (Menamalona Forest, Masoala), C) *Scaphiophryne gottlebei* (Isalo), D) *S. boribory* (captive specimen), E) *S. madagascariensis* (Andringitra), F) *S. marmorata* (Andasibe), G) *S. menabensis* (Tsingy de Bemaraha), H) *S. spinosa* (Betampona), I) *S. brevis* (Isalo), J) *S. matsoko* (Marotandrano), K) *S. calcarata* (Ilakaka), and L) *S. obscura* (Isalo).** (PHOTOS A, C, E, H, I, K, and L by G. M. Rosa; B, D, and F by F. Andreone; G by F. Glaw, and J by A. P. Raselimanana.)

BIOGEOGRAPHY

Species of the genus *Paradoxophyla* and some species of the genus *Scaphiophryne* are among the few pond breeders in Madagascar that are specialized to inhabit moist evergreen forest (Glaw and Vences 2007). The two species of *Paradoxophyla* have a hydrodynamic and flattened body, small eyes, and extensive foot webbing (Andreone et al. 2006a; Glaw and Vences 2007). The two subgenera of *Scaphiophryne* can be distinguished based on general morphology (Vences et al. 2003b; Scherz et al. 2021): the subgenus *Scaphiophryne* (*S. marmorata*, *S. menabensis*, *S. boribory*, *S. spinosa*, *S. madagascariensis*, *S. gottlebei*, and *S. matsoko*) is characterized by species with greenish dorsal color patterns and (except for *S. madagascariensis*) expanded terminal finger discs. Species in this subgenus inhabit lowland and medium-altitude moist evergreen forests or dry deciduous forest areas of central and eastern Madagascar (*S. marmorata*, *S. boribory*, *S. spinosa*, and *S. madagascariensis*, with *S. boribory* also known from the north; Rabearivony et al. 2010), or relict forest fragments in western Madagascar (*S. gottlebei* and *S. menabensis*). *Scaphiophryne matsoko* was recently shown to belong to this subgenus (Scherz et al. 2021). This species has a highly unusual morphology reminiscent of *Paradoxophyla* species (pointed snout, marbled venter). It seems to be restricted to the moist evergreen forests of northeastern Madagascar (Raselimanana et al. 2014).

The subgenus *Pseudohemisus* (*S. calcarata, S. brevis,* and *S. obscura*) is characterized by species with brown to gray, sometimes green, dorsal color patterns and unexpanded terminal finger discs. Species in this subgenus are distributed in the dry deciduous forests and arid environments of central and western Madagascar (Glaw and Vences 2007; Cocca et al. 2018; Scherz et al. 2021).

REPRODUCTION AND ECOLOGY

Most pond-breeding frogs on Madagascar can be found active close to water mostly during the rainy season (Glaw and Vences 2007). All Scaphiophryninae species are strongly seasonal, have explosive breeding habits, reproduce in lentic, often temporary, waters, and deposit a large number of small eggs (Blommers-Schlösser 1975b; Vences et al. 2002c; Glaw and Vences 2007; Rosa et al. 2011b). Reproduction in these species is generally limited to a few days or weeks (especially for *Scaphiophryne*), and several are difficult to encounter in the field outside the reproductive season. In captivity, *S. marmorata* individuals may become dormant through the European summer, even without a decrease in moisture or food availability, and tend to emerge again as temperatures decline from September to October; thereafter they are intermittently active for several months (M. D. Scherz, unpublished data).

Species belonging to the genus *Paradoxophyla*, which are restricted to moist evergreen forests, are specialized pond breeders, and during (explosive) reproduction they are fully aquatic (Glaw and Vences 1994); they probably live in leaf litter on the forest floor outside the breeding season despite very few observations. *Scaphiophryne* species have a typical semi-fossorial lifestyle (maintained to some extent also during the breeding season), and *S. gottlebei* is unique in having rupicolous habits (Mercurio and Andreone 2006). *Scaphiophryne* species are among the most terrestrial of Malagasy microhylids and seek refuge in the soil and detritus during the dry season. Most of them have enlarged and heavily keratinized outer metatarsal tubercles and burrow backward into the soil with their hind limbs. Especially the species living in dry areas (subgenus *Pseudohemisus*) spend much of their life burrowed underground, while the moist evergreen forest species with expanded finger discs, especially subadults of *S. marmorata* and *S. spinosa*, can occasionally also be seen climbing on low rocks or tree trunks. Scaphiophrynines are largely nocturnal, and little is known about the ecology of adults. Most species in the subgenus *Scaphiophryne* emit long and fast series of short melodious notes (Andreone et al. 2005b; Glaw and Vences 2007), those of the subgenus *Pseudohemisus* are loud and pulsed, while the call of *P. palmata* (that of *P. tiarano* is unknown) is a loud, short, cricket-like melodious trill (Glaw and Vences 2007).

All studied *Scaphiophryne* tadpoles lack keratodonts and have keratinized beaks, papillae on the lips, and a sinistral spiracle (a single ventral gill opening on the left side of the body). Tadpoles of *Scaphiophryne* are categorized ecomorphologically as psammonektonic (with horny beaks but lacking keratodonts), an ecomorphological guild only recently proposed to take into account their peculiar morphology (Glos et al. 2005; Mercurio and Andreone 2006; Grosjean et al. 2007; Grosjean and Vences 2009; Glos et al., pp. 1350–53). They are not obligate suspension feeders, as are most of the other members of the family Microhylidae, and during the day they display a singular feeding behavior that consists of burrowing the anterior half of their body into the sand with their tail obliquely upward, while during the night they swim throughout the water column, as obligate suspension-feeding tadpoles do (Mercurio and Andreone 2006; Grosjean et al. 2007). Among the known *Scaphiophryne* species, subgenus *Pseudohemisus* species have relatively small tadpoles (up to 22 mm total length), while tadpoles of the species of subgenus *Scaphiophryne* (e.g., *S. madagascariensis, S. menabensis, S. spinosa, S. gottlebei*) have larger tadpoles (up to 48 mm), and all have an overall balloon-like appearance of their bodies (Mercurio and Andreone 2006; Grosjean et al. 2007).

Paradoxophyla tadpoles do not have keratinized beaks or keratodonts, do not have papillae, have a median spiracle (a single mid-ventral gill opening), and have a typical microhylid suspension filter-feeding morphology that shares many synapomorphies with other microhylids (Grosjean et al. 2007). Since a convergent evolution of these features is unlikely, it is more reasonable that the apparently plesiomorphic larval mouthparts of *Scaphiophryne* instead represent a reversal, with the ancestor of all *Scaphiophryne* species having reacquired its beak and other characters. *Scaphiophryne* (*Pseudohemisus*) species with small tadpoles are restricted to semiarid areas of western and southern Madagascar and breed in temporary lentic waters. It is thought that this condition enables the tadpoles of these species to undergo rapid development and metamorphose at small sizes, before the temporary ponds where they reproduce vanish. In contrast, *Scaphiophryne* (*Scaphiophryne*) species with larger tadpoles are restricted to moist evergreen forests (*S. boribory, S. marmorata,* and *S. spinosa*) or montane (*S. madagascariensis*) and dry deciduous areas (*S. gottlebei* and *S. menabensis*), where lentic waters persist for a longer time and allow them to have a more extended larval development that results in metamorphosis at larger sizes (Grosjean et al. 2007; Grosjean and Vences 2009). This is also valid for species such as *S. gottlebei* and *S. menabensis* that breed in longer-lasting water bodies in canyons or dry deciduous forests (deep and permanent ponds remaining in the bed of temporary streams in the case of *S. gottlebei*, Figure 11.40; ephemeral ponds within the dry deciduous Kirindy Forest CNFEREF in the case of *S. menabensis*), compared to quick-drying pools where *S. calcarata, S. obscura,* and *S. brevis* breed (Glos et al. 2005; Rosa et al. 2011b). Spatial ecology data on *S. gottlebei* revealed no significant differences in activity patterns between sexes and suggest that rain and temperature stimulate the dispersal rate (Andreone et al. 2013), in line with what is expected in explosively breeding species.

Genetic analyses of *S. gottlebei* reveal weak phylogeographic substructure, with most populations sharing a single widespread haplotype, which suggests a high level of gene flow between all known populations (Crottini et al. 2008). Because of the typical semi-fossorial lifestyle of this species, its philopatry to the canyons it inhabits, and the overall limited dispersal capacities of adults (Andreone et al. 2013), it has been proposed that these high levels of gene flow between populations might be explained by the passive dispersal of larvae and metamorphosed individuals during cyclonic floods (Andreone et al. 2013).

FIGURE 11.40 **Natural history and spatial ecology of *Scaphiophryne gottlebei*. Years of research in the canyons of the Isalo Massif have unveiled some secrets of this elusive species. A) Radio-tracking individuals allowed us to better understand movements and dispersal, and B) to discover where these frogs hide and seek refuge. C) This species is highly adapted to live in narrow canyons, as it can climb up vertical walls. D) These are also extremely seasonal breeding habitats, with temporary water basins formed after the first heavy rains that E) dry out afterward. F) Males and females aggregate to breed, and G) and H) the hatching psammonektonic larvae will develop in a race against time to complete their metamorphosis.** (PHOTOS A, B, C, and E by G. M. Rosa; D, F, G, and H by V. Mercurio.)

Species in the subfamily Scaphiophryninae are probably myrmecophagous (preferring to feed on ants), for they possess the tongue-flipping and feeding movements similar to those of many microhylids with this dietary preference outside Madagascar: strikingly, these frogs are able to project the tongue laterally out of the mouth (Meyers et al. 2004). Based on pellet remains, *Scaphiophryne* species are known to be eaten by *Tyto alba* (Barn Owl). *Scaphiophryne* bones were identified from pellets collected most months of the year, including July, indicating that some individuals remain active during the dry season (Goodman et al. 1993b).

CONSERVATION

All nominal Scaphiophryninae species, except *S. obscura,* have been assessed by the IUCN Red List, with almost half the species classified as Least Concern (IUCN 2019). Two *Scaphiophryne* species are Near Threatened, including the recently described *S. matsoko*, whose populations are decreasing in the wild (IUCN SSC Amphibian Specialist Group 2016a), and three species are listed in threatened categories (*S. gottlebei*, Endangered; *S. boribory* and *S. marmorata*, Vulnerable). *Paradoxophyla tiarano* is Data Deficient. It should be noted, however, that the current assessment of *S. calcarata* was based on a taxonomic concept of the species that is now outdated, and its conservation status needs to be revisited (Scherz et al. 2021). Threatened species of *Scaphiophryne* are all assessed under Criterion B (distribution and habitat decline), with the greatest threats involving habitat loss, alteration, and fragmentation. Forested habitat has been receding because of subsistence agriculture (including livestock grazing) but also from fire, wood extraction, mineral mining, and natural expansion of human settlements (IUCN 2019). All species rely on some forest presence, which warrants the minimum humidity levels they need, and they are not found in deforested or heavily degraded areas. Several species of *Scaphiophryne* are internationally traded (all but *S. gottlebei* seemingly in low numbers, though this is hard to quantify). *Scaphiophryne gottlebei* is listed in Appendix II of CITES and may be threatened as a result of exploitation for the pet trade. Further studies are needed to fully understand the impacts of trade on the survival of *Scaphiophryne* populations. Nevertheless, all nominal scaphiophrynine frogs are known to occur in at least one protected area. Individuals of *Scaphiophryne* exported from Madagascar have tested positive for the pathogenic fungus *Batrachochytrium dendrobatidis* (Kolby 2014), but further work is needed to assess the distribution, lineage, and origin of the detected fungal strain (see Bletz et al., pp. 1342–49).

Subject editors: Angelica Crottini, Miguel Vences, and Achille P. Raselimanana

MICROHYLIDAE, DYSCOPHINAE: *DYSCOPHUS*

M. Vences, A. Crottini, M. D. Scherz, and A. Rakotoarison

The genus *Dyscophus*, with only three species (*D. antongilii*, *D. guineti*, and *D. insularis*), is classified in its own subfamily, Dyscophinae, within the Microhylidae and is not closely related to the other two Malagasy microhylid subfamilies (Scaphiophryninae and Cophylinae). Instead, Dyscophinae is related to Asian microhylids (Van Bocxlaer et al. 2006; Van der Meijden et al. 2007; Peloso et al. 2016; Feng et al. 2017) and, according to the most recent analyses, is sister to the Asian subfamily Microhylinae (Tu et al. 2018; Streicher et al. 2020). The ancestor of these frogs thus colonized Madagascar independently from the ancestor of the scaphiophrynine/cophyline clade and probably did so from Asia around 60 million years ago (Crottini et al. 2012b).

MORPHOLOGY AND SYSTEMATICS

The three species of *Dyscophus* are rather stout, medium-size (*D. insularis*) to large terrestrial frogs (*D. guineti* and *D. antongilii*) breeding in stagnant, often temporary waters in arid regions of western Madagascar (*D. insularis*), and in relatively open and marshy areas along Madagascar's eastern coastal plain (*D. antongilii* and *D. guineti*). *Dyscophus antongilii* is currently known from secondary habitats along the northeastern coast, while *D. guineti* inhabits forested areas.

Dyscophus antongilii and *D. guineti* are spectacular orange or red frogs (granting them the subfamily common name "tomato frogs"; Figure 11.41), ranging among the largest microhylids. *Dyscophus antongilii* males reach 60–65 mm and females 85–105 mm from snout to vent. These two species are very similar in morphology, and their status has not yet been fully clarified. Morphologically, the main difference is their color pattern, with *D. antongilii* being orange red, often with some black spots along the flanks, and *D. guineti* often having a dorsal rhomboid marking and, especially, blackish pigment below the dorsolateral ridges. In both species, females are typically a deeper red and males more yellowish orange.

Genetic data (Chiari et al. 2006; Orozco-terWengel et al. 2013) have not been able to fully resolve the taxonomic conundrum surrounding the morphologically similar *D. antongilii* and *D. guineti*. While both species share widely the same mitochondrial alleles, nuclear genetic data (microsatellites) suggest they represent two separate genetic clusters. Furthermore, the single sequenced individual of *D. guineti* from a southeastern locality (Vevembe) had a substantial divergence also in mitochondrial DNA, suggesting that possible mitochondrial introgression has blurred the differentiation among the northern populations of *D. guineti* and *D. antongilii* that most probably were in contact in the recent past. More-detailed hybrid zone analyses will be necessary to ascertain whether they both merit recognition as distinct species.

The third species of *Dyscophus*, *D. insularis*, is much less conspicuous than the two eastern species. It is a medium-size terrestrial frog of up to 40–50 mm snout-to-vent length, varying in color from brown grayish to gray greenish and often with symmetric vermiculated darker markings on the dorsum. Males are characterized by a dark vocal sac.

ECOLOGY AND REPRODUCTION

According to current taxonomy, *D. guineti* inhabits moist evergreen forest areas mostly at middle to low elevations across a large part of eastern Madagascar, whereas *D. antongilii* is found primarily in coastal disturbed sites, almost at sea level, around Antongil

FIGURE 11.41 **A female specimen of *Dyscophus antongilii* (Tomato Frog) from Maroantsetra.** (PHOTO by M. Vences.)

Bay. Both species occur mostly in areas of sandy substrate. *Dyscophus antongilii*, especially, lives in a zone of poorly marked seasonality and thus reproduces year-round (Segev et al. 2012), with activity influenced by minimum air temperature and less so by rainfall.

Calls of the two orange/red species are a series of short, low-pitched notes, which led to the Malagasy name *saogongongo* for this frog. *Dyscophus antongilii* lays 1000–1500 small, sticky black eggs, which hatch 36 hours later. The filter-feeding tadpoles develop in stagnant water and become rather large until metamorphosis. In two studied populations, the age of adult males was 3–7 years and the age of females 3–11 years, sexual maturity was attained between 2 and 3 years, and individual age was correlated to body size and weight (Tessa et al. 2007). The conspicuous red color of these frogs is certainly related to the sticky whitish secretion they can produce. According to Conlon and Kim (2000) and König et al. (2013), the only peptide component in the secretion of *D. guineti* is a trypsin inhibitor, while other toxic substances were not found and no antimicrobial function was demonstrated. The main function of the secretion may thus be mechanical, impeding ingestion through its high adhesivity and viscosity, especially as it is often secreted along with body inflation. *Dyscophus antongilii* is known to be susceptible to the fungal pathogen *Batrachochytrium dendrobatidis* (Oevermann et al. 2005).

The western species, *D. insularis*, reproduces in shallow temporary pools, sometimes of incredibly small dimensions (e.g., a few centimeters in diameter, as observed in Isalo; A. Crottini, unpublished data), and its calls are a series of rapidly repeated low-pitched notes, of similar general structure as in the two eastern species. Tenebrionid beetles, orthopterans, and ants have been identified as prey of this species (Vences et al. 2002d). It is relatively widespread, from Behara Forest (about 40 km north of Amboasary-Atsimo; A. P. Raselimanana, unpublished data) in the south up to at least Ambanja in the Sambirano Region.

CONSERVATION

All three species have been assessed by the IUCN Red List, and all are classified as Least Concern (IUCN 2019). For many years in the 1960s, *D. antongilii* was killed by local people, especially by children, just for the pleasure of seeing its white secretion, which was considered a type of "milk." This and other factors led to a steep decrease in the population density of the species. Currently, numerous environmental education projects are in place to raise awareness of the importance of this frog for the development of the local economy. One such activity is the organization by the IUCN SSC Amphibian Specialist Group Madagascar and the Madagascar Fauna and Flora Group of the "Tomato Frog Festival," which was the first celebration on the island dedicated to an amphibian occurring within a town. This was done at the inauguration of the "Tomato Frog Village," which aims to protect some of the most relevant frog populations in Maroantsetra (Andreone et al. 2012). This specific event was hosted by the College Zanatany Maroantsetra, and the program included "frog races," drawing and frog call competitions, and traditional dancers disguised as frogs. A local artist, Augustin Sarovy, a fervent advocate for environmental protection, wrote a song dedicated especially to the preservation of this species of *Dyscophus* entitled *saogongongo* which has become quite well known among amphibian conservationists on Madagascar.

Subject editors: Miguel Vences and Achille P. Raselimanana

HYPEROLIIDAE: *HETERIXALUS*

M. Vences and F. Glaw

Despite their rather limited diversity, *Heterixalus* species are certainly among the most common amphibians of Madagascar. At night, their advertisement calls are heard throughout unforested habitats on the island, even within the city of Antananarivo. These frogs are restricted to lentic (nonflowing) water for breeding and do not penetrate undisturbed moist evergreen forest. Open swamps and their human-made equivalent, rice fields, are the most likely places to observe them.

SYSTEMATICS

The genus *Heterixalus* is endemic to Madagascar. It belongs to the family Hyperoliidae, which is mainly African in distribution. Besides *Heterixalus*, the only non-African hyperoliid genus is *Tachycnemis* from the Seychelles. Molecular data (Richards and Moore 1996; Wollenberg et al. 2007) indicate that *Heterixalus* and *Tachycnemis* are closely related sister groups that together split from their African relatives between 57 million and 19 million years ago, that *Tachycnemis* split from *Heterixalus* between 21 million and 11 million years ago, and that *Tachycnemis* itself comprises a single species with populations on various islands in the Seychelles archipelago constituting monophyletic but only weakly divergent genetic clades (Vences et al. 2003d; Crottini et al. 2012b; Maddock et al. 2014). A recent study identified the Ethiopian endemic *Afrixalus enseticola* as a possible sister taxon of the *Tachycnemis/Heterixalus* clade (Portik et al. 2019). Molecular studies (Odierna et al. 2007; Wollenberg et al. 2007; Gehring et al. 2012) have substantially contributed to our understanding of the evolutionary history, taxonomy, and geographic distribution of these frogs.

The identity of the Malagasy hyperoliids was clarified only after the pioneering work of Blommers-Schlösser (1982) and Blommers-Schlösser and Blanc (1991), who confirmed that they differ from all other Malagasy frogs by the presence of a conspicuous gular gland in males, which is particularly visible when the large single subgular vocal sac is inflated. Further, all Malagasy hyperoliid species differ from the otherwise morphologically similar African *Hyperolius* by the vertical rhomboid shape of the pupil (horizontal in *Hyperolius*).

ECOLOGY AND REPRODUCTION

Heterixalus species are active at night but can also be observed during the day by close inspection of large sun-exposed leaves (such as taro and *Vernonia* spp.) close to their breeding ponds. It is not unusual to observe several individuals of different species (up to three *Heterixalus* species are known to occur syntopically) together in leaf axils of large-leaved plants such as *Typhonodorum*. They bask in a typical position that minimizes their exposed surface (and thus water loss) and often have a coloration different from that displayed nocturnally: while they are dirty yellowish at night, *H. tricolor*, *H. madagascariensis*, and *H. punctatus* are bright white when basking. Males and females can show sexual dichromatism, as is most distinct in *H. alboguttatus*, in which females have a characteristic spotted pattern dorsally that is much less distinct or even absent in males. The evolution of sexual dichromatism in *Hyperolius* and *Heterixalus* has been studied by Veith et al. (2009) and in a more general context by Portik et al. (2019).

Eggs of *Heterixalus* are rather small; they are attached in small clutches to plants or other structures in the water close to the surface. Because the water level in the (often temporary) breeding ponds may quickly descend, the eggs are sometimes exposed, which does not hinder their development. Vocalizing males of all *Heterixalus* species have been observed in the rainy season, but, at least in *H. madagascariensis*, calling (and thus probably reproduction) is also known in the dry season.

In all species in which tadpoles are known, these are morphologically rather similar. They typically have one continuous row of keratodonts (labial teeth) on the upper lip, and one interrupted and two continuous (or three continuous) rows on the lower lip (keratodont formula 1/1+1:2 or 1/3). They reach lengths of up to 46 mm and are of the generalized type of tadpole. They are rather fragile and show adaptations to a life in nonflowing water, such as a rather high caudal fin. Metamorphs measure 12–20 mm snout-to-vent length. Juveniles of most species (all in which they are known) have dorsolateral bands, which are later lost in many species, being retained in *H. betsileo*, *H. carbonei*, *H. luteostriatus*, *H. andrakata*, and some *H. variabilis*. Sexual maturity in *Heterixalus* is achieved very quickly; a captive-raised *H. boettgeri* female had mature oocytes (visible through the ventral skin) less than four months after metamorphosis (Glaw and Vences 1993). A recent study of *H. tricolor* in the dry deciduous Kirindy Forest CNFEREF found that its mating system corresponded partly to predictions for lek systems, with a highly male-biased operational sex ratio, females visiting the pond only one or a few days per season, unequal frog densities at different microhabitats within their breeding site, absence of size-assortative mating, and no size differences between amplectant and non-amplectant males (Glos et al. 2019).

SPECIES ACCOUNTS

All 11 currently known *Heterixalus* species are rather small (snout-to-vent length 18–40 mm), females generally being larger than males. Feet and hands are partly webbed. Terminal discs of fingers and toes are moderately enlarged, and often yellow or orange. The ventral side is whitish to yellowish, without any darker markings, but the dorsal color is highly variable and can be very colorful. As is typical in hyperoliids, there is high variability in color and pattern, both between and within populations of the same species. A number of problems in the correct definition of species originated through this color variability, in combination with the largely uniform external morphology of most *Heterixalus* species. As a consequence, identifying these frogs by coloration alone may be extremely misleading. For example, at Sambava, specimens of *H. punctatus* are uniformly white dorsally, unlike specimens from the type locality, Andasibe, which have many small black spots (Figure 11.42). In contrast, the generally uniformly white *H. madagascariensis*, which occurs syntopically with *H. punctatus* at Sambava, sometimes has black dorsal spots in this geographic area. Careful identification of calling males, and genetic data, demonstrated that the "typical" color patterns of both species are reversed at this northeastern site compared to those on the central east coast (Wollenberg et al. 2007). In many cases, species that can display very similar color patterns, such as *H. punctatus* and *H. madagascariensis*, *H. luteostriatus* and *H. betsileo*, or *H. tricolor* and *H. madagascariensis*, are not each other's closest relatives and differ strongly in their advertisement calls, which demonstrates their reproductive isolation. On the other hand, the status of several species defined by their color pattern requires confirmation, in particular *H. alboguttatus* and *H. boettgeri*, which are very similar genetically and bioacoustically to *H. madagascariensis*; and *H. variabilis*, which likely represents a synonym of *H. tricolor*.

The most common *Heterixalus* species in the Central Highlands is *H. betsileo*. This species is characterized by its simple call consisting of a single short unharmonious note repeated at irregular intervals, with a note repetition rate of 0.4–0.6 per sec. Most *H. betsileo* are greenish to yellowish, with distinct yellow dorsolateral bands (Figure 11.43), but these bands are indistinct or absent in some populations—at Manjakatompo on the Ankaratra Massif, many specimens are uniformly green. Size differences also exist among individuals from different populations—those from Andasibe are distinctly smaller than those from Antananarivo. These morphological differences partly coincide with the subdivision of the species into various genetic clusters (Gehring et al. 2012). *Heterixalus betsileo* is widespread in the Central Highlands from Ambatondrazaka to the Andringitra Massif (Glaw and Vences 1994, 2007) and is replaced farther west (Kirindy Forest CNFEREF and Bemaraha) and north (Tsaratanàna and Montagne d'Ambre) by the phenotypically similar *H. carbonei*, which differs by a longer note duration in its advertisement call (Vences et al. 2000a; Gehring et al. 2012).

A group of species restricted to northern and western Madagascar contains *H. tricolor*, *H. variabilis*, and *H. andrakata*. These species are characterized by a call composed of two note types, one slightly longer than the other. These notes are arranged in rather rapid series. *Heterixalus andrakata* can be recognized by its yellow color with a bluish-black pattern on the dorsum that excludes the yellow dorsolateral bands. *Heterixalus tricolor* is generally of uniform coloration, especially females displaying a bright white diurnal color, with a typical rounded black patch on each eye. *Heterixalus variabilis* is extremely variable in coloration, especially the females, which often have large black vermiculated patterns on their back. *Heterixalus andrakata* is known from the northeast and north (between Andapa and Sambava, Montagne des Français), while *H. variabilis* was described from Nosy Faly and *H. tricolor* from Nosy Be. Molecular data suggest all these populations are closely related (Wollenberg et al. 2007). While *H. andrakata* shows a certain amount of bioacoustic divergence and can be easily recognized by color pattern, the status of *H. variabilis* is highly doubtful and it may represent a synonym of *H. tricolor*. However, *H. tricolor* was not reconstructed as a genetically monophyletic group in the tree of Wollenberg et al. (2007), respective to *H. variabilis* and *H. andrakata*, suggesting the entire group requires revision.

A further complex of closely related species occurring in Madagascar's eastern lowland zone is made up of *H. boettgeri* (southeastern Madagascar, e.g., Tolagnaro), *H. alboguttatus* (southeast, e.g.,

FIGURE 11.42 A ***Heterixalus punctatus*** **specimen from Andasibe.** (PHOTO by M. Vences.)

FIGURE 11.43 **A *Heterixalus betsileo* specimen from Andasibe, showing the dorsolateral stripe that is typical for this and several other species in adults, and for almost all species in juveniles.** (PHOTO by M. Vences.)

Ranomafana National Park), and *H. madagascariensis* (east and northeast at least up to Sambava). These species are characterized by two very distinct call patterns: one long pulsed note, often followed by a series of rapidly repeated short notes. Species distinction in this complex was initially based only on coloration; however, the species do form monophyletic groups based on genetic data, and the sharp contact zone between *H. alboguttatus* and *H. madagascariensis* coincides with the Mangoro River, a major riverine barrier (Gehring et al. 2012). *Heterixalus boettgeri* is characterized by its uniformly greenish coloration, while *H. madagascariensis* is white during the day and *H. alboguttatus* has (especially in females) a spectacular pattern of colorful dorsal spotting.

A further species with similarities in call pattern to the *H. madagascariensis* complex, but phylogenetically unrelated to it, is *H. luteostriatus*, known in the west from Anja to the north (at least Ankarana). *Heterixalus luteostriatus* has yellowish dorsolateral bands that continue onto the tibia, a pattern that has been observed in all known specimens and therefore does not appear to be variable. Another further phylogenetically isolated species is *H. punctatus*, a species from the east (from Anosibe An'Ala in the central east to at least Sambava in the northeast). Its calls consist of different note types, which are partly arranged in short series.

Finally, the most divergent *Heterixalus* species is *H. rutenbergi*, an attractive highland form with a greenish back with five longitudinal white stripes. In contrast to the whitish or yellowish gular gland of all other species, this is blackish in *H. rutenbergi* and also appears to have a different morphological structure. Furthermore, its sharp and loud trilling calls are not reminiscent of any other known *Heterixalus* species. Very little is known about the biology and ecology of *H. rutenbergi*. It has been collected at several sites at higher elevations (from Ambohitantely to Ambatofitorahana). Near Ambatolampy, a low-density population has been observed syntopically with *H. betsileo* in moorlands. *Heterixalus rutenbergi* calls were never heard from rice fields, where *H. betsileo* is very common. At Ambohitantely we observed both species in swamps at the edge of forest fragments. High-elevation swamps have so far not been given high priority in conservation efforts but are possibly endangered because of transformation into rice cultivation, suggesting that the status and available habitat of *H. rutenbergi* should be monitored more closely. The 11 species of *Heterixalus* have been the subject of IUCN Red List assessments, and all are classified as species of Least Concern (IUCN 2019).

Subject editors: Miguel Vences and Achille P. Raselimanana

PTYCHADENIDAE: *PTYCHADENA*, MASCARENE GRASS FROG

M. Vences, F. Glaw, A. P. Raselimanana, and M. Pabijan

The Mascarene Grass Frog, *Ptychadena mascareniensis* (Figure 11.44), belongs to an almost exclusively African clade. According to Clarke (1981), the genera *Ptychadena*, *Hildebrandtia*, and *Lanzarana* form a well-defined monophyletic group, which was elevated to subfamilial rank as the Ptychadeninae (family Ranidae) by Dubois (1992) and is currently seen as a separate family, Ptychadenidae. Molecular data have corroborated the monophyly of the *Ptychadena*-*Hildebrandtia* clade (Emerson et al. 2000; Pyron and Wiens 2011). *Lanzarana* has not yet been studied genetically.

SYSTEMATICS AND BIOGEOGRAPHY

Ptychadena mascareniensis is the only ptychadenid occurring outside continental Africa. It was originally described in 1841 from La Réunion (Ile Bourbon), part of the Mascarene archipelago, where it was apparently introduced from Madagascar around 1750 (Probst 1997). According to Staub (1993), the Mauritius population was introduced in 1792 from Madagascar. The origin of the Seychelles population remains obscure, but specimens from that archipelago were found to have DNA sequences very similar or identical to those from Madagascar and Mauritius based on a mitochondrial gene (Vences et al. 2004b), making it likely they were introduced to the Seychelles as well.

Ptychadena mascareniensis is also known from a vast area in continental Africa. However, genetic data have shown that the African populations constitute at least nine deeply divergent genetic lineages, which all differ from the Malagasy populations (Zimkus et al. 2017). Phylogenetically, a lineage occurring in eastern Africa (Tanzania) is the sister group of the Malagasy populations, which themselves are subdivided into three rather strongly divergent mitochondrial lineages. This deep differentiation among Malagasy *Ptychadena* species along with a large number of haplotypes (Vences et al. 2004b) leaves no doubt that they are native to the island, and their origin has been reconstructed to have taken place around 8 million years ago (Crottini et al. 2012b). This hypothesis is in line with the fact that the ancestors of another species of *Ptychadena*, *P. newtoni*, successfully colonized an oceanic island in the Gulf of Guinea archipelago and evolved into a distinct species there (Measey et al. 2007). Despite substantial mitochondrial divergence among populations in the humid eastern part of the island, so far there is no evidence that more than one species of *Ptychadena* occurs on Madagascar, which is thus populated by a single endemic species, *P. mascareniensis*, which has also been introduced to Mauritius, La Réunion, and the Seychelles.

MORPHOLOGY

Because of its characteristic morphology, *P. mascareniensis* is not likely to be mistaken for any other anuran, except for *Hoplobatrachus tigerinus* juveniles and perhaps in rare cases some

FIGURE 11.44 **A *Ptychadena mascareniensis* specimen from near Sambava.** (PHOTO by M. Vences.)

Mantidactylus species (e.g., *M. brevipalmatus*). Males have snout-to-vent lengths of up to 40 mm, females up to 50 mm. The feet are largely webbed, and the tips of fingers and toes are not expanded to discs. When hind limbs are appressed forward along the body, the tibiotarsal articulation reaches between eye and nostril. On the back, there is a characteristic pattern of six to eight longitudinal, more or less continuous ridges (there are only two such ridges in some *Mantidactylus* species, and discontinuous tubercle rows in *Hoplobatrachus*). The vocal sacs of males are paired and arranged laterally (not subgular), a unique state in Malagasy frogs. The ventral surface is uniformly white, but the dorsal coloration is quite variable. It ranges from brown to green, with or without a median line or broader median band. These vertebral lines or bands can be yellow whitish or green. A very thin light line is usually present longitudinally on the tibia.

REPRODUCTION, ECOLOGY, AND CONSERVATION

At present, *P. mascareniensis* is without doubt the most common frog species on Madagascar. Blommers-Schlösser and Blanc (1991) and Glaw and Vences (1994) recorded the species from no fewer than 58 localities over the island. It is known from the extremely dry areas of the southwest (Toliara), from disturbed lowland and medium-altitude moist evergreen forest (Andasibe and Nosy Mangabe), and from high montane areas up to more than 2000 m elevation (Plateau d'Andohariana on the Andringitra Massif). It is a semiaquatic species that depends on stagnant or slow-flowing water bodies in open landscapes. It appears to be absent from dense primary moist evergreen forest except in clearings (natural or not), but it is common in rice fields and swamps in human-degraded areas, including Antananarivo. It is quite common even on salt flats around Lake Tsimanapetsotse in the extreme southwest.

On Madagascar, *P. mascareniensis* shows diurnal as well as nocturnal activity. According to Tohé and Gourène (2016), other populations of the *P. mascareniensis* complex in Côte d'Ivoire (probably belonging to another species) have two peaks of food intake, at 12:00 and 24:00, suggesting that this species feeds during the day and overnight. However, it is not clear whether the Malagasy *Ptychadena* species behave similarly. Young and adult individuals are generally found sitting on the ground close to water, and they jump and dive when disturbed. Juveniles and subadults can also be found far from water, for example in grassland, when conditions are sufficiently moist for dispersal.

The typical advertisement calls of *P. mascareniensis* are heard during the night, as well as during the day. According to Blommers-Schlösser and Blanc (1991), calling is especially intense during the first rainfalls, becoming less intense during the rest of the rainy season, and activity is reduced during the dry cold season. Vocalizing males generally sit in the water. Choruses of several individuals often "explosively" emit calls: one animal begins, and several surrounding individuals follow suit. Calling activity is especially intense at dawn, and Malagasy people in the countryside use this call period as a kind of biological clock. The chorus often ends as abruptly as it began after a few seconds, and it may not start again for several minutes. The calls consist of different note types (Passmore 1977) and are difficult to analyze. Slowly pulsed and unharmonious notes are composed of about 15 pulses and last about 450 ms. Glaw and Vences (1992a) stated that the calls of Malagasy individuals were distinct from those reported from South Africa, but another call type, similar to the South African one, was later recorded on Madagascar (Glaw and Vences 1994). This second call type consists of short, regularly repeated notes (note duration 188–194 ms; more than 20 pulses) and was generally heard at dusk or dawn, possibly with territorial functions. More data on the bioacoustics of Malagasy *Ptychadena* frogs, especially from the populations showing distinct mitochondrial divergences, are necessary to ascertain the biological and possibly taxonomic significance of their calls.

Ptychadena mascareniensis has a generalized mode of reproduction. During axillary amplexus (the coupling of male and female frogs during egg laying and fertilization), a large number of small blackish eggs are laid in small clutches. Tadpoles can reach a total length of about 45 mm. They have a typical silvery belly, similar to that of *Laliostoma labrosum*, which can occur in syntopy. The keratodont (labial tooth) formula of *P. mascareniensis* is unique on Madagascar: one continuous and one interrupted row on the upper lip, and two continuous rows on the lower lip (formula 1:1+1/2). Metamorphosed juveniles measure about 15 mm.

Ptychadena mascareniensis feeds on invertebrates, including snails, grasshoppers, and beetles, and has also been observed to consume conspecifics and other frogs (McIntyre and Ramanamanjato 1999). It also eats worms and small butterflies. Fatroandrianjafinonjasolomiovazo et al. (2011) found beetles and ants (16.2% each), orthopterans (13.4%), spiders (11.7%), insect larvae (7.5%), and hemipterans (5.4%) as the most common prey items and confirmed the consumption of a small frog. There was a positive correlation between prey size and frog size, and a significant negative correlation between number and size of prey ingested.

Birds (*Asio madagascariensis*, Madagascar Long-eared Owl; Goodman et al. 1993a, as well as *Bubulcus ibis*, Cattle Egret) and snakes (*Thamnosophis lateralis*, *Madagascarophis colubrinus*, and *Leioheterodon modestus*) are among its main predators. In the countryside, farmers often collect this frog to feed domestic ducks. The species is known to be parasitized by a large number of parasites (Blommers-Schlösser and Blanc 1993), including mites of the genus *Endotrombicula*, and indeed one species (*E. ptychadenae*) may be specialized on this host (Wohltmann et al. 2007). Among its parasites is the flatworm *Metapolystoma brygoonis*, which also appears to be specialized on this host (Euzet and Combes 1964; A. Lambert and Bourgat 1978), and whose divergence from African *Metapolystoma* species 14–2 million years ago appears to match the time by which *Ptychadena* colonized the island (Verneau et al. 2009).

Ptychadena mascareniensis is one of the few Malagasy anuran species that are positively affected by at least some forms of destruction of original habitat, such as swamp forest clearing for rice paddies. The species is clearly not at risk on Madagascar and has been classified as Least Concern by the IUCN Red List (IUCN 2019).

Subject editors: Miguel Vences and Achille P. Raselimanana

DICROGLOSSIDAE: *HOPLOBATRACHUS*, TIGER FROG

M. Vences, A. Crottini, A. P. Raselimanana, and F. Glaw

All but two anuran species found on Madagascar are native to the island. The sole exceptions are the Tiger Frog (or Indian Bullfrog), *Hoplobatrachus tigerinus* (Figure 11.45), and the Black-spined Toad, *Duttaphrynus melanostictus* (see Freeman et al., pp. 1404–10). For a third frog previously thought to be non-native, *Ptychadena mascareniensis*, molecular data have demonstrated substantial genetic diversity within Madagascar, and strong divergence from African populations (Zimkus et al. 2017; see Vences et al., pp. 1400–1401), thus suggesting it indeed reached Madagascar by natural overseas dispersal.

ORIGINS ON MADAGASCAR

In the case of *H. tigerinus*, it is almost certain that humans introduced the species in recent times. Guibé (1953) was the first to mention it being present on Madagascar, based on a specimen collected by R. Paulian in the region of "Majungo" (most probably referring to Mahajanga). Although its provenance is uncertain, Guibé (1953) hypothesized that the species may have been introduced "par les Hindous ou les Chinois" (by the Hindus or the Chinese), and according to people in the Marovoay area, the species was first locally introduced in 1929 to fight the invasion of rats in rice fields (A. P. Raselimanana, unpublished data). The taxonomic identity of these populations was supported by Blommers-Schlösser and Blanc (1991), and molecular data have corroborated that the Malagasy *Hoplobatrachus* specimens are genetically very close to Indian *H. tigerinus*, and that they neither represent an endemic species nor are referable to the African *H. occipitalis* (Kosuch et al. 2001). *Hoplobatrachus tigerinus* has also recently been introduced to the Andaman Islands (Harikrishnan and Vasudevan 2013; Mohanty and Measey 2019; Mohanty et al. 2021). The establishment of a population of this frog on this remote archipelago, where its dietary niche overlaps considerably with that of native anurans (Mohanty and Measey 2018), further confirms its potential as an invasive species (Mohanty et al. 2021).

DISTRIBUTION ON MADAGASCAR

Hoplobatrachus tigerinus is the largest frog on Madagascar, although it is uncertain whether reports of snout-to-vent lengths of 160–170 mm (Guibé 1953, 1978) actually refer to Malagasy specimens. Naturalized populations of *H. tigerinus* have so far been recorded from localities in western, eastern, and northern Madagascar. In the west and north, this alien species is known from Mahajanga, Marovoay, Mahavavy Kinkony, Ampijoroa, Anabohazo Forest, Ankarafa Forest, Ankarafantsika, Antafiabe, Amborovy, Nosy Be (since at least 1964) including Lokobe, Antsirasira near Manongarivo, Ambilobe, Ambanja, Antanambao, Antsiranana (since at least 1972), Montagne des Français, Mitsinjo, Ampitsopitsoka and Ankorikakely villages near Antsiranana (iNaturalist photographic record), Ankarana, Analamerana, 15 km south of Sambava (recorded in 1995), between Antsohihy and Port Bergé, Lake Alaotra (recorded in 2008; M. Vences, unpublished data), Manondro (~30 km southwest of Antsiranana), and Anjiamangirana Forest. Along the eastern coast the

FIGURE 11.45 **A *Hoplobatrachus tigerinus* specimen from Lake Alaotra.** (PHOTO by M. Vences.)

species is known at least from Parc Ivoloina, Toamasina, and Mahasoa-Melville (north of the Ivondro River) (Glaw and Vences 2007; Mohanty et al. 2021).

Although *H. tigerinus* is a very large invasive species, it has received much less attention than the recently introduced toad (*Duttaphrynus melanostictus*), and very little is known about its rapid range extension or the ecology and biology of Malagasy populations. These frogs tend to live in pools in or outside the forest, as well as in rice fields, channels, or stagnant water along small streams.

ECOLOGY AND REPRODUCTION

Calls of this species have not yet been described from Madagascar. Males in breeding condition are yellow and have nuptial pads. The tadpoles of several (probably all) species of the genus have a specialized morphology, with a large horny beak and double rows of keratodonts (Dubois 1992; Grosjean et al. 2004). In contrast to most other anuran larvae, *Hoplobatrachus* tadpoles are adapted to carnivorous habits (Grosjean et al. 2004) and preferably consume tadpoles of other frog species (Rödel 1996). *Hoplobatrachus tigerinus* is known to prey on other frogs at both the larval and adult stage. It also feeds on insects and small mammals, including mice and rats. According to farmers in the Marovoay area, it can even prey on snakes and small birds. At Ambanja, *Ptychadena* and *Heterixalus* have been observed in high densities with *H. tigerinus*, indicating that its occurrence has no negative short-term effect on these species. However, our data also indicate some degree of niche segregation, with *H. tigerinus* occurring mainly in larger ponds, while native species tend to inhabit puddles or shallow swamp areas where only a few *Hoplobatrachus* individuals were seen. This adaptation to larger bodies of water is probably the origin of the Malagasy name *tsirevobe* (which translates as "the big frog that is never sunk deep in the mud") given to this frog by people in western Madagascar (Marovoay).

After the rainy season, *H. tigerinus* seems to undergo estivation. In July 1996, we found specimens of *Mantella betsileo*, *Ptychadena mascareniensis*, and *H. tigerinus* 20–30 cm under the soil in dry seasonal swamps in the Ankarana, while in 2000, we observed a rather high density of *Hoplobatrachus* adults in a swamp close to Ambanja. In the west and northwest, they occur syntopically with *P. mascareniensis*, *Boophis tephraeomystax*, *B. doulioti*, *Heterixalus variabilis*, *H. luteostriatus*, *Blommersia wittei*, and species of *Mantidactylus* (subgenus *Brygoomantis*). In Mahasoa village (ex-Toamasina Province), *Hoplobatrachus tigerinus* is sympatric with *Duttaphrynus melanostictus*. Both of these introduced species became active at dusk and quite common during periods of heavy rain.

CONSERVATION

In general, it can be concluded that the impact of *Hoplobatrachus* on the native anuran fauna of Madagascar may not be high at present, especially as it does not appear to be widespread in moist evergreen forest areas. *Hoplobatrachus* is regularly consumed on Madagascar. From 1991 to 1996, we observed animals sold for food in the Zoma market of Antananarivo, and *Hoplobatrachus* continues to be sold regularly in Madagascar's capital (Jenkins et al. 2009), for instance in many supermarkets and fish markets, but in smaller quantities than endemic Malagasy species such as *Boophis goudotii*. In 2000 at Antsiranana we were told that several professional gatherers specialize in the collection of frogs for their legs, and their main target is *H. tigerinus*. At Lake Alaotra in 2008, we obtained specimens from local fishermen that were destined for the food market. No data are available on the impact at the population level of gathering invasive *Hoplobatrachus* for consumption as human food.

In the plains of the Marovoay area, where *H. tigerinus* is very abundant in the rice fields and channels, farmers are aware of the role this frog may play in controlling *Rattus* populations. Although it is an introduced and invasive species, in the early 1990s a community-based conservation strategy was developed to reduce the hunting of *Hoplobatrachus*. A local convention accepted by all communes and local communities had been established at the time.

Hoplobatrachus tigerinus is listed in Appendix II of CITES. A recent study investigated the status of introduced *H. tigerinus* populations and their global invasion potential (Mohanty et al. 2021). In this work, the authors modeled its potential distribution in the introduced range and globally, and they identified the eastern coast of Madagascar, the Mascarenes, Malaysia, Indonesia, and East Africa as suitable and likely areas for invasion. Finally, using a risk assessment framework, these same authors assigned a species-level score of "moderate" for the ecological and socioeconomic impact this species can have on native ecosystems (Mohanty et al. 2021).

Subject editors: Miguel Vences and Achille P. Raselimanana

BUFONIDAE: *DUTTAPHRYNUS MELANOSTICTUS*, BLACK-SPINED TOAD

K. L. M. Freeman, F. Andreone, T. M. Randriamoria, H. Randrianizahana, A. P. Raselimanana, C. J. Raxworthy, E. Robsomanitrandrasana, and A. Crottini

BLACK-SPINED TOAD INTRODUCTION AND RESPONSE HISTORY

The conservation community and local authorities first signaled the presence of an alien population of the Black-spined Toad or Asian Toad (*Duttaphrynus melanostictus*) on Madagascar (Figures 11.46a and c) in March 2014 in the eastern port town of Toamasina (Andreone et al. 2014b; Crottini et al. 2014a; Kolby et al. 2014). Nursery workers at a private enterprise site alerted their seniors to the presence of toads at Marovato (just south of Toamasina) in November 2013, but it was not until March 2014 that a cross-sectorial team of experts was sent to the site to photograph, collect, and identify the species; the identification was later confirmed by two independent herpetologists (C. J. Raxworthy and M. Vences). During the same trip, skin swabs were taken from a selection of toads and later analyzed for amphibian chytrid fungus (*Batrachochytrium dendrobatidis*), and the results were negative.

By April 2014 a National Toad Advisory Committee (NTAC) had been established under the coordination of Christian Randrianantoandro. Extensive communications ensued across the herpetological and wider conservation community with a keen interest in Madagascar, with varying and occasionally opposing suggestions of suitable actions being shared. To manage the extensive communications more effectively, various subcommittees were set up in June 2014 (Communication; Fundraising; Surveys; Education and Prevention; Feasibility Study and Eradication; Chytrid and Samples

FIGURE 11.46 ***Duttaphrynus melanostictus* on Madagascar and its habitat. A) *D. melanostictus* adult in its Toamasina surroundings; B) magnification of *D. melanostictus* head showing its parotoid glands; C) *D. melanostictus* individual in a village near Toamasina; D) urban area with rubbish heaps that host high densities of *D. melanostictus*; E) secondary scrub vegetation (locally called *savoka*); F) oil palm plantation where recorded toad abundances were the highest in Licata et al. (2019); and G) temporary breeding site of *D. melanostictus* near Toamasina.** (PHOTOS A, B, C, and G by F. Andreone; D and F by F. Licata; and E by M. Melo.)

Analysis), with different people assigned to the most suitable subcommittee to make the best use of their skills and experience (Crottini et al. 2014a). A plan was drafted in the same month and a research permit was sought for gathering more detailed information on the toad and its potential impacts.

The Madagascar Fauna and Flora Group (MFG), Association Mitsinjo, and the Atsinanana Region branch of the Direction Régionale de l'Environnement, de l'Ecologie et des Forêts (DREEF) of the Ministère de l'Environnement, de l'Ecologie et des Forêts (MEEF; now the Ministère de l'Environnement et du Développement Durable, MEDD) were tasked with completing the first distribution surveys, which were carried out between April and November 2014. Students from the Institut Supérieur de Sciences, Environnement et Développement Durable (ISSEDD) of the Université de Toamasina were charged with carrying out preliminary inquiries in local communities to try to ascertain the date and point of origin of the introduction. At the same time, the private enterprise carried out distribution surveys and implemented control efforts on its own restricted-access grounds, and the Mention Zoologie et Biodiversité Animale (MZBA) of the Université d'Antananarivo was contracted to carry out these surveys on its behalf.

In July 2014 various members of the NTAC suggested that a bounty be offered on the toads to encourage local control. However, a member of the Invasive Species Specialist Group (ISSG) of the International Union for the Conservation of Nature (IUCN) advised against this approach, as it had never succeeded when applied in other parts of the world and had, on some occasions, led to increases in the target species through abuse of the bounty system (Kraus 2009).

The initial distribution surveys indicated that the toads had invaded an estimated area of 98 km^2 mainly south and west of the city of Toamasina but, significantly, they had not been recorded at the port of Toamasina (Moore et al. 2015) (Figures 11.47a and b). Although it is likely that the point of entry of the toads was through the port, it seems that the physical release of the species was not within this zone. Within the current distribution range, toads were found in all habitat types ranging from urban environments to rural villages, mixed *Eucalyptus* forest, secondary scrub vegetation, and grassland (Figures 11.46d–g). The highest perceived densities were around villages, particularly in areas with rubbish heaps (Moore et al. 2015).

The population size in and around Toamasina, based on the initial surveys and estimated average toad densities, was calculated to be around 4 million adult toads (McClelland et al. 2015). However, by November 2014, precise density data gathered over a selection of different habitat types prompted a revised estimate of 7 million adult toads (Reardon et al. 2018). The preliminary inquiries made of the local communities indicated that most people

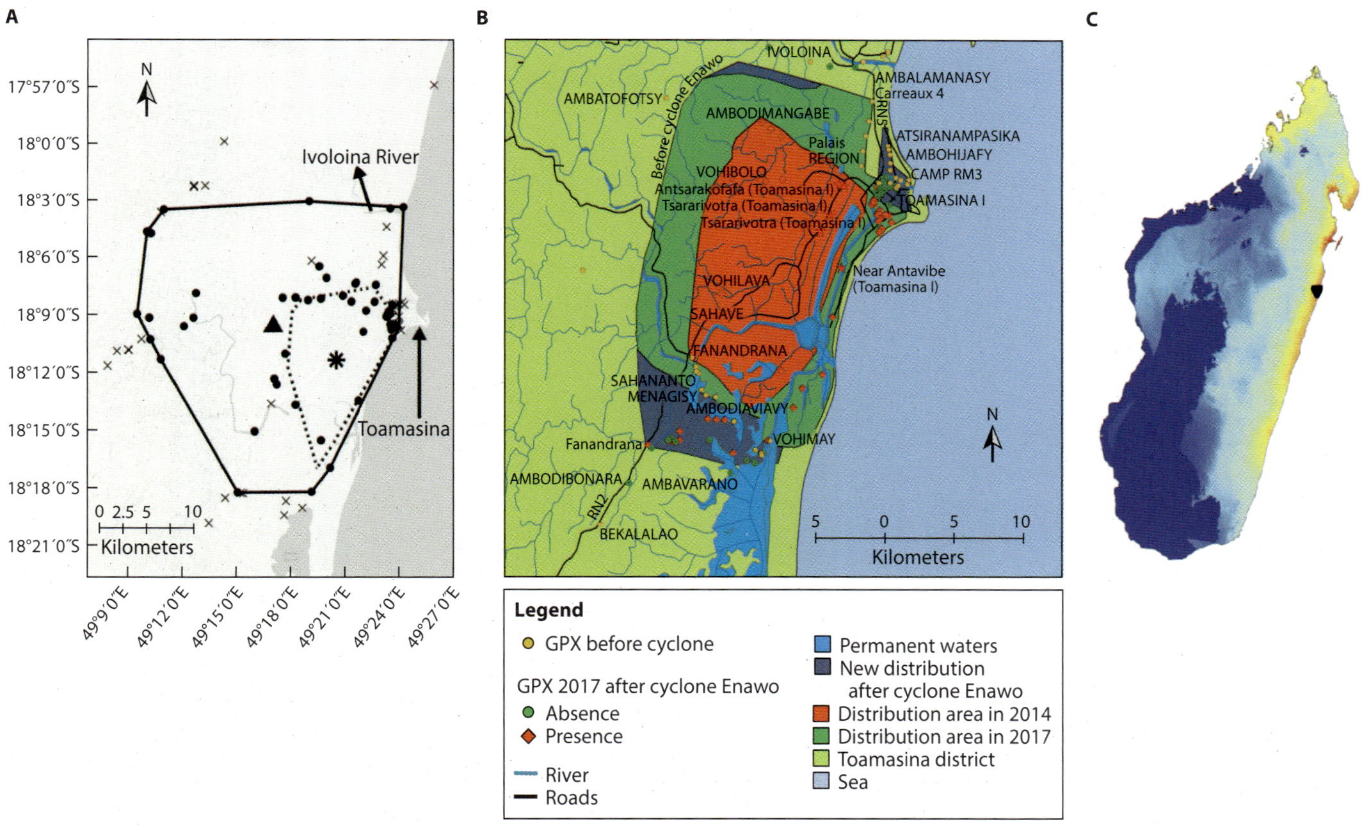

FIGURE 11.47 **A) Distribution map based on data collected in early 2017 (solid line). Filled circles are sites of detection; crosses are sites of nondetection; the dotted line outlines the distribution range in late 2014; the filled triangle is the centroid of distribution in early 2017; the star is the centroid of distribution in late 2014 (modified from Licata et al. 2019). B) Evolution of toad distribution from 2014 to 2017 and distribution difference before and after Cyclone Enawo in March 2017, made available by Angelo Rafilipo (MFG); and C) predicted suitable area for the *D. melanostictus* lineage invasion of Madagascar, with warmer colors indicating higher suitability (modified from Vences et al. 2017a).**

had first observed the toad in 2014, but some reported having seen it as early as 2010 (McClelland et al. 2015; Moore et al. 2015). Simple regression calculations based on the distribution at that time concur with the social surveys, indicating that *D. melanostictus* probably arrived on Madagascar at least by 2010 (McClelland et al. 2015).

After fund-raising efforts by the IUCN SSC Amphibian Specialist Group Madagascar and MFG (also highlighted during the ACSAM2 meeting held in 2014 in Ranomafana; Randrianantoandro et al. 2015), international invasive species and herpetological specialists were brought in to collaborate with local partners to carry out an eradication feasibility study in November 2014. The associated report was finalized in April 2015, highlighting the already daunting challenge and calling for urgent action to eradicate the toad (McClelland et al. 2015). The report also noted that the invasion started most likely as a result of accidental introduction via imported commercial containers from Southeast Asia (McClelland et al. 2015).

Phylogeographic analyses of *D. melanostictus* across its native range revealed it to be a species complex containing at least three evolutionary lineages (Wogan et al. 2016). The analysis of the introduced population of *D. melanostictus* on Madagascar showed that this population was likely the result of a single introduction event of just a few individuals of the recently identified Southeast Asian lineage, and Cambodia or Vietnam was specified as the likely source (Vences et al. 2017a). The inferred timing of the introduction coincides with a period during which a major industrial facility was being built in Toamasina. The introduction pathway of the toad to Madagascar will most likely never be definitively ascertained. As with so many other island nations, tighter biosecurity regulations and procedures are required on Madagascar to prevent this type of incursion. Besides the toad, Madagascar has numerous other invasive plant and animal species, several of which are known to have entered the country through Toamasina (Goodman et al. 2017).

In January 2016, following the initial efforts to ascertain the toad's distribution in Toamasina, an eradication specialist was appointed, in collaboration with students from ISSEDD, to test four potential eradication tools: 1) pitfall trapping and drift fencing, 2) hand-capture removal, 3) citric acid sprays, and 4) tadpole trapping (Reardon et al. 2018). The tests indicated that pitfall trapping is an effective tool for this species; capture by hand is a good method for initial reduction of toad numbers but becomes less effective as toads become rarer in the environment; spraying of a 25% weight by volume (w/v) solution of citric acid is highly effective at eradicating toads from delimited areas; and toad trapping using adult *D. melanostictus* toxins as an attractant did not prove successful in this short trial.

From February 2016 to April 2017 an integrated program including informational posters, radio transmissions, the release of a popular song about the dangers of the toad, and other public awareness-raising events was launched in a partnership among the MFG, Association Vahatra, and DREEF Atsinanana, informing the public of the dangers of handling the toxic toad, asking for help in carrying out simple biosecurity measures to limit the toad's dispersal, and helping to further elucidate the toad's distribution via telephone calls to a toll-free toad hotline. In February 2016 a press conference was organized by various stakeholders who had been involved with the eradication feasibility assessment. The aim of this press conference was to raise awareness of the urgent issue of *D. melanostictus* invasion in Toamasina via local and international media, share the eradication report of McClelland et al. (2015), present preliminary results of the eradication tool trials, and increase pressure on the enterprise that was believed to have introduced the toad to step up its actions and financial support for the called-for eradication. The press conference led to new coverage by local newspapers and TV stations, as well as international reports on the web, but also intensified acrimonious relationships that had already been developing within the NTAC, and eventually the committee became all but dysfunctional. Disappointingly, almost no interest was expressed by the international nongovernmental organization (NGO) community or governmental aid agencies in contributing to an eradication program. In parallel, from January 2016 onward, the private enterprise contracted a team from the Université d'Antananarivo to carry out ongoing control and research efforts on its property, and it also funded a larger control effort managed by DREEF Atsinanana, which was launched in January 2017. However, this was discontinued because agreed-on procedures were not being adhered to.

Given the toad's continued advance into eastern Madagascar and given that, with present technology, it seems unlikely that complete eradication will be possible, much effort in the past few years has been put into capacity building within the country to deal with invasive species, conduct research on the toads, and raise funds to facilitate a wider control effort. These long-term efforts are now starting to bear fruit, and a larger program of control, mitigation, and research is currently being developed by the local and regional branches of the MEDD, MFG, a private enterprise, IUCN SSC Amphibian Specialist Group Madagascar, and the Centro de Investigação em Biodiversidade e Recursos Genéticos in Portugal. Several international and national researchers are now studying the invasion dynamics, taxonomy, evolutionary adaptability, ecology, disease transfer risks, and impacts of the toad on Madagascar, and it is hoped that their findings will help guide the planned control efforts.

DOCUMENTED AND PREDICTED SPREAD AND ABUNDANCE OF *D. MELANOSTICTUS* IN TOAMASINA

Follow-up surveys between November 2016 and September 2017 revealed that the *D. melanostictus* population had increased to an area over five times greater (covering approximately 549 km^2) in the three years since the first surveys in 2014 (Moore et al. 2015; Licata et al. 2019; Figure 11.47a). This study also revealed an apparent rapid expansion toward the northwest, presumably because there were no ecological barriers in that direction. In the north, the Ivoloina River appears to be behaving as at least a partial barrier to the spread of the toads, while the Ivondro River to the south does not appear to be having such a limiting influence, probably because of the numerous interconnected human-made canals associated with this river, which may have further facilitated the southward invasion (Licata et al. 2019). Goodman et al. (2017) noted the significant extensions of the toad's distribution both northward into the Ivoloina River system and southward into the Nosive River system, an area that constitutes the northern portion of the Pangalanes Canal and hence connects to a 550 km stretch of continuous waterways to the south. This was in part associated with Cyclones Enawo (March 2017) and Ava (January 2018), which created large-scale flooding that inundated many areas.

The maximum distance between the putative introduction point (as per Moore et al. 2015) and the farthest location at which the toads were found in this second series of surveys was 21.9 km. If no other introductions occurred, the maximum spread rate of the toad invasion front to this point was 3.3 km per year, while the average spread rate based on all invasion front localities was 2.5 ± 0.6 km per year (Licata et al. 2019). This range of estimates of the rate of spread of the toad into new areas is double that estimated by Moore et al. (2015). This calculated accelerated spread could be an artifact of an underestimated spread rate by Moore et al. (2015), or it could be the result of this species gaining momentum as it became better established (Kraus 2009). A similar acceleration of spread rate has been reported in connection with the cane toad (*Rhinella marina*) invasion of Australia, where it has been associated with rapid adaptive changes in morphological and behavioral traits, and promoted by the absence of ecological pressures (Phillips et al. 2007).

Unpublished data from the MFG revealed a large increase in distribution of the toad following flooding in the wake of Cyclone Enawo in March 2017 (Figure 11.47b). In November 2018, a rapid survey to update the distribution of the toad south of Toamasina confirmed its presence in Ampiranambo (near Ambodibonara, along National Road 2) (Randriamoria et al. 2019), where the toad had not been recorded in March 2017.

Early ecological niche modeling exercises carried out shortly after this species' discovery on Madagascar predicted that the majority of the island provides suitable climate for this species, with no areas having temperatures or rainfall patterns different from those within the toad's native range. The modeling suggested, however, that the eastern escarpment presented climates most appropriate for the toad, while the drier conditions of the Central Highlands and in the west were less conducive, and so an initial northward and southward spread across the eastern escarpment was predicted (Pearson 2015). Using ecological parameters extracted only from the Southeast Asian lineage of the toad (the one present on Madagascar), a different ecological modeling analysis suggested that the suitable range of the invasive population on Madagascar may be narrower than that proposed by Pearson (2015), who used data from the whole *D. melanostictus* species complex (Figure 11.47c; Vences et al. 2017a). This analysis suggested that spread may be restricted to the lowlands of eastern and northern Madagascar, although all these predictions must be treated with caution, as invasive species may be able to occupy novel niches in new areas of introduction (Vences et al. 2017a).

The toad population density in the Toamasina area seems to be highly heterogeneous across the introduced range, with an average abundance of 184 toads per ha (95% CI 132–263) being reported by Licata et al. (2019) and an average 588 toads per ha being recorded by Reardon et al. (2018), who reported maximal densities per hectare of 559 (95% CI 445–695) and 1800 toads, respectively. The regional toad abundance is positively related to the presence of organic waste and negatively related to the density of road networks (Licata et al. 2019). Besides Madagascar, this species has been accidentally introduced and is now invasive in several other regions of the world, including Bali, New Guinea, Sulawesi, Timor-Leste, Maldives, and several small islands of the Sundaic region (Gardiner 1906; Church 1960; van Dijk et al. 2004; Trainor 2009; Reilly et al. 2017).

Currently, however, the great unknown is what the ecological impacts of *D. melanostictus* will be on Madagascar. Early on during the introduction, there were a few reported observations of dead snakes, presumed to be the result of feeding on toads (McClelland et al. 2015). But the actual impacts on native predators as well as competition with and predation on other native species are unknown. This is partly because the current toad distribution is confined mostly to areas with high human impact and low native biodiversity. The likely first major test for native biodiversity can be expected at the Ivoloina Forestry Station on the south bank of the Ivoloina River (Crottini et al. 2014b), and afterward in the Betampona protected area north of the Ivoloina River.

NATURAL HISTORY AND ECOLOGY

Belonging to the family Bufonidae, *D. melanostictus* is a terrestrial species that becomes active at dusk and stays active through the night. It is an ecological and breeding generalist (Daniel and Sekar 1989; Saidapur and Girish 2001) and in its native range is commonly found in disturbed lowland habitats (Hendrix et al. 2008), generally in both rural and urban areas (van Dijk et al. 2004). It is a relatively long-lived species (up to 12 years in wild populations from India; Nayak et al. 2007), although skeletochronological analysis of the invasive population on Madagascar failed to identify lines of arrested growth in the sampled individuals, suggesting that this invasive population does not undergo seasonal changes in physiological growth (F. M. Guarino, unpublished data in Licata et al. 2020). While studying the native population of *D. melanostictus* in Vietnam, Ngo and Ngo (2013) found that this species breeds once per year. However, based on different lines of evidence, the population on Madagascar might reproduce more than once per year (Licata et al. 2020).

Breeding and oviposition on Madagascar occur in ephemeral water bodies, and females can lay up to 10,000 eggs in long double-row strings (Licata et al. 2020). Tadpoles from the native range require 18–20 days to reach metamorphosis (Mahapatra et al. 2017). Cannibalism on conspecific eggs, tadpoles, and adult carrion, as well as predation on other tadpole species, has been described in the native range of this species (Mahapatra et al. 2017). Adult toads are generalist feeders in both native and introduced ranges (Berry and Bullock 1962; Mercy 1999; Döring et al. 2017). *Duttaphrynus melanostictus* can grow up to 200 mm snout-to-vent length, although this measurement in sexually mature individuals from Vietnam ranges from 50.2 to 70.3 mm in males and 65.2 to 97.3 mm in females (Ngo and Ngo 2013).

During the breeding season, males develop a yellowish-orange subgular vocal sac and blackish nuptial pads on the first and second fingers. As is true of most amphibians, females are expected to reach sexual maturity later than males (Ngo and Ngo 2013). Like most true toads, *D. melanostictus* possesses a pair of external parotoid glands on the back of the head (Figure 11.46b; Vitt and Caldwell 2013). This species is known to secrete bufadienolide toxins (commonly referred as bufotoxins) that inhibit the sodium-potassium pump of cells, causing cardiotoxic effects (Lingrel 2010) and thereby deterring predation (Chen and Kovaříková 1967; Ujvari et al. 2015). Most of the native vertebrates of Madagascar have been predicted to be susceptible to the toxin produced by this species (Marshall et al. 2018).

LESSONS LEARNED

The evolution of the response to the invasion of *D. melanostictus* on Madagascar is a salutary tale with many valuable lessons. Though the difficulties are so often avoided, it is important to share such experiences as much as the successes, in order to avoid repeating the same mistakes. Many positive advances have been made in increasing the profile of the potential negative impacts of introduced species as a result of the Madagascar *D. melanostictus* experience; however, it is important to list some key oversights (not in order of importance):

1. In the face of such an extensive and potentially environmentally damaging incursion, feelings ran very high, many accusatory fingers were pointed in several different directions, and little was gained. Precious time and potential funding opportunities were lost in the early stages of the response because of these differences of opinion.
2. Unrealistic expectations were placed on what was then MEEF (now MEDD) and the established NTAC tasked to tackle the invasion. To date, the largest successful amphibian eradication worldwide has been that of the Coqui Frog (*Eleutherodactylus coqui*) on the island of O'ahu, Hawaii; at the height of the invasion it is believed that there were around 1325 individuals across a maximal area of 5.6 ha. The eradication was completed using a combination of habitat modification and repeated high-intensity drenchings with citric acid over eight years (Beachy et al. 2011). On the nearby island of Kaua'i, a population of the same species covering an area of around 6 ha has been eliminated but, as with O'ahu, there are continuing reports of small, incipient populations (Pitt et al. 2012). At the point of "discovery" by the scientific community and Malagasy authorities, the toads were already at an estimated population of 7 million (Reardon et al. 2018), a situation that was already more than three orders of magnitude beyond that of any amphibian eradication that had been achieved at that time. It was most likely an impossible situation at that initial time of discovery (given the technology available) even if the incursion had happened in a rich country with developed biosecurity protocols and trained personnel already in place.
3. At that time, there was no mechanism or system in place to report the existence of newly arrived non-native species, nor any widespread comprehension of the potential risks and impacts of such species within local communities.
4. The National Toad Advisory Committee (NTAC) was quickly established to coordinate the response to *D. melanostictus* incursion, but its role and authority were never officially ratified by the government of Madagascar, and hence it had very limited power and resources to implement actions agreed on by consensus.
5. In an effort to be as inclusive as possible, the NTAC quickly became too large and unwieldy to be able to reach a quick consensus of opinion on key decisions. A smaller, more focused body would have been more effective.
6. The NTAC functioned under the umbrella of what was then MEEF alone, but because the toad posed potential impacts for human health and economic development, as well as for local biodiversity conservation, a select but inter-ministerial team would have been more appropriate to guide the response.
7. During the early stages of the NTAC, coordination was switched from a local Malagasy coordinator to an international NGO. This was an error; coordination of the national response should have remained firmly with a Malagasy individual or organization, with support provided by international partners. While the international organizations and individuals highly invested in Madagascar and the protection of its biodiversity had an extremely important role to play in the incursion response, their efforts would have been more useful in a supporting rather than a leadership role.
8. Jurisdiction between the national and regional branches of MEEF was unclear on this issue, and in some instances this hampered the quick resolution of important topics.
9. External public communications were not always agreed on in advance by the majority of the NTAC and sometimes led to further acrimony between different stakeholders. A clearly defined and agreed-on communications strategy could have prevented some of this discord.
10. There is no emergency group that bodies (governmental or nongovernmental organizations) can turn to for immediate advice/guidance/funding in such an urgent situation. Despite a wealth of biologists and naturalists on Madagascar, both local and international, there were very few individuals with sufficient experience in invasion biology and control to guide the incursion response. It would be of great value if an international invasive species task force could be created to support local reactions to new and potentially highly damaging invasions should its assistance be sought. Such a group could be envisaged, for example, under the umbrella of the IUCN's Invasive Species Specialist Group (ISSG).
11. Greatly needed expert help was provided by the international community, which resulted in the quick production of an eradication feasibility document that was vital to start formulating a national response and to inform fund-raising efforts. Because sufficient funds were lacking in the early stages of the response, these services were generously donated pro bono by the individuals in question. For the follow-up feasibility testing of various potential eradication tools, the fieldwork was organized and carried out quickly, but because the consultant was managing an extremely heavy workload in his own full-time job, the distribution of the published eradication feasibility trial results was delayed. Expert consultants should be engaged and paid to work full time in the country of incursion.
12. Timely reporting of emerging results from key locally based stakeholders was insufficient and further hampered effective decision-making. Calls for reports from MEDD were not re-

spected, and hence there is still little written record of in-country information available on *D. melanostictus*.

13. There was, and still is, insufficient national biosecurity legislation on Madagascar to provide a solid structure on which to build stronger protocols to react to or prevent future invasions (Randriamoria 2019). Supplementary and stronger legislation is required to build on existing text and mechanisms to monitor and enforce control of the new legislation. This will require a large investment on the part of the international community to support Madagascar in this challenging endeavor.
14. There is no effective policing of commitments made by international operators working on the island to respect biosecurity protocols. The environmental consultants tasked with monitoring a specific private operator on Madagascar that is alleged to have accidentally imported the toads were themselves unaware of the contractual World Bank Group's International Finance Corporation Performance Standards on Environmental and Social Sustainability agreements that had been committed to in the terms of financial lending agreements by the operator. Actually, the standards, in an effort to be internationally applicable, are so vaguely written and open to interpretation as to be largely ineffective.

A POSITIVE LOOK FORWARD

It is hard to imagine any positive outcomes resulting from the still-daunting and rapidly expanding toxic toad invasion in eastern Madagascar. However, here we detail various positive outcomes that have resulted from the enhanced awareness of the potential negative impacts of invasive species on Madagascar following the *D. melanostictus* incursion:

1. Far more attention has been given to the incursion of *D. melanostictus* than to earlier invasions (such as the House Sparrow, *Passer domesticus* [see Safford et al., pp. 1553–602], and the Tiger Frog, *Hoplobatrachus tigerinus* [see Vences et al., pp. 1402–3). This is partly because of the rapidly evolving and growing field of invasion biology and management worldwide, but also largely because of the attention-grabbing toxicity of *D. melanostictus*. As a result, the issue of invasive species and how to reduce the risks of new arrivals and manage present incursions is now firmly established on the national agenda within Madagascar, perhaps for the first time, in relation to nature conservation as opposed to human food security and economic interests, as has been mostly the case in the past.
2. For the first time, a dedicated post has been created within MEDD for dealing with invasive species, and an additional post has very recently been added to tackle biosecurity issues. A strong and positive collaboration has emerged between MEDD and a few key NGOs and local associations working on invasive species issues within Madagascar, and they have agreed to begin developing the first national database of invasive species.
3. Within the regional MEDD teams (DREDD), managers have been nominated to be locally responsible for invasive species issues.
4. Through ongoing dialogue with various IUCN officials after the discovery of *D. melanostictus* on Madagascar, stronger links have been forged between the IUCN and certain conservation entities working on Madagascar. Backing from the IUCN has been helpful in securing subsequent funding for various invasive species management projects (see below).
5. Perhaps helped by the wide negative publicity associated with the *D. melanostictus* invasion, a grant has been secured to quickly tackle the recent invasion of the House Crow, *Corvus splendens*, also in Toamasina (Linders and Langrand 2014; see Meier et al., pp. 1704–7), and to build local capacity to deal with this species. With this quick intervention, we hope to avoid the House Crow reaching problematic numbers, as it has in over 30 other countries worldwide where it is has successfully invaded.
6. An invasive species capacity-building workshop was carried out for national and regional authorities in Toamasina in May 2019 at Parc Ivoloina to increase awareness of invasive species issues, gain local support and advice for the implementation of the House Crow eradication, and create a local invasive species interest group. Toamasina is Madagascar's primary marine port and handles most of the country's imports and exports, so it is particularly relevant to promoting improved biosecurity and monitoring for newly arriving non-native species at the point of highest risk of invasion.
7. Two more invasive species capacity-building workshops will be carried out in 2020 or 2021 to a) set up a community-based surveillance and reporting network around Toamasina with local administrative leaders (President Fokontanys and Chefs Carreaux) based around the port and farther afield in Toamasina (imported containers are often opened for the first time outside the port), and b) build capacity for surveying and ecological monitoring of invasive species with ISSEDD of the Université de Toamasina.
8. A proposed motion was submitted to the IUCN for inclusion in the 2020 World Conservation Congress by a selection of local Malagasy and international IUCN members to call for greater capacity building within Madagascar to support the positive development of legislation and to implement systems to manage invasive species issues more effectively moving forward. This motion has successfully been voted on by IUCN members.
9. A strong and positive collaboration has now been forged between the private sector, the Malagasy government, NGOs, and the scientific community to tackle the *D. melanostictus* invasion in a more proactive fashion. Much can be learned to help control this species' population and mitigate negative impacts on people and local wildlife.
10. A special symposium held during the 2020 World Herpetology Congress dealt with tackling the problem of invasive reptiles and amphibians worldwide. During this meeting it was possible to discuss the need for an international task force to support local efforts to tackle herpetological invasive species issues.
11. There is already an emerging class of local scientists and practitioners on Madagascar who are developing greater capacity to deal with invasive species issues in-country. The various projects outlined above all include strong capacity-building aspects to bring in international experts to train local practitioners. The plan is that within a few years there will be a good pool of local invasive species specialists to tackle these issues in a timely and locally appropriate fashion.

12. A study by Randriamoria (2019) highlighted the need for increased capacity, legislation, and implementation of procedures within Madagascar to deal with and protect against the arrival of further invasive species. Recent advances in biosecurity on the neighboring island of La Réunion could be extremely valuable for informing a parallel process on Madagascar.

Despite the many challenges experienced over the past years since the discovery of *D. melanostictus* in eastern Madagascar, and the enormous problems that remain in trying to protect local biodiversity, human health, and the Malagasy economy from the negative impacts of this incursion, it can confidently be stated that large positive steps have been made toward developing a more integrated approach to invasive species knowledge and management on Madagascar as a result of this potentially devastating invasion.

Subject editors: Angelica Crottini, Miguel Vences, and Achille P. Raselimanana

REFERENCES

Agnolín, F. L. 2012. New Calyptocephalellidae (Anura, Neobatrachia) from the Upper Cretaceous of Patagonia, Argentina, with comments on its systematic position. *Studia Geologica Salmanticensia* 48: 129–178.

Aguirre, A. A., Tabor, G. M., and Ostfeld, R. S. 2012. Conservation medicine. In *New Directions in Conservation Medicine*, eds. A. A. Aguirre, R. S. Ostfeld, and P. Daszak, pp. 3–16. Oxford: Oxford University Press.

Ahl, E. 1931. Amphibia, Anura III, Polypedatidae. *Das Tierreich* 55: xvi, 477.

Allnutt, T. F., Ferrier, S., Manion, G., Powell, G.V.N., Ricketts, T. H., et al. 2008. A method for quantifying biodiversity loss and its application to a 50-year record of deforestation across Madagascar. *Conservation Letters* 1: 173–181.

Altig, R., and Johnston, G. F. 1989. Guilds of anuran larvae: Relationships among developmental modes, morphologies, and habits. *Herpetological Monographs* 3: 81–109.

Altig, R., and McDiarmid, R. W. 2006. Descriptions and biological notes on three unusual mantellid tadpoles (Amphibia: Anura: Mantellidae) from southeastern Madagascar. *Proceedings of the Biological Society of Washington* 119: 418–425.

Altig, R., Whiles, M. R., and Taylor, C. L. 2007. What do tadpoles really eat? Assessing the trophic status of an understudied and imperiled group of consumers in freshwater habitats. *Freshwater Biology* 52: 386–395.

Amat, F., Wollenberg, K. C., and Vences, M. 2013. Correlates of eye colour and pattern in mantellid frogs. *Salamandra* 49: 7–17.

Amphibian Ark. 2019. Conservation needs assessments. Accessed 03 Nov. 2019. http://www.conservationneeds.org.

AmphibiaWeb. 2021. University of California, Berkeley. Accessed 15 June 2021. https://AmphibiaWeb.org.

Andreone, F. 1992. Syntopy of *Mantella cowani* Boulenger and *Mantella madagascariensis* (Grandidier) in central-eastern Madagascar, with notes on the coloration in the genus *Mantella* (Anura: Mantellidae). *Bollettino del Museo di Scienze Naturali di Torino* 10: 421–450.

———. 1994. The amphibians of Ranomafana rainforest, Madagascar: Preliminary community analysis and conservation considerations. *Oryx* 28: 207–214.

———, ed. 2008. A conservation strategy for the amphibians of Madagascar. *Monografie del Museo Regionale di Scienze Naturali di Torino* 45: 1–45.

Andreone, F., and Nussbaum, R. A. 2006. A revision of *Mantidactylus microtis* and *M. microtympanum*, and a comparison with other large Madagascan stream frogs (Anura: Mantellidae: Mantellinae). *Zootaxa* 1105: 49–68.

Andreone, F., and Randriamahazo, H. 2008. *Sahonagasy Action Plan: Conservation Programs for the Amphibians of Madagascar*. Turin: Museo Regionale di Scienze Naturali, Conservation International, IUCN/SSC Amphibian Specialist Group.

Andreone, F., and Randrianirina, J. E. 2003. It's not carnival for the harlequin mantella! Urgent actions needed to conserve *Mantella cowani*, an endangered frog from the High Plateau of Madagascar. *FrogLog* 59: 1–2.

———. 2008. An unexpected *Rhombophryne* record at Tsingy de Bemaraha confirms the presence of cophyline frogs in western Madagascar. *Zootaxa* 1812: 46–48.

Andreone, F., Randrianirina, J. E., Jenkins, P. D., and Aprea, G. 2000. Species diversity of Amphibia, Reptilia and Lipotyphla (Mammalia) at Ambolokopatrika, a rainforest between the Anjanajaribe-Sud and Marojejy Massifs, NE Madagascar. *Biodiversity and Conservation* 9: 1587–1622.

Andreone, F., Behler, J., Bloxam, Q., Cadle, J., Kuchling, G., et al. 2001. Rapport du groupe reptiles et amphibiens. In *AAVV, evaluation et plans de gestion pour la conservation (CAMP) de la faune de Madagascar: Lémuriens, autres mammifères, reptiles et amphibiens, poissons d'eau douce*. Mantasoa: Madagascar Fauna Group.

Andreone, F., Vences, M., Guarino, F. M., Glaw, F., and Randrianirina, J. E. 2002. Natural history and larval morphology of *Boophis occidentalis* (Anura: Mantellidae: Boophinae) provide new insights into the phylogeny and adaptive radiation of endemic Malagasy frogs. *Journal of Zoology* 257: 425–438.

Andreone, F., Fenolio, D. B., and Walvoord, M. E. 2003a. Two unknown arboreal frogs (genus *Platypelis*) described from the rainforests of northeastern Madagascar (Microhylidae: Cophylinae). *Current Herpetology* 22: 91–100.

Andreone, F., Glaw, F., Nussbaum, R. A., Randrianirina, J. E., Raxworthy C. J., and Vences, M. 2003b. Diversity and conservation of amphibians and reptiles on offshore islands: The case study of Nosy Be and nearby islets (NW Madagascar). *Journal of Natural History* 37: 2119–2149.

Andreone, F., Cadle, J. E., Cox, N., Glaw, F., Nussbaum, R. A., Raxworthy, C. J., Stuart, S. N., Vallan, D., and Vences, M. 2005a. Species review of amphibian extinction risks in Madagascar: Conclusions from the Global Amphibian Assessment. *Conservation Biology* 19: 1790–1802.

Andreone, F., Mattioli, F., and Mercurio, V. 2005b. The call of *Scaphiophryne gottlebei*, a microhylid frog from the Isalo Massif, southcentral Madagascar. *Current Herpetology* 24: 33–35.

Andreone, F., Vences, M., Vieites, D. R., Glaw, F., and Meyer, A. 2005c. Recurrent ecological adaptations revealed through a molecular analysis of the secretive cophyline frogs of Madagascar. *Molecular Phylogenetics and Evolution* 34: 315–322.

Andreone, F., Aprea, G., Odierna, G., and Vences, M. 2006a. A new narrow-mouthed frog of the genus *Paradoxophyla* (Microhylidae: Scaphiophryninae) from Masoala rainforest, northeastern Madagascar. *Acta Herpetologica* 1: 15–27.

Andreone, F., Mercurio, V., and Mattioli, F. 2006b. Between environmental degradation and international pet trade: Conservation strategies for the threatened amphibians of Madagascar. In Dalla tutela ambientale e faunistica allo sviluppo sostenibile: Esperienze di ricerca e gestione participative in Africa e in Madagascar, ed. F. Andreone. *Atti della Giornata di Studio, Milano, Natura* (*Atti della Società Italiana di Scienze Naturali e del Museo Civico di Storia Naturale di Milano*) 95: 81–96.

Andreone, F., Carpenter, A. I., Cox, N., Du Preez, L., Freeman, K., et al. 2008a. The challenge of conserving amphibian megadiversity in Madagascar. *PLoS Biology* 6: e118.

Andreone, F., Cox, N. A., Glaw, F., Köhler, J., Rabibisoa, N.H.C., et al. 2008b. Update of the Global Amphibian Assessment for Madagascar in light of new species discoveries, nomenclature changes, and new field information. In A Conservation Strategy for the Amphibians of Madagascar. *Monografie del Museo Regionale di Scienze Naturali di Torino* 45: 419–438.

Andreone, F., Rosa, G. M., Noël, J., Crottini, A., Vences, M., and Raxworthy, C. J. 2010. Living within fallen palm leaves: The discovery of an unknown *Blommersia* (Mantellidae: Anura) reveals a new reproductive strategy in the amphibians of Madagascar. *Naturwissenschaften* 97: 525–543.

Andreone, F., Giacoma, C., Guarino, F. M., Mercurio, V., and Tessa, G. 2011. Age profile in nine *Mantella* poison frogs. *Alytes* 27: 73–84.

Andreone, F., Carpenter, A. I., Copsey, J., Crottini, A., Jenkins, R.K.B., Köhler, J., Rabibisoa, N. H. C., Randriamahazo, H., and Raxworthy, C. J. 2012. Saving the diverse Malagasy amphibian fauna: Where are we four years after implementation of the Sahonagasy Action Plan? *Alytes* 29: 44–58.

Andreone, F., Bergò, P. E., Mercurio, V., and Rosa, G. M. 2013. Spatial ecology of *Scaphiophryne gottlebei* in the canyons of the Isalo Massif, Madagascar. *Herpetologica* 69: 11–21.

Andreone, F., Crottini, A., Rabemananjara, F.C.E., Randrianirina, J. E., Razafindrabe, T., and Tessa, G. 2014a. Age structure, population estimate and *Bd*-status of two Critically Endangered frogs from the Ankaratra Massif (Madagascar), *Boophis williamsi* and *Mantidactylus pauliani* (Amphibia: Mantellidae). In Studies on amphibians and reptiles in honour of Benedetto Lanza, eds. M. Capula and C. Corti, pp. 17–29. *Scripta Herpetologica, Monografie Societas Herpetologica Italica*, III. Edizioni Belvedere, Latina.

Andreone, F., Rabibisoa, N., Randrianantoandro, C., Crottini, A., Edmonds, D., et al. 2014b. Madagascar: Risk review is under way for invasive toad. *Nature* 512: 253.

Andreone, F., Cadle, J. E., Crottini, A., Dawson, J., Larney, E., et al. 2015. Frogs of Madagascar: A second ACSAM workshop to prevent a crisis. *FrogLog* 113: 14–16.

Andreone, F., Dawson, J., Rabemananjara, F.C.E., Rabibisoa, N.H.C., and Rakotonanahary, T. eds. 2016. *New Sahonagasy Action Plan 2016–2020 / Nouveau Plan d'Action Sahonagasy 2016–2020*. Turin: Museo Regionale di Scienze Naturali and Amphibian Survival Alliance.

Andreone, F., Andriantsimanarilafy, R. R., Crottini, A., Edmonds, D., Garcia, G., Hansen-Hendrikx, C. M., Rakotoarison, A., and Razafimanahaka, J. H., eds. 2020. Mantella cowanii *Action Plan 2021–2025*. Turin: Museo Regionale di Scienze Naturali and Amphibian Survival Alliance.

Andriamaharavo, N. R., Garraffo, H. M., Spande, T. F., Giddings, L. A., Vieites, D. R., Vences, M., and Saporito, R. A. 2015. Individual and geographic variation of skin alkaloids in three swamp-forest species of Madagascan poison frogs (*Mantella*). *Journal of Chemical Ecology* 41: 837–847.

Aprea, G., Odierna, G., Andreone, F., Glaw, F., and Vences, M. 2007. Karyological evolution and systematics of Malagasy microhylid frogs. *Zoologischer Anzeiger* 246: 23–41.

Arnoult, J., and Razarihelisoa, M. 1966. Contribution à l'étude des batraciens de Madagascar: Ecologie et formes larvaires de *Rhacophorus goudoti* (Tschudi). *Bulletin du Muséum National d'Histoire Naturelle*, Paris 38: 111–117.

Asher, R. J., and Krause, D. W. 1998. The first pre-Holocene (Cretaceous) record of Anura from Madagascar. *Journal of Vertebrate Paleontology* 18: 696–699.

Atmar, W., and Patterson, B. D. 1995. The nestedness temperature calculator: A visual basic program including 294 presence-absence matrices. University Park: AICS Research.

Bain, O., and Brunhes, J. 1968. Un nouveau genre de filaire, parasite de grenouilles malgaches. *Bulletin du Muséum National d'Histoire Naturelle*, Paris 40: 797–801.

Baker, M. 1980. Revision of Old World species of the genus *Aplectana* Railliet and Henry, 1916 (Nematoda. Cosmocercidae). *Bulletin du Muséum National d'Histoire Naturelle*, Paris 2: 995–998.

Beachy, J. R., Neville, R., and Arnott, C. 2011. Successful control of an incipient invasive amphibian: *Eleutherodactylus coqui* on O'ahu, Hawai'i. In *Eradication and Management: Proceedings of the International Conference on Island Invasives*, eds. C. R. Veitch, M. N. Clout, and D. R. Towns, pp. 140–147. Gland: IUCN.

Behra, O. 1991. Exportation des amphibiens de Madagascar: Intérêt, danger et perspectives d'avenir. *Circalytes* 5(4): 45–49.

———. 1993. The export of reptiles and amphibians from Madagascar. *TRAFFIC Bulletin* 13(3): 115–116.

Bellati, A., Scherz, M. D., Megson, S., Hyde Roberts, S., Andreone, F., et al. 2018. Resurrection and re-description of *Plethodontohyla laevis* (Boettger, 1913) and transfer of *Rhombophryne alluaudi* (Mocquard, 1901) to the genus *Plethodontohyla* (Microhylidae: Cophylinae). *Zoosystematics and Evolution* 94: 109–135.

Berry, P. Y., and Bullock, J. A. 1962. The food of the common Malayan toad, *Bufo melanostictus* Schneider. *Copeia* 4: 736–741.

Berthier, P., Du Preez, L. H., Raharivololoniana, L., Vences, M., and Verneau, O. 2014. Two new species of polystomes (Monogenea: Polystomatidae) from the anuran host *Guibemantis liber*. *Parasitology International* 63: 108–119.

Bielby, J., Cooper, N., Cunningam, A. A., Garner, T.W.J., and Purvis, A. 2008. Predictors of rapid decline in frog species. *Conservation Letters* 1: 82–90.

Bletz, M. C., Rosa, G. M., Andreone, F., Courtois, E. A., Schmeller, D. S., et al. 2015a. Consistency of published results on the pathogen *Batrachochytrium dendrobatidis* in Madagascar: Formal comment on Kolby et al. Rapid response to evaluate the presence of amphibian chytrid fungus (*Batrachochytrium dendrobatidis*) and *Ranavirus* in wild amphibian populations in Madagascar. *PLoS One* 10: e0135900.

———. 2015b. Widespread presence of the pathogenic fungus *Batrachochytrium dendrobatidis* in wild amphibian communities in Madagascar. *Scientific Reports* 5: 8633.

Bletz, M. C., Archer, H., Harris, R. N., McKenzie, V. J., Rabemananjara, F.C.E., Rakotoarison, A., and Vences, M. 2017a. Host ecology rather than host phylogeny drives amphibian skin microbial community structure in the biodiversity hotspot of Madagascar. *Frontiers in Microbiology 8: 1530*. doi:10.3389/fmicb.2017.01530.

Bletz, M. C., Myers, J., Woodhams, D. C., Rabemananjara, F.C.E., Rakotonirina, A., Weldon, C., Edmonds, D., Vences, M., and Harris, R. N. 2017b. Estimating herd immunity to amphibian chytridiomycosis in Madagascar based on the defensive function of amphibian skin bacteria. *Frontiers in Microbiology* 8: 1751. doi:10.3389/fmicb.2017.01751.

Bletz, M. C., Scherz, M. D., Rakotoarison, A., Lehtinen, R., Glaw, F., and Vences, M. 2018. Stumbling upon a new frog species of *Guibemantis* (Anura: Mantellidae) on top of the Marojejy Massif in northern Madagascar. *Copeia* 106: 255–263.

Blommers-Schlösser, R.M.A. 1975a. A unique case of mating behaviour in a Malagasy tree frog, *Gephyromantis liber* (Peracca, 1893), with observations on the larval development (Amphibia, Ranidae). *Beaufortia* 23: 15–25.

———. 1975b. Observations on the larval development of some Malagasy frogs, with notes on their ecology and biology (Anura: Dyscophinae, Scaphiophryninae and Cophylinae). *Beaufortia* 24(309): 7–26.

———. 1978. Cytotaxonomy of the Ranidae, Rhacophoridae, Hyperoliidae (Anura) from Madagascar with a note on the karyotype of two amphibians of the Seychelles. *Genetica* 48: 23–40.

———. 1979a. Biosystematics of the Malagasy frogs. I. Mantellinae (Ranidae). *Beaufortia* 29: 1–77.

———. 1979b. Biosytematics of the Malagasy frogs. II. The genus *Boophis* (Rhacophoridae). *Bijdragen tot de Dierkunde* 49: 261–312.

———. 1982. Observations on the Malagasy frog genus *Heterixalus* Laurent, 1944 (Hyperoliidae). *Beaufortia* 32: 1–11.

Blommers-Schlösser, R.M.A., and Blanc, C. P. 1991. Amphibiens, pt. 1. *Faune de Madagascar* 75(1): 1–384.

———. 1993. Amphibiens, pt. 2. *Faune de Madagascar* 75(2): 385–530.

Boettger, O. 1913. Reptilien und Amphibien von Madagascar, den Inseln und dem Festland Ostafrika. In *Reise in Ostafrika*, ed. A. Voeltzkow, pp. 1–269. Stuttgart: Schweizerbart'sche Verlagsbuchhandlung.

Bora, P., Ramilijoana, O., Raminosoa, N., and Vences, M. 2011. A new species of *Mantidactylus* (subgenus *Chonomantis*) from Ranomafana National Park, eastern Madagascar (Amphibia, Anura, Mantellidae). *Zootaxa* 2772: 52–60.

Borkent, A. 2008. The frog-biting midges of the world (Corethrellidae: Diptera). *Zootaxa* 1804: 1–456.

Boulenger, G. A. 1882. *Catalogue of the Batrachia Salientia s. Caudata in the Collection of the British Museum: Addenda*. London: Trustees of the British Museum.

Brown, J. L., Cameron, A., Yoder, A. D., and Vences, M. 2014. A necessarily complex model to explain the biogeography of the amphibians and reptiles of Madagascar. *Nature Communications* 5: e5046.

Brown, J. L., Sillero, N., Glaw, F., Bora, P., Vieites, D. R., and Vences, M. 2016. Spatial biodiversity patterns of Madagascar's amphibians and reptiles. *PLoS One* 11: e0144076.

Busse, K. 1981. Revision der Farbmuster-Variabilität in der madagassischen Gattung *Mantella* (Salientia: Ranidae). *Amphibia-Reptilia* 2: 23–42.

Cadle, J. E. 1995. A new species of *Boophis* (Anura: Rhacophoridae) with unusual skin glands from Madagascar, and a discussion of variation and sexual dimorphism in *Boophis albilabris* (Boulenger). *Zoological Journal of the Linnean Society* 115: 313–345.

———. 1996. Systematics of snakes of the genus *Geodipsas* (Colubridae) from Madagascar, with descriptions of new species and observations on natural history. *Bulletin of the Museum of Comparative Zoology* 155: 33–87.

———. 2014. Natural history and taxonomic notes on *Liopholidophis grandidieri* Mocquard, an upland rainforest snake from Madagascar (Serpentes: Lamprophiidae: Pseudoxyrhophiinae). *Herpetological Conservation and Biology* 9: 406–416.

Canessa, S. 2017. No conservation without representation? Linked decisions and priority setting in amphibian ex situ programmes. *Animal Conservation* 20: 124–125.

Cardiff, S. G., and Goodman, S. M. 2008. Natural history of the red owl (*Tyto soumagnei*) in dry deciduous tropical forest in Madagascar. *Wilson Journal of Ornithology* 120: 891–897.

Chabaud, A. G., and Brygoo, E. R. 1957. Deux nématodes parasites de grenouilles à Madagascar: *Flacaustra golvani* n. sp. et *Harentinema ambocaeca* n. gen. n. sp. *Annales de Parasitologie Humaine et Comparée* 32: 385–397.

———. 1958. Description et cycle évolutif d'*Aplectana courdurieri* n. sp. (Nematoda, Cosmocercidae). *Mémoires de l'Institut Scientifique de Madagascar*, série A, 12: 159–176.

Chabaud, A. G., Brygoo, E. R., and Petter, A. 1961. Déscription et caractères biologiques de deux nouveaux *Rhabdias* malgaches. *Annales de Parasitologie Humaine et Comparée* 36: 752–763.

Chanson, J. S., Hoffmann, M., Cox, N. A., and Stuart, S. N. 2008. The state of the world's amphibians. In *Threatened Amphibians of the World*, eds. S. N. Stuart, M. Hoffmann, J. S. Chanson, N. A. Cox, R. J. Berridge, P. Ramani, and B. E. Young, pp. 33–44. Barcelona: Lynx Edicions.

Chen, K. K., and Kovaříková, A. 1967. Pharmacology and toxicology of toad venom. *Journal of Pharmaceutical Sciences* 56: 1535–1541.

Chiari, Y., Vences, M., Vieites, D. R., Rabemananjara, F., Bora, P., Ramilijaona Ravoahangimalala, O., and Meyer, A. 2004. New evidence for parallel evolution of colour patterns in Malagasy poison frogs (*Mantella*). *Molecular Ecology* 13: 3763–3774.

Chiari, Y., Andreone, F., Vences, M., and Meyer, A. 2005. Genetic variation of an endangered Malagasy frog, *Mantella cowani*, and its phylogeographic relationships to the widespread *M. baroni*. *Conservation Genetics* 6: 1041–1047.

Chiari, Y., Orozco-terWengel, P., Vences, M., Vieites, D. R., Sarovy, A., Randrianirina, J. E., Meyer, A., and Louis, E., Jr. 2006. Genetic identification of units for conservation in tomato frogs, genus *Dyscophus*. *Conservation Genetics* 7: 473–482.

Christe, P., Morand, S., and Michaux, J. 2006. Biological conservation and parasitism. In *Micromammals and Macroparasites*, eds. S. Morand, B. Krasnov, and R. Pouin, pp. 593–613. New York: Springer.

Church, G. 1960. The invasion of Bali by *Bufo melanostictus*. *Herpetologica* 16(1): 15–21.

Clark, V. C., Raxworthy, C. J., Rakotomalala, V., Sierwald, P., and Fisher, B. L. 2005. Convergent evolution of chemical defense in poison frogs and arthropod prey between Madagascar and the Neotropics. *Proceedings of the National Academy of Sciences of the USA* 102: 11617–11622.

Clark, V. C., Rakotomalala, V., Ramilijaona, O., Abrell, L., and Fisher, B. L. 2006. Individual variation in alkaloid content of poison frogs of Madagascar (*Mantella*; Mantellidae). *Journal of Chemical Ecology* 32: 2219–2233.

Clark, V. C., Harinantenaina, L., Zeller, M., Ronto, W., Rocca, J., Dossey, A. T., Rakotondravony, D., Kingston, D. G., and Shaw, C. 2012. An endogenous bile acid and dietary sucrose from skin secretions of alkaloid-sequestering poison frogs. *Journal of Natural Products* 75: 473–478.

Clarke, B. T. 1981. Comparative osteology and evolutionary relationships in the African Raninae (Anura Ranidae). *Monitore Zoologico Italiano (N. S.) Supplemento* 15: 285–331.

———. 1997. The natural history of amphibian skin secretions, their normal functioning and potential medical applications. *Biological Review* 72: 365–379.

Cocca, W., Rosa, G. M., Andreone, F., Aprea, G., Eusebio Bergò, P., et al. 2018. The herpetofauna (Amphibia, Crocodylia, Squamata, Testudines) of the Isalo Massif, southwest Madagascar: Combining morphological, molecular and museum data. *Salamandra* 54: 178–200.

Cocca, W., Andreone, F., Belluardo, F., Rosa, G. M., Randrianirina, J. E., Glaw, F., and Crottini, A. 2020. Resolving a taxonomic and nomenclatural puzzle in mantellid frogs: Synonymization of *Gephyromantis azzurrae* with *G. corvus*, and description of *Gephyromantis kintana* sp. nov. from the Isalo Massif, western Madagascar. *ZooKeys* 951: 133–157.

Collen, B., Dulvy, N. K., Gaston, K. J., Gärdenfors, U., Keith, D. A., et al. 2016. Clarifying misconceptions of extinction risk assessment with the IUCN Red List. *Biology Letters* 12: 20150843.

Colwell, R. K., and Lees, D. C. 2000. The mid-domain effect: Geometric constraints on the geography of species richness. *Trends in Ecology and Evolution* 15: 70–76.

Conlon, J. M., and Kim, J. B. 2000. A protease inhibitor of the Kunitz family from skin secretions of the tomato frog, *Dyscophus guineti* (Microhylidae). *Biochemical and Biophysical Research Communications* 279: 961–964.

Cramer, A. F., Rabibisoa, N.H.C., and Raxworthy, C. J. 2008. Descriptions of two new *Spinomantis* frogs from Madagascar (Amphibia: Mantellidae), and new morphological data for *S. brunae* and *S. massorum*. *American Museum Novitates* 3618: 1–22.

Crottini, A., Chiari, Y., Mercurio, V., Meyer, A., Vences, M., and Andreone, A. 2008. Into the canyons: The phylogeography of the Malagasy frogs *Mantella expectata* and *Scaphiophryne gottlebei* in the arid Isalo Massif, and its significance for conservation (Amphibia: Mantellidae and Microhylidae). *Organisms Diversity and Evolution* 8: 368–377.

Crottini, A., Barbuto, M., Casiraghi, M., and Andreone, F. 2011a. Amphibian survey at Itremo-Ambatofinandrahana, central Madagascar, with confirmed absence of chytrid fungus and recommendations for future monitoring activities. *North-Western Journal of Zoology* 7: 346–351.

Crottini, A., Glaw, F., Casiraghi, M., Jenkins, R.K.B., Mercurio, V., Randrianantoandro, C., Randrianirina, J. E., and Andreone, F. 2011b. A new *Gephyromantis* (*Phylacomantis*) frog species from the pinnacle karst of Bemaraha, western Madagascar. *ZooKeys* 81: 51–71.

Crottini, A., Brown, J. L., Mercurio, V., Glaw, F., Vences, M., and Andreone, F. 2012a. Phylogeography of the poison frog *Mantella viridis* (Amphibia: Mantellidae) reveals chromatic and genetic differentiation across ecotones in northern Madagascar. *Journal of Zoological Systematics and Evolutionary Research* 50: 305–314.

Crottini, A., Madsen, O., Poux, C., Strauß, A., Vieites, D. R., and Vences, M. 2012b. Vertebrate time-tree elucidates the biogeographic pattern of a major biotic change around the K–T boundary in Madagascar. *Proceedings of the National Academy of Sciences of the USA* 109: 5358–5363.

Crottini, A., Andreone, F., Edmonds, D., Hansen, C. M., Lewis, J. P., et al. 2014a. A new challenge for amphibian conservation in Madagascar: The invasion of *Duttaphrynus melanostictus* in Toamasina Province. *FrogLog* 111: 46–47.

Crottini, A., Bollen, A., Weldon, C., Dalton, D. L., Kotze, A., Noël, J., Iambana, B., and Andreone, F. 2014b. Amphibian survey and current absence of *Batrachochytrium dendrobatidis* (*Bd*) in Ivoloina Park, Toamasina (eastern Madagascar). *African Journal of Herpetology* 63: 70–78.

Crottini, A., Orozco-terWengel, P., Rabemananjara, F.C.E., Hauswaldt, J. S., and Vences, M. 2019. Mitochondrial introgression, color pattern variation, and severe demographic bottlenecks in three species of Malagasy poison frogs, genus *Mantella*. *Genes* 10: 317.

Crump, M. L. 2015. Anuran reproductive modes: Evolving perspectives. *Journal of Herpetology* 49: 1–16.

Cushnie, T.P.T., Cushnie, B., and Lamb, A. J. 2014. Alkaloids: An overview of their antibacterial, antibiotic-enhancing and antivirulence activities. *International Journal of Antimicrobial Agents* 44: 377–386.

Daly, J. W., Andriamaharavo, N. R., Andriantsiferana, M., and Myers, C. W. 1996. Madagascan poison frogs (*Mantella*) and their skin alkaloids. *American Museum Novitates* 3177: 1–34.

Daly, J. W., Garraffo, H. M., Spande, T. F., Giddings, L. A., Saporito, R. A., Vieites, D. R., and Vences, M. 2008. Geographic variation of skin alkaloids among individuals of three species of Madagascan poison frogs (*Mantella*). *Journal of Chemical Ecology* 34: 252–279.

Daniel, J. C., and Sekar, A. G. 1989. Field guide to the amphibians of western India, pt. 4. *Journal of the Bombay Natural History Society* 86: 194–202.

Dawson, J., Edmonds, D., Freeman, K., Iambana, B., Moore, M., and Rakotoarisoa, J. C. 2014. Working together to develop Madagascar's amphibian captive breeding capacity. *FrogLog* 22: 61–62.

D'Cruze, N., Henson, D., Olsson, A., and Emmett, D. 2009. The importance of herpetological survey work in conserving Malagasy biodiversity: Are we doing enough? *Herpetological Review* 40: 19.

Delvinquier, B.L.J., Glaw, F., Markus, M. B., and Passmore, N. I. 1998. Opalinidae (Slopalinida) in Madagascan Anura: *Zelleriella* Metcalf, 1920 and *Protoopalina* Metcalf, 1918. *Systematic Parasitology* 41: 187–196.

de Sá, R. O., Steicher, J. W., Sekonyela, R., Forlani, M. C., Loader, S. P., Greenbaum, E., Richards, S., and Haddad, C.F.B. 2012. Molecular phylogeny of microhylid frogs (Anura: Microhylidae) with emphasis on relationships among New World genera. *BMC Evolutionary Biology* 12: 241.

Döring, B., Mecke, S., Kieckbusch, M., O'Shea, M., and Kaiser, H. 2017. Food spectrum analysis of the Asian toad, *Duttaphrynus melanostictus* (Schneider, 1799) (Anura: Bufonidae), from Timor Island, Wallacea. *Journal of Natural History* 51: 607–623.

Dubois, A. 1992. Notes sur la classification des Ranidae (Amphibiens Anoures). *Bulletin Mensuel de la Societé Linnéenne de Lyon* 61: 305–352.

Dubois, A., Ohler, A., and Pyron, R. A. 2021. New concepts and methods for phylogenetic taxonomy and nomenclature in zoology, exemplified by a new ranked cladonomy of recent amphibians (Lissamphibia). *Megataxa* 5: 1–738.

Dubos, N., Morel, L., Crottini, A., Freeman, K., Honoré, J., Lava, H., Nöel, J., Porton, I., Rosa, G. M., and Andreone, F. 2020. High interannual variability of a climate-driven amphibian community in a seasonal rainforest. *Biodiversity and Conservation* 29: 893–912.

Duellman, W. E., and Trueb, L. 1986. *Biology of Amphibians*. Baltimore: Johns Hopkins University Press.

Du Preez, L. H., Raharivololoniaina, L., Verneau, O., and Vences, M. 2010. A new genus of polystomatid parasitic flatworm (Monogenea: Polystomatidae) without free-swimming life stage from the Malagasy poison frogs. *Zootaxa* 2722: 54–68.

Durkin, L., Steer, M. D., and Belle, E. M. 2011. Herpetological surveys of forest fragments between Montagne d'Ambre National Park and Ankarana Special Reserve, northern Madagascar. *Herpetological Conservation and Biology* 6: 114–126.

Edmonds, D. 2009. Extended distribution of two frogs from Madagascar: *Mantella crocea* and *Mantella manery* (Anura: Mantellidae). *Herpetology Notes* 2: 53–57.

Edmonds, D., Rakotoarisoa, J. C., Dolch, R., Pramuk, J., Gagliardo, R., Andreone, F., Rabibisoa, N., Rabemananjara, F.C.E., Rabesihanaka, S., and Robsomanitrandrasana, E. 2012. Building capacity to implement conservation breeding programs for frogs in Madagascar: Results from year one of Mitsinjo's amphibian husbandry research and captive breeding facility. *Amphibian and Reptile Conservation* 5: 57–69.

Edmonds, D., Rakotoarisoa, J. C., Rasoanantenaina, S., Sam, S. S., Soamiarimampionona, J., et al. 2015. Captive husbandry, reproduction, and fecundity of the golden mantella (*Mantella aurantiaca*) at the Mitsinjo breeding facility. *Salamandra* 51: 315–325.

Edmonds, D., Rakotoarisoa, J. C., Rasoanantenaina, S., Sam, S. S., Soamiarimampionona, J., and Tsimialomanana, E. 2016. Captive management and reproduction of the treefrog *Boophis pyrrhus* in Andasibe, Madagascar. *Herpetological Review* 47: 405–409.

Edwards, W. M., Griffiths, R. A., Bungard, M. J., Rakotondrasoa, E. F., Razafimanahaka, J. H., Razafindraibe, P., Andriantsimanarilafy, R. R., and Randrianantoandro, J. C. 2019. Microhabitat preference of the Critically Endangered golden mantella frog in Madagascar. *Herpetological Journal* 29: 207–213.

Emerson, S. B., Richards, C., Drewes, R. C., and Kjer, K. M. 2000. On the relationships among ranoid frogs: A review of the evidence. *Herpetologica* 56: 209–230.

Eudeline, R., Wang, C., and Scherz, M. D. 2015. Predation attempt of *Rhombophryne laevipes* by *Compsophis albiventris*. *Herpetology Notes* 8: 393–394.

Euzet, L., and Combes, C. 1964. Sur un Polystomatidae (Monogenea) récolté à Madagascar chez *Rana mascareniensis* Duméril et Bibon. *Bulletin de la Societé Geologique de France* 89: 392–401.

Evans, S. E., Jones, M. E., and Krause, D. W. 2008. A giant frog with South American affinities from the Late Cretaceous of Madagascar. *Proceedings of the National Academy of Sciences of the USA* 105: 2951–2956.

Evans, S. E., Groenke, J. R., Jones, M. E., Turner, A. H., and Krause, D. W. 2014. New material of *Beelzebufo*, a hyperossified frog (Amphibia: Anura) from the late Cretaceous of Madagascar. *PLoS One* 9: e87236.

Fatroandrianjafinonjasolomiovazo, T.N.L., Rasoamampionona, N. R, Vieites, D. R., and Vences, M. 2011. Diet of the Mascarene grass frog, *Ptychadena mascareniensis*, in Madagascar. *Malagasy Nature* 5: 68–74.

Feng, Y. J., Blackburn, D. C., Liang, D., Hillis, D. M., Wake, D. B., Cannatella, D. C., and Zhang, P. 2017. Phylogenomics reveals rapid, simultaneous diversification of three major clades of Gondwanan frogs at the Cretaceous-Paleogene boundary. *Proceedings of the National Academy of Sciences of the USA* 114: 5864–5870.

Ferrier, S., Manion, G., Elith, J., and Richardson, K. 2007. Using generalized dissimilarity modelling to analyse and predict patterns of beta diversity in regional biodiversity assessment. *Diversity and Distributions* 13: 252–264.

Fischer, E. K., Roland, A. B., Moskowitz, N. A., Vidoudez, C., Ranaivorazo, N., Tapia, E. E., Trauger, S. A., Vences, M., Coloma, L. A., and O'Connell, L. A. 2019. Mechanisms of convergent egg provisioning in poison frogs. *Current Biology* 29: 4145–4151.

Ford, L. S., and Cannatella, D. C. 1993. The major clades of frogs. *Herpetological Monographs* 7: 94–117.

Frost, D. R., Grant, T., Faivovich, J., Bain, R. H., Haas, A., et al. 2006. The amphibian tree of life. *Bulletin of the American Museum of Natural History* 297: 1–370.

García, G., Bock, L., Earle, S., Berridge, R., and Copsey, J. 2008. Captive breeding as a tool for the conservation of Malagasy amphibians: How ready are we to respond to the need? In A conservation strategy for the amphibians of Madagascar, ed. F. Andreone. *Monografie del Museo Regionale di Scienze Naturali di Torino* 45: 321–342.

Gardiner, J. S. 1906. Notes on the distribution of the land and marine animals, with a list of the land plants and some remarks on the coral reefs. In *The Fauna and Geography of the Maldive and Laccadive Archipelagos*, ed. J. S. Gardiner, pp. 1046–1057. Cambridge: Cambridge University Press.

Gardner, C., and Jasper, L. 2009. The urban herpetofauna of Toliara, southwest Madagascar. *Herpetology Notes* 2: 239–242.

Garner, T.W.J., Briggs, C. J., Bielby, J., and Fisher, M. C. 2012. Determining when parasites of amphibians are conservation threats to their hosts. In *New Direction in Conservation Medicine*, eds. A. A. Aguirre, R. S. Ostfeld, and P. Daszak, pp. 521–538. Oxford: Oxford University Press.

Gascon, C., Collins, J. P., Moore, R. D., Church, D. R., McKay, J. E., and Mendelson, J. R., III, eds. 2007. *Amphibian Conservation Action Plan*. Gland and Cambridge: IUCN/SSC Amphibian Specialist Group.

Gehring, P.-S., Pabijan, M., Randrianirina, J. E., Glaw, F., and Vences, M. 2012. The influence of riverine barriers on phylogeographic patterns of Malagasy reed frogs (*Heterixalus*). *Molecular Phylogenetics and Evolution* 64: 618–632.

Glaw, F., and Vences, M. 1992a. *A Fieldguide to the Amphibians and Reptiles of Madagascar*. 1st ed. Cologne: Vences and Glaw Verlag GbR.

———. 1992b. Zur Biologie, Biometrie und Färbung bei *Mantella laevigata* Methuen and Hewitt, 1913. *Sauria* 14: 25–29.

———. 1993. Zur Ökologie, Bioakustik und Systematik der Gattung *Heterixalus* aus Madagaskar (Anura: Hyperoliidae). *Salamandra* 29: 212–231.

———. 1994. *A Fieldguide to the Amphibians and Reptiles of Madagascar*. 2nd ed. Cologne: Vences and Glaw Verlags GbR.

———. 1997a. Neue Ergebnisse zur *Boophis goudoti*-Gruppe aus Madagaskar: Bioakustik, Fortpflanzungsstrategien und Beschreibung von *Boophis rufioculis* sp. nov. *Salamandra* 32: 225–242.

———. 1997b. A review of anuran eye colouration: Definitions, taxonomic implications and possible functions. In *Herpetologia Bonnensis*, eds. W. Böhme, W. Bischoff, and T. Ziegler, pp. 125–138. Bonn: Societas Europaea Herpetologica.

———. 1997c. New species of the *Boophis tephraeomystax* group (Anura: Ranidae: Rhacophorinae) from arid western Madagascar. *Copeia* 1997: 572–578.

———. 2005. A new arboreal microhylid frog of the genus *Anodonthyla* from south-eastern Madagascar. *Spixiana* 28: 181–189.

———. 2006. Phylogeny and genus-level classification of mantellid frogs (Amphibia, Anura). *Organisms Diversity and Evolution* 6: 236–253.

———. 2007. *A Field Guide to the Amphibians and Reptiles of Madagascar*. 3rd ed. Cologne: Vences and Glaw Verlag.

———. 2011. Description of a new frog species of *Gephyromantis* (subgenus *Laurentomantis*) with tibial glands from Madagascar. *Spixiana* 34: 121–127.

Glaw, F., Vences, M., and Böhme, W. 1998. Systematic revision of the genus *Aglyptodactylus* Boulenger, 1919 (Amphibia: Ranidae), and analysis of its phylogenetic relationships to other Madagascan ranid genera (*Tomopterna*, *Boophis*, *Mantidactylus*, and *Mantella*). *Journal of Zoological Systematics and Evolutionary Research* 36: 17–37.

Glaw, F., Vences, M., and Gossmann, V. 2000a. A new species of *Mantidactylus* (subgenus *Guibemantis*) from Madagascar, with a comparative survey of internal femoral gland structure in the genus (Amphibia: Ranidae: Mantellinae). *Journal of Natural History* 34: 1135–1154.

Glaw, F., Vences, M., and Schmidt, K. 2000b. Nachzucht, Juvenilfärbung und Oophagie von *Mantella laevigata* im Vergleich zu anderen Arten der Gattung (Amphibia: Ranidae). *Salamandra* 36: 1–24.

Glaw, F., Vences, M., Andreone, F., and Vallan, D. 2001. Revision of the *Boophis majori* group (Amphibia: Mantellidae) from Madagascar, with descriptions of five new species. *Zoological Journal of the Linnean Society* 133: 495–529.

Glaw, F., Hoegg, S., and Vences, M. 2006. Discovery of a new basal relict lineage of Madagascan frogs and its implications for mantellid evolution. *Zootaxa* 1334: 27–43.

Glaw, F., Köhler, J., Bora, P., Rabibisoa, N.H.C., Ramilijaona, O., and Vences, M. 2007. Discovery of the genus *Plethodontohyla* (Anura: Microhylidae) in dry western Madagascar: Description of a new species and biogeographic implications. *Zootaxa* 1577: 61–68.

Glaw, F., Köhler, J., de la Riva, I., Vieites, D. R., and Vences, M. 2010. Integrative taxonomy of Malagasy treefrogs: Combination of molecular genetics, bioacoustics and comparative morphology reveals twelve additional species of *Boophis*. *Zootaxa* 2383: 1–82.

Glaw, F., Köhler, J., and Vences, M. 2011. New species of *Gephyromantis* from Marojejy National Park, northeast Madagascar. *Journal of Herpetology* 45: 155–160.

Glaw, F., Scherz, M. D., Prötzel, D., and Vences, M. 2018. Eye and webbing colouration as predictors of specific distinctness: A genetically isolated new treefrog species of the *Boophis albilabris* group from the Masoala Peninsula, northeastern Madagascar. *Salamandra* 54: 163–177.

Glaw, F., Hawlitschek, O., Glaw, K., and Vences, M. 2019. Integrative evidence confirms new endemic island frogs and transmarine dispersal of amphibians between Madagascar and Mayotte (Comoro archipelago). *Science of Nature* 106: 19.

Glaw, F., Scherz, M. D., Rakotoarison, A., Crottini, A., Raselimanana, A. P., Andreone, F., Köhler, J., and Vences, M. 2020. Genetic variability and partial integrative revision of partially red-flanked *Platypelis* frogs (Microhylidae) from eastern Madagascar. *Vertebrate Zoology* 70: 141–156.

Glos, J. 2003. The amphibian fauna of the Kirindy dry forest in western Madagascar. *Salamandra* 39: 75–90.

———. 2006. Amphibian communities of the dry forest of western Madagascar: Taxonomy, ecology and conservation. PhD thesis, University of Würzburg.

———. 2009. *Scaphiophryne calcarata* (NCN). Tadpole biology. *Herpetological Review* 40: 211.

Glos, J., and Linsenmair, K. E. 2004. Descriptions of the tadpoles of *Aglyptodactylus laticeps* and *Aglyptodactylus securifer* from western Madagascar, with notes on life history and ecology. *Journal of Herpetology* 38: 131–136.

———. 2005. Description of the tadpoles of *Boophis doulioti* and *Boophis xerophilus* from western Madagascar with notes on larval life history and breeding ecology. *Amphibia-Reptilia* 26: 459–466.

Glos, J., Glaw, F., and Vences, M. 2005. A new species of *Scaphiophryne* from western Madagascar. *Copeia* 2005: 252–261.

Glos, J., Dausmann, K. H., and Linsenmair, K. E. 2007a. Mixed-species social aggregations in Madagascan tadpoles: Determinants and species composition. *Journal of Natural History* 41: 1965–1977.

Glos, J., Erdmann, G., Dausmann, K. H., and Linsenmair, K. E. 2007b. A comparative study of predator-induced social aggregation of tadpoles in two anuran species from western Madagascar. *Herpetological Journal* 17: 261–268.

Glos, J., Teschke, M., and Vences, M. 2007c. Aquatic zebras? The tadpoles of the Madagascan treefrog *Boophis schuboeae* Glaw and Vences 2002 compared to those of *B. ankaratra* Andreone 1993. *Tropical Zoology* 20: 125–133.

Glos, J., Volahy, A. T., Bourou, R., Straka, J., Young, R., and Durbin, J. 2008. Amphibian conservation in Central Menabe. In A conservation strategy for the amphibians of Madagascar, ed. F. Andreone. *Monografie del Museo Regionale di Scienze Naturali di Torino* 45: 107–124.

Glos, J., Metzner, A., Schmidtke, C., and Rödel, M. O. 2019. The mating system of the reed frog *Heterixalus tricolor* (Anura: Hyperoliidae) from western Madagascar's dry forests. *Salamandra* 55: 151–159.

Golvan, Y. J., Brygoo, E. R., and Gassman, M. 1972. *Acanthocephalus domerguei* n. sp., parasite d'un amphibien malgache. *Annales de Parasitologie* 47: 305–308.

Goodman, S. M., Langrand, O., and Raxworthy, C. J. 1993a. Food habits of the Madagascar Long-eared Owl *Asio madagascariensis* in two habitats in southern Madagascar. *Ostrich* 64: 79–85.

Goodman, S. M., Langrand, O., and Raxworthy, C. J. 1993b. The food habits of the Barn Owl *Tyto alba* at three sites on Madagascar. *Ostrich* 64: 160–171.

Goodman, S. M., Rakotondravony, D., Schatz, G., and Wilmé, L. 1996. Species richness of forest-dwelling birds, rodents and insectivores in a planted forest of native trees: A test case from the Ankaratra, Madagascar. *Ecotropica* 2: 109–120.

Goodman, S. M., Raselimanana, A. P., Andriniaina, H. A., Gauthier, N. E., Ravaojanahary, F. F., Sylvestre, M. H., and Raherilalao, M. J. 2017. The distribution and ecology of invasive alien vertebrate species in the greater Toamasina region, central eastern Madagascar. *Malagasy Nature* 12: 95–109.

Goodman, S. M., Raherilalao, M. J., and Wohlhauser, S., eds. 2018. *Les aires protégées terrestres de Madagascar: Leur histoire, description et biote / The Terrestrial Protected Areas of Madagascar: Their History, Description, and Biota*. Antananarivo: Association Vahatra.

Grandidier, M. A. 1872. Description de quelque reptiles nouveaux, découverts à Madagascar en 1870. *Annales Sciences Naturelles*, Paris 5(15): 6–11.

Griffiths, R. A., and Pavajeau, L. 2008. Captive breeding, reintroduction, and the conservation of amphibians. *Conservation Biology* 22: 852–861.

Grosjean, S., and Vences, M. 2009. The tadpole of the toadlet *Scaphiophryne marmorata* from Madagascar. *Zootaxa* 1986: 67–68.

Grosjean, S., Vences, M., and Dubois, A. 2004. Evolutionary significance of oral morphology in the carnivorous tadpoles of tiger frogs, genus *Hoplobatrachus* (Ranidae). *Biological Journal of the Linnean Society* 81: 171–181.

Grosjean, S., Glos, J., Teschke, M., Glaw, F., and Vences, M. 2007. Comparative larval morphology of Madagascan toadlets of the genus *Scaphiophryne*: Phylogenetic and taxonomic inferences. *Zoological Journal of the Linnean Society* 151: 555–576.

Grosjean, S., Randrianiaina, R. D., Strauß, A., and Vences, M. 2011a. Sand-eating tadpoles in Madagascar: Morphology and ecology of the unique larvae of the treefrog *Boophis picturatus*. *Salamandra* 47: 63–76.

Grosjean, S., Strauß, A., Glos, J., Randrianiaina, R. D., Ohler, A., and Vences, M. 2011b. Morphological and ecological uniformity in the funnel-mouthed tadpoles of Malagasy litter frogs, subgenus *Chonomantis*. *Zoological Journal of the Linnean Society* 162: 149–183.

Guarino, F. M., Andreone, F., and Angelini, F. 1998. Growth and longevity by skeletochronological analysis in *Mantidactylus microtympanum*, a rain-forest anuran from southern Madagascar. *Copeia* 1998: 194–198.

Guarino, F. M., Crottini, A., Mezzasalma, M., Randrianirina, J. E., and Andreone, F. 2019. A skeletochronological estimate of age and growth in a large riparian frog from Madagascar (Anura, Mantellidae, *Mantidactylus*). *Herpetozoa* 32: 39–44.

Guibé, J. 1947. Description d'un batracien nouveau de Madgascar (*Boophis laurenti* n. sp.) et synonymie de plusieurs espèces du genre *Boophis*. *Bulletin du Muséum National d'Histoire Naturelle*, Paris, série 2, 19: 438–439.

———. 1952. Recherches sur les batraciens de Madagascar. *Mémoires de l'Institut Scientifique de Madagascar* 7: 109–116.

———. 1953. Au sujet de l'introduction de *Rana tigerina* Daudin à Madagascar. *Le Naturaliste Malgache* 5: 241–242.

———. 1956. La position systemique des genres *Pseudohemisus* et *Scaphiophryne* (Batraciens). *Bulletin du Muséum National d'Histoire Naturelle*, Paris 28: 180–182.

———. 1974. Batraciens nouveaux de Madagascar. *Bulletin Muséum National d'Histoire Naturelle*, Paris 171: 1169–1192.

———. 1978. Les batraciens de Madagascar. *Bonner Zoologische Monographien* 11: 1–140.

Haddad, C.F.B., and Prado, C.P.A. 2005. Reproductive modes in frogs and their unexpected diversity in the Atlantic forest of Brazil. *BioScience* 55: 207–217.

Halajian, A., Bursey, C. R., Goldberg, S. R., and Luus-Powell, W. 2013. Helminths of six species of anurans from the Republic of South Africa: *Amietophrynus garmani*, *Amietophrynus gutturalis*, *Amietophrynus maculatus*, *Schismaderma carens* (Bufonidae), *Amietia angolensis*, and *Strongylopus grayii* (Pyxicephalidae), with a review of South African anuran helminths. *Comparative Parasitology* 80: 80–95.

Harikrishnan, S., and Vasudevan, K. 2013. Recent introduction and spread of Indian bullfrog *Hoplobatrachus tigerinus* (Daudin, 1802) into the Andaman Islands. *Aliens* 33: 42–43.

Harper, G. J., Steininger, M. K., Tucker, C. J., Juhn, D., and Hawkins, F. 2007. Fifty years of deforestation and forest fragmentation in Madagascar. *Environmental Conservation* 34: 325–333.

Heinermann, J., Rodríguez, A., Segev, O., Edmonds, D., Dolch, R., and Vences, M. 2015. Year-round activity patterns in a hyperdiverse community of rainforest amphibians in Madagascar. *Journal of Natural History* 49: 2213–2231.

Hendrix, R., Nguyen, Q. T., Böhme, W., and Ziegler, T. 2008. New anuran records from Phong Nha-Ke Bang National Park, Truong Son, central Vietnam. *Herpetology Notes* 1: 23–31.

Henle, K., Davies, K. F., Kleyer, M., Margules, C., and Settele, J. 2004. Predictors of species sensitivity to fragmentation. *Biodiversity and Conservation* 13: 207–251.

Héritier, L., Badets, M., Du Preez, L. H., Aisien, M. S., Lixian, F., Combes, C., and Verneau, O. 2015. Evolutionary processes involved in the diversification of chelonian and mammal polystomatid parasites (Platyhelminthes, Monogenea, Polystomatidae) revealed by palaeoecology of their hosts. *Molecular Phylogenetics and Evolution* 92: 1–10.

Heying, H. E. 2001. Social and reproductive behaviour in the Madagascan poison frog, *Mantella laevigata*, with comparisons to the dendrobatids. *Animal Behaviour* 61: 567–577.

Hocking, D. J., and Babbitt, K. J. 2014. Amphibian contributions to ecosystem services. *Herpetological Conservation and Biology* 9: 1–17.

Hödl, W., and Gollmann, G. 1986. Distress calls in Neotropical frogs. *Amphibia-Reptilia* 7: 11–21.

Hutter, C. R., Lambert, S. M., Cobb, K. A., Andriampenomanana, Z. F., and Vences, M. 2015. A new species of bright-eyed treefrog (Mantellidae) from Madagascar, with comments on call evolution and patterns of syntopy in the *Boophis ankaratra* complex. *Zootaxa* 4034: 531–555.

Hutter, C. R., Andriampenomanana, Z. F., Razafindraibe, J. H., Rakotoarison, A., and Scherz, M. D. 2018a. New dietary data from *Compsophis* and *Alluaudina* species (Squamata: Lamprophiidae: Pseudoxyrhophiinae), and implications for their dietary complexity and evolution. *Journal of Natural History* 52: 2497–2510.

Hutter, C. R., Lambert, S. M., Andriampenomanana, Z. F., Glaw, F., and Vences, M. 2018b. Molecular systematics and diversification of Malagasy bright-eyed tree frogs (Mantellidae: *Boophis*). *Molecular Phylogenetics and Evolution* 127: 568–578.

International Money Fund. 2019. GDP per capita, current prices. https://www.imf.org/external/datamapper/NGDPDPC@WEO/OEMDC/ADVEC/WEOWORLD.

IUCN. 2012. IUCN Red List Categories and Criteria. Version 3.1. 2nd ed. Gland and Cambridge: IUCN.

———. 2019. IUCN Red List of Threatened Species. Version 2019–2. Accessed 15 June 2021. http://www.iucnredlist.org.

IUCN SSC Amphibian Specialist Group. 2016a. *Scaphiophryne matsoko*. IUCN Red List of Threatened Species 2016: e.T78585464A84185490.

———. 2016b. *Tsingymantis antitra*. IUCN Red List of Threatened Species 2016: e.T135798A515947.

Jenkins, R.K.B., Rabearivelo, A., Chan, C. T., Andre, W. M., Randrianavelona, R., and Randrianantoandro, J. C. 2009. The harvest of endemic amphibians for food in eastern Madagascar. *Tropical Conservation Science* 2: 25–33.

Johnson, K., Baker, A., Buley, K., Carrillo, L., Gibson, R., Gillespie, G., Lacy, R. C., and Zippel, K. 2020. A process for assessing and prioritizing species conservation needs: Going beyond the Red List. *Oryx* 54: 125–132.

Johnson, P.T.J., Hartson, R. B., Larson, D. J., and Sutherland, D. R. 2008. Linking biodiversity loss and disease emergence: Amphibian community structure determines parasite transmission and pathology. *Ecology Letters* 11: 1017–1026.

Jovanovic, O., and Vences, M. 2010. Skeletochronological analysis of age structure in populations of four species of Malagasy poisonous frogs, genus *Mantella*. *Amphibia-Reptilia* 31: 553–557.

Jovanovic, O., Glos, J., Glaw, F., Randrianiaina, R.-D., and Vences, M. 2009a. Comparative larval morphology in Madagascan frogs of the genus *Mantella* (Amphibia: Mantellidae). *Zootaxa* 2124: 21–37.

Jovanovic, O., Vences, M., Safarek, G., Rabemananjara, F.C.E., and Dolch, R. 2009b. Predation upon *Mantella aurantiaca* in the Torotorofotsy wetlands, central-eastern Madagascar. *Herpetology Notes* 2: 95–97.

Junk, A., Wenzel, S., Vences, M., and Nowack, C. 2014. Deviant anatomy of the olfactory system of the Malagasy frog *Mantidactylus betsileanus* (Anura: Mantellidae). *Zoologischer Anzeiger* 253: 338–344.

Junker, K., Lhermitte-Vallarino, N., Barbuto, M., Ineich, I., Wanji, S., and Bain, O. 2010. New species of *Rhabdias* (Nematoda: Rhabdiasidae) from Afrotropical anurans, including molecular evidence and notes on biology. *Folia Parasitologica* 57: 47–61.

Kaffenberger, N., Wollenberg, K. C., Köhler, J., Glaw, F., Vieites, D. R., and Vences, M. 2012. Molecular phylogeny and biogeography of Malagasy frogs of the genus *Gephyromantis*. *Molecular Phylogenetics and Evolution* 62: 555–560.

Kari, S., and Korhonen-Kurki, K. 2013. Framing local outcomes of biodiversity conservation through ecosystem services: A case study from Ranomafana, Madagascar. *Ecosystem Services* 3: e32–e39.

Keesing, F., Brunner, J., Duerr, S., Killilea, M., LoGiudice, K., Schmidt, K., Vuong, H., and Ostfeld, R. S. 2009. Hosts as ecological traps for the vector of Lyme disease. *Proceedings of the Royal Society of London B: Biological Sciences* 276: 3911–3919.

Klages, J., Glaw, F., Köhler, J., Müller, J., Hipsley, C. A., and Vences, M. 2013. Molecular, morphological and osteological differentiation of a new species of microhylid frog of the genus *Stumpffia* from northwestern Madagascar. *Zootaxa* 3717: 280–300.

Klonoski, K., Bi, K., and Rosenblum, E. B. 2019. Phenotypic and genetic diversity in aposematic Malagasy poison frogs (genus *Mantella*). *Ecology and Evolution* 9: 2725–2742.

Knoll, A., Köhler, J., Glaw, F., Teschke, M., and Vences, M. 2007. Larval morphology in four species of Madagascan frogs of the subgenus *Brygoomantis* (Mantellidae: *Mantidactylus*). *Zootaxa* 59: 49–59.

Köhler, J., Glaw, F., and Vences, M. 1997. Notes on the reproduction of *Rhombophryne* (Anura: Microhylidae) at Nosy Be, northern Madagascar. *Revue Française d'Aquariologie* 24: 53–54.

Köhler, J., Vieites, D. R., Bonett, R. M., Hita García, F., Glaw, F., Steinke, D., and Vences, M. 2005. New amphibians and global conservation: A boost in species discoveries in a highly endangered vertebrate group. *Bioscience* 55: 693–696.

Köhler, J., Glaw, F., and Vences, M. 2007. A new green treefrog, genus *Boophis* Tschudi 1838 (Anura Mantellidae), from arid western Madagascar: Phylogenetic relationships and biogeographic implications. *Tropical Zoology* 20: 215–227.

———. 2008. Two additional treefrogs of the *Boophis ulftunni* species group (Anura: Mantellidae) discovered in rainforests of northern and south-eastern Madagascar. *Zootaxa* 1814: 37–48.

Köhler, J., Vences, M., D'Cruze, N., and Glaw, F. 2010. Giant dwarfs: Discovery of a radiation of large-bodied "stump-toed frogs" from karstic cave environments of northern Madagascar. *Journal of Zoology* 282: 21–38.

Köhler, J., Glaw, F., Pabijan, M., and Vences, M. 2015. Integrative taxonomic revision of mantellid frogs of the genus *Aglyptodactylus* (Anura: Mantellidae). *Zootaxa* 4006: 401–438.

Köhler, J., Jansen, M., Rodríguez, A., Kok, P.J.R., Toledo, L. F., Emmrich, M., Glaw, F., Haddad, C.F.B., Rödel, M. O., and Vences, M. 2017. The use of bioacoustics in anuran taxonomy: Theory, terminology, methods and recommendations for best practice. *Zootaxa* 4251: 1–124.

Kolby, J. E. 2014. Presence of the amphibian chytrid fungus *Batrachochytrium dendrobatidis* in native amphibians exported from Madagascar. *PLoS One* 9: e89660.

Kolby, J. E., Kraus, F., Rabemananjara, F.C.E., Rabesihanaka, S., Rabibisoa, N., et al. 2014. Stop Madagascar's toad invasion now. *Nature* 509: 563.

Kolby, J. E., Smith, K. M., Ramirez, S. D., Rabemananjara, F., Pessier, A. P., Brunner, J. L., Goldberg, C. S., Berger, L., and Skerratt, L. F. 2015. Rapid response to evaluate the presence of amphibian chytrid fungus (*Batrachochytrium dendrobatidis*) and Ranavirus in wild amphibian populations in Madagascar. *PLoS One* 10: e0125330.

König, E., Wesse, C., Murphy, A. C., Zhou, M., Wang, L., Chen, T., Shaw, C., and Bininda-Emonds, O.R.P. 2013. Molecular cloning of the trypsin inhibitor from the skin secretion of the Madagascan Tomato Frog, *Dyscophus guineti* (Microhylidae), and insights into its potential defensive role. *Organisms Diversity and Evolution* 13: 453–461.

Kosuch, J., Vences, M., Dubois, A. Ohler, A., and Böhme W. 2001. Out of Asia: Mitochondrial DNA evidence for an Oriental origin of tiger frogs, genus *Hoplobatrachus*. *Molecular Phylogenetics and Evolution* 21: 398–407.

Kraus, F. 2009. *Alien Reptiles and Amphibians: A Scientific Compendium and Analysis*. The Netherlands: Springer.

Kremen, C., Cameron, A., Moilanen, A., Phillips, S. J., Thomas, C. D., et al. 2008. Aligning conservation priorities across taxa in Madagascar with high-resolution planning tools. *Science* 320: 222–226.

Kull, C., Tassin, J., and Carriere, S. 2015. Approaching invasive species in Madagascar. *Madagascar Conservation and Development* 9: 60–70.

Kupfer, A. 2007. Sexual size dimorphism in amphibians: An overview. In *Sex, Size and Gender Roles: Evolutionary Studies of Sexual Size Dimorphism*, eds. D. J. Fairbairn, W. U. Blanckenhorn, and T. Szekely, pp. 50–59. New York: Oxford University Press.

Kurabayashi, A., Sumida, M., Yonekawa, H., Glaw, F., Vences, M., and Hasegawa, M. 2008. Phylogeny, recombination, and mechanisms of stepwise mitochondrial genome reorganization in mantellid frogs from Madagascar. *Molecular Biology and Evolution* 25: 874–891.

Kurabayashi, A., Matsui, M., Belabut, D. M., Yong, H., Ahmad, N., Sudin, A., Kuramoto, M., Hamidy, H., and Sumida, M. 2011. From Antarctica or Asia? New colonization scenario for Australian-New Guinean narrow mouth toads suggested from the findings on a mysterious genus *Gastrophrynoides*. *BMC Evolutionary Biology* 11: 175.

Kuzmin, Y., Junker, K., Du Preez, L., and Bain, O. 2013. A new species of *Rhabdias* Stiles and Hassall, 1905 (Nematoda: Rhabdiasidae) from *Blommersia domerguei* (Guibé) (Amphibia: Mantellidae) in Madagascar. *Folia Parasitologica* 60: 469–474.

Lam, B., Noël, J., Crottini, A., Andreone, F., and Rosa, G. M. 2020. Report of agonistic interaction in Malagasy frogs of the genus *Gephyromantis* (Anura: Mantellidae). *Arxius de Miscel·lània Zoològica* 18: 27–32.

Lambert, A., and Bourgat, R. 1978. L'oncomiracidium de *Metapolystoma brygoonis* (Euzet et Combes, 1964) parasite de l'amphibien malgache *Ptychadena mascareniensis* (Duméril et Bribon). *Annales de Parasitologie Humaine et Comparée* 53: 547–549.

Lambert, S. M., Hutter, C. R., and Scherz, M. D. 2017. Diamond in the rough: A new species of fossorial diamond frog (*Rhombophryne*) from Ranomafana National Park, southeastern Madagascar. *Zoosystematics and Evolution* 93: 143–155.

Landman, W., Verneau, O., and Du Preez, L. H. 2018. First record of viviparity in polystomatid flatworms (Monogenea: Polystomatidae) with the description of two new species of *Madapolystoma* from the Madagascan anuran hosts *Blommersia domerguei* and *Mantella expectata*. *International Journal of Parasitology* 7: 343–354.

Landman, W., Verneau, O., Raharivololoniaina, L., and Du Preez, L. H. 2021. First record of *Metapolystoma* (Monogenea: Polystomatidae) from *Boophis* tree frogs in Madagascar, with the description of five new species. *International Journal for Parasitology* 14: 161–178.

Langrand, O. 2003. Réserve Spéciale d'Ambohitantely. In *The Natural History of Madagascar*, eds. S. M. Goodman and J. P. Benstead, pp. 1472–1476. Chicago: University of Chicago Press.

Laurent, R. 1946. Mises au point dans la taxonomie des ranidés. *Revue de Zoologie et de Botanique Africaines* 34: 336–338.

Laveran, A. 1905. Contribution a l'etude des grandes hemogregarines des grenouilles. *Comptes Rendus des Séances de la Société de Biologie* 59: 172–175.

Lees, D. C. 1996. The Périnet effect? Diversity gradients in an adaptive radiation of butterflies in Madagascar (Satyrinae: Mycalesina) compared with other rainforest taxa. In *Biogéographie de Madagascar*, ed. W. R. Lourenço, pp. 479–490. Paris: Editions de l'ORSTOM.

Lees, D. C., and Colwell, R. K. 2007. A strong Madagascan rainforest MDE and no equatorward increase in species richness: Re-analysis of "The missing Madagascan mid-domain effect," by Kerr J. T., Perring M., and Currie D. J. (*Ecology Letters* 9:149–159, 2006). *Ecology Letters* 10: E4–E8.

Lehtinen, R. M. 2002. The use of screw pines (*Pandanus* spp.) by amphibians and reptiles in Madagascar. *Herpetological Bulletin* 82: 20–25.

———. 2003. Parental care and reproduction in two species of *Mantidactylus* (Anura: Mantellidae). *Journal of Herpetology* 37: 766–768.

———. 2004. Tests for competition, cannibalism, and priority effects in two phytotelm-dwelling tadpoles from Madagascar. *Herpetologica* 60: 1–13.

———. 2005. Competitive interactions and distributional dynamics in two Malagasy frogs. *Journal of Tropical Ecology* 21: 569–576.

———. 2009. The natural history of two plant-breeding frogs from Madagascar, *Guibemantis bicalcaratus* and *G. punctatus* (Anura: Mantellidae). *Salamandra* 45: 39–49.

Lehtinen, R. M., and Carfagno, G.L.F. 2011. Habitat selection, the included niche, and coexistence in plant specialist frogs from Madagascar. *Biotropica* 43: 58–67.

Lehtinen, R. M., and Ramanamanjato, J.-B. 2006. Effects of rainforest fragmentation and correlates of local extinction in a herpetofauna from Madagascar. *Applied Herpetology* 3: 95–110.

Lehtinen, R. M., Ramanamanjato, J.-B., and Raveloarison, J. G. 2003. Edge effects and extinction proneness in a herpetofauna from Madagascar. *Biodiversity and Conservation* 12: 1357–1370.

Lehtinen, R. M., Nussbaum, R. A., Richards, C. M., Cannatella, D. C., and Vences, M. 2007. Mitochondrial genes reveal cryptic diversity in plant-breeding frogs from Madagascar (Anura, Mantellidae, *Guibemantis*). *Molecular Phylogenetics and Evolution* 44: 1121–1129.

Lehtinen, R. M., Glaw, F., and Vences, M. 2011. Two new plant-breeding frog species (*Guibemantis*) from southeastern Madagascar. *Herpetological Journal* 21: 95–112.

Lehtinen, R. M., Glaw, F., Andreone, F., Pabijan, M., and Vences, M. 2012. A new species of putatively pond breeding frog of the genus *Guibemantis* from southeastern Madagascar. *Copeia* 2012: 648–662.

Lehtinen, R. M., Glaw, F., Vences, M., Rakotoarison, A., and Scherz, M. D. 2018. Two new *Pandanus* frogs (*Guibemantis*: Mantellidae: Anura) from northern Madagascar. *European Journal of Taxonomy* 451: 1–20.

Licata, F., Ficetola, G. F., Freeman, K., Mahasoa, R. H., Ravololonarivo, V., Solofo Niaina Fidy, J. F., Koto-Jean, A. B., Rasoanomenjanahary Nahavitatsara, E., Andreone, F., and Crottini A. 2019. Abundance, distribution and spread of the invasive Asian toad *Duttaphrynus melanostictus* in eastern Madagascar. *Biological Invasions* 21: 1615–1626.

Licata, F., Andreone, F., Freeman, K., Rabesihanaka, S., Robsomanitrandrasana, E., Reardon, J., and Crottini A. 2020. The Asian toad (*Duttaphrynus melanostictus*) in Madagascar: A report of an ongoing invasion. In *Problematic Wildlife II: New Conservation and Management Challenges in the Human-Wildlife Interactions*, eds. F. M. Angelici and L. Rossi, pp. 617–638. Berlin: Springer.

Linders, T.E.W., and Langrand, O. 2014. First record of house crow for Madagascar: Potential impacts and suggested management of an invasive bird species. *African Bird Club Bulletin* 21: 216–219.

Lingrel, J. B. 2010. The physiological significance of the cardiotonic steroid/ouabain-binding site of the Na, K-ATPase. *Annual Review of Physiology* 72: 395–412.

Linsenmair, K. E., and Glos, J. 2005. Description of the tadpoles of *Boophis doulioti* and *B. xerophilus* from western Madagascar with notes on larval life history and breeding ecology. *Amphibia-Reptilia* 26: 459–466.

Lötters, S., Rödder, D., Bielby, J., Bosch, J., Garner, T.J.W., et al. 2008. Meeting the challenge of conserving Madagascar's megadiverse amphibians: Addition of a risk-assessment for the chytrid fungus. *PLoS Biology* 6: e118.

Lourenço, W. R., Glaw, F., Cloudsley-Thompson, J. L., and Vences, M. 1997. The Madagascan frog *Plethodontohyla inguinalis* eats scorpions. *British Herpetological Society Bulletin* 60: 26–28.

Lühe, M.F.L. 1910. Parasitische Plattwürmer. II. Cestodes. *Süsswasserfauna* 18: 1–153.

MacPhee, R.D.E., Burney, D. A., and Wells, N. A. 1985. Early Holocene chronology and environment of Ampasambazimba, a Malagasy subfossil lemur site. *International Journal of Primatology* 6: 463–489.

Maddock, S. T., Day, J. J., Nussbaum, R. A., Wilkinson, M., and Gower, D. J. 2014. Evolutionary origins and genetic variation of the Seychelles treefrog, *Tachycnemis seychellensis* (Duméril and Bibron, 1841) (Amphibia: Anura: Hyperoliidae). *Molecular Phylogenetics and Evolution* 75: 194–201.

Maeder, M. N., Raherinjafy, R., Andriamahefa, H., Ramasindrazana, B., and Randrianarivelojosia, M. 2019. Absence of *Trypanosoma* infection among *Hoplobatrachus tigerinus* (Amphibia: Dicroglossidae) from Boeny, western Madagascar. *Malagasy Nature* 13: 173–175.

Mahapatra, S., Dutta, S. K., and Sahoo, G. 2017. Opportunistic predatory behaviour in *Duttaphrynus melanostictus* (Schneider, 1799) tadpoles. *Current Science* 112: 1755–1759.

Marshall, B. M., Casewell, N. R., Vences, M., Glaw, F., Andreone, F., Rakotoarison, A., Zancolli, G., Woog, F., and Wüster, W. 2018. Widespread vulnerability of Malagasy predators to the toxins of an introduced toad. *Current Biology* 28: R654–R655.

McClelland, P., Reardon, J. T., Kraus, F., Raxworthy, C. J., and Randrianantoandro, C. 2015. Asian toad eradication feasibility report for Madagascar. Te Anau.

McGowan, P.J.K., Traylor-Holzer, K., and Leus, K. 2017. IUCN guidelines for determining when and how ex situ management should be used in species conservation. *Conservation Letters* 10: 361–366.

McIntyre, P., and Ramanamanjato, J.-B. 1999. *Ptychadena mascareniensis mascareniensis* diet. *Herpetological Review* 30: 223.

Measey, G. J., Vences, M., Drewes, R. C., Chiari, Y., Melo, M., and Bourles, B. 2007. Freshwater paths across the ocean: Molecular phylogeny of the frog *Ptychadena newtoni* gives insights into amphibian colonization of oceanic islands. *Journal of Biogeography* 34: 7–20.

Mercurio, V., and Andreone, F. 2006. The tadpoles of *Scaphiophryne gottlebei* (Microhylidae: Scaphiophryninae) and *Mantella expectata* (Mantellidae: Mantellinae) from Isalo Massif, southcentral Madagascar. *Alytes* 23: 81–95.

———. 2007. Two new canyon-dwelling frogs from the arid sandstone Isalo Massif, central-southern Madagascar (Mantellidae, Mantellinae). *Zootaxa* 1574: 31–47.

———. 2008. New distribution data of the green mantella, *Mantella viridis*, from northern Madagascar (Anura: Mantellidae). *Herpetology Notes* 1: 3–7.

Mercy, M. 1999. Studies on some aspects of the biology and ecology of the common Indian toad *Bufo melanostictus* Schneider (class Amphibia; order Anura). PhD thesis, Mahatma Gandhi University.

Metcalf, M. M. 1923. The opalinid ciliate infusorians. *Bulletin of the United States National Museum* 120: 1–484.

———. 1940. Further studies on the opalinid ciliate infusorians and their hosts. *Proceedings of the United States National Museum* 87: 465–634.

Methuen, P. A., and Hewitt, J. 1913. On a collection of Batrachia from Madagascar made during the year 1911. *Annals of the Transvaal Museum* 4: 49–64.

Meyers, J. J., O'Reilly J. C., Monroy, J. A., and Nishikawa, K. C. 2004. Mechanism of tongue protraction in microhylid frogs. *Journal of Experimental Biology* 207: 21–31.

Millot, J., and Guibé, J. 1951. Batraciens malgaches a biotope vegetal. *Mémoires de l'Institut Scientifique de Madagascar*, série A, *Biologie Animale* 5: 197–212.

Mittermeier, R. A., Robles, G. P., Hoffman, M., Pilgrim, J., Brooks, T., Mittermeier, C. G., and Lamoreux, J. 2004. *Hotspots Revisited*. Mexico City: CEMEX.

Moen, D. S., Morlon, H., and Wiens, J. J. 2016. Testing convergence versus history: Convergence dominates phenotypic evolution for over 150 million years in frogs. *Systematic Biology* 65: 146–160.

Mohanty, N. P., and Measey, J. 2018. What's for dinner? Diet and potential trophic impact of an invasive anuran *Hoplobatrachus tigerinus* on the Andaman archipelago. *PeerJ* 6: e5698.

———. 2019. Reconstructing biological invasions using public surveys: A new approach to retrospectively assess spatio-temporal changes in invasive spread. *Biological Invasions* 21: 467–480.

Mohanty, N. P., Crottini, A., Garcia, R. A., and Measey, J. 2021. Non-native populations and global invasion potential of the Indian bullfrog *Hoplobatrachus tigerinus*: A synthesis for risk-analysis. *Biological Invasions* 23: 69–81.

Moore, M., Solofo Niaina Fidy, J. F., and Edmonds, D. 2015. The new toad in town: Distribution of the Asian toad, *Duttaphrynus melanostictus*, in the Toamasina area of eastern Madagascar. *Tropical Conservation Science* 8: 440–455.

Mori, A., Ikeuchi, I., and Hasegawa, M. 2015. Calling activity of an anuran assemblage in a temporary pond in a dry forest of Madagascar. *Current Herpetology* 34: 140–148.

Mörs, T., Reguero, M., and Vasilyan, D. 2020. First fossil frog from Antarctica: Implications for Eocene high latitude climate conditions and Gondwanan cosmopolitanism of Australobatrachia. *Scientific Reports* 10: 5051.

Moskowitz, N. A., Roland, A. B., Fischer, E. K., Ranaivorazo, N., Vidoudez, C., et al. 2018. Seasonal changes in diet and chemical defense in the climbing mantella frog (*Mantella laevigata*). *PLoS One* 13: e0207940.

Myers, N., Mittermeier, R. A., Mittermeier, C. G., da Fonseca, G.A.B., and Kent, J. 2000. Biodiversity hotspots for conservation priorities. *Nature* 403: 853–858.

Narins, P. M., Lewis, E. R., and McClelland, B. E. 2000. Hyperextended call note repertoire of the endemic Madagascar treefrog *Boophis madagascariensis* (Rhacophoridae). *Journal of Zoology* 250: 283–298.

Nayak, S., Mahapatra, P. K., Mishra, S., and Dutta, S. K. 2007. Age determination by skeletochronology in the common Indian toad *Bufo melanostictus* Schneider, 1799 (Anura: Bufonidae). *Herpetozoa* 19: 111–119.

Ndriantsoa, S. H., Randrianiaina, R. D., Ravoahangimalala, O. R., Vences, M., and Glos, J. 2012. Description of two tadpoles of Malagasy treefrogs, *Spinomantis* sp. aff. *peraccae* and *Spinomantis tavaratra* (Anura: Mantellidae). *Zootaxa* 3248: 66–68.

Ndriantsoa, S. H., Rakotonanahary, T., Dawson, J., and Edmonds, D. 2014. Predation of the Critically Endangered *Boophis williamsi* by *Boophis goudotii* at Ankaratra Massif, Madagascar. *Herpetology Notes* 7: 343–345.

Ndriantsoa, S. H., Riemann, J. C., Raminosoa, N. R., Rödel, M.-O., and Glos, J. 2017. Amphibian diversity in the matrix of a fragmented landscape around Ranomafana in Madagascar depends on matrix quality. *Tropical Conservation Science* 10: 1–16.

Netherlands, E. C., Cook, C. A., Kruger, D. J., Du Preez, L. H., and Smit, N. J. 2015. Biodiversity of frog haemoparasites from sub-tropical northern KwaZulu-Natal, South Africa. *International Journal for Parasitology* 4: 135–141.

Ngo, B. V., and Ngo, C. D. 2013. Reproductive activity and advertisement calls of the Asian common toad *Duttaphrynus melanostictus* (Amphibia, Anura, Bufonidae) from Bach Ma National Park, Vietnam. *Zoological Studies* 52: 12.

Noble, G. K. 1922. The phylogeny of the Salientia. I. The osteology and the thigh musculature: Their bearing on classification and phylogeny. *Bulletin of the American Museum of Natural History* 46: 1–88.

———. 1931. *Biology of the Amphibia*. New York: McGraw-Hill.

Noble, G. K., and Parker, H. W. 1926. A synopsis of the brevicipitid toads of Madagascar. *American Museum Novitates* 232: 1–21.

Nowack, C., and Vences, M. 2016. Ontogenetic development of the derived olfactory system of the mantellid frog *Mantidactylus betsileanus*. *Anatomical Record* 299: 943–950.

Nowack, C., Peram, P. S., Wenzel, S., Rakotoarison, A., Glaw, F., Poth, D., Schulz, J., and Vences, M. 2017. Volatile compound secretion coincides with modifications of the olfactory organ in mantellid frogs. *Journal of Zoology* 303: 72–81.

Nussbaum, R. A., Raxworthy, C. J., Raselimanana, A. P., and Ramanamanjato, J.-B. 1999. Amphibians and reptiles of the Réserve Naturelle Intégrale d'Andohahela, southern Madagascar. In A floral and faunal inventory of the Réserve Naturelle Intégrale d'Andohahela, Madagascar: With reference to elevational variation, ed. S. M. Goodman. *Fieldiana: Zoology*, new series 94: 155–174.

Odierna, G., Aprea, G., Andreone, F., Böhme, W., and Vences, M. 2007. Cytosystematics of hyperoliid frogs: Phylogeny of *Heterixalus*, low karyotypic variability in hyperoliines and separate phylogenetic position of *Leptopelis*. *Italian Journal of Zoology* 74: 71–81.

Oetter, K., Wanke, S., and Vences, M. 2001. Ergänzende Daten zur Larvalentwicklung von *Mantella laevigata* Methuen and Hewitt, 1913 (Amphibia: Mantellidae). *Salamandra* 37: 99–104.

Oevermann, A., Schildger, B., Feldman, S., and Robert, N. 2005. Chytridiomykosis in amphibians (*Dyscophus antongilii*) in Switzerland. *Tierärztliche Umschau* 60: 211–217.

Orozco-terWengel, P., Andreone, F., Louis, E., Jr., and Vences, M. 2013. Mitochondrial introgressive hybridization following a demographic expansion in the tomato frogs of Madagascar, genus *Dyscophus*. *Molecular Ecology* 22: 6074–6090.

Pabijan, M., Gehring, P.-S., Köhler, J., Glaw, F., and Vences, M. 2011. A new microendemic frog species of the genus *Blommersia* (Anura: Mantellidae) from the east coast of Madagascar. *Zootaxa* 2978: 34–50.

Pabijan, M., Wollenberg, K. C., and Vences, M. 2012. Small body size increases the regional differentiation of populations of tropical mantellid frogs (Anura: Mantellidae). *Journal of Evolutionary Biology* 25: 2310–2324.

Pabijan, M., Brown, J., Chan, L. M., Rakotondravony, H., Raselimanana, A. P., Yoder, A. D., Glaw, F., and Vences, M. 2015. Phylogeography of the arid-adapted Malagasy bullfrog, *Laliostoma labrosum*, influenced by past connectivity and habitat stability. *Molecular Phylogenetics and Evolution* 92: 11–24.

Parker, H. W. 1934. *A Monograph of the Frogs of the Family Microhylidae*. London: British Museum (Natural History).

Passmore, N. I. 1977. Mating calls and other vocalizations of five species of *Ptychadena* (Anura: Ranidae). *South African Journal of Science* 73: 212–214.

Pearson, R. G. 2015. Asian common toads in Madagascar: An urgent effort to inform surveys and eradication efforts. *Global Change Biology* 21: 9.

Peloso, P.L.V., Frost, D. R., Richards, S. J., Rodrigues, M. T., Donnellan, S., et al. 2016. The impact of anchored phylogenomics and taxon sampling on phylogenetic inference in narrow-mouthed frogs (Anura, Microhylidae). *Cladistics* 32: 113–140.

Peloso, P.L.V., Raxworthy, C. J., Wheeler, W. C., and Frost, D. R. 2017. Nomenclatural stability does not justify recognition of paraphyletic taxa: A response to Scherz et al. (2016). *Molecular Phylogenetics and Evolution* 111: 56–64.

Penny, S., Andreone, F., Crottini, A., Holderied, M., Rakotozafy, L., Schwitzer, C., and Rosa, G. 2014. A new species of the *Boophis rappiodes* group (Anura, Mantellidae) from the Sahamalaza Peninsula, northwest Madagascar, with acoustic monitoring of its nocturnal calling activity. *ZooKeys* 435: 111–132.

Perl, R.G.B., Nagy, Z. T., Sonet, G., Glaw, F., Wollenberg, K. C., and Vences, M. 2014. DNA barcoding Madagascar's amphibian fauna. *Amphibia-Reptilia* 35: 197–206.

Phillips, B. L., Brown, G. P., Greenlees, M., Webb, J. K., and Shine, R. 2007. Rapid expansion of the cane toad (*Bufo marinus*) invasion front in tropical Australia. *Austral Ecology* 32: 169–176.

Piludu, N., Dubos, N., Razafimanahaka, J. H., Razafindraibe, P., Randrianantoandro, J. C., and Jenkins, R.K.B. 2015. Distribution, threats and conservation of a Critically Endangered amphibian (*Mantella aurantiaca*) in eastern Madagascar. *Herpetology Notes* 8: 119–123.

Pitt, W. C., Beard, K. H., and Doratt, R. E. 2012. Management of invasive coqui frog populations in Hawaii. *Outlooks on Pest Management* 23: 166–169.

Portik, D. M., Bell, R. C., Blackburn, D. C., Bauer, A. M., Barratt, C. D., et al. 2019. Sexual dichromatism drives diversification within a major radiation of African amphibians. *Systematic Biology* 68: 859–875.

Poth, D., Wollenberg, K. C., Vences, M., and Schulz, S. 2012. Volatile amphibian pheromones: Macrolides of mantellid frogs from Madagascar. *Angewandte Chemie International Edition* 51: 1–5.

Poth, D., Peram, P. S., Vences, M., and Schulz, S. 2013. Macrolides and alcohols as scent gland constituents of the Madagascan frog *Mantidactylus femoralis* and their intraspecific diversity. *Journal of Natural Products* 76: 1548–1558.

Pritchard, D. J., Fa, J. E., Oldfield, S., and Harrop, S. R. 2011. Bring the captive closer to the wild: Redefining the role of ex situ conservation. *Oryx* 46: 18–23.

Probst, J.-M. 1997. *Animaux de la Réunion: Guide d'identification des oiseaux, mammifères, reptiles et amphibiens*. Sainte-Marie: Azalées Editions.

Prod'hon, J. 1969. Description de *Raillietnema petterae* et de *Raillietnema parapetterae* nématodes parasites d'un amphibien malgache *Discophus antongili* Grandidier, 1877. *Bulletin du Muséum National d'Histoire Naturelle*, Paris 40: 1209–1214.

Prod'hon, J., and Bain, O. 1974. *Madochotera landauae* n. sp., nouvelle filaire de grenouille malgache. *Bulletin du Muséum National d'Histoire Naturelle*, Paris 156: 813–817.

Pyron, R. A., and Wiens, J. J. 2011. A large-scale phylogeny of Amphibia including over 2800 species, and a revised classification of extant frogs, salamanders, and caecilians. *Molecular Phylogenetics and Evolution* 61: 543–583.

Rabearivony, J., Raselimanana, A. P., Andriamazava, M. A., Thorstrom, R., and Rene de Roland, L.-A. 2010. A new locality for the endangered microhylid frog *Scaphiophryne boribory* from northern Madagascar and a rapid survey of other amphibians of the Bemanevika region. *Herpetology Notes* 3: 105–109.

Rabemananjara, F.C.E., Chiari, Y., Ravoahangimalala Ramilijaona, O., and Vences, M. 2007a. Evidence for recent gene flow between north-eastern and south-eastern Madagascar from a phylogeography of the *Mantella cowani* group. *Frontiers in Zoology* 4: article 1.

Rabemananjara, F.C.E., Crottini, A., Chiari, Y., Andreone, F., Glaw, F., Duguet, R., Bora, P., Ravoahangimalala Ramilijaona, O., and Vences, M. 2007b. Molecular systematics of Malagasy poison frogs in the *Mantella betsileo* and *M. laevigata* species groups. *Zootaxa* 1501: 31–44.

Rabemananjara, F.C.E., Bora, P., Razafindrabe, T. J., Randriamitso, R., Ravoahangimalala Ramilijaona, O., Rasoamampionona Raminosoa, N., Rakotondravony, D., Vieites, D. R., and Vences, M. 2008a. Rapid assessments of population sizes in ten species of Malagasy poison frogs, genus *Mantella*. In A conservation strategy for the amphibians of Madagascar, ed. F. Andreone. *Monografie del Museo Regionale di Scienze Naturali di Torino* 45: 253–264.

Rabemananjara, F.C.E., Rasoamampionona Raminosoa, N., Ravoahangimalala Ramilijaona, O., Rakotondravony, D., Andreone, F., et al. 2008b. Malagasy poison frogs in the pet trade: A survey of levels of exploitation of species in the genus *Mantella*. In A conservation strategy for the amphibians of Madagascar, ed. F.

Andreone. *Monografie del Museo Regionale di Scienze Naturali di Torino* 45: 277–300.

Rabemananjara, F.C.E., Randrianantoandro, C., Wolf, S., Edmonds, D., Rakotoarisoa, J. C., et al. 2018. The first experience of reintroduction of the Critically Endangered golden mantella frog in Madagascar. *Amphibian Ark Newsletter* 42: 2–3.

Rabibisoa, N. 2008. Mantella cowanii *Action Plan*. Antananarivo: Amphibian Specialist Group Madagascar and Conservation International.

Rabibisoa, N., Ramilijaona Ravoahangimalala, O., and Raxworthy, C. J. 2008. Diversité spécifique et endémisme inattendus dans le nord de Madagascar: Résultats biogéographiques préliminaires de *Mantidactylus* sous-genre *Ochthomantis*. In A conservation strategy for the amphibians of Madagascar, ed. F. Andreone. *Monografie del Museo Regionale di Scienze Naturali di Torino* 45: 233–252.

Rabibisoa, N. H., Anjeriniaina, M., Rakotoniaina, V., Randrianasolo, H., Rabemananjara, F.E.C., and Andreone, F. 2013. The harlequin mantella *Mantella cowanii* in Antoetra region, High Plateau of Madagascar: New steps in conservation. *FrogLog* 107: 50–51.

Rachowicz, L. J., and Briggs, C. 2007. Quantifying the disease transmission function: Effects of density on *Batrachochytrium dendrobatidis* transmission in the mountain yellow-legged frog *Rana muscosa*. *Journal of Animal Ecology* 76: 711–721.

Rage, J.-C., and Rocek, Z. 1989. Redescription of *Triadobatrachus massinoti* (Piveteau, 1936) an anuran amphibian from the early Triassic. *Palaeontographica, Abteilung A*, 206 (1–3): 1–16.

Raharivololoniaina, L., Vieites, D. R., Glaw, F., and Vences, M. 2003. Larval stages, habitat and distribution of the hyperoliid frog *Heterixalus rutenbergi* (Boettger, 1881). *Alytes* 21: 59–65.

Raharivololoniaina, L., Grosjean, S., Raminosoa, N. R., Glaw, F., and Vences, M. 2006. Molecular identification, description, and phylogenetic implications of the tadpoles of 11 species of Malagasy treefrogs, genus *Boophis*. *Journal of Natural History* 40: 1449–1480.

Raharivololoniaina, L., Verneau, O., Berthier, P., Vences, M., and Du Preez, L. H. 2011. First monogenean flatworm from a microhylid frog host: *Kankana*, a new polystome genus from Madagascar. *Parasitology International* 60: 465–473.

Rakotoarisoa, J. C. 2019. Bringing Andasibe frogs to the public: News from Toby Sahona's Education Center, Madagascar. *Amphibian Ark Newsletter* 46: 2–4.

Rakotoarison, A., Glaw, F., Vieites, D. R., Raminosoa, N. R., and Vences, M. 2012. Taxonomy and natural history of arboreal microhylid frogs (*Platypelis*) from the Tsaratanana Massif in northern Madagascar, with description of a new species. *Zootaxa* 3563: 1–25.

Rakotoarison, A., Köhler, J., Glaw, F., and Vences, M. 2013. The advertisement call of the relict frog *Tsingymantis antitra* from Madagascar (Anura, Mantellidae). *Spixiana* 36: 143–148.

Rakotoarison, A., Crottini, A., Müller, J., Rödel, M.-O., Glaw, F., and Vences, M. 2015a. Revision and phylogeny of narrow-mouthed treefrogs (*Cophyla*) from northern Madagascar: Integration of molecular, osteological, and bioacoustic data reveals three new species. *Zootaxa* 3937: 61–89.

Rakotoarison, A., Erens, J., Ratsoavina, F. M., and Vences, M. 2015b. Amphibian and reptile records from around the Betsiboka delta area in north-western Madagascar. *Herpetology Notes* 8: 535–543.

Rakotoarison, A., Scherz, M. D., Glaw, F., Köhler, J., Andreone, F., et al. 2017a. Describing the smaller majority: Integrative taxonomy reveals twenty-six new species of tiny microhylid frogs (genus *Stumpffia*) from Madagascar. *Vertebrate Zoology* 67: 271–398.

Rakotoarison, A., Scherz, M. D., Glaw, F., and Vences, M. 2017b. Rediscovery of frogs belonging to the enigmatic microhylid genus *Madecassophryne* in the Anosy Massif, south-eastern Madagascar. *Salamandra* 53: 507–518.

Rakotoarison, A., Scherz, M. D., Bletz, M. C., Razafindraibe, J. H., Glaw, F., and Vences, M. 2019a. Description of the lucky *Cophyla* (Microhylidae, Cophylinae), a new arboreal frog from Marojejy National Park in north-eastern Madagascar. *Zootaxa* 4651: 271–288.

———. 2019b. Diversity, elevational variation, and phylogeographic origin of stump-toed frogs (Microhylidae: Cophylinae: *Stumpffia*) on the Marojejy Massif, northern Madagascar. *Salamandra* 55: 115–123.

Rakotoarison, A., Scherz, M. D., Köhler, J., Ratsoavina, F. M., Hawlitschek, O., Megson, S., Vences, M., and Glaw, F. 2020. Frogs of the genus *Platypelis* from the Sorata Massif in northern Madagascar: Description of a new species and reports of range extensions. *Zoosystematics and Evolution* 96: 263–274.

Rakotonanahary, T. F., Dawson, J., Andreone, F., Rakotoarisoa, J. C., and Edmonds, D. 2017. Amphibian captive breeding programs for Madagascar: Where we are now and the road ahead. *FrogLog* 25: 118: 37–39.

Rakotondrasoa, E. F., Andriantsimanarilafy, R. R., Andriafidison, D., Razafimanahaka, H. J., Razafindraibe, P., et al. 2017. Species conservation strategy of *Mantella aurantiaca* (the golden mantella frog) 2017–2021. Unpublished report. Madagasikara Voakajy, IUCN/SSC Amphibian Specialist Group, Ambatovy, Asity Madagascar, and Association Mitsinjo.

Rakotondravony, H. A., and Goodman, S. M. 2011. Rapid herpetofaunal surveys within five isolated forests on sedimentary rock in western Madagascar. *Herpetological Conservation and Biology* 6: 297–311.

Ramamonjisoa, N., Rakotonoely, H., and Thomas, H. 2013. Spatial and temporal distribution of call activities of two *Gephyromantis* species (Mantellidae) along forest–farmbush habitat in Ranomafana, Madagascar. *African Journal of Herpetology* 62: 90–99.

Ramanamanjato, J.-B. 2000. Fragmentation effects on reptile and amphibian diversity in the littoral forest of southeastern Madagascar. In Isolated vertebrate communities in the tropics, ed. G. Rheinwald. *Bonner zoologische Monographien* 46: 297–308.

———. 2008. Reptile and amphibian communities along the humidity gradient and fragmentation effects in the littoral forests of southeastern Madagascar. In *Biodiversity, Ecology and Conservation of Littoral Ecosystems in Southeastern Madagascar, Tolagnaro (Fort Dauphin)*, eds. J. U. Ganzhorn, S. M. Goodman, and M. Vincelette, pp. 167–180. Washington, DC: Smithsonian Institution, Monitoring and Assessment of Biodiversity Program.

Rancilhac, L., Bruy, T., Scherz, M. D., Pereira, A. E., Preick, M., et al. 2020. Target-enriched DNA sequencing from historical type material enables a partial revision of the Madagascar giant stream frogs (genus *Mantidactylus*). *Journal of Natural History* 54: 87–118. doi:10.1080/00222933.2020.1748243.

Randriamalala, H., and Liu, Z. 2010. Rosewood of Madagascar: Between democracy and conservation. *Madagascar Conservation and Development* 5: 11–22.

Randriamoria, T. M. 2019. Revue des stratégies nationales sur la biosécurité et perspectives sur la gestion des espèces exotiques envahissantes à Madagascar. *Malagasy Nature* 13: 76–87.

Randriamoria, T. M., Rafilipo, L. A., and Solofo Niaina Fidy, J. F. 2019. Mise à jour de la distribution du crapaud commun d'Asie (*Duttaphrynus melanostictus*) dans le sud de Toamasina, Madagascar. *Malagasy Nature* 13: 162–168.

Randrianantoandro, C., Moore, M., and Edmonds, D. 2015. An overview of actions taken regarding the invasive toad *Duttaphrynus melanostictus* in the Toamasina area since March 2014. In *A Conservation Strategy for the Amphibians of Madagascar 2: Abstract Book*, p. 19. Turin: Museo Regionale di Scienze Naturali.

Randrianavelona, R., Rakotonoely, H., Ratsimbazafy, J., and Jenkins, R.K.B. 2010. Conservation assessment of the Critically Endangered frog *Mantella aurantiaca* in Madagascar. *African Journal of Herpetology* 59: 65–78.

Randrianiaina, R. D., Glaw, F., Thomas, M., Glos, J., Raminosoa, N., and Vences, M. 2007. Descriptions of the tadpoles of two species of *Gephyromantis*, with a discussion of the phylogenetic origin of direct development in mantellid frogs. *Zootaxa* 1401: 53–61.

Randrianiaina, R. D., Raharivololoniaina, L., Preuss, C., Strauß, A., Glaw, F., Teschke, M., Glos, J., Raminosoa, N., and Vences, M. 2009. Descriptions of the tadpoles of seven species of Malagasy treefrogs, genus *Boophis*. *Zootaxa* 2021: 23–41.

Randrianiaina, R. D., Köhler, J., Glos, J., Vences, M., and Glaw, F. 2011a. Where to grow in the Tsingy? Limestone rock pools as breeding habitats of the relict frog *Tsingymantis antitra* from Madagascar and description of its tadpole. *Salamandra* 47: 77–89.

Randrianiaina, R. D., Strauß, A., Glos, J., Glaw, F., and Vences, M. 2011b. Diversity, external morphology and "reverse taxonomy" in the specialized tadpoles of Malagasy river bank frogs of the subgenus *Ochthomantis* (genus *Mantidactylus*). *Contributions to Zoology* 80: 17–65.

Randrianiaina, R. D., Wollenberg, K. C., Hiobiarilanto, T. R., Strauß, A., Glos, J., and Vences, M. 2011c. Nidicolous tadpoles rather than direct development in Malagasy frogs of the genus *Gephyromantis*. *Journal of Natural History* 45: 2871–2900.

Randrianiaina, R. D., Strauß, A., Glos, J., and Vences, M. 2012. Diversity of strongly rheophilous tadpoles of Malagasy tree frogs, genus *Boophis* (Anura, Mantellidae), and identification of new candidate species via larval DNA sequence and morphology. *ZooKeys* 178: 59–124.

Raselimanana, A. P. 1998. La diversité de la faune de reptiles et d'amphibiens. In Inventaire biologique: Forêt d'Andranomany, Anjozorobe, eds. D. Rakotondravony and S. M. Goodman. *Recherches pour le Développement, Série Sciences Biologiques* 13: 43–59.

———. 2018. Field observations of predation events in Malagasy amphibians and reptiles. *Herpetology Notes* 11: 659–662.

Raselimanana, A. P., Raxworthy, C. J., and Nussbaum, R. A. 2000. Herpetofaunal species diversity and elevational distribution within the Parc National de Marojejy. In A floral and faunal inventory of the Parc National de Marojejy, Madagascar: With reference to elevational variation, ed. S. M. Goodman. *Fieldiana: Zoology*, new series 97: 157–174.

Raselimanana, A. P., Glaw, F., and Vences, M. 2007. Lack of secondary sexual characters in a male of *Tsingymantis antitra* confirms its position as most basal mantelline frog lineage. *Zootaxa* 1557: 67–68.

Raselimanana, A. P., Raxworthy, C. J., Andreone, F., Glaw, F., and Vences, M. 2014. An enigmatic new *Scaphiophryne* toadlet from the rainforests of north-eastern Madagascar (Amphibia: Microhylidae). *Vertebrate Zoology* 64: 95–102.

Rasolonjatovo Hiobiarilanto, T., Randrianiaina, R. D., Glos, J., Strauß, A., and Vences, M. 2010. Description of ten tadpoles in the genus *Boophis* from Madagascar. *Zootaxa* 2694: 1–25.

Raxworthy, C. J., and Nussbaum, R. A. 1994. A rainforest survey of amphibians, reptiles and small mammals at Montagne d'Ambre, Madagascar. *Biological Conservation* 69: 65–73.

———. 1995. Systematics, speciation and biogeography of the dwarf chameleons (*Brookesia*; Reptilia, Squamata, Chamaeleontidae) of northern Madagascar. *Journal of Zoology* 235: 525–558.

———. 1996a. Amphibians and reptiles of the Réserve Naturelle Intégrale d'Andringitra, Madagascar, and local endemicity. In A floral and faunal inventory of the eastern slopes of the Réserve Naturelle Intégrale d'Andringitra, Madagascar: With reference to elevational variation, ed. S. M. Goodman. *Fieldiana: Zoology*, new series 85: 158–170.

———. 1996b. Montane amphibian and reptile communities in Madagascar. *Conservation Biology* 10: 750–756.

———. 1996c. Patterns of endemism for terrestrial vertebrates in eastern Madagascar. In *Biogeography of Madagascar*, ed. W. R. Lourenço, pp. 368–384. Paris: Editions de l'ORSTOM.

———. 2000. Extinction and extinction vulnerability of amphibians and reptiles in Madagascar. *Amphibian and Reptile Conservation* 2: 15–23.

Raxworthy, C. J., Ramanamanjato, J.-B., and Raselimanana, A. 1994. Les reptiles et les amphibiens. In Inventaire biologique Forêt de Zombitsy, eds. S. M. Goodman and O. Langrand. *Recherches pour le Développement, Série Sciences Biologiques* No. Spécial: 41–57.

Raxworthy, C. J., Andreone, F., Nussbaum, R. A., Rabibisoa, N., and Randriamahazo, H. 1998. Amphibians and reptiles of the Anjanaharibe-Sud Massif, Madagascar: Elevational distribution and regional endemicity. In A floral and faunal inventory of the eastern slopes of the Réserve Naturelle Intégrale d'Andringitra, Madagascar: With reference to elevational variation, ed. S. M. Goodman. *Fieldiana: Zoology*, new series 90: 79–92.

Raxworthy, C. J., Ingram, C., Rabibisoa, N., and Pearson, R. 2007. Applications of ecological niche modeling for species delimitation: A review and empirical evaluation using day geckos (*Phelsuma*) from Madagascar. *Systematic Biology* 56: 907–923.

Raxworthy, C. J., Pearson, R. G., Rabibisoa, N., Rakotondrazafy, A. M., Ramanamanjato, J.-B., Raselimanana, A. P., Wu, S., Nussbaum, R. A., and Stone, D. 2008. Extinction vulnerability of tropical montane endemism from warming and upslope displacement: A preliminary appraisal for the highest massif in Madagascar. *Global Change Biology* 14: 1703–1720.

Razafindraibe, J. H., Scherz, M. D., Dawson, J. S., Vences, M., and Rakotoarison, A. 2021. First record and probable reproductive mode of a true *Stumpffia* from Ambohitantely Special Reserve in the Central Highlands of Madagascar. *Herpetology Notes* 14: 493–495.

Reardon, J. T., Kraus, F., Moore, M., Rabenantenaina, L., Rabinivo, A., Rakotoarisoa, N. H., and Randrianasolo, H. H. 2018. Testing tools for eradicating the invasive toad *Duttaphrynus melanostictus* in Madagascar. *Conservation Evidence* 15: 12–19.

Reeve, E., Ndriantsoa, S. H., Strauß, A., Randrianiaina, R. D., Hiobiarilanto, T. R., Glaw, F., Glos, J., and Vences, M. 2011. Acoustic underwater signals with a probable function during competitive feeding in a tadpole. *Naturwissenschaften* 98: 135–143.

Reilly, S. B., Wogan, G. O., Stubbs, A. L., Arida, E., Iskandar, D. T., and McGuire, J. A. 2017. Toxic toad invasion of Wallacea: A biodiversity hotspot characterized by extraordinary endemism. *Global Change Biology* 23: 5029–5031.

Richard, J., Chabaud, A. G., and Brygoo, E. R. 1968. Notes sur la morphologie et la biologie des trematodes digenes parasites des grenouilles du jardin de 1'Institut Pasteur a Tananarive. *Archives de l'Institut Pasteur, Madagascar* 37: 31–52.

Richards, C. M., and Moore, W. S. 1996. A phylogeny of the African treefrog family Hyperoliidae based on mitochondrial rDNA. *Molecular Phylogenetics and Evolution* 5: 522–532.

———. 1998. A molecular phylogenetic study of the Old World treefrogs, family Rhacophoridae. *Herpetological Journal* 8: 41–46.

Richards, C. M., Nussbaum, R. A., and Raxworthy, C. A. 2000. Phylogenetic relationships within the Madagascan boophids and mantellids as elucidated by mitochondrial ribosomal genes. *African Journal of Herpetology* 49: 23–32.

Riemann, J. C., Ndriantsoa, S. H., Raminosoa, N. R., Rödel, M.-O., and Glos, J. 2015. The value of forest fragments for maintaining amphibian diversity in Madagascar. *Biological Conservation* 191: 707–715.

Riemann, J. C., Ndriantsoa, S. H., Rödel, M.-O., and Glos, J. 2017. Functional diversity in a fragmented landscape: Habitat alterations affect functional trait composition of frog assemblages in Madagascar. *Global Ecology and Conservation* 10: 173–183.

Robert, V., and Borkent, A. 2014. First record of Corethrellidae (Diptera), frog-biting midges, in Madagascar. *Malagasy Nature* 8: 49–53.

Rocha, R., Borda, E., Andreone, F., and Rosa, G. M. 2012. First reports of leech parasitism in Malagasy anurans. *Comparative Parasitology* 79: 352–356.

Rödel, M.-O. 1996. *Amphibien der westafrikanischen Savanne*. Frankfurt: Chimaira.

Rodríguez, A., Börner, M., Pabijan, M., Gehara, M., Haddad, C.F.B., and Vences, M. 2015. Genetic divergence in tropical anurans: Deeper phylogeographic structure in forest specialists and in topographically complex regions. *Evolutionary Ecology* 29: 765–785.

Rosa, G. M., and Andreone, F. 2012. Fighting for a leaf: Agonistic behaviour in Malagasy frogs of the genus *Guibemantis* (Anura Mantellidae). *Ethology Ecology and Evolution* 24: 198–204.

Rosa, G. M., Marquez, R., and Andreone, F. 2011a. *The Astonishing Calls of the Frogs of Betampona*. Turin: Museo Regionale di Scienze Naturali and Fonoteca Zoológica.

Rosa, G. M., Mercurio, V., Crottini, A., and Andreone, F. 2011b. Explosion into the canyon: Breeding aggregation in *Scaphiophryne gottlebei* Busse and Böhme, 1992. *North-Western Journal of Zoology* 7: 329–333.

Rosa, G. M., Andreone, F., Crottini, A., Hauswaldt, J. S., Noël, J., Rabibisoa, N. H., Randriambahiniarime, M. O., Rebelo, R., and Raxworthy, C. J. 2012. The amphibians of the relict Betampona low-elevation rainforest, eastern Madagascar: An application of the integrative taxonomy approach to biodiversity assessments. *Biodiversity and Conservation* 21: 1531–1559.

Rosa, G. M., Crottini, A., Noël, J., Rabibisoa, N., Raxworthy, C. J., and Andreone, F. 2014a. A new phytotelmic species of *Platypelis* (Microhylidae: Cophylinae) from the Betampona Reserve, eastern Madagascar. *Salamandra* 50: 201–214.

Rosa, G. M., Sabino-Pinto, J., Noël, J., and Andreone, F. 2014b. Predation on the treefrog *Boophis rufioculis* (Anura, Mantellidae) by the freshwater crab *Hydrothelphusa* sp. (Decapoda, Potamonautidae) in Madagascar. *Crustaceana* 87: 890–894.

Ruane, S., Pyron, R. A., and Burbrink, F. T. 2011. Phylogenetic relationships of the Cretaceous frog *Beelzebufo* from Madagascar and the placement of fossil constraints based on temporal and phylogenetic evidence. *Journal of Evolutionary Biology* 24: 274–285.

Sabino-Pinto, J., Rakotoarison, A., Bletz, M., Edmonds, D., Glaw, F., and Vences, M. 2019. A new species of the *Spinomantis bertini* species complex (Anura: Mantellidae) from Pic d'Ivohibe Special Reserve (Madagascar). *Zootaxa* 4656: 133–142.

Safarek, G., Jovanovic, O., Vences, M., Kurrer, H., Carpenter, J. M., and Dolch, R. 2010. Wasp predation on Malagasy frog egg clutches. *Salamandra* 46: 53–54.

Saidapur, S. K., and Girish, S. 2001. Growth and metamorphosis of *Bufo melanostictus* tadpoles: Effects of kinship and density. *Journal of Herpetology* 35(2): 249–254.

Salgado Costa, C., Chuliver Pereyra, M., Alcalde, L., Herrera, R., Trudeau, V. L., and Natale, G. S. 2014. Underwater sound emission as part of an antipredator mechanism in *Ceratophrys cranwelli* tadpoles. *Acta Zoologica* 95: 367–374.

Samonds, K. E., Godfrey, L. R., Ali, J. R., Goodman, S. M., Vences, M., Sutherland, M. R., Irwin, M. T., and Krause, D. W. 2012. Spatial and temporal arrival patterns of Madagascar's vertebrate fauna explained by distance, ocean currents, and ancestor type. *Proceedings of the National Academy of Sciences of the USA* 109: 5352–5357.

———. 2013. Imperfect isolation: Factors and filters shaping Madagascar's extant vertebrate fauna. *PLoS One* 8: e62086.

Santos, J. C., and Cannatella, D. C. 2011. Phenotypic integration emerges from aposematism and scale in poison frogs. *Proceedings of the National Academy of Sciences of the USA* 108: 6175–6180.

Santos-Santos, J. H., Guinovart-Castán, M., and Vieites, D. R. 2020. Descriptive skeletal anatomy of *Blommersia transmarina* (Amphibia: Anura: Mantellidae) from the Comoro islands. *Contributions to Zoology* 89: 14–73.

Saporito, R. A., Garraffo, H. M., Donnelly, M. A., Edwards, A. L., Longino, J. T., and Daly, J. W. 2004. Formicine ants: An arthropod source for the pumiliotoxin alkaloids of dendrobatid frogs. *Proceedings of the National Academy of Sciences of the USA* 101: 8045–8050.

Schaefer, H.-C., Vences, M., and Veith, M. 2002. Molecular phylogeny of Malagasy poison frogs, genus *Mantella* (Anura: Mantellidae): Homoplastic evolution of colour pattern in aposematic amphibians. *Organisms Diversity and Evolution* 2: 97–105.

Scheele, B. C., Pasmans, F., Berger, L., Skerratt, L. F., Martel, A., et al. 2019. The aftermath of an amphibian fungal panzootic reveals unprecedented loss of biodiversity. *Science* 636: 1459–1463.

Scheld, S., Perl, R.G.B., Rauhaus, A., Karbe, D., van der Straeten, K., Hauswaldt, J. S., Randrianiaina, R. D., Gawor, A., Vences, M., and Ziegler, T. 2013. Larval morphology and development of the Malagasy frog *Mantidactylus betsileanus*. *Salamandra* 49: 186–200.

Scherz, M. D. 2020. Diamond frogs forever: A new species of *Rhombophryne* Boettger, 1880 (Microhylidae, Cophylinae) from Montagne d'Ambre National Park, northern Madagascar. *Zoosystematics and Evolution* 96: 313–323. doi:10.3897/zse.96.51372.

Scherz, M. D., Ruthensteiner, B., Vences, M., and Glaw, F. 2014. A new microhylid frog, genus *Rhombophryne*, from northeastern Madagascar, and a re-description of *R. serratopalpebrosa* using micro-computed tomography. *Zootaxa* 3860: 547–560.

Scherz, M. D., Rakotoarison, A., Hawlitschek, O., Vences, M., and Glaw, F. 2015a. Leaping towards a saltatorial lifestyle? An unusually long-legged new species of *Rhombophryne* (Anura, Microhylidae) from the Sorata Massif in northern Madagascar. *Zoosystematics and Evolution* 91: 105–114.

Scherz, M. D., Ruthensteiner, B., Vieites, D. R., Vences, M., and Glaw, F. 2015b. Two new microhylid frogs of the genus *Rhombophryne* with superciliary spines from the Tsaratanana Massif in northern Madagascar. *Herpetologica* 71: 310–321.

Scherz, M. D., Glaw, F., Vences, M., Andreone, F., and Crottini, A. 2016a. Two new species of terrestrial microhylid frogs (Microhylidae: Cophylinae: *Rhombophryne*) from northeastern Madagascar. *Salamandra* 52: 91–106.

Scherz, M. D., Vences, M., Rakotoarison, A., Andreone, F., Köhler, J., Glaw, F., and Crottini, A. 2016b. Reconciling molecular phylogeny, morphological divergence and classification of Madagascan narrow-mouthed frogs (Amphibia: Microhylidae). *Molecular Phylogenetics and Evolution* 100: 372–381.

Scherz, M. D., Vences, M., Borrell, J., Ball, L., Nomenjanahary, D. H., et al. 2017a. A new frog species of the subgenus *Asperomantis* (Anura: Mantellidae: *Gephyromantis*) from the Bealanana District of northern Madagascar. *Zoosystematics and Evolution* 93: 451–466.

Scherz, M. D., Vences, M., Rakotoarison, A., Andreone, F., Köhler, J., Glaw, F., and Crottini, A. 2017b. Lumping or splitting in the Cophylinae (Anura: Microhylidae) and the need for a parsimony of taxonomic changes: A response to Peloso et al. (2017). *Salamandra* 53: 479–483.

Scherz, M. D., Hawlitschek, O., Andreone, F., Rakotoarison, A., Vences, M., and Glaw, F. 2017c. A review of the taxonomy and osteology of the *Rhombophryne serratopalpebrosa* species group (Anura: Microhylidae) from Madagascar, with comments on the value of volume rendering of micro-CT data to taxonomists. *Zootaxa* 4273: 301–340.

Scherz, M. D., Razafindraibe, J. H., Rakotoarison, A., Bletz, M. C., Glaw, F., and Vences, M. 2017d. Yet another small brown frog from high altitude on the Marojejy Massif, northeastern Madagascar. *Zootaxa* 4347: 572–582.

Scherz, M. D., Hawlitschek, O., Razafindraibe, J. H., Megson, S., Ratsoavina, F. M., Rakotoarison, A., Bletz, M. C., Glaw, F., and Vences, M. 2018a. A distinctive new frog species (Anura, Mantellidae) supports the biogeographic linkage of the montane rainforest massifs of northern Madagascar. *Zoosystematics and Evolution* 94: 247–261.

Scherz, M. D., Rakotoarison, A., Ratsoavina, F. M., Hawlitschek, O., Vences, M., and Glaw, F. 2018b. Two new Madagascan frog species of the *Gephyromantis* (*Duboimantis*) *tandroka* complex from northern Madagascar. *Alytes* 36: 130–158.

Scherz, M. D., Glaw, F., Hutter, C. R., Bletz, M. C., Rakotoarison, A., Köhler, J., and Vences, M. 2019a. Species complexes and the importance of Data Deficient classification in Red List assessments: The case of *Hylobatrachus* frogs. *PLoS One* 14: e0219437.

Scherz, M. D., Hutter, C. R., Rakotoarison, A., Riemann, J. C., Rödel, M.-O., et al. 2019b. Morphological and ecological convergence at the lower size limit for vertebrates highlighted by five new miniaturised microhylid frog species from three different Madagascan genera. *PLoS One* 14: e0213314.

Scherz, M. D., Rasolonjatovo, S. M., Köhler, J., Rancilhac, L., Rakotoarison, A., et al. 2020. "Barcode fishing" for archival DNA from historical type material overcomes taxonomic hurdles, enabling the description of a new frog species. *Scientific Reports* 10: 19109.

Scherz, M. D., Schmidt, L., Crottini, A., Miralles, A., Rakotoarison, A., Raselimanana, A. P., Köhler, J., Glaw, F., and Vences, M. 2021. Into the Chamber of Horrors: A proposal for the resolution of nomenclatural chaos in the *Scaphiophryne calcarata* complex (Anura: Microhylidae), with a new species-level phylogenetic hypothesis for Scaphiophryninae. *Zootaxa* 4938: 392–420.

Schmidt, H., Glaw, F., Teschke, M., and Vences, M. 2009a. The tadpole of the Madagascar bullfrog, *Laliostoma labrosum*. *Zootaxa* 2005: 67–68.

Schmidt, H., Strauß, A., Glaw, F., Teschke, M., and Vences, M. 2009b. Description of tadpoles of five frog species in the subgenus *Brygoomantis* from Madagascar (Mantellidae: *Mantidactylus*). *Zootaxa* 1988: 48–60.

Schnell, I. B., Bohmann, K., Schultze, S. E., Richter, S. R., Murray, D. C., et al. 2018. Debugging diversity: A pan-continental exploration of the potential of terrestrial blood-feeding leeches as a vertebrate monitoring tool. *Molecular Ecology Resources* 18: 1282–1298.

Schulze, A., Randrianiaina, R.-D., Perl, B., Glaw, F., and Vences, M. 2016. The unexpectedly dull tadpole of Madagascar's largest frog, *Mantidactylus guttulatus*. *Acta Herpetologica* 11: 119–125.

Segev, O., Andreone, F., Pala, R., Tessa, G., and Vences, M. 2012. Reproductive phenology of the tomato frog, *Dyscophus antongili*, in an urban pond of Madagascar's east coast. *Acta Herpetologica* 7: 331–340.

Shine, R. 1979. Sexual selection and sexual dimorphism in the Amphibia. *Copeia* 1979: 297–306.

Soamiarimampionona, J., Sam, S. S., Dolch, R., Klymus, K., Rabemananjara, F., Robsomanitrandrasana, E., Rakotoarisoa, J. C., and Edmonds, D. 2015. Effects of three diets on development of *Mantidactylus betsileanus* larvae in captivity. *Alytes* 32: 7–15.

Sodhi, N. S., Bickford, D., Diesmos, A. C., Lee, T. M., Koh, L. P., Brook, B. W., Sekercioglu, C. H., and Bradshaw, C.J.A. 2008. Measuring the meltdown: Drivers of global amphibian extinction and decline. *PLoS One* 3: e1636.

Staub, F. 1993. *Fauna of Mauritius and Associated Flora*. Mauritius Precigraph Ltd.

Strauß, A., Reeve, E., Randrianiaina, R. D., Vences, M., and Glos, J. 2010. The world's richest tadpole communities show functional redundancy and low functional diversity: Ecological data on Madagascar's stream-dwelling amphibian larvae. *BMC Ecology* 10: 12.

Strauß, A., Randrianiaina, R. D., Vences, M., and Glos, J. 2013. Species distribution and assembly patterns of frog larvae in rainforest streams of Madagascar. *Hydrobiologia* 702: 27–43.

Strauß, A., Guilhaumon, F., Randrianiaina, R. D., Wollenberg, V.K.C., Vences, M., and Glos, J. 2016. Opposing patterns of seasonal change in functional and phylogenetic diversity of tadpole assemblages. *PLoS One* 11: e0151744.

Streicher, J. W., Loader, S. P., Varela-Jaramillo, A., Montoya, P., and de Sá, R. O. 2020. Analysis of ultraconserved elements supports African origins of narrow-mouthed frogs. *Molecular Phylogenetics and Evolution* 146: 106771.

Stuart, S. N., Chanson, J. S., Cox, N. A., Young, B. E., Rodrigues, A.S.L., Fischman, D. L., and Waller, R. W. 2004. Status and trends of amphibian declines and extinctions worldwide. *Science* 306: 1783–1786.

Suzán, G., Marc, E., Tomasz Giermakowski, J., Armin, B., Pascale, J., et al. 2008. The effect of habitat fragmentation and species diversity loss on hantavirus prevalence in Panama. *Annals of the New York Academy of Sciences* 1149: 80–83.

Svitin, R., and Du Preez, L. 2017. *Amphibiophilus mooiensis* n. sp. (Nematoda: Amphibiophilidae), a parasite of *Amietia delalandii* (Duméril and Bibron) (Amphibia: Pyxicephalidae) from South Africa. *Systematic Parasitology* 95: 81–89.

Tessa, G., Guarino, F. M., Giacoma, C., Mattioli, F., and Andreone, F. 2007. Longevity and body size in three populations of *Dyscophus antongilii* (Microhylidae, Dyscophinae), the tomato frog from north-eastern Madagascar. *Acta Herpetologica* 2: 139–146.

Tessa, G., Mattioli, F., Mercurio, V., and Andreone, F. 2009. Egg numbers and fecundity traits in nine species of *Mantella* poison frogs from arid grasslands and rainforests of Madagascar (Anura: Mantellidae). *Madagascar Conservation and Development* 4: 113–119.

Tessa, G., Crottini, A., Giacoma, C., Guarino, F. M., and Randrianirina, J. E. 2017. Comparative longevity and age at sexual maturity in twelve rainforest frogs of the genera *Boophis*, *Gephyromantis*, and *Mantidactylus* (Anura: Mantellidae) from Madagascar. *Phyllomedusa* 16: 13–21.

Thomas, M., Raharivololoniaina, L., Glaw, F., Vences, M., and Vieites, D. R. 2005. Montane tadpoles in Madagascar: Molecular identification and description of the larval stages of *Mantidactylus elegans*, *Mantidactylus madecassus*, and *Boophis laurenti* from the Andringitra Massif. *Copeia* 2005: 174–183.

Tinsley, R. C. 1996. Parasites of *Xenopus*. In *The Biology of* Xenopus, eds. R. C. Tinsley and H. R. Kobel, pp. 233–261. Oxford: Clarendon Press.

Tohé, B., and Gourène, G. 2016. Food rate of *Ptychadena mascareniensis*, *P. pumilio* and *Hoplobatrachus occipitalis*, three Anura of degraded areas of Banco National Park, Côte d'Ivoire. *International Journal of Fisheries and Aquatic Studies* 4: 1–4.

Trainor, C. R. 2009. *Survey of a Population of Black-Spined Toad* Bufo melanostictus *in Timor-Leste: Confirming Identity, Distribution, Abundance and Impacts of an Invasive and Toxic Toad*. Darwin: Charles Darwin University. doi:10.13140/RG.2.2.31944.93445.

Tschudi, J. J. v., 1838. *Classification der Batrachier mit Berücksichtigung der fossilen Thiere dieser Abtheilung der Reptilien*. Neuchâtel: Petitpierre.

Tu, N., Yang, M., Liang, D., and Zhang, P. 2018. A large-scale phylogeny of Microhylidae inferred from a combined dataset of 121 genes and 427 taxa. *Molecular Phylogenetics and Evolution* 126: 85–91.

Ujvari, B., Casewell, N. R., Sunagar, K., Arbuckle, K., Wüster, W., et al. 2015. Widespread convergence in toxin resistance by predictable molecular evolution. *Proceedings of the National Academy of Sciences of the USA* 112: 11911–11916.

Vallan, D. 2000. Influence of forest fragmentation on amphibian diversity in the nature reserve of Ambohitantely, highland Madagascar. *Biological Conservation* 96: 31–43.

———. 2002. Effects of anthropogenic environmental changes on amphibian diversity in the rain forests of eastern Madagascar. *Journal of Tropical Ecology* 18: 725–742.

Vallan, D., Glaw, F., Andreone, F., and Cadle, J. E. 1998. A new tree frog species of the genus *Boophis* (Anura: Ranidae: Rhacophorinae) with dermal fringes from Madagascar. *Amphibia Reptilia* 19: 357–368.

Vallan, D., Andreone, F., Raherisoa, V. H., and Dolch, R., 2004. Does selective wood exploitation affect amphibian diversity? The case of An'Ala, a tropical rainforest in eastern Madagascar. *Oryx* 38: 410–417.

Van Bocxlaer, I., Roelants, K., Biju, S. D., Nagaraju, J., and Bossuyt, F. 2006. Late Cretaceous vicariance in Gondwanan amphibians. *PLoS One* 1: e74.

Van der Meijden, A., Vences, M., Hoegg, S., Boistel, R., Channing, A., and Meyer, A. 2007. Nuclear gene phylogeny of narrow-mouthed toads (family: Microhylidae) and a discussion of competing hypotheses concerning their biogeographical origins. *Molecular Phylogenetics and Evolution* 44: 1017–1030.

Van Dijk, P. P., Iskandar, D., Lau, M.W.N., Huiqing, G., Baorong, G., et al. 2004. *Duttaphrynus melanostictus*. IUCN Red List of Threatened Species. 2016. www.iucnredlist.org.

Veith, M., Kosuch, J., Rödel, M.-O., Hillers, A., Schmitz, A., Burger, M., and Lötters, S. 2009. Multiple evolution of sexual dichromatism in African reed frogs. *Molecular Phylogenetics and Evolution* 51: 388–393.

Vejarano, S., Thomas, M., Glaw, F., and Vences, M. 2006a. Advertisement call and tadpole morphology of the clutch-guarding frog *Mantidactylus argenteus* from eastern Madagascar. *African Zoology* 41: 164–169.

Vejarano, S., Thomas, M., and Vences, M. 2006b. Comparative larval morphology in Madagascan frogs of the genus *Guibemantis* (Amphibia: Mantellidae). *Zootaxa* 1329: 39–57.

———. 2006c. Comparative tadpole morphology in three species of frogs of the genus *Spinomantis* (Amphibia: Mantellidae). *Contributions to Zoology* 75: 99–108.

Vences, M., and Glaw, F. 1991. Revision der Gattung *Stumpffia* Boettger 1881 aus Madagaskar mit Beschreibung von zwei neuen Arten (Amphibia, Anura, Microhylidae). *Acta Biologica Benrodis* 3: 203–219.

———. 2000. Geographic distribution. *Laliostoma labrosum*. *Herpetological Review* 31: 182.

———. 2001. When molecules claim for taxonomic changes: New proposals on the classification of Old World treefrogs (Amphibia, Anura, Ranoidea). *Spixiana* 24: 85–92.

———. 2002. Two new treefrogs of the *Boophis rappiodes* group from eastern Madagascar. *Tropical Zoology* 15: 141–163.

———. 2003. New microhylid frog (*Plethodontohyla*) with a supraocular crest from Madagascar. *Copeia* 2003: 789–793.

Vences, M., and Raxworthy, C. J. 2008. *Mantella aurantiaca*. IUCN Red List of Threatened Species. 2008. https://www.iucnredlist.org/species/12776/3381123.

Vences, M., and Wake, D. B. 2007. Speciation, species boundaries and phylogeography of amphibians. In *Amphibian Biology*, vol. 6, *Systematics*, eds. H. Heatwole and M. Tyler, pp. 2613–2671. Chipping Norton: Surrey Beatty and Sons.

Vences, M., Glaw, F., and Böhme, W. 1998a. Evolutionary correlates of microphagy in alkaloid-containing frogs (Amphibia: Anura). *Zoologischer Anzeiger* 236: 217–230.

Vences, M., Hille, A., and Glaw, F. 1998b. Allozyme differentiation in the genus *Mantella* (Amphibia: Anura: Mantellinae). *Folia Zoologica* 47: 261–274.

Vences, M., Glaw, F., Mausfeld, P., and Böhme, W. 1998c. Comparative osteology of Malagasy poison frogs of the genus *Mantella* (Amphibia: Ranidae: Mantellinae). *Bonner zoologische Beiträge* 48: 205–215.

Vences, M., Glaw, F., and Böhme, W. 1999a. A review of the genus *Mantella* (Anura, Ranidae, Mantellinae): Taxonomy, distribution and conservation of Malagasy poison frogs. *Alytes* 17(1–2): 3–72.

Vences, M., Glaw, F., and Zapp, C. 1999b. Stomach content analyses in Malagasy frogs of the genera *Tomopterna*, *Aglyptodactylus*, *Boophis* and *Mantidactylus* (Anura: Ranidae). *Herpetozoa* 11: 109–116.

———. 1999c. Bemerkungen zu Eizahlen und Eigrößen bei madagassischen Fröschen der Gattungen *Tomopterna*, *Aglyptodactylus*, *Boophis*, und *Mantidactylus* (Amphibia: Ranidae). *Salamandra* 35: 77–82.

Vences, M., Glaw, F., Jesu, R., and Schimmenti, G. 2000a. A new species of *Heterixalus* (Amphibia: Hyperoliidae) from western Madagascar. *African Zoology* 35: 269–276.

Vences, M., Glaw, F., Kosuch, J., Das, I., and Veith, M. 2000b. Polyphyly of *Tomopterna* (Amphibia: Ranidae) based on sequences of the mitochondrial 16S and 12S rRNA genes, and ecological biogeography of Malagasy relict amphibian groups. In *Diversité et endémisme à Madagascar*, eds. W. R. Lourenço and S. M. Goodman, pp. 229–242. Paris: Mémoires de la Société de Biogéographie.

Vences, M., Andreone, F., Glaw, F., Kosuch, J., Meyer, A., Schaefer, H. C., and Veith, M. 2002a. Exploring the potential of life-history key innovation: Brook breeding in the radiation of the Malagasy treefrog genus *Boophis*. *Molecular Ecology* 11: 1453–1463.

Vences, M., Andreone, F., Glaw, F., Raminosoa, N., Randrianirina, J. E., and Vieites, D. R. 2002b. Amphibians and reptiles of the Ankaratra Massif: Reproductive diversity, biogeography and conservation of a montane fauna in Madagascar. *Italian Journal of Zoology* 69: 263–284.

Vences, M., Aprea, G., Capriglione, T., Andreone, F., and Odierna, G. 2002c. Ancient tetraploidy and slow molecular evolution in *Scaphiophryne*: Ecological correlates of speciation mode in Malagasy relict amphibians. *Chromosome Research* 10: 127–136.

Vences, M., Glaw, F., and Fisher, B. L. 2002d. Notes on the distribution of *Dyscophus insularis* (Anura: Microhylidae). *Herpetological Review* 33: 18–19.

Vences, M., Kosuch, J., Glaw, F., Böhme, W., and Veith, M. 2003a. Molecular phylogeny of hyperoliid treefrogs: Biogeographic origin of Malagasy and Seychellean taxa and re-analysis of familial paraphyly. *Journal of Zoological Systematics and Evolutionary Research* 41: 205–215.

Vences, M., Raxworthy, C. J., Nussbaum, R. A., and Glaw, F. 2003b. A revision of the *Scaphiophryne marmorata* complex of marbled toads from Madagascar, including the description of a new species. *Herpetological Journal* 13: 69–79.

———. 2003c. New microhylid frog (*Plethodontohyla*) from Madagascar, with semiarboreal habits and possible parental care. *Journal of Herpetology* 37: 629–636.

Vences, M., Vieites, D. R., Glaw, F., Brinkmann, H., Kosuch, J., Veith, M., and Meyer, A. 2003d. Multiple overseas dispersal in amphibians. *Proceedings of the Royal Society of London B: Biological Sciences* 270: 2435–2442.

Vences, M., Chiari, Y., Raharivololoniaina, L., and Meyer, A. 2004a. High mitochondrial diversity within and among populations of Malagasy poison frogs. *Molecular Phylogenetics and Evolution* 30: 295–307.

Vences, M., Kosuch, J., Rödel, M.-O., Lötters, S., Channing, A., Glaw, F., and Böhme, W. 2004b. Phylogeography of *Ptychadena mascareniensis* suggests transoceanic dispersal in a widespread African-Malagasy frog lineage. *Journal of Biogeography* 31: 593–601.

Vences, M., Andreone, F., and Glaw, F. 2005. A new microhylid frog of the genus *Cophyla* from a transitional forest in northwestern Madagascar. *African Zoology* 40: 143–149.

Vences, M., Glaw, F., and Marquez, R., eds. 2006. *The Calls of the Frogs of Madagascar*. 3 audio CDs and booklet. Barcelona: Alosa.

Vences, M., Wahl-Boos, G., Hoegg, S., Glaw, F., Oliveira, E. S., Meyer, A., and Perry, S. 2007. Molecular systematics of mantelline frogs from Madagascar and the evolution of their femoral glands. *Biological Journal of the Linnean Society* 92: 529–539.

Vences, M., Chiari, Y., Teschke, M., Randrianiaina, R. D., Raharivololoniaina, L., Bora, P., Vieites, D. R., and Glaw, F. 2008. Which frogs are out there? A preliminary evaluation of survey techniques and identification reliability of Malagasy amphibians. In A conservation strategy for the amphibians of Madagascar, ed. F. Andreone. *Monografie del Museo Regionale di Scienze Naturali di Torino* 45: 233–252.

Vences, M., Wollenberg, K. C., Vieites, D. R., and Lees, D. C. 2009. Madagascar as a model region of species diversification. *Trends in Ecology and Evolution* 24: 456–465.

Vences, M., Glaw, F., Köhler, J., and Wollenberg, K. C. 2010a. Molecular phylogeny, morphology and bioacoustics reveal five additional species of arboreal microhylid frogs of the genus *Anodonthyla* from Madagascar. *Contributions to Zoology* 79: 1–32.

Vences, M., Köhler, J., Pabijan, M., and Glaw, F. 2010b. Two syntopic and microendemic new frogs of the genus *Blommersia* from the east coast of Madagascar. *African Journal of Herpetology* 59: 133–156.

Vences, M., Hauswaldt, S., and Glaw, F. 2011. The advertisement call of *Guibemantis pulcher*, a phytotelmic frog from Madagascar. *Herpetology Notes* 4: 377–379.

Vences, M., Gehara, M., Köhler, J., and Glaw, F. 2012. Description of a new Malagasy treefrog (*Boophis*) occurring syntopically with its sister species, and a plea for studies on non-allopatric speciation in tropical amphibians. *Amphibia-Reptilia* 33: 503–520.

Vences, M., Lyra, M. L., Kueneman, J. G., Bletz, M., Archer, H. M., et al. 2016. Gut bacterial communities across tadpole ecomorphs in two diverse tropical anuran faunas. *Naturwissenschaften* 103: 25.

Vences, M., Brown, J. L., Lathrop, A., Rosa, G. M., Cameron, A., et al. 2017a. Tracing a toad invasion: Lack of mitochondrial DNA variation, haplotype origins, and potential distribution of introduced *Duttaphrynus melanostictus* in Madagascar. *Amphibia-Reptilia* 38: 197–207.

Vences, M., Köhler, J., and Glaw, F. 2017b. A new species of smooth-skinned *Spinomantis* frog (Anura: Mantellidae) from south-eastern Madagascar. *Zootaxa* 4317: 379–390.

Vences, M., Köhler, J., Pabijan, M., Bletz, M., Gehring, P.-S., et al. 2017c. Taxonomy and geographic distribution of Malagasy frogs of the *Gephyromantis asper* clade, with description of a new subgenus and revalidation of *Gephyromantis ceratophrys*. *Salamandra* 53: 77–98.

Vences, M., Hildenbrand, A., Warmuth, K. M., Andreone, F., and Glaw, F. 2018. A new riparian *Mantidactylus* (*Brygoomantis*) frog from the Tsaratanana and Manongarivo Massifs in northern Madagascar. *Zootaxa* 4486: 575–588.

Verneau, O., Du Preez, L. H., Laurent, V., Raharivololoniaina, L., Glaw, F., and Vences, M. 2009. The double odyssey of Madagascan polystome flatworms leads to new insights on the origins of their amphibian hosts. *Proceedings of the Royal Society of London B: Biological Sciences* 276: 1575–1583.

Vieilledent, G., Grinand, C., Rakotomalala, F. A., Ranaivosoa, R., Rakotoarijaona, J.-R., Allnutt, T. F., and Achard, F. 2018. Combining global tree cover loss data with historical national forest cover maps to look at six decades of deforestation and forest fragmentation in Madagascar. *Biological Conservation* 222: 189–197.

Vieites, D. R., Chiari, Y., Vences, M., Andreone, F., Rabemananjara, F.C.E., Bora, P., Nieto-Román, S., and Meyer, A. 2006. Mitochondrial evidence for distinct phylogeographic units in the endangered Malagasy poison frog *Mantella bernhardi*. *Molecular Ecology* 15: 1617–1625.

Vieites, D. R., Wollenberg, K. C., Andreone, F., Köhler, J., Glaw, F., and Vences, M. 2009. Vast underestimation of Madagascar's biodiversity evidenced by an integrative amphibian inventory. *Proceedings of the National Academy of Sciences of the USA* 106: 8267–8272.

Vieites, D. R., Wollenberg, K. C., and Vences, M. 2012. Not all little brown frogs are the same: A new species of secretive and cryptic *Gephyromantis* (Anura: Mantellidae) from Madagascar. *Zootaxa* 3344: 34–46.

Vieites, D. R., Nieto-Roman, S., Fernández, M. P., and Santos-Santos, J. H. 2020. Hidden in plain sight: A new frog species of the genus *Blommersia* from the oceanic island of Mayotte, Comoro archipelago. *ZooKeys* 994: 149–166.

Vitt, L. J., and Caldwell, J. P. 2013. *Herpetology: An Introductory Biology of Amphibians and Reptiles*. Cambridge: Academic Press.

Vredenburg, V., Du Preez, L., Raharivololoniaina, L., Vieites, D. R., Vences, M., and Weldon, C. 2012. A molecular survey across Madagascar does not yield positive records of the amphibian chytrid fungus *Batrachochytrium dendrobatidis*. *Herpetology Notes* 5: 507–517.

Wassersug, R. 1984. The *Pseudohemisus* tadpole: A morphological link between microhylid (Orton type 2) and ranoid (Orton type 4) larvae. *Herpetologica* 40: 138–149.

Weldon, C., and Du Preez, L. 2008. Managing emerging amphibian diseases. Gestion des maladies émergentes des amphibiens. In *Sahonagasy Action Plan*, eds. F. Andreone and H. Randriamahazo, pp. 34–42. Turin: Museo Regionale di Scienze Naturali.

Weldon, C., Du Preez, L., and Vences, M. 2008. Lack of detection of the amphibian chytrid fungus (*Batrachochytrium dendrobatidis*) in Madagascar. In A conservation strategy for the amphibians of Madagascar, ed. F. Andreone. *Monographie del Museo Regionale di Scienze Naturali di Torino* 45: 95–106.

Weldon, C., Crottini, A., Bollen, A., Rabemananjara, F.C.E., Copsey, J., García, G., and Andreone, F. 2013. Pre-emptive national monitoring plan for detecting the amphibian chytrid fungus in Madagascar. *Ecohealth* 10: 234–240.

Wogan, G.O.U., Stuart, B. L., Iskandar, D. T., and McGuire, J. A. 2016. Deep genetic structure and ecological divergence in a widespread human commensal toad. *Biology Letters* 12: 20150807.

Wohltmann, A., Du Preez, L., Rödel, M.-O., Köhler, J., and Vences, M. 2007. Endoparasitic mites of the genus *Endotrombicula* Ewing, 1931 (Acari: Prostigmata: Parasitengona: Trombiculidae) from African and Madagascan anurans, with description of a new species. *Folia Parasitologica* 54: 225–235.

Wolf, S. 2013. A case of male egg guarding behaviour in a stream-dwelling frog, *Mantidactylus* (*Ochthomantis*) sp. (Anura: Mantellidae), from northeastern Madagascar. *Salamandra* 49: 45–47.

———. 2018. Bringing conservation workers together: Mitsinjo expands its public terrarium exhibition. *Amphibian Ark Newsletter* 44: 23.

Wollenberg, K. C., and Harvey, J. 2010. First assessment of the male territorial vocal behaviour of a Malagasy leaf litter frog (*Gephyromantis thelenae*). *Herpetology Notes* 3: 141–150.

Wollenberg, K. C., Glaw, F., Meyer, A., and Vences, M. 2007. Molecular phylogeny of Malagasy reed frogs, *Heterixalus*, and the relative performance of bioacoustics and color-patterns for resolving their systematics. *Molecular Phylogenetics and Evolution* 45: 14–22.

Wollenberg, K. C., Andreone, F., Glaw, F., and Vences, M. 2008a. Pretty in pink: A new treefrog species of the genus *Boophis* from north-eastern Madagascar. *Zootaxa* 1684: 58–68.

Wollenberg, K. C., Vieites, D. R., van der Meijden, A., Glaw, F., Cannatella, D. C., and Vences, M. 2008b. Patterns of endemism and species richness in Malagasy cophyline frogs support a key role of mountainous areas for speciation. *Evolution* 62: 1890–1907.

Wollenberg, K. C., Vieites, D. R., Glaw, F., and Vences, M. 2011. Speciation in little: The role of range and body size in the diversification of Malagasy mantellid frogs. *BMC Evolutionary Biology* 11: e217.

Wollenberg, K. C., Glaw, F., and Vences, M. 2012. Revision of the little brown frogs in the *Gephyromantis decaryi* complex with description of a new species. *Zootaxa* 3421: 32–60.

Wollenberg Valero, K. C. 2015. Evidence for an intrinsic factor promoting landscape genetic divergence in Madagascan leaf-litter frogs. *Frontiers in Genetics* 6: 1–7.

Wollenberg Valero, K. C., Garcia-Porta, J., Rodríguez, A., Arias, M., Shah, A., et al. 2017. Transcriptomic and macroevolutionary evidence for phenotypic uncoupling between frog life history phases. *Nature Communications* 8: 15213.

Woodhead, C., Vences, M., Vieites, D. R., Gamboni, I., Fisher, B. L., and Griffiths, R. A. 2007. Specialist or generalist? Feeding ecology of the Malagasy poison frog *Mantella aurantiaca*. *Herpetological Journal* 17: 225–236.

Yeager, J., and Zarling, A. 2020. Mediating ethical considerations in the conservation and sustainable biocommerce of the jewels of the rainforest. *Journal for Nature Conservation* 54: 125803.

Yuan, Z.-Y., Zhang, B.-L., Raxworthy, C. J., Weisrock, D. W., Hime, P. M., et al. 2019. Natatanuran frogs used the Indian Plate to step-stone disperse and radiate across the Indian Ocean. *National Science Review* 6: 10–14.

Zeisset, I., and Beebee, T. 2008. Amphibian phylogeography: A model for understanding historical aspects of species distributions. *Heredity* 101: 109–119.

Zimkus, B. M., Lawson, L. P., Barej, M. F., Barratt, C. D., Channing, A., et al. 2017. Leapfrogging into new territory: How Mascarene ridged frogs diversified across Africa and Madagascar to maintain their ecological niche. *Molecular Phylogenetics and Evolution* 106: 254–269.

CHAPTER 12

REPTILES

DIVERSITY AND EXPLORATION OF THE MALAGASY REPTILE FAUNA

F. Glaw, M. Vences, and C. J. Raxworthy

Madagascar has an incredible diversity of reptiles, and most of the species are found nowhere else. To date (as of 15 June 2021), not counting marine turtles, marine snakes, and introduced species, 436 named species have been recorded from the island (Table 12.1), and many additional candidate species have already been identified but are still awaiting formal taxonomic revision (Nagy et al. 2012). According to the early assessments of Myers et al. (2000), only two other global biodiversity hotspots (the Caribbean and Mesoamerica) were found to have a greater species diversity of endemic reptiles than Madagascar. The present introductory contribution aims to provide a brief overview of the island's reptile fauna and its most striking ecological and behavioral patterns. In the subsequent contributions, the various major groups of Malagasy reptiles are reviewed in more detail, especially the priorities and challenges for their conservation.

Although this entire chapter deals with reptiles, it is difficult to provide an exact definition of what a "reptile" is. Traditionally reptiles have been considered a class of vertebrates (Reptilia) and, together with the other three classes of primarily four-limbed vertebrates (amphibians, birds, and mammals), placed in the clade of terrestrial vertebrates (tetrapods), a group comprising more than 30,000 species. In this classification scheme, reptiles were defined as vertebrates with scaly skin and without hair or feathers. However, phylogenetic research has revealed that this convenient and intuitive classification does not reflect the phylogenetic relationships of tetrapods. For instance, crocodiles and turtles are more closely related to birds than they are to lizards and snakes, and birds belong to the group of dinosaurs.

Modern taxonomic classification aims to reflect the evolutionary history of different natural lineages by recognizing only those groups that are derived from a shared common ancestor, technically referred to as monophyletic. To render "Reptilia" a monophyletic group, taxonomists today sometimes include birds in Reptilia, or use the term "nonflying reptiles" or "nonavian reptiles" to separate reptiles from birds, or place "Reptilia" in quotation marks to indicate the group's lack of monophyly. Phylogenetically, crocodiles and birds (along with the extinct dinosaurs) are included in the clade Archosauria, and snakes, lizards, and tuataras in the clade Lepidosauria. Turtles are closely related to the Archosauria, as revealed by molecular genetic evidence (e.g., Irisarri et al. 2017). The classification of Uetz et al. (2021) distinguishes the following (monophyletic) extant reptile orders: Testudines (turtles and tortoises, c. 360 species), Rhynchocephalia (tuataras, one species), Squamata (lizards, snakes, and worm lizards, >11,000 species), and Crocodylia (crocodiles, gavials, and alligators, 26 species).

The genetic diversity of Malagasy reptiles and their phylogenetic relationships have been intensively studied in recent years and detailed in numerous publications, including a DNA barcoding study (Nagy et al. 2012) and large phylogenomic studies of snakes (Ruane et al. 2018; Burbrink et al. 2019) that revealed a substantial number of still unrecognized genetic lineages. However, DNA barcoding alone is not sufficient for reliable species delimitation, and in several reptile groups there are genetically divergent populations and lineages that should best be considered as belonging to the same species according to the current state of knowledge (e.g., Ratsoavina et al. 2010; Gehring et al. 2013; Prötzel et al. 2017).

TABLE 12.1. **The modern fauna of nonavian reptiles (crocodiles, chelonians, and squamates) of Madagascar as of 15 June 2021**

FAMILY (SUBFAMILY) GENUS AND SPECIES	DISTRIBUTION	IUCN STATUS
CROCODYLIDAE		
Crocodylus niloticus	Much of island and Africa	LC
Testudinidae		
**Astrochelys radiata*	South	CR
**A. yniphora*	Northwest	CR
Kinixys zombensis	Northwest (Nosy Faly region), probably introduced	LC
**Pyxis arachnoides*	South and southwest	CR
**P. planicauda*	West	CR
PELOMEDUSIDAE		
Pelomedusa subrufa	West and south, probably introduced	LC
Pelusios castanoides	North and west, probably introduced	LC
P. subniger	East, probably introduced	LC
PODOCNEMIDIDAE		
**Erymnochelys madagascariensis*	West	CR
CHAMAELEONIDAE (BROOKESIINAE)		
**Brookesia antakarana*	North (Montagne d'Ambre)	NT
**B. bekolosy*	Northwest (Manongarivo)	EN
**B. betschi*	North	NT
**B. bonsi*	Northwest (Namoroka)	CR
**B. brunoi*	Central Highlands (Anja Private Reserve)	NT
**B. brygooi*	West	LC
**B. confidens*	North (Ankarana)	NT
**B. decaryi*	Northwest (Ankarafantsika)	EN
**B. dentata*	Northwest	EN
**B. desperata*	North (Montagne d'Ambre)	CR
**B. ebenaui*	North and northwest (Sambirano Region)	VU
**B. exarmata*	West (Bemaraha)	EN
**B. griveaudi*	Northeast	NT
**B. karchei*	Northeast	EN
**B. lambertoni*	East (needs rediscovery)	DD
**B. lineata*	Northwest (Manongarivo)	EN
**B. micra*	North (Nosy Hara)	NT
**B. minima*	Northwest (Sambirano Region)	EN
**B. nana*	North (Sorata)	NE
**B. perarmata*	West (Bemaraha)	EN

FAMILY (SUBFAMILY) GENUS AND SPECIES	DISTRIBUTION	IUCN STATUS
**B. peyrierasi*	Northeast	EN
**B. ramanantsoai*	East	EN
**B. stumpffi*	North and northwest	LC
**B. superciliaris*	East	LC
**B. tedi*	Northeast (Marojejy)	NE
**B. therezieni*	East	LC
**B. thieli*	East	LC
**B. tristis*	North (Montagne des Français)	EN
**B. tuberculata*	North (Montagne d'Ambre)	VU
**B. vadoni*	Northeast	VU
**B. valerieae*	Northwest (Manongarivo)	EN
**Palleon lolontany*	North (Tsaratanàna and COMATSA Nord)	NT
**P. nasus*	Southeast	VU
CHAMAELEONIDAE (CHAMAELEONINAE)		
**Calumma amber*	North (Montagne d'Ambre)	NT
**C. ambreense*	North (e.g., Montagne d'Ambre)	NT
**C. andringitraense*	Central east and southeast	EN
**C. boettgeri*	Northwest (Sambirano Region)	LC
**C. brevicorne*	East	LC
**C. capuroni*	Southeast (Andohahela)	VU
**C. crypticum*	East	LC
**C. cucullatum*	Northeast and east	VU
**C. emelinae*	Northern central east	NE
**C. fallax*	Central Highlands and southeast	DD
**C. furcifer*	East	EN
**C. gallus*	East	EN
**C. gastrotaenia*	Central Highlands, east, and southeast	LC
**C. gehringi*	North (Tsaratanàna region)	NE
**C. glawi*	Central southeast	EN
**C. globifer*	Central Highlands	EN
**C. guibei*	North (Tsaratanàna region)	NT
**C. guillaumeti*	North and northeast	LC
**C. hafahafa*	Northwest (Bemanevika)	CR
**C. hilleniusi*	Central Highlands	EN
**C. jejy*	Northeast (Marojejy)	VU
**C. juliae*	East (Moramanga region)	NE

(continued overleaf)

TABLE 12.1. ***continued***

FAMILY (SUBFAMILY) GENUS AND SPECIES	DISTRIBUTION	IUCN STATUS
**C. lefona*	North (Tsaratanàna region)	NE
**C. linotum*	North (Montagne d'Ambre and Tsaratanàna)	LC
**C. malthe*	East	LC
**C. marojezense*	Northeast	NT
**C. nasutum*	East	LC
**C. oshaughnessyi*	Southeast	VU
**C. parsonii*	East	NT
**C. peltierorum*	North	NT
**C. peyrierasi*	Northeast (Marojejy)	VU
**C. radamanus*	North and east	NE
**C. ratnasariae*	North	NE
**C. roaloko*	East (Andasibe region)	NE
**C. tarzan*	East	CR
**C. tjiasmantoi*	Southern central east and southeast	NE
**C. tsaratananense*	Central north (Tsaratanàna)	VU
**C. tsycorne*	Southeast (Andohahela, Ivohibe)	VU
**C. uetzi*	North and northeast (Sorata, Marojejy)	NE
**C. vatosoa*	Northeast	DD
**C. vencesi*	Northeast	EN
**C. vohibola*	East	EN
**Furcifer angeli*	Northwest	LC
**F. antimena*	Southwest	VU
**F. balteatus*	Central southeast	EN
**F. belalandaensis*	Southwest	CR
**F. bifidus*	East	LC
**F. campani*	Central Highlands	VU
**F. labordi*	West	VU
**F. lateralis*	Central Highlands and east	LC
**F. major*	South	LC
**F. minor*	Central Highlands and central southeast	EN
**F. monoceras*	Northwest (needs rediscovery)	NE
**F. nicosiai*	West	EN
**F. oustaleti*	All of island except central southeast	LC
**F. pardalis*	Northwest, north, and east	LC
**F. petteri*	North and northwest	VU
**F. rhinoceratus*	Northwest	VU

FAMILY (SUBFAMILY) GENUS AND SPECIES	DISTRIBUTION	IUCN STATUS
**F. timoni*	North and northeast (Montagne d'Ambre, Marojejy)	NT
**F. tuzetae*	Southwest	DD
**F. verrucosus*	South and southwest	LC
**F. viridis*	West	LC
**F. voeltzkowi*	Northwest	NE
**F. willsii*	East and north	LC
OPLURIDAE		
**Chalarodon madagascariensis*	South and west	LC
**C. steinkampi*	Southeast	NE
Oplurus cuvieri	West Madagascar and Grande Comore Island	LC
**O. cyclurus*	South and west	LC
**O. fierinensis*	Southwest	LC
**O. grandidieri*	Southern Central Highlands	LC
**O. quadrimaculatus*	South and southern Central Highlands	LC
**O. saxicola*	South	LC
GEKKONIDAE		
**Blaesodactylus ambonihazo*	Northwest (Ankarafantsika)	DD
**B. antongilensis*	East and northeast	LC
**B. boivini*	North	VU
**B. microtuberculatus*	North (Ankarana)	NE
**B. sakalava*	West	LC
**B. victori*	Northwest (Namoroka)	NE
Ebenavia boettgeri	East Madagascar, also Mauritius (probably introduced)	NE
**E. inunguis*	Northwest	LC
**E. maintimainty*	Southwest (Tsimanampesotse)	EN
**E. robusta*	Central east	NE
E. safari	Northeast and north, also on Mayotte (Comoros) and Pemba (Tanzania)	NE
Geckolepis humbloti	West and northwest (Bemaraha and Sahamalaza), also Comoro archipelago	NE
**G. maculata*	Northern half of island and southeast (needs taxonomic revision)	LC
**G. megalepis*	North (Ankarana)	NE
**G. polylepis*	West	DD
**G. typica*	South and west	LC
Gehyra mutilata	Northeast, east, and southeast, probably introduced	NE
Hemidactylus frenatus	North, west, and south, probably introduced	LC
H. mercatorius	Much of island	LC

(continued overleaf)

TABLE 12.1. ***continued***

FAMILY (SUBFAMILY) GENUS AND SPECIES	DISTRIBUTION	IUCN STATUS
H. platycephalus	North, probably introduced	NE
**Lygodactylus arnoulti*	Central Highlands	LC
**L. bivittis*	East	VU
**L. blancae*	Central Highlands (Ampefy)	NT
**L. blanci*	Central Highlands (Ibity)	VU
**L. decaryi*	Southeast	DD
**L. expectatus*	North (Ankarana)	NT
**L. guibei*	East	NT
**L. heterurus*	North and northwest (Sambirano Region)	LC
**L. intermedius*	Southern Central Highlands	EN
**L. klemmeri*	West (Bemaraha)	NT
**L. madagascariensis*	North and northwest (Sambirano Region)	VU
**L. miops*	East	LC
**L. mirabilis*	Central Highlands (Ankaratra)	CR
**L. montanus*	Southeast	LC
**L. ornatus*	Central Northern Highlands (Mandritsara)	EN
**L. pauliani*	Central Highlands (Itremo)	DD
**L. pictus*	Central Highlands and southeast	LC
**L. rarus*	North (Ankarana)	NT
**L. roavolana*	Southeast	EN
**L. tolampyae*	West and south	LC
**L. tuberosus*	South	LC
**L. verticillatus*	Southwest	LC
**Matoatoa brevipes*	Southwest	VU
**M. spannringi*	Southeast	DD
**Paragehyra austini*	Southeast	NE
**P. felicitae*	Central Highlands (Anja Private Reserve)	NE
**P. gabriellae*	Southeast	EN
**P. petiti*	Southwest	VU
**Paroedura androyensis*	South	VU
**P. bastardi*	South	LC
**P. fasciata*	North (Nosy Hara)	NE
**P. gracilis*	East and north	LC
**P. guibeae*	West and south	NE
**P. homalorhina*	North (Ankarana)	LC

FAMILY (SUBFAMILY) GENUS AND SPECIES	DISTRIBUTION	IUCN STATUS
**P. hordiesi*	North (Montagne des Français)	NE
**P. ibityensis*	Central Highlands	NT
**P. karstophila*	Northwest and possibly north	LC
**P. kloki*	Northwest	NE
**P. lohatsara*	North (Montagne des Français)	CR
**P. maingoka*	Southwest (Tsimanampesotse)	NT
**P. masobe*	East	EN
**P. neglecta*	West (Bemaraha)	NE
**P. oviceps*	North	NT
**P. picta*	South and west	LC
**P. rennerae*	West	NE
**P. spelaea*	West (Bemaraha)	NE
**P. stumpffi*	North and northwest	LC
**P. tanjaka*	West	EN
**P. vahiny*	West	LC
**P. vazimba*	Northwest	VU
Phelsuma abbotti	North and west, also several Seychelles islands	LC
**P. antanosy*	Southeast	CR
**P. barbouri*	Central Highlands	LC
**P. berghofi*	Southeast	NT
**P. borai*	West and northwest	DD
**P. breviceps*	South	VU
**P. dorsivittata*	North	NT
P. dubia	North and northwest, also Comoro islands	LC
**P. flavigularis*	East	EN
**P. gouldi*	Central Highlands (Anja Private Reserve)	DD
**P. grandis*	North	LC
**P. guttata*	East	LC
**P. hielscheri*	Southwest	VU
**P. hoeschi*	East	DD
**P. kely*	East	DD
**P. klemmeri*	Northwest and west	EN
**P. kochi*	West and northwest	LC
P. laticauda	Northwest and northeast, also Comoro islands	LC
**P. lineata*	East and northwest	LC
**P. madagascariensis*	East	LC

(continued overleaf)

TABLE 12.1. ***continued***

FAMILY (SUBFAMILY) GENUS AND SPECIES	DISTRIBUTION	IUCN STATUS
**P. malamakibo*	Southeast (Andohahela)	NT
**P. masohoala*	Northeast	CR
**P. modesta*	South	LC
**P. mutabilis*	West and south	LC
**P. parva*	East	LC
**P. pronki*	Central Highlands	CR
**P. pusilla*	East	LC
**P. quadriocellata*	East	LC
**P. ravenala*	East	LC
**P. roesleri*	North (Ankarana)	EN
**P. seippi*	Northwest (Sambirano Region)	EN
**P. serraticauda*	East	EN
**P. standingi*	Southwest	VU
**P. vanheygeni*	Northwest (Sambirano Region)	EN
**Uroplatus alluaudi*	North	NT
**U. ebenaui*	North and northwest	VU
**U. fangorn*	Northeast	NE
**U. fetsy*	North (Ankarana)	NE
**U. fiera*	Central Highlands	NE
**U. fimbriatus*	East	LC
**U. finaritra*	Northeast (Marojejy)	NE
**U. finiavana*	North (Montagne d'Ambre)	NT
**U. fivehy*	Northeast	NE
**U. fotsivava*	North (Tsaratanàna)	NE
**U. giganteus*	North and northeast	VU
**U. guentheri*	West	EN
**U. henkeli*	Northwest	VU
**U. kelirambo*	North (Tsaratanàna)	NE
**U. lineatus*	Northeast and east	LC
**U. malahelo*	Southwest and southeast	EN
**U. malama*	Southeast	VU
**U. phantasticus*	East and Central Highlands	LC
**U. pietschmanni*	Central Highlands	EN
**U. sameiti*	East	LC
**U. sikorae*	East and north	LC

FAMILY (SUBFAMILY) GENUS AND SPECIES	DISTRIBUTION	IUCN STATUS
GERRHOSAURIDAE		
**Tracheloptychus madagascariensis*	South and west	LC
**T. petersi*	Southwest	VU
**Zonosaurus aeneus*	East and Central Highlands, isolated records from northeast (Daraina)	LC
**Z. anelanelany*	Southeast	VU
**Z. bemaraha*	West	LC
**Z. boettgeri*	North	VU
**Z. brygooi*	Northeast and east	LC
**Z. haraldmeieri*	North	NT
**Z. karsteni*	West and south	LC
**Z. laticaudatus*	West, north, and southeast	LC
Z. madagascariensis	Much of Madagascar, as well as Glorioso and Cosmoledo Islands	LC
**Z. maramaintso*	West	DD
**Z. maximus*	Southeast	VU
**Z. ornatus*	East and Central Highlands	LC
**Z. quadrilineatus*	Southwest	VU
**Z. rufipes*	Northwest and northeast	NT
**Z. subunicolor*	Northwest and northeast	EN
**Z. trilineatus*	South	LC
**Z. tsingy*	North	LC
SCINCIDAE (SCINCINAE)		
**Amphiglossus astrolabi*	East	LC
**A. reticulatus*	Northwest	LC
**Brachyseps anosyensis*	Southeast and Central Highlands	VU
**B. frontoparietalis*	East	LC
**B. gastrostictus*	Central Highlands and northeast	DD
**B. macrocercus*	Central Highlands	LC
**B. mandady*	Northeast (Masoala)	DD
**B. punctatus*	East	LC
**B. spilostichus*	Northeast (Tsararano)	DD
**B. splendidus*	Southeast, west, and southern Central Highlands	VU
**Flexiseps alluaudi*	North	VU
**F. andranovahensis*	South	DD
**F. ardouini*	North	VU
**F. crenni*	Northeast, east, and Central Highlands	LC

(continued overleaf)

TABLE 12.1. ***continued***

FAMILY (SUBFAMILY) GENUS AND SPECIES	DISTRIBUTION	IUCN STATUS
**F. decaryi*	Southeast	EN
**F. elongatus*	Northwest	DD
**F. mandokava*	North and northwest (Sambirano Region)	VU
**F. melanurus*	Northeast	LC
**F. meva*	Northeast and west (Ambohijanahary)	DD
**F. ornaticeps*	East, south, and southwest (needs taxonomic revision)	LC
**F. stylus*	Northeast (Masoala)	DD
**F. tanysoma*	Northwest	LC
**F. tsaratananensis*	North (Tsaratanàna)	LC
**Grandidierina fierinensis*	Southwest	LC
**G. lineata*	South	LC
**G. petiti*	Southwest	NT
**G. rubrocaudata*	West and southwest	LC
**Madascincus ankodabensis*	Southeast	DD
**M. arenicola*	North (Oronjia and Ampombofofo)	CR
**M. igneocaudatus*	Southwest and south	LC
**M. macrolepis*	Central Highlands (Ambositra-Vondrozo)	EN
**M. melanopleura*	East and north	LC
**M. miafina*	North	NE
**M. minutus*	North	LC
**M. mouroundavae*	North, east, and possibly west	LC
**M. nanus*	Northeast	VU
**M. polleni*	West	LC
**M. pyrurus*	Central Highlands (Ibity and Itremo)	NE
**M. stumpffi*	North	NT
**Paracontias ampijoroensis*	Northwest (Ankarafantsika)	NE
**P. brocchii*	North (Montagne d'Ambre)	NT
**P. fasika*	North (Oronjia)	CR
**P. hafa*	Northeast (Anjanaharibe-Sud)	NT
**P. hildebrandti*	North	LC
**P. holomelas*	East and northeast	LC
**P. kankana*	East (Mahasoa)	VU
**P. mahamavo*	Northwest	NE
**P. manify*	North (Tsaratanàna)	DD
**P. milloti*	Northwest (Sambirano Region)	DD
**P. minimus*	North (between Oronjia and Ampombofofo)	CR

FAMILY (SUBFAMILY) GENUS AND SPECIES	DISTRIBUTION	IUCN STATUS
**P. rothschildi*	North (Oronjia)	CR
**P. tsararano*	Northeast (Tsararano)	DD
**P. vermisaurus*	Northeast (Makira)	DD
**Pseudoacontias angelorum*	Northeast (Marojejy)	EN
**P. madagascariensis*	Unknown	DD
**P. menamainty*	Northwest (Sahamalaza)	CR
**P. unicolor*	Northwest (Nosy Be)	VU
**Pygomeles braconnieri*	Southwest	LC
**P. petteri*	Northwest	EN
**P. trivittatus*	South	LC
**Voeltzkowia mira*	Northwest	EN
**V. mobydick*	Northwest	NE
**V. yamagishii*	Northwest	EN
SCINCIDAE (EUGONGYLINAE)		
Cryptoblepharus boutoni	Coastal north, west, and south	NE
SCINCIDAE (MABUYINAE)		
**Trachylepis aureopunctata*	West and south	LC
**T. boettgeri*	Central Highlands	LC
T. comorensis	Northwest (Nosy Tanikely, probably introduced), Comoro islands	LC
**T. dumasi*	South, southwest, and west	VU
**T. elegans*	Much of island	LC
**T. gravenhorstii*	Much of island	LC
**T. lavarambo*	Northwest and northeast	VU
**T. madagascariensis*	Central Highlands	LC
**T. nancycoutuae*	Southern Central Highlands (Isalo)	NT
**T. tandrefana*	West	LC
**T. tavaratra*	North	VU
**T. vato*	South and southern Central Highlands	LC
**T. vezo*	Southwest	DD
**T. volamenaloha*	West (Bemaraha)	NT
SANZINIIDAE		
**Acrantophis dumerili*	South	LC
**A. madagascariensis*	North	LC
**Sanzinia madagascariensis*	East	LC
**S. volontany*	West, north, and south	NE

(continued overleaf)

TABLE 12.1. ***continued***

FAMILY (SUBFAMILY) GENUS AND SPECIES	DISTRIBUTION	IUCN STATUS
PSEUDOXYROPHIIDAE		
**Alluaudina bellyi*	North	LC
**A. mocquardi*	North (Ankarana)	EN
**Brygophis coulangesi*	East and northeast	VU
**Compsophis albiventris*	North (Montagne d'Ambre)	NT
**C. boulengeri*	Northeast and east	LC
**C. fatsibe*	North and northeast	NT
**C. infralineatus*	Central Highlands, east, and southeast	LC
**C. laphystius*	East and northeast	LC
**C. vinckei*	East and northeast	EN
**C. zeny*	Southeast	VU
**Dromicodryas bernieri*	Much of island	NT
**D. quadrilineatus*	North and east	NT
**Elapotinus picteti*	North and east	LC as *Exallodontophis albignaci*
**Heteroliodon fohy*	North	EN
**H. lava*	North and west	NT
**H. occipitalis*	West and south	LC
**Ithycyphus blanci*	Northeast (Marojejy)	DD
**I. goudoti*	East	LC
**I. miniatus*	West and north	LC
**I. oursi*	West and south	LC
**I. perineti*	East	LC
**Langaha alluaudi*	West and south	LC
**L. madagascariensis*	Much of coastal lowlands	LC
**L. pseudoalluaudi*	North and northwest	LC
**Leioheterodon geayi*	West and south	LC
**L. madagascariensis*	Much of island except Central Highlands	LC
**L. modestus*	North, west, south, and Central Highlands	LC
**Liophidium apperti*	South	DD
**L. chabaudi*	West	LC
**L. maintikibo*	West and northwest	DD
**L. pattoni*	Northeast	NT
**L. rhodogaster*	East and north	LC
**L. therezieni*	North	VU

FAMILY (SUBFAMILY) GENUS AND SPECIES	DISTRIBUTION	IUCN STATUS
**L. torquatum*	Much of island except south	LC
**L. trilineatum*	South	DD
**L. vaillanti*	West and south	LC
**Liopholidophis baderi*	East (Andasibe and Zahamena)	NE
**L. dimorphus*	North (Montagne d'Ambre)	NT
**L. dolicocercus*	East and Central Highlands	LC
**L. grandidieri*	Central Highlands	VU
**L. oligolepis*	Northeast (Marojejy and COMATSA)	NE
**L. rhadinaea*	East	LC
**L. sexlineatus*	East and Central Highlands	LC
**L. varius*	East	LC
Lycodryas capuroni	Northwest (Ankarana)	NE
**L. citrinus*	West	VU
**L. gaimardi*	Northeast and east	LC
**L. granuliceps*	North	LC
**L. guentheri*	Central Highlands (Itremo) and south	EN
**L. inopinae*	North	EN
**L. inornatus*	South	VU
**L. pseudogranuliceps*	Northwest, west, and southwest	LC
**Madagascarophis colubrinus*	Much of island	LC
**M. fuchsi*	North (Montagne des Français)	NE
**M. lolo*	North (Ankarana)	NE
**M. meridionalis*	South and west	LC
**M. ocellatus*	Southwest	LC
**Micropisthodon ochraceus*	North and east	LC
**Pararhadinaea melanogaster*	North	VU
**Parastenophis betsileanus*	East and northwest	LC
**Phisalixella arctifasciata*	East	LC
**P. tulearensis*	Northwest, west, and southwest	LC
**P. variabilis*	North and northwest	EN
**Pseudoxyrhopus ambreensis*	North (Montagne d'Ambre)	NT
**P. analabe*	Northeast	NT
**P. ankafinaensis*	Southern Central Highlands (probably extinct)	CR
**P. heterurus*	East	LC
**P. imerinae*	Central Highlands	NT
**P. kely*	Southeast	EN

(continued overleaf)

TABLE 12.1. ***continued***

FAMILY (SUBFAMILY) GENUS AND SPECIES	DISTRIBUTION	IUCN STATUS
**P. microps*	East and northwest	LC
**P. oblectator*	Central Highlands and southeast	VU
**P. quinquelineatus*	North, west, south, and central east	LC
**P. sokosoko*	Southeast	VU
**P. tritaeniatus*	East	LC
**Thamnosophis epistibes*	East	LC
**T. infrasignatus*	East	LC
**T. lateralis*	Much of island	LC
**T. martae*	North (Montagne des Français, Montagne d'Ambre, and Ankarana)	EN
**T. mavotenda*	West and southwest	NT
**T. stumpffi*	Northwest	VU
PSAMMOPHIIDAE		
**Mimophis mahfalensis*	Central Highlands, west, and southwest	LC
**M. occultus*	North, northwest, and west	NE
TYPHLOPIDAE (ASIATYPHLOPINAE)		
Indotyphlops braminus	Much of island (introduced), pantropical	LC
TYPHLOPIDAE (MADATYPHLOPINAE)		
**Madatyphlops andasibensis*	East (Andasibe)	DD
**M. arenarius*	West and south	LC
**M. boettgeri*	South	LC
**M. decorsei*	West	LC
**M. domerguei*	Central southeast (Ranomafana)	DD
**M. madagascariensis*	Northwest (Nosy Be)	DD
**M. microcephalus*	North	DD
**M. mucronatus*	Northwest (Nosy Be)	DD
**M. ocularis*	Northeast and southeast	DD
**M. rajeryi*	Central southeast (Ranomafana)	DD
**M. reuteri*	Northwest (Nosy Be)	DD
XENOTYPHLOPIDAE		
**Xenotyphlops grandidieri*	North (sandy coast)	CR

Notes: The IUCN status is after the IUCN Red List of Threatened Species (IUCN 2019); more recently described species have not yet been officially assessed for their Red List status. CR, Critically Endangered; DD, Data Deficient; EN, Endangered; LC, Least Concern; NE, Not Evaluated; NT, Near Threatened; VU, Vulnerable. The vast majority of terrestrial reptile species presented in this table are endemic to Madagascar, and these are preceded by an asterisk (*). The nonendemic species include those that occur outside Madagascar or have been introduced to the island. Extinct species (*Voay robustus*, *Aldabrachelys abrupta/gigantea*, and *A. grandidieri*), marine species (sea turtles and the sea snake *Hydrophis platurus*), and species with unconfirmed extant populations or dubious occurrence on Madagascar (*Phelsuma cepediana*, *Trachylepis betsileana*, and *Agama agama*) are excluded from this list. While this book was in press, Shea (2021) proposed that the genus *Mesomycterus* Cope, 1892 represents a senior synonym of *Brachyseps* Erens et al., 2017, but this taxonomic action requires additional scrutiny and has not been adopted here as it probably qualifies as *nomen oblitum*.

THE HISTORY OF EXPLORATION OF MADAGASCAR'S REPTILE FAUNA

When Madagascar was first colonized by humans, now estimated to perhaps be over 10,000 years ago (see Wright and Rakotoarisoa, pp. 181–90), the first settlers probably faced a reptile fauna very similar to that of today. Apart from an extinct crocodile (*Voay robustus*), one main exception would have been giant tortoises, which were probably a common and important component of ecosystems in the drier regions of the island (much as they are today on the Aldabra Atoll in the western Seychelles). On Madagascar, giant tortoises probably coexisted with humans for an extended period but eventually went extinct, possibly from overexploitation as a food resource. The same is likely true for other elements of Madagascar's megafauna, as indicated by cut marks on bones of hippos, elephant birds, and giant lemurs (e.g., Dewar 1984; MacPhee and Burney 1991; Dewar et al. 2013; Hansford et al. 2018).

If the interior Central Highlands once included forest-grassland mosaics as suggested by a number of researchers (e.g., Burney 1997; Vorontsova et al. 2016), then it is striking that today there are no locally endemic grassland reptile communities in this region. During many millennia humans have modified the landscape of Madagascar, probably with a dramatic influence on reptile species distributions. Humans have also probably introduced several commensal reptile species (e.g., *Hemidactylus frenatus*, *Gehyra mutilata*, *Indotyphlops braminus*).

The earliest known natural history accounts of Malagasy reptiles were published in 1658 by Etienne de Flacourt, including his observations of the *Uroplatus* leaf-tailed geckos (see C. Blanc 1984). However, it was another 130 years after Flacourt before the first endemic species was scientifically described from Madagascar—the Malagasy Leaf-nosed Snake, *Langaha madagascariensis*, named by Pierre Joseph Bonnaterre in 1790 (Figure 12.1). In general, the exploration of Malagasy reptile diversity started several decades earlier than the corresponding research on amphibians. The first reptiles formally named from Madagascar were highly conspicuous—besides the Malagasy Leaf-nosed Snake, these were the Giant Leaf-tailed Gecko (*U. fimbriatus*) in 1792, and a chameleon (*Furcifer bifidus*) in 1800. From 1824 to 1829, the French zoologist and paleontologist Georges Cuvier (1769–1832) described three large chameleons (*Calumma parsonii*, *F. pardalis*, and *F. verrucosus*), and in 1837 Hermann Schlegel published a book on snakes with new species descriptions and excellent color figures.

In the following decades, European museums started to receive new reptile collections from Madagascar, and the number of described species increased substantially. Most of these specimens were studied in Paris by André Marie Constant Duméril (1774–1860), Gabriel Bibron (1805–1848), and Francois Mocquard (1834–1917); in London by John Edward Gray (1800–1875), Albert Günther (1830–1914), and George Albert Boulenger (1858–1937); in Frankfurt by Oskar Boettger (1844–1910); and in Berlin by Wilhelm Peters (1815–1883). Early collections were often confined to coastal regions around major trading areas (such as Toamasina or Nosy Be), and specific locality information or collector names were frequently incomplete or missing. Most of these species were described by authors who had little opportunity to gain information on living specimens and their natural habitats, with the major exception of Alfred Grandidier (1836–1921), who explored the island and described numerous new reptiles between 1867 and 1872. The notable increase in knowledge of the island's reptile diversity was summarized by Fernand Angel (1881–1950) in his monograph of Malagasy lizards (in 1942), and by Jean Guibé (1910–1999) in his revision of Malagasy snakes (in 1958).

The next major phase of fieldwork took place between 1960 and 1975 (the period of the first Malagasy Republic), when many remote regions (especially montane areas) of Madagascar were surveyed, in part by large multidisciplinary expeditions. This led to the discovery and description of numerous new species and the appearance of researchers increasingly specialized on different reptile groups: Guy Ramanantsoa, the first Malagasy reptile researcher, published several papers on chameleons between 1974 and 1984. Edouard R. Brygoo (1920–2016) provided comprehensive revisions of Malagasy chameleons (1971, 1978), gerrhosaurid lizards (1985a), and scincid skinks (for example, 1983a). Charles A.

FIGURE 12.1 The Malagasy Leaf-nosed Snake, *Langaha madagascariensis*, was the first of Madagascar's endemic reptile species to be scientifically named (by Bonaterre in 1790). The different shape of the rostral appendages in males (below) and females (above), as well as the sexually dimorphic coloration, suggests that these features play a role as signals in mate choice, but the behavior of this species is incompletely known, despite its spectacular external appearance. (PHOTO by F. Glaw.)

Domergue (1914–2008) published papers on the snakes of Madagascar from 1970 to 1994 and coauthored numerous descriptions of new chameleon species. Georges Pasteur (1930–2015) described numerous new species of day geckos in the genus *Lygodactylus*, and Harald Meier (1922–2007) named several *Phelsuma* species. Charles P. Blanc published a monograph on Malagasy iguanids (1977; now in their own family, Opluridae) and many additional contributions on reptiles and frogs, including aspects of their biogeography. Species descriptions of this period were also often enhanced by behavioral and ecological observations. However, in 1975 a dramatic political change on Madagascar created a hiatus in herpetological field research that was to last for approximately 15 years.

A new era in research on Malagasy reptiles started after 1990, when Ronald A. Nussbaum and Christopher J. Raxworthy described numerous new species, including chameleons, geckos, skinks, and snakes, partly in cooperation with Achille P. Raselimanana and Jean-Baptiste Ramanamanjato. John Cadle revised several groups of snakes, and Wolfgang Böhme and Pierre Ibisch described new species of *Uroplatus* geckos. Roger Bour and Gerald Kuchling studied different aspects of turtle and tortoise biology and taxonomy, and Franco Andreone and Allen Greer revised several genera of skinks. Numerous new species of reptiles were also discovered and described by teams assembled by Frank Glaw and Miguel Vences, including the taxonomic revisions of *Uroplatus* led by Fanomezana M. Ratsoavina, of skinks led by Aurélien Miralles, and of one group of *Calumma* chameleons led by David Prötzel.

Despite the intensified research, the inventory of Madagascar's reptiles is still far from complete, and the discovery and description of forms unknown to science remains an important field of research. Numerous candidate species are awaiting in-depth study, and new collections in remote areas are still needed to achieve a comprehensive view of the island's true diversity, which in turn is essential to objectively define conservation priorities. Just between 2000 and 2019, an additional 94 reptile species were described. Herpetologists who coauthored five or more new reptile species in this period include Franco Andreone, Angelica Crottini, Michael Franzen, Philip-Sebastian Gehring, Frank Glaw, Allen Greer, Oliver Hawlitschek, Jörn Köhler, Aurélien Miralles, Zoltan T. Nagy, Ronald A. Nussbaum, David Prötzel, Achille P. Raselimanana, Fanomezana M. Ratsoavina, Christopher J. Raxworthy, Mark D. Scherz, Miguel Vences, and David R. Vieites.

Since the beginning of the 21st century, Madagascar has increasingly become a model region for biogeographic and evolutionary research (Vences et al. 2009), and accordingly, the research on Malagasy reptiles has diversified substantially beyond taxonomy, with intensive research programs on molecular phylogeny (e.g., Tolley et al. 2013), phylogenomics (e.g., Ruane et al. 2015, 2018), DNA barcoding (Nagy et al. 2012), behavior (e.g., Anderson 2016), life history (e.g., Karsten et al. 2008), reproduction (e.g., Randriamahazo and Mori 2001), habitat use (e.g., D'Cruze et al. 2009a; Randrianantoandro et al. 2010), species inventories (e.g., Raselimanana 2008; Penny et al. 2017; Cocca et al. 2018; Belluardo et al. 2021), distribution, biogeography, and evolution of endemism (e.g., Boumans et al. 2007; Raselimanana 2008; Pearson and Raxworthy 2009), extinction vulnerability and conservation (e.g., Pedrono et al. 2004; Leuteritz et al. 2005; Raxworthy et al. 2008b; Jenkins et al. 2014), karyology (e.g., Mezzasalma et al. 2014, 2017, 2019), and micro-CT based osteology (e.g., Prötzel et al. 2015, 2018c, 2020; Scherz et al. 2017). Simultaneously, the contributions of Malagasy researchers to the scientific literature on reptiles have increased enormously, especially in ecology, natural history, conservation biology, and species inventories, as exemplified by over 135 publications with Malagasy coauthors included in the reference list for this chapter.

DIVERSITY OF REPTILES ON MADAGASCAR

Except for crocodiles and sea snakes, Madagascar has no dangerous reptiles. No terrestrial snakes can inflict life-threatening bites. Despite this, most Malagasy remain frightened of snakes, even though presumably no one has died of a snakebite on the island since it was first occupied by people millennia ago. One of the most feared snakes is the *menarana* (*Leioheterodon madagascariensis*), a species that was even included in early Malagasy translations of the Bible, as the serpent in the Garden of Eden. Chameleons are also frequently feared and respected for being both intelligent and supernatural, and other species (e.g., *Astrochelys radiata*, *Uroplatus* geckos) are considered *fady* (taboo) by certain cultural groups, although in many areas of the island these taboos are breaking down due to a number of sociocultural factors.

Madagascar has a cosmopolitan marine reptile fauna, representing two families of sea turtles: Cheloniidae and Dermochelyidae, and probably one or two species of one family of marine snakes (Elapidae) can occasionally be encountered, although no recent records for these species exist. By comparison, the terrestrial fauna is largely endemic. At the family level, Madagascar is especially remarkable for what is absent compared to Africa and (to a lesser extent) other islands in the western Indian Ocean. Omissions compared to Africa include the families Trionychidae, Agamidae, Amphisbaenidae, Eublepharidae, Lacertidae, Leptotyphlopidae, Trogonophidae, Varanidae, Pythonidae, Atractaspididae, and Viperidae. Other absent African groups include the subfamilies Erycinae and Elapinae. Compared to elsewhere in the western Indian Ocean, Madagascar is also missing representatives of the Bolyeriidae (Round Island boas), a family now confined to a single surviving species on Round Island, northeast of Mauritius.

Chelonians on Madagascar are relatively species poor, represented by four endemic and one probably introduced extant species of terrestrial tortoise, plus two probably extinct giant species (see Pedrono et al., pp. 1463–68), and one endemic, ancient species plus three possibly introduced species of freshwater turtles (besides the marine species) (see Kuchling et al., pp. 1469–74). Crocodiles are today represented by the widespread Nile Crocodile (see Kuchling et al., pp. 1458–63), but many subfossils from Madagascar are attributed to the endemic genus and species *Voay robustus*, which went extinct less than a few thousand years ago (Brochu 2007), though the possibility that relict populations of *V. robustus* survive in remote areas cannot be entirely excluded.

Most Malagasy reptiles belong to the squamates (lizards and snakes), a group in which number, size, and arrangement of scales are often important characters for species identification. An important characteristic of squamates is the presence of a transverse cloacal opening, and a paired genital organ in males (called a hemipenis), which can also display species-specific differences and is often used in the taxonomy of chameleons, snakes, and other groups (e.g., Domergue 1983; Klaver and Böhme 1986). Within Malagasy squamates, there are several lizard families: Chamaeleonidae, Gekkonidae, Gerrhosauridae, Opluridae, and Scincidae; and among snakes, the island harbors blind snakes (Typhlopidae and Xenotyphlopidae), giant snakes (Sanziniidae), colubroid snakes (Pseudoxyrhophiidae and Psammophiidae), and a sea snake (Elapidae).

Among the lizards, Madagascar hosts almost 90 species of chameleons, more than 40% of the worldwide diversity of this group, including the largest species, *Calumma parsonii* and *Furcifer oustaleti*, and the smallest species, *Brookesia nana* (Glaw et al. 2021; see Scherz et al., pp. 1506–16). Iguanas are probably one of the oldest groups among the extant Malagasy reptiles, with eight species currently distinguished on Madagascar and classified in the family Opluridae (see Cadle et al., pp. 1502–5); these lizards belong to a group distributed primarily in the New World, with a few endemic species occurring on remote Pacific Ocean islands—and on Madagascar (Welt and Raxworthy 2022). The plated or gerrhosaurid lizards are mostly terrestrial and sometimes arboreal lizards distributed in sub-Saharan Africa (subfamily Gerrhosaurinae) and on Madagascar (subfamily Zonosaurinae, with two genera) (see Raselimanana et al., pp. 1490–94). Skinks are a very species-rich group occurring across all continents except Antarctica, and on Madagascar they are represented by three subfamilies; of these, the Scincinae, with over 60 species on Madagascar, is an impressive radiation on the island, including a wide range of morphological diversity and numerous cases of convergent limb reduction and limb loss (Miralles et al. 2015b; Erens et al. 2017; see Miralles et al., pp. 1494–502); the Mabuyinae comprises 14 species of *Trachylepis* on Madagascar; and the Eugongylinae is represented on the island only by a species in the genus *Cryptoblepharus*, specialized to live on coastal rocks. Another species-rich lizard group is the geckos (see Bauer et al., pp. 1474–79), most of which are easily recognizable by their lack of eyelids and the presence of adhesive lamellae under the toes, which enable them to climb on vertical and smooth surfaces and provide taxonomists a variety of characters to identify different genera. About 10% of the worldwide diversity of geckos, around 110 species, is found on Madagascar, including spectacular forms like the colorful day geckos (*Phelsuma*; see Gehring and Ratsoavina, pp. 1485–90), bizarre leaf-tailed geckos (*Uroplatus*; see Gehring et al., pp. 1480–85), and skin-shading fish-scale geckos (*Geckolepis*; see Bauer et al., pp. 1474–79). About 50% of the island's gecko species are active during the day, most notably the genera *Lygodactylus* and *Phelsuma*.

Among snakes, the Malagasy giant snakes comprise two terrestrial (*Acrantophis*) and two semiarboreal (*Sanzinia*) species; the colubroids contain about 80 species, of which two belong to the Psammophiidae and all others to the Pseudoxyrhophiidae (Ruane et al. 2018), which comprises a large diversity of adaptations including diurnal, terrestrial, and partly aquatic forms. More secretive and rarely seen are the fossorial, wormlike blind snakes (see Raxworthy, pp. 1532–34), which are often not even recognized as snakes at first glance. Most blind snakes are relatively small, the eyes are largely reduced or even absent, and the tail is extremely short. On Madagascar they are represented by the Xenotyphlopidae, with a single species of an ancient evolutionary lineage endemic to Madagascar; and the Typhlopidae (subfamily Madatyphlopinae), which currently has 11 endemic Malagasy species whose taxonomy and genus-level classification are in need of revision, and one introduced species.

ECOLOGY AND BEHAVIOR

Reptiles are often considered to be behaviorally inflexible and to have poor learning capacity, but recent studies have found remarkable cognitive abilities, such as long-term memory in Aldabra and Galapagos giant tortoises (Gutnick et al. 2020). Individual behavior of reptiles is often influenced by environmental factors including egg incubation temperatures (Matsubara et al. 2017), and the Madagascar Ground Gecko, *Paroedura picta*, is one of the model species used to study a variety of behavioral and developmental research questions (e.g., Blumberg et al. 2002; Noro et al. 2009; Kubička et al. 2012). However, the ecology and behavior of most Malagasy reptiles are still poorly studied and certainly need much more attention in the future.

Nutrition

Although most Malagasy reptiles are carnivorous or insectivorous (Figure 12.2), their diet is more variable than in amphibians. Terrestrial tortoises are almost completely herbivorous, feeding on leaves and fruits, while freshwater and many marine turtles (except *Chelonia mydas*) are largely carnivorous, at least as adults. Lizards are in general carnivorous and insectivorous, hunting all prey types of suitable size, but an increasing number of recent observations have reported consumption of food items of vegetable origin, showing that the general diet of reptiles might often be complemented, with more variability than generally assumed. Gerrhosaurids (*Zonosaurus* and *Tracheloptychus*) and oplurids have been observed consuming fruit and flowers (Brillet 1982). Day geckos (*Phelsuma*) are known to feed on nectar, fruits, and pollen (e.g., Taylor and Gardner 2014), and in urban environments, natural and artificial sources of sugar (including fruit, honey, sugar, syrup, and chocolate) can become a substantial part of their diet (C. Gardner and Jasper 2015). Geckos of the genera *Phelsuma*, *Lygodactylus*, and *Blaesodactylus* "milk" honeydew-producing planthoppers (Fölling et al. 2001) by licking honeydew from their abdomens (Figure 12.2; see Świerczewski and Stroiński, pp. 987–91). A similar behavior, but also simple licking of tree sap, was observed in *Geckolepis* (Jono et al. 2015). Some lizards are able to consume relatively large prey. Cannibalism has been recorded in the iguana *Chalarodon madagascariensis* (C. Gardner and Jasper 2012), and the day gecko *P. kochi* is known to feed on smaller *Hemidactylus* geckos (García and Vences 2002a). Chameleons have special adaptations to capture insect prey, especially their very long projectile tongue, used to precisely "shoot" insects. Malagasy chameleons are not known to consume vegetable items other than by mistake, but large chameleons prey on other vertebrates such as young birds (García and Vences 2002b).

Apart from the microphagous blind snakes (Typhlopidae and Xenotyphlopidae), Malagasy snakes usually consume larger vertebrate prey, especially frogs (Figure 12.3), reptiles, and mammals, but several snakes are also oophagous: *Leioheterodon madagascariensis* and *L. geayi* are well known to feed on the eggs of *Oplurus* iguanas, and *Compsophis* snakes consume mantellid frog eggs (Glaw

FIGURE 12.2 **Prey capture and nutrition in geckos. *Phelsuma* lizards are primarily insectivorous A), D) but also consume flower nectar C). Different species of geckos, like the *Blaesodactylus* gecko shown in B), lick the sugar-rich excrement of hemipteran insects.** (PHOTO A by C. R. Hutter; B, C, and D by P.-S. Gehring.)

and Vences 2007). *Pseudoxyrhopus* species feed on eggs of chameleons, skinks, and probably *Oplurus*; they apparently use their posterior fangs to slit the eggshell before swallowing the contents, a technique that facilitates digestion (Cadle 1999; Andreone et al. 2007; Knoll et al. 2009).

Activity Patterns

Most Malagasy reptile genera can be classified as either diurnal or nocturnal. Chameleons, iguanas, gerrhosaurids, scincid lizards of the genera *Trachylepis* and *Cryptoblepharus*, geckos of the genera *Phelsuma* and *Lygodactylus*, and several genera of pseudoxyrhophiid snakes (e.g., *Dromicodryas*, *Ithycyphus*, *Liopholidophis*, *Thamnosophis*) are diurnal. Other snakes (e.g., *Acrantophis*, *Compsophis*, *Lycodryas*, *Madagascarophis*, *Parastenophis*, *Phisalixella*, *Pseudoxyrhopus*, *Sanzinia*) are largely nocturnal, although some of these taxa can occasionally be active during the day. A basically nocturnal activity pattern is also found in most geckos, although some species of *Blaesodactylus* and *Paroedura*, for example, can on rare occasions be observed basking during the day. Crocodiles as well as freshwater turtles are known to show diurnal and nocturnal activity, as is also the case for many scincine lizards. As a general rule (although some exceptions exist), nocturnal species can be recognized by their slit-like vertical pupils, whereas diurnal species usually have rounded pupils. Reptiles need relatively high temperatures to maintain activity, which explains why nocturnal reptiles (e.g., geckos) are very rare in forests above 1500 m. Arboreal species of chameleons and many *Lygodactylus* geckos spend the night inactive roosting on tree twigs and leaves. Some terrestrial chameleons of the genus *Brookesia* climb at dusk onto branches and leaves of low vegetation, apparently to avoid the risk of nocturnal terrestrial predators. Other lizards and snakes, when not active, hide in burrows or rock fissures, under stones or under the bark of dead tree trunks, or in similar shelters.

An important aspect of reptile behavior is active thermoregulation through basking. This is especially important in high mountain habitats where environmental temperatures are relatively low. The annual activity period of reptiles in such settings appears to be concentrated around the warm and rainy season. Although reptile reproduction is less dependent on environmental humidity than that of amphibians, it still occurs mainly during this period. Only a few reptile species, including *Phelsuma barbouri* and *L. mirabilis* on the Ankaratra Massif, and other *Lygodactylus* species from the southwest, are known to reproduce year-round on Madagascar.

FIGURE 12.3 **The nocturnal pseudoxyrhophiid snake *Compsophis laphystius* is often seen preying on the eggs of arboreal frogs such as *Guibemantis* and *Spinomantis* (above), but it also consumes adult frogs (below).** (PHOTOS by C. R. Hutter.)

Reproductive Diversity

Compared to amphibians with their enormous diversity of reproductive modes, reptiles have a rather invariable reproduction, with large, shelled eggs and internal fertilization by the male using either paired hemipenes (in lizards and snakes) or unpaired penes (in crocodiles and chelonians). The eggshell is usually a leathery and partly flexible structure that allows the egg to become larger as the embryo grows and humidity is taken up from the environment. The eggs of Malagasy geckos have a strongly calcified, hard, inflexible shell similar to that of bird eggs. Egg laying is the typical mode of reproduction in all reptile groups, but viviparity (live bearing) and ovoviviparity have repeatedly evolved in different groups. So-called ovoviviparous species may even still lay eggs, often with a very fragile or rudimentary shell, and the young hatch immediately after the clutch has been laid. Except for chelonians, the reproductive mode of most Malagasy reptiles is poorly known, and it is therefore easier to distinguish in more general terms, between egg-laying and live-bearing species. In this sense, live bearing is known from several snakes (*Sanzinia*, *Acrantophis*, *Liopholidophis sexlineatus*, *Lycodryas citrinus*, and probably *L. pseudogranuliceps*), and scincid lizards (*Brachyseps macrocercus* and *B. punctatus*).

A special mode of reproduction that is occasionally found in reptiles is parthenogenesis, where females produce offspring without fertilization by a male. Such parthenogenetic reproduction is known from the (probably introduced) burrowing blind snake *Indotyphlops braminus*. Reptile eggs are usually buried underground or deposited in hidden sites such as rock crevices, tree trunk cavities, under bark, or under dead trees. Some species use communal sites to lay their eggs, especially rock-dwelling geckos such as *Phelsuma malamakibo* and *Paragehyra gabriellae*. The eggs take a few weeks to many months to hatch, with large chameleons generally having particularly long incubation times. In many reptiles, the

FIGURE 12.4 **Death feigning is an antipredator strategy often seen in ground chameleons of the genera *Brookesia* and *Palleon*, as in these *P. lolontany* chameleons from Sorata.** (PHOTO by F. Glaw.)

temperature that the eggs experience during incubation determines the sex of the hatchlings, a mechanism called temperature-dependent sex determination.

Predation and Antipredator Strategies

Reptiles are an important component in the food web and are fed on by a large variety of other animals. Birds are among the main diurnal predators of chameleons (Jenkins et al. 2009) but also consume many other lizards and snakes. Several snake genera (e.g., *Liophidium*) appear to be specialized to prey on lizards, and hinged teeth in these snakes are considered an adaptation for swallowing this hard-bodied prey (Savitzky 1981). Mammals (tenrecs, carnivorans, and lemurs), invertebrates (centipedes), and sometimes even frogs consume juvenile reptiles as well. Reptiles have evolved a number of strategies to reduce the risk of predation. In many cases the dorsal coloration has an obvious function of camouflage. For example, the color of dwarf geckos (*Lygodactylus*) living on trees is rather similar to that of tree bark, and the brownish color of dwarf chameleons (*Brookesia*) together with the pointed laterovertebral tubercles and the diamond-shaped pelvic shield resembles the leaf litter where they live. Sometimes this effect is enhanced by the shape of the animal's body, as is very obvious in the small species of *Uroplatus* geckos (e.g., *U. phantasticus*). In species of *Brookesia* and *Palleon*, immobile death-feigning postures are often observed upon disturbance (Figure 12.4).

A typical antipredator behavior of lizards is tail autotomy; when these lizards are attacked, the tail will fracture at special breaking segments. Tail autotomy is known in all Malagasy geckos, gerrhosaurids, and skinks but is absent in chameleons and occurs only exceptionally in Malagasy iguanas. Autotomized tails can be regenerated, but always without vertebrae. Some lizards on Madagascar also shed much of their skin and scales when captured. This phenomenon is expressed in an extreme manner in fish-scale geckos of the genus *Geckolepis*, which can completely shed their skin (Scherz et al. 2017; Bauer et al., pp. 1474–79). Although the antipredator function of this adaptation is obvious, it has not yet been studied in any detail, and the main predators of these geckos remain unknown. Very fragile skin is also observed in some *Zonosaurus* species, where it also likely serves an antipredator purpose.

Subject editors: Miguel Vences and Achille P. Raselimanana

SPECIES INVENTORIES, BIOGEOGRAPHY, PHYLOGEOGRAPHY, AND SPECIES FORMATION OF REPTILES ON MADAGASCAR

M. Vences, J. L. Brown, A. Crottini, N. D'Cruze, C. J. Gardner, A. Miralles, A. P. Raselimanana, and C. J. Raxworthy

Biogeographic studies of Madagascar's reptiles have a relatively long history: Angel (1942) defined biogeographic regions based on the occurrence of lizards on the island, and several subsequent authors such as Pasteur (1965), C. Blanc (1972), and C. Blanc and Paulian (1996) further analyzed these biogeographic patterns. Raxworthy and Nussbaum (1995, 1996a, 1997) used area cladograms to analyze reptile distribution patterns on Madagascar and provided an explicit suggestion of speciation mechanisms using ground chameleons (genus *Brookesia*) as a model group. Many subsequent studies have addressed biogeographic and phylogeographic questions using reptile communities or specific reptile taxa on Madagascar as model systems; however, there are still several taxonomic gaps, and only a few studies have addressed population genetic structure and speciation mechanisms in these animals (Raxworthy et al. 2008a; Florio et al. 2012; Gehring et al. 2013; Florio and Raxworthy 2016). Certainly, understanding the species distribution patterns of Madagascar's reptiles is a prerequisite for insight into the mechanisms underlying their diversification (Yoder et al. 2005; Raxworthy et al. 2007; Pearson and Raxworthy 2009; Blair et al. 2015).

SPECIES INVENTORIES

The field identification of many reptile species is more straightforward than that of amphibians, and as a result, a larger number and higher density of reliable occurrence records exist for numerous reptile species. Over the past three decades, a broad range of surveys have targeted the herpetofauna, with a particular focus on protected areas (Raxworthy 1988; Raxworthy and Nussbaum 1994a, 1995, 1996a, 1996b; Raxworthy et al. 1994, 1998, 2008b; Goodman et al. 1997, 2018; Raselimanana 1998, 1999, 2004, 2008, 2013; Raselimanana et al. 1998, 2000a; Nussbaum et al. 1999b; Andreone et al. 2000, 2003, 2007, 2009; Rakotomalala 2002; Ramanamanjato and Rabibisoa 2002; Rakotomalala and Raselimanana 2003; D'Cruze et al. 2006, 2007, 2008, 2009b; Bora et al. 2007, 2010; C. Gardner et al. 2015b; Blumgart et al. 2017; Penny et al. 2017; Cocca et al. 2018; Belluardo et al. 2021). From 1996 to 2007, between one and five inventory studies that included reptiles were published every year (D'Cruze et al. 2009b), and many additional surveys exist as unpublished reports.

Three complementary field techniques advocated by Raxworthy and Nussbaum (1994a) have been primarily used during the last three decades to investigate reptile diversity. These methods include direct observation (such as opportunistic searches during the day and night along sampling itineraries in different microhabitats); systematic sampling of potential refuges (e.g., under rocks or bark, and inspection of dead wood, rotten logs, leaf litter, plant axils, and tree holes); and pitfall traps, including buckets (generally between 12 and 15 L) and vertical plastic drift fences. In addition, "funnel traps" and sticky traps have also been used for snake and lizard capture. These standard survey techniques have facilitated the comparative analysis of herpetofaunal diversity across field sites, resulting in improved understanding of species assemblages. Increased field exploration, the availability of field guides that enable the comparatively easy field identification of living specimens, the growth of museum collections, and the release of a barcoding reference database for the reptiles of Madagascar (Nagy et al. 2012) have enabled much easier identification of encountered animals and candidate species (*sensu* Vieites et al. 2009).

Madagascar's western and southwestern herpetofaunal communities are dominated by reptiles, whereas their proportion (relative to the amphibians) is comparatively lower in eastern Madagascar. However, in the moist evergreen forests of the northeast and in the northwestern Sambirano Region, reptiles still make up a higher proportion of the herpetofauna, often accounting for more than 50% of encountered species (J. Brown et al. 2016). This may reflect the small-scale mosaic of more humid and drier habitats in this part of Madagascar, where more reptile species are able to colonize moist evergreen forest habitat from the arid biomes. Also, as expected, community composition (for amphibians and reptiles) reflects major biomes, with dry and subarid sites differing from humid, subhumid, and montane sites, while communities from the latter three biomes are less distinct from each other (J. Brown et al. 2016). Detectability (the proportion of species found in a survey relative to those that should occur in an area based on known distribution ranges) is particularly low in snakes and highest in iguanids and chelonians, probably reflecting a density component, with snakes, as tertiary consumers, occurring at lower density than their main prey, lizards and frogs. This may contribute to the lower community similarity indices found among reptiles compared to amphibians (Andreone and Randrianirina 2000). It should be noted that detectability is also low for arboreal species that are upper-canopy specialists, and for most fossorial species, especially skinks and blind snakes, without extensive pitfall trapping (Figure 12.5). As a general conclusion, complete species sampling of reptile community assemblages continues to be a major challenge (Raxworthy et al. 2012).

BIOGEOGRAPHY

Better knowledge of reptile distributions and alpha taxonomy has facilitated more robust biogeographic analyses than have been done for amphibians. Specifically, species distribution modeling has enabled insights into differences in the bioclimatic envelopes of closely related species (Raxworthy et al. 2007, 2008a; Florio et al. 2012; Florio and Raxworthy 2016) and hinted toward regions where extended distributions of known species, or new species, could be expected (Raxworthy et al. 2003). Species richness of Malagasy reptiles peaks in the eastern moist evergreen forests, but in contrast to amphibians, substantial richness is also present in the dry western and southwestern biomes (J. Brown et al. 2016). Regional endemism is concentrated in northern Madagascar, but also in some areas in the central eastern moist evergreen forests and in the southwest (J. Brown et al. 2016); this partly coincides with a concentrated occurrence of threatened species, usually because these are range restricted, in the north, southeast, and southwest (Jenkins et al. 2014). Geckos and gerrhosaurids, especially, have a high richness of threatened species occurring exclusively in the southeast and southwest (Jenkins et al. 2014; C. Gardner et al. 2015a).

Cases of microendemism seem to be particularly frequent in fossorial taxa. Several species of *Madatyphlops*, *Grandidierina*, *Voeltzkowia*, *Paracontias*, and *Pseudoacontias*, for instance, are known only from their type locality (Wegener et al. 2013; Miralles et al. 2016a). Although this trend might be explained by their restricted dispersal capacity, it could also be partly artifactual, given the difficulty of observing or correctly identifying these very inconspicuous and poorly studied organisms. Other examples of microendemism

FIGURE 12.5 **Burrowing skinks such as this *Grandidierina rubrocaudata* individual from Andranomaitso (Commune Rurale de Sakaraha) are difficult to detect and are usually recorded by researchers using pitfall traps.** (PHOTO by G. M. Rosa.)

appear to be well supported (based on ease of identification, and surveys of many sites), such as *Brookesia perarmata* at Bemaraha, and *Phelsuma antanosy* in the Tolagnaro area (Raxworthy and Nussbaum 1993a, 2000).

The elevational distribution of reptiles, averaged over the entire island, peaks at low elevations of 100 m above sea level and gradually decreases toward higher elevations (Raxworthy and Nussbaum 1994a, 1996b; Raxworthy et al. 1998; Nussbaum et al. 1999b; Raselimanana et al. 2000a; J. Brown et al. 2016). This can be explained by the many reptile species occurring at low elevations in the west, and perhaps also by the many reptiles that prefer warm temperatures and are less adaptable to mid- and high-elevation habitats. However, it is worth mentioning that high-elevation areas (together with some specific and isolated habitat associated with karstic environments) are also home to several reptile microendemics (Raxworthy and Nussbaum 1996c; Raxworthy et al. 2008a; Prötzel et al. 2018c; Scherz et al. 2019).

Compared to the distributional ranges of amphibians, those of reptiles are generally larger but are also strongly dependent on body size, with small species (Figure 12.6) having smaller distributions (J. Brown et al. 2016). Interestingly, the occupancy of suitable available habitat (range filling) is higher in reptiles than in amphibians, probably because of the higher dispersal abilities of reptiles. On average reptile species can colonize a higher proportion of an area that offers bioclimatically suitable conditions for them. Within reptiles, a comparison between lizards and snakes suggests that the latter, based on similar body sizes, have on average significantly larger distributional ranges (J. Brown et al. 2016), a pattern that has also been found globally (Böhm et al. 2013). In contrast to sites in continental Africa, on Madagascar snake communities have a higher proportion of species specialized on lizard and amphibian diets and comparatively fewer species feed on mammals or fish (Andreone and Luiselli 2000).

FIGURE 12.6 **Miniaturized species such as this tiny *Brookesia micra* individual from Nosy Hara often occur in very small distributional ranges, following a general trend of decreasing range size with decreasing body size. These small species are highly threatened by destruction of their remaining habitat, but because they can persist in very small forest fragments, conservation management of such small animals is alleviated.** (PHOTO by F. Glaw.)

PHYLOGEOGRAPHY

Because reptiles are characterized by high dispersal capacity and tolerance of arid habitats, they can be expected to display limited phylogeographic structure. However, an analysis of various reptile species by Boumans et al. (2007) revealed deep genetic lineages even in widespread species adapted to a variety of habitats. Remarkably high genetic divergence has also been observed in various other widespread species from moist evergreen forests, such as *Brookesia superciliaris* (Ratsoavina et al. 2010) and *Uroplatus phantasticus* (Ratsoavina et al. 2012), as well as in species of more open habitats such as *Furcifer pardalis* (Grbic et al. 2015), *F. lateralis* (Florio et al. 2012), the genera *Sanzinia* and *Acrantophis* (Orozco-terWengel et al. 2008), and *Mimophis mahfalensis* (Ruane et al. 2018). In some of these species, such as the chameleon *F. lateralis* and the snake *M. mahfalensis*, research has shown that the deep lineages represent cryptic species (Florio et al. 2012; Ruane et al. 2018). Further, the two main lineages of *Sanzinia* are today recognized as distinct species because of their substantial genetic differences and a few morphological differences, despite a lack of thorough study of contact zones. In other cases relatively large genetic differences are considered to fall within intraspecific variation, for example in *F. oustaleti* and *F. verrucosus* (Florio and Raxworthy 2016), *Trachylepis gravenhorstii* (Vences et al. 2014), *Uroplatus phantasticus* and *U. ebenaui*, and *Brookesia superciliaris* (Ratsoavina et al. 2010, 2012, 2019a). Even some highly restricted local endemics show substantial genetic diversity (e.g., Chiari et al. 2009).

A meta-analysis of phylogeographic units across Madagascar, to determine possible agreements among the ranges occupied by distinct intraspecific genetic units, has so far not been undertaken. In many cases, the genetic subdivisions of widespread species do not coincide with any obvious current barriers to gene flow and therefore may have evolved during past climatic shifts and secondary contact during subsequent range expansions. Among the more interesting apparent patterns is the presence of distinct haplotypes of some very widespread and vagile species in the extreme north of the island around Antsiranana; this is observed in *Trachylepis elegans* (Vences et al. 2014) and to a certain degree in the gecko *Hemidactylus mercatorius*, as well as in the probably introduced *H. frenatus* (Vences et al. 2004b).

Almost all phylogeographic studies to date on Madagascar's reptiles rely on analysis of mitochondrial genes. Unfortunately, this approach alone does not allow a reliable delimitation of deep conspecific lineages from closely related species—that is, lineages on independent evolutionary trajectories (Padial et al. 2010). Given that a lack of taxonomic resolution can lead to phylogeographic misinterpretations, it is crucial to apply phylogenomic approaches to these taxa to understand whether the high mitochondrial divergence observed among geographically separated populations is paralleled in the nuclear genome. There are indications this may not be the case in at least some circumstances. For instance, in *Phelsuma lineata*, minimal divergence was found between subspecies in the nuclear RAG-1 gene despite strong differentiation in mitochondrial genes among these lineages (Gehring et al. 2013). Contact zones with syntopic occurrence of distinct haplotypes have been identified for subspecies of *P. lineata* (Gehring et al. 2013) and for deep lineages in the *Madascincus melanopleura* complex (Miralles and Vences 2013; Miralles et al. 2016a). Given the high and relatively constant rate of new species descriptions from the island, it seems essential to increase the accuracy of species delimitation in Malagasy reptiles. This can be achieved by using rigorous phylogenomic approaches to quantify the shape and breadth of contact/hybrid zones across Madagascar.

SPECIES FORMATION

Processes of species formation have so far been poorly studied in Malagasy reptiles. Based on overall distribution patterns, Raxworthy and Nussbaum (1995) suggested a role of montane refugia in generating the current species diversity of *Brookesia* chameleons. J. Brown et al. (2014) analyzed spatial patterns of different reptile groups and found that a combination of multiple mechanisms best explained the overall diversification of reptiles, but they also found that in certain reptile subgroups (e.g., *Brookesia* chameleons), there was a strong contribution of their "sanctuary" model (speciation by lineages persisting in refugia stable over time), validating the initial hypothesis of Raxworthy and Nussbaum (1995). Pearson and Raxworthy (2009) also found support for multiple drivers of speciation and regional endemism for reptile groups on Madagascar, and they especially highlighted the importance of climatic variation and ecotones, while finding poor support for the Pleistocene "watershed hypothesis" of Wilmé et al. (2006). A sanctuary model, together with climate stability models, also explained a large proportion of spatial species richness and endemism in iguanas but not in *Phelsuma* day geckos, where instead a so-called montane museum mechanism had a higher contribution (J. Brown et al. 2014). Scantlebury (2013) observed that speciation rates in several groups of Malagasy reptiles (*Brookesia*, *Paroedura*, *Phelsuma*, and *Uroplatus*) declined over time, suggesting that possibly these clades on the island represent adaptive radiations; however, since the underlying phylogenies did not include many of the deep intraspecific lineages that may represent young incipient speciation events, this conclusion needs confirmation. More recently, a detailed study of speciation rates for the entire pseudoxyrhophiid snake radiation demonstrated support for constant rates of diversification during the Neogene, followed by a decline during the Pleistocene (Burbrink et al. 2019).

An important habitat for several reptile groups is *tsingy* formations, areas of exposed karstic limestone eroded in a rather particular fashion (Veress et al. 2008, 2009). In particular, the northern Ankarana Massif is known to harbor many microendemic reptile (and amphibian) species, some of which (e.g., *Paroedura homalorhina*, *Geckolepis megalepis*, *Blaesodactylus microtuberculatus*, *Uroplatus fetsy*, *Madagascarophis lolo*) are genetically deeply divergent from related species that occur in neighboring areas. It is appealing to hypothesize that these species diverged after becoming specialized to this habitat (Ruane et al. 2016; Glaw et al. 2018); its many deep crevices and caves probably allow persistence of species even during severe climatic fluctuations. This hypothesis is supported by similar patterns of microendemism in limestone karsts worldwide, such as in Asian *Cyrtodactylus* geckos (e.g., Davis et al. 2019).

OUTLOOK

The ongoing scientific process of reptile species discovery and exploration on Madagascar means that we still have an incomplete knowledge of the island's biodiversity and the distribution of these animals. However, we are also at an exciting point where we can now explore patterns and processes of diversification in many species and radiations, and target research to address more specific issues such as genetic introgression, community assembly, competition, behavior, dispersal, population demography, and population extinction.

The most urgent issues will center on those species most vulnerable to extinction, with the greatest threat coming from habitat loss because of human activity (landscape modification), and for some species (especially chelonians) from illegal collection and trade. In the very near future, climate change is likely to constitute a serious threat for many species even within protected areas, and invasive species and pathogens could equally lead to dramatic declines if they become established on Madagascar. To date, we have only one candidate modern reptile extinction: the snake *Pseudoxyrhopus ankafinaensis*, which appears to have been restricted to medium-altitude moist evergreen forests in the southern portion of the Central Highlands (Raxworthy and Nussbaum 1994b). The forest habitat where this snake was collected has now been cleared, and the species has not been seen in more than 100 years. Unfortunately, more reptile extinctions seem likely over the next decades if their habitats continue to fragment and degrade. The inclusion (over the past 10 years) of all the Malagasy reptile species in the IUCN Red List represents an important contribution to increasing the visibility of these animals and having them better integrated in conservation planning and management. We are therefore optimistic that Madagascar's reptiles will play a more prominent role in future conservation efforts, as they also continue to reveal new insights into processes of diversification and evolution.

Subject editors: Miguel Vences and Achille P. Raselimanana

CONSERVATION CHALLENGES AND IN SITU AND EX SITU APPROACHES TO REPTILE CONSERVATION

A. Crottini, C. J. Gardner, M. Pedrono, R. K. B. Jenkins, O. Behra, A. Ramy, and C. J. Raxworthy

Enormous research effort over the last three decades has led to a good understanding of the taxonomy, evolution, and biogeographic origins of Malagasy reptiles (Crottini et al. 2012a; J. Brown et al. 2014). Although almost no subfossil material is available for amphibians, some notable Holocene reptile extinctions are known from Madagascar. These include the horned crocodile *Voay robustus* and probably two giant tortoises of the genus *Aldabrachelys* (*A. grandidieri* and populations of the *A. abrupta/gigantea* lineage), taxa that went extinct following the colonization of Madagascar by humans (Goodman and Jungers 2014). The drivers of their extinctions are not yet understood but may include hunting (for bushmeat), loss of habitat from fire or other human activities, climate change, predation (e.g., of clutches) by introduced mammals, and/or competition with other species (e.g., *Voay robustus* versus *Crocodylus niloticus*) (see Kuchling et al., pp. 1458–63).

A recent assessment of the conservation status of a randomized sample of global reptile species reveals that the vast majority of threatened reptile species are distributed in the tropics, and habitat loss and harvesting have been identified as the major threats to their survival (Böhm et al. 2013). Reptiles, on Madagascar and elsewhere, are known to have special ecological adaptations and dependency on specific habitats and environmental conditions (Raxworthy et al. 2007; Pearson and Raxworthy 2009), making them highly susceptible to changes in the extent and quality of their habitats (e.g., Huey et al. 2009; Sinervo et al. 2010). Reptiles represent an important portion of the endemic vertebrate fauna of Madagascar, where habitat destruction and fragmentation are among the major threats affecting not only reptiles but also other components of the island's unique biodiversity (Jenkins et al. 2014).

C. Blanc and Blommers-Schlösser (1987) were the first to approach the issue of conservation prioritization for amphibian and reptile species of Madagascar, stressing the need to preserve a representative set of all natural environments of Madagascar. After this first call, a survey of the situation of crocodiles was conducted by Behra and Hutton (1990) at the end of the 1980s, and Conservation International coordinated the first global conservation assessment on Madagascar, which included reptiles (Ganzhorn et al. 1997), followed by the Conservation and Assessment Management Plan (CAMP) workshop in 2001 (Ministère de l'Environnement Malgache et al. 2001). After this first phase, a randomized group of Malagasy reptile species was assessed according to IUCN criteria in the framework of a global study (Böhm et al. 2013), followed by assessments of chelonians in 2008, and of all remaining species in 2011 (Jenkins et al. 2014). As of December 2011, 373 Malagasy reptile species were included in the IUCN Red List, and all but one species (*Pseudoxyrhopus ankafinaensis*), which is most likely extinct (Raxworthy and Nussbaum 1994b), appeared to persist at that time. If species considered Data Deficient or not assessed are excluded, 39% were classified in one of the "threatened with extinction" categories of the IUCN Red List, with 22 listed as Critically Endangered, 49 as Endangered, 59 as Vulnerable, and a further 43 species assessed as Near Threatened (Jenkins et al. 2014); see IUCN (2019) for updated information. In accordance with the observed patterns of total reptile species richness, these authors found that coastal and peripheral zones hosted the greatest number of threatened species. About 10 years after this last effort and with more than 50 newly described species, we currently need a new update to the conservation status of Malagasy reptiles in order to identify the species at greatest risk of extinction and improve the accuracy of their conservation status.

THREATS

Deforestation

Prior to human arrival on Madagascar, the island was covered predominantly by forests (especially outside the Central Highlands), and most of its endemic reptiles are forest dwelling. Deforestation driven by largely small-scale agricultural expansion has reduced natural forest cover to less than 15% of the island, and 46% of the remainder is within 100 m of the forest edge (Vielledent et al. 2018). In addition, many areas of remaining forests are highly degraded, having undergone structural and floristic composition changes as the result of different anthropogenic factors, including habitat loss and degradation, which impact Madagascar's reptiles (Jenkins et al. 2014). The prediction of species' vulnerability is particularly important because many of the country's protected areas are designed as multiple-use sites in which resource extraction is permitted (C. Gardner 2009; C. Gardner et al. 2018; Goodman et al. 2018). However, while over the last two decades some important research on this topic has been conducted, available information is patchy and lacks synthesis. Although some reptile species are known to depend on habitats other than forests, little to no information is available on these habitat requirements and we therefore concentrate on the impacts of forest habitat modification.

Reptile Resilience to Habitat Disturbance

Several researchers have carried out reptile inventories within forests and nearby anthropogenically cleared areas (see Glaw et al., pp. 1305–22). In most of these studies, cleared areas retain 25–63% of the species richness of intact forests (mean 45.6%, n = 7) (D'Cruze et al. 2007; Megson et al. 2009a; Rakotondravony and Goodman 2011; Theisinger and Ratianarivo 2015; C. Gardner et al. 2016; Nopper et al. 2017a, 2018). In two studies investigating only lizard communities, the percentage of species retained following forest clearance is also within this range (Scott et al. 2006; D'Cruze and Kumar 2011). The exceptions to this pattern involve areas in which the anthropogenic landscapes retain a high proportion of trees (sometimes also of non-native origin, such as fruit tree orchards) or hedges around field boundaries: in these cases the anthropogenic landscapes retain 78–83% of species as compared to adjacent forests (Blumgart et al. 2017; Nopper et al. 2017a). As the latter examples highlight, the richness of reptiles in deforested landscapes is correlated to the proportion of woody vegetation cover (D'Cruze and Kumar 2011; Nopper et al. 2017a, 2018): indeed, a minimum of 10–30% appears to be required in a landscape to retain most reptile species (Nopper et al. 2018).

The presence of trees may therefore be important for many species, even if the trees are non-native. For example, fruit tree orchards may retain high species richness (Blumgart et al. 2017), and they appear to be a particularly suitable habitat for some species of *Phelsuma* day geckos. On Nosy Be, three (out of five) species of *Phelsuma* are more abundant in fruit tree or ylang-ylang orchards than in natural forest, while orchards harbor a greater richness and abundance of *Phelsuma* species than forests overall (Humphrey and Ward 2018). Similarly, orchards in northern Madagascar hold a significantly greater density of *P. grandis* than natural forests (D'Cruze et al. 2009a), and ylang-ylang and coffee plantations along roads on Nosy Be can sustain a diverse herpetofauna outside the protected areas (Andreone et al. 2003). However, although other forms of plantation (such as *Eucalyptus* and *Pinus*) cover a significant amount of land (especially in the east and Central Highlands) and are often close to degraded natural forest, the extent to which they support native reptile communities is unknown.

The presence of trees may explain the persistence of some reptile species in even the most anthropogenically disturbed habitats—towns and cities. Although little herpetological research has been carried out in such environments, at least 17 reptile species occur in the city of Toliara (C. Gardner and Jasper 2009; C. Gardner et al. 2015b), and some genera seem to occur in towns throughout the country (e.g., *Phelsuma*, *Lygodactylus*, *Hemidactylus*, *Trachylepis*, *Furcifer*; C. J. Gardner and C. J. Raxworthy, unpublished data).

While the body of research reviewed above suggests than an important proportion of the original forest reptile community can persist following deforestation, it is critical to note that all these inventories were carried out in cleared areas adjacent to remaining forests or in a mosaic of forest patches within a nonforest matrix. Little herpetological survey work has been carried out away from forest areas (D'Cruze et al. 2009b), so there is no information on the persistence of reptiles in most anthropogenic habitats that have been long disconnected from forest source areas. It is therefore not possible to know whether the reviewed nonforest areas support viable populations of the species, or whether these populations are maintained only through source-sink dynamics and the immigration of individuals from adjacent forest areas (Pulliam 1988; Barlow et al. 2007).

The use of species richness to quantify reptile communities following deforestation may mask declines in the abundance of persisting species. For example, while the gecko *Uroplatus henkeli* was recorded within coffee plantations on Nosy Komba, it was observed in that habitat only once, whereas it was unfailingly recorded on all transects within forests (Blumgart et al. 2017). In studies where abundance data are presented, 77–100% of species recorded in both forests and cleared areas were more abundant in forests (mean 86.5%, n = 4) (Scott et al. 2006; Theisinger and Ratianarivo 2015; C. Gardner et al. 2016; Nopper et al. 2017a). Again, a landscape in which cleared areas retain hedges around field boundaries provides an exception: of the 14 species recorded in both forests and cleared areas with hedges, only 36% were more abundant within forests (Nopper et al. 2017a). Because of the low detectability of snakes and fossorial species, data on the effect of habitat disturbance on them are largely missing.

Forest Degradation

While deforestation consistently reduces reptile richness, forest degradation (in which forests are "opened up" but some tree cover remains) causes idiosyncratic responses in reptile communities. Of the eight available comparisons between degraded and less degraded forests, moderate levels of degradation led to observed or predicted increases in reptile richness in half the cases, while at least 75% of species were retained following degradation in the remainder (Theisinger and Ratianarivo 2015; C. Gardner et al. 2016; Blumgart et al. 2017; Nopper et al. 2017a, 2017b, 2018). In addition, selective logging had no effect on reptile community composition in the dry deciduous forest of Kirindy Forest CNFEREF (Centre National de Formation, d'Etudes et de Recherche en Environnement et Foresterie) (Bloxam et al. 1996).

Forest degradation may lead to increases in species richness because of an increase in structural complexity and microhabitat heterogeneity (C. Gardner 2009; C. Gardner et al. 2016; Nopper et al. 2017a), or because of increasing solar radiation that favors heliothermic species, which are generally found outside forests (Theisinger and Ratianarivo 2015). As a result, degraded forest areas may retain many species from the original, intact forest but additionally support some species adapted to more open areas that otherwise avoid intact forest (e.g., Blumgart et al. 2017).

Beyond studies of whole reptile communities, chameleons have been a particular focus of some research. In moist evergreen forests at Andranomay, four *Calumma* species and two *Brookesia* species were recorded in low-disturbance forest (impacted by selective logging); all species except *B. ramanantsoai* also occurred in high-disturbance forest (recovering after fire), though four of the five species occurred at higher densities in the less degraded site (Jenkins et al. 2003). The establishment of paths through otherwise largely intact forests also impacts chameleon densities: chameleons in both western dry deciduous forests (*Furcifer oustaleti* and *F. rhinoceratus*) and moist evergreen forests (*C. brevicorne* and *Palleon nasus*) occurred at greater density near paths than away from them (Jenkins et al. 1999; Metcalf et al. 2005b). In dry deciduous forests of Menabe, selective logging had no clear overall effect on the chameleon community, although *B. brygooi* was associated with patches of dense ground vegetation arising from timber extraction (Randrianantoandro et al. 2010).

Habitat Fragmentation and Edge Effects

Fragmentation is a particular form of habitat change that can impact forest species through two mechanisms: 1) decline in habitat area and increasing isolation from other habitat patches, and 2) edge effects (changes to forest structure and composition because of increased solar radiation and other effects at the forest edge). In littoral forests in the extreme southeast, species richness is positively correlated with fragment size, and the species occurring in the smallest fragments form a nested subset of the reptile community in larger areas: of the 28 species recorded in a fragment of 427 ha, 21% did not occur in a fragment of 221 ha, and 64% were absent from a 10 ha fragment (Lehtinen and Ramanamanjato 2006). Forest specialists and rare species were the most extinction prone, and there was a negative correlation between extinction risk and tolerance of the matrix (nonforest) habitat, so a greater proportion of the community was composed of matrix-tolerant species as fragment size decreased. Edge effects in this community vary seasonally, with some species avoiding forest edges (i.e., preferring the interior) during the dry season but not the wet season, and vice versa. There was no significant relationship between the strength of edge avoidance and extinction vulnerability (Lehtinen et al. 2003). In contrast, fragment size had less influence on reptile communities in dry deciduous forests of Loky Manambato than the heterogeneity of habitats within forest patches. In this region even small forest fragments contained species that did not occur in larger areas, highlighting the lack of a nested pattern and the value of small habitat patches (Rakotondravony 2007).

Reptile species vary greatly in their sensitivity to habitat change, and it is not possible to reliably determine patterns based on ecology or species group. Indeed, in several cases, the same genus (e.g., *Phelsuma*, *Furcifer*) may contain species dependent on intact forests and others that are common in highly disturbed habitats, such as agricultural land and urban areas (Brady and Griffiths 1999; Raxworthy and Nussbaum 2000; Humphrey and Ward 2018). Nocturnal species appear to be more sensitive to habitat change than diurnal species. In the dry spiny thickets, for example, nocturnal species richness declines rapidly after only moderate habitat changes, while diurnal richness declines after greater levels of degradation (Nopper et al. 2018). Substrate preference may also affect sensitivity to habitat change, with arboreal species tending to decline in richness at lower levels of habitat degradation than terrestrial species (Theisinger and Ratianarivo 2015; C. Gardner et al. 2016; Nopper et al. 2017a); however, no such differences have been detected in some cases (Nopper et al. 2018). Fossorial species were the first to disappear following light degradation in one case (Theisinger and Ratianarivo 2015) but were most abundant in an area of moderate degradation elsewhere (C. Gardner et al. 2016), although limited information is available for this group of reptiles.

Forest degradation and clearance trigger turnover in reptile communities (C. Gardner et al. 2016): as habitats become more open, forest specialists tend to be lost, and only a subset of degradation-tolerant species are retained in the landscape (Nopper et al. 2018). Habitat specialists are, logically, more vulnerable to habitat change than generalists because of their specific habitat requirements. Specialists also tend to be less abundant, more range restricted, and more extinction prone than generalist species, which are often widespread and able to tolerate a range of habitats including anthropogenically disturbed ones (McKinney 1997; Segura et al. 2007; Colles et al. 2009). Intact forests are likely to harbor range-restricted and threatened habitat specialists that require the maintenance of these habitats for their survival, while the species that persist in highly degraded habitats are not dependent on conservation action and therefore assume lower conservation value (C. Gardner 2009; Nopper et al. 2017a).

Climate Change

One of the greatest long-term concerns for the conservation of biodiversity on Madagascar is conserving suitable species habitat under the stress of climate change. For reptiles, the biggest threat is likely from changes to thermal environments and precipitation, because most species are restricted to specific climatic conditions on the island. This is evident in elevational transects where all species are confined to relatively narrow elevations of habitat (e.g., Raxworthy and Nussbaum 1994a, 1996a; Raxworthy et al. 1998; Nussbaum et al. 1999b; Raselimanana et al. 2000a) and has been demonstrated repeatedly by species ecological niche modeling, where species distribution models require both temperature and precipitation layers to be highly predictive (e.g., Raxworthy et al. 2003, 2008a, 2008b; Florio et al. 2012; Florio and Raxworthy 2016).

The impacts of changing precipitation patterns on Madagascar, which may be shifting the dry season and making rainfall more unpredictable and more intense (Hannah et al. 2008), have not yet been studied for Malagasy reptiles. However, warming temperatures have been documented for the island (see Jury, pp. 91–98), and this is associated with records of elevational upslope shifts (movements) for reptiles and amphibians, as observed on the Tsaratanàna Massif by Raxworthy et al. (2008b). These upslope population movements are in line with predictions based on warming trends and the moist adiabatic lapse rate of a 6°C temperature difference per 1000 m of elevational change. Of major concern are species endemic to habitats close to summits of isolated massif systems, which will be the first to lose all their available habitat with a warming climate and are thus especially vulnerable to extinction. For Malagasy montane amphibians, temperature increases greater than 1.5°C and upslope displacements greater than 250 m are predicted to substantially increase extinction rates (Raxworthy 2008), and similar patterns can be expected for montane reptiles. Extinction from warming and upslope shifts will be further exacerbated by habitat fragmentation if species are unable to cross habitat barriers and thus move upslope.

Pet Trade

The global pet trade is regulated by national and international laws, and thousands of wild Malagasy animals are caught and harvested from the wild and then traded legitimately, although illegal commerce is also fueling this market. The legal trade is ruled by CITES (Convention on International Trade in Endangered Species of Wild Fauna and Flora), which is responsible for controlling all imports and exports of species it covers, while the illegal trade operates outside these channels.

Some of Madagascar's reptile species are included in Appendix I of CITES and cannot be traded (e.g., *Astrochelys* spp., *Pyxis* spp., *Brookesia perarmata*, *Acrantophis* spp., *Sanzinia madagascariensis*), although some continue to suffer under the pressure of the international illicit wildlife trade (e.g., *Astrochelys* spp.; Carpenter et al. 2004, 2005). Some other iconic Malagasy reptile species can legally be traded (e.g., *Furcifer* spp., *Calumma* spp., *Phelsuma* spp., *Uroplatus* spp., *Paroedura* spp.), with some species being heavily traded (Carpenter et al. 2004, 2005; Todd 2011), and with many populations declining in abundance and distribution because of intense pressure from both the legal and illicit wildlife trade (e.g., Nussbaum and Raxworthy 2000a; Raxworthy and Nussbaum 2000; Carpenter et al. 2004). The pet trade saw a massive increase at the end of the 1980s with the opening of Madagascar to the international economic community (Behra and Raxworthy 1991). A general trend has emerged where novel species and groups become targeted by the pet trade (based on evolving customer demand), which is rapidly followed by nonsustainable legal and illegal international trade, in some instances leading to their listing in a CITES appendix some three to five years later.

A crocodile ranching program for the sustainable production of skins was launched in 1989 in partnership with rural communities (Behra and Ramandimbison 1992), but its management was too complex to result in effective curbing of illegal hunting, and the program was stopped a few years ago. All extant tortoise species of Madagascar are classified as Critically Endangered under IUCN Red List criteria (IUCN 2019) and are currently listed in Appendix I of CITES. They are also protected under Malagasy national law, and their export for the international pet trade is entirely illegal. However, their illegal trade remains highly attractive and thousands of tortoises are smuggled out of Madagascar each year (Gray 2018).

The demand for some species such as the Ploughshare Tortoise (*Astrochelys yniphora*, which on the illegal market can fetch from US$510 to $47,000 each) by tortoise hobbyists has destroyed 30 years of previously successful conservation efforts (Auliya et al. 2016), and their wild populations are currently reduced to just a few dozen adult individuals (Pedrono and Clausen 2018). As a result, this species is now one of the rarest reptile species in the world (IUCN 2019). Unlike *A. yniphora*, large-bodied individuals of the Radiated Tortoise (*A. radiata*) are also traded within Madagascar for bushmeat (Walker and Rafeliarisoa 2012b), and this species is currently facing significant risk of large-scale population declines if this additional threat is not halted. However, *A. radiata*, particularly small-bodied animals, is also heavily exploited in the illegal pet trade, and the numbers of occasional seizures, reaching in recent years up to several thousand individuals, provide an index of the massive pressure that the illegal international trade adds to the threats facing wild populations of this species (Walker 2011a; Jenkins et al. 2014). Boas of the genera *Sanzinia* and *Acrantophis* are also illegally collected for the international pet trade, but many fewer than in the past (IUCN 2019).

Recently it has been shown that outside of traditional trade channels (e.g., physical markets), internet-based platforms are facilitating the illegal international trade of Malagasy reptiles, exacerbating the pressure of the pet trade on native wild populations (Walker 2011b; Morgan and Chng 2018; Runhovde 2018). The way these virtual markets operate makes it difficult to effectively monitor their activities, and these platforms currently have the dangerous potential to scale up what can currently be considered a niche interest into a global demand. Madagascar is one of the world's poorest countries (International Money Fund 2019) where wildlife crime has recently increased (Jones et al. 2019). The collection of native reptiles to supply the legal and illegal international pet trade relies on local communities; however, this activity is generally sporadic and communities perceive it as opportunistic, risky, and unreliable (Robinson et al. 2018a, 2018b). As these latter authors suggest, improved understanding of the dimensions of wildlife trade on Madagascar should be used to plan ad hoc conservation policies that consider the socioeconomic situation of Madagascar. Chameleons represent a significant portion of the reptile diversity of the island and suffer from both widespread habitat loss and over-collection for the pet trade (Auliya et al. 2016). A recent project developed in collaboration with Madagasikara Voakajy, the Malagasy government, IUCN, Conservation International, the Université d'Antananarivo, and the University of Kent is trying to fill this gap by exploring whether the sustainable use of some key species of chameleons is achievable.

Bushmeat

With the notable exception of *Astrochelys radiata*, very little is known about the potential pressure that bushmeat hunting and consumption can have on native Malagasy wildlife (Jenkins et al. 2011), and this is especially true for reptile species. It is expected that both Malagasy ground and tree boas (*Acrantophis* spp. and *Sanzinia* spp.) suffer pressure from bushmeat hunting to some degree. Further, crocodiles (*Crocodylus niloticus*), an endemic freshwater turtle (*Erymnochelys madagascariensis*), and sea turtle populations have suffered and continue to suffer from hunting and egg collection (Kuchling 1988).

Biological Invasions

Biological invasions are a human-mediated phenomenon that occurs when a non-native species is introduced to a new area and becomes established. This process can generate a multitude of impacts on human societies and is currently considered one of the major drivers of change in ecosystem services (Millennium Ecosystem Assessment 2005). Unlike in other island contexts, biological invasions have received only limited attention on Madagascar (Kull et al. 2014), and the impact of invasive species on native biota is still largely underexplored. The recent invasion of the Asian toad (*Duttaphrynus melanostictus*) (see Freeman et al., pp. 1404–10), and the media attention that this phenomenon received, led to increased interest in the "invasive species" problems of Madagascar, stimulated discussion aimed at defining a national strategy to reduce the risks of new invasions, and placed the management of invasive species at the core of the priority actions to protect the unique ecosystems of Madagascar and promote their sustainable use. Asian toads secrete bufotoxins to deter predation (Chen and Kovaříková 1967; Ujvari et al. 2015), and a recent study revealed widespread predicted susceptibility of most native vertebrates of Madagascar (including all analyzed native reptiles) to the toxins of this toad (Marshall et al. 2018). With respect to native reptiles, these results raise concerns about the snake fauna, which is known to widely prey on amphibians (e.g., Jovanovic et al. 2009; Rosa et al. 2010).

The Gold-dust Day Gecko (*Phelsuma laticauda*) and the Madagascar Giant Day Gecko (*P. grandis*) are endemic to northern Madagascar (Glaw and Vences 2007; Dubos et al. 2014). They occur in both degraded and relatively intact habitats (e.g., in open spots in intact forest) and have succeeded in colonizing and becoming established in multiple sites around the world (e.g., Allison 2002;

Krysko et al. 2003; Ota and Ineich 2006). After multiple introductions, probably as accidental escapees from commercial pet-trade export facilities, these species have been able to colonize and expand their distribution both overseas and on Madagascar (Pearson and Raxworthy 2009; Gehring et al. 2010a; Dubos et al. 2014). The impact of these multiple introductions needs to be further investigated, but at least in the case of the introduced population of *P. laticauda* in Toamasina, it is evident that this establishment is having a negative impact (in terms of both occurrence and abundance) on the natural local populations of *P. lineata*, which are becoming rare. Another potential problem might be *Agama agama*, one individual of which was observed in 2004 close to Ivato Airport near Antananarivo (Wagner et al. 2009), and which could compete with endemic species if it manages to establish a permanent breeding population.

The identification of parasites and the characterization of host-parasite interactions remain poorly explored in Malagasy reptiles and certainly represent an important area for future investigations (e.g., Maia et al. 2014). *Ranavirus* has been identified in wild amphibian populations on Madagascar (Kolby et al. 2015). The transmission of novel strains of *Ranavirus* from amphibians may potentially threaten Madagascar's endangered reptile species (Brenes et al. 2014), but there is a general knowledge gap regarding the distribution, prevalence, and virulence of *Ranavirus* on the island.

IN SITU CONSERVATION

Madagascar has over 100 terrestrial protected areas of various IUCN statuses covering more than 10% of landscapes and seascapes (Goodman et al. 2018; Waeber et al. 2019). The intent of the island's protected area network is to conserve important habitats and preserve the multiple endemic species that live therein. On average around 40% of the geographic range of Malagasy reptiles currently receives formal protection (Jenkins et al. 2014). Coverage tends to be lower for Critically Endangered and Vulnerable species, and as of December 2011, four Critically Endangered species (*Calumma hafahafa*, *Phelsuma masohoala*, *P. pronki*, and *Pseudoxyrhopus ankafinaensis* [the latter might be extinct]) and one Endangered species (*Lygodactylus ornatus*) were not included in any protected area. Several species occur only in intact or slightly degraded forest habitats, suggesting that in several cases intact forests are irreplaceable (C. Gardner 2009; Gibson et al. 2011; Watson et al. 2018) and must be maintained if the full complement of Malagasy reptile species is to be conserved.

The IUCN classifies protected areas in different categories based on their management objectives (Dudley 2008). Madagascar hosts some "strict" protected areas (IUCN category Ia, Strict Nature Reserve) where human visitation, use, and impacts are strictly controlled and limited. However, given that many of the country's new protected areas permit resource extraction (IUCN category V or VI), which can be expected to contribute to forest degradation (C. Gardner et al. 2018), these areas may suffer the loss of disturbance-sensitive species. The country's network of strict protected areas may therefore be more important for the long-term conservation of reptile species (C. Gardner 2009).

In addition, as mentioned above, several Malagasy reptile species have narrow climate envelopes and are particularly vulnerable to climate change (e.g., Raxworthy et al. 2008b). To buffer these effects, protection of climate refugia through the existing Malagasy protected area network should be the cornerstone of the reptile conservation strategy for two reasons: 1) the prohibitively high costs and questionable effectiveness of other strategies including large-scale restoration and ex situ activities, and 2) the ability to make the best use of hard-won existing conservation gains. This effort should be coupled with complementary restoration activities to enhance reptile species dispersion to and between climate refugia. Finally, long-term, sustainable monitoring and adaptive management systems need to be implemented to maintain the effectiveness of the proposed measurements.

EX SITU CONSERVATION

Because of the beautiful coloration (e.g., *Phelsuma* spp., *Calumma* spp., *Furcifer* spp.), remarkable appearance (small *Pyxis* or larger *Astrochelys* tortoises; small tree or ground boas, *Sanzinia* spp. and *Acrantophis* spp.), or peculiarity (*Uroplatus* geckos) of the reptiles of Madagascar, several zoos and aquaria around the world are dedicating part of their exhibit sections and husbandry facilities to them (Mattioli et al. 2006). Most of these species are currently bred in these facilities and play an important role in the development of ex situ reproduction protocols, and in maintaining sustainable captive populations. These captive-bred populations, if properly managed, could potentially also be bred intensively and traded, to reduce the number of wild-caught animals for the pet trade. All *Phelsuma* species generally have a similar reproductive biology (Rundquist 1994), usually laying two eggs, and incubation is normally successful, making them a relatively easy group of reptiles to maintain in captivity and a good candidate group to become commercially viable. *Uroplatus* species, on the other hand, are more difficult to maintain and breed in captivity, yet they are among the most in-demand species in the pet trade. Only four *Furcifer* species can regularly be legally imported into Europe, with *F. pardalis* being the most sought-after species. *Furcifer pardalis* is relatively easy to maintain and reproduce in captivity, and it is also a good candidate to become commercially viable. Unlike *F. pardalis*, most species of *Calumma* cannot be exported from Madagascar, and the number of specimens outside Madagascar associated with zoos, aquaria, and private breeders is very small. In addition, sustainable reproduction of one of the most sought-after species of this genus, *C. parsonii* (Figure 12.7), has not yet been achieved (Mattioli et al. 2006). Breeding protocols for both *Astrochelys radiata* and *Pyxis arachnoides* are well established, while other species (e.g., of the genera *Paroedura*, *Zonosaurus*, *Oplurus*, *Chalarodon*) are in very low demand, and therefore there seems to be no need to establish intensive captive-breeding programs for these species to supplement the pet trade.

Within Madagascar there are long-term and successful captive-breeding programs focusing on the endemic tortoises and freshwater turtles. These programs aim to breed these Critically Endangered species and reintroduce them in the wild. The

FIGURE 12.7 **Large forest chameleons such as *Calumma parsonii* are sought after in the international pet trade but there is no ex situ captive-breeding program for this species.** (PHOTO by F. Glaw and M. Vences.)

FIGURE 12.8 **The Angonoka (*Astrochelys yniphora*), one of the most endangered tortoise species in the world, is now reduced to just a few individuals in the wild because of overcollecting for the illegal pet trade, and it persists mainly in captive-breeding colonies.** (PHOTO by M. Vences.)

conservation of the Ploughshare Tortoise (or Angonoka, *Astrochelys yniphora*; Figure 12.8) was launched in 1986 by the Durrell Wildlife Conservation Trust, a project developed in collaboration with the Direction Générale des Eaux et Forêts and the World Wildlife Fund (WWF). A total of 17 adult individuals were used at the beginning of this project, and within about 30 years it generated about 600 captive-bred juveniles. The same project also started to develop conservation plans in partnership with local communities inhabiting the areas adjacent to Angonoka habitat. Within the framework of this project local communities have been involved in creating firebreaks and establishing Baly Bay National Park. Captive-breeding programs for two Critically Endangered tortoise species (*A. yniphora* and *Pyxis planicauda*) and the freshwater Malagasy Big-headed Turtle (*Erymnochelys madagascariensis*) are currently active at the Chelonian Captive Breeding Center at Ampijoroa Forestry Station, Ankarafantsika National Park (Razandrimamilafiniarivo et al. 2000).

Other captive-breeding programs for reptiles have also been developing in other regions of Madagascar. These include Ivoloina Park and Research Station just north of Toamasina (managed by the Madagascar Fauna and Flora Group [MFG]) for *A. radiata*; Croc Farm at Antananarivo (private enterprise) for *Crocodylus niloticus*; and the Mangily Tortoise Village just north of Toliara (managed by the Station for the Observation and Protection of Tortoises and Their Environment [SOPTOM] and Association de Sauvegarde de l'Environnement [ASE]) for *A. radiata* and *P. arachnoides*. In addition, the Anjajavy protected area is currently conducting the first (re)introduction of giant tortoises on Madagascar, using captive-bred individuals of *Aldabrachelys gigantea*. The long-term goal of this innovative project is to develop a rewilding program based on the establishment of a viable population of giant tortoises (Pedrono et al. 2013). Two hatchlings were born in November 2019, the first to be born on Madagascar since the extinction of Madagascar's giant tortoises over 500 years ago (Pedrono et al. 2020).

Captive breeding with reintroduction has long been considered a viable conservation strategy for long-lived species of Malagasy reptiles with delayed maturity, low mortality, and innate behavior (Pedrono and Sarovy 2000), although it would need to be coupled with in situ conservation approaches to become sustainable (Pedrono 2011). Theoretically, any reptile species whose populations in the wild are no longer viable can still avoid extinction through reintroduction of captive individuals if a healthy, sustainable, reproductive ex situ population exists and suitable habitat remains. However, the effectiveness of reintroduction projects still lacks a robust standardized protocol.

Radiated Tortoises are regularly seized by authorities both on Madagascar and overseas, and some of these animals are repatriated to the wild. Their release has become the default solution to overcrowded rescue centers in southern Madagascar and is also considered to be a means of boosting wild populations, but it is crucial to evaluate the success of these reintroductions. This would ensure that the risks associated with this approach—including the spread of non-native and native diseases and the disruption of genetic diversity of wild populations—do not exceed its benefits. This is especially true for species like endemic tortoises where released individuals are likely at some level to be re-collected by poachers.

Until now, ex situ facilities have played a small role in the conservation of Malagasy reptile biodiversity, and it is unrealistic to hope that such facilities will sustain and manage hundreds of threatened reptile species long term (Lees and Wilcken 2009). However, it is worth exploring the captive-breeding option to supply the international market and invest part of the profits in conservation activities (Mattioli et al. 2006). There also is a need to diversify knowledge on captive-breeding of threatened Malagasy reptile species, involving zoos and aquaria, including refocusing such activities on threatened and microendemic species.

Subject editors: Angelica Crottini, Miguel Vences, and Achille P. Raselimanana

VALORIZATION OF REPTILES AND AMPHIBIANS FROM THE WILDLIFE TRADE AND ECOTOURISM

A. I. Carpenter, F. C. E. Rabemananjara, O. Behra, A. P. Raselimanana, F. M. Ratsoavina, K. C. Wollenberg Valero, and N. D'Cruze

SOCIOECONOMIC ASPECTS OF WILDLIFE VALORIZATION ON MADAGASCAR

It is a long-standing ambition to align conservation requirements and poverty alleviation to engender mutual benefits (D. Brown 1998; Milner-Gulland and Mace 1998; Low et al. 1999). While conservation benefits have been cited globally from the sustainable exploitation of wildlife resources (Norman 1987; Milner-Gulland and Mace 1998), on Madagascar the actual harvesting impacts on wild reptile and amphibian populations, and on the welfare of individual animals, are relatively poorly known. Moreover, in recent years it has been more commonly stated that unsustainable trade in wildlife is one of the major drivers of species decline globally (Gibbons et al. 2000; IPBES 2019). Specifically on Madagascar, where unsustainable wildlife harvesting occurs both within and outside protected areas (Jenkins et al. 2014), this situation is further compounded by the high numbers of new species, endemic to Madagascar, that are still being described (Glaw and Vences 2000; Vieites et al. 2009; see Glaw et al., pp. 1305–22 and pp. 1423–42). Hence, it has been suggested that alternative nonextractive methods of valorizing environments, such as wildlife ecotourism, also need to be considered (Dixon and Pagiola 2001; Ormsby and Mannle 2006). However, this too needs to be responsibly managed to minimize negative impacts on Madagascar's unique herpetofauna (Moorhouse et al. 2015).

Historically, local communities had little or no involvement in the formal establishment of protected areas on Madagascar (Shyamsundar and Kramer 1997), yet in many cases they have ostensibly received varying degrees of negative impact from their creation (Durbin and Ralambo 1994). Furthermore, it has also been stated that many local communities do not perceive protected areas as bringing any direct benefits because the people are prevented from utilizing these areas, and the natural resources therein, for either subsistence or commerce (Nicoll and Langrand 1989; Durbin and Ralambo 1994; Shyamsundar and Kramer 1997). Similarly, not all local communities are enthusiastic about engaging in the live trade for international markets (which typically omits bushmeat, other derivatives, and domestic uses) for many reasons, such as the repulsion some feel for reptiles, concerns about payment security, fear of legal repercussions, or traditional reluctance to harvest certain species, especially snakes and chameleons (Brady and Griffiths 1999; Robinson et al. 2018b). Nevertheless, the live trade for international markets appears to be flourishing on Madagascar, with relatively high levels of trade in Malagasy reptiles and amphibians supplying international demands (Carpenter et al. 2004, 2014; Rabemananjara et al. 2007; Carpenter and Robson 2008).

REPTILE AND AMPHIBIAN TRADE REVENUES

Various publications have provided estimated values for certain taxonomic groups, such as chameleons generating over US$14.5 million (Carpenter et al. 2004), amphibians traded between 2000 and 2006 generating up to US$906,750 (Carpenter and Robson 2008), or *Mantella* traded between 2001 and 2003 generating up to US$246,372 (Rabemananjara et al. 2007). In 2013 alone, the trade in reptiles and amphibians was estimated to generate up to US$646,000 (Robinson et al. 2018a). While supply chain structures can vary on Madagascar (Carpenter 2003; Carpenter et al. 2005), the three-actor chain is reported as the most common, with collector and intermediary positions filled by Malagasy people. That is, locals collect animals in the wild and sell them to intermediary traders, who in turn sell them to exporters (Rabemananjara et al. 2007; Robinson et al. 2018a). However, wildlife trade comes with potential hazards to the already challenging protection of Madagascar's wildlife, such as the possibility of introducing the amphibian disease chytridiomycosis into pristine areas (Andreone et al. 2008; Wollenberg et al. 2010; see Bletz et al., pp. 1342–49).

Collating trade data from the CITES (Convention on International Trade in Endangered Species of Wild Fauna and Flora) database (on 7 November 2019 with purpose code "T" [commercial], source code "W" [wild], and trade term "LIV" [live]) for all CITES-listed reptiles and amphibians exported from Madagascar between 2007 and 2018 revealed a total of 167,754 individual reptiles and 71,050 individual amphibians (Figure 12.9). Frogs of the genus *Mantella* made up nearly 97% of the amphibian total, while

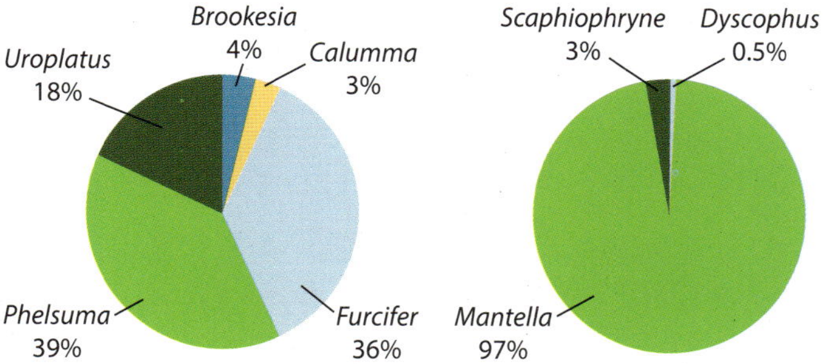

FIGURE 12.9 **The percentage breakdown of reptiles (left) and amphibians (right) exported from Madagascar between 2007 and 2018 by genera. Utilizing the CITES database with purpose code "T" (commercial), source code "W" (wild), and trade term "LIV" (live), the trade data were newly collated on 7 November 2019 for all reptiles and amphibians exported from Madagascar between 2007 and 2018. Four other genera also included in the collated data make up small percentages of the total trade in reptiles: *Zonosaurus* (0.09%), *Erymnochelys* (0.06%), "*Chamaeleo*" (which refers to *Calumma* and *Furcifer* and the older genus name for large chameleons), and *Palleon* (0.02%). Note that trade in non-CITES species is not included here.**

day geckos of the genus *Phelsuma* (nearly 40%) and chameleons of the genus *Furcifer* (nearly 36%) made up the majority of the reptile total.

The top three species from within the most-traded genera (*Mantella*, *Phelsuma*, and *Furcifer*; Figure 12.9) were, for the amphibian *Mantella*, *M. betsileo* (n = 22,737, 33%), *M. baroni* (31%), and *M. nigricans* (11%). For the reptiles, the top three species of *Furcifer* were *F. pardalis* (n = 19,600, 33%), *F. lateralis* (26%), and *F. verrucosus* (18.8%), and the top three species of *Phelsuma* were *P. lineata* (n = 17,939, 28%), *P. quadriocellata* (24%), and *P. laticauda* (22%). Consequently, based on dedicated species prices extracted from the published scientific literature (Table 12.2), an estimated total of US$401,470 (just over 15% of the more than US$2.6 million generated for exporters) was generated from the trade between 2007 and 2018 and theoretically made available to Malagasy people; approximately 21% was received at the collector level and 79% at the intermediary level (Table 12.2).

WILDLIFE ECOTOURISM REVENUE

An alternative to the extractive approach to valorizing wildlife is viewing it in situ—that is, ecotourism. This is often considered a panacea for resolving potential conflicts between local people's needs and the conservation of protected areas, by bringing tourists

TABLE 12.2. **Value (US$ in 2019) of the reptile and amphibian trade to the three actor levels involved with the wildlife trade on Madagascar between 2007 and 2018**

GENUS	VALUE PER INDIVIDUAL TO WILDLIFE TRADE ACTORS			NUMBER TRADED	TOTAL VALUE TO WILDLIFE TRADE ACTORS		
	COLLECTOR	INTERMEDIARY	EXPORTER		COLLECTOR	INTERMEDIARY	EXPORTER
Calumma[1]	0.36	0.42	34.57	4843	1743	2034	167,423
Furcifer[1]	0.36	0.42	34.57	60,263	21,694	25,311	2,083,292
"*Chamaeleo*"[1]	0.36	0.42	34.57	10	4	4	346
Mantella[2]	0.43	1.74	2.92	68,798	29,583	119,709	200,890
Erymnochelys	0.3	1.62	1.62	110	33	179	178
Palleon	0.3	1.62	1.62	32	10	52	52
Phelsuma	0.3	1.62	1.62	65,329	19,599	105,833	105,833
Uroplatus	0.3	1.62	1.62	30,335	9101	49,143	49,143
Brookesia	0.3	1.62	1.62	6686	2006	10,831	10,831
Zonosaurus	0.3	1.62	1.62	146	44	237	237
Dyscophus	0.3	1.62	1.62	342	103	554	554
Scaphiophryne	0.3	1.62	1.62	1910	573	3094	3094
Total					84,491	316,979	2,621,872

Note: "*Chamaeleo*" refers to species of *Calumma* and *Furcifer* listed under the old inclusive scientific name applied to all large chameleons; these values do not include species that are not CITES listed (e.g., *Boophis* frogs).

[1] Denotes dedicated chameleon prices extracted from Carpenter et al. (2005) and adjusted for inflation in US$.

[2] Denotes dedicated *Mantella* prices extracted from Rabemananjara et al. (2007) and adjusted for inflation in Malagasy ariary before conversion to US$; all remaining prices extracted from Robinson et al. (2018a) and adjusted for inflation in US$.

to see the wildlife and developing associated services around this premise (Dixon and Pagiola 2001). Several studies have estimated the value of ecotourism to Madagascar, often at the level of the protected area. For example, in the early 1990s at Mantadia, the economic revenue generated by ecotourists was estimated at US$24–$65 per individual visitor, or a total of US$0.8–$2.2 million per annum. At Ranomafana, in 2002, it was estimated that a total of up to US$31,246 was generated per annum, with US$15,836 going to local communities. While lemurs are considered the main attraction for most visitors (J. Peters 1998; Duffy 2006), chameleons ranked second in a survey of over 600 ecotourists visiting different protected areas on Madagascar (Wollenberg et al. 2011). Additionally, when shown pictures of local herpetofauna, most tourists expressed interest in learning more about these animals. Estimated revenue received by local communities around the Masoala Peninsula ranged from US$700 in 1999 to US$500 in 2001 (Ormsby and Mannle 2006). At the national scale, it was estimated based on 2006 data that ecotourism generated between US$26 million and $29 million, with approximately 17% of total tourists visiting protected areas (Wollenberg et al. 2011).

Using data from the Ministère du Tourisme (Table 12.3), we can conclude that between 2007 and 2018, the approximately 27% of ecotourists with an interest in herpetofauna generated a total of over US$51 million, using the values of Wollenberg et al. (2011). Alternatively, ecotourism generated from over US$17 million to over US$46 million, using the lower and upper values of Dixon and Pagiola (2001) (Table 12.3).

CONCLUSION

Over the period for which data exist (2007–2018), the international live trade in Malagasy herpetofauna generated estimated total revenue of US$401,470, a portion of which reached local Malagasy people and communities. Ecotourism focused on reptiles and amphibians was valued at US$17 million to $46 million, with maximum estimates of over US$51 million. These estimates were greater than the estimated revenue generated from the wildlife trade, but it is unclear how much revenue reached local people. For comparison, however, in just 2018, Madagascar's top revenue generators were, in order of importance, coffee, tea, and spices (valued at US$1 billion; vanilla alone was worth US$855.4 million and cloves US$149 million); in 10th place among revenue generators was mineral fuels, including oil (valued at US$51.5 million) (World's Top Exports 2019).

While revenue from ecotourism with a herpetological focus was over two orders of magnitude higher than that generated from the international live trade, the revenue was focused toward zones with protected areas, bringing benefits to adjacent communities. Conversely, those involved with the live trade were more geographically dispersed and in most cases had no clear association with protected

TABLE 12.3. Estimated value (US$ in 2019) of ecotourism to Madagascar from 2007 to 2018

	NUMBER OF TOURISTS ARRIVING[1]	17% ECOTOURISTS	ESTIMATED REVENUE GENERATION[2]	DIXON AND PAGIOLA UPPER LIMIT[3]	DIXON AND PAGIOLA LOWER LIMIT[‡3]	27% OF ECOTOURISTS WHO PRIORITIZE WANTING TO SEE HERPS	ESTIMATED REVENUE GENERATION[†]
2007	344,348	58,539	22,590,262	5,519,657	2,037,748	15,806	6,099,371
2008	375,010	63,752	24,601,781	6,011,148	2,219,197	17,213	6,642,481
2009	162,687	27,657	10,672,755	2,607,759	962,733	7467	2,881,644
2010	19,052	3239	1,249,868	305,390	112,744	874	337,464
2011	225,055	38,259	14,764,283	3,607,474	1,331,808	10,330	3,986,356
2012	255,942	43,510	16,790,563	4,102,571	1,514,588	11,748	4,533,452
2013	196,375	33,384	12,882,789	3,147,754	1,162,088	9014	3,478,353
2014	222,374	37,804	14,588,402	3,564,500	1,315,943	10,207	3,938,868
2015	244,321	41,535	16,028,191	3,916,295	1,445,818	11,214	4,327,611
2016	293,185	49,841	19,233,816	4,699,550	1,734,981	13,457	5,193,130
2017	255,460	43,428	16,758,942	4,094,845	1,511,736	11,726	4,524,914
2018	291,299	49,521	19,110,088	4,669,319	1,723,820	13,371	5,159,724

Notes: Values were obtained using the multipliers of Wollenberg et al. (2011), assuming 17% of tourists are ecotourists and 27% of ecotourists prioritize herps (reptiles and amphibians) as their target taxa; the "aggregated average value" is provided. Also, the upper and lower estimated values provided by Dixon and Pagiola (2001) were used to calculate the estimated value of ecotourism. All values converted to 2019 US$ rates.

[1] Data from Ministère du Tourisme/PAF/ADEMA/RAVINALA AIR-PORTS/APMF (collated October 2019).

[2] Denotes Wollenberg et al. (2011), average value per protected area used to perform calculation, adjusted for inflation in US$.

[3] Denotes the estimated per person values of Dixon and Pagiola (2001), adjusted for inflation in US$, multiplied by the number of ecotourists each year.

areas. Hence, the two sources of revenue generation were possibly complementary in that each could potentially engage with different local communities. Therefore, they should be seen not as alternatives, but rather as activities that can operate in parallel, as long as wildlife trade is conducted sustainably.

Despite the short-term economic benefits, the long-term conservation impact resulting from the current scope and scale of the consumptive use of wildlife is being increasingly brought into question (IPBES 2019). The potential negative impacts of unsustainable exploitation are not limited to extractive use of Madagascar's herpetofauna alone. For example, broad-scale issues can arise from ecotourism operators' environmental responsibility, such as deleterious impacts from the demand for water supplies or waste disposal (Kasim 2007). Alternatively, at a finer scale, irresponsible ecotourism can also bring net negative impacts to both the conservation and welfare of wild animals, including reptiles (Moorhouse et al. 2015, 2017; D'Cruze et al. 2017, 2018). For example, regular proximity of tourists to free-ranging wildlife outside Madagascar can negatively impact an array of animal behaviors, such as breeding (Jacobson and Lopez 1994) and foraging (Meissner et al. 2015). Direct physical contact with wild-caught wildlife can also lead to the unintentional death of individual animals or to species, potentially threatened species, being brought into captivity to show to tourists. Lastly, although no reptile pathogens are known to be immediately transmittable to humans, these animals harbor a large number of viruses, bacteria, and protozoans, and minimizing their physical contact with humans also minimizes the risk of zoonotic pandemics spreading from reptile hosts into the human population. Often these types of negative impacts are difficult to detect, especially by tourists themselves (Moorhouse et al. 2015), while different attitudes and societal expectations further complicate such decision-making (Moorhouse et al. 2017). Ultimately, there are positives and negatives associated with the valorization of both the live trade and ecotourism, and managers will need to ensure the long-term sustainability and minimal environmental impact of both going forward.

Subject editors: Angus I. Carpenter, Miguel Vences, and Achille P. Raselimanana

REPTILES INTRODUCED TO AND FROM MADAGASCAR

A. P. Raselimanana and M. Vences

Voluntary or accidental introductions of non-native fauna and flora to Madagascar started when human settlers first arrived on the island many centuries ago (see Wright and Rakotoarisoa, pp. 181–90), and it has continued up to the present. Several reasons exist for the introduction of these organisms (Randriamoria 2019): use for food, as biological control associated with agricultural problems, as pets, and for display in zoological gardens (e.g., Indian Python in the Parc Botanique et Zoologique de Tsimbazaza); they are also introduced by accident.

Assessment of the native or introduced nature of a species on Madagascar is useful for two reasons. First, to understand the biogeographic origins and age of the extant Malagasy fauna, it is important to base analyses only on native species. Second, species introductions may threaten the native fauna through competition, predation, or zoonotic diseases. This is especially obvious in the island's freshwater habitats, where non-native species (e.g., *Channa* cf. *striata*, nonendemic cichlids) are partly responsible for the highly endangered status of many native fish taxa (see Sparks and Stiassny, pp. 1245–60). No similar threats have yet been identified from introduced reptiles. Assessing the origin of the non-native reptile species of Madagascar can be complex. In the following sections, we review those species for which introduction has been postulated or is likely, followed by Malagasy species on neighboring regional islands, and then Malagasy species that have been introduced to other areas.

TURTLES

Kinixys zombensis

The Hinge-back Tortoise, *Kinixys zombensis*, may have been introduced to Madagascar about 1000–1500 years ago by African immigrants. This tortoise reaches up to 230 mm in carapace length. The Malagasy populations have usually been referred to as *K. belliana* (Bour 1979) and even described as the distinct subspecies *K. b. domerguei* (Bour 1987), until Kindler et al. (2012) provided molecular data assigning them to *K. zombensis*. On Madagascar, this tortoise is known from Nosy Faly in the Sambirano Region, and from adjacent mainland localities near Ambanja. Kindler et al. (2012) analyzed 17 Malagasy samples and found that all had the same mitochondrial haplotype, and they interpreted this genetic uniformity as evidence for a non-native origin. The Malagasy samples were genetically divergent from South African material, but the latter covered only the southernmost tip of the species' range. To clarify the origins of Malagasy *Kinixys*, a wider sampling across the continental range of *K. zombensis* is necessary.

Little is known about the ecology and behavior of this species on Madagascar, but Mifsud et al. (2017) recently provided detailed information on its natural history (also see Pedrono et al., pp. 1463–68). This tortoise was found across Nosy Faly and portions of the adjacent peninsula, with most encounters in the central portion of the island. It occurs in various habitats including grasslands, secondary forests, plantations, and village gardens and rubbish piles.

Pelusios castanoides and *Pelusios subniger*

It is difficult to definitively conclude whether these two species of hinged terrapins were introduced to Madagascar or are the result of a recent natural colonization by individuals rafting across the Mozambique Channel from Africa, where both species are widely distributed. *Pelusios* species are regularly consumed in many parts of Madagascar and thus constitute a food resource, and they may have originally been brought to Madagascar by humans. However, their consumption is now decreasing because of population declines related to habitat transformation.

Fritz et al. (2010, 2012) found almost no genetic differentiation of the Malagasy and Seychellois populations of *P. subniger* and concluded that for this species, an introduction was likely. In the case of *P. castanoides*, these same authors found that samples from Madagascar and from the Seychelles were weakly differentiated from continental African samples and from each other, but because there were no samples from eastern Africa in the comparisons, no clear conclusion could be drawn as to whether the western Indian Ocean populations were introduced or natural. However, within the Madagascar individuals, no haplotype differentiation was found, which argues for a non-native origin (or an extremely young colonization by a small group of founders). In some areas of the northern portion of the Central Highlands, people in the countryside keep *P. castanoides* in and around their chicken coops to reduce poultry lice, as they believe that the urine of the turtle reduces the development of these ectoparasites.

Pelomedusa subrufa

The African Helmeted Terrapin is widespread on Madagascar and in continental Africa, where several deep genetic lineages occur (Vargas-Ramírez et al. 2010). The Malagasy populations belong to a lineage occurring in eastern and central Africa (e.g., Malawi, Botswana, Democratic Republic of Congo) and are only weakly divergent from these African populations. Because three haplotypes were encountered within the Malagasy samples, it can be hypothesized that either this species was introduced to Madagascar on multiple occasions or perhaps from different source areas, or sufficient time has passed for local genetic differentiation to arise. However, the weak differentiation between the Malagasy and African haplotypes argues for human-mediated introduction. This is a very common, generalist aquatic species and can be found inhabiting swamps, streams, small shallow lakes, and lentic waters in the west and southeast regions of Madagascar.

GECKOS

Phelsuma cepediana

There are only a few records of *Phelsuma cepediana* on Madagascar. Apparently this gecko, which is native to Mauritius, was deliberately introduced to Madagascar at Ivoloina (Mertens 1963), just north of Toamasina, but nothing is known about the date of the introduction or its purpose. Whether this species was able to successfully establish a local population is uncertain; this may have been hindered by competition and hybridization with the local native *Phelsuma* species (Raxworthy and Nussbaum 1993a). *Phelsuma cepediana* has also been reported from a locality along Ampasindava Bay, near Ambanja. Gravid females lay two hard-shelled, cemented eggs, typical of day geckos, onto hard surfaces. It cannot be excluded that the introduction of this species to Madagascar was the result of accidentally transported eggs.

Gehyra mutilata, *Hemidactylus frenatus*, *H. mercatorius*, and *H. platycephalus*

Geckos of the genera *Gehyra* and *Hemidactylus* (Figure 12.10) are among the most cosmopolitan reptiles and are often found in port cities of tropical countries, where they are almost certainly the result of accidental transport on ships. They are quite common in and around human habitations in cities and towns. For *G. mutilata*, Rocha et al. (2009a) showed that Malagasy animals share identical mitochondrial haplotypes with populations from the Seychelles, Mascarenes, Myanmar, Malaysia, and the Philippines, suggesting that it is an introduced species and has been widely transported by humans. For the three species of *Hemidactylus*, the situation is more diverse. *Hemidactylus mercatorius*, a species that is widespread across Madagascar including in natural environments, shows substantial genetic variation across its Malagasy range (Vences et al. 2004b), which suggests it is native to the island. Malagasy

FIGURE 12.10 **House geckos are among the reptile species most commonly introduced in tropical areas around the world. The Tender-skinned House Gecko, *Gehyra mutilata* (upper specimen), on Madagascar is almost certainly an introduction, while Gray's Leaf-toed Gecko, *Hemidactylus mercatorius* (lower specimen) shows notable genetic variation across Madagascar and may therefore have colonized the island naturally.** (PHOTOS by M. Vences.)

populations of *H. platycephalus*, as far as is known, are genetically uniform and closely related to the populations of this species on the Comoro islands, providing support for an introduction. For *H. frenatus*, a species that has been introduced to many areas worldwide, samples from the extreme north of Madagascar differ genetically from those collected in other areas of the island, probably pointing to multiple introduction events or possibly to a native species that has evolved some level of genetic differentiation over time.

SKINKS AND OTHER LIZARDS

Trachylepis comorensis

This lizard species is endemic to the Comoro islands (Brygoo 1981c). On Madagascar, it is known from Nosy Tanikely, close to Nosy Be. The occurrence of this species on the island has been assumed to be the result of an introduction, possibly via the frequent boat traffic between the Comoros and northwestern Madagascar (J. Köhler et al. 1998; Nussbaum et al. 1999a). This is also supported by the molecular study of Rocha et al. (2010a), who found that the Malagasy specimens of *T. comorensis* had mitochondrial DNA sequences identical to those of specimens from Mohéli Island, suggesting a very recent origin, probably introduced, from a Comorian source population.

Cryptoblepharus boutonii

This small skink inhabits coastal habitats and has undergone an enormous expansion on islands throughout the Indian and Pacific Oceans (Blom et al. 2019). According to Rocha et al. (2006), the northern and southern populations on Madagascar are genetically distinct from each other, and from those on other islands in the region. This suggests they probably have independent origins on Madagascar, presumably by natural colonization.

Agama agama

This lizard species is widespread in Africa, and introduced populations occur on La Réunion and Grande Comore Island, and in Florida. Wagner et al. (2009) reported an individual of this species was photographed on a wall close to Ivato Airport in Antananarivo in 2004, but no subsequent records are known from Madagascar. Because *A. agama* potentially occupies a niche similar to that of the native *Oplurus* iguanas and could outcompete these, it is important to prevent this species from becoming established on Madagascar.

CROCODILES

Crocodylus niloticus

Natural rafting is the most probable origin of crocodiles on Madagascar, and Malagasy populations are sometimes considered an endemic subspecies, *C. n. madagascariensis* (see Kuchling et al., pp. 1458–63). For one mitochondrial gene analyzed, no difference was observed between Malagasy and continental African samples from Zimbabwe (Meredith et al. 2011). Malagasy crocodile populations also showed affinities to those from Zimbabwe in microsatellites (Meredith et al. 2011), but with these high-resolution markers they also had unique genetic characteristics, suggesting a recent natural colonization from eastern Africa (see also Crottini et al. 2012a). This species is hunted on Madagascar for its skin and meat, or simply killed because of the threat it poses to people and their cattle. However, among certain cultural groups, such as the Sakalava in northern Madagascar, they are venerated in the context of ancestor cults. Crocodile oil is used in certain areas of the island to treat asthma.

BLIND SNAKES

Indotyphlops braminus

This small, very widespread parthenogenetic subterranean blind snake occurs in different areas of tropical Asia and Africa (see Raxworthy, pp. 1532–34). Because of its mode of reproduction, introduction or natural dispersal of a single female would suffice to constitute a founder population, and this species has accordingly been introduced to many parts of the world. It almost certainly also arrived on Madagascar by human-mediated introduction, and it is common in different areas of the island, including village and town gardens, particularly during the rainy season. When local children and adults find it, they call it a "strange worm with a tongue."

INTRODUCTIONS FROM MADAGASCAR

A few native Malagasy reptile species are also known from neighboring islands. For instance, the Comoros population of *Oplurus cuvieri*, which is limited to Grande Comore, and the Glorioso and Cosmoledo populations in the western Seychelles of *Zonosaurus madagascariensis* have been considered separate subspecies (*O. c. comorensis* and *Z. m. insulanus*). Hence, it has usually been assumed that their colonization of these other islands was natural. The population genetics of *Z. madagascariensis* have not been analyzed in depth, despite the existence of mDNA sequences for one specimen from the Seychelles (Raselimanana et al. 2009). The *Oplurus* from Grande Comore shows only negligible genetic divergence compared to Malagasy populations (Münchenberg et al. 2008), suggesting it may instead have been introduced.

It is worth mentioning that several species occur both on Madagascar and on neighboring islands in the western Indian Ocean (e.g., *Indotyphlops braminus*, *Leioheterodon madagascariensis*, *Cryptoblepharus boutonii*, *Zonosaurus madagascariensis*, *Gehyra mutilata*, *Hemidactylus mercatorius*, *H. frenatus*, *Ebenavia safari*, *Geckolepis humbloti*, *Phelsuma dubia*, *P. laticauda*, *P. cepediana*, *Oplurus cuvieri*, *Furcifer pardalis*). Virtually all of these species on Madagascar are found in the Sambirano Region or nearby northern and northwestern portions of the island. This observation is interesting in two regards. First, this zone of Madagascar was an important trade entrepôt during the Islamic period, with the relatively large village of Mahilaka being the largest known from this time, dating from the 11th century, and a hub of maritime trade (Radimilahy 1997).

This situation would favor exchanges and introductions to and from Madagascar. Second, the Sambirano Region presents the shortest route from Madagascar to the Comoro islands, which in association with favorable ocean currents would provide enhanced possibilities of natural dispersal between Madagascar and these small islands, and perhaps also from the African coast.

MALAGASY REPTILES AS INVASIVE SPECIES

Several Malagasy reptile species have in recent years been introduced to other parts of the world. This especially concerns day geckos: some examples are *Phelsuma dubia*, which was probably introduced to eastern Africa; *P. laticauda* to Moorea (French Polynesia), Hawai'i, and other islands in the Pacific; and *P. grandis* to Florida. These *Phelsuma* species are also invasive in the Mascarenes and Comoros, for instance *P. grandis* on La Réunion and Mauritius; the Panther Chameleon, *Furcifer pardalis*, has become established in Florida and on La Réunion, and the snake *Leioheterodon madagascariensis* on Grande Comore.

Subject editors: Miguel Vences and Achille P. Raselimanana

SYSTEMATIC ACCOUNTS

CROCODYLIDAE: *CROCODYLUS NILOTICUS* AND *VOAY ROBUSTUS* (SUBFOSSIL), *VOAY, MAMBA*

G. Kuchling, C. Lippai, O. Behra, and F. Glaw

The genus *Crocodylus* of the family Crocodylidae can be found in tropical and subtropical regions around the world. *Crocodylus niloticus* is the largest surviving terrestrial vertebrate of Madagascar. As with all crocodiles, this species is sexually dimorphic, with the larger males reaching about 4.5 m in length, although in the past some individuals may have reached larger sizes. *Crocodylus niloticus* once inhabited much of Madagascar, except for high mountain areas, and could be found in various habitats ranging from large rivers to brackish-water environments, small forest streams, lakes, and swamps. According to current knowledge, only one extant crocodile species, the nonendemic Nile Crocodile (*Crocodylus niloticus*; Figure 12.11), occurs on Madagascar, whereas a second endemic

FIGURE 12.11 ***Crocodylus niloticus*** **is widespread in Africa. On Madagascar, crocodiles occur across many areas of the island but are becoming increasingly uncommon, largely because of human persecution.** (PHOTO by H. Schütz.)

genus and species (*Voay robustus*) became extinct a few hundred or thousand years ago and is known only from subfossils.

EXTINCT MALAGASY CROCODILES

Vaillant and Grandidier (1872) described *Crocodylus robustus* based on subfossil remains from Ambolisatra in southwestern Madagascar. However, in a subsequent paper (1910) these authors expressed doubts that *C. madagascariensis* and *C. robustus* were morphologically distinct. During the 20th century most taxonomists considered *C. robustus* an invalid taxon and assumed that previously cited morphological differences were age related and associated with ontogeny (e.g., C. Blanc 1972; Fuchs et al. 1974). However, Brochu (2000) demonstrated that *C. robustus* is a valid subfossil taxon and suggested that it may be phylogenetically more closely related to the African dwarf crocodile in the genus *Osteolaemus* than to any living species of the genus *Crocodylus*. *Crocodylus robustus*, bearing squamosal horns, was placed in its own genus, *Voay*, endemic to Madagascar, which shares similarities in cranial features with the genus *Osteolaemus* (Brochu 2007). *Voay*'s phylogenetic position was recently analyzed using ancient DNA (a partial mitochondrial genome). This study recovered a sister group relationship between *Voay* and the genus *Crocodylus* and unambiguously confirmed the specific distinctness of *V. robustus* (Hekkala et al. 2021). This result is particularly interesting with respect to the recency and circumstances of its extinction, since it is more or less similar in stature and size to *C. niloticus*, potentially making them direct rivals for ecological resources. *Voay robustus* was still extant when humans first settled Madagascar many millennia ago and may have been a casualty of a megafaunal extinction event on the island (Brochu 2007). No matter whether humans extirpated *V. robustus* or whether it became extinct because of changes in habitat and/or prey (Bickelmann and Klein 2009), both species so far have not been found together in the same strata of a subfossil site. Hence, a general hypothesis is that *C. niloticus* successfully invaded Madagascar only after *V. robustus* became extinct.

In the late 19th century Voeltzkow was based in Mahajanga researching crocodiles and their embryology in the lower Betsiboka River drainage. He reported that the natives distinguished two species of crocodiles, one (*C. niloticus*) with a longer head and another one with a shorter head and larger body. The latter reportedly lived only in large streams in primeval forest, was particularly feared by natives for its ferocity, and was "dürfte wohl mit *Cr. robustus* Vaill. Grandid. identisch sein" (probably identical to *Cr. robustus* Vaill. Grandid.) (Voeltzkow 1891: 115). Even though Voeltzkow never received or saw a specimen of this second species, these reports suggest the possibility that *V. robustus* survived for longer than indicated in the subfossil record, long enough for it to persist at least in tales of local people into the 19th century. The report that a second species may still have been present in remote forested zones during the 19th century supports the hypothesis that *V. robustus* may have been slowly driven to extinction through competition with *C. niloticus*.

Interestingly, a horned dwarf crocodile, *Aldabrachampsus dilophus*, has also been described from the Quaternary of the Aldabra Atoll in the western Seychelles, about 400 km northwest of northern Madagascar (Brochu 2006). A close relationship with *V. robustus* appears plausible, as both genera share some unique morphological characters. Furthermore, strong marine currents support overseas dispersal from Madagascar to Aldabra, and the fossil herpetofauna of Aldabra is apparently of Malagasy origin (Arnold 1976; Hawlitschek et al. 2017a). *Aldabrachampsus* was very likely an immigrant from elsewhere and not endemic to the Aldabra Atoll, as it occurs in deposits formed shortly after a period of submergence that ended 100,000 years ago (Brochu 2006). It could be a dispersal case parallel to that of extinct Malagasy giant tortoises, some of which are closely related to *A. gigantea* still living on Aldabra.

SYSTEMATICS AND GENETIC DIFFERENTIATION OF *CROCODYLUS NILOTICUS*

Grandidier (1872) described *Crocodylus madagascariensis*, but several years later Boulenger (1889) synonymized this taxon with *C. niloticus*. Until recently *C. niloticus* was regarded as a single widespread species occurring throughout Africa and Madagascar. However, the populations from western and central Africa are now recognized as a separate species, *C. suchus*, an old lineage that is sister to a group containing *C. niloticus* plus all New World species of the genus (Schmitz et al. 2003; Hekkala et al. 2011; Meredith et al. 2011). Thus, *C. niloticus* is now restricted to eastern and southern Africa, including Madagascar, with the species historically also extending into southern Israel and perhaps the Comoro islands.

Hekkala et al. (2010) described the biogeographic substructuring of *C. niloticus* associated with major river drainages in Africa and Madagascar. The crocodile populations of Madagascar exhibit genetic clustering consistent with isolation from neighboring mainland Africa by the Mozambique Channel. A weaker divergence was observed between populations in northwestern Madagascar (Betsiboka) and Zimbabwe (Zambezi River drainage) across the Mozambique Channel than between populations from southeastern and northern Madagascar. Individuals from the isolated Ankarana cave population in extreme northern Madagascar exhibited the lowest level of heterozygosity and multiple fixed alleles.

The genetic differentiation of *C. niloticus* within Madagascar is consistent with a natural origin of these populations and supports previously described morphological differences between populations of mainland Africa and Madagascar that were used for diagnosing Malagasy populations as a distinct subspecies, *C. n. madagascariensis* (Fuchs et al. 1974; Wermuth and Fuchs 1978). However, the origin of the species on Madagascar is poorly known. The only dated subfossil crocodilian described from Madagascar is a specimen presumably of *C. niloticus* dated to 460–310 years ago (Crowley and Samonds 2013), providing a minimum date for arrival of this species on the island. The genetic differentiation within Madagascar reported by Hekkala et al. (2010) could indicate that *C. niloticus* may have dispersed to Madagascar through multiple events (Mathews and Samonds 2016). In any case, molecular clock analyses (Crottini et al. 2012a) clearly support close relationships between African and Malagasy populations and a quite recent, probably Pleistocene or Holocene, colonization of the island.

ECOLOGY

Although this has not been investigated on Madagascar in any detail, *Crocodylus niloticus* elsewhere within its range generally shows a shift in diet, from insects and small aquatic invertebrates when young to predominantly vertebrate prey among older individuals. At Lake Ngezi, Zimbabwe, the diet of juveniles changed at a size of 600 mm snout-to-vent length from a predominance of insects to fish and birds. A concurrent reversal of several important allometric relationships of the head seems to be an adaptation for the efficient capture of prey of increasing size. A fundamental change of home range behavior also occurs in these animals, and the abruptness of the dietary transition may partly reflect a change in prey availability (Hutton 1987a). Very large crocodiles on the African mainland also feed on ungulates, of which no native form is present on Madagascar. It has been reported that large Malagasy crocodiles kill African Bush Pigs (*Potamochoerus larvatus*), cattle, and dogs (Petit 1925), and even humans are part of the prey of *C. niloticus*.

Juvenile growth is confined to the hot season. Large animals grow in irregular spurts. Hatchlings are able to develop at lower temperatures than older animals (Hutton 1987a). A large adult can be five orders of magnitude heavier than a hatchling. *Crocodylus niloticus* individuals 0.4–2.2 m long have home ranges of about 0.1 km^2 but enter a dispersal phase when approximately 1.2 m long. Juvenile crocodiles can move overland through forest during the wet season and may also inhabit temporary ponds (Kofron 1993). When crocodiles reach 2.2 m in length, which coincides with the subadult phase, the range of movement increases again and they abandon home ranges and travel widely throughout much of the available habitat. Large breeding females (>2.8 m) have small home ranges near prime nesting sites. The size-class separation is part of a density-dependent regulation mechanism and based on adults becoming increasingly intolerant of intermediate-size crocodiles (Hutton 1989).

REPRODUCTION

In Zimbabwe, *Crocodylus niloticus* females attain sexual maturity when 262–287 cm in total length and males when 270–295 cm. Males produce viable sperm from mid-May to mid-September (i.e., during the Southern Hemisphere winter). Ovarian follicle growth, the synthesis of yolk protein in the liver, and subsequent yolk deposition in the developing eggs in the ovaries (vitellogenesis) occur from April through mid-August, during the dry season. Courtship takes place from late June through mid-August, the coldest months. Ovulation occurs during the latter half of August, and females nest during September and early October (Kofron 1990). Some adult females nest only every other year (Kofron 1989).

The best description of nesting behavior, nests, hatching, and parental care of *C. niloticus* on Madagascar is provided by Voeltzkow (1891, 1893, 1899). In the general Mahajanga area, egg deposition takes place from the end of August to the end of September. Nests contain 20–30 eggs, sometimes up to 40. Most nests are constructed during the night, often following rain, in banks of relatively dry, white sand; only a few are in more humus-rich soil. The egg deposition hole is 45–65 cm deep, partly has steep sides, and has two compartments with slightly higher ground in the middle. Eggs therefore roll to both sides during oviposition. The nest is then closed with the loose sand or earth and the female sleeps on it. Embryonic development to the hatching stage takes about three months. At its completion, hatchlings start to vocalize inside the unopened egg, in particular following vibrations, such as when the female moves on top of the nest. The female then scratches the sand out of the nest hole. After the eggs hatch, the female walks with the young to the water. The first young hatch in November with a total length of about 280 mm.

Crocodylus niloticus has temperature-dependent sex determination. At constant incubation temperatures, females are produced at 31°C and below, while the threshold temperature for males is between 31°C and 34°C. The duration of incubation varies with temperature and is 110 days at 28°C, falling to 85 days at 34°C (Hutton 1987b). Temperatures in wild nests fluctuate, and the eggs at shallow depths have higher mean temperatures and more advanced embryos than eggs positioned deeper in the ground.

BEHAVIOR

Crocodylus niloticus basks most frequently during the cool dry season and least during the hot wet season. Groups of subadults and adults of both sexes can bask together, but juveniles are excluded. Spacing and distribution of basking crocodiles is not controlled by sex, dominance, or reproductive status, and basking sites are not defended as exclusive territories (Kofron 1993).

Crocodylus niloticus courts and mates in a shared courtship-mating arena in front of a shared basking ground during the winter months. Courtship and mating usually occur shortly after the morning arrival of individuals, in water about 1 m deep. After courting and mating, individuals bask and sleep. Young adult males show group courtship, but the arena is time partitioned by the larger bulls: fights between the largest bulls are avoided by staggered entry into the arena. Adult and subadult males and subadult females all exhibit submissive behavior to larger bulls. Female crocodiles often initiate mating. Four different head postures and tail displays (arching the tail above the water) are used during courtship and submissive behavior. Courtship and mating also include blowing audible bubbles by mouth or nostrils, narial geysering, slamming the head against the water; making water ripples that radiate outward from the head; expanding the neck; opening the mouth; vocalizing; splashing water with the tail; submerging and surfacing; and rolling over. Courting individuals frequently smell the head and tail base of one another and rub the gular skin about the other's head. Three positions of copulation can occur: the male on the female's back (most frequent), venter to venter (male on top), and the female on the male's back (Kofron 1991).

Since Voeltzkow (1893) first described the formation of crèches (groups of hatchlings, often accompanied by adults) and maternal protection of newly hatched *C. niloticus*, these phenomena have now been well documented for crocodiles. Hatchling crocodiles vocalize when distressed, evoking defense reactions from adults. However, juvenile Nile Crocodiles commonly kill and eat hatchlings when they are held together in captivity, even when adequate food is present. Loss of hatchlings through cannibalism in the wild may occur mainly among individuals of intermediate age classes and not adults. Adults, on the other hand, show cannibalism toward crocodiles of dispersal size and larger. Intermediate age classes suffer high mortality wherever they are unable to avoid adults (Hutton 1989).

STATUS AND CONSERVATION

The Malagasy have a long history of crocodile lore and beliefs. Prior to 1925, trial by ordeal was common, in which the accused was forced to cross a crocodile-infested river in both directions. An untouched survivor was considered innocent. Several ethnic groups on Madagascar consider the crocodile to be sacred. A taboo (*fady*) surrounds these sacred crocodiles, and they (and their eggs) are not touched or disturbed. The Sakalava (in the north and northwest of Madagascar) protected and fed crocodiles; teeth taken from live crocodiles became part of the king's relics to be passed down to his successors (Petit 1925). Several localities are named after *Crocodylus niloticus*, for example Marovoay, Marovoaykely, and Bevoay (meaning "many crocodiles," "many small crocodiles," and "large crocodile," respectively).

The Nile Crocodile is widely distributed throughout Madagascar, but in particular in the river and lake systems descending from the northwestern and western sides of the Central Highlands, and in the northeast of the country, including the Maningoza, Sambao, Marotrondro, Bemarivo, Hafay, Ampandrana, and Maningozamaty Rivers, and Marovoaikely, Marovoaibe, Ankiliholiho, Befandraria, Ampanihy, Sotria, Ankiliolio, Sahapy, and Ampandra Lakes. During the wet season, crocodiles may follow floodwaters and occasionally turn up in seasonal rivers such as Begogo, Antsorobalala, Betsotaky, Amborometroka, Mokarana, Betombotomboky, Manarihena, Mangotroka, and Anjanambo (Republic of Madagascar 1997).

In 1988, 25 aerial surveys were conducted over selected rivers and lakes on Madagascar, covering a total shoreline distance of 2380 km, with 150 Nile Crocodiles observed. The same year 12 spotlight boat counts were also conducted, covering 101 km, and 46 individuals were observed; in 1997, 10 more aerials surveys were conducted, covering 1033 km, and 10 individuals were observed. In July and August 2008, 12 spotlight counts from a boat were conducted, covering 129.8 km, and 53 individuals were observed (Ottley et al. 2008).

The reported survey data from 1988 and 2008 indicate that the densities of wild Nile Crocodiles were low throughout the rivers and lakes of Madagascar, even in the areas where crocodiles were previously relatively abundant, and it is possible that the situation since then has degraded even more. This is the result of continued unregulated hunting of crocodiles of all sizes, which is depleting wild populations. Survey results indicate that Madagascar's wild crocodile population needs time and space to recover. Protected areas may play a key role as refuge areas, provided they contain sufficient crocodiles and quality nesting habitats (Ottley et al. 2008). In this regard a unique site is Lake Tsimaloto and the Andranomiditra River in the northeastern part of Ankarafantsika National Park. A strong local *fady* protects the lake, which has a breeding population of huge adult sacred crocodiles, locally called *fitra*, which nest on a peninsula some distance from the water within thin, open forest on sandy soil. Lake Tsimaloto is still surrounded by forested hills and has a year-round overflow and outflow, the Andranomiditra River, a relatively small tributary of the Mahajamba River. Early this century, interviewed crocodile hunters in different areas of the northwest mentioned the Andranomiditra as the best site for (illegal) crocodile hunting (G. Kuchling, unpublished data). This appears to be because the Andranomiditra River has a consistent supply of dispersing juveniles from the protected breeding population in Lake Tsimaloto.

Additional surveys were carried out in 2013 during a CITES (Convention on International Trade in Endangered Species of Wild Fauna and Flora) capacity building project on Madagascar and covered previously unsurveyed areas, thus precluding any analysis of temporal trends from previously surveyed populations. Further surveys have been carried out (2015 and 2016), albeit on a small scale, under the recently developed Madagascar Crocodile Conservation and Sustainable Use Program, covering the following river systems: the "complexe" Mahavavy Kinkony, Ikopa (17 km before joining the Betsiboka at Maevatanana), Betsiboka (11 km of the river near Ambato Boeny, and 18 km near Maroala) and Lakes Bemakamba-Bekipoly (7 km). However, because of security reasons, the survey team was not able to complete its anticipated trajectory in the Betsiboka area. A total of 34 individual crocodiles were observed during these surveys, with an additional 16 eye shines counted.

Crocodylus utilization on the island has taken several forms in the past. Prior to the arrival of Europeans, the killing of crocodiles is thought to have been minimal, as most Malagasy do not eat the animal (if given a choice). In the late 19th century Voeltzkow (1891) suggested that *C. niloticus* was probably the most common reptile, if not vertebrate, on Madagascar. This species was still found in high densities early in the 20th century, particularly in the northwest, where it was very common in rivers, lakes, and ponds of all sizes (Kaudern 1922; Petit 1925). Since crocodiles attack and kill both humans and livestock, Europeans considered them a dangerous nuisance, and in 1915 the colonial government, in an effort to control the numbers of crocodiles, granted bonuses for the killing of these animals and the destruction of their eggs. Petit (1925) criticized these bounties for straining the finances of the colony; he proposed that a better strategy to get rid of crocodiles on the island or to at least reduce their numbers would be to use them industrially for leather production.

In the middle of the 20th century crocodiles were extensively hunted on the island for commercial sale of their skin. For example, 1000 skins per month were exported in 1947 (Behra and Hutton 1990). Decary (1950) also reported that someone from Marovoay brought 7000 eggs to the colonial administration in three weeks. Eggs were collected at that time for the systematic reduction and destruction of crocodile populations, which were severely depleted by overexploitation, particularly toward the end of the colonial period (1960). C. Blanc (1984) suggested that crocodiles were nearly eradicated from the lakes and rivers of Madagascar through hunting and egg collection and that they were confined to a few sacred lakes and limited regions where access was difficult, such as the subterranean rivers of the Ankarana. However, it seems that this assessment was erroneous, since the crocodile survived in most wetlands of the west. *Crocodylus niloticus* was found to be widespread and locally common in western Madagascar during the mid-1980s, suggesting that populations may have recovered after the end of the colonial period, during the 1970s and 1980s (Kuchling 1989). At the end of the 20th century crocodiles were again fairly abundant in the western lowlands. Little undisturbed habitat was and is left in the Central Highlands, where crocodiles are scarce or extirpated. Pressure from the human population has also made crocodiles scarce along the east coast.

As a species, *C. niloticus* is not threatened and is listed in the IUCN Red List as Least Concern (LC), although it may be threatened in some parts of its range, including Madagascar (Isberg et al. 2019). During the 1980s, the CITES Nile Crocodile program played an important role in developing sustainable use programs, with ranching promoted as the preferred means of obtaining conservation benefits from crocodile utilization. The Madagascar population was transferred from CITES Appendix I to Appendix II in 1985, subject to an export quota. Countries given quotas were permitted to export cropped skins with the understanding that the future development of crocodile management programs would move toward ranching (Ross 1998).

A program to promote crocodile farming on Madagascar began in 1989 with the CITES Nile Crocodile project, which carried out the first formal surveys (Behra and Hutton 1990). This led to the application of a project funded by the Food and Agriculture Organization (FAO) that identified sites and entrepreneurs suitable for farming and ranching (Bolton 1991) and divided Madagascar into three zones. The western zone was designated for the development of ranching and egg collection programs, while the eastern zone was set aside for crocodile hunting; a third zone was identified in the center of the island, where little suitable habitat remains and crocodiles have nearly disappeared. No hunting was allowed in the western zone (Games et al. 1997). After exploratory egg collection, the potential of egg collection in the Besalampy area was estimated to be 15,000–20,000 eggs in the area of the Sambao and Maningoza Rivers and 20,000–25,000 eggs in the area between the Mahavavy and Manambolo Rivers. Along the Maningoza River, 54 nests were found in a 6.5 km stretch in 1990 (Bolton 1991). Detailed historical data (from 1990 to 2006) on nest/egg harvests are available for the Maningoza, Sambao, Hafay, and Bemarivo Rivers (Ramandimbison et al. 1998). The data indicate that new nesting sites were continually added to the egg collection program (from six nest sites in 1991 to 23 sites in 2001). This made it difficult to establish temporal trends for nesting areas. Even though search effort was not quantified, it might be worth noting that 30 total nests were collected in 1990, increasing to 135 in 1994, but after 2001 there was a consistent decline to 73 nests in 2006 (Ottley et al. 2008). Since 2010, there has been no authorized egg collection for the ranching program and, accordingly, no data to update knowledge of nesting trends.

For 12 nesting areas, sufficient data were available from 1996 to 2003 to allow quantification of trends in nesting effort. Each of the 12 nesting areas has shown reduced nesting, ranging from −33% in the Bemarivo and Marotrondro Rivers to −52% in the Maningoza River, and −55% in the Sambao River. For all areas together, the estimated decrease in nesting is −45%, which better reflects the change for the area as a whole, as it takes into account the differences in absolute nesting effort between the different rivers. This decrease over seven years is equivalent to a mean rate of decrease in nesting of around −10% per annum.

HUNTING

Crocodile hunting probably always existed on Madagascar for a variety of reasons. It is part of the customs of some ethnic groups and was never a serious threat to the survival of the species (Zehrer 2013). First reports of crocodile hunting on the island date back to the early 17th century. Voeltzkow (1893) described four local methods used in Marovoay (lower Betsiboka River region) to hunt crocodiles: first, a wooden cross with sharpened ends is hidden in floating cattle entrails (e.g., lungs) and tethered to the shore with a rope. When the bait is taken, the wooden tips penetrate the crocodile's throat, and since it frantically tries to keep its mouth shut, it can be pulled to shore. Second, floating bait is attached at the top of a noose of about 0.5 m diameter made from a strong rope tethered to the shore, with the noose kept open and vertically floating with thin branches. When the crocodile takes the bait, it vigorously shakes its head and the noose tightens on its upper or lower jaw. Third, shark nets are used, but this is costly because many are ripped by trapped crocodiles. Fourth, crocodiles dig 10–15 m long tunnels that rise gently upward into the bank for hiding, with entries under the water line, and end with a chamber where the animal can turn around. Native hunters locate the chamber by finding the two or three aeration holes the crocodiles push through the ceiling. By throwing stones and making a lot of noise, people chase the crocodile into its tunnel, which is then blocked by bashing poles or tree trunks through the earth some distance from the chamber. The crocodile is then dug out.

Hunting effort between the 1940s and 1960s resulted in dramatic declines in the population of *C. niloticus*. Exports of Malagasy crocodile skins from the hunting of wild animals officially stopped after the ratification of the Washington Convention in November 1975. When the Malagasy population of Nile Crocodiles was transferred to CITES Appendix II (in 1997) pursuant to the ranching resolution (Resolution Conf. 11.16 [Rev. Cop15]), this included provision for an export quota on wild skins derived from "problem" crocodiles. However, under the current management regime, problem crocodiles can no longer be traded, and the killing of these crocodiles must be authorized by local authorities.

Illegal hunting of *C. niloticus* is problematic on the island and takes place even in protected areas (e.g., Ankarafantsika). Illegal hunting is done mainly for the domestic trade of crocodile oil and finished skin products. Hunting is considered the main reason for the declines in egg numbers mentioned above and has increased since 2000, with traps commonly sighted during the egg collection period, September to October. This decline in nesting suggests a significant and serious reduction in the wild Nile Crocodile breeding population, and apart from the intense hunting pressure on animals of all sizes, there appears to be no regulation or enforcement of stated harvest quotas (Ottley et al. 2008). After a socioeconomic crisis that affected the country between 2009 and 2014, coupled with a CITES ban on all crocodile exports from Madagascar (2010–2014), ranching has not taken place and egg collection for it has therefore ceased. The ranching program now exists in name alone.

MONITORING

There is a need to develop a crocodile and nest monitoring program for Madagascar's wild crocodiles that is simple to implement but can still detect significant changes in the population and breeding segment (Ottley et al. 2008). The Madagascar Crocodile Conservation and Sustainable Use Program (MCCSUP), established on Madagascar with assistance from the Crocodile Specialist Group, led to the creation of a dedicated Crocodile Management Unit (CMU) affiliated with the Direction Générale des Forêts. The CMU is responsible for all aspects of crocodile management in the country, including monitoring of wild populations and control of the harvest and offtake of wild crocodilians to supply the national artisanal crocodile leather industry. Funding constraints currently limit the capacity of the CMU to fully implement its National Crocodile Management Plan (2016–2020), which still needs to be finalized and validated by the Malagasy government.

Closely related to the issue of "problem" crocodiles is that of human-crocodile conflict, which is a serious issue on Madagascar. Available human-crocodile conflict data have been analyzed (Maheritafika et al. 2016) and a database created and updated with available information. Human-crocodile conflicts have become a major problem in some western areas of the island. Efforts to mitigate human-crocodile conflict, or to tailor strategies already in existence, were made through the MCCSUP by a public service announcement in the form of a cartoon with a message through song. An accompanying coloring book was also produced, the target audience being schools in the north and northwest, where most crocodile hunting takes place. A poster was also produced that provides guidance on the new size limits for offtake.

Subject editors: Miguel Vences, Achille P. Raselimanana, and Frank Glaw

TESTUDINIDAE, LAND TORTOISES

M. Pedrono, L. L. Smith, and R. C. J. Walker

The diverse reptile fauna of Madagascar includes four extant species of land tortoises within two endemic genera, *Astrochelys radiata*, *A. yniphora*, *Pyxis arachnoides*, and *P. planicauda*. A fifth species, *Aldabrachelys gigantea*, occurs on the Seychelles and is very closely related, possibly conspecific with the extinct Malagasy populations known as *A. abrupta*. Specimens of *A. gigantea* have recently been (re)introduced on Madagascar (Arnold 1979; Pedrono et al. 2013, 2020). A further giant tortoise native to Madagascar, *A. grandidieri*, is now extinct (Bour 1994), most likely because of over-hunting (Burleigh and Arnold 1986; Pedrono et al. 2013). Another species, *Kinixys zombensis*, is believed to have been introduced to the island from mainland Africa by humans (see Raselimanana and Vences, pp. 1455–58). Tortoises are among the best-studied reptiles on Madagascar, at least in part because they are highly threatened. The natural history of *Astrochelys yniphora* and *A. radiata* in particular is well known.

ASTROCHELYS RADIATA, RADIATED TORTOISE, *SOKAKE*

This species (Figure 12.12) inhabits dry spiny thickets in the southern portion of the island, roughly from Toliara to Tolagnaro. The core of its range comprises the Mahafaly and Karimbola plateaus and a coastal band extending as far as 50 km inland. This region receives less than 400 mm of rainfall per year and supports unique xerophytic vegetation. Radiated Tortoises occur in low spiny thicket habitat with a grassy understory (Juvik 1975). Subfossil remains assigned to this species have been discovered in the Morondava region (Bour 1994), more than 300 km north of its current geographic distribution. If these are confirmed, then this dramatic reduction in range is likely a result of centuries of heavy exploitation by humans for food. There is also strong evidence that this species underwent a second dramatic range contraction during the 20th century for the same reason (Leuteritz 2002; O'Brien et al. 2003; Rafeliarisoa et al. 2013). Today, populations at the periphery of the range and close to towns and villages are rapidly being depleted by human harvest for food and the pet trade (both local and international). The highest densities of this tortoise occur in the core of its current range between southern Lake Tsimanampesotse and Cap Sainte Marie. Hammer and Ramilijaona (2009) estimated densities of 0.32–0.47 tortoise per ha in Tsimanampesotse in a survey carried out during the dry season, whereas Rafeliarisoa et al. (2013) estimated an average population density of 4.2 individuals per ha in this area in 2011. However, in the recent past *A. radiata* occurred in very high densities within the core of its range (>50 tortoises per ha; Pedrono 2008), and such densities were among the highest estimates for tortoise populations in the world. These rapid and dramatic declines are a direct result of intensive exploitation.

Some consider *A. radiata* to be the most strikingly patterned of all the Malagasy tortoises, with a dark brown to black carapace and yellow stripes radiating from the areolae of the vertebral and pleural scutes (Figure 12.12). The plastron is yellow with dark triangles extending from all but the anal and gular scutes. There is great

FIGURE 12.12 Mating individuals of the Radiated Tortoise, *Astrochelys radiata*, from southwestern Madagascar. (PHOTO by M. Pedrono.)

variation among individuals in the same population. Juveniles are quite colorfully marked, but the pattern typically fades with age. Older individuals often lose the yellow striations entirely and the shell may appear uniformly dark brown. This species has a highly domed shell with slightly flared, serrated rear marginals. A cervical scute is present and the gular scutes are typically paired. The head and limbs are yellow to tan, although the crown of the head may be darkly pigmented. The tail lacks a large terminal scale. Adults may reach a length of 40 cm and weigh approximately 11 kg (Pedrono 2008). Radiated Tortoises exhibit sexual dimorphism; adult males are larger than females and have a concave plastron, a thicker xiphiplastron or posterior plate of the plastron, and a longer tail than adult females. This species is quite similar in appearance to the Ploughshare Tortoise, *A. yniphora* (see below), and mitochondrial DNA supports their close relationship (Caccone et al. 1999). *Astrochelys yniphora*, however, is larger than *A. radiata* and has a single, fused gular scute. *Astrochelys radiata* is characterized by substantial genetic diversity (Rioux Paquette et al. 2005).

The climate in southern Madagascar is hot and dry and *A. radiata* is usually active only during the coolest times of the day, such as in the early morning or late afternoon, or during rainy weather. The tortoises become more active during the wet season (November through March) and less active during the dry season (May through October), when juveniles become dormant, seeking refuge under vegetative debris. Rainfall triggers activity in this species, particularly mating. It is known to eat succulent plants, grasses, and fruits, including those of the non-native cactus *Opuntia*. Rasoma et al. (2013) found *A. radiata* to use individual ranges between 0.5 and 2.3 ha, depending on the statistical method used, with larger ranges in littoral forests than on limestone. According to these authors, the tortoises consumed leaves (91%), flowers (5%), and fruits (4%) from 109 plant species.

Astrochelys radiata reaches sexual maturity between 16 and 21 years old, depending on individual growth rates. Females lay from one to five eggs per nest and may nest up to three times within a season; the number of nests per season is positively related to female size. Clutch sizes are lower during dry years and appear to reflect resource availability. The eggs are typically hard shelled and round, weighing between 28 and 55 g. After covering the eggs, captive *A. radiata* females urinate above the nest, presumably to mask the scent of the eggs. The incubation period is relatively long but highly variable, ranging between 263 and 342 days in the wild (Leuteritz and Ravolanaivo 2005). Diapause (a period of suspended growth) affects the development of the embryo during the cool season. With rising temperature, embryonic development continues, and hatchlings emerge from the nest with the onset of seasonal rains. Sex is determined by temperature in the nest, but the adult sex ratio is at equilibrium in wild populations. Hammer (2015) observed seasonal breeding activity in Tsimanampesotse, with egg deposition from February to October and a mean clutch size of 2.5 eggs. Larger females produced larger eggs (Hammer 2013, 2015).

Adult mortality is very low and juvenile mortality is notably high in this species, with most offspring never reaching sexual maturity. Although data on longevity in the wild are lacking, captive individuals have been reported to live for more than 150 years. One famous *A. radiata* individual, Tui Malila, was a gift to the queen of Tonga from Captain Cook in 1777. This tortoise died in 1966 at more than 188 years of age.

ASTROCHELYS YNIPHORA, PLOUGHSHARE TORTOISE, *ANGONOKA*

Astrochelys yniphora is the largest of Madagascar's extant tortoises. It received its English name for the distinctive long, plow-like gular projection on the anterior plastron of adult males. This species occurred in bamboo-scrub habitat within dry deciduous forests on the west coast of Madagascar. As of 2015, *A. yniphora* populations were restricted to small patches of habitat within a 30 km radius of Baly Bay. Population densities ranged from 0.55 to 0.71 tortoise per ha during the 1990s (Pedrono 2000), but the species is now considered functionally extinct in the wild, or no longer reproductively viable, because of intensive poaching to supply the international trade (Pedrono and Clausen 2018). Currently, *A. yniphora* exists mainly as two large captive populations, one within the historic range of the species in Baly Bay National Park, and the second outside the historic range, in Ampijoroa (in Ankarafantsika National Park). There are a few scattered individuals in zoological parks overseas, and likely more individuals in the illegal collections of tortoise hobbyists in Southeast Asia.

Astrochelys yniphora occurred in secondary growth habitat consisting of bamboo (*Perrierbambus madagascariensis*) and shrub thickets (*Terminalia boivinii* and *Bauhinia pervillei*), shrub-palm (*Bismarckia nobilis*) grassland, and forest edges. Today, much of the region is covered in grassland perpetuated by anthropogenic bushfires, although a few small patches of secondary growth and dry deciduous forest still exist. It is hypothesized that this habitat is suboptimal for this species, but it may have afforded refuge to a few tortoises because it is virtually impenetrable to humans (Pedrono and Clausen 2018). The first reported specimens of *A. yniphora* were sent to overseas museums by fishermen in the late 18th century. In addition, bones of *A. yniphora* have been identified from archaeological sites dating from the 11th to 14th centuries in northwestern Madagascar (L. Rakotozafy 1996) and the Comoro islands (Allibert 1989), demonstrating that this species was exploited and exported for food by Arab traders because, like other large tortoises, they can survive on boats for extended periods without food or water. Such exploitation soon outstripped the maximum sustainable harvest rates for *A. yniphora* population viability. The cessation of this historical exploitation likely allowed populations to stabilize, with a very low but continuous annual growth rate of 1% (Pedrono 2000). However, recent exploitation (since about the year 2000) has led to the functional extinction of the species in the wild (Pedrono and Clausen 2018).

Astrochelys yniphora adults reach an average length of 43 cm. The shell is highly domed and somewhat less colorful than that of *A. radiata*. Shell color of *A. yniphora* adults is yellow to tan, with dark brown to black margins on the vertebral and costal scutes. The marginal scutes are transected by a dark triangular pattern that extends ventrally. Dark triangles also appear on the plastron, where they radiate from the midline through the pectoral, abdominal, and femoral scutes. Large, presumably old tortoises tend to be uniformly dull yellow or tan. Hatchlings also have dark margins on the vertebral and costal scutes, but the marginal scutes lack the dark triangles visible in larger individuals. The skin of this species across all sizes is tan, although the heads of some adults are dark brown to nearly black. The scales on the front limbs are quite large. A cervical scute is present in most individuals and is often greatly recurved. The most distinctive characteristic is the single, fused gular scute. The gular is greatly elongated in both sexes but may exceed 10 cm in length in adult males. *Astrochelys yniphora* males reach a larger body size than females. The largest male captured in the wild measured 51.9 cm in length (straight-line carapace length) and weighed 20 kg, whereas the largest female measured 41.6 cm and weighed 15.5 kg (Mandimbihasina and Currylow 2014). Adult *A. yniphora* males have a concave plastron and an elongated gular projection. Males also have a longer tail and a wider epiplastral opening than females. These differences typically cannot be distinguished until the tortoises reach a length of more than 30 cm (Smith et al. 2000).

In the wild, this species reaches sexual maturity between 20 and 23 years of age, depending on individual growth rates. Breeding activity begins early in the wet season (November and December), when males compete for access to females. Males use the elongated gular projection to engage in combat with other males and to corral females before mating. The large, thick scales on the forelimbs may offer protection from the gular projection of rival males. Scent may play an important role in enabling males to locate females during the mating season. In the wild, *A. yniphora* females nest from January through late May. They typically nest in open areas, often directly adjacent to shrubs, or in recently burned areas. Females produce between one and four clutches of one to six eggs per year, with an average incubation period of 240 days. Both clutch frequency and mean clutch mass are correlated with maternal body mass. Hatchlings emerge at the onset of seasonal rains in November and, on average, are 4.5 cm long and weigh 24 g (Pedrono et al. 2001). Like most chelonians, *A. yniphora* grows slowly and experiences an attenuated growth pattern. Juveniles grow approximately 15% per year, compared to only 5% per year in adults (Pedrono 2000).

Activity in *A. yniphora* is closely tied to seasonal rainfall. Tortoises are most active during the wet season, from November through April. During the dry season, May through October, they rest under vegetative cover and are rarely observed feeding. Males are particularly mobile following the first rains of November and December, during which they fight and search for a sexual partner. Females are especially active during January and May after mating, when they search for a site to lay their clutches. Home range size in *A. yniphora* varies greatly among individuals but is positively correlated with body size; males use a larger area than females. The home range of an adult female is on average 12 ha, whereas for adult males it is about 21 ha (Smith et al. 1999). *Astrochelys yniphora* juveniles are rather sedentary and apparently do not disperse great distances (Pedrono and Sarovy 2000). In addition, juveniles exhibit site fidelity; it is not uncommon to recapture an individual at the same locality from one year to the next. *Astrochelys yniphora* feeds on grasses, sedges, and small forbs.

Annual survival rate of *A. yniphora* has been estimated to be 97% for adults and 40–96% for juveniles, depending on their size (Pedrono 2000). Other than humans, *A. yniphora* subadults and adults (>23 cm carapace length) have no known predators. However, African Bush Pigs (*Potamochoerus larvatus*), a non-native species, are known to destroy *A. yniphora* nests (Pedrono et al. 2001). Other potential predators of eggs and young tortoises include the Madagascar Buzzard (*Buteo brachypterus*), the Fosa (*Cryptoprocta ferox*), and the introduced Small Indian Civet (*Viverricula indica*). Additional threats to Ploughshare Tortoise populations include bushfires, which can kill tortoises of all sizes. Ectoparasites of this species include the mite *Geckobia enigmatica* and an ixodid tick, *Amblyomma geochelone* (Bertrand and Pedrono 1999; Durden et al. 2002).

PYXIS ARACHNOIDES, SPIDER TORTOISE, *TSAFAKY, KAPIKA*

Pyxis arachnoides (Figure 12.13) occurs in coastal areas of southern Madagascar between the region of Morombe in the north and areas west of Amboasary-Atsimo in the south. Historical distribution of

FIGURE 12.13 An individual of the Spider Tortoise, *Pyxis arachnoides*, from southwestern Madagascar. (PHOTO by M. Pedrono.)

the species is thought to have encompassed a contiguous band of more than 500 km of coastline (Pedrono 2008); however, the range has contracted by up to 71%, to form a current occupancy area spanning 2464 km^2 of coastal forest habitat (Walker et al. 2013). The species is now confined to eight distinct, fragmented subpopulations. This small species is morphologically and phylogenetically similar to the Flat-tailed Tortoise, *P. planicauda* (Bour 1981; Caccone et al. 1999). However, *P. arachnoides* is unique among tortoises in that it has an anterior plastral hinge.

Three subspecies of *P. arachnoides* are recognized based on geographic distribution and morphological differences. Work on the genetics of this species using a mitochondrial marker found low levels of differentiation between recognized subspecies, and in certain cases intrapopulation variation was greater than interpopulation variation (Chiari et al. 2005). In addition, there are two populations of intergrades between the morphologically distinct subspecies (Walker et al. 2013). The most obvious morphological difference between the three subspecies is variation in the flexibility of the plastral hinge. *Pyxis a. brygooi*, the northernmost subspecies, is found within approximately 500 km^2 of dry spiny thicket across three fragmented populations from east of Morombe to north of the Manombo River (Walker 2010). This subspecies has a rigid plastron and a strongly projecting gular. *Pyxis a. arachnoides* occurs from south of the Onilahy River to south of the Linta River, with an occupancy area spanning approximately 1000 km^2 of coastal dry spiny thicket. This subspecies possesses a semi-ridged plastron. *Pyxis a. oblonga* is the most southern form, spanning approximately 570 km^2 and occupying the area around Cap Sainte Marie, with a population stretching through the coastal dunes to about 70 km east of the Manambovo River (Walker et al. 2013). Because of the extensive cultivation of land east of Faux Cap, this subspecies is confined to a few localized areas of dunes within the coastal zone (Walker and Rafeliarisoa 2012a). In this latter subspecies, the anterior lobe of the plastron is completely mobile and often supports dark pigmentation to the periphery of the plastron (Bour 1981; Pedrono 2008).

Pyxis arachnoides is sympatric with *Astrochelys radiata* across a portion of its range; however, *P. arachnoides* prefers coastal dunes and is often found under dry vegetation with a sandy substrate. Spider Tortoise density varies widely within the range, with recent studies recording from 1.5 to 9.2 tortoises per ha (Walker et al. 2012; Barley and Walker 2013). Densities of more than 16 tortoises per ha have also been reported in areas of good habitat (Pedrono 2008). However, the Spider Tortoise has declined in population density in many areas, as indicated by more recent data compared to data from several decades ago. Today, *P. a. oblonga* is thought to support the smallest population of the three subspecies, with perhaps as few as 6200 total individuals (Walker 2014).

Pyxis arachnoides is one of the smallest tortoises in the world at less than 15 cm in length. The species is named for its shell pattern, which somewhat resembles a spiderweb. The background of the shell is dark brown, and yellow striations radiate from the light-colored rings (areolae) on the central scutes of the carapace. The pattern fades with age, with the carapace of older individuals appearing uniformly yellowish. The rear of the carapace is domed and somewhat flattened anteriorly. Individuals of *P. a. oblonga* have a black plastron, but the plastron of the other two subspecies is lightly pigmented. The plastral hinge, when present, is located between the humeral and pectoral scutes. This species typically has 11 marginal scutes per side, and the margins are smooth rather than serrated. The head and limbs are black dorsally and pale yellow ventrally. The tail is flattened and has a spinelike terminal scale, which is particularly well developed in males. The anterior plastral hinge allows the tortoise to enclose its head and forelimbs for protection from predators. Male and female Spider Tortoises are about the same size, with a mean carapace length of 11 cm, a mean adult male mass of 194 g, and a mean female mass of 205 g (Pedrono 2008). This species exhibits morphological sexual dimorphism. As with other tortoises, the plastron of a *P. arachnoides* male is more concave and the tail is enlarged.

Knowledge of the biology of *P. arachnoides* in the wild is limited. The species is crepuscular, similar to other Malagasy tortoises, but seasonally shows distinct variation in activity. The high activity period begins in December with the first rains. The species goes through an annual period of estivation during the cooler dry season (May through November). During estivation *P. arachnoides* generally spends extended periods buried with only part of the top of the carapace exposed (Walker et al. 2007; Pedrono 2008).

This species is characterized by early sexual maturity, between eight and 11 years of age, and a consequently short generation time. Females are thought to deposit only one to three eggs per year, and they lay a single egg per nest. The eggs are relatively large in proportion to their body size (Bour 1981) and are laid in sandy substrate during the wet season, then go through a diapause during the dry season before hatching the following wet season. As a consequence, incubation is very long, on average 276 days in captivity when eggs are incubated under natural conditions.

Very little is known about the foraging habits or diet of this species. Casual field observations suggest that the species is an opportunistic browser, taking grasses, low vegetation, and flowers during the wet season. Individuals do not feed during the dry season (Walker et al. 2007). Like all other native Malagasy tortoises, this species appears to have the ability to drink through its nostrils—that is, it can close off the pathway to its lungs and take up water from puddles with its nose.

Remains of this genus have been recovered from 11th- to 14th-century human middens at the archaeological site of Mahilaka (south of Ambanja), indicating a long history of use as food (L. Rakotozafy 1996). Today, *P. a. arachnoides* is collected for the pet trade and has become a human food source in areas where *Astrochelys radiata* populations have been depleted or drought has restricted crop yields. It appears that *P. arachnoides* has been seriously impacted by hunting within the Mikea region (Walker 2010). In recent years this species has been turning up with increasing regularity in confiscated illegal tortoise shipments of predominantly *A. radiata.* Given the very low reproductive potential of this species, any exploitation could have serious consequences for individual populations. However, habitat loss is most likely the greatest threat to the long-term survival of *P. arachnoides*. Population matrix modeling using data from the Anakao area revealed that this population is declining by 1.4% per year (Walker et al. 2012). Other subpopulations of lower densities facing habitat loss are thought to be at even greater risk of local extinction.

PYXIS PLANICAUDA, FLAT-TAILED TORTOISE, *KAPIDOLO*

This small, secretive tortoise is found in the region of Morondava; its current distribution extends from Menahavo in the north to the Morondava River in the south. The species inhabits fragments of dry deciduous forest, as well as more open degraded habitat in the Menabe Region, which is characterized by strongly seasonal rainfall. It prefers secondary forests mixed with open areas over natural undisturbed forests (Pedrono 2008). Estimations of population densities for this tortoise are extremely variable, ranging from 0.40 to 6 individuals per ha in the dry deciduous forest of Kirindy Forest CNFEREF (Bloxam et al. 1996; Rakotombololona 1998; Bloxam 1999; Young et al. 2008).

Pyxis planicauda adults are generally less than 15 cm in length and weigh 700 g, and adult females are on average larger and heavier than adult males (Kuchling and Bloxam 1988; M. Rakotozafy 2009). Hatchling body mass is about 18 g and carapace length is 40 mm. The carapace is flattened dorsally and somewhat elongated. The species received its common name from its flattened tail, which terminates in a blunt tubercle (thickened skin projection). The aperture between the posterior of the carapace and plastron is quite narrow. However, the posterior lobe of the plastron of females is slightly mobile to facilitate passage of relatively large eggs. The nuchal scale is elongated but is lacking in some individuals. The gular scales are somewhat pronounced and are anteriorly divided. There are eight to nine flared, serrated marginal scales per side. Unlike *P. arachnoides*, *P. planicauda* has no plastral hinge on the anterior lobe of the plastron. This species is cryptically colored, with each brown-orange scute having a single dark band. This color patterns blends quite well with leaf litter. The plastron is yellow. The shell pattern of *P. planicauda* juveniles is monomorphic, more striking than that of adults, with brightly patterned black and yellow stripes that fade with age. The shell of older individuals is sometimes covered with algae.

Pyxis planicauda is active only when it rains (generally early December through early May). It estivates under leaf litter during the extended dry season. Preliminary data indicate that adult males and females have minimum ranges of 0.5 and 0.4 ha, respectively. Juveniles also are very sedentary, with a minimum home range of only 0.02 ha (M. Rakotozafy 2009). Flat-tailed Tortoises are often found basking in the early morning or after rain in places where sunshine reaches the forest floor. In the wild, *P. planicauda* eats fallen fruits, flowers, seedlings, leaves, fungi, snails, and insects and has been observed scavenging animal corpses (Kuchling and Bloxam 1988).

Pyxis planicauda reaches maturity between 9 and 13 years of age. Males become very active and fight for access to females with the first rains, which can start as early as November. Like *P. arachnoides*, *P. planicauda* has a very limited reproductive output and recruitment potential. In captivity, one to three nests are laid per season, at night or in the early morning (one egg per nest). The hatchlings emerge from the nest in the wet season, after a long incubation period of 254 to 343 days (Razandrimamilafiniarivo et al. 2000), which varies with the season of egg deposition. A diapause of several months likely affects the development of the embryo during the cool dry season to ensure that premature dry season emergence does not occur.

Pyxis planicauda is not regularly collected for food, given that it is taboo for the local Sakalava people; their local name for the species is *kapidolo*, meaning "tomb tortoise" (*kipaka*, "tortoise"; *lolo*, "tomb"). However, there was a pulse of exploitation for the international trade in this species between 2000 and 2004, raising serious concern about the status of remaining populations (J. Durbin, unpublished data). *Pyxis planicauda* probably still faces ongoing illegal collection to supply the international traffic of exotic species. Even more disturbing is the significant increase in deforestation of the Menabe Region since 2010 because of swidden agriculture for the cultivation of cash crops, as well as uncontrolled fires in open pastures, resulting in the extinction of many *P. planicauda* populations.

KINIXYS ZOMBENSIS, MADAGASCAR HINGE-BACKED TORTOISE, *KAPILA, ANGONOKA*

Previously considered a subspecies of *Kinixys belliana* (Bour 2006), *K. zombensis* has recently been recognized as a full species (Kindler et al. 2012). The Malagasy population is sometimes differentiated as a distinct subspecies, *K. domerguei*, but is thought to have been introduced from Africa by humans (see Raselimanana and Vences, pp. 1455–58). This species is found on the west coast of northern Madagascar from Nosy Faly and the adjacent Ambato Peninsula in the Sambirano Region. This region is characterized by a hot, humid climate. The highest densities of this subspecies have been reported on the small island of Nosy Faly, where the tortoises use secondary forest and cultivated fields such as coconut and cashew plantations and grasslands and are occasionally encountered in villages hidden under cover in gardens and rubbish piles (Kuchling 1986; Pedrono 2008). They also forage on Soursop (*Annona muricata*), mushrooms, slugs and snails, and carrion (mostly slaughtered chicken remains). Population assessment across the known historical range reported an occupancy area of 13.5 km^2 on Nosy Faly and 31.1 km^2 on the Ambato Peninsula. This subspecies is believed to number about 6600 individuals in total, with highest population densities on Nosy Faly (Walker et al. 2016). This insular population most likely represents the highest density of *Kinixys* tortoises in the world, and this subspecies, if indeed a natural population, has the most restricted range within this genus.

The largest individuals of *K. zombensis* on Madagascar may attain a carapace length of 25 cm and weigh up to 2.3 kg (Mifsud et al. 2017). Males and females are equal in size. Adults of this species possess a well-developed hinge between the fourth and fifth or second and third bilateral scutes of the carapace. This hinge allows the rear of the carapace to be lowered over the hind limbs. The carapace is elongated, slightly domed, and flattened posteriorly. The plastron of this species is not hinged. The hatchlings are round and more flattened than adults, with serrated marginal scales. The hinge is absent in hatchlings but starts to develop at one year of age. The carapace is yellow to brown with a black radial pattern, and the head and limbs are entirely yellow. This pattern usually fades to uniform brown with age. The males have a concave plastron and an enlarged tail.

In southeast Africa, *K. zombensis* attains sexual maturity at about 11 years of age. Males fight during the breeding season, which is also the wet season (October through May), and eggs are laid from November to April. Females produce 2 to 10 eggs per clutch and lay more than one clutch per season (Broadley 1989). Little is known of the reproductive ecology of the Malagasy population. However, Kuchling (1986) determined that female tortoises on Nosy Faly had an annual reproductive potential of 10–45 eggs per year. Hatchling body mass is about 20 g and carapace length is 40 mm. Sex ratio is at equilibrium on Nosy Faly (Pedrono 2008).

Kinixys zombensis may play an important role in its environment as a seed disperser (Mifsud et al. 2017). Activity diminishes in the dry season, when the tortoises estivate in burrows beneath the litter. They become very active with the onset of the rainy season at the end of October. The African Bush Pig (*Potamochoerus larvatus*), which is present on Nosy Faly, constitutes its main predator, but the local population of *Kinixys* does not seem to suffer significantly from such predation. The discovery of remains of *Kinixys* in human middens at the 11th- to 14th-century Mahilaka archaeological site in northwestern Madagascar (south of Ambanja) indicates that this species was exploited in the past (L. Rakotozafy 1996). *Kinixys zombensis* has recently entered the international pet trade. People on Nosy Faly traditionally support the conservation of these tortoises associated with a local cultural taboo and even sometimes feed them. However, *K. zombensis* on Madagascar may be threatened because of uncontrolled bushfires and the extremely small range of this species (Pedrono 2008; Mifsud et al. 2017).

Subject editors: Miguel Pedrono, Miguel Vences, and Achille P. Raselimanana

PODOCNEMIDIDAE AND PELOMEDUSIDAE, FRESHWATER TURTLES

G. Kuchling, J. Velosoa, and G. García

Four species of freshwater turtles are found on Madagascar, all members of the Pelomedusoides clade of side-necked turtles, with two extant families, the Podocnemididae and Pelomedusidae. Besides these extant species, three extinct genera and species of side-necked turtles have been described from the Cretaceous of Madagascar, *Kinkonychelys rogersi*, *Sokatra antitra*, and *Sahonachelys mailakavava* (Gaffney et al. 2009; Gaffney and Krause 2011; Joyce et al. 2021).

TAXONOMY AND SYSTEMATICS

Erymnochelys madagascariensis (*rere*, *rerehy*, *bihara* in Malagasy; Figure 12.14), representing a monotypic genus and subfamily (Erymnochelinae), is endemic to Madagascar and the only extant Old World representative of the family Podocnemididae. The other living members of the subfamily Podocnemidinae include seven species in two genera (*Podocnemis* and *Peltocephalus*) occurring in tropical South America, but fossils of the family Podocnemididae are also known from mainland Africa, Asia, Europe, and North America (Lapparent de Broin 2000). Given the long separate evolutionary history of *E. madagascariensis*, a prioritization of threatened species based on their evolutionary distinctiveness (ED) and global endangerment (GE) identified it as the world's single highest-ranked EDGE tetrapod (amphibians, birds, mammals, and reptiles; Gumbs et al. 2018). Because of its phylogenetic uniqueness and age, the significance of *E. madagascariensis* for biodiversity conservation simply cannot be overstated.

Erymnochelys has a wide distribution in western Madagascar, with at least two genetically distinct populations. Mitochondrial DNA sequencing data indicate a deep genealogical split between a southwestern group of the Mangoky-Tsiribihina-Tsingy de Bemaraha drainages and a northwestern group of the Mahajamba-Betsiboka-Sofia drainages (Kuchling et al. 2006; Velosoa et al. 2013). The type specimen of *E. madagascariensis* originated from the southwestern group (Grandidier 1867; type locality: "fleuves Morondava et Tsiribihina, côte ouest malgache"). If the northwestern group is considered to represent a separate taxon, a name is available based on a subspecies described from the Betsiboka: *Podocnemis madagascariensis bifilaris* (Boettger 1893; type locality: Majunga [Mahajanga]). There is some genetic divergence among drainage systems, which is poorly understood. Further genetic data from mitochondrial and nuclear markers are needed to determine the full extent of genetic variation for the species.

The other three species of Malagasy freshwater turtles belong to the family Pelomedusidae and are also found in mainland Africa: *Pelomedusa subrufa* (*kapidolo*, *tsimbao*, *kapika*; Figure 12.15), *Pelusios castanoides* (*kapika*, *kapibatana*; Figure 12.16), and *P. subniger* (*kapika*). Their native or introduced origin on Madagascar is still not fully clarified (see Raselimanana and Vences, pp. 1455–58). Chiefly, *Pelomedusa* does show some genetic variation within Madagascar, and differentiation from African specimens studied so far (Vargas-Ramírez et al. 2010); it is therefore likely to have colonized Madagascar naturally, although quite recently. In contrast, the two *Pelusios* species did not show any variation within Madagascar for the markers studied, which would agree with an introduction to Madagascar by humans.

FIGURE 12.14 ***Erymnochelys madagascariensis*, a representative of a monotypic genus whose closest relatives live in South America, is the world's single highest-ranked tetrapod species based on the EDGE assessment in terms of evolutionary distinctiveness (ED) and global endangerment (GE). This individual is from Lake Andranomena.** (PHOTO by G. Kuchling.)

FIGURE 12.15 ***Pelomedusa subrufa* is found from southern and western Madagascar north to Mahajanga. This individual was found in the Andranoheza River, at the foot of the Analavelona Massif.** (PHOTO by H. Schütz.)

FIGURE 12.16 **The Yellow-bellied Mud Turtle, *Pelusios castanoides*, occurs in Africa as well as Madagascar, and it is still uncertain whether it reached Madagascar naturally or was introduced by humans.** (PHOTO by M. Vences.)

DISTRIBUTION

Erymnochelys madagascariensis is a large turtle (carapace length up to 50 cm) found in the lowlands of western Madagascar, between the Mangoky River in the south and the Ankitribiky Marsh in the Sambirano watershed in the north. The species inhabits permanent wetlands, mainly rivers and lakes, and prefers clear and open water. *Pelomedusa subrufa* may grow up to 25 cm in carapace length and is found in southern and western Madagascar north to Mahajanga. It inhabits seasonal and ephemeral wetlands including pools of temporary flowing creeks, swamps, temporarily inundated areas, and rice fields. *Pelusios castanoides* (up to 30 cm carapace length) apparently occurs over most of Madagascar, including the Central Highlands. *Pelusios subniger* (up to 20 cm carapace length) is found along the central east coast. Both *Pelusios* species inhabit a wide variety of permanent and seasonal wetlands and seem to prefer areas with dense aquatic plants. They are also found in rice fields and channels. *Pelusios* and *Pelomedusa* are bottom walkers rather than swimmers and prefer rather shallow and vegetated areas of stagnant water or water with very little current. *Erymnochelys* is a good swimmer, occurring in deeper water bodies and flowing sections of rivers. Basking sites, like protruding tree trunks or rocks, are also important habitat structures for *Erymnochelys*.

DIETARY HABITS

The older literature reported *Erymnochelys madagascariensis* to be entirely carnivorous, eating mollusks, arthropods, fish, and amphibians (Siebenrock 1903; Vaillant and Grandidier 1910; Decary

1950; Tronc and Vuillemin 1974; IUCN 1982). Recent studies demonstrate that the species is omnivorous (Kuchling and Mittermeier 1987; Kuchling 1993a; García 2005; García and Lourenço 2007). The type of food consumed depends on the size of the turtle, the habitat, and the season. Data from stomach contents and fecal samples are available from Ankarafantsika National Park, in small natural wetlands and rivers surrounded by native dry deciduous forests (García 2005; García and Lourenço 2007), and from Marofilao, a shallow floodplain lake of the Kamoro River surrounded by degraded grassland near Ambato-Boeny (Kuchling and Mittermeier 1987; Kuchling 1993a). Limited data also exist from floodplain lakes and a side creek of the Tsiribihina River (Kuchling 1993a).

Smaller juveniles (<100 mm carapace length) of *E. madagascariensis* are largely carnivorous. In Ankarafantsika small juveniles eat mainly aquatic invertebrates in rivers, particularly Trichoptera larvae, but also mollusks and terrestrial arthropods that fall into the water. In a side creek of the Tsiribihina River, the stomach contents of juveniles under 100 mm carapace length contained mainly Ephemeroptera and Odonata larvae and aquatic coleopterans, whereas juveniles of 100–150 mm carapace length also had fish, seeds, nuts, and leaves in their stomachs. At Marofilao, however, even juveniles under 100 mm carapace length had already consumed large quantities of *Phragmites* shoots. When evidence of fish consumption has been found, generally consisting of scales and bones of relatively large fish rather than whole fish or bitten-off pieces, the turtles seem to have mainly scavenged dead fish or leftovers (e.g., scales) from other predators (crocodiles and humans) rather than hunting live fish; at many study sites people clean fish at the water's edge and discard waste in the water.

In Ankarafantsika, stomach samples of larger juveniles contained 59% animal and 41% plant material, whereas those of *E. madagascariensis* adults contained 72% plant and 28% animal material with no difference between sexes (García and Lourenço 2007). Adults consumed mainly aquatic plants, shoots and stems of *Phragmites* sp., leaves from trees adjacent to the water, terrestrial fungi, flowers (e.g., *Pandanus* sp.) that fell into the water, and various fruits (especially *Ficus* sp., *Raphia farinifera*, lianas, and mangos) and seeds (e.g., *Typhonodorum lindleyanum*, those from different trees). Most seeds were not fully digested and could germinate after their passage through the digestive tract (García 2005). *Erymnochelys* may thus be a seed disperser for various riparian plant species. Adults also utilize animal protein in their diet, consuming mollusks, fish, insects and arachnids including bees and scorpions, hatchlings of *Crocodylus niloticus*, and birds (*Foudia madagascariensis*). Much of the animal matter may be taken by scavenging dead animals rather than by active predation. At Marofilao, the diet of adults and larger juveniles was mainly *Phragmites* and a small aquatic snail (*Melanoides tuberculata*). The turtles crushed the largest coils of snail shells but still swallowed the entire shell of snails less than about 30 mm long. Additional food items at Marofilao included fish, crustaceans, small seeds, nuts, and the remains of an introduced mouse (*Mus musculus*).

Erymnochelys madagascariensis feeds less during the cool period of the dry season (May through August), when its stomach is frequently empty. Although turtles feed opportunistically on seasonally available food sources like fruits and seeds, there is no seasonal shift between herbivory and carnivory in the relatively small permanent lakes and rivers of the Ankarafantsika Plateau, which show only minor seasonal water level fluctuations and are surrounded by natural forest. However, the flood lakes in the alluvial plains of the large rivers of western Madagascar show dramatic seasonal water level fluctuations. Reed beds typically cover vast areas along the shores. Most reed beds are without much water during the dry season, and little or no plant material is available for turtles during the time of year when water is restricted to the deeper sections of lakes. In these habitats, all size classes of *Erymnochelys* show an overwhelmingly carnivorous diet during the late dry season (mainly snails) but shift to herbivory (mainly *Phragmites*) with rising water levels at the onset of the wet season (Kuchling 1993a). This is also the time when *Phragmites* produces new green shoots and roots that are preferentially eaten.

Data on food composition of *Pelusios castanoides* and *Pelomedusa subrufa* are available for Ankarafantsika (G. García, unpublished data). *Pelusios castanoides* shows a preference for aquatic invertebrates, but adults also consume some plant material such as shoots, stems, grains, and fruits. They also opportunistically take terrestrial animals that fall into the water, such as Lepidoptera larvae, terrestrial coleopterans, or even lizards (*Oplurus cuvieri*). *Pelomedusa* is carnivorous and consumes aquatic invertebrates (including Odonata larvae and aquatic heteropterans) and tadpoles, but also terrestrial insects that fall into the water. During the cool part of the dry season, from June to September, both *Pelusios castanoides* and *Pelomedusa subrufa* leave the wetlands, hide in forest leaf litter, and apparently do not feed. Only small juveniles of these species may stay in the water, remaining active throughout the year and feeding during the dry season. No information is available concerning the diet of *Pelusios subniger* on Madagascar, but African populations of this species are generally considered to be omnivorous (Loveridge 1941).

REPRODUCTION

Erymnochelys madagascariensis females reach sexual maturity when they attain about 26 cm carapace length, while males possibly mature at a slightly smaller size (Kuchling 1988). This corresponds to an age of between 22 and 25 years (García 2005). Gravid females have been observed in September, but the nesting season seems to start in October with the first rains. Given that the onset of rains varies across the zone where this species occurs, it is reasonable to assume regional variation in its nesting season. Females typically lay several clutches per season, and the nesting season generally extends until January (Kuchling 1993a). However, recent ultrasonographic data show that some females can produce eggs until April or May (G. Kuchling, unpublished data). Thus, *E. madagascariensis* nests from the first rains until the end of the wet season. Preliminary data suggesting a biennial ovarian cycle of *E. madagascariensis* (Kuchling 1993b) were confirmed with more extensive ultrasonographic and coelioscopic data at Ankarafantsika: females produce several clutches of eggs every second year (Blanvillain et al. 2011).

Erymnochelys is not a communal sand beach nester like the large *Podocnemis* species of South America but instead nests solitarily along shores in bushland and forest. In this respect it resembles its South American relative *Peltocephalus dumerilianus* (Vogt et al. 1994). At Ankarafantsika, *E. madagascariensis* females construct nests between 3.2 and 67.1 m from the water's edge. They nest during the night, particularly after rainstorms when the ground is moist and easy to dig. Nests are 15–20 cm deep and are often close to vegetation, although females generally seem to prefer rather open and sunny locations (García 2005). At Ankarafantsika, clutch size ranges from 6 to 25 eggs; a clutch size of 29 eggs has been reported at Lake Marofilao adjacent to the Kamoro River (Kuchling 1993a), and clutch sizes of 8–32 eggs at Lake Ambondrobe (J. Velosoa, unpublished data). Voeltzkow (1901) reported an egg length of 34–40 mm and a width of 22–25 mm. At Lake Antsilomba, Ankarafantsika (1998–2000), eggs had a mean length of 39.24 ± 2.24 (SD) mm (range 28.2–47.1 mm, n = 399), a mean width of 25.10 ± 1.65 mm (range 20.6–29.95 mm, n = 399), and a mean mass of 14.81 ± 2.74 g (5.0–22.0 g, n = 395) (García 2005). These large ranges suggest that clutch and egg size may increase with female body size and that large and older females may have better reproductive success than small ones, but these hypotheses have yet to be tested.

Wild nests of *E. madagascariensis* at Ankarafantsika have an incubation period of 73–75 days. Nests constructed early in the wet season (October or November) tend to receive more solar radiation (i.e., they are warmer) than nests constructed later in the wet season. The hatchlings do not emerge immediately but stay in the nest cavity for two or three days before leaving. They may wait for the most favorable moment to emerge, for example during rain. Hatchlings have a supply of internal yolk when they emerge from the nest but start feeding as soon as they reach the water (García 2005).

Pelusios castanoides and *Pelomedusa subrufa* both nest at the end of the dry season or beginning of the wet season. They tend to nest slightly earlier than *Erymnochelys*. Both species have an annual ovarian cycle. *Pelusios castanoides* females reach maturity at about 140 mm carapace length and males between 120 and 125 mm. *Pelomedusa* females are mature when they reach a carapace length of 130 mm, while males are mature at about 108 mm. Ultrasound examination during the pre-nesting season suggested clutch sizes of about 10 eggs for *Pelusios castanoides* and about seven eggs for *Pelomedusa subrufa* (G. Kuchling, unpublished data), but large females may produce larger clutches. It is possible that some females produce more than one clutch per season. Kaudern (1922) reported that a clutch of a Malagasy *Pelusios castanoides* contained 12 eggs. Ernst and Barbour (1989) reported clutch sizes of up to 25 eggs for *P. castanoides* and up to 42 eggs for *Pelomedusa subrufa* on the African mainland. Interestingly, Kaudern (1922) reported that *Pelusios castanoides* females excavate a flask-shaped nest cavity with their front legs and head. It has been suggested that this observation was erroneous (Ernst and Barbour 1989), since it is generally assumed that all turtles dig the nest chamber with their hind legs. However, nest digging with front legs has been described for the Australian turtle *Pseudemydura umbrina* (family Chelidae; Kuchling 1993c). Clearly, nest-digging behavior in *Pelusios castanoides* should be reexamined to clarify whether Kaudern's observation was correct.

Little is known about male reproductive cycles of Malagasy turtles. Endoscopic examinations suggest that spermatogenesis (formation of spermatozoa in the testis) and spermiation (transport of spermatozoa from the testis into the epididymis) peak in *Pelusios castanoides* and *Pelomedusa subrufa* in April, toward the end of the wet season, whereas the testes of *Erymnochelys* are in the early recrudescent phase during that time of year (Blanvillain et al. 2011). The time of mating is unknown in Malagasy freshwater turtles, but it may possibly take place before and during the early nesting season. Preliminary data indicate that *Pelusios castanoides* and *Pelomedusa subrufa* have postnuptial spermatogenetic cycles, whereas *E. madagascariensis* has a prenuptial spermatogenetic cycle.

To summarize, the reproductive cycles of *Pelusios castanoides* and *Pelomedusa subrufa* follow a typical freshwater turtle pattern. In contrast, that of *E. madagascariensis* is unusual for freshwater turtles in that it has an extended nesting season, multiyear ovarian cycle, and prenuptial spermatogenesis, all characteristics reminiscent of the reproductive cycles of sea turtles. The only other freshwater turtle for which the female reproductive cycle is comparable to that of *Erymnochelys* is the mainly herbivorous large river turtle *Carettochelys insculpta*, which produces two clutches of eggs also only every second year (Doody et al. 2003); this species occurs in northern Australia and in a climatic zone comparable to that of northwestern Madagascar. Nothing is known about the reproduction of *Pelusios subniger* on Madagascar.

PREDATION

The turtle life stages most prone to predation are eggs and hatchlings. Predators on Madagascar include African Bush Pigs, *Potamochoerus larvatus*, which dig out nests, and possibly the Tailless Tenrec, *Tenrec ecaudatus*. The snakes *Leioheterodon madagascariensis* and *L. modestus* can also often be seen foraging in nesting areas and may opportunistically consume turtle eggs and hatchlings. Waterbirds like egrets and herons can certainly feed on hatchlings and small juveniles. *Crocodylus niloticus* may be the major predator of *Erymnochelys madagascariensis* juveniles (and possibly also *Pelusios* and *Pelomedusa*). However, it seems that once *Erymnochelys* reaches adult size, it is more or less secure from crocodiles because of the strength of its shell. During turtle trapping over the years, several juveniles have been found crushed by crocodiles inside turtle traps (J. Velosoa, unpublished data), and several small adults have been found with crocodile tooth imprints on the shell; they obviously survived the attack because their shell could not be crushed (J. Velosoa et al., unpublished data).

The single most important predator of *Erymnochelys* subadults and adults is humans. Exploitation is mainly at the local subsistence level. The turtles are captured primarily during fishing, an activity that has expanded dramatically over the past 15 years. Usually all turtles captured are killed and consumed. In contrast to fish, turtles are generally not marketed because they are considered to be protected by Malagasy law. Exploitation is directed mainly toward large turtles, but given that their meat is highly appreciated as food, some animals are harvested before reaching sexual maturity. In the past at sites with substantial populations, only turtles larger than about 18 cm shell length were taken. In habitats where fishing pressure suddenly increases because of an influx of people with better fishing technology (seine nets), the extirpation pattern of *Erymnochelys* populations is characterized by their abrupt disappearance: people who exploit them often have the impression there are plenty of turtles until they are suddenly gone. The reason for this phenomenon is that once all reproducing females are extirpated and no further recruitment of hatchlings takes place, there are still, for several years, younger age classes from previous reproductive seasons growing up to a size that makes them attractive for human consumption. Once all these age classes have been captured, extinction is so abrupt that local people are often mystified by the sudden disappearance of the species. The smaller the habitat surface area, the faster *Erymnochelys* populations crash under exploitation pressure; under continuing exploitation, persistence at a low population level over several years is found only in very extensive habitats (Kuchling and Mittermeier 1993; Kuchling 1997a). However, once turtle numbers are reduced, all size classes are consumed (Velosoa et al. 2015).

Humans throughout Madagascar also exploit *Pelusios* and *Pelomedusa*, but they are less appreciated for consumption than *Erymnochelys*. Their smaller size and different habitat preferences make them much less prone to extirpation under human exploitation pressure.

CONSERVATION STATUS WITH A FOCUS ON *ERYMNOCHELYS*

In contrast to *Pelusios* and *Pelomedusa*, for which the Malagasy populations are not threatened, *Erymnochelys madagascariensis* is Critically Endangered (IUCN 2019) and in serious, noncyclical decline over its complete distributional range. Little is known about the historic abundance of *Erymnochelys* and its ecological role in the rivers and lakes of western Madagascar. Its closest relatives, the large river turtles of the genus *Podocnemis*, which occur over vast areas in the Amazon and Orinoco River drainages, had historically huge populations and played an important role in these ecosystems through their large standing crop biomass, high secondary productivity, and contribution to energy flow within and between ecosystems. However, in the 19th century the unsustainable harvest of eggs and meat by humans had already depleted populations across the species' range (Humboldt 1820; H. Bates 1892), a situation that dramatically accelerated throughout the 20th century (Forero-Medina et al. 2021). It appears plausible that in precolonial times, *Erymnochelys* had comparable dense populations, biomass, and ecological significance in the slow-moving rivers, backwaters, and floodplain lakes of western Madagascar: it was still considered very common in the late 19th century (Voeltzkow 1901; Siebenrock 1903). However, the very limited extent (compared to South America) of this species' required habitats in western Madagascar, combined with exploitation by a growing human population, led to depletion of *Erymnochelys* populations during the 20th century that was much more pronounced than that of its South American relatives.

Large, shallow lakes in alluvial plains that are seasonally inundated by flooding rivers are the core habitat areas and former strongholds of *Erymnochelys* and are where the largest populations occurred historically. In 1991 and 1992 most major *Erymnochelys* habitats and populations were assessed by a rapid survey technique, based on interviews with local fishermen. In flood lakes of the Tsiribihina where *Erymnochelys* was still common in the early 1970s (Tronc and Vuillemin 1974), the species was depleted or heavily depleted by the early 1990s. The best-studied population of the 1980s, in a flood lake in the alluvial plain of the Kamoro River (Kuchling 1988, 1993a), was extirpated by the early 1990s (Kuchling and Mittermeier 1993). A survey of 46 localities revealed serious depletion and local extirpation of populations from overexploitation. Eleven percent of the populations were considered to be "exploited but relatively good," 28% "exploited and declining," 28% "heavily exploited and depleted," 31% "possibly extinct" or "extinct," and at one locality, this species may have "never existed" (Kuchling 1997a). However, only two of the five sites with "exploited but relatively good" populations, Lake Ambondrobe and Lake Masama, are relatively large flood lakes in alluvial plains with presumably large *Erymnochelys* populations (Kuchling 1992). All other sites identified then and since then with relatively good persisting populations are small in comparison because they occur in small and marginal habitat areas and can be considered relict populations at the margins of much wider former occurrences. However, even though small, they can still be significant for conservation, particularly if found in protected areas, typically water catchment areas with small streams adjacent to alluvial plains where the species has largely disappeared, such as Ankarafantsika National Park.

By the late 1990s, several of the surveyed populations had further declined, although no additional extirpation was recorded (Velosoa 2000). Since then, the decrease in population sizes during the first decade of this century averaged 70%, and only eight sites, or 7.6%, supported stable populations by 2010 (Velosoa et al. 2013). Although the species is still widespread, the continuing downward trend in *Erymnochelys* populations is alarming.

Thirty years ago, no *Erymnochelys* population was known to occur in a protected area (Nicoll and Langrand 1989), but several small populations were identified in 1996 at Ankarafantsika (Kuchling 1996, 1997b). Later in the 1990s small populations of *Erymnochelys* were also recorded at Bemaraha and Baly Bay. However, the small populations at these sites are also under exploitation pressure and partly depleted. At Ankarafantsika, a particular problem is an increasing human population together with the loss of old traditions and taboos (*fady*) concerning wetland use. Fishing nets and pirogues are now used on several lakes where they were traditionally *fady*. This has resulted in increased exploitation pressure on these small *Erymnochelys* populations (Kuchling 1997b; García and Goodman 2003).

A program for the conservation of *Erymnochelys* was started in 1997 at Ankarafantsika under the direction of the Durrell Wildlife Conservation Trust and Conservation International, and involving Madagascar National Parks (Kuchling 1997b). It includes ecological and population studies (García 2005), captive breeding (Kuchling 2000), and the active management of wild populations, including nest protection, head starting (raising young animals in captive settings and then releasing them into the wild), and reintroduction. Originally collected as hatchlings from protected nests at Lake Antsilomba and raised in captivity, 158 head-started juveniles were released at Lake Ankomakoma in 2004 to reinforce this population, with another 180 released in 2009. Since 2010, hatchlings from Antsilomba have also been directly translocated to Ankomakoma (Velosoa et al. 2013). Approximately 19% of released turtles have been recaptured post-release, and population estimates based on mark-recapture demonstrate that the population in Ankomakoma increased significantly as a result of the releases (Velosoa et al. 2011). In 2015, 114 juveniles bred and raised in captivity were released into Lake Ravelobe adjacent to Ampijoroa, and the lake habitat was improved by cleaning out Water Hyacinths (*Eichhornia crassipes*) in a cooperative effort by Fikambanana Sakaizan-d'Ravelobe (Friends of Ravelobe), Madagascar National Park, and the Durrell Wildlife Conservation Trust.

Based on efforts by the Durrell Wildlife Conservation Trust, the largest *Erymnochelys* population identified as "exploited but relatively good" by Kuchling (1992), possibly still today harboring the largest, most significant surviving populations of the species, is now the focus of conservation management with the creation of the new Ambondrobe protected area (7049 ha) in 2008 (Velosoa et al. 2015, 2019). From the 2008 to 2019 breeding seasons, the Durrell Wildlife Conservation Trust, in collaboration with local communities, protected 783 *Erymnochelys* nests, from which 6807 hatchlings emerged and were released into the lake. After the creation of the Mahavavy Kinkony protected area, managed by Asity Madagascar since 2002, what probably used to be one of the historically largest populations of *Erymnochelys*, which was already heavily depleted in the 1980s (Kuchling 1992; Kuchling and Mittermeier 1993), may now also receive some active protection (Chechia 2018).

To summarize, with the creation of new protected areas on Madagascar over the past couple of decades, *Erymnochelys* populations are now known to occur in a total of 10 protected areas, five of which are Ramsar sites (roughly north to south): Antrema, Ankarafantsika, Mahavavy Kinkony, Baly Bay, Mandrozo, Bemaraha, Tsimembo-Manambolomaty, Ambondrobe, Menabe Antimena, and Mangoky Ihotry complex.

Subject editors: Gerald Kuchling, Miguel Vences, and Achille P. Raselimanana

GEKKONIDAE, GECKOS, *KATSATSAKA, TSATSAKE*

A. M. Bauer, M. D. Scherz, A. Crottini, F. M. Ratsoavina, and F. Glaw

The Gekkota, or geckos, with more than 2000 species, is the most species-rich group of lizards in the world (Uetz et al. 2021). On Madagascar, geckos are the most diverse group of lizards, with 121 species and 11 genera represented (Table 12.4). Gekkota is an ancient clade of lizards that includes seven families (Gamble et al. 2012), of which only the Gekkonidae is represented on Madagascar. Gekkonids occur on all inhabitable continents and are among the only lizards able to colonize remote oceanic islands.

The nine Malagasy genera (Table 12.4) with endemic species are all part of a large clade of mostly Afro-Malagasy geckos (Gamble et

TABLE 12.4. **Genera of gekkonid lizards occurring on Madagascar**

GENUS	ENDEMIC MALAGASY SPECIES/ MALAGASY SPECIES/TOTAL SPECIES	SUBSTRATE TYPE (IN ORDER OF SIGNIFICANCE)	PRIMARY ACTIVITY PERIOD
Blaesodactylus	6/6/6	Ar, Ru	Nocturnal
Ebenavia	4/5/6	Ar, Ru	Nocturnal
Geckolepis	4/5/5	Ar, Ed	Nocturnal
Gehyra	0/1/63	Ed, Ar	Nocturnal
Hemidactylus	0/3/158	Ed, Ar	Nocturnal
Lygodactylus	22/22/65	Ar, Ru	Diurnal
Matoatoa	2/2/2	Ar	Nocturnal
Paragehyra	4/4/4	Ru	Nocturnal
Paroedura	22/22/24	Te, Ru, Ar	Nocturnal
Phelsuma	33/34/52	Ar, Ed, Ru	Diurnal
Uroplatus	21/21/21	Ar, Ed	Nocturnal

Note: Ar, arboreal; Ed, edificarian (using human-built structures); Ru, rupicolous; Te, terrestrial.

FIGURE 12.17 **Because gekkonid geckos lack eyelids, they rely on their flexible tongue to clean their eyes, as this *Phelsuma guttata* individual from Masoala is doing.** (PHOTO by G. M. Rosa.)

al. 2012, 2015). The extralimital genera in this clade include the endemic southern African and Seychelles taxa, as well as some from the Indian subcontinent. Within this group there is no evidence for the collective monophyly of the Malagasy geckos, which appear to represent multiple independent colonization events on the island (Gamble et al. 2015). The Afro-Malagasy clade appears to have undergone a rapid radiation about 80 million years ago (Mya), and there is little support for some of the basal relationships within the group. The genera *Hemidactylus* and *Gehyra* are not members of the Afro-Malagasy clade and are clearly relatively recent arrivals from Africa and Asia, respectively (Bauer 1993; Vences et al. 2004b; Rocha et al. 2009a; see Raselimanana and Vences, pp. 1455–58).

All gekkonids are small to moderately sized, fully limbed lizards, and most are characterized by relatively short tails and large heads with rounded snouts and large eyes (all retained juvenile traits). Since they lack eyelids they cannot "close" their eyes (Figure 12.17), and they use their tongue to clean or moisten the transparent brille (or spectacle) that covers the eye. Malagasy geckos span almost the entire size range seen in the family, from species of *Lygodactylus* and *Ebenavia* less than 25 mm snout-to-vent length to *Uroplatus giganteus*, which at 200 mm snout-to-vent length is the largest living representative of the Gekkonidae, and one of the largest living geckos in the world (Bauer 2013).

ASPECTS OF NATURAL HISTORY

Gekkonids in general are noted for their climbing, and while all Malagasy species are capable of this activity to some extent, the more terrestrial species have limited abilities. At the global level, most geckos are rupicolous (living on rocks), but a large minority, including most species occurring on Madagascar, are arboreal (Bauer 2013). Climbing involves the use of both claws (absent or reduced, however, in *Phelsuma* and *Ebenavia*) and a complex system of subdigital scansors (Figure 12.18) bearing millions of branched, hairlike setae. These interact to form weak, temporary molecular bonds with the surfaces to which they are applied (Autumn et al. 2000; Autumn and Peattie 2002). These systems are controlled by a series of tendons and a diversity of tissues that distribute forces uniformly across the setal fields (Russell 1986, 2002; Higham et al. 2017). The scansors may run along the basal part of the toe or, as in some Malagasy genera (e.g., *Matoatoa*, *Paroedura*, *Uroplatus*), may be distal only.

The tails of some species, especially in the genera *Lygodactylus*, *Matoatoa*, and to some extent *Phelsuma*, are prehensile and may bear adhesive pads or setal fields on the tip (Mertens 1964; Maderson 1971; Bauer 1998; Nussbaum et al. 1998). The tails of most

FIGURE 12.18 **Geckos are excellent climbers thanks to a complex system of subdigital scansors bearing millions of branched, hairlike setae that interact to form weak, temporary molecular bonds with the surfaces to which they are applied. The morphology of these scansors is also distinct among genera of geckos and can be an excellent character for diagnosis. The photograph shows the ventral side of the toes of *Phelsuma grandis*, each with a single row of lamella-like scansors.** (PHOTO by M. Vences.)

Malagasy geckos can break and be regenerated. Tail breakage in *Uroplatus* is restricted to the tail base (Bauer and Russell 1989), and regeneration seems to be possible in only some species (see Gehring et al., pp. 1480–85). Tail break frequencies among most geckos are high and probably reflect both failed predation attempts and the results of intraspecific interactions (Bauer and Russell 1994; Itescu et al. 2016). Parts of the skin, too, can be "shed" as an antipredator escape mechanism. This facility is moderately well developed in some *Phelsuma* species (Raxworthy and Nussbaum 1994a; see Gehring and Ratsoavina, pp. 1485–90) and exceptionally so in members of the genus *Geckolepis* (Meier 1980; Paluh et al. 2017; Scherz et al. 2017).

Geckos are ancestrally nocturnal, but diurnality evolved in the common ancestor of *Phelsuma* and *Lygodactylus* (Gamble et al. 2015), genera characterized by bold patterns and rounded pupils. These geckos use a variety of visual cues in their behavioral repertoire, especially in the maintenance of territories and the acquisition of mates (Heselhaus 1986; Hallmann et al. 1997). Open-mouthed threat postures involving body inflation or compression and slow tail waving occur in *Uroplatus* (Raxworthy 1988; Andreone 1991a, 1991b). Some *Paroedura* species curl the tail over the back, scorpion-like, when threatened (Nussbaum and Raxworthy 2000b), some wave the tail vigorously (e.g., *P. masobe*), and others, including *P. bastardi* (Glaw and Vences 2007), gape and vocalize. Most geckos emit distress calls if threatened or handled, but many also use complex calls as social signals, chiefly to maintain spacing and warn away rivals (Rohtla et al. 2019). *Ebenavia robusta* has been regularly observed emitting soft purring vocalizations of unknown function in captivity (Hawlitschek et al. 2018). In *Paroedura* and other geckos, conspecifics may also communicate by means of chemosensory cues detected by tongue flicking (Brillet 1990).

All geckos are principally insectivorous. Many ambush their prey (Bauer 2007), but *Uroplatus* species are active foragers, walking slowly along branches in search of invertebrates (Raxworthy 1988), and some *Phelsuma*, *Lygodactylus*, and *Blaesodactylus* species milk honeydew-producing planthoppers (Fölling et al. 2001; see Figure 12.2b and Świerczewski and Stroiński, pp. 987–91). Insular geckos frequently supplement their diets with nectar, pollen, and fruit (Rösler 1995; Valido and Olesen 2019). On Madagascar and other Indian Ocean islands, such behavior has been noted chiefly in *Phelsuma* (Cheke 1984; A. Gardner 1984; Hallmann et al. 1997). In turn, geckos are preyed on by a variety of birds, snakes, primates, and other carnivorous mammals (Meier 1977; Bauer and Russell 1992; Goodman et al. 1993a, 1993b); at least three lemurs prey on geckos and other lizards (Petter 1978; Hladik et al. 1980; Pages 1980). Smaller or juvenile geckos may fall prey to other geckos (e.g., *P. laticauda* preys on juvenile *Hemidactylus* sp.; Gehring et al. 2010a), spiders (e.g., *Ebenavia boettgeri*; A. Crottini, unpublished data), and other predatory arthropods, including scorpions (Glaw et al. 2002) and centipedes (D. Prötzel and F. Glaw, unpublished data).

Gekkonids are oviparous and virtually all have clutches of two hard-shelled eggs. Some species are known to lay in communal nests (e.g., *Paragehyra gabriellae*; Nussbaum and Raxworthy 1994c). Reproductive cycles are generally poorly documented in the wild, but most tropical geckos probably produce multiple clutches per year, peaking at the beginning of and during the warm rainy season. Paradoxically, some high-elevation *Lygodactylus* species are winter breeders (Pasteur 1959), while a species of this genus from western Madagascar has been documented to breed year-round (Vences et al. 2004a). Mating gekkonids tend to exhibit stereotypic precopulatory behaviors, and the male often restrains the female by biting or, as in *Paroedura picta*, holding her with his forelegs (Brillet 1991).

Reproductive females often store calcium, presumably for use in eggshell production, in endolymphatic sacs (fluid-filled extensions of the inner ear apparatus) that usually extend along the neck (Bauer 1989). These structures may be huge in *Phelsuma* (A. Gardner 1985), *Uroplatus*, *Ebenavia*, and other Malagasy geckos. Eggs are laid most often in tree hollows, palm frond petioles, rock crevices, or shallow excavated nests on the ground. Defense of the eggs has been reported in a number of species of *Phelsuma* (Osadnik 1984).

In most geckos sex is genetically determined, but temperature-dependent sex determination occurs in some *Phelsuma* species (Gamble 2010). Parthenogenetic reproduction has been suggested for one species occurring on the island, *Lygodactylus pauliani* (Pasteur and Blanc 1991), but this remains to be verified. Although gekkonids generally show little sexual dimorphism, males of Malagasy geckos (except *Ebenavia* and *Uroplatus*) possess precloacal glands that produce waxy secretions used in intraspecific chemical communication. Pronounced size and color dimorphism are characteristic of some *Phelsuma* species (Glaw and Vences 2007).

Little is known about community ecology, population structure, or population dynamics of Malagasy geckos, but at least some species have relatively long life spans (Rösler 1995; Hallmann et al. 1997) and may best be regarded as *k*-selected. *Phelsuma* in the Seychelles (and probably Madagascar) can reach relatively high densities, and sympatric congeners appear to achieve niche partitioning chiefly through differential habitat (vegetation) utilization (Thorpe and Crawford 1979). The potential instability of populations is exemplified by *L. tuberosus*, which, at Lake Ihotry in southwestern Madagascar, underwent a huge increase in relative abundance over several years before ultimately crashing back to original levels in just six months (Pasteur 1977).

On Madagascar most gecko species are restricted to mesic forest habitats; however, several species of *Blaesodactylus*, *Ebenavia*, *Geckolepis*, *Matoatoa*, *Paroedura*, *Paragehyra*, *Phelsuma*, and *Lygodactylus* occur in the arid west and southwest, and virtually all habitat types, including karst areas and littoral forests, have some endemics (Raxworthy and Nussbaum 1993a, 1994c; Nussbaum and Raxworthy 2000b; Crottini et al. 2014). Most gecko species are restricted to lowland habitats or extend to only about 1000 m elevation (Raxworthy and Nussbaum 1994c; Nussbaum et al. 1999b; Raselimanana et al. 2000a). At the extreme, some *Lygodactylus* and *Phelsuma* species occur only at elevations well above 2000 m in montane ericoid thicket or montane grassland (Pasteur 1995; Glaw and Vences 2007).

Several Malagasy geckos, especially those in the genera *Phelsuma*, *Uroplatus*, and *Paroedura*, are particularly popular with herpetoculturists (Mattioli et al. 2006), and several species are therefore included in Appendix II of CITES (Convention on International Trade in Endangered Species of Wild Fauna and Flora). These are regularly exported for the international pet trade, and numbers of species and individuals are controlled under a quota system that, at present, may be sustainable (see Carpenter et al., pp. 1452–55).

Malagasy geckos are at risk mostly from habitat destruction and transformation. Because so many of the island's geckos are arboreal, deforestation and habitat fragmentation are the most significant sources of imperilment (Jenkins et al. 2014). Many species are known only from single forest blocks or are limited to narrow elevational bands (Nussbaum and Raxworthy 1994b; Crottini et al. 2011, 2014; Jono et al. 2015).

GENERA OF MALAGASY GEKKONIDS

Blaesodactylus species (all six are endemic) are large (up to 140 mm snout-to-vent length), heavy-bodied, long-lived geckos with scattered dorsal tubercles. They are arboreal or rock dwelling (Böhme and Meier 1980), and at least some species are known to be extremely philopatric (e.g., individuals of *B. antongilensis* at Betampona may inhabit the same tree trunk for all, or almost all, their lives; A. Crottini, unpublished data). Two eggs are laid in the ground, and at least *B. boivini* has been reported to protect both the eggs and hatchlings (Henkel and Schmidt 2000). Although most *Blaesodactylus* activity appears to take place at night, *B. boivini* has been considered at least partly diurnal (Glaw and Vences 2007). The latest taxonomic work on this genus was by Ineich et al. (2016). *Blaesodactylus* is the sister taxon of the mainland African *Homopholis* (Gamble et al. 2012).

Ebenavia species (six total, of which five occur on Madagascar and four are endemic) are among the smallest of the island's geckos, with one species reaching only 24 mm snout-to-vent length. These are leaf-toed geckos with multi-carinate (bearing multiple keels) dorsal scales. Claws are entirely or almost entirely lacking (Nussbaum and Raxworthy 1998a; Hawlitschek et al. 2018). These geckos are usually arboreal and occur in several forest types but can also be found on buildings, both on Madagascar and on Mauritius (introduced), the Comoro islands, and Pemba Island (Tanzania) (Andreone 1991a, 1991b; Hawlitschek et al. 2017b, 2018). They may be active night and day (Andreone 1991a, 1991b; Nussbaum and Raxworthy 1998a). *Ebenavia maintimainty* may be rupicolous and appears to be restricted to the dry spiny thickets of the limestone Mahafaly Plateau. The natural history of all species remains poorly known, but *E. maintimainty* appears to lay only a single egg (Nussbaum and Raxworthy 1998a). Multiple deep phylogeographic lineages and numerous cases of overseas dispersal were identified by Hawlitschek et al. (2017a), and the taxonomy of this genus was revised by Hawlitschek et al. (2018). *Ebenavia* shares its closest affinities with *Paroedura* (Gamble et al. 2012).

Matoatoa (two species, both endemic) is a relatively recently described genus (Nussbaum et al. 1998) that was separated from *Phyllodactylus,* which is now known to be a member of a different gekkotan family and restricted to the New World (Bauer et al. 1997). These are relatively small geckos (<60 mm snout-to-vent length) with slender, elongated bodies, short limbs, fat tails, and small, blunt heads. The digits end in a pair of distal scansors (enlarged scales bearing hairlike setae that permit climbing). Both dorsal and ventral scales are arranged in transverse rows of granular scales that overlap weakly or not at all, and the tail is adhesive (Nussbaum et al. 1998). Virtually nothing is known about their biology, but they are nocturnal and arboreal (Funnell et al. 2012). One species is restricted to moist evergreen forests and the other to dry spiny thickets. *Matoatoa* is closely related to several mainland African genera and to *Christinus* of Australia, all of which share similar "leaf-toed" morphology (Heinicke et al. 2014).

Paragehyra species (all four are endemic) are moderately large (up to 75 mm snout-to-vent length), flattened, granular-scaled geckos with long limbs, and basal toe pads. The populations of *P. petiti* from Bemaraha and Toliara are morphologically distinct, and the former might represent a new species (Crottini et al. 2014). A confirmed candidate species of *Paragehyra* has recently been identified in Tsaranoro (western side of the Andringitra Massif; Belluardo et al. 2021), not too far from the recently described *P. felicitae* (Figure 12.19), which is known to live on large granitic boulders close to small streams in dry deciduous forests. *Paragehyra gabriellae* lives in association with boulders along water courses at the southern end of the eastern moist evergreen forests in the Vohimena and Anosyenne Mountains. Eggs are laid in communal nests on protected rock surfaces and reproduction may be seasonal, with

FIGURE 12.19 Like many lizards, geckos often consume their shed skin, as this *Paragehyra felicitae* individual from Sakaviro is doing. (PHOTO by G. M. Rosa.)

hatching occurring from January to March (Nussbaum and Raxworthy 1994c). The taxonomy of this genus was revised by Crottini et al. (2014). The phylogenetic position of *Paragehyra* remains difficult to assess, but striking convergences in digital structure with the West Indian sphaerodactylid *Aristelliger* (Nussbaum and Raxworthy 1994b) and a Cretaceous amber-embedded fossil gecko from Myanmar (Daza et al. 2016) have been noted.

Geckolepis species (five total, four endemic to Madagascar) are highly distinctive arboreal geckos with very fragile skin (Meier 1980; Bauer et al. 1989; G. Köhler et al. 2009). Their large or very large, overlapping, fishlike scales, which contain thin osteoderms, or dermal bone structures, are unique among all geckos (Paluh et al. 2017; Scherz et al. 2017). The body is usually stout and small to moderate in size (up to 75 mm snout-to-vent length; Lemme et al. 2013), and the toe pads are wide. Some species occupy human habitations and can occur in aggregations (e.g., *G. polylepis*; Henkel and Schmidt 2000), but they are chiefly arboreal and nocturnal, sheltering under bark by day (Glaw and Vences 1994). *Geckolepis polylepis* and *G. typica* are restricted to the subarid west of the island, *G. megalepis* (Figure 12.20) inhabits the limestone formations (locally known as *tsingy*) of the Ankarana Massif, and the *G. maculata* species group inhabits moist evergreen forests of the east and north. Eggs are laid in the soil or in palm frond petioles (C. Blanc 1966). *Geckolepis* includes numerous undescribed species (Lemme et al. 2013), and a comprehensive revision of the genus is still needed. The taxonomy remains very difficult to resolve because of confounding inter- and intraspecific variance in the skeleton (Hawlitschek et al. 2016; Scherz et al. 2017) and scale patterns, exacerbated by the fragile skin and often damaged specimens (Lemme et al. 2013). *Geckolepis* is strongly supported as the sister to *Homopholis* + *Blaesodactylus* (Gamble et al. 2012).

Paroedura is a genus restricted chiefly to Madagascar, with 22 endemic species, and two in the Comoros (Hawlitschek and Glaw 2012; Glaw et al. 2018; J. Köhler et al. 2019; Miralles et al. 2021). These are nocturnal geckos, 40–100 mm snout-to-vent length, with relatively tuberculate dorsal scales, large heads, large eyes, and relatively slender tails that often bear spines. Most occur in transitional or dry deciduous forest habitats, although some are present in moist evergreen forests (Nussbaum and Raxworthy 2000b). Most species climb and are often found a few meters above the ground, but a few are exclusively terrestrial (Figure 12.21), and others are active on rocky faces or in caves (Nussbaum and Raxworthy 1994a; Glaw et al. 2003; Miralles et al. 2021). Although a comprehensive revision of this genus has not recently been undertaken, work has progressed on certain species groups (Glaw et al. 2014c, 2018; Miralles et al. 2021). Molecular phylogenetics supports a relationship with *Ebenavia*. *Paroedura picta* has been established as a model organism for developmental biology (Noro et al. 2009; Hara et al. 2018).

Uroplatus (21 species) is an endemic genus of leaf-tailed geckos of uncertain relationships within the clade of Afro-Malagasy geckos (Gamble et al. 2012). They are among the most distinctive geckos in the world and have become emblematic of Madagascar. They are treated in detail in a separate contribution herein (see Gehring et al., pp. 1480–85).

Lygodactylus includes about 65 species, of which 22 are endemic to Madagascar. All are small (typically <40 mm snout-to-vent length), diurnal geckos with round pupils. They have partially divided subdigital scansors and often well-developed subcaudal pads (Pasteur 1965; Maderson 1971; Bauer 1998). Species are either arboreal or rupicolous and occur in a variety of habitats including different types of moist evergreen forests, dry deciduous forests, dry spiny thickets, arid grasslands, and montane grasslands, and some species are also known to inhabit highly human-altered areas (Glaw and Vences 1994). The taxonomy of Madagascar's *Lygodactylus* species was revised by Puente et al. (2005, 2009), who recognized an eastern *L. madagascariensis* group (formerly the subgenus *Domerguella*), the chiefly arid-zone

FIGURE 12.20 **Fish-scale geckos of the genus *Geckolepis*, here *G. megalepis*, have a uniquely delicate skin, which they can shed as defensive behavior when grabbed by a predator, and which then regenerates very fast even in a largely "naked" specimen.** (PHOTOS by F. Glaw.)

FIGURE 12.21 **Although geckos on Madagascar are generally arboreal, some species, such as *Paroedura picta*, have secondarily reevolved adaptations to a terrestrial lifestyle.** (PHOTO by P.-S. Gehring.)

L. verticillatus group, and a geographically restricted, high-elevation *L. mirabilis* group, among others. The first two of these groups appear to represent endemic Malagasy lineages within the genus, whereas the remaining Malagasy *Lygodactylus* species may represent one or several recolonizations of the island from mainland Africa (Puente et al. 2005; Röll et al. 2010; Mezzasalma et al. 2017; Gippner et al. 2021). *Lygodactylus bivittis*, which differs from its congeners in having undivided subdigital scansors, was previously placed in a separate genus, *Microscalabotes*, but has been shown to be embedded among other *Lygodactylus* species (Kluge and Nussbaum 1995; Röll et al. 2010; Mezzasalma et al. 2017). A recent chromosomal analysis including many Malagasy species revealed a variety of karyotypes within this genus, with values of 2n varying from 34 to 40 (Mezzasalma et al. 2017), which is at least partly consistent with known phylogenetic relationships and species group composition. Chromosome evolution occurred independently in different lineages, possibly through reduction from a putative ancestral karyotype of 2n = 40.

Phelsuma species are day-active geckos that are typically bright green in background color. Thirty-four of the 52 extant species occur on Madagascar, of which about 33 are endemic to the island. They are closely related to *Lygodactylus* and the South African endemic genus *Rhoptropella*. They are treated in detail in a separate contribution herein (see Gehring and Ratsoavina, pp. 1485–90).

Two genera are represented on Madagascar only by nonendemic species, which are or may be introduced (see Raselimanana and Vences, pp. 1455–58). *Gehyra mutilata* is often found as a house gecko in eastern Madagascar, but it can also utilize rocks and a variety of vegetation types. It is nocturnal, smooth skinned, and almost translucent. *Hemidactylus* is represented by *H. frenatus*, a tropical Asian species occurring on the west coast; *H. platycephalus*, an eastern African species found in lowland habitats in northwestern Madagascar; and *H. mercatorius*, which is both widespread and genetically diverse within Madagascar, suggesting that its occurrence may pre-date human occupation of the island (Vences et al. 2004b). The first two of these species are almost exclusively synanthropic (inhabiting built structures and often observed on walls) and may occur in large numbers in towns and villages (Andreone 1991a, 1991b; Henkel and Schmidt 2000). In contrast, *H. mercatorius* occurs in plantations and secondary vegetation, as well as on buildings and throughout the dry spiny thickets of southern Madagascar (M. D. Scherz, unpublished data). All of these geckos lay two hard-shelled eggs and are generalist insectivores.

Subject editors: Aaron M. Bauer, Miguel Vences, and Achille P. Raselimanana

GEKKONIDAE: *UROPLATUS*, LEAF-TAILED GECKOS, *TAHAFISAKA*

P.-S. Gehring, F. M. Ratsoavina, A. P. Raselimanana, C. J. Raxworthy, and M. D. Scherz

The genus *Uroplatus* includes nocturnal, forest-dwelling geckos endemic to Madagascar, famed for their impressive camouflage. Since the description of the first species, *U. fimbriatus*, in 1792, these geckos have thrilled researchers and naturalists with their unique appearance. The monophyly of the genus is well established from molecular data and unique morphological features (autapomorphies), including structures of the lung, shoulder girdle, inscriptional ribs (posterior ribs not attached to the sternum), and dentition. Currently 21 described species are known for this genus, but the number is still on the rise, with new species recently described from the Tsaratanàna Massif (Ratsoavina et al. 2017), the Marojejy Massif (Ratsoavina et al. 2019a, 2020), and the Ankarana Massif (Ratsoavina et al. 2019b). These nocturnal geckos are characterized by their large eyes with a vertical pupil, their triangular head with a large mouth, and their flattened tail, which is leaf shaped in some species and paddle shaped or rectangular in others. Most species in the genus can be grossly divided into two morphotypes, namely bark-mimicking (Figures 12.22 and 12.23) and leaf-mimicking

FIGURE 12.22 **The large bark-mimicking *Uroplatus* species such as *U. fimbriatus* spend the day resting on tree trunks with the head downward. They display an open mouth when threatened by a predator.** (PHOTO by P.-S. Gehring.)

FIGURE 12.23 ***Uroplatus lineatus* is found mostly on bamboo and *Ravenala*. This specimen was found at Sahafina, near Brickaville.** (PHOTO by P.-S. Gehring.)

FIGURE 12.24 ***Uroplatus ebenaui* from Sahamalaza, a representative of the small leaf-mimicking species of this genus.** (PHOTO by G. M. Rosa.)

(Figure 12.24) forms, which also correspond to the species' habits during the day. Bark mimics rest flat on tree trunks and branches, mostly with the head facing downward, and leaf mimics hide among leaves (or in leaf axils) and rest with a bent body posture, sometimes with one leg held out like a twig, or take refuge under tree bark. *Uroplatus giganteus* is among the largest geckos in the world, with males reaching at least 198 mm snout-to-vent length (SVL), while in the smallest species of the *U. ebenaui* group, this measurement is often between only 50 and 60 mm. All species are insectivorous but also eat snails and other invertebrates. They lay two eggs (which are protected by a calcified shell and are not stuck together), deposited under dead wood or in thick leaf litter on the ground.

SPECIES AND SPECIES GROUPS

The leaf-mimicking forms belong to a single species-rich clade, the *Uroplatus ebenaui* species group. Comprising 11 nominal species (*U. ebenaui*, *U. fangorn*, *U. fetsy*, *U. fiera*, *U. finaritra*, *U. finiavana*, *U. fivehy*, *U. fotsivava*, *U. kelirambo*, *U. malama*, and *U. phantasticus*), this group has the broadest distribution range on the island of all *Uroplatus* species groups. Representatives of the group have colonized many types of forest habitat and a wide elevational range. Species can be encountered in lowland and medium-altitude moist evergreen forests, low-elevation dry deciduous forests, and montane forests close to the tree line. Some members of this group tolerate the rather cold climate of high elevations, which is unique for nocturnal geckos on Madagascar; the species *U. kelirambo* from Tsaratanàna has been recorded from as high as 2200 m, making it the only known forest-dwelling nocturnal gecko to reach such high elevations on Madagascar at present. Besides various other aspects of body shape, these geckos differ from other *Uroplatus* species by a sexual dimorphism in tail shape, which is almost always laterally smooth in females and notched along its edges in males, whereas tail length and width appear to be rather species specific, with only limited variation between the sexes. Moreover, the tail dimensions and the color of the inner portion of the mouth (oral mucosa) constitute the key taxonomic characters within this group.

A great deal of work remains in the integrative taxonomy of the leaf-mimicking, smaller-bodied species of the *U. ebenaui* group, and local endemism is high (Nussbaum and Raxworthy 1995a). Several candidate species have been identified in the northern part of Madagascar, and most of these are now taxonomically described (Raxworthy et al. 2008a; Ratsoavina et al. 2013, 2017, 2019a, 2020), but the group still needs deeper integrative studies.

The species of the *U. alluaudi* (*U. alluaudi* and *U. pietschmanni*) and the *U. guentheri* (*U. guentheri* and *U. malahelo*) species groups might be confused with other geckos since their heads are less obviously triangular and not distinctly set off from the body, although the flattened tail and the shape and structure of the toes and digits are typical of *Uroplatus*. Despite the morphological similarities of these species, phylogenetic studies (e.g., Greenbaum et al. 2007; Raxworthy et al. 2008a; Ratsoavina et al. 2013) have clearly shown that the four species belong to two separate clades within the genus and are not monophyletic. *Uroplatus alluaudi* is encountered in medium-altitude moist evergreen humid forest of northern Madagascar, while its sister species *U. pietschmanni* is restricted to intact areas of the same formation of the central east. *Uroplatus pietschmanni* is morphologically rather unique and differs from other species of *Uroplatus* by its rough skin and characteristic reddish bark coloration on its venter. Both species have particularly broad toe pads, and both occur more than 4 m above the ground, while *U. pietschmanni* seems to be a strict canopy-dwelling species, bound to tall moist evergreen forest trees and sometimes found as high as 15 m above the ground.

The dry deciduous forests of the northwest and west are inhabited by *U. guentheri*. This species can be found roosting at an average of 1.5 m above the ground, hiding under tree bark or in tree holes during the day. It is well differentiated from all other *Uroplatus* species both morphologically and genetically; its sister species, *U. malahelo*, occurs in the southeast in rather different habitat. The type locality of the latter species is a tiny forest patch at the southern limit of the Anosyenne Mountains (Nussbaum and Raxworthy 1994b; Raxworthy et al. 2008a). The rapid decline of forest in the southern part of Madagascar leaves the habitat of this species in a patchwork pattern. *Uroplatus malahelo* is not common and may be quite threatened. Until now, only a few individuals have been found, in few localities exclusively in largely intact lowland and medium-altitude moist evergreen forests.

The *U. lineatus* species group comprises only one species (*U. lineatus*), which is morphologically unique with an elongated slender body and limbs, and longitudinal markings on the body (Figure 12.23); it is easily distinguishable from all other species of leaf-tailed geckos. This species inhabits lowland moist evergreen forests in eastern Madagascar, especially areas with bamboo. Morphologically, it constitutes a very distinctive taxon by its rather smooth appearance and peculiar yellow-brownish body coloration with longitudinal stripes in females but usually light dots in males. Dermal fringes are missing in *U. lineatus*; however, the species has striking dermal spines above each eye. In phylogenetic studies, it is consistently resolved as the sister lineage of the *U. fimbriatus* group (Raxworthy et al. 2008a; Ratsoavina et al. 2013).

The *U. fimbriatus* species group includes *U. fimbriatus*, *U. giganteus*, *U. sikorae*, *U. sameiti*, *U. henkeli*, and at least one candidate species that is morphologically close to *U. henkeli* and referred to by Ratsoavina et al. (2013) as *U. henkeli* [Ca11] (i.e., candidate species no. 11). The species included in this group are large bark-mimicking leaf-tailed geckos that can reach more than 30 cm in total length (Figure 12.22). They are characterized by dermal fringes along the lateral side of the body. The coloration is mostly a gradient of gray to dark brown, but during the day, roosting specimens can also be at least partly white. In some species, a mimetic lichen-like color pattern is observed, for instance in *U. sikorae* and *U. sameiti*. Because of the morphological similarity among several of the species and candidate species in this complex, and the presence of deep genealogical lineages within species, the taxonomy of this species group needs integrative revision. Based on morphological similarity only, three complexes can be distinguished in this group: the *U. fimbriatus* complex, including *U. fimbriatus* and *U. giganteus* (recently taxonomically treated by Gehring et al. 2018 and confirmed to be distinct); the *U. henkeli* complex, including *U. henkeli* and the candidate species *U. henkeli* [Ca11]; and the *U. sikorae* complex, including *U. sikorae* and *U. sameiti*. The taxonomic situation is quite difficult, especially in the *U. sikorae* complex, because on the one hand there are numerous deep mitochondrial lineages, and on the other, the main genetic subdivision does not correspond fully with the pigmentation of the oral mucosa, which is supposed to be a diagnostic character to distinguish the two species. However, most species of this group are distributed in the lowland and medium-altitude moist evergreen forests of the north and east. In the dry deciduous forests of the west, large *Uroplatus* individuals occur, which all belong to *U. henkeli*. The south and southwest regions, specifically the dry spiny thickets, are not known to harbor any *Uroplatus* species.

ORIGINS AND DIVERSIFICATION

Leaf-tailed geckos represent a striking example of gekkonid species diversification. *Uroplatus* is estimated to have initially diverged during the mid-Tertiary on Madagascar, long after the island had become isolated from all other landmasses at around 87–91 Mya (Raxworthy et al. 2008a). At present, their relationships to other genera are not entirely clear. Raxworthy et al. (2008a) recovered them as being sister to *Paroedura*, together sister to *Ebenavia*, and diverging from the former during the Oligocene, with the youngest sister-species pairs having evolved during the Miocene (*U. sameiti* and *U. sikorae*), and all intraspecific divergence estimated to date from the Miocene. However, studies with much broader taxon sampling of geckos have most frequently found *Uroplatus* to be sister to part of the polyphyletic genus *Cnemaspis* (Gamble et al. 2012, 2015; Garcia-Porta et al. 2016; Zheng and Wiens 2016), although one study found them sister to *Ptenopus* (Wright et al. 2015). The former is an enormous genus (>140 species) of diurnal, saxicolous geckos from Africa and Asia, while the latter consists of burrowing, nocturnal geckos from southern Africa. Clearly, more work is needed on the generic-level systematics of geckos to clarify the outgroup relationships of *Uroplatus*. Zheng and Wiens (2016) place the earliest divergence within *Uroplatus* (the split of *U. guentheri* + *U. malahelo* from all other species) at around 70 Mya (which may be an overestimate; see Crottini et al. 2012a), with gradual subsequent divergences and the youngest species pair in their tree being *U. giganteus* + *U. fimbriatus*, dated to around 14 Mya.

The diversification of leaf-tailed geckos is related to the complexity of the topography and hydrographic system supported by the mountains and existing vegetation on Madagascar (J. Brown et al. 2016). Recent phylogenetic and phylogeographic analyses (e.g., Raxworthy et al. 2008a; Ratsoavina et al. 2011, 2013, 2019a, 2019b; J. Brown et al. 2016) demonstrate not only that these geckos are most species rich in northern Madagascar but also that their diversification has in part taken place in this geographic region. This can be inferred from species of the *U. ebenaui* species group. Ratsoavina et al. (2011) hypothesized that after an initial split between a southern clade composed of *U. malama* and a northern ancestral species, the latter diversified in the northern regions into *U. ebenaui*-like forms with rather short tails. Most of these species appear to have a distribution restricted chiefly to the eastern half of northern Madagascar, and very likely they have diversified in this region, possibly by a combination of vicariant isolation and ecological specialization to different elevational bands. For instance, the occurrence of *U. finiavana* at Montagne d'Ambre might be interpreted as a consequence of vicariance on this isolated mountain, whereas the occurrence of *U. kelirambo* at high elevations over 2000 m might be an ecological specialization restricting gene flow with neighboring populations of *U. fivehy* from the Makira Plateau.

Tail length evolution in the *U. ebenaui* species group is more complex than this initial picture (Ratsoavina et al. 2019a). The four species with substantial tail lengths, *U. phantasticus*, *U. finaritra*, *U. ebenaui* [Ca10], and *U. malama*, do not form a monophyletic group; *U. malama* is the earliest-diverging member of the *U. ebenaui* species group. *Uroplatus phantasticus* is sister to *U. fiera* + *U. fotsivava* + *U. ebenaui* [Ca8]. *Uroplatus finaritra* is sister to *U. ebenaui* [Ca10], which is similar to *U. phantasticus*, and these together fall sister to the aforementioned *U. phantasticus* + *U. fiera* clade. The exact process of tail length evolution in the group has not been explicitly analyzed to date but appears to be characterized by multiple convergence and/or reversal events.

A genetic divergence of lineages occurring exclusively or mainly in northern Madagascar was also found in other *Uroplatus* species groups, such as *U. giganteus* (north) versus *U. fimbriatus* (south), *U. lineatus* (with a genetically divergent lineage apparently being distributed in the northeast), the *U. alluaudi* group (with *U. alluaudi* being restricted to the north), and the *U. henkeli* complex (one candidate species present in the north), but this pattern is much less obvious than it is in the *U. ebenaui* group (Ratsoavina et al. 2011, 2013, 2019a, 2019b; Gehring et al. 2018). Within the large distribution range of *U. phantasticus*, a strong phylogeographic structure and regional genetic differentiation were observed, which were associated with rivers that acted, at least temporarily, as barriers to gene flow among populations (Ratsoavina et al. 2012).

UNIQUE MORPHOLOGY

Morphologically, *Uroplatus* geckos are so distinctive that they were for some time considered a separate family (Boulenger 1884, 1885; Werner 1912a). Boulenger (1885) stated, "This family contains a single genus, the aberrant *Uroplates* [*sic*] of Madagascar, which combines with a Geckoid [*sic*] structure a peculiar sternal apparatus and the union of the nasal bones." The peculiarity of that sternal apparatus is the slender, nondilated clavicle and the reduced interclavicle; Boulenger (1884) noted that a similar configuration was known only in chameleons. Indeed, further research on the pectoral girdle across all geckos has shown that it is indeed highly derived in *Uroplatus* (Russell and Bauer 2008). The fusion of the nasal bones was a feature Boulenger knew only from monitor lizards (Varanidae), but today it is known from a wider variety of geckos, including *Ebenavia*, *Phelsuma*, and *Afroedura* (Evans 2008).

The tail of *Uroplatus* is perhaps the most distinctive feature. It is composed of a narrow vertebral structure as in all other geckos, with a broad, thin skin flap on either side of this central muscular tail. When this flap of skin is wrapped around (as sometimes occurs in stressed or sick animals), it resembles a "normal" lizard tail. Unlike in most other geckos, the tail of *Uroplatus* is autotomized only at its base and cannot be broken along its length where skin fringes are present. The tail is remarkably movable (Ratsoavina et al. 2019a) and in some of the larger members may indeed be considered prehensile (Bauer and Russell 1989); it is wrapped around branches during foraging. Each species group has a somewhat unique tail shape, but overall the bark-mimicking species tend to have more rectangular tails, while members of the *U. ebenaui* species group have the most leaf-like (or spear-like) tails of all tetrapods. As briefly mentioned above, males of this species group tend to have notches in the edges of their tails, resembling insect damage, while females have edges that are smooth and complete; the function of this dimorphism is not known, but it is consistent across the group (Ratsoavina et al. 2013, 2019a, 2019b). Australian carphodactylid leaf-tailed geckos of the genera *Phyllurus* and *Saltuarius* have convergently evolved broad, flattened tails that aid in their crypsis, but they differ structurally.

In addition to their characteristic broad, flat snout, unique tail shapes, and presence of dermal fringing in some species, *Uroplatus* species possess several internal anatomical features that are highly distinctive among geckos. Bauer and Russell (1989) summarized these autapomorphies in their systematic treatment of the genus. Subsequent work has focused largely on the taxonomy, systematics, and evolution of these geckos, and fairly little in the way of additional information on their morphology has been published, except pertaining to their laryngotracheal morphology (see below). For the sake of brevity, therefore, we here briefly mention the features highlighted by Bauer and Russel (1989):

1. Tooth counts in *Uroplatus* are extremely high—up to 169 teeth in the upper jaw, up to 148 in the lower jaw (Edmund 1969). These counts are far higher than in any other gecko genus and are indeed perhaps the highest of any tetrapod.
2. Abdominal musculature and presence of 11–13 inscriptional ribs in *Uroplatus* are unique among geckos (Meckel 1819).
3. Tail autotomy is restricted to caudal vertebrae seven and eight or eight and nine (Hoffstetter and Gasc 1969). All *Uroplatus* species can autotomize their tails, and most species can regenerate a rounder, shorter, smoother, and less fringed tail. However, no member of the *U. ebenaui* species group can completely regenerate its tail, producing at most a small projection from the stump.
4. Lung and laryngeal morphology of *Uroplatus* have received considerable attention. *Uroplatus* lungs have fingerlike diverticula, otherwise best known from chameleons (Meckel 1819; Werner 1912b; Guibé 1970). The function of these diverticula has not, however, been established.
5. The laryngotracheal morphology of *Uroplatus* was described by Rittenhouse et al. (1997) and Russell et al. (2014). It differs from that of most other geckos in having thicker cricoid cartilage, an anteriorly dilated and depressed trachea, and a thick, fibrous membrane on the dorsal surface of the anterior trachea, among other features.

Finally, although not unique to the genus, the coloration of the oral (buccal) mucosa has received much attention, as it is highly diagnostic at the species level, especially within the *U. ebenaui* species complex. Coloration ranges from light pink to black and includes oranges and reds. Recent species descriptions by Ratsoavina et al. (2015, 2017, 2019a, 2019b, 2020) have emphasized how diverse and diagnostic this feature is, yet neither the anatomical basis of this coloration nor its function is yet understood.

BIOLOGY AND ECOLOGY

Despite the general interest in these geckos, little is known about the ecology, biology, or distribution ranges of most of the recognized forms, which remain rather poorly understood (Nussbaum and Raxworthy 1994b, 1995a; Glaw et al. 2006; Greenbaum et al. 2007; Raxworthy et al. 2008a; Gehring 2020). Growth rates, longevity, and population density have not yet been studied in detail because of the difficulty in locating and observing these cryptic and arboreal geckos, making the collection of detailed data sets challenging. We suspect that moist evergreen forest *Uroplatus* species, unlike many reptiles, remain active throughout most of the Malagasy winter months, based on numerous nocturnal observations made by us and others for some species. However, dry deciduous forest and montane species may estivate or become inactive during this season. Reproduction (mating and egg laying) occurs during the rainy season. Female leaf-tailed geckos are oviparous and usually lay two or three eggs that hatch after 45–160 days, depending on climatic conditions such as temperature and humidity (Svatek and Van Duin 2002; Gehring 2020). Hatchlings and small juveniles are especially difficult to observe, which suggests they may be occupying overlooked microhabitats.

The behavior of *Uroplatus* species is also poorly recorded, but clearly these geckos are notably active at night, frequently seen covering significant distances in the canopy over the space of a few minutes, and they likely occupy large home ranges that also include much of the vertical range of vegetation available to them. Diet is probably larger arthropods and other invertebrates that are nocturnal and active on plant stems, lianas, and tree branches. The prey size depends on the species' body size. Leaf-tailed geckos are also known to eat ripe fruits in their natural habitat. The few studies on feeding have reported a preponderance of orthopterans in the diet, such as in *U. giganteus* (Ingady 2011). In captivity, they also eagerly feed on gastropods.

When handled at night (or when resting by day), *Uroplatus* species will bite and sometimes emit a high-pitched scream, presumably to deter predators, and break off their tail if it is seized. At rest, two camouflage strategies can be distinguished according to the species' size. For large-bodied species, dermal fringes and an imitation of the substrate color allow them to become almost invisible in their habitat and escape detection by vision-guided predators. Smaller species use phytomimicry and imitate the color and position of dead leaves on branches. The main predators of *Uroplatus* species are birds (including raptors), snakes, and other large geckos. Some bird species like *Coua caerulea* (Blue Coua) actively move through tree foliage to hunt. Upon being attacked, large species of *Uroplatus* open their mouth to intimidate while raising their body from the substrate and pointing their tail upward to look bigger (Figure 12.22).

Species in the *U. ebenaui* group have colonized almost the full range of elevations available to them on Madagascar, from lowland moist evergreen forests (*U. ebenaui*; Figure 12.24) up to 2200 m (*U. kelirambo*). Of the other species groups, only the *U. fimbriatus* group approaches this elevational range, though it does not occur at elevations as high as *U. kelirambo*. *Uroplatus lineatus* and the *U. guentheri* group are generally found in the lowlands, whereas the *U. alluaudi* group occurs at intermediate elevations.

It is remarkable that in many locations a substantial assemblage of *Uroplatus* species exists. For example, in Montagne d'Ambre National Park, *U. alluaudi*, *U. ebenaui*, *U. finiavana*, *U. giganteus*, *U. henkeli* [Ca11], and *U. sikorae* are present, and in Marojejy National Park, *U. fangorn*, *U. finaritra*, *U. fivehy*, *U. giganteus*, *U. lineatus*, and *U. sikorae* are present. In such mountain assemblages, elevational segregation seems important; for example, in Montagne d'Ambre the ecologically similar *U. finiavana* and *U. ebenaui* do not occur in syntopy; rather, *U. ebenaui* occurs at low elevations up to around 800 m, and *U. finiavana* from 800 m to the peak at about 1400 m.

All species of *Uroplatus* are associated with forests, and many have a relatively narrow elevational range. They occupy littoral, lowland and medium-altitude moist evergreen forests up to 2200 m, as well as dry deciduous forests, but they are absent from the dry spiny thickets of the south and southwest. The reasons for these narrow ecological specializations are not yet well understood, but clearly climate is an important factor (Raxworthy et al. 2008a). This is best indicated by elevational range, which has been documented for many montane transects including the massifs of Montagne d'Ambre, Tsaratanàna, Marojejy, Anjanaharibe-Sud, Andringitra, and Andohahela (Raxworthy and Nussbaum 1994a, 1996b; Raxworthy at al. 1998; Nussbaum et al. 1999b; Raselimanana et al. 2000a). The ecological characteristics of *Uroplatus* as intact habitat specialists, with a broad generic distribution across Madagascar yet with regional endemism and high species diversity, make them an ideal group to use for setting conservation priorities. They were one of the reptile groups employed by Kremen et al. (2008) to evaluate the protected area network on the island.

CONSERVATION AND CURRENT THREATS

Because of their spectacular body shape and appearance, *Uroplatus* species are among the animals most coveted by hobbyists and are therefore regularly commercialized in the international pet trade. All species within the genus are listed in Appendix II of CITES (Convention on International Trade in Endangered Species of Wild Fauna and Flora). Their trade is regulated under the supervision of the management authority of CITES, with a limited quota for commercial international export, which for some species is currently set at zero. However, overharvesting at specific sites of easy access might constitute an additional threat toward local extirpation, especially for species with restricted distribution ranges like *U. pietschmanni*, in spite of a sustainable export quota system that is now well established for these and other reptiles. Except for *U. fiera*, all members of the genus are known from at least one protected area. However, most species are known from only a few localities, often in fragmented forest habitat, and in general they need relatively intact forest. Consequently, fragmentation of natural forests prevents dispersal between populations and makes these geckos especially vulnerable to habitat shifts induced by anthropogenic climate change (Raxworthy et al. 2008b). Habitat loss and overharvesting for the pet trade represent the main threats to *Uroplatus* geckos.

UROPLATUS AS MODEL ORGANISMS FOR RESEARCH

This group of geckos has been used to investigate speciation patterns on Madagascar, using both ecological niche models (Pearson et al. 2007; Raxworthy et al. 2008a) and correlations between spatial patterns of species distributions and landscape or climate features (Pearson and Raxworthy 2009). *Uroplatus* locality data are patchy because field observations are difficult, which thus makes these cryptic geckos an ideal group to test validation techniques for species ecological niche modeling and predicting species distributions (Pearson et al. 2007). Niche modeling data for sister species of *Uroplatus* support different scenarios in different species pairs: 1) conservative niches and vicariance, and 2) divergent niches in parapatry and between populations, on ecological gradients supporting speciation (Raxworthy et al. 2008a). Relict distributions were also identified between the sister species *U. alluaudi* and *U. pietschmanni*. A comparison of *Uroplatus* species distribution patterns with the 14 major watersheds and 14 climate clusters on Madagascar failed to find a close association with either (Pearson and Raxworthy 2009), indicating that *Uroplatus* speciation and endemism have not been promoted by these features. More work is needed to further investigate drivers of species formation within this group, but it is evident that there are multiple mechanisms (e.g., vicariance, parapatric speciation at ecotones), and that ecological factors are prominent.

Subject editors: Philip-Sebastian Gehring, Miguel Vences, and Achille P. Raselimanana

GEKKONIDAE: *PHELSUMA*, DAY GECKOS, *KATSATSAKA*, *TSATSAKE*

P.-S. Gehring and F. M. Ratsoavina

Day geckos of the genus *Phelsuma* represent one of the most successful reptile radiations on Madagascar and nearby archipelagoes in the western Indian Ocean (Malagasy Region). Most of the 50 extant species and several subspecies of *Phelsuma* occur on Madagascar (Glaw and Rösler 2015), but these geckos have also naturally colonized the Comoros, Mascarenes, Seychelles, Andamans, Zanzibar, and Pemba, as well as several other small islands and a few localities on the African mainland. They have additionally been widely introduced, in locations like Hawai'i (Lever 2003), Moorea, in French Polynesia (Ota and Ineich 2006), and Florida (Glaw and Rösler 2015), as well as in closer archipelagoes like the Mascarenes (Cheke and Hume 2008). Their splendid coloration and diurnal activity make them very conspicuous animals and one of the most prominent groups of lizards in the Malagasy Region, but despite intensive research efforts, the taxonomy and phylogenetic relationships of several taxa are still unclear, and new species of *Phelsuma* are regularly discovered and described (e.g., Berghof and Trautmann 2009; Glaw et al. 2009b, 2010; Crottini et al. 2011). Day geckos have received enormous attention in the last decades, from scientists as well as from hobbyists who keep and breed them in vivaria. Thus, considerable literature on *Phelsuma* has been published in recent years.

SPECIES AND SPECIES GROUPS

Species of *Phelsuma* are remarkably similar to each other based on their morphology, including round pupils and undivided toe lamellae. The largest living species of the genus on Madagascar, *P. grandis*, can reach a total length of up to 30 cm, while the smallest species, *P. kely*, has a total length of not even 7 cm. Besides body size, few morphological characters are known that can be used to distinguish species, and therefore their taxonomy is based largely on color. Many species from moist evergreen forest areas have a bright green ground coloration, often with reddish markings and spots. *Phelsuma* species often rely on their green coloration to aid in camouflage and to avoid predators, and clinging to similar-colored structures helps them blend with their tropical and arboreal environment. Species from drier regions tend to be more brown and grayish. Individuals can change color very quickly and usually become dark when stressed. Currently, 34 species and 11 subspecies of *Phelsuma* are recognized on Madagascar, which belong to seven species groups (Rocha et al. 2010b; Glaw and Rösler 2015). These species groups reflect evolutionary relationships within the genus based on clades and biogeographically meaningful groupings. In the following summary only the Malagasy species are considered and we follow the taxonomic groups of Rocha et al. (2010b).

Phelsuma dubia Group (including *P. berghofi*, *P. dubia*, *P. flavigularis*, *P. hielscheri*, *P. malamakibo*, *P. modesta*, and *P. ravenala*)

Species in the *P. dubia* group have a weak expression of green color and share egg-gluing behavior. Morphologically they are characterized by the absence of nostril-rostral contact, a relatively low number of femoral pores in males (30 or fewer), and keeled dorsal and lateral scales (except for *P. ravenala*). The species in this group show a great variety of ecological adaptations and specializations. For example, *P. malamakibo* is restricted to rock substrates either along streams in intact, open-canopy moist evergreen forests, or in montane ericoid thicket and montane grassland between 800 and 2000 m in the Anosyenne Mountains in the southeast, where communal nesting sites can often be found. *Phelsuma flavigularis* is reliably reported only from moist evergreen forests in the Andasibe area, where it is rarely encountered, mainly in *Ravenala* and tall palm trees. In contrast, *P. dubia* is rather common in coastal areas from the north to the central west, where it inhabits dry deciduous forests, secondary vegetation, and anthropogenic habitats (gardens and houses).

The taxonomy of the *P. dubia* group merits further investigation, as *P. dubia* is paraphyletic with respect to *P. ravenala* and possibly contains yet further undescribed species, with the western Antsalova population being one candidate. Also, the validity of *P. ravenala* needs confirmation, especially regarding its morphological differentiation.

Phelsuma barbouri Group (including *P. barbouri* and *P. pronki*)

These two species are sister taxa with a genetic distance of only 5.1% (uncorrected p-distance, cytochrome b), which is low compared to other interspecific differentiation values within this genus and points to their recent differentiation. *Phelsuma barbouri* and *P. pronki* share a rather depressed body and head shape, and a rather similar and distinct color pattern without clear predominance of green, but they differ in the number of mid-body scales (higher in *P. barbouri*), number of ventral scales, and egg-gluing behavior (*P. pronki* is an egg gluer and *P. barbouri* is not).

Phelsuma barbouri is the most ground-dwelling species within the genus, found on and around exposed rocky outcrops and boulders of nonforested habitat in the Central Highlands. In contrast, *P. pronki* is an arboreal species in the moist evergreen forests at the base of the Central Highlands. The divergence between these two species is likely recent and may have been driven by ecological specialization along a sharp ecotone. The distribution of *P. pronki* is very poorly known (Glaw and Vences 2007; Jenkins et al. 2014), and the species is probably rare and localized. According to A. P. Raselimanana (unpublished data), it occurs in the Anjozorobe area in degraded and secondary forests, possibly suggesting that it prefers dead trees with loose bark in rather open-canopy forest or forest edges. Additional surveys are needed to understand whether these two taxa are geographically isolated or have a contact or hybrid zone.

Phelsuma mutabilis Group (including *P. breviceps*, *P. gouldi*, *P. mutabilis*, and *P. borai*)

Species in the *P. mutabilis* group share, among other character states, the absence of bright green color, non-gluing egg-laying behavior, a relatively low number of sublabials (five or six), smooth ventrals and subcaudals, and absence of nostril-rostral contact. The four species in this group inhabit southwestern (*P. breviceps* and *P. mutabilis*), south-central (*P. gouldi*), and western (*P. mutabilis* and *P. borai*) portions of Madagascar. Close relationships between *P. breviceps* and *P. mutabilis* have already been hypothesized based on morphometric and scale features; in fact, the two species have been synonymized and resurrected several times (Loveridge 1942; C. Blanc 1972; Kluge 1991; Raxworthy and Nussbaum 1994c). They are, however, clearly distinct and can occur in sympatry, such as around Sept Lacs in Mahaleotse Forest and in Salary Bay Forest (A. P. Raselimanana, unpublished data). The species of this group occupy a rather basal position in the phylogeny of this genus, with high genetic divergence (up to 20%) observed among all species, indicating a long divergent evolutionary history.

Phelsuma madagascariensis Group (including *P. abbotti* [*chekei*], *P. guttata*, *P. grandis*, *P. kochi*, *P. madagascariensis*, *P. seippi*, and probably *P. masohoala*)

Species in the *Phelsuma madagascariensis* group are characterized by non-gluing egg-laying behavior, smooth ventral and subcaudal scales, keeled dorsal and lateral scales, absence of nostril-rostral contact, and smaller vertebral scales, whereas other characters are variable among species in the group, possibly in part related to size differences. For example, the number of femoral pores is higher in the larger species (*P. grandis*, *P. kochi*, *P. madagascariensis*, and *P. parkeri*; the latter is the only non-Malagasy member of the group and is endemic to Pemba Island, Tanzania).

The species in this group show a green to grayish (sometimes bluish) back with red to brownish spots. A largely reddish stripe between nostril and eye is present. One of the few *Phelsuma* species for which no DNA sequence is available to date is *P. masohoala*. As discussed by Meier and Böhme (1996), it is possible that *P. masohoala* is related to *P. abbotti* and thus belongs to the *P. madagascariensis* group. Two additional records have recently been added to the known distribution of *P. masohoala*: near Antalaha and in Marojejy National Park (Stanley and Raxworthy 2016). *Phelsuma masohoala* apparently dwells in the canopy, where its drab, cryptic coloration provides good camouflage on tree branches.

Phelsuma lineata Group (*P. antanosy*, *P. dorsivittata*, *P. hoeschi*, *P. kely*, *P. lineata*, *P. pusilla*, and *P. quadriocellata*)

The *Phelsuma lineata* group is characterized by a predominant green color with usually a pattern of lateral/sublateral stripes. Loveridge (1942) hypothesized that the dark spots of *P. quadriocellata* are derived from the dark lateral band of *P. lineata*. Members of this group typically have keeled ventral and subcaudal scales (except *P. l. punctulata*, *P. l. elanthana*, and the non-Malagasy *P. comorensis*), absence of rostral-nostril contact, a relatively low number of mid-body scales (fewer than 98, except for *P. antanosy*), and vertebral scales not reduced in size. Eggs are not glued to the substrate in this species group.

The *P. lineata* group as defined here is one of the most genetically diverse clades within *Phelsuma* and will probably turn out to be the most species-rich clade after thorough taxonomic study. According to molecular data (Rocha et al. 2009b, 2010b), two clades can be defined within this species group: 1) all *P. quadriocellata* subspecies, *P. parva*, and *P. antanosy*, and 2) *P. lineata*, *P. dorsivittata*, *P. pusilla*, and *P. kely*. Phylogenetic studies clearly show that a systematic revision and the description of new species within the *P. lineata* group are necessary (Rocha et al. 2009b, 2010b; Gehring et al. 2013) because 1) molecular data demonstrate a paraphyletic position of *P. l. lineata*, *P. l. bombetokensis*, *P. l. punctulata*, and *P. l. elanthana*, and currently they are recognized as subspecies but most likely some of them require full species rank, although the phylogenetic placement of *P. l. bombetokensis* requires further study; 2) the mitochondrial phylogeny suggests at least three independent colonization events in Madagascar's northeastern coastal lowlands by *P. pusilla*; therefore, in its current taxonomic position, *P. pusilla* is paraphyletic given that *P. p. hallmanni* is deeply nested within the *P. kely/hoeschi* clade; 3) the relationships between the nominal taxa *P. hoeschi* and *P. p. hallmanni* need to be studied in detail, since it cannot be excluded that these two taxa might be conspecific; 4) the taxonomic status of *P. q. bimaculata* and *P. q. lepida* likely requires the recognition of both at the species level; besides molecular characteristics, these forms have differences in color patterns that are distinct from each other, from *P. q. quadriocellata*, and from *P. parva*.

Several of these taxa are rather widespread in both intact and secondary habitats, and a few have relatively narrow elevational ranges (Glaw and Vences 2007). This applies to *P. p. pusilla* and to some of the sublineages of *P. lineata*, which are rather poorly defined thus far. *Phelsuma kely*, *P. hoeschi*, and *P. p. hallmanni*, as presently delineated, are microendemic taxa known only from very small ranges, and *P. l. lineata* (*sensu lato*) is presumably a more generalized taxon and a comparatively good colonizer, as suggested by its wide occurrence in both mid-elevation and low-elevation sites along the east coast.

Phelsuma laticauda Group (*P. laticauda* and *P. roesleri*)

The *P. laticauda* group is a well-defined clade that is characterized by non-gluers with smooth ventral and subcaudal scales, three nasals, and no nostril-rostral contact. They are mostly bright green and have no lateral or dorsal stripes.

Phelsuma roesleri is the sister species of *P. laticauda* and is known from only a single locality on the Ankarana Massif, where it appears to be specialized to live in *Pandanus*. *Phelsuma laticauda* (Figure 12.25) is very abundant in the moist evergreen forest regions of northern Madagascar, especially along the northeastern coast and in the Sambirano Region. It is more generalist in terms of habitat, with a high capacity to adapt to degraded and secondary forest or even human habitation, and to fences made from natural materials. The southernmost record along the northeast coast is Cap Est on the east side of the Masoala Peninsula, but Gehring et al. (2010a) reported its occurrence at Andranokoditra and around Lake Ampitambe, which is part of Pangalanes Canal and along the central east coast; these populations might be introduced. *Phelsuma l. angularis* from Antsohihy, in the northwest, is genetically differentiated, confirming its subspecific status and suggesting that the east coast populations are the result of more recent immigration from the Sambirano Region.

FIGURE 12.25 **Phelsuma laticauda is a common species of day gecko in northern Madagascar that is known from forest habitats and is also associated with human settlements.** (PHOTO by M. Vences.)

Phelsuma klemmeri Group (*P. klemmeri*)

The coloration of *P. klemmeri* is very characteristic and strongly differs from that of all other *Phelsuma* species. The dorsal coloration is brown to turquoise with turquoise dorsolateral bands. Before and after the ear, *P. klemmeri* has one or more rather large turquoise tubercle scales. The head and neck are yellow, and the ventral coloration is whitish. *Phelsuma klemmeri* has a very flat appearance, likely an adaptation to using bamboo fissures, and the scales are extremely small and smooth. It has a very restricted distribution and the population is severely fragmented, known only from two separate and isolated locations, the Ampasindava Peninsula in the northwest, and Mandrozo (Razafimahatratra et al. 2010). This species occurs in bamboo patches and secondary bamboo forests within or on the edge of intact forests.

Phelsuma standingi Group (*P. standingi*)

This species stands out because of the high number of pre-anofemoral pores and mid-body scales. By being a non-gluer without nostril-rostral contact, it resembles the other large Malagasy day geckos in the *P. madagascariensis* group but differs by having vertebral scales not reduced in size, and subcaudal scales not broadened. The back of adults is gray or bluish green with dark reticulations, whereas the head is mostly green and the tail bluish. Juveniles show a distinct coloration consisting of light transverse bars on a brown background.

Phelsuma standingi, a species for which relationships with *P. madagascariensis* have been suggested, instead is a separate deep lineage in the genus. It seems not to have any close living relatives. This is a large species occurring in the transitional dry forest in the Sakaraha region and the dry spiny thickets of the southwest. It is apparently associated with large trees such as baobabs (A. P. Raselimanana, unpublished data).

Species Not Included in Any Group

The phylogenetic relationships of two species, *P. serraticauda* and *P. vanheygeni*, are at present largely unresolved, and their assignment to a species group is pending further analyses.

Morphologically, *P. serraticauda* shares most characters with species of the *P. laticauda* group but differs in the absence (versus presence) of keeled ventral and subcaudal scales and is unique in having a broad, flattened tail. The phylogenetic analyses of Rocha et al. (2010b) placed it instead in the *P. dubia* group, although without strong support. This very territorial species seems to be restricted to a small coastal range along the northeast coast, where it is found mainly in coconut palms (Figure 12.26).

Phelsuma vanheygeni was excluded by Lerner (2004) from possibly belonging to the *P. madagascariensis* species group because of its egg-gluing behavior. In the work of Rocha et al. (2010b) its relationships with the *P. astriata* and *P. madagascariensis* groups are clearly supported, but it remains uncertain whether the species

FIGURE 12.26 A specimen of *Phelsuma serraticauda* in its typical habitat, on a coconut palm tree. (PHOTO by P.-S. Gehring.)

splits from a node basal to the *P. madagascariensis* group (and thus merits inclusion in its own species group), or basal to the *P. astriata* group (and thus could be included as the only Malagasy species in this otherwise Seychellois species group).

ORIGINS AND DIVERSIFICATION

Day geckos have most likely evolved from an African nocturnal gekkonid ancestor. A putative synapomorphy of *Phelsuma* might be the contact between the prefrontal and post-orbitofrontal bones, a feature otherwise present only among pygopodids (Daza and Bauer 2010). The genus is well supported by molecular data as monophyletic (Austin et al. 2004; Rocha et al. 2009b, 2010b). The closest known relative of *Phelsuma* is probably *Rhoptropella ocellata*, a cryptically colored gecko from dry habitats in South Africa and Namibia (Austin et al. 2004). Depending on the data set used, estimates for the age of crown diversification within *Phelsuma* and its split from *Rhoptropella/Lygodactylus* are substantially different (Austin et al. 2004; Rocha 2010). A comprehensive assessment of Malagasy vertebrate ages places the stem age of *Phelsuma* around 62.3 Mya after overseas dispersal from Africa, and a crown diversification age at 29.7 Mya (Crottini et al. 2012a).

The complex geological history of Madagascar provided numerous opportunities for isolation and diversification of day geckos. After diversification on Madagascar, several independent colonizations of other western Indian Ocean archipelagoes took place. The dispersal of day geckos to the Mascarene archipelago occurred around 22 Mya, and to the granitic Seychelles and to the Andamans in the Oligocene and Eocene (36–28 Mya) (Crottini et al. 2012a). The colonization of this group in the Comoro archipelago was recovered post-Oligocene. The Comoros was the subject of three other independent colonizations, which is more than any other archipelago; after successful dispersal to other islands, these geckos often radiated, producing several sets of endemic species.

BIOLOGY AND ECOLOGY

Within Madagascar, *Phelsuma* species are found in a variety of habitats across the island, mainly in intact forest regions (e.g., *P. masohoala*), including dry spiny thickets (e.g., *P. breviceps*), coastal dry spiny thicket scrublands (e.g., *P. mutabilis*, *P. modesta*, *P. hielscheri*), western coastal forests of different vegetational types (e.g., *P. abbotti*), lowland moist evergreen forests (e.g., *P. guttata*, *P. lineata* ssp., *P. quadriocellata* ssp.), and even mid-elevation moist evergreen and montane grasslands (e.g., *P. barbouri*, *P. malamakibo*). The members of the genus span the spectrum of habitat degradation tolerance from obligate forest-dwelling species, such as *P. flavigularis*, to strict human commensals rarely if ever recorded in forests, such as *P. modesta*. Numerous other species may be common in urban environments but also occur in intact or degraded forests (e.g., *P. laticauda*, *P. lineata*, *P. madagascariensis*, *P. quadriocellata*; Glaw and Vences 2007; Hallmann et al. 2008; C. Gardner and Jasper 2009).

Phelsuma species are territorial sit-and-wait predators that occupy a niche similar to that of other diurnal arboreal lizards such as *Anolis* lizards in the Caribbean. Like most geckos worldwide, *Phelsuma* species are thought to be primarily insectivorous (Bauer 2003); however, many species include significant amounts of fruit, pollen, or nectar in their diets (Murphy and Myers 1996; Taylor and Gardner 2014), and several may be the obligate pollinators of endemic plant species (Hansen et al. 2007). Other species are known to steal pollen from bees (Clémencet et al. 2013) and milk honeydew from planthoppers (Fölling et al. 2001; see Świerczewski and Stroiński, pp. 987–91), while some of the largest *Phelsuma* species are known to prey on vertebrates, including other geckos (García and Vences 2002a; Gehring et al. 2010a; Buckland et al. 2014). Furthermore, some *Phelsuma* species can take advantage of artificial light sources to prey on nocturnal invertebrates (Baxter-Gilbert et al. 2021).

In intact habitats the abundance of tree-dwelling species of day geckos is positively correlated with foliar cover and the number of trees (D'Cruze et al. 2009a). These diurnal arboreal lizards select and utilize perch microhabitats based on several factors including thermoregulatory aspects, prey density, protection from predators, interspecific competition, morphology-related aspects, and intraspecific competition (D'Cruze et al. 2009a). Sympatric species of *Phelsuma* often subtly differ in their habitat use, choosing different perch height, perch diameter, and tree type. One intriguing possibility is that habitat-use differences among day gecko species are a by-product of specialization to feed on certain types of nectar, pollen, tree sap, or other nonarthropod resources (Harmon et al. 2007). For instance, *P. klemmeri* is sympatric with other species such as *P. grandis*, *P. seippi*, and *P. vanheygeni* in the Sambirano Region, yet at other western localities, specifically at Mandrozo, it is found with *P. kochi* and *P. mutabilis*. To avoid competition, *P. klemmeri* seems to prefer bamboo trees close to the forest edge (Razafimahatratra et al. 2010) and often uses dry, dead bamboo for refuge and egg-laying sites (A. P. Raselimanana, unpublished data). Visual signals are extensively employed in courtship and other intraspecific encounters (Figure 12.27) but are poorly understood.

FIGURE 12.27 A *Phelsuma lineata* male (below) in a typical display posture directed toward a conspecific individual (above), illustrating how these day geckos use their conspicuous color pattern for intraspecific communication. (PHOTO by P.-S. Gehring.)

Male day geckos have well-developed femoral pores on the undersurface of their rear limbs. These pores are less developed or absent in females. Males usually are notably larger than females. Females often have well-developed endolymphatic chalk sacs on the sides of their necks. These sacs store calcium, which is needed for egg production. Madagascar day geckos reproduce sexually and during courtship males approach females with a jerky head-swaying motion. This male behavior is usually accompanied by rapid tongue flicking by the female. Males grab females between the head and neck with their teeth during copulation. A female may produce multiple clutches in a single breeding season, and a clutch usually consists of two hard-shelled eggs, often attached to one another. With respect to egg deposition, there are two different techniques employed by *Phelsuma* species: "gluers" attach their eggs to the substrate and "non-gluers" do not attach their eggs. The female generally holds the eggs with her hind limbs until the shell hardens. After an incubation period of 40 to 90 days, the young hatch and are immediately self-sufficient and independent. The sex of *Phelsuma* specimens is determined by the incubation temperature of the eggs. The young feed primarily on small insects and become sexually mature within one to two years (Hallmann et al. 2008).

CONSERVATION AND CURRENT TRENDS

Although morphological diversity in the genus *Phelsuma* is relatively limited, the distribution range, abundance, and utilization of natural habitats vary greatly among species. Many taxa are microendemic, and sometimes their distribution range may be restricted to only a few square kilometers (e.g., *P. kely*, *P. hoeschi*, *P. p. hallmanni*, *P. pronki*), whereas other species are rather widespread (e.g., *P. lineata*, *P. mutabilis*). Some species seem to be restricted to specific natural habitats (e.g., *P. roesleri*), whereas many others (e.g., *P. dubia*, *P. grandis*, *P. laticauda*, *P. lineata*) are well adapted to anthropogenic habitats. The IUCN Red List status has recently been assessed for most *Phelsuma* species in the framework of the Global Reptile Assessment, especially for those species found on Madagascar. Regardless of their IUCN Red List status, all *Phelsuma* species are at least listed in Appendix II of CITES (Convention on International Trade in Endangered Species of Wild Fauna and Flora). This means that widespread and abundant species classified as Least Concern have the same level of protection by CITES associated with international trade as microendemic species listed as Critically Endangered. However, Malagasy authorities have developed an annual quota system that allows the exportation of a defined number of usually widespread and abundant reptile and amphibian species for the international pet trade (Carpenter et al. 2005; see Carpenter et al., pp. 1452–55). Also, the collection for the international pet trade of vulnerable *Phelsuma* populations at several localities, including some close to protected areas, was prohibited. In 2019, six *Phelsuma* species were approved to be exported: *P. grandis*, *P. kochi*, *P. laticauda*, *P. lineata*, *P. madagascariensis*, and *P. quadriocellata*. The illegal trade of *Phelsuma* species from Madagascar potentially threatens the survival of some local endemic species (e.g.,

P. antanosy, *P. pronki*), and some species with specific habitats, such as *P. standingi*, may be threatened by overharvesting.

As with other Malagasy reptiles, habitat loss and land transformation caused by expanding swidden agriculture, as well as a range of other associated activities, affect the majority of *Phelsuma* species (Jenkins et al. 2014). However, day geckos vary in their responses to the modification of natural landscapes. Several adaptive, generalist species (e.g., *P. laticauda*, *P. grandis*) tolerate land clearing; they are capable of using agricultural areas and human infrastructure and may even benefit from ongoing deforestation on the island (e.g., D'Cruze et al. 2009a; Humphery and Ward 2018), but others are sensitive to anthropogenic disturbance (e.g., *P. seippi*, *P. antanosy*) (Irwin et al. 2010; Humphery and Ward 2018). At least one Critically Endangered species, *P. pronki*, does not seem to be present in any protected area (Jenkins et al. 2014). Knowledge of the distribution, response, and tolerance of *Phelsuma* species to anthropogenic land-use change will be crucial for the formulation of conservation efforts for Malagasy day geckos.

Subject editors: Philip-Sebastian Gehring, Miguel Vences, and Achille P. Raselimanana

GERRHOSAURIDAE, PLATED LIZARDS, *BEKARATSAKA*, *ANTALABOSY*, *ANDRONGO*

A. P. Raselimanana, M. D. Scherz, D. Prötzel, and F. Glaw

The family Gerrhosauridae, or plated lizards, occurs in Africa south of 13°N latitude, on Madagascar and on Glorioso and Cosmoledo Islands in the western Seychelles. Two genera of Gerrhosauridae are endemic or largely endemic to Madagascar: *Tracheloptychus* and *Zonosaurus*. *Tracheloptychus* is easy to differentiate from *Zonosaurus*—the lateral fold of skin stops at the insertion point of the forelimbs, while in *Zonosaurus* it extends toward the inguinal region. Two species of *Tracheloptychus* and 17 species of *Zonosaurus* are recognized from Madagascar, with *Z. maramaintso* being the most recently described species (Raselimanana et al. 2006). In 1831 Gray described the first Malagasy gerrhosaurid under the name *Cicigna madagascariensis*, today known as *Zonosaurus madagascariensis*. The genus *Zonosaurus* was created in 1887 by Boulenger, and *Tracheloptychus* in 1854 by W. Peters. The Malagasy Gerrhosauridae species were revised by Brygoo (1985a), and the small species of the "*aeneus*-group" by Vences et al. (1996) and Raselimanana et al. (2000b).

The Malagasy Gerrhosauridae forms a monophyletic group (Raselimanana 2000; Recknagel et al. 2013), the Zonosaurinae. *Zonosaurus* consists of four clades (*Z. boettgeri*, *Z. madagascariensis*, *Z. ornatus*, and *Z. rufipes* groups). It is still uncertain whether *Tracheloptychus* is sister to or nested within *Zonosaurus* (Recknagel et al. 2013; Blair et al. 2015). Molecular data show that the Malagasy plated lizards arose from a single colonization event, presumably from Africa in the Paleocene or early Eocene (Raselimanana et al. 2009). A multigene analysis combined with fossil information dates the most recent African common ancestor to about 30 million years ago (Blair et al. 2015). Five genera of African Gerrhosauridae are currently distinguished: *Broadleysaurus*, *Cordylosaurus*, *Gerrhosaurus*, *Matobosaurus*, and *Tetradactylus* (M. Bates et al. 2013). The karyotypes of Malagasy gerrhosaurid species are very similar to each other (Odierna et al. 2002).

CHARACTERISTICS

In the genera *Tracheloptychus* and *Zonosaurus*, the head is covered with symmetrical plates, hence the English common name "plated lizard." The mobile eyelids are well developed, and the lower eyelid is covered with scales. The tympanum is very distinct, overhung by one small scale. Both sexes have femoral pores. The nostril is pierced between two nasal scales and surrounded on the sides by the first upper labial scales and anteriorly by the rostral scale. In *Zonosaurus* the ventral scales are hexagonal and arranged in eight longitudinal rows, whereas in *Tracheloptychus* the dorsal and ventral scales are in staggered rows. The tongue is covered with rhomboid papillae, and neither of the two genera has a fronto-parietal scale. Most scales, especially those of the main trunk and head, are osseous. The scales of the dorsal trunk are arranged in clear, regular bands.

BIOLOGY AND ECOLOGY

The Malagasy gerrhosaurids are oviparous. They lay their eggs in the ground, under dead wood, under rocks, or in grass tufts (Raselimanana et al. 2000b). A ground nest is found in most species, including *Z. aeneus*, *Z. haraldmeieri*, *Z. karsteni*, and *Z. rufipes*. The nest is dug obliquely into the earth, usually on a gentle slope (Raselimanana 2000). A clutch consists of two to six eggs, depending on the species, with *Z. madagascariensis* laying up to six eggs and *Z. rufipes* two or three eggs. *Tracheloptychus madagascariensis* generally lays three eggs.

Sexual maturity is discreet. There are no distinctive signs when a female becomes sexually active for the first time. In the adult male the hemipenis becomes swollen at the base of the tail. The lateral scales behind the cloaca thicken and harden to resemble a triangular spine. When a male is reproductively active, the femoral pores exude a yellowish substance, which probably communicates species, sex, and reproductive status, as is common for these structures (e.g., Cooper et al. 1996). The internal testes are large, rounded, and yellow, whereas in the young and the subadults they are flat and white.

The post-reproductive phase is marked by the accumulation of fat in the abdominal region. The gonads become small and pale. It is presumed that numerous species of Malagasy gerrhosaurids hibernate. A definitive case of hibernation was documented in *Z. haraldmeieri*—a dormant individual was found in dead wood (A. P. Raselimanana, unpublished data).

Growth is rapid following hatching. A neonate *Z. ornatus* measured 27 mm, and four days later it had already reached a length of 35 mm. In the wild, three different subadult generations can be observed at the same time and locality: the newly hatched, the young with a visible umbilical slit, and subadults.

Regeneration of limbs has been observed in *Z. ornatus* (Brygoo 1985a) and in *Z. haraldmeieri* (Raselimanana 2000). Regeneration of the caudal region is common to all forms. Desquamation (detachment of the skin from the dermis) and skin regeneration are frequent in *Z. bemaraha*, *Z. tsingy*, and *Z. subunicolor*. Regenerated skin does not have the same structure as the original. Skin flimsiness is considered to be part of the defense system (Raselimanana et al. 2000b). Snakes of the genus *Leioheterodon* (see Cadle et al., pp. 1525–31), the Ring-tailed Vontsira (*Galidia elegans*; see Farris and Goodman, pp. 1989–92), and birds of prey (see Rene de Roland and Thorstrom, pp. 1668–79) are the main predators of *Zonosaurus*. Several other snakes have also been observed to prey on Malagasy gerrhosaurids, including *Liophidium torquatum* (Cadle 1999), *Dromicodryas bernieri* (C. Y. Wang-Claypool and collaborators, unpublished data), *Mimophis mahfalensis* (Clause 2017), and *M. occultus* (Raselimanana 2018).

The operculum plate, which covers the hearing orifice of *Tracheloptychus*, may be an adaptation to life in sandy habitats, preventing sand from entering the tympanum (Brygoo 1985a). This feature is also found in the African *Gerrhosaurus skoogi*, which also lives in sandy areas. The well-developed pads under the fingers and toes of *Zonosaurus* are used during locomotion. The upper and lower posterior labial scales overlap and prevent food from being expelled from the corners of the muzzle.

The relative length of the tail in relation to the rest of the body, its thickness, and its fragility vary in reptiles according to their lifestyles (Etheridge 1967). The arboreal species (*Z. boettgeri* and *Z. maramaintso*), the rupicolous species (*Z. tsingy*), and the semiaquatic form (*Z. maximus*) tend to have proportionately longer tails. The elongation of the tail may help to balance or to hold on to a substrate and is not necessarily related to locomotion. The strong claws on the fingers and toes also help to grip. The toes and very long posterior limbs are used to scratch the face and head.

Habitat specificity is rather variable, with species often showing preferences. *Zonosaurus rufipes* prefers exposed areas in forest that receive direct solar radiation, whereas *Z. subunicolor* frequents closed-canopy forests. *Zonosaurus haraldmeieri* occurs in dry deciduous forests, transitional forests, and moist evergreen forests, whereas *Z. madagascariensis* is found in moist evergreen forests. *Zonosaurus laticaudatus* is among the species that use

FIGURE 12.28 A *Zonosaurus laticaudatus* individual preying on a frog, *Aglyptodactylus laticeps*, at Kirindy Forest CNFEREF. (PHOTO by H. Schütz.)

different types of substrate. Normally it is rupicolous, but it has been observed on the ground or climbing cacao trees. This species has also been observed using vertical or horizontal crevices in boulders or talus as a refuge. *Zonosaurus quadrilineatus*, *Z. trilineatus*, *Tracheloptychus madagascariensis*, and *T. petersi* prefer the dry subarid areas in the south and southwest. At certain localities, *Z. laticaudatus* and *Z. madagascariensis* are often the most abundant lizards.

Gerrhosaurids are usually insectivorous, but various types of seeds have been found in the stomach of *Z. laticaudatus*. Plated lizards generally hunt on the ground, under leaves, under the bark of dead trees, and in anthills. *Zonosaurus madagascariensis* and *Z. laticaudatus* prey on cicadas and crickets. *Zonosaurus laticaudatus* sometimes climbs introduced cacao trees to eat fruits and insects, and even small vertebrates (Raselimanana 2018). After a heavy rainstorm an individual was observed eating a large earthworm that came to the surface. In Ankarafantsika, a *Z. laticaudatus* adult was observed preying on a wasp nest, grasping the nest in its teeth, shaking it vigorously, and running several meters away; this was repeated several times until all wasps had been chased away, and the lizard then consumed the entire nest, which contained the wasp eggs and larvae (M. Vences, unpublished data). At Kirindy Forest CNFEREF, a *Z. laticaudatus* individual was photographed preying on a frog (Figure 12.28). In *Z. ornatus* a case of partial cannibalism has been recorded—an adult male had a piece of tail of a conspecific in its stomach. *Zonosaurus karsteni* has been documented feeding on terrestrial prey such as large cockroaches, which usually live under bark of dead trees, as well as Coleoptera, caterpillars, and spiders. Although *Z. maximus* can be semiaquatic, it does not seem to hunt extensively in the water. However, it sometimes attacks aquatic animals that surface near riverbanks; remains of aquatic insects, such as water beetles (probably Gyrinidae; see Gustafson et al., pp. 1034–41), have been found in the stomach of this species.

As ectotherms, gerrhosaurids use external sources of heat for thermoregulation. They attempt to maintain a relatively constant body temperature by adjusting their position and behavior. Individuals often spend several hours in the sun, especially in the early morning. Time spent sunbathing varies with the species. Large species such as *Z. laticaudatus* and *Z. madagascariensis* spend more time resting in the sunlight than smaller species. Late afternoon sunbathing has been observed in *Z. aeneus*. Sunbathing takes place on bare ground or in leaf litter, on tree trunks or on rocks, in positions that allow the animal to be exposed to the sun's rays. The animal lies with its throat on the substrate and keeps its eyes open; these lizards belong to a group that Avery (1979) termed "shuttling heliotherms." The resting metabolic rate of *Z. laticaudatus* was studied by Berg et al. (2017) in parcel 1 of Andohahela. It does not exhibit metabolic differences between the wet and dry seasons, possibly because ambient temperature is elevated enough and relatively stable, and food sources are available year-round.

DISTRIBUTION

The climatological consequences of Madagascar's eastern escarpment—its rainfall, and its rivers predominantly along the east side—have played an important role in molding the distribution of gerrhosaurids. The geographic distributions of these lizards can be grouped into three main categories: 1) those with very restricted distributions, 2) those occurring across regions within well-defined bioclimatic areas, and 3) those with very broad distributions across different bioclimatic zones. These distributions were most recently summarized by Glaw and Vences (2007) and Raselimanana and Goodman (2013). The greatest species richness of the Malagasy gerrhosaurids is in the northwest (Nosy Be, Ankarana) and southeast (Andohahela), and endemism is also high in these areas, although it is highest in the north (J. Brown et al. 2016).

Numerous species have restricted geographic ranges. *Tracheloptychus madagascariensis* (Figure 12.29) occurs in the dry deciduous forests of the central west and the dry spiny thickets of the south. It is present from Tolagnaro, the southeastern limit, up to Befandriana-Sud, the northwestern limit. Its counterpart, *T. petersi*, is found in a very restricted zone from north of the Onilahy River to south of the Mangoky River (Raselimanana and Goodman 2013).

Zonosaurus haraldmeieri is known only in the extreme north in the protected areas of Montagne d'Ambre, Ankarana, and Analamerana, while in the same immediate area *Z. tsingy* is found from Montagne des Français, Nosy Hara, and Ankarana. *Zonosaurus trilineatus* occurs in the dry spiny thickets of the south, in a small area between the Onilahy and Mandrare Rivers. Its counterpart *Z. quadrilineatus* occupies a zone to the north between the Onilahy and Mangoky Rivers. The Onilahy River probably forms a dispersal barrier between these two species. *Zonosaurus bemaraha* is known only from the west in the dry deciduous forests of Andranopasazy in the Tsingy de Bemaraha. Despite its preference for rivers and lake shores, *Z. maximus* does not occur outside the southeast and is restricted to the area between Tolongoina and Tolagnaro. *Zonosaurus anelanelany* is known only from the southeast in lowland moist evergreen forests, from Grande Lavasoa in the south to Befotaka–Midongy du Sud National Park in the north (A. P. Raselimanana, unpublished data). Hence, it seems that the Itomampy River is the northern limit of its distribution. *Zonosaurus boettgeri* occurs in the lowland moist evergreen forests in Lokobe on Nosy Be in the northwest, in Loky Manambato, and on the Masoala Peninsula in the northeast, as well as in dry deciduous forests of Montagne des Français and Ankarana in the north (Glaw and Vences 2007).

The open anthropogenic habitats and montane ericoid thickets of the Central Highlands, up to over 2000 m elevation on the Ankaratra and Andringitra Massifs, are generally occupied by *Z. ornatus*. This species is rather adaptable to urban zones and is quite common, for example, around the Université d'Antananarivo. Interestingly, *Z. ornatus* in southeastern Madagascar also occurs at low elevations, for instance near sea level in Manombo Special Reserve. *Zonosaurus karsteni* is confined to the dry and subarid bioclimate of the south, southwest, and west. This species and *Z. ornatus* are closely related (Blair et al. 2015), and these two forms have never been found occurring in sympatry, while *Z. laticaudatus* is known to overlap in its distribution with one or the other species.

Some species have broad distributions, such as *Z. brygooi*, which is found in lowland moist evergreen forests and littoral forests along the east coast from sea level up to 750 m, and in a geographic range from the Masoala Peninsula in the north to its southern limit near

FIGURE 12.29 **A *Tracheloptychus madagascariensis* specimen from Berenty.** (PHOTO by F. Glaw and M. Vences.)

FIGURE 12.30 **A colorful *Zonosaurus subunicolor* specimen from Marojejy.** (PHOTO by F. Glaw and M. Vences.)

Fenoarivo-Atsinanana. *Zonosaurus rufipes* occurs across much of northern Madagascar, from Lokobe (Nosy Be) in the northwest to the Masoala Peninsula in the northeast, and throughout portions of this zone it occurs in sympatry with *Z. subunicolor* (Figure 12.30).

Three species are ubiquitous. *Zonosaurus laticaudatus* is spread over a broad area that is broken up into three separate blocks: the northwest, west, and south. This species presumably had a continuous distribution in the past. The current disjunct ranges may be the result of local extirpation in certain zones or separation of populations associated with ecological changes (e.g., climate and human perturbation). Molecular studies are needed to examine genetic distances between these populations. *Zonosaurus madagascariensis* is sympatric with *Z. laticaudatus* at several localities, and the former species is absent from the extreme southeast but is common throughout the balance of the eastern moist evergreen forests. *Zonosaurus aeneus* is found across this same zone, as well as in the Central Highlands from Andohahela in the south to the Loky Manambato area in the northeast. However, the Loky Manambato population near Daraina shows some distinct morphological characters and is genetically different from the typical *Z. aeneus*, instead clustering with *Z. subunicolor* based on DNA evidence (Recknagel et al. 2013).

ORIGINS AND RADIATION

The Malagasy Zonosaurinae is the result of a single colonization event of Madagascar from Africa (Raselimanana et al. 2009). Blair et al. (2015) found that the common ancestor arrived about 30 Mya when oceanic currents were favorable for dispersal from the mainland. Compared to the radiation of other taxa, such as the chameleon genera *Brookesia* or *Furcifer* (see Scherz et al., pp. 1506–16), that of plated lizard species is rather young (Blair et al. 2015).

The phylogeography of Madagascar's Gerrhosauridae was modeled by Blair et al. (2015). They found that the biogeographic origin of the subfamily Zonosaurinae could not be traced, but *Zonosaurus* did not originate in the subarid south, whereas *Tracheloptychus* seemingly did. The south and southwest were secondarily colonized by the ancestor of *Z. quadrilineatus* and *Z. trilineatus* (and possibly *Z. laticaudatus* and *Z. anelanelany*), which probably arrived from more northerly areas of the central west. Most of the diversification of *Zonosaurus* was found to have taken place in the dry western forests, with several independent movements into the moist evergreen forests of the east.

CONSERVATION

Among the 19 species of gerrhosaurids known from Madagascar, five species are threatened, with four listed as Vulnerable (*Zonosaurus anelanelany*, *Z. boettgeri*, *Z. quadrilineatus*, and *Z. maximus*) and one as Endangered (*Z. subunicolor*); one species is Data Deficient (*Z. maramaintso*). *Tracheloptychus petersi*, *Z. anelanelany*, *Z. maximus*, *Z. quadrilineatus*, and *Zonosaurus maramaintso* have very restricted ranges. *Tracheloptychus petersi* is known from three protected areas (Mangoky Ihotry, Ranobe PK32, and Mikea). *Zonosaurus anelanelany* is restricted to the protected areas of Andohahela and Befotaka–Midongy du Sud. *Zonosaurus maximus* is known only from the protected area of Ambositra-Vondrozo, whereas *Z. maramaintso* is not known to occur in a protected area. At least one species, *Z. maximus*, is a subject of the international pet trade, but this is not very regular (Raxworthy et al. 2011).

Subject editors: David Prötzel, Miguel Vences, and Achille P. Raselimanana

SCINCIDAE, SKINKS, *ANDRONGO, MATAHOTRANDRO*

A. Miralles, A. P. Raselimanana, D. Rakotomalala, and A. Crottini

Skinks of the family Scincidae represent one of the largest lizard families in the world, with about 1700 described species (Uetz et al. 2021). This family has a cosmopolitan distribution and occurs in diverse habitats except in boreal and polar regions, showing multiple morphological adaptations to various microhabitats (especially in the subfamily Scincinae). They are most often opportunistic carnivores and generally feed on small invertebrates, although some species can be omnivorous, and one arboreal species from the Solomon Islands (*Corucia zebrata*) is known to be strictly herbivorous. Skinks can be identified by the presence of ossified scales (osteoderms), which are most often cycloid, smooth, and glossy (this feature is shared with gerrhosaurids; the latter can be most easily distinguished by the lateral fold, which is absent in skinks, and dorsal scales arranged in bands; see Raselimanana et al., pp. 1490–94). Like chain mail, this envelope of osteoderms helps protect their bodies from predators.

The phylogenetic relationships of several Scincidae clades remain unclarified. A major confounding characteristic that hampered the resolution of their phylogenetic relationships is the ability of several representatives of this group to adopt a fossorial lifestyle. Limb regression, the presence of a pointed rostral shield (a modification of the scales of the head), eye reduction, and body lengthening often characterize this adaptation (Miralles et al. 2011b, 2015b, 2016a). This phenomenon has evolved independently numerous times during skink evolutionary history (Whiting et al. 2003; Brandley et al. 2005; Daniels et al. 2005, 2006; Wiens et al. 2006) and enabled them to colonize various microhabitats usually inaccessible to other lizard species (sandy dunes, forest humus, leaf litter, rock crevices, and dense grass).

With 78 species (one species, *T. comorensis*, is likely introduced; see Raselimanana and Vences, pp. 1455–58), Madagascar is a diversity hotspot for skinks (c. 5% of the world's species diversity for this family). Half of the currently recognized Malagasy skink species were described during the 19th and 20th centuries (Figure 12.31), although the first serious treatment of the group was done by Edouard-Raoul Brygoo in a series of 18 papers (Brygoo 1979, 1980a, 1980b, 1980c, 1981a, 1981b, 1981c, 1981d, 1983a, 1983b, 1984a, 1984b, 1984c, 1984d, 1984e, 1985b, 1986, 1987). A new era of intense field exploration (in both remote and more accessible areas of Madagascar) toward the end of the 20th century allowed the acquisition of many new specimens. This resulted in a considerable expansion of biological, ecological, and distributional information on this group and led to the description of several new species (Raxworthy and Nussbaum 1993b; Nussbaum and Raxworthy 1994d, 1995b, 1995c, 1998b; Nussbaum et al. 1999a; Ramanamanjato et al. 1999a, 1999b; Andreone and Greer 2002; Sakata and Hikida 2003a, 2003b).

Three of the seven Scincidae subfamilies known worldwide are present on Madagascar (subfamilies Scincinae, Eugongylinae, and Mabuyinae). The Scincinae of Madagascar forms a monophyletic group that colonized the island during the Paleocene/Eocene and diversified into a remarkably species-rich evolutionary radiation. The Mabuyinae colonized Madagascar with the genus *Trachylepis* (during the Miocene), and the Eugongylinae colonized the island more recently with the rock-dwelling skink genus *Cryptoblepharus* (Crottini et al. 2012a). Studies on the evolutionary history of these three groups have intensified in recent years, with the publication of several molecular phylogenies. These works led to major classification changes and contributed to maintaining the high pace of new species discovery and description by revealing the existence of several species complexes (Whiting et al. 2004;

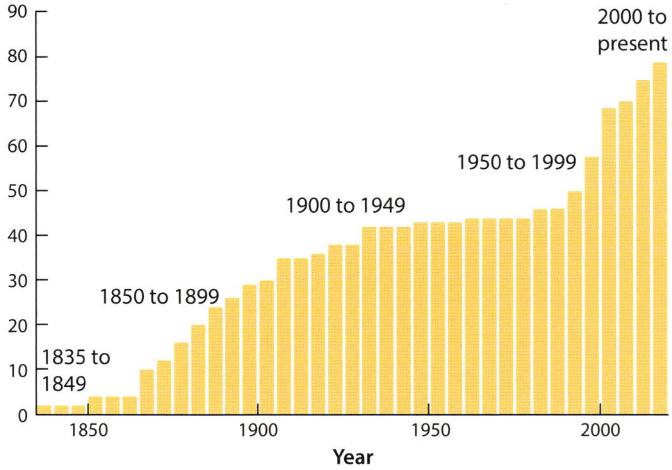

FIGURE 12.31 Number of Malagasy skink species described over time, broken down into cumulative five-year periods until March 2020.

Brandley et al. 2005; Schmitz et al. 2005; Rocha et al. 2006; Crottini et al. 2009; J. Köhler et al. 2009, 2010; Miralles et al. 2011a, 2011b, 2011c, 2012, 2015b, 2016a, 2016b; Lima et al. 2013; Miralles and Vences 2013; Vences et al. 2014; Erens et al. 2017). The relatively constant rate of description over the last two decades suggests that a significant number of new species—especially miniaturized, fossorial, and morphologically conservative species complexes—are still waiting to be discovered and/or formally described (Figure 12.31).

Malagasy skinks exhibit a wide spectrum of different lifestyles, including terrestrial, fossorial, rock-dwelling, semiaquatic, and partly arboreal species. Many of these species have microendemic distribution ranges, making this group particularly relevant for biogeographic studies.

SYSTEMATICS AND NATURAL HISTORY

Scincinae

The scincine skinks of Madagascar are an ancient and species-rich monophyletic group composed of nine genera (*Amphiglossus, Brachyseps, Flexiseps, Grandidierina, Madascincus, Paracontias, Pseudoacontias, Pygomeles,* and *Voeltzkowia*; Figures 12.32 and 12.33; Table 12.5) and around 63 currently recognized species (Erens et al. 2017; Uetz et al. 2021; see notes to Table 12.1 regarding the use of the genus name *Brachyseps*). On Madagascar, this group succeeded to evolve into extremely diversified morphologies and to adapt to different types of habitats, from generalized forms (e.g., *Brachyseps*) to giant semiaquatic species (e.g., *Amphiglossus*) and to leaf-litter (e.g., *Pseudoacontias, Paracontias*) or sand burrowers (*Grandidierina, Paracontias, Pygomeles,* and *Voeltzkowia*) with reduced limbs and/or eyes. This evolutionary radiation on Madagascar has seemingly evolved in parallel into most of the ecological and morphological spaces explored by this subfamily worldwide.

Members of this subfamily have colonized and succeeded in adapting to all types of environments, from the scorching dunes of littoral forests to the upper montane zones of the Central Highlands and other high-elevation areas (e.g., *Madascincus pyrurus*, found up to 1700 m on Mont Ibity, as well as *Brachyseps macrocercus* and *Flexiseps tsaratananensis*, both occurring well above 2000 m on several massifs), and from the dry spiny thickets and dry deciduous forests in the south and west to the moist evergreen forests in the east. Some species have evolved toward ultra-miniaturized leaf-litter forms (e.g., *M. nanus*, maximum snout-to-vent length [SVL] <3 cm), whereas others such as *A. astrolabi* and *A. reticulatus* have taken the opposite path, with SVL reaching more than 22 cm. Their ecological and morphological flexibility is strikingly illustrated through the diversity of body shapes present within the group (Figures 12.32, 12.33). Although several genera are fundamentally tetrapodal and pentadactyl (e.g., *Amphiglossus, Madascincus, Brachyseps, Flexiseps*), many lineages have secondarily and recurrently evolved toward totally or partly limbless forms, in conjunction with their progressive shift toward new and unoccupied ecological niches. Serpentine species, which are totally limbless (e.g., *Paracontias, Pseudoacontias*) and frequently miniaturized (e.g., some species of *Paracontias*), are probably the most morphologically divergent forms. Some of these are specialized to live in the leaf litter and forest humus of the north and eastern moist evergreen forest belt (e.g., *Pseudoacontias, Flexiseps stylus,* most *Paracontias* species).

All these taxa are frequently characterized by the presence of a robust, rounded, short snout, frequently covered with a rostral shield (i.e., an aggregation of snout scales into a single enlarged plate that protects the anterior part of the head during head-first progression into the substrate). In contrast, other serpentine species are highly specialized to sandy substrates in dry regions (e.g., *Grandidierina, Voeltzkowia, Paracontias minimus*). Species of these genera are often pale or even totally depigmented and are considered to be "blind" because their eyes are very regressed and covered by skin (although little is known about their visual acuity). Their generally pointed snout is flattened to function as a shovel, enabling them to "swim" in fine sand. It seems likely that these species can track and catch their prey by orienting themselves within the sand, thanks to the vibrations the latter emit by moving on the surface (e.g., *G. fierinensis*; A. Miralles, unpublished data).

A vast spectrum of extant forms represents persisting stages of evolutionary transition from a four-limbed to a limbless skink. The body of scincine skinks can be more or less elongated (the number of presacral vertebrae runs from a minimum of 29 within the fully pentadactyl genus *Madascincus* up to a maximum of 67 in the apodal genus *Pseudoacontias*). Their digits can be absent, more or less regressed (from reduced number of digits to reduced number of phalanges in pentadactyl species), or fully developed. Among the species with regressed limbs, extreme regression may affect only the hind limbs (several species of *Grandidierina* and *Pygomeles*) or the forelimbs (two species of the genus *Voeltzkowia*).

Some remarkable ecological adaptations are also present among the tetrapodal species. For instance, a few species are known to be aquatic or semiaquatic, especially *Amphiglossus astrolabi* and *A. reticulatus*, and to a lesser degree *Flexiseps mandokava* and *Brachyseps frontoparietalis* (Millot 1951; Raxworthy and Nussbaum 1993b; A. Crottini, unpublished data), and at least in the *Amphiglossus* species, the nostril aperture is turned posteriorly, typically an adaptation to life underwater (Raxworthy and Nussbaum 1993b).

FIGURE 12.32 **An overview of Malagasy scincine diversity. A) *Pseudoacontias menamainty*, Berara; B) *Brachyseps macrocercus*, Ankaratra; C) *B. frontoparietalis*, Betampona; D) *Madascincus* sp. (of the "*nanus*" group), Betampona; E) *M. igneocaudatus*, Ifaty; F) *M. polleni*, dry forest of Kirindy Forest CNFEREF; G) *Flexiseps ornaticeps*, Ifaty; H) *F. meva*, Makira; I) *Amphiglossus reticulatus* juvenile, Berara; J) *Voeltzkowia yamagishii*, Ankarafantsika; K) *Paracontias vermisaurus*, Makira; L) *Pygomeles trivittatus*, Tolagnaro; M) and N) *P. braconnieri*, near Ifaty; O) *Grandidierina rubrocaudata*, near Ifaty; P) *G. fierinensis*, from Anakao; Q) gravid female of *Madascincus* sp. ("*nanus*" group), Betampona, whose single large egg is visible (Porcel et al. 2021); and R) characteristic zigzag traces left on the sand by *G. fierinensis*.** (PHOTOS A and I by F. Andreone; B by F. Glaw and M. Vences; C, D, E, and G by G. M. Rosa; F, L–P, and R by A. Miralles; H by M. Vences and D. R. Vieites; J by F. Eckhard; K by M. Vences; and Q by A. Crottini.)

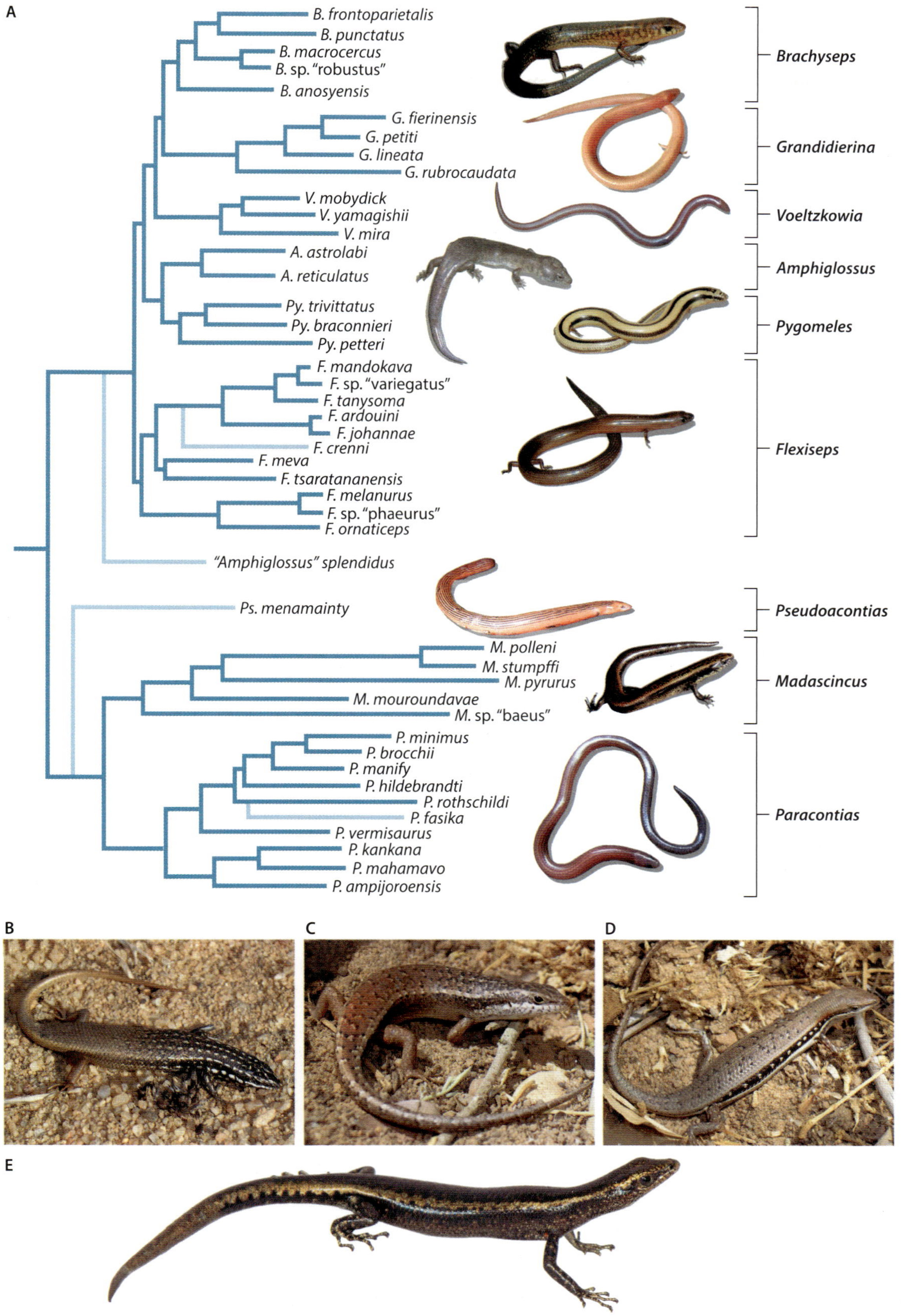

FIGURE 12.33 **A) Phylogenetic tree of the Scincinae of Madagascar (redrawn from Erens et al. 2017). Overview of Mabuyinae and Eugongylinae skink diversity on the island: B) *Trachylepis vato*, near Ambalavao; C) *T. dumasi*, Kirindy Forest CNFEREF (both belonging to the "*aureopunctata*" group); D) *T. elegans*, Kirindy Forest CNFEREF ("*elegans*" group); and E) *Cryptoblepharus boutonii cognatus*, Nosy Ambariobe.** (PHOTOS B–D by A. Miralles, and E by M. D. Scherz.)

TABLE 12.5. **Ecological and geographic distribution of Malagasy Scincidae species**

SUBFAMILY (NUMBER OF SPECIES) SPECIES	GENERAL HABITAT	HABITAT TYPE AND DISTRIBUTION
EUGONGYLINAE (1)		
Cryptoblepharus boutonii cognatus	Northern coast	Coral islets and littoral rocks
C. b. voeltzkowi	Southern, southwestern, western, and northwestern coasts	Coral islets and littoral rocks
MABUYINAE (14)		
Trachylepis aureopunctata	Dry spiny thickets and dry deciduous forests	Dry forests and thickets, and open habitat in the S and SW from Tolagnaro to the Manambolo River
T. boettgeri	Central Highlands	Grasslands from central east
T. comorensis	Nosy Tanikely (probably introduced)	Ubiquitous species on Nosy Tanikely, in the Comoros in urban areas, degraded habitats, forests and plantations
T. dumasi	Dry spiny thickets and dry deciduous forests	Dry forests, spiny thickets, and woodlands in the S and W
T. elegans	Widespread	Ubiquitous species, common in forest edges, open habitat, grasslands
T. gravenhorstii	Widespread	Ubiquitous species, common in forest edges, grasslands
T. lavarambo	Moist evergreen forests	Lokobe (Sambirano Region)
T. madagascariensis	Central Highlands and dry deciduous forests	Forests and grasslands in Central Highlands
T. nancycoutuae	Dry deciduous forests	Grasslands and sclerophyllous woodlands near Isalo
T. tandrefana	Dry deciduous forests	Dry deciduous forests between Morondava, Antsalova, and Namoroka
T. tavaratra	Dry deciduous forests	Dry and transitional forests in the N
T. vato	Dry spiny thickets and dry deciduous forests	Rupicolous species, open habitat, dry forests and thickets in the S and SW
T. vezo	Dry spiny thickets and dry deciduous forests	Rupicolous species on Mahafaly Plateau south of Onilahy River
T. volamenaloha	Dry deciduous forests	Dry deciduous forests associated with limestone *tsingy*
SCINCINAE (63)		
Amphiglossus astrolabi	Moist evergreen forests, Central Highlands	Along streams in the E
A. reticulatus	Moist evergreen forests, dry deciduous forests, and Central Highlands	Transitional forests and wetlands (streams/marshland) in the NW
Brachyseps anosyensis	Moist evergreen forests, Central Highlands	In the E
B. frontoparietalis	Moist evergreen forests, Central Highlands	Along rivers in the E
B. gastrostictus	Moist evergreen forests, montane ericoid thickets, and Central Highlands	Forests in the NE and Central Highlands
B. macrocercus	Moist evergreen forests, montane ericoid thickets, and Central Highlands	Forests in the E, SE, and Central Highlands

SUBFAMILY (NUMBER OF SPECIES) SPECIES	GENERAL HABITAT	HABITAT TYPE AND DISTRIBUTION
B. mandady	Moist evergreen forests	In the NE
B. punctatus	Moist evergreen forests, Central Highlands	In the E
B. spilostichus	Moist evergreen forests	In the NE
B. splendidus	Dry deciduous forests	Open habitat near forests, often under woods or rocks
Flexiseps alluaudi	Dry deciduous forests	Dry deciduous forests in the extreme N
F. andranovahensis	Dry spiny thickets	In the S
F. ardouini	Dry deciduous forests	Dry deciduous and transitional forests in the N
F. crenni	Moist evergreen forests and Central Highlands	In the E and in the Central Highlands
F. decaryi	Moist evergreen forests	Littoral forests in the SE
F. elongatus	Moist evergreen forests	Moist evergreen or transitional forests in the N and NW
F. mandokava	Moist evergreen forests, montane ericoid thickets, dry deciduous forests, and Central Highlands	Moist evergreen and transitional forests in the NW
F. melanurus	Moist evergreen forests, Central Highlands	In the E and in the Central Highlands
F. meva	Central Highlands	In the NE and W
F. ornaticeps	Moist evergreen forests and dry spiny thickets	Dry forests and thickets in the S and SW, and coastal moist evergreen forests in the E
F. stylus	Moist evergreen forests	In the NE
F. tanysoma	Moist evergreen forests and dry deciduous forests	In the NW
F. tsaratananensis	Montane ericoid thickets and Central Highlands	In the NW
Grandidierina fierinensis	Dry spiny thickets	Fossorial species living in sand and humus along the coast in the S and SW
G. lineata	Dry spiny thickets, dry deciduous forests	Fossorial species living in sand and humus. Littoral forests, riparian forests, and dunes in the S and SW
G. petiti	Dry spiny thickets	Fossorial species living in dunes in the SW
G. rubrocaudata	Dry spiny thickets, dry deciduous forests	Fossorial species living in sand, humus, and leaf litter in dunes and riparian forests in the SW
Madascincus ankodabensis	Moist evergreen forests, Central Highlands	Humid, subhumid, and littoral forests in the SE
M. arenicola	Dry deciduous forests	Dunes in the N
M. igneocaudatus	Dry spiny thickets, dry deciduous forests	In the S and SW
M. macrolepis	Dry deciduous forests, medium-altitude moist evergreen forests	Subhumid formations in western Central Highlands
M. melanopleura	Moist evergreen forests	In the central E and in the Central Highlands
M. miafina	Dry deciduous forests	In the N
M. minutus	Dry deciduous forests and moist evergreen forests	Humid and transitional forests of the N, NE, and Sambirano Region
M. mouroundavae	Moist evergreen forests and montane ericoid thickets	NW, NE, and Central Highlands

(continued overleaf)

TABLE 12.5. ***continued***

SUBFAMILY (NUMBER OF SPECIES) SPECIES	GENERAL HABITAT	HABITAT TYPE AND DISTRIBUTION
M. nanus	Moist evergreen forests	In the NE
M. polleni	Dry deciduous forests	Between Morondava and Mahajanga
M. pyrurus	Central Highlands	Subhumid and dry deciduous forests
M. stumpffi	Moist evergreen forests, montane ericoid thickets, and dry deciduous forests	Humid and transitional forests in the NW and Central Highlands
Paracontias ampijoroensis	Dry deciduous forests	In the NW
P. brocchii	Moist evergreen forests	Montagne d'Ambre (N)
P. fasika	Dry deciduous forests	Sand, in the N
P. hafa	Moist evergreen forests	In the NE
P. hildebrandti	Moist evergreen forests and dry deciduous forests	Humid and transitional forests in the N and NW
P. holomelas	Moist evergreen forests	In the E
P. kankana	Lowland moist evergreen forests	In the E
P. mahamavo	Dry deciduous forests	In the NW
P. manify	Moist evergreen forests	Tsaratanàna (NW)
P. milloti	Moist evergreen forests	Known only by its type from the Sambirano Region (Nosy Mamoko)
P. minimus	Dry deciduous forests	Known only from sand in the N
P. rothschildi	Dry deciduous forests	Known only from sand in the N
P. tsararano	Moist evergreen forests	In the NE
P. vermisaurus	Lowland moist evergreen forests	In the NE
Pseudoacontias angelorum	Moist evergreen forests	In the NE
P. madagascariensis	Unknown	No information
P. menamainty	Moist evergreen forests	Transitional forests in the NW
P. unicolor	Moist evergreen forests	In Lokobe (Sambirano Region)
Pygomeles bracconieri	Dry spiny thickets	In the SW
P. petteri	Dry deciduous forests	In the W
P. trivittatus	Dry spiny thickets and riparian forests	In the S and SW
Voeltzkowia mira	Dry deciduous forests	Fossorial species living in sand in the NW
V. mobydick	Dry deciduous forests	Fossorial species living in sand in the NW
V. yamagishii	Dry deciduous forests	Fossorial species living in sand in the NW

Knowledge of the biology and ecology of most members of the subfamily Scincinae is deficient because most are relatively difficult to observe in the field. Several species are fossorial or semi-fossorial, nocturnal or crepuscular, microendemic or present at very low density. For instance, information on habitat utilization, competition, and predation is generally lacking. Most species seem to be oviparous and lay between one and 10 fibrous eggs (e.g., Figure 12.32q). Nevertheless, ovoviviparity (live birth but with embryonic development taking place in eggs within the mother) evolved several times independently in a couple of species such as *Brachyseps punctatus* (Raxworthy and Nussbaum 1993b) and *Madascincus igneocaudatus* (Glaw and Vences 2007; Miralles et al. 2016b), and it appears to be likely in *Grandidierina lineata* (A. Miralles, unpublished data) and *B. macrocercus* (Glaw and Vences 2007). *Brachyseps punctatus* has strong, well-developed limb claws, and individuals have been captured up to 1.5 m off the ground inside dead tree trunks or under tree bark (Raxworthy and Nussbaum 1993b), most probably to find a refuge and to profit from the presence of insect larvae. These latter authors also observed a female *B. punctatus* on a *Ravenala* tree and suspected that the female climbed up the trunk to the leaf axil to deposit young, as this individual gave birth to three fully developed young skinks the day after being captured. *Brachyseps anosyensis* has been reported to occur in zones with bamboo cover and to be fossorial, and it is often observed inside dead tree trunks inhabited by termites on which it probably feeds.

The genus *Madascincus* contains species adapted to the leaf litter of moist evergreen and dry deciduous forests. Most species occur in allopatry, although some *Madascincus* species are known to occur sympatrically at some localities. At Analamazaotra, a probable hybrid individual between the closely related *M. minutus* and *M. melanopleura* has recently been collected (A. Crottini, unpublished data). Ancestral range reconstruction analyzed across the entire group shows that the moist evergreen forest biome has been the most relevant in the diversification of the group (A. Crottini, unpublished data).

Cryptoblepharus, "Snake-eyed Skinks"

The genus *Cryptoblepharus* (Eugongylinae) is composed of 53 species (Uetz et al. 2021). Thanks to its remarkable transoceanic dispersal capacities, it is distributed across a vast portion of the Indo-Pacific region (Australia, Indonesia, New Guinea, Pacific area, east coast of Africa, and Madagascar) and is one of the most widespread genera of the family (Brygoo 1986; Horner and Adams 2007; Blom et al. 2019). Snake-eyed skinks exhibit a marked degree of morphological conservatism. They are relatively small (SVL <55 mm), and easily recognizable by their pointed snout, slender body shape with well-developed pentadactyl limbs, and lack of eyelids (Brygoo 1986; Horner 2007; Horner and Adams 2007) (Figure 12.33e). Skinks of this genus are heliotropic, arboreal, or saxicolous. They are remarkably adept water-surface swimmers and are kept afloat on seawater by surface tension. This has likely contributed to their dispersal capacity.

Several distinct lineages of *Cryptoblepharus* belonging to the *boutonii* group are present in the western Indian Ocean (from the east coast of Africa to Mauritius, including Madagascar, the Comoros, and several other neighboring islands), and several taxa have been described to reflect the associated phenotypic and geographic diversity. Based on current data, two lineages are documented on Madagascar, which are distinct morphologically and phylogenetically as well as in their distribution ranges: *C. boutonii cognatus* is restricted to the extreme north, and *C. b. voeltzkowi* is present in the south (Rocha et al. 2006). It should be noted that certain authors (Horner 2007; Uetz et al. 2021) regard these taxa as different species, but given their rather weak genetic divergence (Blom et al. 2019), it seems more plausible to assign them to subspecies.

On Madagascar, *Cryptoblepharus* lives on coral islets and littoral rocks along the southern, southwestern, western, northwestern, and northern coasts. In such areas the abundant flies associated with the remains of stranded marine organisms constitute an important food resource for these lizards. Moreover, fissures and various holes in coastal rocks and old coral beds provide refuge. Glaw and Vences (1994) reported that on Nosy Be this species feeds in the intertidal zone on insects, crustaceans, and fish.

Trachylepis, "African Mabuyas"

The genus *Trachylepis* (Mabuyinae) originates from Africa, where most of the 87 recognized species are distributed (Uetz et al. 2021). The remarkable dispersal capacity of this genus has furthermore enabled it to colonize the Arabian Peninsula, the island of Fernando de Noronha (Brazil), and several islands in the Indian Ocean (Carranza and Arnold 2003; Rocha et al. 2010a; Weinell et al. 2019). These episodes of transoceanic dispersal allowed them to arrive around 20 million years ago on Madagascar (Crottini et al. 2012a), where they diversified into 13 recognized species and adapted to almost all bioclimatic zones on the island (Glaw and Vences 2007). Thirteen species are endemic to the island, whereas *T. comorensis*, which is present on the Malagasy offshore islet of Nosy Tanikely, probably represents an anthropogenic introduction from the Comoros (J. Köhler et al. 1998). Malagasy *Trachylepis* species are relatively conserved from a morphological point of view: they are all characterized by a moderate size (SVL varies only from 5 to 10 cm) and a robust constitution with four well-developed pentadactyl limbs, and all are strictly oviparous. A molecular phylogeny supports the existence of two monophyletic groups that are morphologically distinct (Figures 12.33b–d): 1) the "*aureopunctata*" group, which comprises 10 species characterized by a rectangular subocular, and 2) the "*elegans*" group, with three species showing a trapezoidal subocular (Lima et al. 2013; Weinell et al. 2019).

The species of the "*elegans*" group (*T. elegans*, *T. gravenhorstii*, and to a lesser extent *T. madagascariensis*) are relatively ubiquitous and have colonized very diverse environments across the island (Vences et al. 2014). In contrast, the species of the "*aureopunctata*" group (*T. aureopunctata*, *T. boettgeri*, *T. dumasi*, *T. lavarambo*, *T. nancycoutuae*, *T. tandrefana*, *T. tavaratra*, *T. vato*, *T. vezo*, and *T. volamenaloha*) appear to be ecologically more constrained, being mostly microendemic or restricted to given bioclimatic zones.

Trachylepis species are mostly diurnal and terrestrial, and most are adapted to arid habitats of southern, southwestern, western, and northwestern Madagascar, such as grasslands, dry deciduous forests, transitional forests, and dry spiny thickets (Raselimanana 1993; Raxworthy and Nussbaum 1993b; Nussbaum and Raxworthy 1994d, 1995c; Nussbaum et al. 1999a; Ramanamanjato et al. 1999a; Glaw and Vences 2007). Nevertheless, moist evergreen forest specialist species also exist (e.g., *T. lavarambo*), although they are typically found at the edge or in forest clearings, and a few generalists such as *T. boettgeri* and *T. madagascariensis* can be found both in dry deciduous forests of the west and in moist evergreen forests of the Central Highlands (Goodman et al. 1998; Raselimanana 1998). Some species seem to be adapted to a rupicolous lifestyle, such as *T. volamenaloha*, which occurs in dry deciduous forests typical of *tsingy* formations (Nussbaum et al. 1999a); or *T. vato* and *T. vezo*, which are found on a variety of rock substrates (Glaw and Vences 2007).

Arboreality is limited within this genus, although *T. gravenhorstii* and *T. aureopunctata* have been observed climbing tree trunks. These species seem to use this microhabitat for hunting, as they have been observed feeding on insects living in dead wood and tree bark, and they almost certainly use holes and crevices in tree trunks as a refuge. *Trachylepis comorensis* has been observed several times at night on Nosy Tanikely perched on shrub branches 3 m off the ground (D. Rakotomalala, unpublished data).

MALAGASY SKINK CONSERVATION AND CULTURAL BELIEFS

The convictions of the Malagasy people relating to the Scincidae vary according to region. When referring to these reptiles, people often make parallels between the animals' lives and their own behavior. For instance, in the Central Highlands, particularly in the Imerina area, the following proverb is commonly used: "Androngo anaty asa, samy miaro ny rambony tsy ho tapaka," which can be literally translated as "Like lizards in an agricultural field, each one takes care not to lose his tail." This can be interpreted as "When imperiled, everyone should be concerned with their own life." There are also some popular beliefs associated with skinks that might result in their persecution. For example, in the southeast many people living in the countryside believe that when *Amphiglossus astrolabi* (commonly known as *langaso*) bites someone, this person will live for only the number of years corresponding to the number of skink teeth embedded in the skin associated with the bite. Because of this, people are generally afraid of these animals. These skinks are regularly killed and chopped into pieces, because it is commonly thought that otherwise they can revive.

A recent effort to provide an overview of the vertebrate fauna of most terrestrial protected areas of Madagascar revealed that most skink species occur in at least one protected area (Goodman et al. 2018). However, a few exceptions exist: for example, *T. vezo*, *Paracontias fasika*, *P. kankana*, *P. minimus*, and *P. rothschildi* as far as known do not occur within the current protected area network.

The conservation status of the 74 native skink species occurring on Madagascar has been recently assessed. Of these, 22 species are listed among the highest threatened categories of the IUCN (IUCN 2019; see Table 12.1). Five have been classified as Critically Endangered, six as Endangered, and 11 as Vulnerable. As underlined above, most species in this family show remarkable adaptations to the microhabitat they occur in, and for this reason habitat loss and fragmentation are the most serious threats affecting these taxa.

Subject editors: Angelica Crottini, Miguel Vences, and Achille P. Raselimanana

OPLURIDAE, MALAGASY IGUANAS, *ANDRONGOVATO*

J. E. Cadle, L. Chan, and A. Miralles

INTRODUCTION AND SYSTEMATICS

Malagasy iguanas (Figure 12.34) comprise two genera: *Chalarodon* with two species (*C. madagascariensis* and *C. steinkampi*) and *Oplurus* with six species (*O. cuvieri*, *O. cyclurus*, *O. quadrimaculatus*, *O. saxicola*, *O. fierinensis*, and *O. grandidieri*). *Oplurus* and *Chalarodon* are part of a large cosmopolitan clade known as the Iguania, which includes chameleons, agamids, and iguanids in the broad sense (Pough et al. 2015). The two Malagasy genera, referred to collectively as oplurids (family Opluridae), are part of the large clade of iguanians known as the pleurodont iguanians (based on tooth structure), which includes all iguanians except chameleons and agamids. "Pleurodont Iguania" is strongly supported as a clade by molecular and morphological data. The monophyly of oplurids is corroborated by the reduction of inscriptional ribs (posterior ribs not attached to the sternum) to paired splints and by the ulnar nerve pathway deep to the limb muscle; both characters are unique among iguanids *sensu lato* (Etheridge and De Queiroz 1988). In addition, a wealth of molecular data support oplurid monophyly (Münchenberg et al. 2008). Their karyotype is rather conserved, with 36 chromosomes as in most iguanas, but oplurid species differ in the position of the nucleolar organizer region and heterochromatic blocks (Altmanová et al. 2016).

Apart from the Malagasy species, iguanids in the broad sense are found primarily in the Americas, but one genus (four species) also occurs on Fiji. The relationship of oplurids to other pleurodont iguanians is unresolved. Macey et al. (1997) concluded that oplurids were nested well within the iguanid clade, but support for their relationship to other specific iguanid taxa is weak. Etheridge and De Queiroz (1988) and Williams (1988) concluded that oplurids were perhaps more closely related to the Neotropical Polychrotidae and/or Hoplocercidae than to other pleurodont iguanians. Recent molecular studies recovered oplurids as a sister clade to the Leiosauridae (Townsend et al. 2011a; Zheng and Wiens 2016). There is general agreement that the isolation of oplurids on Madagascar is a result of Gondwanan plate tectonic events (Noonan and Chippindale 2006b). Based on complete mitochondrial genomes, Okajima and Kumazawa (2009) concluded that oplurids were the earliest-diverging lineage of pleurodont iguanians, and that this divergence occurred during the Middle to Late Jurassic; however, the robustness of this result is still controversial considering a wealth of other DNA sequence data indicating poor resolution of the relationships of pleurodont iguanians (e.g., Townsend et al. 2011a).

The morphological distinction between *Oplurus* and *Chalarodon* is weak (Etheridge and De Queiroz 1988). Both Münchenberg et al. (2008) and Chan et al. (2012) analyzed relationships among

FIGURE 12.34 **Overview of the diversity of Malagasy iguanas. A) *Chalarodon madagascariensis* in the Ifaty dry spiny thicket; B) *C. steinkampi* between Amboasary-Atsimo and Esomony; C and D) *Oplurus cuvieri* in the dry deciduous forest of Kirindy Forest CNFEREF; E) *O. quadrimaculatus* near Ambalavao; and F) *O. saxicola* southeast of Toliara.** (PHOTOS by A. Miralles.)

oplurid species using mitochondrial and nuclear DNA sequences. The estimated phylogeny of Münchenberg et al. (2008) recovered *Chalarodon* as sister to *Oplurus*. Within the latter, a clade containing *O. cuvieri* and *O. cyclurus* was sister to a clade with all other species; *O. grandidieri* was sister to *O. fierinensis*; the clade of these two species was sister to *O. saxicola*; and the clade of *O. fierinensis*, *O. grandidieri*, and *O. saxicola* was sister to *O. quadrimaculatus*. Data from Chan et al. (2012) corroborated the relationships and found support for the monophyly of *Oplurus*.

DISTRIBUTION

Oplurids are typically found in open areas in the Central Highlands or in arid areas of western and southern Madagascar (C. Blanc 1977). Most of the known localities for these species are in the southern half of the island, although *Oplurus cuvieri* occurs mainly in the northwestern quadrant. An endemic subspecies, *O. cuvieri comorensis*, occurs in the Comoro islands (Grande Comore). Only two species, *O. grandidieri* and *O. quadrimaculatus*, occur in scattered localities within mesic areas of the moist evergreen forest belt, and all these localities are in the southern portion of this region, although these species appear to be restricted to relatively open rock outcrops within that area. Populations of oplurids often differ in coloration, which seems to some extent to represent background matching of the substrate (Meier 1981) and may thus confer some protection against predation. For example, individuals in populations of *O. quadrimaculatus* from dark granitic rock outcrops within moist evergreen forests of the southeast are usually much darker than individuals from populations inhabiting open areas with light-colored rocks or patches of sand.

The phylogeny of oplurids (Titus and Frost 1996; Münchenberg et al. 2008; Chan et al. 2012) reflects the general macrohabitat associations. The terrestrial species of *Chalarodon* represent the sister clade to *Oplurus*. The two sister species *O. cuvieri* and *O. cyclurus* are arboreal, whereas all other *Oplurus* species are saxicolous, or rock dwelling (C. Blanc 1977), and form a monophyletic group sister to the *cuvieri-cyclurus* clade.

NATURAL HISTORY OF *CHALARODON*

Both species of *Chalarodon* are terrestrial and measure up to about 200 mm in total length. They occur in areas of sparse vegetation and where at least some patches of sand are present. The availability of open sandy areas determines, in part, the density of *C. madagascariensis* occupying a given site (C. Blanc 1970). Its distribution is limited to areas that receive 500 mm or less of rainfall per year, distributed primarily from November to April. Like many lizards that inhabit open sandy habitats (Luke 1986), this species has relatively long limbs and fringes on the digits that aid locomotion in loose sand (C. Blanc 1970). *Chalarodon madagascariensis* digs retreat burrows up to 25 cm deep, often with two entrances and usually near vegetation, where the roots help stabilize the sand. They are heliophilic ("sun loving") and become much less active during the cooler dry season. During rapid movements, *C. madagascariensis* becomes bipedal for short distances (C. Blanc 1982). Brillet (1982) reported that it ate winged ants, small flowers, and, in coastal populations, small intertidal crustaceans. Males are larger than females and become brightly colored during the breeding season, which takes place during the warm rainy season (C. Blanc 1969). Clutches consist of two eggs, which are deposited in sand (Glaw and Vences 2007). The young reach sexual maturity in 8 to 10 months and reproduce their first year, and most die before the second year of reproduction (C. Blanc 1969). *Chalarodon madagascariensis* is preyed on by the colubrid snake *Mimophis mahfalensis* (C. Blanc 1969, 1977) and by birds of prey (e.g., *Falco newtoni*, *Milvus aegyptius*; C. Blanc 1970; Preston-Mafham 1991). Very little is known about the biology of *C. steinkampi*, a species apparently microendemic to the southeast. Its high morphological and environmental similarities with *C. madagascariensis* nevertheless suggest that both species probably share very similar ecological traits (Miralles et al. 2015a).

DIVERSITY OF *OPLURUS*

Oplurus fierinensis is a rather gracile species, 25–30 g and 300 mm total length, whereas *O. cuvieri* is a heavy-bodied species, reaching nearly 200 g for a large male 350 mm in length. The other species are intermediate in length and mass (220–300 mm; 32–80 g). Species of *Oplurus* are primarily insectivorous (Brillet 1982). *Oplurus quadrimaculatus* eats a high proportion of ants but also consumes small lizards and plant material. According to Brillet (1982), *O. cuvieri* also feeds on small mammals, but it is unclear whether this was observed in nature or in captivity.

All species of *Oplurus* are oviparous. The arboreal *O. cyclurus* buries its eggs in the ground, whereas the saxicolous *O. quadrimaculatus* deposits its eggs in rock crevices or under large rocks (Glaw and Vences 2007). In some areas of the southeast, a single large rock may harbor dozens of clutches of *O. quadrimaculatus*, obviously the product of many females over time. Breeding males of *O. saxicola* develop bright colors, but this has not been documented in other *Oplurus* species. Members of this genus appear to reproduce during the warm rainy season, but no studies of the complete reproductive cycle of any species have been conducted.

The arboreal species, *O. cuvieri* and *O. cyclurus*, are typically found on the trunks and larger branches of trees. They perch in a head-down position, usually with the head at nearly a right angle to the trunk. They have relatively short tails armored with heavy spines. Retreat sites are large cavities in trees or under bark, and the spiny tail provides some defense at the cavity opening. The distributions of *O. cuvieri* and *O. cyclurus* overlap in the central west, but the former is widely distributed in the northwest and north in more mesic environments than *O. cyclurus*, which is found in the southwest and south. Body temperatures of active *O. cyclurus* and *O. cuvieri* averaged 36–38°C in one study (Randriamahazo 1998). At Ampijoroa *O. cyclurus* prefers hot, open, north-facing slopes to south-facing slopes with a similar vegetation type (Preston-Mafham 1991).

Oplurus cuvieri and *O. cyclurus* are sit-and-wait predators that use their arboreal perches to survey for potential prey as well as to give territorial displays. A single individual of *O. cuvieri* uses the same perch for long periods, and perches are usually located near a retreat hole (Preston-Mafham 1991). Once within a retreat hole, they can inflate their bodies, making extraction of the animals by predators rather difficult. Mori and Randriamahazo (2002a) analyzed quantitative movement data of *O. cuvieri* that indicated the species is a typical ambusher, occasionally feeding on plant materials by active foraging. Additional details on the prey of *O. cuvieri* were published by Ito (2013), Rosa and Rakotozafy (2013), Itoh and Ito (2015), and Kawai (2016).

Oplurus fierinensis, *O. saxicola*, and *O. grandidieri* have depressed bodies and lack extremely spinose tails. They retreat into crevices or fissures in rocks. Preston-Mafham (1991) reported that up to 20 *O. saxicola* individuals could be found in a single retreat. *Oplurus quadrimaculatus* has a longer, less spinose tail than the other saxicolous species, and a less flattened body. It has the broadest elevational distribution of all the oplurids: sea level to more than 2000 m (C. Blanc 1977; Brillet 1982). This species has been considered less specialized for scansorial or saxicolous microhabitats than the other saxicolous species.

BEHAVIOR OF *OPLURUS*

Brillet (1982) studied the behavior of four species of *Oplurus* (*O. quadrimaculatus*, *O. cyclurus*, *O. fierinensis*, and *O. cuvieri*) in the field, and these four plus *O. grandidieri* in captivity. Both sexes gave territorial displays typical of many iguanians: head bobbing and raising of the anterior body, often accompanied by slight inflation of the throat and arching of the back. In the arboreal species, *O. cuvieri* and *O. cyclurus*, the nuchal crest (a fold of skin or series of spines on the mid-dorsal posterior part of the head) is also erected and the body is compressed laterally. These displays are exaggerated when directed specifically toward another individual. In the saxicolous species, movements of the head are usually manifested by raising the entire anterior part of the body using the forelimbs, whereas the arboreal species usually bob the head and neck independently of forelimb movement. Nonetheless, both the arboreal and saxicolous lizards use each type of movement.

In direct aggressive interactions between individuals, behaviors such as elevation of the entire body, short jumping movements, arching of the back, and lateral body orientation with respect to the other individual are observed. Hissing resulting from sudden expulsion of air is also characteristic, and fighting events in which individuals are bitten have been documented. Interactions between males of *O. grandidieri*, *O. fierinensis*, and *O. quadrimaculatus* sometimes involve lengthy contact between or crossing of their raised tails. Territorial interactions between two *O. grandidieri* males were photographically documented by Lobón-Rovira et al. (2019), including lateral flattening, head bobbing, vertebral band display, and physical attacks.

Interspecific differences in territorial and aggressive displays occur in *Oplurus*. Primarily these are differences between the arboreal and saxicolous species. Arboreal species (*O. cuvieri* and *O. cyclurus*) compress the body laterally during interactions, whereas the saxicolous species (*O. grandidieri* and *O. fierinensis*) depress the body, often inclining it toward other individuals and thus exposing the broad dorsum. The displays of *O. quadrimaculatus* are somewhat intermediate between those of *O. cuvieri* and *O. cyclurus* on the one hand, and of *O. grandidieri* and *O. fierinensis* on the other.

With one exception, the species studied by Brillet (1982) established dominance hierarchies and discrete territories. However, in *O. fierinensis* dominance hierarchies seemed poorly developed and territories less discrete than in the other species. In the remaining four species, males defended territories that included one or more females. In some areas, populations of *O. saxicola* and *O. quadrimaculatus* reach very high densities, and it is unknown how territories in these high-density populations are arranged, or how the sexes are distributed. Females also seemed to be somewhat territorial with other females, but to a lesser extent than males.

Territory size in lizards depends heavily on both biotic and abiotic factors. A territory of an *O. cyclurus* male studied by Brillet (1982) in a disturbed area near Toliara covered 30 m^2 and included five trees as well as other perches. In this area, individuals of this species usually perched 1.5–2.5 m above the ground on tree trunks and large branches. In the same region but in a littoral zone, *O. quadrimaculatus* males had territories greater than 100 m^2, and population densities were fewer than 12 individuals per 100 m of linear habitat. However, at least in some more mesic areas in southeastern Madagascar, *O. quadrimaculatus* reaches much higher densities.

Theisinger et al. (2017) studied thermoregulation of *O. quadrimaculatus* across a gradient from cool and humid to hot and dry habitat and found no variation in activity body temperatures, suggesting that the species relies on behavioral mechanisms rather than physiological adjustments to compensate for thermal differences between habitats. However, daily activity time and field resting costs were reduced by 35% and 28% in the cool compared to the hot habitat. Randriamahazo and Mori (2005) found that the number of black dorsal bands of *O. cuvieri* varies ontogenetically and is affected by thermal conditions, implying a thermoregulatory function of this color pattern.

Ito and Mori (2010) found that *O. cuvieri* recognizes mobbing calls of the Madagascar Paradise-flycatcher (*Terpsiphone mutata*) and increases its vigilance accordingly. Ito and Mori (2012) observed this same species reacting to exposure to a snake model by push-up and dewlapping behavior, followed by fleeing, while exposure to a hawk model elicited just fleeing.

CONSERVATION

All oplurid species (except *C. steinkampi*, which has not yet been assessed) are listed as Least Concern according to the IUCN Red List of Threatened Species (IUCN 2019). Oplurids tend to occupy areas that are not heavily exploited by humans such as dry, sandy or rocky habitats that are poor for agriculture or timber exploitation. Thus, it is reasoned that they should be little affected by large-scale habitat alteration. However, the conversion of areas of the Central Highlands to rice cultivation, and of western dry deciduous forests to agricultural and livestock uses, is ongoing and progressive. These factors may affect some populations of oplurids. Thus, the response of oplurid populations to such landscape alterations clearly warrants study.

Subject editors: Aurélien Miralles, Miguel Vences, and Achille P. Raselimanana

CHAMAELEONIDAE, CHAMELEONS, *TANALAHY, SAKORIKITA, TARONDRO*

M. D. Scherz, D. Prötzel, J. C. Randrianantoandro, D. Rakotomalala, K. B. Karsten, and C. J. Raxworthy

The Chamaeleonidae, a widespread Old World group of lizards, includes some of the best-studied reptiles on Madagascar. The family consists of more than 200 species, distributed throughout Africa, with a few representatives also in Asia and southern and southeastern Europe, but Madagascar has almost half of all the world's species—97 as of July 2021. Most chameleons are arboreal, but several groups are primarily terrestrial and venture off the forest floor only to roost at night on narrow branches. The diversity of body shapes, striking levels of endemism, highly varied ecology and habitat requirements, and zoogeography of these animals continue to draw the attention of numerous researchers and naturalists. For all these reasons, Brygoo (1971) stressed that chameleons are among the fauna that makes Madagascar a naturalist's paradise.

Chameleons are represented on Madagascar by four endemic genera (Klaver and Böhme 1986; Glaw et al. 2014a): *Brookesia*, *Palleon*, *Calumma*, and *Furcifer*. *Brookesia* and *Palleon* together constitute the Brookesiinae, a subfamily of dwarf chameleons wholly endemic to Madagascar. With 31 currently recognized species, *Brookesia* is one of the most diverse chameleon genera, whereas *Palleon* is represented by just two species. The other two genera, *Calumma* and *Furcifer*, representatives of the more widespread subfamily Chamaeleoninae, currently comprise 42 and 24 species, respectively. The distinction between Madagascar's chamaeleonine and brookesiine chameleons is straightforward: *Brookesia* and *Palleon* have short, only distally prehensile tails (typically about the same length as the body), are largely terrestrial and brown in coloration (Figures 12.35a and b), and have the capacity (at least in some species) to strongly vibrate their whole bodies when seized. Their skeletal anatomy is also highly distinct.

Recent field, taxonomic, and especially molecular phylogenetic studies have revealed a great deal of undescribed diversity in Malagasy chameleons, nearly doubling previously recognized diversity in some species groups. This is especially evident in the *C. nasutum* species group, which has expanded from seven to 20 species following genetic investigation by Philip-Sebastian Gehring and collaborators (2012), and intensive taxonomic work by David Prötzel and colleagues (2015, 2016b, 2017, 2018b, 2018c, 2020). Recent progress on the phylogenetics of chameleons, both on Madagascar and as a whole, has shed light on their biogeography, but much remains to be studied.

The moist evergreen forest zones of the eastern region have the greatest richness in chameleon species. The region north of latitude 16°S, for example, shelters about 87% of the known *Brookesia* species. Except for ubiquitous species, most Malagasy chameleons have specific preferences for a particular habitat type, often within relatively narrow elevational limits (Raselimanana et al. 2000a). Further, many species have rather limited geographic distributions, especially miniaturized species of the *B. minima* species group (Townsend et al. 2009; Glaw et al. 2012, 2021; Scherz et al. 2019).

The last 30 years, and especially the last 15 years, have seen a dramatic increase in research on Madagascar's chameleons. Most of this work has been taxonomic, but there is a rapidly growing body of literature on topics including community structure (Rakotomalala 1998; Rabearivony 1999; Rakotondravony 2001; Fideline et al. 2007; Rabearivony et al. 2007; Lowin 2012), life history (F. Blanc 1970a, 1970b; Andreone et al. 2005; Karsten et al. 2008, 2009b, 2009c; Eckhardt et al. 2012, 2017; Tessa et al. 2017), population density (Brady et al. 1996; Rabemananjara 1998; Brady and Griffiths 1999; Jenkins et al. 1999, 2003; Raxworthy and Nussbaum 2002; Rabearivony et al. 2007; Randrianantoandro et al. 2007; Karsten et al. 2009a; Lowin 2012; Villeneuve 2017), behavior (Parcher 1974; Raxworthy 1991; Ferguson et al. 1995; Kaufmann et al. 1997; Razafimahatratra et al. 2008; Takahashi 2008; Karsten et al. 2009b, 2009c, 2009d; C. Gardner 2013; Prötzel et al. 2016a; Resetarits and Raxworthy 2016; Miller 2017), ecology and niches (Jenkins et al. 2003; Raxworthy et al. 2003; Metcalf et al. 2005a; Fideline et al. 2007; Rabearivony et al. 2007; Randrianantoandro et al. 2010; Villeneuve 2017), conservation and the international pet trade (Brady and Griffiths 1999; Andreone 2004; Carpenter 2004; Carpenter and Robson 2005; Carpenter et al. 2005; D'Cruze et al. 2008; Randrianantoandro et al. 2008; Karsten et al. 2009a), biogeography and evolution (Raxworthy et al. 2002; Andreone et al. 2007; Boumans et al. 2007; Townsend et al. 2009; Andrews and Karsten 2010; Ratsoavina et al. 2010; Crottini et al. 2012a; Florio et al. 2012; Gehring et al. 2012; Glaw et al. 2012; Tolley et al. 2013; Grbic et al. 2015; Florio and Raxworthy 2016), predation (Jenkins et al. 2009; Knoll et al. 2009; Hutter et al. 2018), physiology (Andrews 2008), parasites (Lhermitte-Vallarino et al. 2010a, 2010b; McAllister et al. 2011; McAllister 2012; Morton and Krysko 2012; Eckhardt et al. 2019b; Rasoanoro et al. 2019), and color change (Teyssier et al. 2015), not to mention the literature on their taxonomy, systematics, and evolution discussed in the following sections.

PHYLOGENETICS AND HIGHER SYSTEMATICS

Morphologically, chameleons, with their anisodactyl (or "chamaeleodactyl") feet, ballistic tongues, prehensile non-autotomizable tails, and independently pivoting eyes, are indisputably a monophyletic group. However, in the past, hypothesized relationships within the family based on morphological characters differed quite considerably among studies (Rieppel 1987). Hillenius (1986, 1988), for example, concluded that species of the *Calumma nasutum* species group were more closely related to the African genus *Rhampholeon*, and that *Brookesia* and *Rhampholeon* constituted a monophyletic group that had differentiated from the true chameleons. Klaver and Böhme (1986) used lung and genital morphology

FIGURE 12.35 **The chameleon genera of Madagascar, showcasing sexual dimorphism. A) *Brookesia vadoni* male (below) and female (above), side by side; B) *Palleon nasus*, a species largely lacking sexual dimorphism; *Furcifer* cf. *timoni* "Marojejy" C) male (relaxed coloration) and D) female (stressed coloration); *Calumma gallus* E) female and F) male, showcasing their highly dimorphic rostral appendages.** (PHOTOS A–D by M. D. Scherz, and E and F by D. Prötzel.)

and arrived at a rather different phylogenetic hypothesis. Such findings were strongly influenced by homoplasy and convergent evolution, even of apparently highly derived features such as dermal rostral appendages and occipital lobes, as became clear in later phylogenetic reconstructions based on genetic data.

DNA-based molecular phylogenetics over the last 20 years has dramatically changed our understanding of the systematics of Madagascar's chameleons, overturning numerous morphology-based hypotheses. The earliest of these, by Raxworthy et al. (2002), combined genetic and morphological data and found Brookesiinae to form a clade splitting from the base of the chameleon phylogeny, while Madagascar's Chamaeleoninae was paraphyletic with respect to African species. A later study by Townsend et al. (2011b), based only on genetics, recovered Brookesiinae as a clade and showed that *Archaius tigris* of the Seychelles was in fact most closely related to *Rieppeleon* from Africa, and its previous placement in *Calumma* had been the result of convergent morphology. This study, however, also found *Calumma* to be paraphyletic.

The most comprehensive molecular study on chameleons to date is that of Tolley et al. (2013), who used 13 genes and a reduced taxon set to try to solve the deeper phylogeny of the chameleons, and six genes with much more comprehensive taxon sampling to produce a species tree. Their 13-gene tree recovered the monophyly of *Calumma* + *Furcifer* and of the Brookesiinae. Their six-gene tree showed that several phenetic groups, especially the *C. nasutum* species group, are potentially para- or polyphyletic. They also confirmed the affinity of *A. tigris* and *Rieppeleon*.

ORIGINS

Despite recent major strides in chameleon systematics and the deep phylogeny of all reptiles, the origins of the chameleons are only a little clearer, and hardly less controversial than they were nearly 50 years ago (Brygoo 1971). The fossil record of chameleons is generally poor, especially before the Cenozoic—one Cretaceous fossil originally thought to be a stem chamaeleonid (Daza et al. 2016) is actually an amphibian (Matsumoto and Evans 2018). Despite this shortcoming, recent molecular systematic work based on extraneous calibration points has estimated that chameleons diverged from agamid lizards either over 100 Mya (Irisarri et al. 2017) or at 100 Mya (Burbrink et al. 2020), and the crown-group chameleons split into Chamaeleoninae and Brookesiinae around either 65 Mya (Tolley et al. 2013; M. D. Scherz et al., unpublished data) or 40 Mya (Burbrink et al. 2020). This relatively late divergence of crown groups means that the split was not a result of the breakup of Gondwana, as suggested by Hillenius (1959) and Klaver and Böhme (1986), but was rather related to post-Gondwana dispersal (Raxworthy et al. 2002; Tolley et al. 2013).

Now that the approximate timing of their origins has been resolved, the question remains: Where did chameleons originate? And, more specifically relevant here, what are the origins of Madagascar's chameleons? On this point, a consensus has not yet been reached. Raxworthy et al. (2002) concluded that chameleons originated on Madagascar and subsequently dispersed to Africa on repeated occasions. Based on a more comprehensive genetic dataset, Tolley et al. (2013) concluded that chameleons originated in Africa and colonized Madagascar twice. The latest results by M. D. Scherz et al. (unpublished data) based on genomic data sets indicate that a concrete answer will not be reached in the immediate future; even with genomic resolution, out-of-Africa and out-of-Madagascar scenarios are equally well supported. However, it is clear that the basally divergent Brookesiinae are endemic to Madagascar, indicating that the chameleons have an ancient history on Madagascar in any case.

The genera *Calumma* and *Furcifer* also clearly have a common ancestor that was on Madagascar, but the affinities of these chameleons to other extant groups are not clear; Tolley et al. (2013) and the most recent results (M. D. Scherz et al., unpublished data) do not agree on the relative position of these genera. From within this group, one pair of *Furcifer* species, *F. polleni* and *F. cephalolepis*, are native to the Comoros and originated by relatively recent colonization from Madagascar (Crottini et al. 2012a; Tolley et al. 2013).

The first complete fossil chameleon skull was recently described from Kenya by Čerňanský et al. (2020). This fossil was dated to the early Miocene, around 18 Mya (Collinson et al. 2009). Based on a suite of osteological features, the authors assigned the fossil to the genus *Calumma*, naming it *C. benovskyi*. This is surprising, given that the genus *Calumma* is not present in mainland Africa today, but several other genera are present that are morphologically highly similar to *Calumma* and would seem, at least superficially, to be more likely relatives of this taxon. Čerňanský et al. (2020) state that this fossil suggests an African origin of Madagascar's chamaeleonine chameleons, but in reality, this fossil substantially postdating the origins of *Calumma* could instead also suggest a moderately recent (re)colonization of mainland Africa by *Calumma*. The identity of this fossil will require further scrutiny before a conclusion can be reached on its biogeographic implications.

KARYOTYPE EVOLUTION

Cytological studies of chameleons have long been considered important. Hillenius (1963) used karyotype to infer possible phylogenetic relationships, but these findings do not agree with later work. Bourgat (1973) demonstrated a relationship between chromosome number and habitat characteristics, suggesting that chromosomal formula may be influenced by environmental conditions. More recently, Rovatsos et al. (2017) reconstructed the evolution of chameleon karyotypes, concluding that $2n = 36$ is the ancestral state among chameleons, and numerous groups have independently reduced their chromosome numbers, especially among Malagasy chameleons.

TAXONOMY

Until the late 1980s, Madagascar's chamaeleonine species were considered members of the genus *Chamaeleo*, but investigation of male genital characteristics by Klaver and Böhme (1986) led to the resurrection of the two genera *Furcifer* and *Calumma* for these highly distinct groups of chameleons. The most comprehensive historic taxonomic revisions of Madagascar's chameleons were by Brygoo, first concerning the chamaeleonine species (Brygoo 1971), and later also the brookesiine species (Brygoo 1978). Glaw and Vences

(1992, 1994, 2007) also contributed considerably to the knowledge of Madagascar's chameleons in their field guides to the amphibians and reptiles of the island.

Glaw (2015) provided a complete checklist of the family Chamaeleonidae, which of course lacks species described subsequently. Taxonomic progress on Madagascar's chameleons is currently proceeding at an unprecedented pace. Between 1978 and 2003, 10 species were described (one *Furcifer*, one *Calumma*, and eight *Brookesia*; Raxworthy 1991; Raxworthy and Nussbaum 1995; Schimmenti and Jesu 1996; Böhme 1997; Jesu et al. 1999). Between 2003 and 2021, 22 new species were described, four were revalidated or raised to species level, and one was synonymized (two *Furcifer* + three revalidated, 16 *Calumma* + two revalidated + one raised to species level, seven *Brookesia* – one synonymized; Raxworthy and Nussbaum 2006; Glaw et al. 2009a, 2012, 2021; Gehring et al. 2010b, 2011, 2012; Crottini et al. 2012b; Florio et al. 2012; Prötzel et al. 2015, 2016b, 2017, 2018b, 2018c, 2020; Scherz et al. 2018, 2019; Sentís et al. 2018). Moreover, molecular work has shown that numerous species await description (e.g., Gehring et al. 2012), and that several morphologically highly similar groups are not monophyletic (Tolley et al. 2013). Further changes to the taxonomy of Madagascar's chameleons can therefore be anticipated.

Male genital morphology has often been used in the taxonomy and systematics of the Malagasy chameleons (Bourgat and Brygoo 1968; Brygoo et al. 1973 [1974]). At present, hemipenis morphology data are still fragmentary and not available for many species, which has impeded taxonomic progress in some groups (Raxworthy and Nussbaum 1995). However, major strides are being made using micro–computed tomography (micro-CT) with contrast agents (e.g., iodine), enabling the production of 3-D models of hemipenis morphology (Prötzel et al. 2015, 2017, 2018c). The results of this new method indicate that sister species often do not differ much in hemipenial morphology, counter to expectation; rather, hemipenial differences, at least in the *C. nasutum* species group, evolve relatively slowly compared to meristic and coloration differences (Prötzel et al. 2017). Recently, Glaw et al. (2021) showed that there is a general negative correlation between body size and relative hemipenis size, with diminutive members of the *Brookesia tuberculata* species group having the largest male genitalia relative to their body size. In these species, hemipenis morphology is indeed species specific.

On the other hand, external morphology, in particular the shape and size of various ornaments borne especially by males, can be very informative for taxonomic studies of *Calumma* and *Furcifer*, as well as adult morphometric head shape data (Florio et al. 2012). Head ornamentation characters include the presence or absence of occipital lobes, and of foliaceous or bony rostral appendages (single or bifurcated). Sexual dimorphism is also frequent among *Furcifer* and *Calumma*, the males often being bigger, and more ornamented and colorful than females (Figures 12.35c–f and 12.36c). As a result, Glaw and Vences (1994) produced separate keys for male and female chameleons. Females of several groups remain particularly difficult to distinguish.

The distinction between some species remains complicated, despite genetic data being available from recently collected material. Most such problems derive from uncertainty surrounding the type material. The *C. nasutum* species group is a typical example: *C. nasutum* was described from "Madagascar," and its assignment to a specific clade among the various possible genetic lineages to which it could be assigned is challenging because of the variation in several morphological characters, and the lack of definitive molecular evidence (Prötzel et al. 2020).

Skeletal morphology has proved a useful source of taxonomic information in a wide variety of animals, and chameleons are certainly no exception. Osteology is particularly valuable in species complexes and for the identification of diagnostic characters in externally cryptic species. Variation and diversity of chameleon skull morphology was first treated in detail by Rieppel and Crumly (1997). Recently, the reduced cost of micro-CT methods has enabled the nondestructive exploration of skull morphology from type material, helping to resolve species complexes. This has been most extensively exploited in the resolution of the *C. nasutum* group (Prötzel et al. 2015, 2017, 2018b, 2018c), but also recently for some *Furcifer* species (Sentís et al. 2018). It is likely that osteological data will prove valuable in *Brookesia* as well, but as of yet, no major osteological work has been undertaken on that genus.

One group of *Brookesia* species, the *B. minima* species group, recently reinstated as the subgenus *Evoluticauda* (Glaw et al. 2021), consists of species numbered among the smallest amniotes on Earth (Glaw et al. 2012, 2021; see Figure 12.6). This group, today consisting of 12 species, is distributed primarily across northern Madagascar but has individual representatives also in the west and central east. In his review of *Brookesia*, Brygoo (1978) had difficulty distinguishing between these small species and turned to geographic distribution to help separate the different forms. However, the collection of new material enabled Raxworthy and Nussbaum (1995), and later also Schimmenti and Jesu (1996) and Glaw et al. (1999, 2012, 2021), to reanalyze these small species in greater detail and identify a number of useful characters to distinguish among them. Some of these characters, such as the number of dorsolateral spines, are astonishingly variable within species, however (Glaw et al. 2012; Scherz et al. 2019), and geographic distribution remains very useful in narrowing species down to a few possibilities.

DISTRIBUTION AND BIOGEOGRAPHY

Most chameleon species have very restricted or localized ranges, and those species that are widespread often show high levels of genetic differentiation among populations (Boumans et al. 2007; Florio et al. 2012; Grbic et al. 2015; Florio and Raxworthy 2016; Prötzel et al. 2020). Biological inventories in different mountainous regions of Madagascar have highlighted well-defined elevational zonation within chameleons (Raxworthy and Nussbaum 1994a, 1996a, 1996b, 1996c; Raxworthy et al. 1998; Nussbaum et al. 1999b; Raselimanana 1999; Raselimanana et al. 2000a; Andreone et al. 2009; Prötzel et al. 2017), and several species are known from only narrow elevational bands (Brygoo et al. 1973 [1974]; Nussbaum et al. 1999b; Raselimanana 1999; Raselimanana et al. 2000a; Raxworthy and Nussbaum 2006; Andreone et al. 2009; Prötzel et al. 2018b, 2018c, 2020; Scherz et al. 2019). Raxworthy and Nussbaum (1995) specified two ecological abiotic variables—elevation and climate—as the determining factors in the distribution of *Brookesia*, but this is apparently not generalizable among chameleons, as Pearson and

FIGURE 12.36 **Aspects of chameleon biology. A) An estivating *Calumma malthe* individual; B) color communication among females of *C.* cf. *radamanus* on Nosy Be, with the dominant female (left) and submissive female (right) exhibiting strongly different colors and behaviors; C) copulation of *Furcifer labordi*, showing the strong sexual dimorphism in body size and ornamentation; D) nest digging in *F. oustaleti*, also showing the gravid coloration of this species; E) threat display of *C. amber*, with an open mouth, extended gular skin, contrasting coloration, and hissing; F) *Brookesia superciliaris* and G) *F. pardalis* with blue-green fluorescence under ultraviolet light.** (PHOTOS A, F, and G by D. Prötzel, and B–E by M. D. Scherz.)

Raxworthy (2009) showed that neither climate nor watershed explained patterns in the distribution of *Furcifer* species.

The vast majority of Madagascar's chameleon species are found in forests below 1300 m, but the number of species from above this elevation has steadily increased over the last 15 years as a result of taxonomic advances. Notably high-elevation species include *Palleon lolontany* (1650–2130 m), *Calumma peyrierasi* (1675–2130 m), *C. jejy* (1800–2130 m), *C. peltierorum* (1700–2580 m), *C. guibei* (1590–2020 m), *C. lefona* (1720 m), and *C. uetzi* (1100–1500 m). Besides elevation, climate, and physical surroundings, rivers probably constitute an important barrier in the dispersion of some species. For example, *F. antimena* and *F. belalandaensis* are known only from sites between the Onilahy and Mangoky Rivers. It is necessary, however, to emphasize that other factors might be important as well.

Local endemism is particularly remarkable among *Brookesia* species, especially in the north of the island (Raxworthy and Nussbaum 1995; Glaw et al. 1999, 2012, 2021; Ratsoavina et al. 2010; Scherz et al. 2019). The dry spiny thickets of the south and southwest do not host any species of *Brookesia*, while the transitional and dry deciduous forests of the west and less extreme southwest contain five endemic species: *B. bonsi*, *B. brygooi*, *B. decaryi*, *B. exarmata*, and *B. perarmata*. Schimmenti and Jesu (1996) suggested that *B. dentata*, *B. exarmata*, and *B. peyrierasi* were vicariant species. It should be noted that *B. peyrierasi* is a form found in eastern moist evergreen forests. Raxworthy and Nussbaum (1995) hypothesized that an interglacial period of the Pleistocene initiated westward extension of eastern lowland forest, providing corridors for dispersal. This hypothesis was rejected by Townsend et al. (2009), who instead found support for the mountain refuge effect proposed by Raxworthy and Nussbaum (1995). They also found that rivers apparently have not acted as barriers to *Brookesia*.

The genera *Calumma* and *Furcifer* generally exhibit strong niche separation, with *Furcifer* dominating in drier and more open habitats, and *Calumma* dominating in more closed and humid environments. No *Calumma* species are known from the west, but that area is home to a wide array of *Furcifer* species (Glaw et al. 2020). Additionally, there are very few widespread *Calumma* species, the most widespread being *C. parsonii* and *C. gastrotaenia* (Glaw and Vences 2007). *Calumma nasutum* was formerly thought to be widespread, but its range contains several species-level units, and *C. nasutum* itself is now thought to be rather range restricted (Prötzel et al. 2020).

Several *Furcifer* species do occur in moist evergreen forests (e.g., *F. balteatus*, *F. bifidus*, *F. pardalis*), and in general *Furcifer* species tend to be more widespread than *Calumma*. Close investigation of individual species has shown that even widespread species of *Furcifer* do in fact consist of deep genetic lineages or a species complex, however. Florio et al. (2012) conducted a broad-scale sampling of the *F. lateralis* species complex and showed that it consisted of three ecologically distinct deep lineages, which they recognized as *F. lateralis* in central areas, *F. viridis* in the northwest, and *F. major* in the south and southwest. Florio and Raxworthy (2016) investigated the biogeography of the *F. verrucosus* + *F. oustaleti* clade and found deep, biogeographically separated lineages in both of these "species" that may eventually warrant species-level recognition. Grbic et al. (2015) studied the phylogeography of *F. pardalis* and found several deep mitochondrial lineages, but these are of uncertain evolutionary significance, as they have a great deal of nuclear haplotype sharing. Similar patterns are evident in *Brookesia*, with *B. superciliaris* likewise showing highly divergent lineages among populations (Ratsoavina et al. 2010).

BIOLOGY AND ECOLOGY

Habitat

Chameleons are usually arboreal and the vast majority live in forest and wooded habitats. There are a few exceptions: *Furcifer campani*, *F. lateralis*, *F. major*, and *F. viridis* occur in herbaceous and shrubby formations or at the forest edge and are unknown from deep within the forest. *Furcifer pardalis* and *F. oustaleti* can be found along beaches and roads, in grassland and bushland, and deep within the forest, and these are the two chameleons most frequently encountered crossing roads. *Furcifer minor* is found in *Uapaca* forest (see Kull and Birkinshaw, pp. 121–27) and even in coffee plantations (Ramanantsoa 1974). *Calumma jejy*, *C. tsaratananense*, and *C. hilleniusi* live in montane ericoid thicket and grassland, often above the tree line. Forest chameleons tend to occur in places where insects swarm and where undergrowth, shrubs, and lianas provide an assortment of perches. Several species can be found in degraded forest zones and in plantations at the forest edge (e.g., *C. brevicorne*, *F. pardalis*).

The sensitivity of chameleons to habitat disturbance has been a field of particular interest, given the apparent ecological differentiation between *Brookesia* + *Palleon*, *Calumma*, and *Furcifer*. Tolerance of edge habitats varies strongly among species. Most *Furcifer* species are abundant along edges (Metcalf et al. 2005b), as are several different groups of *Calumma* species (*C. brevicorne* species group and *C. nasutum* species group). On the other hand, many *Calumma* species (especially the *C. parsonii* species group, e.g., Rabearivony et al. 2007) and moist evergreen forest–preferring *Furcifer* species (e.g., *F. balteatus*, *F. minor*, *F. timoni*, *F. willsii*) are generally found only well within moist evergreen forests. Edge effects are also not known among *Brookesia* species, but certain species, such as *B. tuberculata* and *B. antakarana* on Montagne d'Ambre and *B. superciliaris* in eastern moist evergreen forests, are abundant everywhere within their distribution range, as long as there is at least some canopy (i.e., they are not found in grasslands). Particularly species that favor open habitats, most notably *F. pardalis*, are at least as abundant in anthropogenic habitats as they are along forest edges and are seldom found deep within forests (e.g., Rabearivony et al. 2007), possibly because they live in the canopy of closed forests, out of the range of observation and detection (Raxworthy 1988). Nevertheless, chameleon abundance is generally higher in low-disturbance habitats (Jenkins et al. 2003).

Diet

All chameleons are generalist predators, but their diet is made up largely of invertebrates, particularly dipterans and orthopterans (Raxworthy 1991), and large species can also feed on small vertebrates. Reports of *Calumma parsonii* catching passerine birds such as *Hypsipetes madagascariensis* (Madagascar Bulbul) and even *Treron australis* (Madagascar Green-Pigeon) (Risley 1997) may be questionable, but it is certain that these large chameleons can eat young birds, as documented for *Furcifer oustaleti* (García and Vences 2002b). Abate (1998) reported that small lizards such as *Phelsuma* are consumed by *C. parsonii*.

Arboreality and Roosting

In general chameleons have several adaptations to arboreal life—anisodactyl fingers and toes and a prehensile tail. The exception is in *Brookesia* species, which seldom use their tails as a prehensile appendage. All chameleons, regardless of their diurnal habits, roost above the ground. The substratum type, position, and orientation during the night vary according to the species and with meteorological conditions. For example, during rain chameleons may remain hidden under sheltering leaves. Small chameleons, such as members of the *Calumma nasutum* group and *Brookesia*, perch on vertical or angled supports. Among large chameleons, the tail is usually rolled up when the animal is asleep, and the diameter of the perch does not exceed the internal diameter of the fingers and toes of the animal. Smaller chamaeleonine species (members of the *C. nasutum* group) may sleep with their tails extended or rolled up, and some sleep on leaves instead of twigs or branches. Most *Brookesia* species sleep on perches low to the ground at night, but *B. ebenaui* is peculiar in often choosing much higher roosts, up to several meters above the ground. This is also the most arboreal *Brookesia* species. Boistel et al. (2010) documented a unique mode of locomotion in *Brookesia*, where the tail is placed on the substrate when walking on broad substrates, thus improving stability.

The micro-ornamentation of the chameleon sole and tail has received particular recent interest. Spinner et al. (2013) found that chameleon feet possess a great number of setae (similar to those of anole and skink feet, and much larger than those of geckos), which in *Calumma* and *Furcifer* are spatulate at the tip. Similar structures are also present on the tail. These are apparently at least genus specific in morphology. These structures increase friction (Khannoon et al. 2014; Spinner et al. 2014) but probably do not function in an adhesive manner like those of geckos and anoles. Riedel et al. (2015) followed this up with a study of micro-ornamentation of dwarf chameleon feet and found that *Brookesia* toes have thorny or conical scales with honeycomb microstructures, convergently similar to those of the terrestrial chameleons of Africa.

Other Behaviors

Chameleons move slowly and often do so with a slight swinging or swaying of the body. Color change, famed among chameleons, is used mostly in intraspecific communication (Figure 12.36b), but coloration at rest is generally quite cryptic (except in males and gravid females of several species, such as *Furcifer oustaleti*, Figure 12.36d), aiding in predation avoidance and hunting. Chameleons are not able to change their color patterns but can change the level of contrast and the hues in particular regions, achieving a similar effect. Teyssier et al. (2015) showed that chameleons have two superposed layers of iridophores, and color shifts occur by active tuning of a lattice of guanine nanocrystals in one of these iridophore layers. Some species of *Furcifer* and *Calumma* have ventral line markings that help disrupt their body outline when they move around their perch in response to predators (Resetarits and Raxworthy 2016).

Chameleons hunt with a ballistic tongue, which can be up to 2.5 times their body length and shoot out with an acceleration and power greater than that of any other amniote vertebrate, with the highest speed achieved by *Brookesia* (Anderson et al. 2012; Anderson 2016). The speed of this ballistic tongue projection is robust to environmental temperature (Anderson and Deban 2010), which is important, as some chameleons may be thermoconformers that maintain a relatively low body temperature (Andrews 2008), while others may be more active in behavioral adjustment of exposure to sunlight (Karsten et al. 2009d). Chameleon eyesight is also remarkable, having an extremely high magnification and allowing the animal to focus monocularly (see Anderson and Higham 2013). Dwarf and small chameleons (*Brookesia* in particular) fall and feign death when touched (see Figure 12.4). Among *Brookesia* species, defense behaviors also include flattening the body, coiling up, and vibrating internally (Brygoo 1978; Glaw and Vences 1994; Raxworthy and Nussbaum 1995). This vibration may be emitted to surprise a predator holding the chameleon, so that the prey is dropped. Most *Brookesia* species are brownish in overall coloration (sometimes also orangish or with cream stripes), except for *B. vadoni*, in which females are cryptic and brown, but males are bright green (Figures 12.35a and 12.37), which serves as an excellent camouflage in the mosses of their high-elevation habitat.

Reproduction

In contrast to many African species, all chameleons on Madagascar are oviparous (lay eggs). This is remarkable, as viviparity has evolved presumably as an adaption for cooler habitats at high elevation in African species (Andrews and Karsten 2010; Hughes and Blackburn 2020), but apparently not in montane species on Madagascar, such as *Calumma hilleniusi*, *C. tsaratananense*, or *Furcifer campani*. This may be explained by an unknown minimum elevation threshold, since African viviparous chameleons are found as high as 4000 m in temperate zones, and the highest mountain on Madagascar is almost two-thirds of that, at 2876 m, and in a tropical zone; mainland Africa provided much broader geographic and temperature ranges for viviparity to evolve (Andrews and Karsten 2010).

In areas with distinct seasons, juvenile chameleons often hatch quasi-synchronously at the beginning of the rainy season. The mechanism for this phenomenon is a distinct diapause stage of the developing embryo (Andrews and Karsten 2010). Embryos are oviposited in the last gastrula phase and remain in that stage for several months during the cooler dry season. The diapause ends in the late dry season, but embryonic development does not resume until nest temperatures exceed a threshold for development, 20°C in non-Malagasy species (Andrews et al. 2008). Long incubation periods of eight or nine months with a diapause stage are most common in the genus *Furcifer* (Karsten et al. 2008; Andrews and Karsten 2010; Table 12.6). Some Malagasy species have extremely long incubation periods lasting over one year, best known in *C. parsonii* (Nečas 2004). The strict seasonality of reproduction has resulted in an annual life cycle in at least one species (*F. labordi*; see "Life History" section below) and is being recognized in an increasing number of species, even large ones (e.g., *F.* cf. *nicosiai*; Eckhardt et al. 2019a). In habitats of eastern Madagascar that provide enough humidity throughout the year, reproduction is less periodic and

FIGURE 12.37 ***Brookesia vadoni*, a partially green species among the otherwise mostly brown ground chameleons. This male specimen was found at Marojejy.** (PHOTO by M. Vences.)

individuals of different ages can be found at the same time, such as *C. radamanus* or *Brookesia superciliaris* (M. D. Scherz et al., unpublished data). Individuals of different age classes are also found at the same time of year in perennial species that have seasonal reproduction with diapause (e.g., *F. verrucosus*; Karsten et al. 2008).

In general, adult males show courtship behavior, including changing to display coloration and laterally flattening their bodies as soon as a female comes into sight. Nonreceptive females can react with an equally spectacular rejection coloration in some species, such as *F. labordi*, *F. lateralis*, and *F. minor*, to signal the male not to approach more closely. Male response to female communication signals is variable. For example, *F. labordi* males adjusted their courtship behavior in response to receptive/unreceptive female behavioral signals, whereas *F. verrucosus* males vigorously courted—and forcibly copulated with—females regardless of their behavioral signals (Karsten et al. 2009b). In *Brookesia*, especially in species of the *B. minima* group, males tend to be smaller than females and ride on the female's back during the mating season (Nečas and Schmidt 2004). The occipital lobes that some species possess are used in various ways during courtship (Parcher 1974).

As predicted by life history theory, both clutch size and offspring size are positively correlated with female size and there is a trade-off between clutch size and hatchling size, varying from larger clutches with relatively smaller hatchlings to smaller clutches with relatively larger hatchlings (Andrews and Karsten 2010). Clutch size varies according to species but in general is significantly and positively correlated with female body size, ranging from a clutch size of one to two in some *Brookesia* species to more than 60 in large *Furcifer* species (see Table 12.6 for data on known clutch sizes). Occasionally, eggs are laid over a series of days (Brygoo 1978; Nečas and Schmidt 2004; Karsten and Andriamandimbiarisoa 2008), and most species can have multiple clutches per year (Glaw and Vences 2007). Annual species, such as *F. labordi*, lay only one clutch per year (Karsten et al. 2008). The chameleon egg is enclosed in a fibrous envelope that can quickly dry out when exposed to the air. Nests are dug by almost all oviparous chameleons, although at least some *Brookesia* species deposit their clutches in the leaf litter (Raxworthy 1991). Nest digging for chameleons like *F. pardalis* can take a whole day. Nesting sites are often chosen in extremely solid ground (we have observed this in *F. pardalis*, *F. oustaleti*, *F. lateralis*, and *F. campani*). However, *F. labordi* digs nests in loose, sandy soil (Karsten and Andriamandimbiarisoa 2008). Unlike most chameleons in captivity, in which females dig a burrow and then reenter posterior first, *F. labordi* builds a V-shaped nest in which a female digs headfirst at a 45° angle, deposits the eggs without reentering posterior first, and then builds an exit burrow perpendicular to the entrance burrow. After exiting, she backfills the exit burrow and returns to the entrance burrow to backfill and complete the nest. The depth at which eggs are placed in the ground is known to vary among species, for example 10–15 cm in *C. brevicorne* (Parcher 1974) and *F. labordi* (Karsten and Andriamandimbiarisoa 2008), but only 8 cm in *F. lateralis* (A. P. Raselimanana, unpublished data). Incubation duration also varies substantially among species; see Table 12.6 for known durations at various temperatures.

Life History

On the whole, chameleons are short-lived reptiles and have rapid life histories. Apparently, a number of Malagasy species have evolved a rapid life cycle of just one rainy season. Famously, *Furcifer labordi* from western Madagascar has the shortest life span of all known amniotes, living for just three or four months outside the egg (Karsten et al. 2008). More recent work on this species has revealed that its life span can be variable, and in rare cases (in the field) single individuals can survive the dry season (Eckhardt et al. 2017). Based on life history theory and observations of numerous unexplained adult mortality events, Karsten et al. (2008) predicted that a physiological stressor in adults could likely drive the evolution of such short life spans. In a recent follow-up study, Eckhardt et al. (2019b) demonstrated that the short life span of these chameleons is partly due to a high parasite burden, a result of investment in reproduction over immune defense. Thus, it appears that these short-lived species follow the "live fast, die young" strategy, with heavy investment toward early growth and reproduction with concomitant reduction in longevity. Several *Furcifer* species seem to have similarly short life spans (Eckhardt et al. 2019a), though most probably live one or two years longer. At the opposite end of the spectrum, *Calumma parsonii* may be the longest-lived chameleon.

TABLE 12.6. **Clutch size and incubation temperature of Malagasy chameleons**

SPECIES	CLUTCH SIZE	WILD OR CAPTIVE	TEMPERATURE (°C)	TIME (DAYS)	SOURCE (s)
Brookesia antakarana (published as *B. ambreensis*)	1 every few weeks	Captive	–	–	1
B. antakarana	2–5	Captive	16–22	70	1
B. brygooi	2–5	Captive	22–24	52–71	1
B. decaryi	2–5	Captive	–	–	2
B. ebenaui	2–5	Captive	23–24	65	3
B. griveaudi	4	Captive	–	–	2
B. minima	2	Unknown	18–22	29–68	1,3
B. minima species group	1–2	Wild	–	–	2
B. perarmata	2–5	Captive	20–24	60	1
B. stumpffi	2–5	Captive	20–23	60	1
B. superciliaris	2–5	Captive	18–23	59–70	1
B. thieli	2–5	Captive	18–22	39–45	1
Calumma boettgeri	2–6	Captive	20–24	90	1,4
C. brevicorne	10–30	Captive	–	–	5
C. furcifer	4	Captive	–	–	4
C. gallus	2–4	Captive	20–24	130	4
C. globifer	17–30	Captive	12–24	540	2,3,4,5
C. hilleniusi	7	Wild	–	–	2
C. hilleniusi	6–8	Captive	20	90	4
C. linotum	5	Wild	20–23.5	90	2,4
C. malthe	12	Captive	23.5	94	4,6
C. nasutum complex	2–4	Captive	23.5	90	4,5
C. parsonii	20–60	Captive	21–24 and diapause at 15–18	400–520	2,3,4,7
Furcifer antimena	16, 8–20	Captive	27–28	300	2,3
F. bifidus	21–24	Captive	20	9 months	3,6
F. campani	6–16	Captive	25–28 and diapause at 10–15	228–236	2,5
F. cephalolepis	5–7	Captive	26–28	244–310	5
F. labordi	8–18	Captive	28	215–305	2,3,8
F. lateralis	4–23	Captive	25–28 and diapause at 10–15	154–378[1]	2,5,9
F. minor	12	Wild	20–23	275	2,3
F. oustaleti	42–61	Captive	28	210–280	2,3,5,10
F. pardalis	12–46	Captive	26–28	139–319	2,3
F. petteri	8–20	Captive	25–26	240	3
F. polleni	6–12	Captive	28–31	260–270	5
F. rhinoceratus	–	–	25	~200	3
F. verrucosus	30–50	Captive	26–28	200	2,3

Sources: References are numbered as follows: 1) Nečas and Schmidt (2004); 2) Glaw and Vences (2007); 3) Masurat (2005); 4) Schmidt et al. (2010); 5) Nečas (1999); 6) Schmidt (1992); 7) Brady and Griffiths (1999); 8) Karsten and Andriamandimbiarisoa (2008); 9) D. Prötzel (unpublished data); and 10) Brygoo (1971).

[1] Usually 7–8 months, of which 45 days are spent in hibernation.

Wild specimens have been recorded reaching nine years old (Tessa et al. 2017), and captive specimens perhaps up to 13 years. Given their short life spans, it is no surprise that many chameleons reach sexual maturity quickly: *F. labordi* within 60 days (Karsten et al. 2008) or 70 days (Eckhardt et al. 2017); *F. lateralis* within two months (F. Blanc 1970a, 1970b); *F. campani* three months after hatching; *F. willsii* in four months; *F. minor* in five months; and *C. brevicorne* in eight months (Le Berre 1995). *Calumma p. cristifer*, however, does not reach sexual maturity before the age of 1.5 years (Le Berre 1995) and perhaps even between 3 and 5 years (Brady and Griffiths 1999). To endure the cooler dry season, at least one species (*C. malthe*) is capable of brumating, or showing partial inactivity/dormancy (Prötzel et al. 2016a). This behavior (Figure 12.36a) is probably more widespread among chameleons, but no other records are known.

Ornamentation

Sexual dimorphism is modest among *Brookesia* and *Palleon*, manifesting most strongly as a female-biased size dimorphism—males of several dwarf chameleon species are known to ride around on the female's back until she is ready to mate (Glaw and Vences 2007). As mentioned above, a notable exception to this is *B. vadoni*, wherein males and females differ in size and numerous morphological characters including color, spiny integument, and presence/absence of long laterovertebral spines (Figures 12.35a and 12.37). Dimorphism is much more pronounced in *Calumma* and *Furcifer* in terms of both size and ornamentation. Often, the shape of the rostral appendage can be sufficient to distinguish males and females, by presence versus absence (e.g., *F. labordi*, *F. pardalis*, *F. timoni* [Figures 12.35c and d]), length (e.g., *F. rhinoceratus*), shape (e.g., *C. gallus* [Figures 12.35e and f]). These appendages manifest in various ways, including dermal accessories in the *C. nasutum* species group; single bony structures in the *C. brevicorne* species group and the *F. rhinoceratus* species group; bifid in *C. furcifer*; spatulate in *F. labordi*, and forming two distinct bony structures in the *C. parsonii* species group, as well as in *F. minor*, *F. bifidus*, *F. timoni*, *F. balteatus*, *F. petteri*, and *F. willsii*. Among members of the *C. nasutum* species group, the coloration of the rostral appendage is also species specific, even among closely related sister taxa (Prötzel et al. 2015, 2017, 2018c, 2020). For this reason, it is thought that the rostral appendage probably plays a role in sexual selection. Indeed, *F. labordi* males have been observed using their rostral appendages to manipulate females directly, sometimes resulting in a switch from antagonistic to receptive behavior (Karsten et al. 2009b, 2009c).

Fluorescence

It was recently discovered that chameleons show fluorescing cyan patterns under ultraviolet light (Prötzel et al. 2018a; see Figures 12.36f and g). This phenomenon is widespread among the whole family and occurs in three of the four Malagasy genera, particularly in species living in moist evergreen and shady forest habitats. The fluorescence on the head results from bony tubercles of the skull. These seem to grow up through the dermal layers, displacing them and leaving them covered by only a thin, transparent layer of epidermis, which acts as a "window" onto the bone. In *Brookesia* the fluorescent tubercles are distributed from the head along the vertebrae to the tail, and the skin is also thin enough to see fluorescence of other bones through it (Figure 12.36f). In *Calumma* the number of tubercles, which are concentrated on the head region, is sexually dimorphic, with more tubercles in males than females, and also reflects species groups. Further, the emission of blue light with a maximum at 430 nm contrasts well with the green and brown background reflectance of the forest, and it is suggested that chameleons use fluorescence for intraspecific signaling (Prötzel et al. 2018a).

Predators

Data on predators of chameleons were summarized by Jenkins et al. (2009): birds and snakes are the dominant predators of chameleons, and a few mammals may also opportunistically take chameleons as meals. *Falco zoniventris* (Banded Kestrel) and *Eutriorchis astur* (Madagascar Serpent-eagle) are apparently particularly partial to chameleons (see Rene de Roland and Thorstom, pp. 1668–79). Many snakes probably consume chameleons opportunistically, and at present no snakes are known to specialize on chameleons. At least one snake, *Pseudoxyrhopus ambreensis*, consumes chameleon eggs (*Calumma linotum*) by slitting them open (Knoll et al. 2009), and both *Madagascarophis meridionalis* and *Mimophis mahfalensis* prey heavily on *Furcifer labordi* in the Toliara region (K. B. Karsten, unpublished data).

CULTURAL ASPECTS

For the Malagasy, chameleons are omnipresent in daily life, and there is a wide variety of cultural beliefs pertaining to them (Ramanantsoa 1984; Jones et al. 2008). As far as we have been able to deduce, only one ethnozoological study has been done on the cultural significance of chameleons on the island (Ramanantsoa 1984). Beliefs vary widely among regions, ethnic groups, and chameleon species. Generally, Malagasy people are afraid of chameleons, except in the Central Highlands, where children play with them. In some regions it is held that they can blind a human with their projectile tongues. Another common feeling is that they are ugly animals, with several phrases and proverbs expressing this sentiment. In several areas, a chameleon should not be pointed at, or should be pointed at only with a curled finger.

There is a widespread belief on Madagascar that needlessly killing animals can result in their spirits avenging them. This belief is generalized but pertains especially to chameleons: in the Central Highlands, it is believed that children die after killing *Furcifer oustaleti*. This same belief has led to a particular fear of *Brookesia* species, which are small enough to be trampled underfoot (Ramanantsoa 1984). In several areas, chameleons are thought to be evil spirits, often representing the reincarnation of people who did evil things when they were alive, leading certain groups, such as the Betsimisaraka, to avoid touching them.

Chameleons are also used in traditional medicine and as talismans. In the southwest, the local people make a collar out of chameleons' claws for children, to protect them against evil spirits. In the central east, a powder of burned chameleon skin is prepared as a tea to treat *ambalavelona*, a psychological illness. Whole chameleons are also eaten to treat throat tumors.

Chameleons are invoked by several Malagasy proverbs. Politicians who constantly change their opinions or are not trustworthy are labeled "chameleon." Chameleons are also considered wise, however: the most famous Malagasy proverb pertaining to chameleons is "Hataovy dian-tana ny fiainana, hatreo ny eo aloha ary todiho ny any afara," which translates as "Go about life the way a chameleon walks: face what is ahead and look back at what is behind," conveying a need for prudence and vigilance. Some Malagasy also consider chameleons to be symbols of intelligence, as they are slow and physically rather weak, but seemingly bright animals. A Malagasy fable tells the story of a bush pig and a chameleon that wanted to decide who was strongest. The bush pig, with its formidable strength and its robust and powerful body, believed that the chameleon could never beat it in a race, but in the end the chameleon won by jumping onto the bush pig's neck at the sound of the starting signal, and jumping ahead of its unwitting carrier at the finish line.

CONSERVATION STATUS

Among the 85 Malagasy chameleon species assessed in the IUCN Red List, 44 are currently in threatened categories—five Critically Endangered, 23 Endangered, and 16 Vulnerable. Four other species are classified as Data Deficient and 13 species have yet to be assessed.

The most important threat to chameleons is the loss of natural habitat associated with human activities (Jenkins et al. 2014). Although some species of *Calumma* and *Furcifer* occur and apparently thrive in secondary forest or plantations (Blumgart et al. 2017), most species, especially *Brookesia*, are true forest-dwelling animals whose survival depends on preferably undisturbed forest habitat. Global warming is also driving species to higher elevation, and this is a particular threat to montane species endemic to the upper portions of massifs, such as *C. jejy* and *C. tsaratananense* (Raxworthy and Nussbaum 2006).

Because of their high levels of endemicity, distinctive features, and diverse morphology, coloration, size, and behavior, Malagasy chameleons are also of major importance in the international pet trade (see Carpenter et al., pp. 1452–55). Most if not all the chameleons exported from Madagascar are taken from the wild. All chameleons are currently listed in Appendix II of CITES (Convention on International Trade in Endangered Species of Wild Fauna and Flora) except *B. perarmata*, which is in Appendix I and has a very small distribution (Raxworthy and Nussbaum 2002). Usually there are export quotas of 150–500 (exceptionally up to 3000) individuals per year for about 30 species of chameleons from Madagascar (CITES 2019). However, it is also clear that several species have been exported under incorrect scientific names, emphasizing the importance of taxonomic work and the production of usable idenitifcation keys to avoid confusion with "look-alike" species that are prohibited for exportation (Alfino and Roberts 2019). So far, although population density estimates exist for some species (see Carpenter et al., pp. 1452–55), we are aware of no sustainability studies that have assessed the impact of exploitation of chameleons. This will be an important future endeavor. However, it is unlikely that commercial international trade is the primary threat to any species on Madagascar, as deforestation is likely having a much more devastating effect on population sizes. The export of chameleons, which are sold for reasonably high prices especially in Europe and the United States, could also be seen as a sustainable opportunity for the Malagasy to gain economic value from their forests and thus help prevent deforestation (Carpenter et al. 2005; Robinson et al. 2018b).

Subject editors: Mark D. Scherz, Miguel Vences, and Achille P. Raselimanana

ESTIMATES OF CHAMELEON DENSITY ON MADAGASCAR

R. R. Andriantsimanarilafy, J. C. Randrianantoandro, R. A. Griffiths, M. A. F. Raholdina, C. J. H. Radafiarimanana, F. Andriamaharavo, E. F. Rakotondrasoa, A. J. V. Rakotondrina, Randriamialisoa, J. Rabearivony, L. D. Brady, M. Soazandry, M. Raselimanana, A. René de Rolland, and R. K. B. Jenkins

With recent descriptions of new taxa during the last decade, Madagascar is now home to 96 chameleon species (see Scherz et al., pp. 1506–16). Until now, 87 species have been assessed in the IUCN Red List, with 44 listed as threatened, specifically five as Critically Endangered, 23 as Endangered, and 16 as Vulnerable (IUCN 2019). An additional four species that are Data Deficient could also be threatened. *Calumma* species are found in moist evergreen forests, while *Furcifer* chameleons occur in different types of forests, as well as in montane ericoid thickets and grasslands and urban areas (Glaw and Vences 2007). The dwarf chameleons, *Brookesia*, occupy both moist evergreen and dry deciduous forests, and *Palleon* is associated only with moist evergreen forests (Rakotomalala and Raselimanana 2003). Published herpetological surveys from Madagascar often present information about the occurrence of different species at particular sites. This information is used to develop a better understanding of the taxonomy, distribution, and natural history of reptiles and amphibians. It is particularly useful for informing conservation when collated in a standardized manner, such as the IUCN Red List of Threatened Species (e.g., Jenkins et al. 2014), or used in conservation planning (e.g., Kremen et al. 2008).

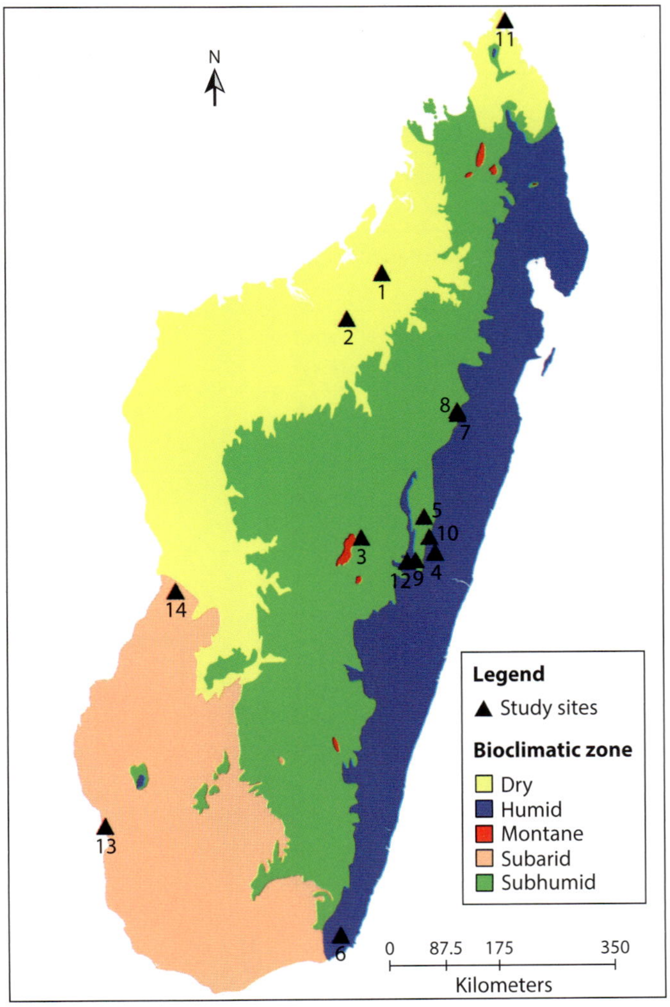

FIGURE 12.38 **Locations of 14 sites where chameleon density surveys have been carried out (numbers as in Table 12.7) and reported in this contribution.**

Quantitative information on population abundance is often more difficult to obtain, either because the species are difficult to survey or because the survey methods require additional investments in time and equipment. While the cryptic behavior of snakes, burrowing skinks, and geckos renders them relatively difficult to study, tortoises and chameleons by contrast are well suited to standard surveys using line transects, and these methods have been used for a number of species on Madagascar (e.g., Jenkins et al. 2003; Young et al. 2008; Karsten et al. 2009a; Randrianantoandro et al. 2010; Walker 2010). Because population density is useful when comparing key sites (protected and not protected), habitats (various types and disturbance), or years, or when monitoring the impact of illegal or legal collection, additional information on the density of key Malagasy species is needed.

Malagasy chameleons are in demand for the international pet trade, and annual quotas are established annually by the Malagasy governement under the auspices of the Convention on International Trade in Endangered Species of Wild Fauna and Flora (CITES) (see Carpenter et al., pp. 1452–55). Such quotas are expected to be derived from the best available scientific data, including information on population densities, although this is not always available. Here we report the unpublished results of a series of field studies conducted between 2009 and 2018 (Figure 12.38; Table 12.7) and provide population density estimates for 28 chameleon species.

TECHNICAL ASPECTS

We surveyed chameleons at night along randomly located 150 m line transects divided into three parallel lines of 50 m positioned 20 m apart. The survey protocol followed the approach described in detail elsewhere (Brady and Griffiths 1999; Randrianantoandro et al. 2008). Surveys were done inside or outside existing protected areas across five of Madagascar's bioclimatic zones, described in Cornet (1974) (Figure 12.38). We visited a total of 14 sites, some on more than one occasion, across a range of elevations and habitat types (Table 12.7). Data analysis was done using Distance software (release 6.2), with model combinations suggested by Thomas et al. (2010). We performed density estimations where there were at least

TABLE 12.7. **Sites on Madagascar where nocturnal chameleon surveys were conducted and reported in this contribution**

SITE NAME	REGION	COORDINATES	SURVEY EFFORT (m)	HABITAT TYPE	ELEVATION (m ABOVE SEA LEVEL)
1. Bongolava	Sofia	S15°39′05.9″ E047°34′56.3″	16,986	Dry deciduous forests	40–300
2. Andranomiditra	Boeny	S16°17′30.5″ E047°04′56.5″	3400	Dry deciduous forests	140–210
3. Ankaratra	Vakinankaratra	S19°19′59.4″ E047°16′13.5″	17,004	Montane ericoid thickets and montane grasslands	1600–2490
4. Ambatofotsy	Alaotra Mangoro	S19°32′24.9″ E048°18′37.5″	7076	Moist evergreen forests	790–1140
5. Mangabe	Alaotra Mangoro	S19°02′48.8″ E048°09′31.8″	1800	Moist evergreen forests	910–1020
6. Tsitongambarika	Anosy	S24°49′25.6″ E046°56′56.9″	4405	Lowland moist evergreen forests	290–360
7. Analabe Betanantana	Alaotra Mangoro	S17°37′04.19″ E048°38′04.07″	750	Lowland moist evergreen forests	970–1300
8. Analalava	Alaotra Mangoro	S17°34′39.07″ E048°37′49.83″	1050	Moist evergreen forests	1050–1200
9. Ankorabe	Alaotra Mangoro	S19°38′45.21″ E048°02′02.23″	1629	Lowland moist evergreen forests	700–790
10. Tarzanville	Alaotra Mangoro	S19°19′38.72″ E048°13′31.61″	1460	Lowland moist evergreen forests	810–960
11. Complexe Bobaomby	DIANA	S12°07′21.55″ E049°19′27.35″	6150	Dry deciduous forests	10–200
12. Ambalaomby	Alaotra Mangoro	S19°40′0.65″ E047°55′02.58″	5400	Medium-altitude moist evergreen forests	1240–1480
13. Sakabera-Belalanda	Atsimo Andrefana	S23°17′51.4″ E043°39′07.6″	1800	Dry spiny thickets	10–30
14. Kirindy Forest CNFEREF	Menabe	S20°03′23.6″ E044°39′29.3″	3000	Dry deciduous forests	20–40

Note: Elevation values are rounded to the nearest 10 m.

15 sightings of a species, as these yielded coefficients of variation (CV) that were all moderate to low (Table 12.7).

MEASURES OF DENSITY

We encountered 2445 individual chameleons comprising nine *Furcifer*, four *Brookesia*, one *Palleon*, and 13 *Calumma* species (Table 12.8). The estimated population densities varied from low values for larger species in dry areas (e.g., *F. oustaleti* 2.3–7.6/ha) to relatively high densities of medium-size species in montane grassland or other forms of grassland (e.g., *F. campani* up to 32.0/ha) and moist evergreen forests (e.g., *C. gallus* at 94.4/ha), with the highest of all densities recorded for forest-dwelling terrestrial *Brookesia* and *Palleon* species (e.g., *B. superciliaris* up to 43.0/ha and *P. nasus* up to 67.4/ha). In the western dry deciduous forests of Bongolava, *F. oustaleti* and *F. angeli* occurred at similar density, with highest values recorded at the end of the wet season (February–March) for both species. At the same site, *B. stumpffi* occurred at relatively high densities during February and March but was absent during the winter survey in June and July. In the montane grasslands of Ankaratra, the highest density of *F. campani* was recorded in the middle of the wet season (January), with lower values during April before a notable reduction in midwinter (August). Five *Calumma* species were observed at Ambatofotsy during April and May, with a sixth species detected during the May survey (Table 12.8). *Calumma gallus* and *C. parsonii* were infrequently detected and it was not possible to calculate population densities

TABLE 12.8. **Summary of population densities for chameleons on Madagascar using Distance sampling**

SPECIES	SITE	PERIOD	YEAR	CHAMELEONS (n)	DENSITY (ind.ha^{-1})	CV (%)	CI 95%	MODEL SELECTED
Brookesia brygooi	14	Nov–Dec	2017	2	–	–	–	–
	14	Jan–Feb	2018	42	92.30	46.01	38.38–221.97	Hazard/Polynomial
B. stumpffi	1	Feb–Mar	2010	119	29.00	32.37	15.44–54.49	Half-normal/Cosine
	1	Jun–Jul	2010	0	–	–	–	–
	11	Feb–Mar	2018	93	33.5	28.87	19.01–59.02	Hazard/Polynomial
B. superciliaris	4	Mar–Apr	2011	191	42.92	12.14	33.66–54.70	Uniform/Cosine
	4	Feb–Mar	2016	72	63.947	26.52	37.07–110.31	Uniform/Cosine
	9	Feb–Mar	2015	54	66.237	27.09	37.340–117.50	Hazard/Polynomial
	10	Feb–Mar	2015	10	–	–	–	–
B. therezieni	5	Feb–Mar	2012	16	13.47	29.94	7.18–25.27	Uniform/Cosine
B. thieli	4	Mar–Apr	2011	70	22.09	26.05	13.22–36.89	Half-normal/ Polynomial
	4	Feb–Mar	2016	7	–	–	–	–
	5	Feb–Mar	2012	4	–	–	–	–
	7	Nov	2015	1	–	–	–	–
	12	Oct–Nov	2018	1	–	–	–	–
Calumma brevicorne	12	Oct–Nov	2018	3	–	–	–	–
C. crypticum	7	Nov	2015	3	–	–	–	–
	8	Nov	2015	10	–	–	–	–
C. cucullatum	4	Mar–Apr	2011	18	5.18	40.01	2.40–11.21	Half-normal/Cosine
	4	Feb–Mar	2016	24	16.80	35.05	8.11–34.82	Uniform/Cosine
C. fallax	12	Oct–Nov	2018	6	–	–	–	–
C. gallus	4	Mar–Apr	2011	2	–	–	–	–
	4	Feb–Mar	2016	10	–	–	–	–
	9	Feb–Mar	2015	72	94.388	18.80	63.549–140.19	Half-normal/ Polynomial
	10	Feb–Mar	2015	57	65.342	32.11	34.398–124.12	Half-normal/Cosine
C. gastrotaenia	4	Mar–Apr	2011	216	40.45	18.63	28.01–58.40	Uniform/Cosine
	4	Feb–Mar	2016	18	13.04	47.88	4.88–34.80	Uniform/Cosine
	7	Nov	2015	14	–	–	–	–
	8	Nov	2015	36	46.56	28.88	25.38–85.42	Hazard/Polynomial
	12	Oct–Nov	2018	114	36.12	13.70	27.60–47.26	Uniform/Cosine
C. globifer	7	Nov	2015	2	–	–	–	–
C. hilleniusi	3	May	2010	59	55.69	31.23	26.82–115.64	Uniform/Cosine
C. malthe	12	Oct–Nov	2018	4	–	–	–	–

(continued overleaf)

TABLE 12.8. ***continued***

SPECIES	SITE	PERIOD	YEAR	CHAMELEONS (n)	DENSITY (ind.ha^{-1})	CV (%)	CI 95%	MODEL SELECTED
C. nasutum	4	Mar–Apr	2011	26	6.12	27.32	3.58–10.45	Uniform/Cosine
	4	Feb–Mar	2016	4	–	–	–	–
	9	Feb–Mar	2015	14	–	–	–	–
	10	Feb–Mar	2015	4	–	–	–	–
	5	Feb–Mar	2012	14	–	–	–	–
	7	Nov	2015	3	–	–	–	–
	8	Nov	2015	2	–	–	–	–
	12	Oct–Nov	2018	6	–	–	–	–
C. oshaughnessyi	12	Oct–Nov	2018	4	–	–	–	–
C. parsonii	4	Mar–Apr	2011	1	–	–	–	–
	4	Feb–Mar	2016	2	–	–	–	–
C. tarzan	4	Mar–Apr	2011	78	16.59	30.42	9.12–30.14	Uniform/Cosine
Furcifer angeli	1	Feb–Mar	2010	55	12.62	20.56	8.41–18.92	Uniform/Cosine
	1	Jun–Jul	2010	43	7.51	17.28	5.32–10.61	Hazard/ Polynomial
	1	Apr	2013	22	4.70	30.21	2.5–8.5	Uniform/Cosine
F. antimena	13	Feb–Mar	2009	11	–	–	–	–
F. campani	3	Jan	2010	72	31.91	29.68	17.65–57.67	Half-normal/Cosine
	3	Aug	2010	9	–	–	–	–
	3	Sep	2011	28	10.42	31.34	5.53–19.63	Uniform/Cosine
	3	Apr	2012	61	15.48	22.16	9.88–24.24	Half-normal/ Polynomial
F. labordi	14	Nov–Dec	2017	23	10.64	22.42	6.72–16.86	Hazard/Polynomial
	14	Jan–Feb	2018	77	35.15	17.07	24.81–49.91	Uniform/Cosine
F. nicosiai	14	Nov–Dec	2017	21	10.53	26.08	6.21–17.87	Uniform/Cosine
	14	Jan–Feb	2018	63	29.31	23.28	18.36–46.8	Half-normal/ Polynomial
F. oustaleti	1	Feb–Mar	2010	60	11.36	18.21	7.91–16.32	Hazard/Polynomial
	1	Jun–Jul	2010	47	8.26	21.78	5.36–12.71	Uniform/Cosine
	1	Apr	2013	18	4.20	30.79	2.3–7.6	Uniform/Cosine
	2	May	2013	17	5.40	27.02	3.1–9.5	Hazard/Polynomial
	11	Feb–Mar	2018	2	–	–	–	–
F. pardalis	11	Feb–Mar	2018	38	6.71	23.83	4.19–10.73	Half-normal/Cosine
F. petteri	11	Feb–Mar	2018	42	12.96	42.39	5.70–29.45	Uniform/Cosine
F. rhinoceratus	2	May	2013	13	–	–	–	–
Palleon nasus	6	Nov–Dec	2009	215	67.36	22	43.61–104.89	Hazard/Cosine

Notes: Site numbers are as follows: 1) Bongolava, 2) Andranomiditra, 3) Ankaratra, 4) Ambatofotsy, 5) Mangabe, 6) Tsitongambarika, 7) Analabe Betanantana, 8) Analalava, 9) Ankorabe, 10) Tarzanville, 11) Complexe Bobaomby, 12) Ambalaomby, 13) Sakabera-Belalanda, and 14) Kirindy Forest CNFEREF. Note that density values were estimated by statistical models, and the reporting of values to the second decimal does not imply a true precision of these estimates, as is obvious from the large coefficient of variation (CV) and confidence interval (CI) values.

for these species. *Calumma cucullatum* and *C. nasutum* were present at relatively low densities (5.6–6.1/ha), and two morphologically similar species, *C. gastrotaenia* and *C. tarzan*, were observed at higher densities (16.6–40.5/ha), the former having the third highest density of any species in the study. *Brookesia superciliaris* occurred at relatively high densities (42.9/ha) in Ambatofotsy. Three chameleon species were recorded from Mangabe, and of the two *Brookesia* species, *B. thieli* was notably scarce and *B. therezieni* occurred at higher densities.

The population density of chameleons varied with the species, season, and habitat. In general, the larger species, *F. oustaleti* and *C. parsonii*, occurred at lowest densities, while the density of the smaller arboreal species varied widely, with some species notably scarce (e.g., *C. gallus*, *C. cucullatum*) and others locally abundant (e.g., *C. gastrotaenia*). Ground-dwelling species also exhibited a wide range of densities, with *B. thieli* occurring at relatively low densities, and *P. nasus*, *B. superciliaris*, and *B. stumpffi* at relatively high densities (Table 12.8).

In a lowland moist evergreen forests, Rabearivony et al. (2007) also found *C. p. parsonii* at very low density, while Rakotondravony (2004) found *C. p. cristifer* in only four out of eight suitable forests and at a relatively low density. Brady and Griffiths (1999) found *C. p. cristifer* in five out of nine suitable forests, usually at low densities. This species may use the canopy and therefore render itself difficult to observe from ground-based surveys. Two individuals were observed 10 m from the ground in Mantadia (1989) and Makira (2003) forests (J. C. Randrianantoandro, unpublished data). Consequently, this species may be difficult to detect in dense vegetation in the eastern moist evergreen forests. Despite its relatively wide distribution and occasional use of degraded forests, this species appears to be one of the rarest members of the Malagasy moist evergreen forest chameleon community. Our estimates of *F. oustaleti* and *F. rhinoceratus* were consistent with those reported by Metcalf et al. (2005a), while the high local abundance of *C. gastrotaenia* and *P. nasus* has been noted from other sites elsewhere (Brady and Griffiths 1999; Jenkins et al. 1999, 2003). Herein we provide the first published population density estimates for two threatened species. The Critically Endangered *C. tarzan* was less abundant than the similar *C. gastrotaenia*, and it appears that although they can be found at the same site, the two species differ in elevational preferences, with the former occurring at lower elevation. If the relatively low density noted herein is representative of *C. cucullatum* across its range, then the conservation of this Vulnerable species, which is a lowland moist evergreen forest specialist, is of concern.

While the data are insufficient to explore seasonality in any great detail, it is clear that despite high search effort, *B. stumpffi* was not found in the winter even though high density was recorded a few months earlier. The population abundance of three *Furcifer* species (*F. angeli*, *F. campani*, and *F. oustaleti*) was highest in the middle of the austral summer and declined notably thereafter. *Furcifer campani* was particularly scarce during the winter compared to the summer period between November and December (Randrianantoandro et al. 2010).

These results show that the local density of chameleons varies with the species, season, and forest, and other studies have demonstrated how other factors can influence density (e.g., Jenkins et al. 2003; Andreone et al. 2005; Karsten et al. 2009a). Legal harvest management regimes for wild chameleons should therefore explicitly consider the local population density in actual sites of collection, and this is particularly important for species that appear to occur at low densities, such as *C. gallus*, *C. parsonii*, and *C. cucullatum*.

Subject editors: Raphali R. Andriantsimanarilafy, Miguel Vences, and Achille P. Raselimanana

SANZINIIDAE, MALAGASY BOAS

C. J. Raxworthy and F. Glaw

Four species of boas are known from Madagascar: two ground boas (*Acrantophis dumerili* and *A. madagascariensis*) and two tree boas (*Sanzinia madagascariensis* and *S. volontany*). These species represent the largest, and in many respects the most charismatic component of the Malagasy snake fauna. They are also surrounded by controversy concerning taxonomy, evolutionary history, and conservation status. In addition, the Malagasy boas have traditional and economic importance. They feature in several legends, and each species is usually recognized by a specific local name.

TAXONOMY

The classification of boas and pythons has changed radically in recent decades. These changes are based mostly on molecular phylogenetic studies (e.g., Pyron et al. 2013; Reynolds et al. 2014), and it is likely that further changes will follow. Malagasy boas were traditionally considered to have close biogeographic relationships to South America. The strong similarities between Neotropical and Malagasy boas prompted Kluge (1991) to synonymize the two Malagasy genera *Sanzinia* and *Acrantophis* with the South American genus *Boa*. Subsequent genetic studies revealed that this arrangement conflicted with the phylogenetic relationships of these snakes, and this classification was rejected (e.g., Vences et al. 2001). More recent studies suggested relatively close phylogenetic relationships between Malagasy boids and the African Burrowing Python, *Calabaria reinhardtii* (Noonan and Chippindale 2006a, 2006b; Noonan and Sites 2010), and the Malagasy boas have been placed in the endemic subfamily Sanziniinae (Pyron et al. 2013) and subsequently in the family Sanziniidae (Pyron et al. 2014). Reynolds et al. (2014) recently revised the Malagasy boids and elevated the western subspecies *S. madagascariensis volontany* to species level based on its genetic distinctiveness. *Sanzinia* can be readily distinguished from *Acrantophis* by the vertically enlarged labial (lip) scales, which are thought to contain thermosensitive receptors that allow the snakes to locate their prey, as is known in other boas and pythons. All Malagasy boas share a karyotype with 2n = 34 chromosomes (Mezzasalma et al. 2019).

NATURAL HISTORY

Sanzinia madagascariensis, Eastern Madagascar Tree Boa, *Manditra*, *Bado*

This species almost always has a greenish coloration (Figure 12.39), which is often paler in populations in the southeast and can be very dark at mid-elevations in moist evergreen forests. Juveniles can be brown or orange. It is found on the ground or above the ground in trees or scrub. It occupies a large variety of habitats (below approximately 1000 m) throughout eastern Madagascar. These include intact lowland moist evergreen forests, littoral forests, transitional moist evergreen–dry deciduous forests in the southeast, secondary and degraded forests, and many other types of secondary habitats including areas around human habitations, as well as in partially open areas such as palm plantations. It is not known from the Central Highlands. The tail is prehensile. Activity is mostly nocturnal. Natural diet comprises mainly mammals, including lemurs (see Goodman and Ganzhorn, pp. 1829–38), *Rattus rattus* (Black Rats), tenrecs, and most likely also frogs and birds (Raxworthy 2003; Glaw and Vences 2007). In captivity amphibians and birds are taken (Branch and Erasmus 1976). This species is viviparous, with gestation reported to take six to seven months, captive litter sizes reported between one and 19, and maturation in 18 months (Branch and Erasmus 1976; Brygoo 1982). Adults reach a length of up to about 2.0 m (Brygoo 1982), although most individuals do not reach more than 1.8 m.

Sanzinia volontany, Western Madagascar Tree Boa, *Manditra*, *Bado*

Sanzinia volontany was originally described as a subspecies of *S. madagascariensis* by Vences and Glaw (2003) but was subsequently elevated to species level because of the relatively large genetic distance to its sister species (Orozco-terWengel et al. 2008; Reynolds et al. 2014; Reynolds and Henderson 2018). However, a thorough analysis of hybrid zones between the two taxa is lacking to confirm their species-level status. *Sanzinia volontany* is morphologically very similar to its eastern sister species but can rather easily be distinguished by its predominantly brownish ground coloration, which is usually greenish in *S. madagascariensis*. A recent osteological study also found a number of possibly diagnostic features of the skull (L. Senici et al., unpublished data). *Sanzinia volontany* occurs in lowland moist evergreen forests in northern Madagascar, dry deciduous forests in the north, west, and south, and a variety of secondary habitats, including village garbage dumps (Vences and Glaw 2003). The habits are partially arboreal and partially terrestrial. Diet is very similar to that of *S. madagascariensis*, and this species typically consumes rats (*Rattus rattus*) around villages. Reproduction is still poorly known, but the reported litter size of one to 16 juveniles is similar to that of *S. madagascariensis* (Glaw and Vences 2007).

Acrantophis madagascariensis, Madagascar Ground Boa, *Do*, *Ankoma*

This species is ground dwelling. It occupies a large variety of habitats (below approximately 800 m) in northeastern and northwestern Madagascar. These include intact evergreen forests, littoral forests, dry deciduous forests, secondary and degraded forests, and many other types of secondary habitats including areas around human

FIGURE 12.39 **A *Sanzinia madagascariensis* individual from eastern Madagascar.** (PHOTO by P.-S. Gehring.)

habitations. It is frequently found close to streams and rivers. It is not known from the Central Highlands. Activity is both diurnal and nocturnal. Diet includes Black Rats (*Rattus rattus*), fruit bats, tenrecs, lemurs, ducks, and even *Oplurus* lizards (Brygoo 1982; Glaw and Vences 2007; Borer 2013); in captivity, birds (chicks and pigeons) are also taken (Branch and Erasmus 1976). This species is viviparous, with gestation reported to take eight to nine months and captive litter sizes reported between one and six. Freshly born juveniles are very large (55–70 cm total length) and weigh up to 270 g (Höß et al. 2005). Maturation takes longer than two years (Branch and Erasmus 1976; Brygoo 1982). Adults can reach a length of up to 3.2 m (Brygoo 1982), but 2.4–2.5 m appears more typical (Huff 1984). The maximum recorded weight is 8.2 kg (C. Gardner et al. 2013).

Acrantophis dumerili, Dumeril's Ground Boa, *Do*, *Bado*

This species is ground dwelling (Figure 12.40). It occupies a large variety of habitats (below approximately 1300 m) in southern and western Madagascar. These include intact moist evergreen forests (only in the extreme southeast), littoral forests, dry spiny thickets, dry deciduous forests, secondary and degraded forests, and many other types of secondary habitats including areas around human habitations. Activity is both diurnal and nocturnal and in the south is particularly elevated after rains. Diet comprises rodents such as *Rattus rattus* and *Hypogeomys antimena* (Madagascar Giant Jumping Rat) (Sommer 2000), tenrecs (Brygoo 1982), and domestic chickens (Glaw and Glaw 2004). This species is viviparous, with gestation reported to take between 200 and 241 days, and captive litter sizes between six and 13 (Huff 1984). Freshly born juveniles (44–52.5 cm total length, 60–108 g) are much smaller and lighter than those of *A. madagascariensis* (Glaw and Vences 2007). Adults reach a length of between 1.3 and 1.5 m (Huff 1984), making this the smallest Malagasy boa.

The two *Acrantophis* species are rather similar to each other and have sometimes been considered conspecific geographic forms (Stull 1935; Mertens 1955, 1972), although more recent authors have followed Guibé (1949, 1958), who gave both taxa species rank. Guibé separated these species based on the following: *A. madagascariensis*, head dorsally covered in large plates, two loreal scales, and six to 10 scales around the eye; *A. dumerili*, head dorsally covered in smaller scales, four loreal scales, and 11 to 16 scales around the eye. There are also several osteological differences between their skulls (L. Senici et al., unpublished data).

FIGURE 12.40 **A specimen of Dumeril's Ground Boa, *Acrantophis dumerili*, from Ifaty in southwestern Madagascar. Despite their resemblance, the Malagasy boas are not direct relatives of South American boas and are today classified in their own family, Sanziniidae.** (PHOTO by F. Glaw.)

Acrantophis madagascariensis is found in northern Madagascar and along the east coast approximately as far south as Toamasina, in contrast to *A. dumerili* in southern Madagascar, including the southern Central Highlands; it is the only boa occurring in the latter area. The distribution limits of the two species are not well known in the west, specifically between Mahajanga and Morondava, where there are reports of intermediate forms (suggesting hybrids or a single *Acrantophis* species). Clearly, detailed molecular and morphological studies, and especially a molecular analysis of introgression across this hybrid zone, are required based on vouchers with accurate locality information to determine whether their specific status is justified. It will also be important to study more in depth the *A. dumerili* populations from the southern and southeastern part of its range, which appear to be genetically divergent (Orozco-terWengel et al. 2008).

CONSERVATION

The boas of Madagascar are protected by a national decree (dated 16 February 1961; IUCN/UNEP/WWF 1987) that prevents commercial collecting without authorization, and they have been listed in Appendix I of CITES (Convention on International Trade in Endangered Species of Wild Fauna and Flora) since 2 April 1977. The CITES listing prevents commercial exportation of these species from Madagascar. In the 1996 IUCN Red List, the Malagasy boas are stated to be rare (Branch and Erasmus 1976), Endangered (Huff 1984), and Vulnerable. However, since 2011, all Malagasy boas have been listed as Least Concern in the IUCN Red List.

The general decreasing trend in the IUCN threat category over time reflects improving field-based knowledge of these snakes. Some decades ago, the international zoological community was under the impression that boas on Madagascar had restrictive distributions and were rare (e.g., Huff 1984), and field-based observations that claimed these snakes were common were discounted as outdated (because of the dramatic increase in habitat loss). It is now clear, however, that each species actually has a broad distribution and is surprisingly tolerant of human habitat modification (Raxworthy and Nussbaum 2000; Vences and Glaw 2003; Blumgart et al. 2017).

Despite national protection on Madagascar, boas are collected commercially for their skins and used primarily in the souvenir leather trade for belts, wallets, handbags, and stuffed whole mounts. Almost all commercial boa skin is *Acrantophis*, and many snakes are reported to come from the Mahajanga and Marovoay regions and are thus likely to be *A. madagascariensis*. In addition, some snakes are also reportedly collected for food by Malagasy of Chinese origin. The impact of commercial collecting on wild populations remains almost unknown. However, all four boa species are among the most common snakes seen throughout most of the island. During the rainy season, roadkill boas can frequently be found on all the major routes, and dead snakes are often found close to villages and in areas of intense agriculture.

Their unusual tolerance of heavy human disturbance suggests that none of the boas are threatened with extinction, despite the ongoing decline in natural forest cover. It is likely that these large snakes are providing a valuable ecosystem service to many rural communities by helping to control populations of introduced pest mammals such as rats (*Rattus rattus* and *R. norvegicus*), and possibly also *Suncus murinus* (Asian Musk Shrews) and *Mus musculus* (House Mice).

Ironically, the CITES Appendix I listing of the boas may have produced some undesirable conservation results. Although dealers have widely sold captive-bred stock of all four species outside Madagascar, no opportunity to create revenue from locally breeding and exporting live boas has existed. This has provided little incentive to manage or protect populations as a valuable local resource. Second, to some extent, the Appendix I listing has also hindered international scientific research because the permit application process is much more complicated. However, despite these problems, it is hoped that more research will be conducted on these charismatic snakes in the near future that will provide valuable new insights concerning the evolutionary history and conservation biology of the Malagasy boas.

Subject editors: Frank Glaw, Miguel Vences, and Achille P. Raselimanana

PSEUDOXYRHOPHIIDAE AND PSAMMOPHIIDAE, COLUBROID SNAKES, *BIBILAVA*

J. E. Cadle, M. D. Scherz, S. Ruane, F. T. Burbrink, C. J. Raxworthy, and F. Glaw

Two clades of colubroid snakes, now recognized as families, are present on Madagascar: Psammophiidae and Pseudoxyrhophiidae. Both clades are within the large clade Colubroides, which includes most extant snakes. Within Colubroides, Psammophiidae and Pseudoxyrhophiidae are in the subclade Elapoidea but are related to different, primarily African lineages within that group (Zaher et al. 2019). Both groups contain only species with medically rather insignificant venom, if they are venomous at all (few reports of envenomation are known; see below). Psammophiidae is widely distributed in Africa and southern Eurasia but on Madagascar includes only *Mimophis*, with just two described species. Psammophiidae, and the inclusion of *Mimophis* in it, have been recognized for well over a century based on morphological and molecular data (reviews in Bogert 1943; Cadle 2003; Nagy et al. 2003; Kelly et al. 2008). Most of Madagascar's snakes, including 19 genera and 80 species, belong to the Pseudoxyrhophiidae. These are highly diverse in terms of ecology and morphology. Unlike the psammophiids, the pseudoxyrhophiids were only relatively recently recognized as a distinct clade, which was eventually considered a full family after the restructuring of the Colubridae (Dowling 1975; Kelly et al. 2009; Pyron et al. 2013; Zaher et al. 2019). They too are related to African genera (*Amplorhinus*, *Ditypophis*, and *Duberria* from Africa and Socotra Island [Nagy et al. 2003; Pyron et al. 2013; Burbrink et al. 2019]), and members of three Malagasy genera are also present on the Comoro archipelago (Hawlitschek et al. 2011; Augros 2019): *Liophidium* (one endemic species on Mayotte, nine on Madagascar), *Lycodryas* (one endemic species on Anjouan and Mayotte, one endemic species on Grande Comore and Mohéli, and seven on Madagascar), and *Leioheterodon madagascariensis* (Grande Comore and Madagascar), although the latter has not been seen recently on Grande Comore and may have been introduced (Wallach 1986; Augros 2019). All other genera of pseudoxyrhophiids are endemic to Madagascar. Many new species within Pseudoxyrhophiidae continue to be described, and candidate species in several genera await description (e.g., Nagy et al. 2010; Burbrink et al. 2019).

PSEUDOXYRHOPHIIDAE

Phylogeny

Most of the current pseudoxyrhophiid genera were erected more than a century ago but have yet to be fully characterized on the basis of more than superficial characteristics of external form, scalation, and a few dental characters, although extensive osteological data sets derived from micro-CT scans have been assembled for Malagasy snake species and will doubtless be published in the near future (P. Skipwith et al., unpublished data; C. Wang-Claypool et al., unpublished data).

In the pre-molecular era, researchers recognized an assemblage of genera including *Pseudoxyrhopus*, *Heteroliodon*, *Liophidium*, *Elapotinus* (formerly *Exallodontophis*), and *Pararhadinaea* (Raxworthy and Nussbaum 1994b; Cadle 1999), which Cadle (1999) referred to as the "*Pseudoxyrhopus* group." Cadle (1999) suggested that *Pseudoxyrhopus* and *Elapotinus* were sister groups, with *Heteroliodon* outside their clade and an unclear relationship between this clade and *Pararhadinaea* and *Liophidium*. Apart from the *Pseudoxyrhopus* group, only *Alluaudina* and *Compsophis* among the other Malagasy pseudoxyrhophiids have specifically been noted to share derived characters that might indicate their close relationship (Cadle 1996b), and molecular data have likewise consistently supported this hypothesis (Nagy et al. 2003; Ruane et al. 2015, Burbrink et al. 2019).

Systematic knowledge of the Malagasy pseudoxyrhophiid radiation has greatly increased with the advent of molecular phylogenetics (e.g., Glaw et al. 2007a, 2007b; Nagy et al. 2010; Ruane et al. 2015; Burbrink et al. 2019). The most recent and comprehensive of these studies was by Burbrink et al. (2019). They showed that the Malagasy Pseudoxyrhophiidae consists of four major clades: 1) the terrestrial and fossorial *Elapotinus*, *Liophidium*, *Liopholidophis*, *Heteroliodon*, *Pseudoxyrhopus*, and *Pararhadinaea* (no molecular data), substantiating the *Pseudoxyrhopus* group of Cadle (1999), albeit with different relationships among genera; 2) the "racer"-like *Thamnosophis* and *Dromicodryas*; 3) the nocturnal and terrestrial or arboreal *Compsophis* and *Alluaudina*; and 4) the mostly arboreal *Parastenophis*, *Leioheterodon*, *Ithycyphus*, *Micropisthodon*, *Langaha*, *Madagascarophis*, *Phisalixella*, and *Lycodryas*. In their reconstruction, the *Pseudoxyrhopus* group and racer-like species fall sister to one another, together sister to *Compsophis* + *Alluaudina*, with the mostly arboreal clade falling sister to this clade. The relationships of *Brygophis* remain uncertain, and several relationships are still quite poorly resolved, meaning that more work remains to be done on the systematics of these snakes.

Molecular clock estimates of divergence times suggest that Psammophiidae and Pseudoxyrhophiidae originated in the Oligocene 25 to 30 Mya, but that the Malagasy lineages date from the early Miocene, 20 to 25 Mya (Nagy et al. 2003; Crottini et al. 2012; Zaher et al. 2019; Burbrink et al. 2020). The four major lineages of pseudoxyrhophiids originated by 20 to 25 Mya, but most speciation of extant species within this group on Madagascar probably dates from the Pleistocene (Burbrink et al. 2019).

Diversity

With over 80 species, the Pseudoxyrhophiidae is a highly diverse endemic radiation. There is also a very high rate of species discovery and description, with 28 species named as new to science between 1980 and 2000, and 15 species described since 2003. Additionally, several candidate species in different genera await description (e.g., Nagy et al. 2010; Burbrink et al. 2019). In the following, we provide brief accounts of the diversity and literature for each of the 19 Malagasy genera currently recognized within the Pseudoxyrhophiidae.

Elapotinus: A monotypic genus consisting of *Elapotinus picteti*. This species was formerly referred to as *Exallodontophis albignaci* (and even earlier as *Pararhadinaea albignaci*), but the synonymy of this species with the mystery taxon *E. picteti* was clarified by Kucharzewski et al. (2014). This poorly known species is fossorial, terrestrial, and small (up to 42 cm including tail) and has a stark white nuchal (neck) collar. It dwells in moist evergreen forests in the east and north of the island. It has hinged teeth and is unique in having massively enlarged teeth in the middle of the maxillary tooth row, followed by a broad diastema and very large rear fangs.

Liophidium: Nine species of slender, diurnal, and terrestrial moist evergreen and dry deciduous forest snakes. At least two species (*Liophidium rhodogaster* and *L. pattoni*) have bright-colored ventral scales, and the latter has an overall very vivid coloration (Vieites et al. 2010; Figure 12.41). These snakes have blunt, distally compressed, hinged teeth suited to consuming hard-bodied prey. *Liophidium torquatum* can be found in grassland and degraded habitats, as well as intact forest.

Liopholidophis: Eight species of slender, diurnal, and terrestrial moist evergreen forest and wetland snakes. Some species of *Liopholidophis* can get rather large, up to 1.6 m in an adult *L. grandidieri*. They share 15–17 mid-body scale rows and strongly sexually dimorphic tail length. The significance of this tail length dimorphism is unclear, and it is much less pronounced in the smaller species of the genus (Glaw et al. 2007b, 2014b; Cadle 2014). *Liopholidophis sexlineatus*, occurring in the eastern lowlands and escarpment and in the Central Highlands, is semiaquatic and is found naturally in marshy enclaves or flooded meadows within forests and adjacent to

FIGURE 12.41 **This spectacularly colored species from moist evergreen forests in northeastern Madagascar was only recently described as *Liophidium pattoni*. So far, very few specimens of this snake have been collected, and its natural history and the function of its contrasting colors remain unstudied.** (PHOTO by P.-S. Gehring.)

rivers; it is also common in overgrown rice fields. The remaining species of *Liopholidophis* are terrestrial inhabitants of closed-canopy forests of the eastern escarpment and lowlands. *Liopholidophis sexlineatus* is viviparous (Glaw and Vences 2007), but the other species are oviparous or probably oviparous. *Liopholidophis* eats primarily frogs (Cadle 1996a). *Liopholidophis rhadinaea* occasionally becomes immobile when disturbed. *Liopholidophis grandidieri* has been considered one of the rarest snakes on Madagascar, but recent collections suggest that it might be relatively common in intact highland moist evergreen forests above about 1200 m (Cadle 2014; Glaw et al. 2014b).

Heteroliodon: Three rather small, semi-fossorial, nocturnal, terrestrial snakes that are found in drier areas of Madagascar. These species are often found inside dead wood during the day, and all three species have distinct nuchal collars. They have hinged teeth, including enlarged dentary teeth. Extremely little of their ecology or behavior is understood, and one species, *H. fohy*, is known from very few specimens (Glaw et al. 2005a; Megson et al. 2009b).

Pararhadinaea: A monotypic genus consisting of *Pararhadinaea melanogaster*. This species is small, terrestrial, and diurnal and is found in moist evergreen forests and transitional dry deciduous–moist evergreen forests. This species is divided into two subspecies, with *P. m. melanogaster* occurring on Nosy Be and in the Loky Manambato region, and *P. m. marojejyensis* on Marojejy. These snakes have blunt, distally compressed, hinged teeth suited to consuming hard-bodied prey.

Pseudoxyrhopus: Eleven species of rather thick-bodied, mostly nocturnal, terrestrial or fossorial snakes with small eyes, rounded snouts, and highly varied ecologies. Several species are found in association with streams, and others are known to burrow. The largest species, *P. microps*, can reach up to 1.4 m total length. These snakes have hinged teeth, enlarged on the dentary, and a diastema associated with consuming hard-bodied prey (e.g., skinks, plated lizards). The diet of *Pseudoxyrhopus* is poorly known, but some species probably eat frogs, others eat lizards, and at least *P. tritaeniatus* also eats small mammals as adults, which is a common dietary shift observed widely among snakes. Prey tentatively identified as *Nesomys rufus* (Nesomyidae) was found in a large *P. tritaeniatus* specimen (Cadle 1999), and another specimen contained *Oryzorictes hova* (Tenrecidae) (Goodman et al. 1999). One species, *P. imerinae*, is known from the Central Highlands and occupies montane ericoid thicket and grassland, and *P. quinquelineatus* has a broad ecological range including the Central Highlands, eastern moist evergreen forests, western and northern dry deciduous forests, and southern dry spiny thickets (Raxworthy and Nussbaum 1994b). *Pseudoxyrhopus kely* lives in littoral and riparian forest in the transitional dry–wet region of the southeast and burrows extensively in sandy soils.

Thamnosophis: Six species of slender, diurnal, terrestrial snakes often found near water. Members of this genus were, for a time, placed in the genus *Bibilava* by Glaw et al. (2007b), but Cadle and Ineich (2008) showed that the genus name *Thamnosophis* was already available for the group. These species are very similar in morphology and ecology to American garter snakes, *Thamnophis*. They have white skin that shows between their scales, 19 mid-body scale rows, and little sexual dimorphism in tail length (Cadle 1996a; Glaw et al. 2005b, 2009c), distinguishing them from the superficially similar but not closely related *Liopholidophis*. *Thamnosophis lateralis* is the most widespread species, being found in the eastern lowlands and escarpment, Central Highlands, and the west, and occurs primarily outside closed-canopy forests. It is commonly seen in disturbed areas, including rice fields, secondary forests, and grasslands. Some species also occur in drier areas, for instance in Montagne des Français in the north (*T. stumpffi* and *T. martae*), and Tsingy de Bemaraha in the west (*T. mavotenda*). Other species such as *T. infrasignatus* and *T. epistibes* occupy only moist evergreen forests. Species of *Thamnosophis* horizontally flatten the neck and/or body as a defensive display and bite readily, though harmlessly.

Dromicodryas: Two species of slender, diurnal, terrestrial snakes. These species are very fast, active hunters. They have a wide distribution, with *D. bernieri* in particular occurring over most of Madagascar. *Dromicodryas bernieri* is sometimes associated with ant nests of the genus *Aphaenogaster* (Cadle 2003); adults use the nests as retreats, and numerous egg clutches and recently hatched young can be found within ant nests. In fact, the vernacular names *marolongo*, *marohavana* (many relatives or family), and *maroandavaka* (many in the hole) may refer to the presence of numerous individuals of this species in ant nests. Preston-Mafham (1991) reported similar behavior in *D. quadrilineatus*. Lizards are likely the main prey of these snakes; *D. bernieri* is known to eat terrestrial and nocturnal geckos (*Paroedura bastardi*), which it subdues by constriction (Preston-Mafham 1991), and these snakes have also been observed stalking and chasing diurnal *Trachylepis* skink species in midmorning (S. Ruane, unpublished data).

Compsophis: Seven species of nocturnal, arboreal, moist evergreen forest snakes (Mercurio and Andreone 2005). Several species are widespread, with *Compsophis laphystius* being a locally common snake often seen at night. Most members of the genus were formerly placed in *Geodipsas*, an African genus, but Cadle (1996b) and Ziegler et al. (1997) provided evidence that African and Malagasy *Geodipsas* species were not closely related, and the African species were transferred to a new genus, *Buhoma*, which today represents an isolated snake clade (Zaher et al. 2018). It was later clarified that *Geodipsas* and *Compsophis* were synonyms at the genus level, with *Compsophis* taking priority (Glaw et al. 2007a). At least one species, *C. boulengeri*, is partly diurnal and terrestrial, and *C. zeny* may likewise be diurnal (or constantly active) on the ground and in low shrubs. Several species need taxonomic reassessment. When caught, several *Compsophis* species emit a foul-smelling secretion from glands at the base of the tail.

Compsophis laphystius is most often found on low vegetation adjacent to, or overhanging, streams or forest pools, whereas *C. infralineatus* is usually not so closely associated with water and often occurs high up in trees. *Compsophis laphystius* is a voracious predator of frogs and their eggs (see Figure 12.3), especially mantellines and *Boophis*, but also geckos and chameleons (Cadle 1996b; Hutter et al. 2018). This species is often active during rains when its frog prey is active as well. *Compsophis infralineatus* is known to eat frogs (unidentified) and mammals (Cadle 1996b). In response to mobbing by a Tylas Vanga (*Tylas eduardi*, Vangidae), one specimen of *C. infralineatus* flattened its neck. *Compsophis infralineatus* is highly polychromatic, even within a population; individuals may be bright yellow to gray, brown, or nearly black. The significance of this variation is unknown. *Compsophis zeny* is most frequently encountered active at night, apparently foraging in a similar manner to *C. laphystius*, although no food records are yet known for *C. zeny*. This latter species has been found both terrestrially active and concealed in leaf litter during the day, which suggests that it might be partially diurnal. Apart from activity period, no observations of behavior or diet exist for *C. boulengeri*. *Compsophis albiventris* was for many years known only from the juvenile holotype collected at Montagne d'Ambre, but recent surveys found several individuals of this species (Raxworthy and Nussbaum 1994a; Glaw et al. 2007a).

Alluaudina: Two species of small, nocturnal, mostly terrestrial moist evergreen or deciduous dry forest snakes with very distinctive keeled scales and a checkerboard ventral scale pattern. One species, *Alluaudina bellyi*, is rather widespread and can be commonly encountered in some areas. The other, *A. mocquardi*, is microendemic to the limestone karst of Ankarana and is known from only a few specimens, two of which were found deep inside caves (Lanza 1990), and a third was found in the evening crawling along karst rock in the protected area during moderate rainfall (C. J. Raxworthy and S. Ruane, unpublished data). In the field, *A. bellyi* has been observed to form a defensive coil with the head at the center (Hutter et al. 2018). Diet includes *Stumpffia* frogs (Hutter et al. 2018) and *Boophis* tree frogs (C. J. Raxworthy, unpublished data). Lanza (1990) reported that *A. mocquardi* bites in defense. He also speculated that the two specimens found in caves may have entered the caves in search of higher humidity, not because they were true cave-dwelling species. *Alluaudina bellyi* is oviparous, and a clutch size of five has been reported (Glaw and Vences 1994). The reproductive biology and diet of *A. mocquardi* are unknown.

Parastenophis: A monotypic genus consisting of *Parastenophis betsileanus*. This species is nocturnal, mostly arboreal, and rather large (up to 1.3 m total length) and is found in most moist evergreen forest areas. It was formerly placed in the paraphyletic genus *Stenophis* (Domergue 1995; Nagy et al. 2010; Ruane et al. 2015; Burbrink et al. 2019). It is a highly distinctive snake with bright white and black or brown bands (sometimes faded). This species is sister to *Leioheterodon*. *Parastenophis betsileanus* is known to prey on nestling birds (Cadle 2003) and chameleons such as *Furcifer willsii* and *F. balteatus* (Glaw and Vences 2007; C. J. Raxworthy, unpublished data).

Leioheterodon: Three species of large, diurnal, terrestrial snakes characterized by an upturned, pointed snout, convergent with the similar snouts of American hognose snakes, *Heterodon* and *Xenodon*. These are some of the most frequently encountered snakes on Madagascar, with much local folklore about the largest species, *L. madagascariensis* (reaching up to at least 1.5 m). These snakes are well known for feeding on lizard eggs buried in the soil. Although *L. madagascariensis* has aglyphous dentition, bites by these snakes can result in localized swellings (Razafimahatratra et al. 2015), and interestingly, *Leioheterodon* is included within the primarily opisthoglyphous clade of Malagasy pseudoxyrhophiids (Ruane et al. 2015; Burbrink et al. 2019).

Leioheterodon madagascariensis and *L. modestus* are widely distributed throughout Madagascar, whereas *L. geayi* is restricted to the arid southwest. Members of this genus are found in forests and more open areas. *Leioheterodon madagascariensis* is oviparous. Clutch sizes of 10 and 13 eggs have been reported (Conant 1938; Campbell and Murphy 1977). Maternal attendance of eggs was reported in *L. madagascariensis* (Mori and Randriamboavonjy 2010). Conant (1938) noted that *L. madagascariensis* uses neck flattening as a defensive threat behavior, and this behavior is sometimes observed in the field, especially in juveniles (C. J. Raxworthy, unpublished data). The diet of *L. modestus* and *L. madagascariensis* includes frogs (Preston-Mafham 1991; Rosa et al. 2010); the former also eats *Zonosaurus ornatus*, rodents, and birds, as well as eggs of snakes, *Oplurus cuvieri*, and birds (Mori 2002; Mori and Randriamahazo 2002b; Cadle 2003). Frogs are at least sometimes located by digging into soil (Preston-Mafham 1991). *Leioheterodon madagascariensis* constricts larger prey, but small prey items are swallowed directly without constriction (Conant 1938). Spectacular male combats of *L. modestus* have been described and photographed by Gebhardt (2004). All three species have been found living in large underground ant nests in southern and western Madagascar, and they also occupy burrows (C. J. Raxworthy, unpublished data).

Ithycyphus: Five species of large, diurnal, mostly arboreal forest snakes. These are species of moist evergreen forests (*Ithycyphus goudoti*, *I. blanci*, and *I. perineti*) and dry deciduous forests (*I. miniatus* and *I. oursi*). Three species exceed 1.5 m total length. A frog was reported in the diet of *I. miniatus* (Domergue 1986), whereas *Furcifer oustaleti* and *Calumma brevicorne* are prey of *I. oursi* and *I. perineti*, respectively (Domergue 1986; Crottini et al. 2010). When threatened, *I. perineti* raises itself into a defensive posture, flattening the neck and gaping the mouth (Domergue 1986). *Ithycyphus miniatus* might be sexually dichromatic in some regions: females with a pale brown head, males with a bright red head. Mild envenomations by *I. miniatus* were reported by Mori and Mizuta (2006).

Micropisthodon: A monotypic genus consisting of *Micropisthodon ochraceus* (Figure 12.42). This species is diurnal and arboreal but very poorly known. Yet records of it span most of eastern and northern Madagascar. This snake attains approximately 850 mm total length (Domergue 1993). A few specimens have been found crossing roads, but one was obtained from the canopy of a large tree (nearly 30 m tall) that had been felled (Domergue 1993), and several have been found curled in branches a few meters above the ground at night (M. D. Scherz, unpublished data). One museum specimen contained remains of at least four snails, including shells and undigested soft parts (Cadle 2003), but no other prey records are known. *Micropisthodon ochraceus* is oviparous, and Domergue (1993) reported a clutch size of 10 eggs laid at the beginning of May.

Langaha: Three species of slender, diurnal, arboreal snakes with remarkable dermal snout appendages. These are perhaps Madagascar's most famous snakes and are regularly seen in the pet trade. The

FIGURE 12.42 ***Micropisthodon ochraceus* is one of the least known Malagasy snakes and is rarely observed, probably because of its arboreal habits. This individual was photographed at Montagne d'Ambre National Park.** (PHOTO by M. D. Scherz.)

rostral appendage is sexually dimorphic, being more denticulated in females and forming a single hornlike structure in males. Two species also have horns above their eyes. *Langaha madagascariensis* males are pale brown or yellowish, whereas females are gray with obscure irregular markings (see Figure 12.1). Limited observations suggest that such sexual dichromatism may be characteristic of the other species as well. *Langaha* species are known primarily from dry deciduous forests of the west, but *L. madagascariensis* is known also from scattered localities in the eastern moist evergreen forests. *Langaha madagascariensis* is largely a sit-and-wait predator and feeds on both arboreal and terrestrial lizards such as *Phelsuma modesta* and *Chalarodon madagascariensis* (Tingle 2012). *Langaha pseudoalluaudi* and *L. madagascariensis* are known to be oviparous (Domergue 1988); clutch sizes for the latter species were 10 and 11 eggs. *Langaha madagascariensis* is very cryptic when moving slowly through tree branches, which it does with a slight swaying motion. It also uses rapid flight followed by immobility as an escape tactic. Mild envenomation by the bite of *L. madagascariensis* was reported by D'Cruze (2008).

Madagascarophis: Five species of thick-bodied, nocturnal, terrestrial to semiarboreal snakes (Glaw et al. 2013; Ruane et al. 2016). These snakes are widespread and often occur in villages and degraded habitats. They can be found during the day under different objects and are frequently found in ant nests (Preston-Mafham 1991; Cadle 2003). Reproduction is by oviparity, and a clutch size of six eggs has been reported (Campbell and Murphy 1977). At least one species (*M. colubrinus*) has an exceptionally bright, sparkling yellow eye shine at night. Recorded food items of *Madagascarophis* are small terrestrial vertebrates, including frogs, lizards (geckos, skinks, and chameleons), snakes, introduced rats and mice, endemic rodents, and ground-dwelling birds (Domergue 1987; Cadle 2003; Neaves et al. 2019). Domergue (1987) observed captive individuals of *Madagascarophis* constricting mice, although lizards and snakes were envenomated and ingested without constriction. Marked local reactions have been reported for human bites by *Madagascarophis* (Domergue 1987, 1989).

Phisalixella: Three species of slender, nocturnal, arboreal forest snakes. They were formerly placed in the genus *Stenophis* (Domergue 1995), which was shown to be paraphyletic (Nagy et al. 2010; Ruane et al. 2015; Burbrink et al. 2019). Species occur in moist evergreen forests (*P. arctifasciata*) or dry deciduous forests (*P. variabilis* and *P. tulearensis*). *Phisalixella* can reach total lengths up to 1.5 m (Glaw and Vences 2007). All three species typically have red irises and can have at least a suggestion of a dark nuchal collar, though this is often faded in *P. variabilis*. *Phisalixella variabilis* is known to feed on *Brookesia antakarana* (M. D. Scherz, unpublished data).

Lycodryas: The genus *Lycodryas* currently includes eight species of slender, nocturnal, arboreal forest snakes from Madagascar (Burbrink et al. 2019) plus two species on the Comoro archipelago (Hawlitschek et al. 2012) (Figure 12.43). They were formerly placed in the paraphyletic genus *Stenophis* (Domergue 1995). This genus rather neatly divides up Madagascar, with *L. citrinus* in the west, *L. pseudogranuliceps* in the west and southwest, *L. inornatus* in the southwest, *L. guentheri* in the south and center, *L. gaimardi* in the east, and *L. granuliceps*, *L. capuroni*, and *L. inopinae* in the north. In a few locations, two species may co-occur. Most species are brown with dark brown crossbands, but *L. citrinus* is bright yellow with black diamonds, making it highly distinctive. *Lycodryas pseudogranuliceps* and *L. citrinus* are viviparous (Vences et al. 1998), as is the Comorian species *L. maculatus* (Augros 2019). *Lycodryas gaimardi* (*carleti*) is oviparous, but the reproductive biology of other species of *Lycodryas* is unknown.

Brygophis: A monotypic genus consisting of *Brygophis coulangesi*. This arboreal species is known from two specimens from central and northeastern Madagascar (Domergue 1988; Andreone and Raxworthy 1998). *Brygophis* has not been adequately diagnosed from *Compsophis*, the only distinctions noted being some minor scale differences that possibly vary within *Compsophis*. Like the arboreal species of *Compsophis*, *Brygophis* has a laterally compressed body. One specimen fell from a large tree and disgorged a *Calumma parsonii*; the other specimen was on a low shrub at night in an apparent sleeping coil, suggesting that *Brygophis* may be diurnal. This species may have proven difficult to detect because it occupies high canopy in intact moist evergreen forests (Andreone and Raxworthy 1998).

FIGURE 12.43 **The slender and elegant arboreal snakes of the genera *Lycodryas* and *Phisalixella* are regularly observed at night in Madagascar's forests, but their natural history is poorly studied. This *Lycodryas* cf. *gaimardi* specimen was photographed in Marojejy National Park.** (PHOTO by M. D. Scherz.)

Ecomorphological Diversity

Malagasy pseudoxyrhophiids display a surprising array of ecomorphs. Although these are fewer than are observed in the Neotropics or tropical Asia, certain resemblances in terms of ecomorphs are present: shovel-snouted species (*Xenodon* in the Neotropics, *Leioheterodon* on Madagascar), vine snakes (various taxa in the Neotropics and Asia, *Langaha* on Madagascar), snail-eating snakes (*Dipsas* in the Neotropics, *Micropisthodon* on Madagascar), and so on. These recapitulations of basic snake ecomorphs within a single radiation of snakes make the Pseudoxyrhophiidae an excellent group for the study of ecomorphological evolution. Burbrink et al. (2019) have already shown, for example, that arboreality and opisthoglyphous dentition are phylogenetically correlated, supporting hypotheses on the evolution of opisthoglyphous dentition for handling arboreal prey (or aglyphous dentition for handling terrestrial prey). They also showed that arboreality and dentition do not relate to diversification rates in this family of snakes.

Yet it is also instructive to consider the ecomorphological types that are absent from these Malagasy snake assemblages. Compared to Neotropical snake assemblages (Cadle and Greene 1993), no extensive diversification of aquatic or fossorial snakes has occurred on Madagascar; only *Liopholidophis sexlineatus* and perhaps *L. varius* are aquatic (fully submerging) snakes, and neither shows any of the peculiar morphological characteristics commonly associated with strongly aquatic adaptation in colubroids, such as nostril valves or dorsal placement of the eyes. Although *Thamnosophis* and *Madagascarophis* species are often found near water, they have not been found to dive. *Heteroliodon* species are at least partly fossorial, but too little is known about their ecology at present; this genus is certainly not diverse. In several Neotropical colubroid assemblages, snakes using aquatic and fossorial macrohabitats make up 10–15% of the total colubroid species diversity. No Malagasy pseudoxyrhophiid is known to feed on fish, and none on non-molluscan invertebrates (see below), such as earthworms or insects.

Most Malagasy pseudoxyrhophiids have enlarged teeth on the posterior end of the maxilla, although the enlargement is subtle in some genera such as *Liophidium* and *Pararhadinaea* (Cadle 1999). Only *Micropisthodon* lacks indications of posterior maxillary tooth enlargement. In addition, the enlarged rear teeth are grooved in *Alluaudina*, *Compsophis*, *Ithycyphus*, *Langaha*, *Madagascarophis*, and *Mimophis*. This groove likely channels venom into the prey while it is being ingested.

Perhaps the most striking adaptations are seen in the clade of five genera and more than 20 species with dietary specializations for feeding on hard-bodied lizards (Savitzky 1981; Cadle 1999), of which hinged teeth are the most unusual specialization. There are far more species with this suite of adaptations than are found in any single continental fauna, although Cadle (1999) indicated that these specializations are probably more frequent among colubroids than is currently recognized.

Only a single dietary record (see *Micropisthodon ochraceus*) suggests that any Malagasy snake preys on the diverse and abundant molluscan fauna on Madagascar (see Griffiths and Herbert, pp. 860–72), and whether this is typical prey for this species is unknown. In contrast, diverse radiations of colubroids in the Neotropics and tropical Asia specialize on mollusks, and an array of small colubroids in the Neotropics prey on earthworms (Cadle and Greene 1993). Snail-eating is also known from the African pseudoxyrhophiid *Duberria*. Interestingly, the single Malagasy record of predation on snails indicates that this prey type is consumed entire rather than the soft parts being extracted from the shells, as in most Neotropical and Asian colubroid molluscivores (Sazima 1989; for an example of a Neotropical snake consuming entire snails, see Greene 1975).

The Pseudoxyrhophiidae therefore contains one species-enriched clade with specialized dentition, and several other, less diverse groups of highly distinct ecomorphology, mimicking a continental colubroid snake fauna from a single common ancestor (similar to what has been achieved by the mantellid frogs [see Vences et al., pp. 1360–65] and vangid birds [see Schulenburg, pp. 1694–99]). Compared to the phylogenetic diversity of other islands, that of Madagascar is off the scale (Pyron and Burbrink 2014). It may have been the early availability of a great deal of lizard diversity that enabled the comparatively large radiation of hinge-toothed species—diversification through ecological opportunity.

PSAMMOPHIIDAE

Researchers of the Malagasy snake fauna have long recognized both the distinctiveness of the genus *Mimophis* from other Malagasy genera, and its close similarity to some species of the Afro-Asian genus *Psammophis* (Mocquard 1895, 1909). *Mimophis* is unique among Malagasy colubroids in lacking hypapophyses (ventral projections) on the posterior trunk vertebrae and in having very reduced, threadlike hemipenes. In these respects, and also in aspects of its dentition, it resembles *Psammophis* and related genera from Africa, which on morphological grounds already suggested a close affinity with the Psammophiidae. Molecular phylogenetic studies have confirmed this relationship (Nagy et al. 2003; Ruane et al. 2015; Burbrink et al. 2019). Recent work by Ruane et al. (2018) focused on *Mimophis* phylogeography has found that there are two species in the genus rather than a single monotypic species. Here we provide a brief account of *Mimophis*.

Mimophis

Mimophis mahfalensis and its recently described northern sister species, *M. occultus*, are widespread in the Central Highlands and in western, southern, and northern Madagascar (Ruane et al. 2018). The two species have a parapatric distribution and are separated by elevation and latitude. Primarily snakes of open habitats and highly tolerant of habitat degradation, they are also occasionally found within forests (Glaw and Vences 1994). *Mimophis* species are largely diurnal and terrestrial but may sometimes be found in low vegetation and are seen active at night. Preston-Mafham (1991) reported, without documentation, that *Mimophis* feeds on other snakes, and C. Blanc (1970, 1977) reported that this species feeds on *Chalarodon madagascariensis*. A specimen collected in 2014 in Antoetra regurgitated a *Furcifer lateralis* upon capture (S. Ruane and C. J. Raxworthy, unpublished data); this species had also been seen hunting *Trachylepis elegans* skinks, and *Ptychadena* frogs have been recovered from its stomach (C. J. Raxworthy, unpublished data). An *M. occultus* individual was found swallowing a *Zonosaurus laticaudatus* subadult in Anjiamangirana forest in the northwest (Raselimanana 2018). Both *Mimophis* species show extensive variation in color and pattern across Madagascar, with striped, zigzag, and uniform color morphs (Ruane et al. 2018), similar to African psammophiine species.

CONSERVATION

Although several species of pseudoxyrhophiids on Madagascar are known from very few specimens, rarity itself is not necessarily a cause for concern since tropical herpetofaunas usually include several apparently "rare" snake species (Dunn 1949). Moreover, very few herpetofaunas (and none on Madagascar) have been sampled quantitatively, meaning that relative abundances of snake species or population trends cannot be estimated. Snakes are encountered infrequently enough in tropical areas that years of intensive effort are required to make inferences about their relative abundances.

The primary threat to snakes, as to the vast majority of Madagascar's flora and fauna, is deforestation and loss of habitat. Several species of pseudoxyrhophiids are unknown outside relatively undisturbed moist evergreen forests, a habitat that has been considerably reduced in recent decades. Species that are restricted to higher-elevation forests of the medium-altitude moist evergreen forests or Central Highlands, as well as lowland moist evergreen forest species, are likely to be the snakes most affected by habitat destruction since these forest components have been the most severely reduced. Examples of such high-elevation species are *Pseudoxyrhopus ankafinaensis* and *Liopholidophis grandidieri*, which are known from only one or a few localities above 1200 m in the Central Highlands (the former is probably now extinct; Raxworthy and Nussbaum 1994b). Montane snake species in the genera *Compsophis* and *Pseudoxyrhopus* are also vulnerable to habitat loss from climate change (Raxworthy et al. 2008b). Similarly, *Pararhadinaea melanogaster* is apparently restricted to highly fragmented lowland forests in northern Madagascar (Franzen et al. 2009; Labanowski and Lowin 2011).

These examples also illustrate the consequences of widespread habitat destruction: species restricted to small ranges or areas outside protected areas are particularly vulnerable. Fortunately, however, many Malagasy pseudoxyrhophiids seem to have broad geographic ranges. It is difficult to assess the impact of exploitation of pseudoxyrhophiids for the pet trade, but current levels of exportation seem to be very low. However, wild-caught individuals of several species (e.g., *Langaha madagascariensis*, *Lycodryas citrinus*, *Leioheterodon madagascariensis*) have appeared in American and European markets.

Subject editors: Mark D. Scherz, Miguel Vences, and Achille P. Raselimanana

TYPHLOPIDAE AND XENOTYPHLOPIDAE, BLIND SNAKES, *MATAHOTRANDRO*

C. J. Raxworthy

The blind snakes of Madagascar are arguably one of the most overlooked and neglected components of the island's herpetofauna. For example, in the precursor to this book (Goodman and Benstead 2003), there was no contribution devoted to this group (unlike all other reptile groups with endemic species) because before the publication of this current volume, little work had been conducted on Malagasy blind snakes and no herpetologist had an active research program on these animals. The reasons for this neglect stem from two problems: 1) they are highly secretive and rarely encountered in the field, and 2) when encountered, they are often mistaken for worms or other invertebrates. Compared to all the other reptile groups on Madagascar, blind snakes are always the rarest herpetological specimens deposited in research collections, and this scarcity of material (and field observations) has made them also the most poorly known. Yet the increased use of pitfall trapping during field inventories and the greater number of specimens collected over the last two decades have led to a somewhat improved state of knowledge.

Blind snakes can be readily identified by their wormlike appearance (but with a mouth, tongue, and reduced but sometimes visible eyes), cylindrical body with a head never broader than the body, smooth glossy scales that are the same size dorsally and ventrally, extremely short tail, and burrowing behavior. No Malagasy species exceeds 600 mm in total length, with most species less than 300 mm.

All blind snakes on the island are from either the family Typhlopidae (12 species in two genera: *Indotyphlops* and *Madatyphlops*) or the family Xenotyphlopidae (one genus and species: *Xenotyphlops grandidieri*); the latter family is endemic to Madagascar. The first modern review of the group on Madagascar was done by Guibé (1958), with more recent summaries given by Brygoo (1982), Glaw and Vences (2007), and Nagy et al. (2015). In the past 10 years considerable progress has been made regarding Malagasy blind snakes, including description of new species, recognition of synonyms and species of previous uncertain status or origin, and better understanding of their evolutionary relationships. However, much more work is still clearly needed; even though new species are almost certain to be discovered, we still lack a basic understanding of most species' distributions, and very little is known concerning their ecology and behavior.

XENOTYPHLOPIDAE

Xenotyphlops grandidieri

For more than 100 years after this species (Figure 12.44) was first described, no new specimen was collected, and frustratingly, the two known type specimens had only the vague locality "Madagascar." However, finally in 2005, a specimen of *Xenotyphlops* was collected in northern Madagascar, which was formally described as a second species, *X. mocquardi* (Wallach et al. 2007). Since that time, more *Xenotyphlops* specimens have been collected in littoral forests on sand dunes along the east coast, east of the town of Antsiranana (Wegener et al. 2013), and on a near-shore island in the northeast (Goodman et al. 2017). Based on an analysis of the morphological variation of all known *Xenotyphlops* specimens, and mtDNA variation, *X. mocquardi* is now considered to be a junior synonym of *X. grandidieri* (Wegener et al. 2013). These authors report that *X. grandidieri* is currently known from at least four sites in northern Madagascar, and it appears that the original "Madagascar" type specimens (part of the Rothschild collection) were also collected from this region, specifically Oronjia.

This species is pale pink and has a total length of less than 300 mm, no visible eyes, a remarkable "bulldozer"-shaped head in lateral view, and a greatly enlarged and nearly circular rostral shield that is nearly vertical in lateral view. The bizarre shape of the head results in the mouth opening being more ventrally oriented than in any other known blind snake (see Chretien et al. 2019, who described

FIGURE 12.44 ***Xenotyphlops grandidieri* represents extreme microendemism. This blind snake is the only representative of a genus and family and occurs only in a very restricted area of dunes and sand in northern Madagascar.** (PHOTOS by J. Köhler.)

the unusual skull of *X. grandidieri* in detail). This may be an adaptation to feed in sand substrates, to help consume larvae or eggs of ants or termites, to aid in sensory perception, or to defend burrows. *Xenotyphlops* is also unique among typhlopids in lacking a tracheal lung (Wallach et al. 2007).

Field observations have included a blind snake active on the surface along a small, almost dried-up stream in sandy soil (Wallach et al. 2007), a snake under wood in sand, and snakes collected by digging in sand to a depth of about 30 cm, in reddish fine-sand dunes with dense scrub forest (Wegener et al. 2013). This species may be restricted to sand dunes with scrub littoral forest in this northern part of Madagascar, and it is found sympatric with two locally endemic legless skinks: *Paracontias rothschildi* and *P. minimus*.

TYPHLOPIDAE

Indotyphlops braminus

This species, known by its English name Brahminy blind snake, is frequently also called the "flowerpot snake" because it has dispersed so widely across the globe as a result of accidental human-assisted translocation, often in horticultural products. It is now found in most tropical countries (Wallach 2009; Uetz et al. 2021) and presumably was introduced to Madagascar around the same time that it became established elsewhere on western Indian Ocean islands, including Mauritius, Rodrigues, La Réunion, Comoros, and Seychelles. *Indotyphlops braminus* is a triploid parthenogenetic species: all individuals are female and reproduce asexually (Wynn et al. 1987; Ota et al. 1991). This obligate parthenogenetic life history (which might be unique to this species within this genus) may also have greatly aided the dispersal ability of this species.

On Madagascar, this snake occurs in all regions up to about 1500 m but is typically found only in degraded habitats, in gardens, and around human habitations—that is to say, outside intact forests with closed canopy. Remarkably, it is tolerant of all climates on the island except in montane regions above 1500 m, which are presumably too cold during the winter months. It occupies sand and soil substrates and can also be found under surface debris and inside rotten wood. Based on the timing of pitfall trap captures, this species appears to be mostly surface active at night. It is relatively slender, never exceeding 200 mm total length, and on Madagascar always has a dark brown coloration.

The *Madatyphlops* Group

The vast majority of blind snake species on Madagascar belong to this group, which also represents the only blind snake species radiation on the island. There are currently 11 species recognized as endemic to Madagascar, with the two most recently described species, *M. andasibensis* and *M. rajeryi*, dating from 2009 (Renoult and Raselimanana 2009; Wallach and Glaw 2009). In addition, one species, *M. boettgeri*, was resurrected from synonymy (Wallach and Glaw 2009). The genus *Madatyphlops* also includes one tentatively assigned fossil species from Mauritius (*M. carieri*), two species from the Comoros—specifically *M. comorensis* from the islands of Grande Comore and Anjouan and *M. eudelini* from Mayotte (Hawlitschek et al. 2021)—and *M. albanalis*, possibly a valid species of unknown locality (Rendahl 1918). Because several African *Afrotyphlops* and *Rhinotyphlops* species are also morphologically very similar to Malagasy *Madatyphlops*, future taxonomic research may yet further modify species membership within the genus (Pyron and Wallach 2014; Nagy et al. 2015).

The first species described from Madagascar was *M. arenarius* in 1872, a small and slender, pink species that has a broad distribution in southern and western Madagascar. It is frequently found in sandy soils, including even pure sand, often in proximity to the coast, and is associated with both intact and degraded habitats. Most specimens are found under or in debris such as dead wood, but it is also surface active at night and can be sampled using pitfall traps. Genetic data (Nagy et al. 2015) and the broad spatial and ecological distribution suggest that this species may actually represent a species complex. The very similar *M. boettgeri* was resurrected from synonymy with *M. arenarius* by Wallach and Glaw (2009). Both species have similar ecologies and can occur sympatrically in southern Madagascar at the same sites. *Madatyphlops boettgeri* has a dorsal coloration of beige (not pink), transverse rather than oblique parietal scales, and other morphological differences compared to *M. arenarius*. The third species broadly distributed in dry deciduous forests of the west is *M. decorsei*, and this is also the largest known Malagasy blind snake, reaching up to 600 mm in total length. It is brown in dorsal coloration with a paler (sometimes yellow) ventral surface, and it has visible eyes. It is encountered rarely, but most often during the peak rainy season, when it may be surface active after heavy rains. This species is known from sites with intact forest and sandy soils.

The remaining eight *Madatyphlops* species are all found in more humid regions of Madagascar and are associated with intact forest, or in degraded habitat close to intact forest. All eight species are highly secretive, and their distribution limits are still poorly understood. Four species are known from Montagne d'Ambre, the extreme north, and the Sambirano Region: *M. madagascariensis*, *M. microcephalus*, *M. reuteri*, and *M. mucronatus*; three species from the east: *M. mucronatus* (Figure 12.45), *M. ocularis*, and *M. andasibensis*; and two species from the southeast, including Ranomafana: *M. domerguei* and *M. rajeryi*. These species have been collected in pitfall traps using drift fences, inside and under rotten wood, and in leaf litter, or they have been picked up off roads and trails after heavy rain. Most specimens have been obtained during the rainy season, and surface-active observations are extremely rare. All these species are

FIGURE 12.45 A *Madatyphlops* specimen, probably *M. mucronatus*, from Marojejy National Park. (PHOTO by M. Vences.)

brown or dark brown and vary in length from 90 to 420 mm. A useful key to their identification is given by Wallach and Glaw (2009).

BIOLOGY

Remarkably little is reliably known about the biology of the Malagasy endemic species of the two families of blind snakes, and to date, no field studies have targeted this group. This is because blind snakes are so difficult to find. We suspect Malagasy blind snakes feed primarily on ants and termites (including eggs and larvae), as is typical of other species of blind snakes (Chretien et al. 2019), and their frequent occurrence in dead wood and rotting vegetation also supports this impression. A recent study by Jono et al. (2019) showed that *Madatyphlops decorsei* elicits nest evacuation in *Aphaenogaster swammerdami* ants, and that these ants have apparently developed a symbiotic relationship with the snake *Madagascarophis colubrinus*, a potential *Madatyphlops* predator, to aid in nest defense. Sand-specialist blind snake species probably prey on other invertebrate groups adapted to this substrate. Life history and reproductive biology are especially poorly documented, with juveniles and neonates being rare in collections.

EVOLUTIONARY HISTORY AND ORIGINS

Although evolutionary relationships and taxonomy have been (at times) controversial and unstable over the past 10 years, it is now well established that the Malagasy blind snakes represent at least three independent origins on Madagascar. The arrival of *Indotyphlops braminus* is the most recent and was almost certainly mediated by human introduction. The two endemic groups of blind snakes on the island represent different families and are not closely related (Pyron and Wallach 2014; Nagy et al. 2015). The xenotyphlopid group is represented by only a single species lineage: *Xenotyphlops grandidieri*, microendemic to northern Madagascar. This species should therefore be viewed as a biogeographic and evolutionary relict. The date of divergence of *Xenotyphlops* from its sister lineage, the Typhlopidae clade, has not yet been estimated (Pyron and Wallach 2014; Nagy et al. 2015). However, based on the divergence date of the typhlopid lineage from other blind snakes (Burbrink et al. 2020), the origin of the *Xenotyphlops* lineage could be as old as the mid-Cretaceous, around 100 Mya (Vidal et al. 2010). But even at this earliest date, Indo-Madagascar (Madagascar still attached to India) was already an island isolated from greater Gondwana. The *Madatyphlops* arrival to Madagascar was certainly later, and based on the divergence dating within the major lineages of the Typhlopidae clade, this occurred during the Paleogene (63–23 Mya) (Vidal et al. 2010).

Evolutionary relationships within the genus *Madatyphlops* have not yet been well established, as many species and populations have not been sampled for tissues, but the most complete study to date is that of Nagy et al. (2015). Generic and family-level relationships are becoming better resolved, with support for a monophyletic genus *Madatyphlops* (Hedges et al. 2014), which includes *M. microcephalus*, *M. reuteri*, and *M. domerguei* (Nagy et al. 2015)—species that had been previously assigned to a recently proposed genus, *Lemuriatyphlops* (Pyron and Wallach 2014). As more localities are sampled and more species are included in evolutionary studies, it will soon be possible to start exploring the drivers of speciation within the *Madatyphlops* species radiation of Madagascar.

CONSERVATION AND THREATS

All species of blind snakes on Madagascar are listed by the 2019 IUCN Red List as either Least Concern or Data Deficient, with the sole exception of *Xenotyphlops grandidieri*, which is given Critically Endangered status. This status is based on the snake having been recorded from only a single locality at the time of its assessment in 2011, and because of the ongoing loss of dune habitat for charcoal production. Although more sites have now been documented (see above), *X. grandidieri* is still clearly vulnerable to extinction from habitat loss.

Other Data Deficient *Madatyphlops* species are expected to also qualify for a category of threat as new field data are collected. The exact dependence of *Madatyphlops* species on intact forest is still unclear, but we suspect that most species do not persist in heavily degraded areas (based on the limited observations made to date). Thus, the protected area network will likely play a crucial future role in conserving populations for most of the endemic blind snake species.

Subject editors: Christopher J. Raxworthy, Miguel Vences, and Achille P. Raselimanana

REFERENCES

Abate, A. 1998. Reports from the field: Parson's chameleon. *Chamaeleon Information Network* 29: 17–25.

Alfino, S., and Roberts, D. L. 2019. Estimating identification uncertainties in CITES "look-alike" species. *Global Ecology and Conservation* 18: e00648.

Allibert, C. J. 1989. Early settlement on the Comoro archipelago. *National Geographic Research* 5: 392–393.

Allison, A. 2002. New record of *Phelsuma madagascariensis* in Hawaii. Geckoweb. https://www.geckoweb.org/biogeography-hawaii.html.

Altmanová, M., Rovatsos, M., Kratochvíl, L., and Johnson Pokorn, M. 2016. Minute Y chromosomes and karyotype evolution in Madagascan iguanas (Squamata: Iguania: Opluridae). *Biological Journal of the Linnean Society* 118: 618–633.

Anderson, C. V. 2016. Off like a shot: Scaling of ballistic tongue projection reveals extremely high performance in small chameleons. *Scientific Reports* 6: 18625.

Anderson, C. V., and Deban, S. M. 2010. Ballistic tongue projection in chameleons maintains high performance at low temperature. *Proceedings of the National Academy of Sciences of the USA* 107: 5495–5499.

Anderson, C. V., and Higham, T. E. 2013. Chameleon anatomy. In *Biology of the Chameleons*, eds. K. A. Tolley and A. Herrel, pp. 7–56. Berkeley: University of California Press.

Anderson, C. V., Sheridan, T., and Deban, S. M. 2012. Scaling of the ballistic tongue apparatus in chameleons. *Journal of Morphology* 273: 1214–1226.

Andreone, F. 1991a. Reptile field records from Malagasy rainforests. *Bollettino del Museo Regionale di Scienze Naturali di Torino* 9: 437–460.
———. 1991b. Conservation aspects of the herpetofauna of Malagasy rain forests. *Zoological Society "La Torbiera" Scientific Reports* 1: 1–45.
———. 2004. Crossroads of herpetological diversity: Survey work for an integrated conservation of amphibians and reptiles in northern Madagascar. *Italian Journal of Zoology* 71: 229–235.
Andreone, F., and Greer, A. E. 2002. Madagascan scincid lizards: Descriptions of nine new species, with notes on the morphology, reproduction and taxonomy of some previously described species (Reptilia, Squamata, Scincidae). *Journal of Zoology* 258: 139–181.
Andreone, F., and Luiselli, L. 2000. Are there shared patterns of specific diversity, abundance, and guild structure in snake communities of tropical forests of Madagascar and continental Africa? *Revue d'Ecologie (La Terre et la Vie)* 55: 215–239.
Andreone, F., and Randrianirina, J. E. 2000. Biodiversity, rainforests and herpetological communities in Madagascar: What about differences between amphibians and reptiles? In *Diversity and Endemism in Madagascar*, eds. W. R. Lourenço and S. M. Goodman, pp. 217–228. Paris: Mémoires de la Société de Biogéographie.
Andreone, F., and Raxworthy, C. J. 1998. The colubrid snake *Brygophis coulangesi* (Domergue 1988) rediscovered in north-eastern Madagascar. *Tropical Zoology* 11: 249–257.
Andreone, F., Randrianirina, J. E., Jenkins, P. D., and Aprea, G. 2000. Species diversity of Amphibia, Reptilia and Lipotyphla (Mammalia) at Ambolokopatrika, a rainforest between the Anjanaharibe-Sud and Marojejy massifs, NE Madagascar. *Biodiversity and Conservation* 9: 1587–1622.
Andreone, F., Glaw, F., Nussbaum, R. A., Raxworthy, C. J., Vences, M., and Randrianirina, J. E. 2003. The amphibians and reptiles of Nosy Be (NW Madagascar) and nearby islands: A case study of diversity and conservation of an insular fauna. *Journal of Natural History* 37: 2119–2149.
Andreone, F., Guarino, F. M., and Randrianirina, J. E. 2005. Life history traits, age profile, and conservation of the panther chameleon, *Furcifer pardalis* (Cuvier 1829), at Nosy Be, NW Madagascar. *Tropical Zoology* 18: 209–225.
Andreone, F., Glaw, F., Randrianirina, J. E., and Vences, M. 2007. Remarkable records of amphibians and reptiles on Madagascar's central high plateau. *Tropical Zoology* 20: 19–39.
Andreone, F., Carpenter, A. I., Cox, N., Du Preez, L., Freeman, K., et al. 2008. The challenge of conserving amphibian megadiversity in Madagascar. *PLoS Biology* 6: 943–946.
Andreone, F., Glaw, F., Mattioli, F., Jesu, R., Schimmenti, G., Randrianirina, J. E., and Vences, M. 2009. The peculiar herpetofauna of some Tsaratanana rainforests and its affinities with Manongarivo and other massifs and forests of northern Madagascar. *Italian Journal of Zoology* 76: 92–110.
Andrews, R. M. 2008. Lizards in the slow lane: Thermal biology of chameleons. *Journal of Thermal Biology* 33: 57–61.
Andrews, R. M., and Karsten, K. B. 2010. Evolutionary innovations of squamate reproductive and developmental biology within the family Chamaeleonidae. *Biological Journal of the Linnean Society* 100: 656–668.
Andrews, R. M., Díaz-Paniagua, C., Marco, A., and Portheault, A. 2008. Developmental arrest during embryonic development of the common chameleon (*Chamaeleo chamaeleon*) in Spain. *Physiological and Biochemical Zoology* 81: 336–344.
Angel, F. 1942. Les lézards de Madagascar. *Mémoires de l'Académie Malgache* 36: 1–193.
Arnold, E. N. 1976. Fossil reptiles from Aldabra Atoll, Indian Ocean. *Bulletin of the British Museum of Natural History* 29: 83–116.
———. 1979. Indian Ocean giant tortoises: Their systematics and island adaptations. *Philosophical Transactions of the Royal Society of London B: Biological Sciences* 286: 127–145.
Augros, S. 2019. *Atlas des amphibiens et des reptiles terrestres de l'archipel des Comores*. Mèze and Paris: Biotope Editions and MNHN.
Auliya, M., Altherr, S., Ariano-Sanchez, D., Baard, E. H., Brown, C., et al. 2016. Trade in live reptiles, its impact on wild populations, and the role of the European market. *Biological Conservation* 204: 103–119.
Austin, J. J., Arnold, E. N., and Jones, C. G. 2004. Reconstructing an island radiation using ancient and recent DNA: The extinct and living day geckos (*Phelsuma*) of the Mascarene islands. *Molecular Phylogenetics and Evolution* 31: 102–109.
Autumn, K., and Peattie, A. M. 2002. Mechanisms of adhesion in geckos. *Integrative and Comparative Biology* 42: 1081–1090.
Autumn, K., Liang, Y. A., Hsieh, S. T., Zesch, W., Chan, W. P., Kenny, T. W., Fearing, R., and Full, R. J. 2000. Adhesive force of a single gecko foot-hair. *Nature* 405: 681–685.
Avery, R. A. 1979. Lizards: A study in thermoregulation. *Studies in Biology* 109: 1–56.
Barley, S. B., and Walker, R.C.J. 2013. Population density and seasonal detection rates of a unique population of critically endangered northern Madagascar spider tortoise (*Pyxis arachnoides brygooi*). *Herpetological Conservation and Biology* 8: 616–621.
Barlow, J., Gardner, T. A., Araujo, I. S., Avila-Peres, T. C., Bonaldo, A. B., et al. 2007. Quantifying the biodiversity value of tropical primary, secondary, and plantation forests. *Proceedings of the National Academy of Sciences of the USA* 104: 18555–18560.
Bates, H. W. 1892. *The Naturalist on the River Amazon*. London: John Murray.
Bates, M. F., Tolley, K. A., Edwards, S., Davids, Z., da Silva, J. M., and Branch, W. R. 2013. A molecular phylogeny of the African plated lizards, genus *Gerrhosaurus* Wiegmann, 1828 (Squamata: Gerrhosauridae), with the description of two new genera. *Zootaxa* 3750: 465–493.
Bauer, A. M. 1989. Extracranial endolymphatic sacs in *Eurydactylodes* (Reptilia: Gekkonidae), with comments on endolymphatic function in lizards. *Journal of Herpetology* 23: 172–175.
———. 1993. African–South American relationships: A perspective from the Reptilia. In *Biological Relationships between Africa and South America*, ed. P. Goldblatt, pp. 244–288. New Haven: Yale University Press.
———. 1998. Morphology of the adhesive tail tips of carphodactyline geckos (Reptilia: Diplodactylidae). *Journal of Morphology* 235: 41–58.
———. 2003. Gekkonidae, geckos. In *The Natural History of Madagascar*, eds. S. M. Goodman and J. P. Benstead, pp. 973–977. Chicago: University of Chicago Press.
———. 2007. The foraging biology of the Gekkota: Life in the middle. In *Lizard Ecology: The Evolutionary Consequences of Foraging Mode in Lizards*, eds. S. M. Reilly, L. B. McBrayer, and D. B. Miles, pp. 371–404. New York: Cambridge University Press.
———. 2013. *Geckos: The Animal Answer Guide*. Baltimore: Johns Hopkins University Press.
Bauer, A. M., and Russell, A. P. 1989. A systematic review of the genus *Uroplatus* (Reptilia: Gekkonidae) with comments on its biology. *Journal of Natural History* 23: 169–203.
———. 1992. The evolutionary significance of regional integumentary loss in island geckos: A complement to caudal autotomy. *Ethology, Ecology and Evolution* 4: 343–358.
———. 1994. Is autotomy frequency reduced in geckos with "actively functional" tails? *Herpetological Natural History* 2(2): 1–15.
Bauer, A. M., Russell, A. P., and Shadwick, R. E. 1989. Mechanical properties and morphological correlates of fragile skin in gekkonid lizards. *Journal of Experimental Biology* 145: 79–102.
Bauer, A. M., Good, D. A., and Branch, W. R. 1997. The taxonomy of the southern African leaf-toed geckos (Squamata: Gekkonidae), with a review of Old World "*Phyllodactylus*" and the description of five new genera. *Proceedings of the California Academy of Sciences* 49: 447–497.
Baxter-Gilbert, J., Baider, C., Florens, F.B.V., Hawlitschek, O., Mohan, A. V., Mohanty, N. P., Wagener, C., Webster, K. C., and Riley, J. L. 2021. Nocturnal foraging and activity by diurnal lizards: Six species of day geckos (*Phelsuma* spp.) using the night-light niche. *Austral Ecology* 46: 501–506.
Behra, O., and Hutton, J. M. 1990. Rapport sur l'état et la conservation des populations des crocodiles à Madagascar. In *The CITES Nile Crocodile Project*, eds. J. M. Hutton and I. Games. Lausanne: Secretariat of the Convention on International Trade in Endangered Species of Wild Fauna and Flora (CITES).
Behra, O., and Ramandimbison. 1992. The involvement of rural communities in the crocodile ranching program in Madagascar. In *Crocodiles: Proceedings of the 11th Working Meeting of the Crocodile Specialist Group of the SSC of the IUCN; The World Conservation Union Convened at Victoria Falls, Zimbabwe, 2 to 7 August 1992*, ed. IUCN Species Survival Commission (SSC), Crocodile Specialist Group, vol. 1, pp. 43–52. Gland: IUCN.
Behra, O., and Raxworthy, C. J. 1991. Exportation des amphibiens de Madagascar: Intérêt, danger et perspectives d'avenir. *Circalytes* 5(4): 45–49.
Belluardo, F., Quirós, D. D., Lobón-Rovira, J., Rosa, G. M., Rasoazanany, M., Andreone, F., and Crottini, A. 2021. Uncovering the herpetological diversity of small forest fragments in south-eastern Madagascar (Haute Matsiatra). *Zoosystematics and Evolution* 97(2): 315–343.
Berg, W., Theisinger, O., and Dausmann, K. H. 2017. Acclimatization patterns in tropical reptiles: Uncoupling temperature and energetics. *Science of Nature* 104: 91.
Berghof, H. P., and Trautmann, G. 2009. Eine neue Art der Gattung *Phelsuma* Gray, 1825 (Sauria: Gekkonidae) von der Ostküste Madagaskars. *Sauria* 31: 5–14.

Bertrand, M., and Pedrono, M. 1999. Euryxenie et stenoxenie du genre *Geckobia* Megnin 1878 (Actinedida: Pterygosomatidae): Récolte de *Geckobia enigmatica* n. sp. sur une tortue terrestre malgache (*Geochelone yniphora*). *Acarologia* 11: 41–47.

Bickelmann, C., and Klein, N. 2009. The late Pleistocene horned crocodile *Voay robustus* (Grandidier and Vaillant, 1872) from Madagascar in the Museum für Naturkunde Berlin. *Fossil Record* 12: 13–21.

Blair, C., Noonan, B. P., Brown, J. L., Raselimanana, A. P., Vences, M., and Yoder, A. D. 2015. Multilocus phylogenetic and geospatial analyses illuminate diversification patterns and the biogeographic history of Malagasy endemic plated lizards (Gerrhosauridae: Zonosaurinae). *Journal of Evolutionary Biology* 28: 481–492.

Blanc, C. P. 1966. Notes sur les Gekkonidae de Madagascar. I. Observations relatives a deux espèces de *Geckolepis*: *G. maculata* Peters, 1880 et *G. typica* Grandidier, 1867. *Vie et Milieu* 17: 453–460.

———. 1969. Etudes sur les Iguanidae de Madagascar. II. Observations sur l'écologie de *Chalarodon madagascariensis* Peters, 1854. *Oecologia* 2: 292–318.

———. 1970. Analyse des facteurs de l'environnement dans l'aire de répartition de *Chalarodon madagascariensis*: Leurs implications biologiques. *Annales de l'Université de Madagascar, Sciences* 7: 279–306.

———. 1972. Les reptiles de Madagascar et des îles voisines. In *Biogeography and Ecology in Madagascar*, eds. R. Battistini and G. Richard-Vindard, pp. 501–614. The Hague: W. Junk.

———. 1977. Reptiles Sauriens Iguanidae. *Faune de Madagascar* 45: 1–199.

———. 1982. Les iguanes. *La Recherche* 13(139): 1398–1408.

———. 1984. The reptiles. In *Madagascar (Key Environments)*, eds. A. Jolly, P. Oberlé, and R. Albignac, pp. 104–114. Oxford: Pergamon.

Blanc, C. P., and Blommers-Schlösser, R. 1987. Priorités en matière de conservation des reptiles et amphibiens de Madagascar. *Occasional Papers, IUCN Species Survival Commission (Suisse)* 2: 117–120.

Blanc, C. P., and Paulian, R. 1996. Originalité biogéographique de la faune du sud Malgache. In *Biogéographie de Madagascar*, ed. W. R. Lourenço, pp. 231–244. Paris: ORSTOM.

Blanc, F. 1970a. Contribution à l'étude de la croissance post-embryonnaire de *Chamaeleo lateralis* Gray, 1831. *Annales de l'Université de Madagascar, Sciences* 7: 321–343.

———. 1970b. Le cycle reproducteur chez la femelle de *Chamaeleo lateralis* Gray, 1831. *Annales de l'Université de Madagascar, Sciences* 7: 345–358.

Blanvillain, G., Owens, D. W., and Kuchling, G. 2011. Reptiles: Hormones and reproductive cycles in turtles. In *Hormones and Reproduction of Vertebrates*, eds. D. Norris and K. Lopez, pp. 277–303. London: Elsevier, Academic Press.

Blom, M.P.K., Matzke, N. J., Bragg, J. G., Arida, E., Austin, C. C., et al. 2019. Habitat preference modulates transoceanic dispersal in a terrestrial vertebrate. *Proceedings of the Royal Society of London B: Biological Sciences* 286: 20182575.

Bloxam, Q.M.C. 1999. Distribution and density and abundance of the Madagascar flat-tailed tortoise *Pyxis planicauda*. *Testudo* 4: 28–40.

Bloxam, Q.M.C., Behler, J. L., Rakotovao, E. R., Randriamahazo, H.J.A.R., Hayes, K. T., Tonge, S. T., and Ganzhorn, J. U. 1996. Effects of logging on the reptile fauna of the Kirindy forest with special emphasis on the flat-tailed tortoise (*Pyxis planicauda*). In Ecology and economy of a tropical dry forest in Madagascar, eds. J. U. Ganzhorn and J.-P. Sorg. *Primate Report* 46–1: 189–201.

Blumberg, M. S., Lewis, S. J., and Sokoloff, G. 2002. Incubation temperature modulates post-hatching thermoregulatory behavior in the Madagascar ground gecko, *Paroedura pictus*. *Journal of Experimental Biology* 205: 2777–2784.

Blumgart, D., Dolhem, J., and Raxworthy C. J. 2017. Herpetological richness and abundance across intact and modified habitats of Nosy Komba Island, Madagascar. *Journal of Natural History* 51: 625–642.

Boettger, O. 1893. *Katalog der Reptilien-Sammlung im Museum der Senckenbergischen Naturforschenden Gesellschaft in Frankfurt am Main*. Vol. 1, *Rhynchocephalen, Schildkröten, Krokodile, Eidechsen, Chamäleons*. Frankfurt a. M.: Gebrüder Knauer.

Bogert, C. M. 1943. Dentitional phenomena in cobras and other elapids with notes on adaptive modifications of fangs. *Bulletin of the American Museum of Natural History* 81: 285–360.

Böhm, M., Collen, B., Baillie, J. E., Bowles, P., Chanson, J., et al. 2013. The conservation status of the world's reptiles. *Biological Conservation* 57: 372–385.

Böhme, W. 1997. Eine neue Chamäeleonart aus der *Calumma gastrotaenia*-Verwandtschaft Ost-Madagaskars. *Herpetofauna* 19: 5–10.

Böhme, W., and Meier, H. 1980. Revision der madagasischen *Homopholis* (*Blaesodactylus*)-Arten (Sauria: Gekkonidae). *Senckenbergiana Biologica* 60(1979): 303–315.

Boistel, R., Herrel, A., Daghfous, G., Libourel, P. A., Boller, E., Tafforeau, P., and Bels, V. 2010. Assisted walking in Malagasy dwarf chamaeleons. *Biology Letters* 6: 740–743.

Bolton, M. 1991. Développement de l'élevage de crocodiles à Madagascar. United Nations FAO Report TCP/MAG/8954.

Bora, P., Randriambahiniarime, O. M., Rabemananjara, F.C.E, Ramilijaona, O. R., Glaw, F., and Vences, M. 2007. A rapid assessment survey of the herpetofauna at Befotaka–Midongy National Park, south-eastern Madagascar. *Zoosystematics and Evolution* 83: 170–178.

Bora, P., Randrianantoandro, J. C., Randrianavelona, R., Hantalalaina, E. F., Andriantsimanarilafy, R. R., et al. 2010. Amphibians and reptiles of the Tsingy de Bemaraha Plateau, western Madagascar: Checklist, biogeography and conservation. *Herpetological Conservation and Biology* 5: 111–125.

Borer, M. 2013. *Madagaskarboas* Acrantophis *und* Sanzinia: *Lebensweise, Pflege und Fortpflanzung*. Rheinstetten: KUS-Verlag.

Boulenger, G. A. 1884. Synopsis of the families of existing Lacertilia. *Annals and Magazine of Natural History*, series 5, 14: 117–122.

———. 1885. *Catalogue of the Lizards of the British Museum*. Vol. 1, *Geckonidæ, Eublepharidæ, Uroplatidæ, Pygopodidæ, Agamidæ*. 2nd ed. London: Taylor and Francis.

———. 1887. *Catalogue of the Lizards in the British Museum (Natural History)*. Vol. 3, *Lacertidae, Gerrhosauridae, Scincidae, Anelytropidea, Dibamidae, Chamaeloentidae*. 2nd ed. London: British Museum (Natural History).

———. 1889. *Catalogue of the Chelonians, Rhynchocephalians and Crocodiles in the British Museum (Natural History)*. London: Taylor and Francis.

Boumans, L., Vieites, D. R., Glaw, F., and Vences, M. 2007. Geographical patterns of deep mitochondrial differentiation in widespread Malagasy reptiles. *Molecular Phylogenetics and Evolution* 45: 822–839.

Bour, R. 1979. Les tortues actuelles de Madagascar (République Malgache): Liste systématique et description de deux sous-espèces nouvelles. *Bulletin de la Société pour les Etudes Scientifiques Anjouan*, nouvelle série, 10: 141–154.

———. 1981. Etude systématique du genre endémique malgache *Pyxis* Bell, 1827 (Reptilia, Chelonii). *Bulletin Mensuel de la Société Linnéenne de Lyon* 50: 154–176.

———. 1987. Les tortues terrestres et d'eau douce de Madagascar et des îles voisines. II. Clé de détermination des tortues malgaches actuelles. *Bulletin de l'Association pour l'Avancement de la Recherche Scientifique concernant Madagascar et la Région Malgache* 20: 1–11.

———. 1994. Recherches sur des animaux doublement disparus: Les tortues géantes subfossiles de Madagascar. *Mémoire Ecole Pratique des Hautes Etudes* 19: 1–253.

———. 2006. *Kinixys belliana domerguei* (Vuillemin, 1972), la tortue à dos articulé de Madagascar: Données historiques et écologiques. *Chéloniens* 3: 42–56.

Bourgat, R. M. 1973. Cytogénétique des caméléons de Madagascar: Incidences taxonomiques, biogéographiques et phylogénétiques. *Bulletin de la Société Zoologique de France* 98: 1.

Bourgat, R. M., and Brygoo, E. R. 1968. Apport de l'étude des hémipénis à la systématique du complexe *Chamaeleo verrucosus* Cuvier, 1829: *Chamaeleo oustaleti* Mocquard, 1894. *Annales de l'Université de Madagascar, Sciences* 6: 419–424.

Brady, L. D., and Griffiths, R. A. 1999. *Status Assessment of Chameleons in Madagascar*. Gland: IUCN Species Survival Commission.

Brady, L. D., Huston, K., Jenkins, R.K.B., Kauffmann, J.J.L., Rabearivony, J., Raveloson, G., and Rowcliffe, M. 1996. *UEA Madagascar Expedition 93*. Final report. Norwich: University of East Anglia.

Branch, W. R., and Erasmus, H. 1976. Reproduction in Madagascar ground and tree boas *Acrantophis dumerili* and *Sanzinia madagascariensis*. *International Zoo Year Book* 16: 78–80.

Brandley, M., Schmitz, A., and Reeder, T. 2005. Partitioned Bayesian analyses, partition choice, and the phylogenetic relationships of scincid lizards. *Systematic Biology* 54: 373–390.

Brenes, R., Gray, M. J., Waltzek, T. B., Wilkes, R. P., and Miller, D. L. 2014. Transmission of Ranavirus between ectothermic vertebrate hosts. *PLoS One* 9(3): e92476.

Brillet, C. 1982. Contribution à l'étude des relations entre individus chez cinq espèces d'iguanes malgaches du genre *Oplurus*. *Revue d'Ecologie (La Terre et la Vie)* 36: 79–148.

———. 1990. Rôle des informations olfactives et visuelles dans la discrimination du sexe chez deux espèces de geckos nocturnes: *Eublepharis macularius* et *Paroedura pictus*. *Biology of Behaviour* 15: 1–22.

———. 1991. Analyse comparative de la structure du comportement sexuel chez deux espèces de geckos nocturnes: *Eublepharis macularius* et *Paroedura pictus* (Sauria, Gekkonidae). *Behaviour* 117: 117–143.

Broadley, D. G. 1989. *Kinixys belliana*. In *The Conservation Biology of Tortoises*, eds. I. R. Swingland and M. W. Klemens, pp. 49–54. Occasional Papers of the Species Survival Commission No. 5. Gland: IUCN.

Brochu, C. A. 2000. Phylogenetic relationships and divergence timing of *Crocodylus* based on morphology and the fossil record. *Copeia* 2000: 657–673.
———. 2006. A new miniature horned crocodile from the Quaternary of Aldabra Atoll, western Indian Ocean. *Copeia* 2006: 149–158.
———. 2007. Morphology, relationships, and biogeographical significance of an extinct horned crocodile (Crocodylia, Crocodylidae) from the Quaternary of Madagascar. *Zoological Journal of the Linnean Society* 150: 835–863.
Brown, D. 1998. *Participatory Biodiversity Conservation Rethinking the Strategy in the Low Potential Areas of Tropical Africa*. Natural Resource Perspectives No. 44. London: Overseas Development Institute.
Brown, J. L., Cameron, A., Yoder, A. D., and Vences, M. 2014. A necessarily complex model to explain the biogeography of the amphibians and reptiles of Madagascar. *Nature Communications* 5: e5046.
Brown, J. L., Sillero, N., Glaw, F., Bora, P., Vieites, D. R., and Vences, M. 2016. Spatial biodiversity patterns of Madagascar's amphibians and reptiles. *PLoS One* 11: e0144076.
Brygoo, E. R. 1971. Reptiles Sauriens Chamaeleonidae: Genre *Chamaeleo*. *Faune de Madagascar* 33: 1–318.
———. 1978. Reptiles Sauriens Chamaeleonidae: Genre *Brookesia* et complément pour le genre *Chamaeleo*. *Faune de Madagascar* 47: 1–173.
———. 1979. Systématique des lézards scincidés de la région malgache. I. *Scelotes trivittatus* (Boulenger, 1896) nov. comb. synonyme de *Scelotes trilineatus* Angel, 1949. *Bulletin du Muséum National d'Histoire Naturelle*, Paris, série 4, 1(4): 1115–1120.
———. 1980a. Systématique des lézards scincidés de la région malgache. II. *Amphiglossus astrolabi* Duméril et Bibron, 1839, *Gongylus polleni* Grandidier, 1869, *Gongylus stumpffi* Boettger, 1882, et *Scelotes waterloti* Angel, 1930. *Bulletin du Muséum National d'Histoire Naturelle*, Paris, série 4, 2(2): 525–539.
———. 1980b. Systématique des lézards scincidés de la région malgache. III. Les "Acontias" de Madagascar: *Pseudoacontias* Barboza du Bocage, 1889, *Paracontias* Mocquard, 1894, *Pseudoacontias* Hewitt, 1929, et *Malacontias* Green, 1970. IV. *Amphiglossus reticulatus* (Kaudern, 1922) nov. comb., troisième espèce du genre: Ses rapports avec *Amphiglossus waterloti* (Angel, 1920). *Bulletin du Muséum National d'Histoire Naturelle*, Paris, série 4, 2(3): 905–918.
———. 1980c. Systématique des lézards scincidés de la région malgache. V. *Scelotes praeornatus* Angel, 1938, synonyme de *Scelotes* s. l. *frontoparietalis* (Boulenger, 1889). *Bulletin du Muséum National d'Histoire Naturelle*, Paris, série 4, 2(4): 1155–1160.
———. 1981a. Systématique des lézards scincidés de la région malgache. VI. Deux scincinés nouveaux. *Bulletin du Muséum National d'Histoire Naturelle*, Paris, série 4, 3(1): 261–268.
———. 1981b. Systématique des lézards scincidés de la région malgache. VII. Révision des genres *Voeltzkowia* Boettger, 1893, *Grandidierina* Mocquard, 1894, et *Cryptoscincus* Mocquard, 1894. *Bulletin du Muséum National d'Histoire Naturelle*, Paris, série 4, 3(2): 675–688.
———. 1981c. Systématique des lézards scincidés de la région malgache. VIII. Les *Mabuya* des îles de l'océan Indien occidental: Comores, Europa, Séchelles. *Bulletin du Muséum National d'Histoire Naturelle*, Paris, série 4, 3(3): 911–930.
———. 1981d. Systématique des lézards scincidés de la région malgache. IX. Nouvelles unités taxinomiques pour les *Scelotes* s. l. *Bulletin du Muséum National d'Histoire Naturelle*, Paris, série 4, 3(4): 1193–1204.
———. 1982. Les ophidiens de Madagascar. *Memorias do Instituto Butantan* 46: 19–58.
———. 1983a. Systématique des lézards scincidés de la région malgache. X. Rapports de *Gongylus johannae* Günther, 1880, des Comores, et de *Sepsina valhallae* Boulenger, 1909, des Glorieuses, avec les espèces malgaches. *Bulletin du Muséum National d'Histoire Naturelle*, Paris, série 4, 5(2): 651–660.
———. 1983b. Systématique des lézards scincidés de la région malgache. XI. Les *Mabuya* de Madagascar. *Bulletin du Muséum National d'Histoire Naturelle*, Paris, série 4, 5(4): 1079–1108.
———. 1984a. Systématique des lézards scincidés de la région malgache. XII. Le groupe d'espèces *Gongylus melanurus* Günther, 1877, *G. gastrostictus* O'Shaughnessy, 1879, et *G. macrocercus* Günther, 1882. *Bulletin du Muséum National d'Histoire Naturelle*, Paris, série 4, 6(1): 131–148.
———. 1984b. Systématique des lézards scincidés de la région malgache. XIII. Les *Amphiglossus* du sous-genre *Madascincus*. *Bulletin du Muséum National d'Histoire Naturelle*, Paris, série 4, 6(2): 527–536.
———. 1984c. Systématique des lézards scincidés de la région malgache. XIV. Le genre *Pygomeles* A. Grandidier, 1867. *Bulletin du Muséum National d'Histoire Naturelle*, Paris, série 4, 6(3): 769–777.
———. 1984d. Systématique des lézards scincidés de la région malgache. XV. *Gongylus igneocaudatus* A. Grandidier, 1867, et *Scelotes intermedius* Boettger, 1913. Les *Amphiglossus* du groupe *igneocaudatus*. *Bulletin du Muséum National d'Histoire Naturelle*, Paris, série 4, 6(3): 779–789.
———. 1984e. Systématique des lézards scincidés de la région malgache. XVI. Les *Amphiglossus* du groupe *ornaticeps*. *Bulletin du Muséum National d'Histoire Naturelle*, Paris, série 4, 6(4): 1153–1160.
———. 1985a. Les Gerrhosaurinae de Madagascar (Sauria: Cordylidae). *Mémoires du Muséum National d'Histoire Naturelle*, Paris, *Zoologie*, 134: 1–65.
———. 1985b. Systématique des lézards scincidés de la région malgache. XVII. *Gongylus splendidus* A. Grandidier, 1872, *Scelotes macrolepis* Boulenger, 1888, et *Scelotes decaryi* Angel 1930. *Bulletin du Muséum National d'Histoire Naturelle*, Paris, série 4, 7(1): 235–247.
———. 1986. Systématique des lézards scincidés de la région malgache. XVIII. Les *Cryptoblepharus*. *Bulletin du Muséum National d'Histoire Naturelle*, Paris, série 4, 8(3): 643–690.
———. 1987. Systématique des lézards scincidés de la région malgache. XIX. Données nouvelles sur le genre *Androngo*. *Bulletin du Muséum National d'Histoire Naturelle*, Paris, série 4, 9(1): 255–263.
Brygoo, E. R., Blanc, C. P., and Domergue, C. A. 1973 [1974]. Notes sur les *Chamaeleo* de Madagascar. XII. Caméléons du Marojezy: *C. peyrierasi* n. sp. et *C. gastrotaenia guillaumeti* n. subsp. (Reptilia, Squamata, Chameleonidae). *Bulletin de l'Académie Malgache* 51: 151–164.
Buckland, S., Cole, N. C., Aguirre-Gutiérrez, J., Gallagher, L. E., Henshaw, S. M., Besnard, A., Tucker, R. M., Bachraz, V., Ruhomaun, K., and Harris, S. 2014. Ecological effects of the invasive giant Madagascar day gecko on endemic Mauritian geckos: Applications of binomial mixture and species distribution models. *PLoS One* 9: e88798. doi:10.1371/journal.pone.0088798.
Burbrink, F. T., Ruane, S., Kuhn, A., Rabibisoa, N., Randriamahatantsoa, B., et al. 2019. The origins and diversification of the exceptionally rich gemsnakes (Colubroidea: Lamprophiidae: Pseudoxyrhophiinae) in Madagascar. *Systematic Biology* 68: 918–936.
Burbrink, F., Grazziotin, F. G., Pyron, R. A., Cundall, D., Donnellan, S., et al. 2020. Interrogating the genomes of Squamata (lizards, snakes, and amphisbaenians) with novel machine-learning techniques shows no support for deeper traditional morphological relationships. *Systematic Biology* 69: 502–520.
Burleigh, R., and Arnold, E. N. 1986. Age and dietary differences of recently extinct Indian Ocean tortoises (*Geochelone s. lat.*) revealed by carbon isotope analysis. *Proceedings of the Royal Society of London B: Biological Sciences* 227: 137–144.
Burney, D. A. 1997. Theories and facts regarding Holocene environmental change before and after human colonization. In *Natural Change and Human Impact in Madagascar*, eds. S. M. Goodman and B. D. Patterson, pp. 75–92. Washington, DC: Smithsonian Institution Press.
Caccone, A., Amato, G., Gratry, O. C., Behler, J., and Powell, J. R. 1999. A molecular phylogeny of four endangered Madagascar tortoises based on mtDNA sequences. *Molecular Phylogenetics and Evolution* 12: 1–9.
Cadle, J. E. 1996a. Snakes of the genus *Liopholidophis* (Colubridae) from eastern Madagascar: New species, revisionary notes, and an estimate of phylogeny. *Bulletin of the Museum of Comparative Zoology* 154(5): 369–464.
———. 1996b. Systematics of snakes of the genus *Geodipsas* (Colubridae) from Madagascar, with descriptions of new species and observations on natural history. *Bulletin of the Museum of Comparative Zoology* 155(2): 33–87.
———. 1999. The dentition, systematics, and phylogeny of *Pseudoxyrhopus* and related genera from Madagascar, with description of a new species and a new genus. *Bulletin of the Museum of Comparative Zoology* 155(8): 381–443.
———. 2003. Colubridae, snakes. In *The Natural History of Madagascar*, eds. S. M. Goodman and J. P. Benstead, pp. 997–1004. Chicago: University of Chicago Press.
———. 2014. Natural history and taxonomic notes on *Liopholidophis grandidieri* Mocquard, an upland rain forest snake from Madagascar (Serpentes: Lamprophiidae: Pseudoxyrhophiinae). *Herpetological Conservation and Biology* 9(2): 406–416.
Cadle, J. E., and Greene, H. W. 1993. Phylogenetic patterns, biogeography, and the composition of Neotropical snake assemblages. In *Species Diversity in Ecological Communities: Historical and Geographical Perspectives*, eds. R. E. Ricklefs and D. Schluter, pp. 281–293. Chicago: University of Chicago Press.
Cadle, J. E., and Ineich, I. 2008. Nomenclatural status of the Malagasy snake genus *Bibilava* Glaw, Nagy, Franzen, and Vences, 2007: Resurrection of *Thamnosophis* Jan and designation of a lectotype for *Leptophis lateralis* Duméril, Bibron, and Duméril (Serpentes: Colubridae). *Herpetological Review* 39(3): 285–288.
Campbell, J. A., and Murphy, J. B. 1977. Miscellaneous notes on the reproductive biology of reptiles. I. Two colubrid snake species from the Malagasy Republic,

Leioheterodon madagascariensis and *Madagascarophis colubrina* (Reptilia, Serpentes, Colubridae). *Journal of Herpetology* 11: 225–228.

Carpenter, A. I. 2003. The ecology and exploitation of chameleons in Madagascar. PhD thesis, University of East Anglia.

———. 2004. The dynamics of the global trade in chameleons. *Biological Conservation* 120: 291–301.

Carpenter, A. I., and Robson, O. 2005. A review of the endemic chameleon genus *Brookesia* from Madagascar, and the rationale for its listing on CITES Appendix II. *Oryx* 39: 375.

———. 2008. Madagascan amphibians as a wildlife resource and their potential as a conservation tool: Species and numbers exported, revenue generation and bio-economic models to explore conservation benefits. In A conservation strategy for the amphibians of Madagascar, ed. F. Andreone. *Monografie del Museo Regionale di Scienze Naturali di Torino* 45: 357–376.

Carpenter, A. I., Rowcliffe, M., and Watkinson, A. R. 2004. The dynamics of the global trade in chameleons. *Biological Conservation* 120: 295–305.

Carpenter, A. I., Robson, O., Rowcliffe, J. M., and Watkinson, A. R. 2005. The impacts of international and national governance changes on a traded resource: A case study of Madagascar and its chameleon trade. *Biological Conservation* 123: 279–287.

Carpenter, A. I., Andreone, F., Moore, R. D., and Griffiths, R. A. 2014. A review of the global trade in amphibians: The types of trade, levels and dynamics in CITES listed species. *Oryx* 48: 565–574.

Carranza, S., and Arnold, E. N. 2003. Investigating the origin of transoceanic distributions: mtDNA shows *Mabuya* lizards (Reptilia, Scincidae) crossed the Atlantic twice. *Systematics and Biodiversity* 1(2): 275–282.

Čerňanský, A., Herrel, A., Kibii, J. M., Anderson, C. V., Boistel, R., and Lehmann, T. 2020. The only complete articulated early Miocene chameleon skull (Rusinga Island, Kenya) suggests an African origin for Madagascar's endemic chameleons. *Scientific Reports* 10: 109.

Chan, L. M., Choi, D., Raselimanana, A. P., Rakotondravony, H. A., and Yoder, A. D. 2012. Defining spatial and temporal patterns of phylogeographic structure in Madagascar's iguanid lizards (genus *Oplurus*). *Molecular Ecology* 21: 3839–3851.

Chechia, A. M. 2018. Nest protection and population evaluation of the critically endangered big-headed Turtle or the rere (*Erymnochelys madagascariensis*) at Lake Kinkony. Unpublished final project evaluation report. Rufford Foundation.

Cheke, A. S. 1984. Lizards of the Seychelles. In *Biogeography and Ecology of the Seychelles Islands*, ed. D. R. Stoddart, pp. 331–360. The Hague: W. Junk.

Cheke, A. S., and Hume, J. 2008. *Lost Land of the Dodo: The Ecological History of Mauritius, Réunion and Rodrigues*. London: A and C Black.

Chen, K. K., and Kovaříková, A. 1967. Pharmacology and toxicology of toad venom. *Journal of Pharmaceutical Sciences* 56: 1535–1541.

Chiari, Y., Thomas, M., Pedrono, M., and Vieites, D. R. 2005. Preliminary data on genetic differentiation within the Madagascar spider tortoise, *Pyxis arachnoides* (Bell, 1827). *Salamandra* 41: 35–44.

Chiari, Y., Vieites, D. R., Guo, J., Bora, P., and Vences, M. 2009. High haplotype diversity in a microendemic Malagasy gecko species, *Lygodactylus mirabilis* (Pasteur, 1962). *Zootaxa* 2269: 43–52.

Chretien, J., Wang-Claypool, C. Y., Glaw, F., and Scherz, M. D. 2019. The bizarre skull of *Xenotyphlops* sheds light on synapomorphies of Typhlopoidea. *Journal of Anatomy* 234: 637–655.

CITES. 2019. Convention on International Trade in Endangered Species of Wild Fauna and Flora. Accessed 12 Oct. 2019. https://cites.org.

Clause, J. K. 2017. *Mimophis mahfalensis* (Malagasy big-eyed snake) diet. *Herpetological Review* 48: 454–455.

Clémencet, J., Aubert, C., Blottière, D., and Sanchez, M. 2013. Kleptoparasitism in the endemic gecko *Phelsuma inexpectata*: Pollen theft from foraging honeybees on Réunion. *Journal of Tropical Ecology* 29: 251–254.

Cocca, W., Rosa, G. M., Andreone, F., Aprea, G., Bergò, P. E., et al. 2018. The herpetofauna (Amphibia, Crocodylia, Squamata, Testudines) of the Isalo Massif, southwest Madagascar: Combining morphological, molecular and museum data. *Salamandra* 54: 178–200.

Colles, A., Liow, L. H., and Prinzing, A. 2009. Are specialists at risk under environmental change? Neoecological, paleoecological and phylogenetic approaches. *Ecology Letters* 12: 849–863.

Collinson, M. E., Andrews, P., and Bamford, M. K. 2009. Taphonomy of the early Miocene flora, Hiwegi Formation, Rusinga Island, Kenya. *Journal of Human Evolution* 57: 149–162.

Conant, R. 1938. A note on eggs and young of *Leioheterodon madagascariensis* (Duméril and Bibron). *Zoologica* 23(19): 389–391.

Cooper, W. E., van Wyk, J. H., and Mouton, P.L.F.N. 1996. Pheromonal detection and sex discrimination of conspecific substrate deposits by the rock-dwelling cordylid lizard *Cordylus cordylus*. *Copeia* 1996: 839–845.

Cornet, A. 1974. *Essai de cartographie bioclimatique à Madagascar*. Paris: Office de la Recherche Scientifique et Technique Outre-Mer.

Crottini, A., Dordel, J., Köhler, J., Glaw, F., Schmitz, A., and Vences, M. 2009. A multilocus phylogeny of Malagasy scincid lizards elucidates the relationships of the fossorial genera *Androngo* and *Cryptoscincus*. *Molecular Phylogenetics and Evolution* 53(1): 345–350.

Crottini, A., Harris, D. J., Irisarri, I., Lima, A., Rasamison, S., and Rosa, G. M. 2010. Confirming Domergue: *Ithycyphus oursi* Domergue, 1986 predation upon *Furcifer oustaleti* (Mocquard, 1894). *Herpetology Notes* 3: 127–131.

Crottini, A., Gehring, P.-S., Glaw, F., Harris, D. J., Lima, A., and Vences, M. 2011. Deciphering the cryptic species diversity of dull-coloured day geckos *Phelsuma* (Squamata: Gekkonidae) from Madagascar, with description of a new species. *Zootaxa* 2982: 40–48.

Crottini, A., Madsen, O., Poux, C., Strauß, A., Vieites, D. R., and Vences, M. 2012a. Vertebrate time-tree elucidates the biogeographic pattern of a major biotic change around the K-T boundary in Madagascar. *Proceedings of the National Academy of Sciences of the USA* 109: 5358–5363.

Crottini, A., Miralles, A., Glaw, F., Harris, D. J., Lima, A., and Vences, M. 2012b. Description of a new pygmy chameleon (Chamaeleonidae: *Brookesia*) from central Madagascar. *Zootaxa* 3490: 63–74.

Crottini, A., Harris, D. J., Miralles, A., Glaw, F., Jenkins, R.K.B., Randrianantoandro, J. C., Bauer, A. M., and Vences, M. 2014. Morphology and molecules reveal two new species of the poorly studied gecko genus *Paragehyra* (Squamata: Gekkonidae) from Madagascar. *Organisms Diversity and Evolution* 15: 175–198.

Crowley, B. E., and Samonds, K. E. 2013. Stable carbon isotope values confirm a recent increase in grasslands in northwestern Madagascar. *Holocene* 23: 1066–1073.

Daniels, S. R., Heideman, N.J.L., Hendricks, M.G.J., Mokone, M.-E., and Crandall, K. A. 2005. Unraveling evolutionary lineages in the limbless fossorial skink genus *Acontias* (Sauria: Scincidae): Are subspecies equivalent systematic units? *Molecular Phylogenetics and Evolution* 34: 645–654.

Daniels, S. R., Heideman, N.J.L., Hendricks, M.G.J., and Crandall, K. A. 2006. Taxonomic subdivision within the fossorial skink subfamily Acontinae (Squamata: Scincidae) reconsidered: A multilocus perspective. *Zoologica Scripta* 35: 353–362.

Davis, H. R., Bauer, A. M., Jackman, T. R., Nashriq, I., and Das, I. 2019. Uncovering karst endemism within Borneo: Two new *Cyrtodactylus* species from Sarawak, Malaysia. *Zootaxa* 4614(2): 331–352.

Daza, J. D., and Bauer, A. M. 2010. The circumorbital bones of the Gekkota (Reptilia: Squamata). *Anatomical Record* 293: 402–413.

Daza, J. D., Stanley, E. L., Wagner, P., Bauer, A. M., and Grimaldi, D. A. 2016. Mid-Cretaceous amber fossils illuminate the past diversity of tropical lizards. *Science Advances* 2: e1501080.

D'Cruze, N. C. 2008. Envenomation by the Malagasy colubrid snake *Langaha madagascariensis*. *Journal of Venomous Animals and Toxins including Tropical Diseases* 14: 546–551.

D'Cruze, N., and Kumar, S. 2011. Effects of anthropogenic activities on lizard communities in northern Madagascar. *Animal Conservation* 14: 542–552.

D'Cruze, N., Green, K. E., Robinson, J. E., and Gardner, C. J. 2006. A rapid assessment of the amphibians and reptiles of an unprotected area of dry deciduous forest in north Madagascar. *Herpetological Bulletin* 96: 17–25.

D'Cruze, N., Sabel, J., Green, K., Dawson, J., Gardner, C., Robinson, J., Starkie, G., Vences, M., and Glaw, V. 2007. The first comprehensive survey of amphibians and reptiles at Montagne des Français, Madagascar. *Herpetological Conservation and Biology* 2: 87–99.

D'Cruze, N., Köhler, J., Franzen, M., and Glaw, F. 2008. A conservation assessment of the amphibians and reptiles of the Forêt d'Ambre Special Reserve, north Madagascar. *Madagascar Conservation and Development* 3: 44–54.

D'Cruze, N., Sabel, J., Dawson, J., and Kumar, S. 2009a. The influence of habitat type and structure on the abundance of *Phelsuma madagascariensis grandis* (Gekkonidae) in northern Madagascar. *Herpetological Conservation and Biology* 4: 55–61.

D'Cruze, N., Henson, D., Olsson, A., and Emmett, D. 2009b. The importance of herpetological survey work in conserving Malagasy biodiversity: Are we doing enough? *Herpetological Review* 40: 19–25.

D'Cruze, N., Machado, F. C., Matthews, N., Balaskas, M., Carder, G., Richardson, V., and Vieto, R. 2017. A review of wildlife ecotourism in Manaus, Brazil. *Nature Conservation* 22: 1–16.

D'Cruze, N., Neihaus, C., Balaskas, M., Vieto, R., Carder, G., Richardson, V. A., Moorhouse, T., Harrington, L. A., and Macdonald, D. W. 2018. Wildlife tourism in Latin America: Taxonomy and conservation status. *Journal of Sustainable Tourism* 26: 1562–1576.

Decary, R. 1950. *La faune malgache*. Paris: Payot.

Dewar, R. E. 1984. Extinctions in Madagascar. In *Quaternary Extinctions: A Prehistoric Revolution*, eds. P. S. Martin and R. G. Klein, pp. 574–593. Tucson: University of Arizona Press.

Dewar, R. E., Radimilahy, C., Wright, H. T., Jacobs, Z., Kelly, G. O., and Berna, F. 2013. Stone tools and foraging in northern Madagascar challenge Holocene extinction models. *Proceedings of the National Academy of Sciences of the USA* 110: 12583–12588.

Dixon, J. A., and Pagiola, S. 2001. *Ecotourism: Incentives for Conservation Success*. Washington DC: Environment Department, World Bank.

Domergue, C. A. 1983. Notes sur les serpents de la région malgache. III. Description de trois espèces nouvelles rapportées au genre *Liophidium* Boulenger, 1896. *Bulletin du Muséum National d'Histoire Naturelle*, Paris 4(5): 1109–1122.

———. 1986. Notes sur les serpents de la région malgache. VI. Le genre *Ithycyphus* Gunther, 1873: Description de deux espèces nouvelles. *Bulletin du Muséum National d'Histoire Naturelle*, Paris, série 4, 8 (section A, no. 2): 409–434.

———. 1987. Notes sur les serpents de la région malgache. VII. Révision du genre *Madagascarophis* Mertens, 1952. *Bulletin du Muséum National d'Histoire Naturelle*, Paris, série 4, 9 (section A, no. 2): 455–489.

———. 1988. Notes sur les serpents de la région malgache. VIII. Colubridae nouveaux. *Bulletin du Muséum National d'Histoire Naturelle*, Paris, série 4, 10 (section A, no. 1): 135–146.

———. 1989. Un serpent venimeux de Madagascar: Observation de deux cas de morsure par *Madagascarophis* (colubridé opisthoglyphe). *Archives de l'Institut Pasteur de Madagascar* 56: 299–311.

———. 1993. Notes sur les serpents de la région malgache. IX. Un Colubrinae rare: *Micropisthodon ochraceus* Mocquard, 1894. *Archives de l'Institut Pasteur de Madagascar* 59: 139–151.

———. 1995 [1994]. Serpents de Madagascar: Note liminaire sur des espèces nouvelles du genre *Stenophis* Boulenger, 1896 (Colubridae-Boiginae). *Archives de l'Institut Pasteur de Madagascar* 61: 121–122.

Doody, J. S., Georges, A., and Young, J. E. 2003. Twice every second year: Reproduction in the pig-nosed turtle, *Carettochelys insculpta*, in the wet-dry tropics of Australia. *Journal of Zoology* 259: 179–188.

Dowling, H. G. 1975. A provisional classification of snakes. In *1974 Yearbook of Herpetology*, ed. H. G. Dowling, pp. 167–170. New York: Herpetological Information Search Systems.

Dubos, N., Piludu, N., Andriantsimanarilafy, R. R., Randrianantoandro, J. C., and Andreone, F. 2014. New findings of *Phelsuma grandis* and *P. laticauda* (Sauria: Gekkonidae) at the southern edge of the range of the endangered *Phelsuma serraticauda* in eastern Madagascar. *Herpetology Notes* 7: 21–23.

Dudley, N. 2008. *Guidelines for Applying Protected Area Management Categories*. Gland: IUCN.

Duffy, R. 2006. Global environmental governance and the politics of ecotourism in Madagascar. *Journal of Ecotourism* 5: 128–144.

Dunn, E. R. 1949. Relative abundance of some Panamanian snakes. *Ecology* 30: 39–57.

Durbin, J., and Ralambo, J. A. 1994. The role of local people in the successful maintenance of protected areas in Madagascar. *Environmental Conservation* 21: 115–120.

Durden, L. A., Keirans, J. E., and Smith, L. L. 2002. *Amblyomma geochelone*, a new species of tick (Acari: Ixodidae) from the Madagascan ploughshare tortoise. *Journal of Medical Entomology* 39: 398–403.

Eckhardt, F., Gehring, P.-S., Bartel, L., Bellmann, J., Beuker, J., et al. 2012. Assessing sexual dimorphism in a species of Malagasy chameleon with a newly defined set of morphometric and meristic measurements. *Herpetology Notes* 5: 335–344.

Eckhardt, F., Kappeler, P. M., and Kraus, C. 2017. Highly variable lifespan in an annual reptile, Labord's chameleon (*Furcifer labordi*). *Scientific Reports* 7: 11397.

Eckhardt, F., Kraus, C., and Kappeler, P. M. 2019a. Life histories, demographies and population dynamics of three sympatric chameleon species (*Furcifer* spp.) from western Madagascar. *Amphibia-Reptilia* 40: 41–54.

Eckhardt, F., Stube, C., Mathes, K. A., Mutschmann, F., Thiesler, H., Kraus, C., and Kappeler, P. M. 2019b. Parasite burden in a short-lived chameleon, *Furcifer labordi*. *IJP: Parasites and Wildlife* 10: 231–240.

Edmund, A. G. 1969. Dentition. In *Biology of the Reptilia*, vol. 1, eds. C. Gans, A. d'A. Bellairs, and T. S. Parsons, pp. 117–200. New York: Academic Press.

Erens, J., Miralles, A., Glaw, F., Chatrou, L., and Vences, M. 2017. Extended molecular phylogenetics and revised systematics of Malagasy scincine lizards. *Molecular Phylogenetics and Evolution* 107: 466–472.

Ernst, C. H., and Barbour, R. W. 1989. *Turtles of the World*. Washington, DC: Smithsonian Institution Press.

Etheridge, R. 1967. Lizard caudal vertebrae. *Copeia* 4: 699–721.

Etheridge, R., and De Queiroz, K. 1988. A phylogeny of Iguanidae. In *Phylogenetic Relationships of the Lizard Families: Essays Commemorating Charles L. Camp*, eds. R. Estes and G. Pregill, pp. 283–367. Stanford: Stanford University Press.

Evans, S. E. 2008. The skull of lizards and tuatara. In *The Skull of Lepidosauria*, eds. A. S. Gaunt and K. Adler, pp. 1–348. Ithaca: Society for the Study of Amphibians and Reptiles.

Ferguson, G., Murphy, J. B., Raselimanana, A. P., and Ramanamanjato, J.-B. 1995. Panther chameleon (*Chamaeleo pardalis*): Natural history, captive management and breeding. In *Care and Breeding of Panther, Jackson's, Veiled, and Parson's Chameleons*, eds. P. de Vosjoli and G. Ferguson, pp. 5–32. Santee: Advanced Vivarium Systems.

Fideline, H. E., Andriantsimanarilafy, R. R., Rakotondravony, D., Randrianantoandro, C., Randrianavelona, R., and Jenkins, R.K.B. 2007. Roost site characteristics of sympatric dwarf chameleons (genus *Brookesia*) from western Madagascar. *Amphibia-Reptilia* 28: 577–581.

Florio, A. M., and Raxworthy, C. J. 2016. A phylogeographic assessment of the Malagasy giant chameleons (*Furcifer verrucosus* and *Furcifer oustaleti*). *PLoS One* 11: e0154144.

Florio, A. M., Ingram, C. M., Rakotondravony, H. A., Louis, E. E., and Raxworthy, C. J. 2012. Detecting cryptic speciation in the widespread and morphologically conservative carpet chameleon (*Furcifer lateralis*) of Madagascar. *Journal of Evolutionary Biology* 25: 1399–1414.

Fölling, M., Knogge, C., and Böhme, W. 2001. Geckos are milking honeydew-producing planthoppers in Madagascar. *Journal of Natural History* 35: 279–284.

Forero-Medina, G., Ferrara, C., Vogt, R., Fagundes, C., Balestra, R., et al. 2021. On the future of the giant South American river turtle *Podocnemis expansa*. *Oryx* 55: 73–80. doi:10.1017/S0030605318001370.

Franzen, M., Jones, J., Raselimanana, A. P., Nagy, Z. T., D'Cruze, N., Glaw, F., and Vences, M. 2009. A new black-bellied snake (Pseudoxyrhophiinae: *Liophidium*) from western Madagascar, with notes on the genus *Pararhadinaea*. *Amphibia-Reptilia* 30: 173–183.

Fritz, U., Branch, W. R., Hofmeyr, M. D., Maran, J., Prokop, H., et al. 2010. Molecular phylogeny of African hinged and helmeted terrapins (Testudines: Pelomedusidae: *Pelusios* and *Pelomedusa*). *Zoologica Scripta* 40: 115–125.

Fritz, U., Branch, W. R., Gehring, P.-S., Harvey, J., Kindler, C., Meyer, L., Du Preez, L., Široký, P., Vieites, D. R., and Vences, M. 2012. Weak divergence among African, Malagasy and Seychellois hinged terrapins (*Pelusios castanoides*, *P. subniger*) and evidence for human-mediated oversea dispersal. *Organisms Diversity and Evolution* 13: 215–224.

Fuchs, K., Mertens, R., and Wermuth, H. 1974. Die Unterarten des Nilkrokodils, *Crocodylus niloticus*. *Salamandra* 10: 107–114.

Funnell, S., Shrum, M., Ellis, E., and Andreone, F. 2012. A new record of the phantom gecko *Matoatoa spannringi* from Sainte Luce, SE Madagascar augments the species' known range. *Herpetology Notes* 5: 151–153.

Gaffney, E. S., and Krause, D. W. 2011. *Sokatra*, a new side-necked turtle (Late Cretaceous, Madagascar) and the diversification of the main groups of Pelomedusoides. *American Museum Novitates* 3728: 1–28.

Gaffney, E. S., Krause, D. W., and Zalmout, I. S. 2009. *Kinkonychelys*, a new side-necked turtle (Pelomedusoides: Bothremydidae) from the Late Cretaceous of Madagascar. *American Museum Novitates* 3662: 1–25.

Gamble, T. 2010. A review of sex determining mechanisms in geckos (Gekkota: Squamata). *Sexual Development* 4: 88–103.

Gamble, T., Greenbaum, E., Jackman, T. R., Russell, A. P., and Bauer, A. M. 2012. Repeated origin and loss of adhesive toepads in geckos. *PLoS One* 7: e39429.

Gamble, T., Greenbaum, E., Jackman, T. R., and Bauer, A. M. 2015. Into the light: Diurnality has evolved multiple times in geckos. *Biological Journal of the Linnean Society* 115: 896–910.

Games, I., Ramandimbison, and Lippai, C. 1997. Madagascar crocodile survey. Report to CITES Secretariat.

Ganzhorn, J. U., Rakotosamimanana, B., Hannah, L., Hough, J., Iyer, L., Olivieri, S., Rajaobelina, S., Rodstrom, C., and Tilkin, G. 1997. Priorities for biodiversity conservation in Madagascar. *Primate Report* 48–1: 1–81.

García, G. 2005. Ecology, human impact and conservation for the Madagascan side-necked turtle (*Erymnochelys madagascariensis* (Grandidier, 1876)) at Ankarafantsika National Park, Madagascar. PhD thesis, University of Kent.

García, G., and Goodman, S. M. 2003. Hunting of protected animals in the National Park Ankarafantsika, north-western Madagascar. *Oryx* 37: 115–118.

García, G., and Lourenço, W. 2007. *Erymnochelys madagascariensis* diet. *Herpetological Review* 38: 330–331.

García, G., and Vences, M. 2002a. *Phelsuma madagascariensis kochi* (Madagascar day gecko) diet. *Herpetological Review* 33: 53–54.

———. 2002b. *Furcifer oustaleti* (Oustalet's chameleon) diet. *Herpetological Review* 33: 134–135.

Garcia-Porta, J., Morales, H. E., Gómez-Díaz, E., Sindaco, R., and Carranza, S. 2016. Patterns of diversification in islands: A comparative study across three gecko genera in the Socotra archipelago. *Molecular Phylogenetics and Evolution* 98: 288–299.

Gardner, A. S. 1984. The evolutionary ecology and population systematics of day geckos (*Phelsuma*) in the Seychelles. PhD thesis, University of Aberdeen.

———. 1985. The calcium cycle of female day-geckos (*Phelsuma*). *Herpetological Journal* 1: 37–39.

Gardner, C. J. 2009. A review of the impacts of anthropogenic habitat change on terrestrial biodiversity in Madagascar: Implications for the design and management of new protected areas. *Malagasy Nature* 2: 2–29.

———. 2013. Observation of reed bed use by *Furcifer verrucosus* (Squamata: Chamaeleonidae) in southwest Madagascar. *Herpetology Notes* 6: 21–22.

Gardner, C. J., and Jasper, L. D. 2009. The urban herpetofauna of Toliara, southwest Madagascar. *Herpetology Notes* 2: 239–242.

Gardner, C. [J.], and Jasper, L. 2012. Cannibalism in *Chalarodon madagascariensis* (Squamata: Iguanidae) from southwest Madagascar. *Herpetology Notes* 5: 127–128.

Gardner, C. [J.], and Jasper, L. 2015. Diet of the endemic Malagasy day gecko *Phelsuma modesta leiogaster* Mertens, 1970 in an urban environment. *Herpetology Notes* 8: 489–492.

Gardner, C. [J.], Germain, N., and de Foucault, C. 2013. Heaviest recorded specimen of Madagascar ground boa *Acrantophis madagascariensis* (Serpentes: Boidae). *Herpetology Notes* 6: 553–554.

Gardner, C. J., Raxworthy, C. J., Metcalfe, K., Raselimanana, A. P., Smith, R. J., and Davies, Z. G. 2015a. Comparing methods for prioritising between existing protected areas: A case study using Madagascar's dry forest reptiles. *PLoS One* 10: e0132803

Gardner, C. [J.], Vincke, X., and Jasper, L. 2015b. Additions to the urban herpetofauna of Toliara, southwest Madagascar. *Herpetology Notes* 8: 47–49.

Gardner, C. J., Jasper, L. D., Eonintsoa, C., Duchene, J. J., and Davies, Z. G. 2016. The impact of natural resource use on bird and reptile communities within multiple-use protected areas: Evidence from sub-arid southern Madagascar. *Biodiversity and Conservation* 25: 1773–1793.

Gardner, C. J., Nicoll, M. E., Birkinshaw, C., Harris, A., Lewis, R. E., Rakotomalala, D., and Ratsifandrihamana, A. N. 2018. The rapid expansion of Madagascar's protected area system. *Biological Conservation* 220: 29–36.

Gebhardt, R. 2004. Beobachtung eines Kommentkampfes bei *Leioheterodon modestus* (Günther, 1863) während einer Reise durch den Südwesten Madagaskars. *Sauria* 26(3): 29–31.

Gehring, P.-S. 2020. *Leaf-tailed Geckos: The Complete* Uroplatus. Frankfurt am Main: Chimaira.

Gehring, P.-S., Crottini, A., Glaw, F., Hauswaldt, S., and Ratsoavina, F. M. 2010a. Notes on the natural history, distribution and malformations of day geckos (*Phelsuma*) from Madagascar. *Herpetology Notes* 3: 321–327.

Gehring, P.-S., Pabijan, M., Ratsoavina, F. M., Köhler, J., Vences, M., and Glaw, F. 2010b. A Tarzan yell for conservation: A new chameleon, *Calumma tarzan* sp. n., proposed as a flagship species for the creation of new nature reserves in Madagascar. *Salamandra* 46: 167–179.

Gehring, P.-S., Ratsoavina, F. M., Vences, M., and Glaw, F. 2011. *Calumma vohibola*, a new chameleon species (Squamata: Chamaeleonidae) from the littoral forests of eastern Madagascar. *African Journal of Herpetology* 60: 130–154.

Gehring, P.-S., Tolley, K. A., Eckhardt, F. S., Townsend, T. M., Ziegler, T., Ratsoavina, F. M., Glaw, F., and Vences, M. 2012. Hiding deep in the trees: Discovery of divergent mitochondrial lineages in Malagasy chameleons of the *Calumma nasutum* group. *Ecology and Evolution* 2: 1468–1479.

Gehring, P.-S., Glaw, F., Gehara, M., Ratsoavina, F. M., and Vences, M. 2013. Northern origin and diversification in the central lowlands? Complex phylogeography and taxonomy of widespread day geckos (*Phelsuma*) from Madagascar. *Organisms Diversity and Evolution* 13: 605–620.

Gehring, P.-S., Siarabi, S., Scherz, M. D., Ratsoavina, F. M., Rakotoarison, A., Glaw, F., and Vences, M. 2018. Genetic differentiation and species status of the large-bodied leaf-tailed geckos *Uroplatus fimbriatus* and *U. giganteus*. *Salamandra* 54: 132–146.

Gibbons, J. W., Scott, D. E., Ryan, T. J., Buhlmann, K. A., Tuberville, T. D., et al. 2000. The global decline of reptiles, déjà vu amphibians. *BioScience* 50: 653–666.

Gibson, L., Lee, T. M., Koh, L. P., Brook, B. W., Gardner, T. A., et al. 2011. Primary forests are irreplaceable for sustaining tropical biodiversity. *Nature* 478: 378–381.

Gippner, S., Travers, S. L., Scherz, M. D., Colston, T. J., Lyra, M. L., et al. 2021. A comprehensive phylogeny of dwarf geckos of the genus *Lygodactylus*, with insights into their systematics and morphological variation. *Molecular Phylogenetics and Evolution* 165: 107311.

Glaw, F. 2015. Taxonomic checklist of chameleons (Squamata: Chamaeleonidae). *Vertebrate Zoology* 65: 167–246.

Glaw, F., and Glaw, K. 2004. Geheimnisvolle Madagaskarboas: *Sanzinia* und *Acrantophis*. *Draco* 5(19): 37–43.

Glaw, F., and Rösler, H. 2015. Taxonomic checklist of the day geckos of the genera *Phelsuma* Gray, 1825 and *Rhoptropella* Hewitt, 1937 (Squamata: Gekkonidae). *Vertebrate Zoology* 65: 247–283.

Glaw, F., and Vences, M. 1992. *A Fieldguide to the Amphibians and Reptiles of Madagascar*. 1st ed. Cologne: Vences and Glaw Verlags.

———. 1994. *A Fieldguide to the Amphibians and Reptiles of Madagascar*. 2nd ed. Cologne: Vences and Glaw Verlags.

———. 2000. Current counts of species diversity and endemism of Malagasy amphibians and reptiles. In *Diversité et endémisme à Madagascar*, eds. W. R. Lourenço and S. M. Goodman, pp. 243–248. Paris: Mémoires de la Société de Biogéographie.

———. 2007. *A Field Guide to the Amphibians and Reptiles of Madagascar*. 3rd ed. Cologne: Vences and Glaw Verlags.

Glaw, F., Vences, M., Ziegler, T., Böhme, W., and Köhler, J. 1999. Specific distinctness and biogeography of the dwarf chameleons *Brookesia minima*, *B. peyrierasi* and *B. tuberculata* (Reptilia: Chamaeleonidae): Evidence from hemipenial and external morphology. *Journal of Zoology* 247: 225–238.

Glaw, F., Vences, M., and Lourenço, W. R. 2002. *Geckolepis maculata* (spotted fishscale gecko): Predation. *Herpetological Review* 33: 135.

Glaw, F., Schmidt, K., and Vences, M. 2003. Nachtgeckos aus Madagaskar. *Die Aquarien- und Terrarien-Zeitschrift* 56(9): 6–11.

Glaw, F., Vences, M., and Nussbaum, R. A. 2005a. A new species of *Heteroliodon* (Reptilia: Squamata: Colubridae) from Montagne des Français, far northern Madagascar. *Herpetologica* 61: 275–280.

Glaw, F., Franzen, M, and Vences, M. 2005b. A new species of colubrid snake (*Liopholidophis*) from northern Madagascar. *Salamandra* 41: 83–90.

Glaw, F., Kosuch, J., Henkel, F.-W., Sound, P., and Böhme, W. 2006. Genetic and morphological variation of the leaf-tailed gecko *Uroplatus fimbriatus* from Madagascar, with description of a new giant species. *Salamandra* 42: 129–144.

Glaw, F., Nagy, Z. T., and Vences, M. 2007a. Phylogenetic relationships and classification of the Malagasy pseudoxyrhophiine snake genera *Geodipsas* and *Compsophis* based on morphological and molecular data. *Zootaxa* 1517: 53–62.

Glaw, F., Nagy, Z. T., Franzen, M., and Vences, M. 2007b. Molecular phylogeny and systematics of the pseudoxyrhophiine snake genus *Liopholidophis* (Reptilia, Colubridae): Evolution of its exceptional sexual dimorphism and descriptions of new taxa. *Zoologica Scripta* 36: 291–300.

Glaw, F., Köhler, J., and Vences, M. 2009a. A distinctive new species of chameleon of the genus *Furcifer* from the Montagne d'Ambre rainforest of northern Madagascar. *Zootaxa* 2269: 32–42.

———. 2009b. A new species of cryptically coloured day gecko (*Phelsuma*) from the Tsingy de Bemaraha National Park in western Madagascar. *Zootaxa* 2195: 61–68.

Glaw, F., Nagy, Z. T., Köhler, J., Franzen, M., and Vences, M. 2009c. Phylogenetic relationships of a new species of pseudoxyrhophiine snake (Reptilia: Lamprophiidae: *Thamnosophis*) suggest a biogeographical link between western and northern Madagascar. *Organisms Diversity and Evolution* 9: 13–22.

Glaw, F., Gehring, P.-S., Köhler, J., Franzen, M., and Vences, M. 2010. A new dwarf species of day gecko, genus *Phelsuma*, from the Ankarana pinnacle karst in northern Madagascar. *Salamandra* 46: 83–92.

Glaw, F., Köhler, J., Townsend, T. M., and Vences, M. 2012. Rivaling the world's smallest reptiles: Discovery of miniaturized and microendemic new species of leaf chameleons (*Brookesia*) from northern Madagascar. *PLoS One* 7: e31314.

Glaw, F., Kucharzewski, C., Köhler, J., Vences, M., and Nagy, Z. T. 2013. Resolving an enigma by integrative taxonomy: *Madagascarophis fuchsi* (Serpentes: Lamprophiidae), a new opisthoglyphous and microendemic snake from northern Madagascar. *Zootaxa* 3630: 317–332.

Glaw, F., Hawlitschek, O., and Ruthensteiner, B. 2014a. A new genus name for an ancient Malagasy chameleon clade and a PDF-embedded 3D model of its skeleton. *Salamandra* 49: 237–238.

Glaw, F., Kucharzewski, C., Nagy, Z. T., Hawlitschek, O., and Vences, M. 2014b. New insights into the systematics and molecular phylogeny of the Malagasy snake genus *Liopholidophis* suggest at least one rapid reversal of extreme sexual dimorphism in tail length. *Organisms Diversity and Evolution*, 14: 121–132.

Glaw, F., Rösler, H., Ineich, I., Gehring, P.-S., Köhler, J., and Vences, M. 2014c. A new species of nocturnal gecko (*Paroedura*) from karstic limestone in northern Madagascar. *Zoosystematics and Evolution* 90: 249–259.

Glaw, F., Köhler, J., and Vences, M. 2018. Three new species of nocturnal geckos of the *Paroedura oviceps* clade from xeric environments of Madagascar (Squamata: Gekkonidae). *Zootaxa* 4433: 305–324.

Glaw, F., Prötzel, D., Eckhardt, F., Raharinoro, N. A., Ravelojaona, R. N., Glaw, T. Glaw, K., Forster, J., and Vences, M. 2020. Rediscovery, conservation status and genetic relationships of the Malagasy chameleon *Furcifer voeltzkowi*. *Salamandra* 56: 342–354.

Glaw, F., Köhler, J., Hawlitschek, O., Ratsoavina, F. M., Rakotoarison, A., Scherz, M. D., and Vences, M. 2021. Extreme miniaturization of a new amniote vertebrate and insights into the evolution of genital size in chameleons. *Scientific Reports* 11: 2522.

Goodman, S. M., and Benstead, J. P., eds. 2003. *The Natural History of Madagascar.* Chicago: University of Chicago Press.

Goodman, S. M., and Jungers, W. L. 2014. *Extinct Madagascar: Picturing the Island's Past*. Chicago: University of Chicago Press.

Goodman, S. M., Langrand, O., and Raxworthy, C. J. 1993a. Food habits of the Madagascar long-eared owl *Asio madagascariensis* in two habitats in southern Madagascar. *Ostrich* 64: 79–85.

———. 1993b. Food habits of the barn owl *Tyto alba* at three sites on Madagascar. *Ostrich* 64: 160–171.

Goodman, S. M., Ramanamanjato, J.-B., and Raselimanana, A. P. 1997. Les amphibiens et les reptiles. In Inventaire biologique Forêts de Vohibasia et Isoky-Vohimena, eds. O. Langrand and S. M. Goodman. *Recherches pour le Développement, Série Sciences Biologiques* 12: 110–129.

Goodman, S. M., Duplantier, J.-M., Rakotomalaza, P. J., Raselimanana, A. P., Rasoloarison, R., Ravokatra, M., Soarimalala, V., and Wilmé, L. 1998. Inventaire biologique de la forêt d'Ankazomivady, Ambositra. *Akon'ny Ala* 24: 19–32.

Goodman, S. M., Jenkins, P. D., and Pidgeon, M. 1999. The Lipotyphla (Tenrecidae and Soricidae) of the Réserve Naturelle Intégrale d'Andohahela, Madagascar. In A floral and faunal inventory of the Réserve Naturelle Intégrale d'Andohahela, Madagascar: With reference to elevational variation, ed. S. M. Goodman. *Fieldiana: Zoology*, new series, 94: 187–216.

Goodman, S. M., Anbdou, Y., Andriamiarantsoa, Y., Fisher, B. L., Griffiths, O., et al. 2017. Results of a biological inventory of the Nosy Ankao island group, Parc National de Loky-Manambato, northeastern Madagascar. *Malagasy Nature* 11: 1–59.

Goodman, S. M., Raherilalao M. J., and Wohlhauser, S. 2018. *The Terrestrial Protected Areas of Madagascar: Their History, Description, and Biota*. Antananarivo: Association Vahatra.

Grandidier, A. 1867. Liste des reptiles nouveaux découverts, en 1866, sur la côte sud-ouest de Madagascar. *Revue et Magazine de Zoologie*, Paris, série 2, 19: 232–234.

———. 1872. Description de quelques reptiles nouveaux découverts á Madagascar en 1870. *Annales des Sciences Naturelles*, Paris, *Zoologie et Biologie Animale* 15: 6–11.

Gray, J. 2018. Turtle Survival Alliance launches rescue mission to nearly 11,000 Critically Endangered radiated tortoises discovered in massive poaching bust. https://turtlesurvival.org/blog/page/22/.

Gray, J. E. 1831. A synopsis of the species of class Reptilia. In *The Animal Kingdom Arranged in Conformity with Its Organisation by the Baron Cuvier with Additional Descriptions of All the Species Hither Named, and of Many before Noticed*, eds. E. Griffith and E. Pidgeon. London: V. Whittaker, Treacher.

Grbic, D., Sanko, S. V., Randriamoria, T. M., Derby, A., Raselimanana, A. P., and Milinkovitch, M. C. 2015. Phylogeography and support vector machine classification of colour variation in panther chameleons. *Molecular Ecology* 24: 3455–3466.

Greenbaum, E., Bauer, A. M., Jackman, T., and Vences, M. 2007. A phylogeny of the enigmatic Madagascan geckos of the genus *Uroplatus* (Sauria: Gekkonidae). *Zootaxa* 1493: 41–51.

Greene, H. W. 1975. Ecological observations on the red coffee snake, *Ninia sebae*, in southern Veracruz, Mexico. *American Midland Naturalist* 93: 478–484.

Guibé, J. 1949. Révision des boidés de Madagascar. *Mémoires de l'Institut Scientifique de Madagascar*, série A, 3: 95–105.

———. 1958. Les serpents de Madagascar. *Mémoires de l'Institut Scientifique de Madagascar*, série A, 12: 189–260.

———. 1970. L'appareil respiratoire. In *Traité de zoologie: Anatomie, systématique, biologie*. Vol. 14, *Reptiles: Caractères généraux et anatomiques*, ed. P.-P. Grassé, pp. 489–520. Paris: Masson.

Gumbs, R., Gray, C. L., Wearn, O. R., and Owen, N. R. 2018. Tetrapods on the EDGE: Overcoming data limitations to identify phylogenetic conservation priorities. *PLoS One* 13: e0194680.

Gutnick, T., Weissenbacher, A., and Kuba, M. J. 2020. The underestimated giants: Operant conditioning, visual discrimination and long-term memory in giant tortoises. *Animal Cognition* 23: 159–167.

Hallmann, G., Krüger, J., and Trautmann, G., eds. 1997. *Faszinierende Taggeckos: Die Gattung* Phelsuma. Münster: Natur und Tier Verlag.

———, eds. 2008. *Faszinierende Taggeckos: Die Gattung* Phelsuma. 2nd ed. Münster: Natur und Tier-Verlag.

Hammer, J. M. 2013. Do bigger females produce bigger eggs? The influence of female body mass on egg mass in *Astrochelys radiata*. *Chelonian Research Monographs* 6: 119–123.

———. 2015. Reproduction as a function of living conditions: The breeding biology of the radiated tortoise (*Astrochelys radiata*) under natural and captive conditions in southwest Madagascar. *Journal of Herpetology* 49: 633–640.

Hammer, J. M., and Ramilijaona, O. 2009. Population study on *Astrochelys radiata* (Shaw, 1802) in the Tsimanampetsotsa National Park, southwest Madagascar. *Salamandra* 45: 219–232.

Hannah, L., Dave, R., Lowry, P. P., Andelman, S., Andrianarisata, M., et al. 2008. Climate change adaptation for conservation in Madagascar. *Biology Letters* 4(5): 590–594.

Hansen, D. M., Kiesbüy, H. C., Jones, C. G., and Müller, C. B. 2007. Positive indirect interactions between neighboring plant species via a lizard pollinator. *American Naturalist* 169: 534–542.

Hansford, J., Wright, P. C., Rasoamiaramanana, A., Pérez, V. R., Godfrey, L. R., Errickson, D., Thompson, T., and Turvey, S. T. 2018. Early Holocene human presence in Madagascar evidenced by exploitation of avian megafauna. *Science Advances* 4: eaat6925.

Hara, Y., Takeuchi, M., Kageyama, Y., Tatsumi, K., Hibi, M., Kiyonari, H., and Kuraku, S. 2018. Madagascar ground gecko genome analysis characterizes asymmetric fates of duplicated genes. *BMC Biology* 16: 40.

Harmon, L., Harmon, L., and Jones, C. 2007. Competition and community structure in diurnal arboreal geckos (genus *Phelsuma*) in the Indian Ocean. *Oikos* 116: 1863–1878.

Hawlitschek, O., and Glaw, F. 2012. The complex colonization history of nocturnal geckos (*Paroedura*) in the Comoro archipelago. *Zoologica Scripta* 42: 135–150.

Hawlitschek, O., Brückmann, B., Berger, J., Green, K., and Glaw, F. 2011. Integrating field surveys and remote sensing data to study distribution, habitat use, and conservation status of the herpetofauna of the Comoro islands. *ZooKeys* 144: 21–79.

Hawlitschek, O., Nagy, Z. T., and Glaw, F. 2012. Island evolution and systematic revision of Comoran snakes: Why and when subspecies still make sense. *PLoS One* 7(8): e42970.

Hawlitschek, O., Scherz, M. D., Straube, N., and Glaw, F. 2016. Resurrection of the Comoran fish scale gecko *Geckolepis humbloti* Vaillant, 1887 reveals a disjointed distribution caused by natural overseas dispersal. *Organisms Diversity and Evolution* 16: 289–298.

Hawlitschek, O., Ramirez Garrido, S., and Glaw, F. 2017a. How marine currents influenced the widespread natural overseas dispersal of reptiles in the western Indian Ocean region. *Journal of Biogeography* 44: 1435–1440.

Hawlitschek, O., Toussaint, E.F.A., Gehring, P.-S., Ratsoavina, F. M., Cole, N., Crottini, A., Nopper, J., Lam, A. W., Vences, M., and Glaw, F. 2017b. Gecko phylogeography in the western Indian Ocean region: The oldest clade of *Ebenavia inunguis* lives on the youngest island. *Journal of Biogeography* 44: 409–420.

Hawlitschek, O., Scherz, M. D., Ruthensteiner, B., Crottini, A., and Glaw, F. 2018. Computational molecular species delimitation and taxonomic revision of the gecko genus *Ebenavia* Boettger, 1878. *Science of Nature* 105: 49.

Hawlitschek, O., Scherz, M. D., Webster, K. C., Ineich, I., and Glaw, F. 2021. Morphological, osteological, and genetic data support a new species of *Madatyphlops* (Serpentes: Typhlopidae) endemic to Mayotte Island, Comoro archipelago. *Anatomical Record* 2021: 1–15.

Hedges, S. B., Marion, A. B., Lipp, K. M., Marin, J., and Vidal, N. 2014. A taxonomic framework for typhlopid snakes from the Caribbean and other regions (Reptilia, Squamata). *Caribbean Herpetology* 49: 1–61.

Heinicke, M., Daza, J. D., Greenbaum, E., Jackman, T. R., and Bauer, A. M. 2014. Phylogeny, taxonomy, and biogeography of a circum-Indian Ocean clade of

leaf-toed geckos (Reptilia: Gekkota), with a description of two new genera. *Systematics and Biodiversity* 12: 23–42.
Hekkala, E., Amato, G., DeSalle, R., and Blum M. 2010. Molecular assessment of population differentiation and individual assignment potential of Nile crocodile (*Crocodylus niloticus*) populations. *Conservation Genetics* 11: 1435–1443.
Hekkala, E., Shirley, M. H., Amato, G., Austin, J. D., Charter, S., Thorbjarnarson, J., Vliet, K. A., Houck, M. L., Desalle, R., and Blum, M. J. 2011. An ancient icon reveals new mysteries: Mummy DNA resurrects a cryptic species within the Nile crocodile. *Molecular Ecology* 20: 4199–4215.
Hekkala, E., Gatesy, J., Narechania, A., Meredith, R., Russello, M., et al. 2021. Paleogenomics illuminates the evolutionary history of the extinct Holocene "horned" crocodile of Madagascar, *Voay robustus*. *Communications Biology* 4: 648.
Henkel, F.-W., and Schmidt, W. 2000. *Amphibians and Reptiles of Madagascar and the Mascarene, Seychelles, and Comoro Islands*. Malabar: Krieger.
Heselhaus, R. 1986. *Taggeckos, praktische Winke zur Pflege und Zucht*. Essen: Edition Kernen.
Higham, T. E., Gamble, T., and Russell, A. P. 2017. On the origin of frictional adhesion in geckos: Small morphological changes lead to a major biomechanical transition in the genus *Gonatodes*. *Biological Journal of the Linnean Society* 120: 503–517.
Hillenius, D. 1959. The differentiation within the genus *Chamaeleo* Laurenti, 1768. *Beaufortia* 8: 1–92.
———. 1963. Comparative cytology: Aid and new complications in chamaeleon-taxonomy. *Beaufortia* 9: 201–218.
———. 1986. The relationship of *Brookesia*, *Rhampholeon* and *Chamaeleo* (Chamaeleontidae, Reptilia). *Bijdragen tot de Dierkunde* 56: 29–38.
———. 1988. The skull of *Chamaeleo nasutus* adds more information to the relationship of *Chamaeleo*, *Rhampholeon* and *Brookesia* (Chamaeleontidae, Reptilia). *Bijdragen tot de Dierkunde* 58: 7–11.
Hladik, C. M., Charles-Dominique, P., and Petter, J.-J. 1980. Feeding strategies of five nocturnal prosimians in the dry forest of the west coast of Madagascar. In *Nocturnal Malagasy Primates: Ecology, Physiology and Behavior*, eds. P. Charles-Dominique, H. M. Cooper, A. Hladik, C. M. Hladik, E. Pages, G. F. Pariente, A. Petter-Rousseaux, J.-J. Petter, and A. Schilling, pp. 41–73. New York: Academic Press.
Hoffstetter, R., and Gasc, J.-P. 1969. Vertebrae and ribs of modern reptiles. In *Biology of the Reptilia*, vol. 1., eds. C. Gans, A. d'A. Bellairs, and T. S. Parsons, pp. 201–310. New York: Academic Press.
Horner, P. 2007. Systematics of the snake-eyed skinks, *Cryptoblepharus* Wiegmann (Reptilia: Squamata: Scincidae): An Australian based review. *Beagle Supplement* 3: 21–198.
Horner, P., and Adams, M. 2007. A molecular systematic assessment of species boundaries in Australian *Cryptoblepharus* (Reptilia: Squamata: Scincidae): A case study for the combined use of allozymes and morphology to explore cryptic biodiversity. *Beagle Supplement* 3: 1–19.
Höß, S., Höß, D., and Glaw, F. 2005. Nachzucht bei der Nördlichen Madagaskarboa (*Acrantophis madagascariensis*). *Reptilia* 10(6): 6–7.
Huey, R. B., Deutsch, C. A., Tewksbury, J. J., Vitt, L. J., Hertz, P. E., Perez, H.J.A., and Garland, T. 2009. Why tropical forest lizards are vulnerable to climate warming. *Proceedings of the Royal Society of London B: Biological Sciences* 276: 1939–1948.
Huff, T. A. 1984. The husbandry and propagation of the Madagascar ground boa, *Acrantophis dumerili* in captivity. *Acta Zoologica et Pathologica Antverpiensia* 78: 255–270.
Hughes, D. F., and Blackburn, D. C. 2020. Evolutionary origins of viviparity in Chamaeleonidae. *Journal of Zoological Systematics and Evolutionary Research* 58: 284–302.
Humboldt, A. V. 1820. *Voyages aux régions equinoxiales du nouveau continent fait en 1799–1804 par A. Humboldt et A. Bonpland*. Vol. 6. Paris: Chez N. Maze.
Humphrey, J. E., and Ward, C.F.M. 2018. Madagascan day geckos (*Phelsuma* spp.) exhibit differing responses along a gradient of land-use change. *Tropical Conservation Science* 11: 1–10.
Hutter, C. R., Andriampenomanana, Z. F., Razafindraibe, J. H., Rakotoarison, A., and Scherz, M. D. 2018. New dietary data from *Compsophis* and *Alluaudina* species (Squamata: Lamprophiidae: Pseudoxyrhophiinae), and implications for their dietary complexity and evolution. *Journal of Natural History* 52: 2497–2510.
Hutton, J. M. 1987a. Growth and feeding ecology of the Nile crocodile *Crocodylus niloticus* at Ngezi, Zimbabwe. *Journal of Animal Ecology* 56: 25–38.
———. 1987b. Incubation temperatures, sex ratios and sex determination in a population of Nile crocodiles *Crocodylus niloticus*. *Journal of Zoology* 211: 143–156.
———. 1989. Movements, home range, dispersal and the separation of size classes in Nile crocodiles. *American Zoologist* 29: 1033–1050.
Ineich, I., Glaw, F., and Vences, M. 2016. A new species of *Blaesodactylus* (Squamata: Gekkonidae) from Tsingy limestone outcrops in Namoroka National Park, north-western Madagascar. *Zootaxa* 4109: 523–541.
Ingady, M.Z.L. 2011. Habitat préférentiel d'*Uroplatus giganteus* (Reptilia, Gekkonidae), dans le complexe de la Montagne d'Ambre, nord de Madagascar. *Malagasy Nature* 5: 89–103.
International Money Fund. 2019. GDP per capita, current prices. https://www.imf.org/external/datamapper/NGDPDPC@WEO/OEMDC/ADVEC/WEOWORLD.
IPBES. 2019. *Global Assessment Report on Biodiversity and Ecosystem Services of the 733 Intergovernmental Science-Policy Platform on Biodiversity and Ecosystem Services*, eds. J. Brondizio, S. Settele, S. Díaz, and H. T. Ngo. Bonn: IPBES Secretariat.
Irisarri, I., Baurain, D., Brinkmann, H., Delsuc, F., Sire, J.-Y., et al. 2017. Phylotranscriptomic consolidation of the jawed vertebrate timetree. *Nature Ecology and Evolution* 1: 1370–1378.
Irwin, M. T., Wright, P. C., Birkinshaw, C., Fisher, B. L., Gardner, C. J., et al. 2010. Patterns of species change in anthropogenically disturbed forests of Madagascar. *Biological Conservation* 143: 2351–2362.
Isberg, S., Combrink, X., Lippai, C., and Balaguera-Reina, S. A. 2019. *Crocodylus niloticus*. IUCN Red List of Threatened Species 2019: e.T45433088A3010181. http://dx.doi.org/10.2305/IUCN.UK.2019–1.RLTS.T45433088A3010181.
Itescu, Y., Schwarz, R., Meiri, S., and Pafillis, P. 2016. Intraspecific competition, not predation, drives lizard tail loss on islands. *Journal of Animal Ecology* 86: 66–74.
Ito, R. 2013. *Oplurus cuvieri cuvieri* (Madagascan spiny-tailed iguana) prey. *Herpetological Review* 44: 678.
Ito, R., and Mori, A. 2010. Vigilance against predators induced by eavesdropping on heterospecific alarm calls in a non-vocal lizard *Oplurus cuvieri cuvieri* (Reptilia: Iguania). *Proceedings of the Royal Society of London B: Biological Sciences* 277: 1275–1280.
———. 2012. The Madagascan spiny-tailed iguana alters the sequence of anti-predator responses depending on predator types. *African Journal of Herpetology* 61: 58-68.
Itoh, M. M., and Ito, R. 2015. *Oplurus cuvieri cuvieri* (Madagascan spiny-tailed iguana) diet. *Herpetological Review* 46: 632-633.
IUCN. 1982. *Red Data Book: Amphibia-Reptilia*. Pt. 1. Morges: International Union for the Conservation of Nature and Natural Resources.
———. 1996. *1996 IUCN Red List of Threatened Animals*. Gland: IUCN.
———. 2019. IUCN Red List of Threatened Species. Version 2019–2. Accessed 15 June 2021. http://www.iucnredlist.org.
IUCN/UNEP/WWF. 1987. *Madagascar: An Environmental Profile*, ed. M. D. Jenkins. Cambridge: IUCN.
Jacobson, S. K., and Lopez, A. F. 1994. Biological impacts of ecotourism: Tourists and nesting turtles in Tortuguero National Park, Costa Rica. *Wildlife Society Bulletin* 22: 414–419.
Jenkins, R.K.B., Brady, L. D., Huston, K., Kauffmann, J.L.D., Rabearivony, J., Raveloson, G., and Rowcliffe, J. M. 1999. The population status of chameleons within Ranomafana National Park, Madagascar, and recommendations for future monitoring. *Oryx* 33: 38–46.
Jenkins, R.K.B., Brady, L. D., Bisoa, M., Rabearivony, J., and Griffiths, R. A. 2003. Forest disturbance and river proximity influence chameleon abundance in Madagascar. *Biological Conservation* 109: 407–415.
Jenkins, R.K.B., Rabearivony, J., and Rakotomanana, H. 2009. Predation on chameleons in Madagascar: A review. *African Journal of Herpetology* 58: 131–136.
Jenkins, R.K.B., Keane, A., Rakotoarivelo, A. R., Rakotomboavonjy, V., Randrianandrianina, F. H., Razafimanahaka, H. J., Ralaiarimalala, S. R., and Jones, J.P.G. 2011. Analysis of patterns of bushmeat consumption reveals extensive exploitation of protected species in eastern Madagascar. *PLoS One* 6: e27570.
Jenkins, R.K.B., Tongelli, M. F., Bowles, P., Cox, N., Brown, J. L., et al. 2014. Extinction risks and the conservation of Madagascar's reptiles. *PLoS One* 9: e100173.
Jesu, R., Mattioli, F., and Schimmenti, G. 1999. On the discovery of a new large chameleon inhabiting the limestone outcrops of western Madagascar: *Furcifer nicosiai* sp. nov. (Reptilia, Chamaeleonidae). *Doriana* 7(311): 1–14.
Jones, J.P.G., Andriamarovololona, M. M., and Hockley, N. 2008. The importance of taboos and social norms to conservation in Madagascar. *Conservation Biology* 22: 976–986.
Jones, J.P.G., Ratsimbazafy, J., Ratsifandrihamanana, A. N., Watson, J.E.M., Andrianandrasana, H. T., et al. 2019. Madagascar: Crime threatens biodiversity. *Science* 363: 825.

Jono, T., Bauer, A. M., Brennan, I., and Mori, A. 2015. New species of *Blaesodactylus* (Squamata: Gekkonidae) from Tsingy karstic outcrops in Ankarana National Park, northern Madagascar. *Zootaxa* 3980: 406–416.

Jono, T., Kojima, Y., and Takafumi, M. 2019. Novel cooperative antipredator tactics of an ant specialized against a snake. *Royal Society Open Science* 6(8): 190283.

Jovanovic, O., Vences, M., Safarek, G., Rabemananjara, F.C.E., and Dolch, R. 2009. Predation upon *Mantella aurantiaca* in the Torotorofotsy wetlands, central-eastern Madagascar. *Herpetology Notes* 2: 95–97.

Joyce, W. G., Rollot, Y., Evers, S. W., Lyson, T. R., Rahantarisoa, L. J., and Krause, D. W. 2021. A new pelomedusoid turtle, *Sahonachelys mailakavava*, from the Late Cretaceous of Madagascar provides evidence for convergent evolution of specialized suction feeding among pleurodires. *Royal Society Open Science* 8: 210098.

Juvik, J. O. 1975. The radiated tortoise of Madagascar. *Oryx* 13: 145–148.

Karsten, K. B., and Andriamandimbiarisoa, L. N. 2008. *Furcifer labordi* (Labord's chameleon) reproduction. *Herpetological Review* 39: 224.

Karsten, K. B., Andriamandimbiarisoa, L. N., Fox, S. F., and Raxworthy, C. J. 2008. A unique life history among tetrapods: An annual chameleon living mostly as an egg. *Proceedings of the National Academy of Sciences of the USA* 105: 8980–8984.

———. 2009a. Population densities and conservation assessments for three species of chameleons in the Toliara region of south-western Madagascar. *Amphibia-Reptilia* 30: 341–350.

———. 2009b. Sexual selection on body size and secondary sexual characters in 2 closely related, sympatric chameleons in Madagascar. *Behavioral Ecology* 20: 1079–1088.

———. 2009c. Social behavior of two species of chameleons in Madagascar: Insights into sexual selection. *Herpetologica* 65: 54–69.

Karsten, K. B., Ferguson, G. W., Holick, M. F., and Chen, T. C. 2009d. Panther chameleons, *Furcifer pardalis*, behaviorally regulate optimal exposure to UV depending on dietary vitamin D status. *Physiological and Biochemical Zoology* 82: 218–225.

Kasim, K. 2007. Towards a wider adoption of environmental responsibility in the hotel sector. *International Journal of Hospitality and Tourism Administration* 8: 25–49.

Kaudern, W. 1922. Sauropsiden aus Madagascar. *Zoologisches Jahrbuch, Abteilung für Systematic* 45: 395–458.

Kaufmann, J.L.D., Brady, L. D., and Jenkins, R.K.B. 1997. Behavioural observations of the chameleon *Calumma oshaughnessyi* in Madagascar. *Journal of Herpetology* 7: 77–80.

Kawai, U. 2016. *Oplurus cuvieri* (Madagascan spiny-tailed iguana) diet. *Herpetological Review* 47: 300-301.

Kelly, C.M.R., Barker, N. P., Villet, M. H., Broadley, D. G., and Branch, W. R. 2008. The snake family Psammophiidae (Reptilia: Serpentes): Phylogenetics and species delimitation in the African sand snakes (*Psammophis* Boie, 1825) and allied genera. *Molecular Phylogenetics and Evolution* 47: 1045–1060.

Kelly, C.M.R., Barker, N. P., Villet, M. H., and Broadley, D. G. 2009. Phylogeny, biogeography and classification of the snake superfamily Elapoidea: A rapid radiation in the late Eocene. *Cladistics* 25: 38–63.

Khannoon, E. R., Endlein, T., Russell, A. P., and Autumn, K. 2014. Experimental evidence for friction-enhancing integumentary modifications of chameleons and associated functional and evolutionary implications. *Proceedings of the Royal Society of London B: Biological Sciences* 281: 20132334.

Kindler, C., Branch, W. R., Hofmeyr, M. D., Maran, J., Široký, P., et al. 2012. Molecular phylogeny of African hinge-back tortoises (*Kinixys*): Implications for phylogeography and taxonomy (Testudines: Testudinidae). *Journal of Zoological Systematics and Evolutionary Research* 50: 192–201.

Klaver, C., and Böhme, W. 1986. Phylogeny and classification of the Chamaeleonidae (Sauria) with special reference to hemipenis morphology. *Bonner zoologische Monographien* 22: 1–64.

Kluge, A. G. 1991. Boine snake phylogeny and research cycles. *Miscellaneous Publications, Museum of Zoology, University of Michigan* 178: 1–58.

Kluge, A. G., and Nussbaum, R. A. 1995. A review of African-Madagascan gekkonid lizard phylogeny and biogeography (Squamata). *Miscellaneous Publications, Museum of Zoology, University of Michigan* 183: 1–20.

Knoll, A., Glaw, F., and Köhler, J. 2009. The Malagasy snake *Pseudoxyrhopus ambreensis* preys upon chameleon eggs by shell slitting. *Herpetology Notes* 2: 161–162.

Kofron, C. P. 1989. Nesting ecology of the Nile crocodile *Crocodylus niloticus*. *African Journal of Ecology* 27: 335–342.

———. 1990. The reproductive cycle of the Nile crocodile *Crocodylus niloticus*. *Journal of Zoology* 221: 477–488.

———. 1991. Courtship and mating of the Nile crocodile (*Crocodylus niloticus*). *Amphibia-Reptilia* 12: 39–48.

———. 1993. Behavior of Nile crocodiles in a seasonal river in Zimbabwe. *Copeia* 1993: 463–469.

Köhler, G., Diethert, H.-H., Nussbaum, R. A., and Raxworthy, C. J. 2009. A revision of the fish scale geckos, genus *Geckolepis* Grandidier (Squamata, Gekkonidae) from Madagascar and the Comoros. *Herpetologica* 65: 419–435.

Köhler, J., Glaw, F., and Vences, M. 1998. First record of *Mabuya comorensis* (Reptilia: Scincidae) for the Madagascan fauna, with notes on the reptile fauna of the offshore island Nosy Tanikely. *Bollettino del Museo Regionale di Scienze Naturali Torino* 15: 75–82.

Köhler, J., Vieites, D. R., Glaw, F., Kaffenberger, N., and Vences, M. 2009. A further new species of limbless skink, genus *Paracontias*, from eastern Madagascar. *African Journal of Herpetology* 58: 98–105.

Köhler, J., Vences, M., Erbacher, M., and Glaw, F. 2010. Systematics of limbless scincid lizards from northern Madagascar: Morphology, phylogenetic relationships and implications for classification (Squamata: Scincidae). *Organisms Diversity and Evolution* 10: 147–159.

Köhler, J., Vences, M., Scherz, M. D., and Glaw, F. 2019. A new species of nocturnal gecko, genus *Paroedura*, from the karstic Tsingy de Bemaraha formation in western Madagascar. *Salamandra* 55: 73–81.

Kolby, J. E., Smith, K. M., Ramirez, S. D., Rabemananjara, F.C.E., Pessier, A. P., Brunner, J. L., Goldberg, C. S., Berger, L., and Skerratt, L. F. 2015. Rapid response to evaluate the presence of amphibian chytrid fungus (*Batrachochytrium dendrobatidis*) and Ranavirus in wild amphibian populations in Madagascar. *PLoS One* 10(6): e0125330.

Kremen, C., Cameron, A., Moilanen, A., Phillips, S., Thomas, C. D., et al. 2008. Aligning conservation priorities across taxa in Madagascar with high-resolution planning tools. *Science* 320: 222–225.

Krysko, K. L., Hooper, A. N., and Sheehy, C. M. 2003. The Madagascar giant day gecko, *Phelsuma madagascariensis grandis* Gray 1870 (Sauria: Gekkonidae): A new established species in Florida. *Florida Scientist* 66: 222–225.

Kubička, L., Starostová, Z., and Kratochvíl, L. 2012. Temperature-dependent rate of clutch production in a tropical lizard (*Paroedura picta:* Gekkonidae): Intraspecific test of the metabolic theory of ecology. *Journal of Thermal Biology* 37: 179–184.

Kucharzewski, C., Raselimanana, A. P., Wang, C., and Glaw, F. 2014. A taxonomic mystery for more than 150 years: Identity, systematic position and Malagasy origin of the snake *Elapotinus picteti* Jan, 1862, and synonymy of *Exallodontophis* Cadle, 1999 (Serpentes: Lamprophiidae). *Zootaxa* 3852: 179–202.

Kuchling, G. 1986. Biology of *Kinixys belliana* at Nosy Faly, Madagascar. In *Studies in Herpetology*, ed. Z. Rocek, pp. 435–440. Prague: Charles University.

———. 1988. Population structure, reproductive potential and increasing exploitation of the freshwater turtle *Erymnochelys madagascariensis*. *Biological Conservation* 43: 107–113.

———. 1989. *Crocodilus niloticus* in Madagascar. *Biological Conservation* 47: 315–317.

———. 1992. Distribution and status of *Erymnochelys madagascariensis* (Grandidier, 1867). Unpublished report to MPAEF and Conservation International.

———. 1993a. Biologie und Lebensraum von *Erymnochelys madagascariensis* (Grandidier, 1867) und Vergleich mit den anderen Wasserschildkröten Madagaskars. *Salamandra* 28: 231–250.

———. 1993b. Possible biennial ovarian cycle of the freshwater turtle *Erymnochelys madagascariensis*. *Journal of Herpetology* 27: 470–472.

———. 1993c. Nesting of *Pseudemydura umbrina* (Testudines: Chelidae): The other way round. *Herpetologica* 49: 479–487.

———. 1996. Feasibility of captive propagation of *Erymnochelys madagascariensis* in Madagascar. Unpublished report to the Madagascar Fauna Group, Direction des Eaux et Forêts, Ministère de l'Agriculture et du Développement Rural de Madagascar, and Conservation International. Subiaco: Chelonia Enterprises.

———. 1997a. Patterns of exploitation, decline, and extinction of *Erymnochelys madagascariensis*: Implications for the conservation of the species. In *Proceedings: Conservation, Management, and Restoration of Tortoises and Turtles, 11–16 July 1993*, ed. J. Van Abbema, pp. 113–117. New York: New York Turtle and Tortoise Society.

———. 1997b. Conservation strategy for the natural populations of *Erymnochelys madagascariensis* at Ankarafantsika. Unpublished report to Conservation International and Jersey Wildlife Preservation Trust. Subiaco: Chelonia Enterprises.

———. 2000. Concept and design of the Madagascar side-necked turtle *Erymnochelys madagascariensis* breeding facility at Ampijoroa, Madagascar. *Dodo* 36: 62–74.

Kuchling, G., and Bloxam, Q.M.C. 1988. Field-data on the Madagascan flat-tailed tortoise *Pyxis (Acinixys) planicauda*. *Amphibia-Reptilia* 9: 175–180.

Kuchling, G., and Mittermeier, R. A. 1987. Biologie et statut d'*Erymnochelys madagascariensis* et commentaires sur d'autres chéloniens de Madagascar. In *Priorités en matière de conservation des espèces à Madagascar*, eds. R. A. Mittermeier, L. H. Rakotovao, V. Randrianosolo, E. J. Sterling, and D. Devitre, pp. 121–124. Occasional Papers, IUCN Species Survival Commission 2. Gland: IUCN.

———. 1993. Field-data on status and exploitation of *Erymnochelys madagascariensis*. *Chelonian Conservation and Biology* 1: 19–30.

Kuchling, G., Velosoa, J., Starkey, D. E., and Shaffer, H. B. 2006. Conservation of *Erymnochelys madagascariensis*: Distribution, exploitation and management units. Proceedings 2nd International Congress on Chelonian Conservation 18 to 22 June 2003, Senegal. *Chelonii* 4: 138.

Kull, C., Tassin, J., and Carrière, S. 2014. Approaching invasive species in Madagascar. *Madagascar Conservation and Development* 9: 60–70. Labanowski, R. J., and Lowin, A. J. 2011. A reptile survey in a dry deciduous forest fragment in northern Madagascar showing new records for the little-known snake *Pararhadinaea melanogaster* and a range extension for the skink *Amphiglossus tanysoma*. *Herpetology Notes* 4: 113–121.

Lanza, B. 1990. Rediscovery of the Malagasy colubrid snake *Alluaudina mocquardi* Angel 1939. *Tropical Zoology* 3: 219–223.

Lapparent de Broin, F. 2000. African chelonians from the Jurassic to the present: Phases of development and preliminary catalogue of the fossil record. *Paleontologica Africana* 36: 43–82.

Le Berre, F. 1995. *The New Chameleon Handbook*. Hong Kong: Barron's Press.

Lees, C. M., and Wilcken, J. 2009. Sustaining the ark: The challenges faced by zoos in maintaining viable populations. *International Zoo Yearbook* 43: 6–18.

Lehtinen, R. M., and Ramanamanjato, J.-B. 2006. Effects of rainforest fragmentation and correlates of local extinction in a herpetofauna from Madagascar. *Applied Herpetology* 3: 95–110.

Lehtinen, R. M., Ramanamanjato, J.-B., and Raveloarison, J. G. 2003. Edge effects and extinction proneness in a herpetofauna from Madagascar. *Biodiversity and Conservation* 12: 1357–1370.

Lemme, I., Erbacher, M., Kaffenberger, N., Vences, M., and Köhler, J. 2013. Molecules and morphology suggest cryptic species diversity and an overall complex taxonomy of fish scale geckos, genus *Geckolepis*. *Organisms Diversity and Evolution* 13: 87–95.

Lerner, A. 2004. A new taxonomically isolated species of the genus *Phelsuma* Gray, 1825 from the Ampasindava peninsula, Madagascar. *Phelsuma* 12: 91–98.

Leuteritz, T.E.J. 2002. Distribution, status and reproductive biology of the radiated tortoise, *Geochelone radiata* (Shaw, 1802) in south-west Madagascar. PhD thesis, George Mason University.

Leuteritz, T.E.J., and Ravolanaivo, R. 2005. Reproductive ecology and egg production of the radiated tortoise (*Geochelone radiata*) in southern Madagascar. *African Zoology* 40: 233–242.

Leuteritz, T.E.J., Lamb, T., and Limberaza, J. C. 2005. Distribution, status and conservation of radiated tortoises (*Geochelone radiata*) in Madagascar. *Biological Conservation* 124: 451–461.

Lever, C. 2003. *Naturalized Reptiles and Amphibians of the World*. Oxford: Oxford University Press.

Lhermitte-Vallarino, N., Barbuto, M., Junker, K., Wanji, S., Ineich, I., Schmitz, A., and Bain, O. 2010a. The lung nematode parasites of the genus *Rhabdias* (Rhabdiasidae): Diversity and biology in the Chamaeleonidae (Squamata) and hypotheses on their evolution. *Bulletin de la Société Zoologique de France* 135: 109–118.

Lhermitte-Vallarino, N., Junker, K., Boistel, R., and Bain, O. 2010b. *Rhabdias* (Nematoda: Rhabdiasidae) from Chamaeleonidae (Sauria): Two new species from *Trioceros ellioti* in east Africa and one from *Brookesia superciliaris* in Madagascar. *Parasite* 17: 91–105.

Lima, A., Harris, D. J., Rocha, S., Miralles, A., Glaw, F., and Vences, M. 2013. Phylogenetic relationships of *Trachylepis* skink species from Madagascar and the Seychelles (Scincidae: Lygosominae). *Molecular Phylogenetics and Evolution* 67(3): 615–620.

Lobón-Rovira, J., Belluardo, F., Crottini, A., and Rosa, G. M. 2019. Territorial behaviour in *Oplurus grandidieri* (Mocquard, 1900), a rock dwelling lizard from Madagascar. *Herpetology Notes* 12: 783–786.

Loveridge, A. 1941. Revision of the African terrapin of the family Pelomedusidae. *Bulletin of the Museum of Comparative Zoology* 788: 467–524.

———. 1942. Revision of the Afro-Oriental geckos of the genus *Phelsuma*. *Bulletin of the Museum of Comparative Zoology* 89: 439–482.

Low, B. R., Costanza, E., Ostrom, J., and Wilson, S. C. 1999. Human-ecosystem interactions: A dynamic integrated model. *Ecological Economics* 31: 227–242.

Lowin, A. J. 2012. Chameleon species composition and density estimates of three unprotected dry deciduous forests between Montagne d'Ambre Parc National and Ankarana Réserve Spéciale in northern Madagascar. *Herpetology Notes* 5: 107–113.

Luke, C. 1986. Convergent evolution of lizard toe fringes. *Biological Journal of the Linnean Society* 27: 1–16.

Macey, J. R., Larson, A., Ananjeva, N. B., and Papenfuss, T. J. 1997. Evolutionary shifts in three major structural features of the mitochondrial genome among iguanian lizards. *Journal of Molecular Evolution* 44: 660–674.

MacPhee, R.D.E., and Burney, D. A. 1991. Dating of modified femora of extinct dwarf *Hippopotamus* from southern Madagascar: Implications for constraining human colonization and vertebrate extinction events. *Journal of Archaeological Science* 18: 695–706.

Maderson, P.F.A. 1971. The regeneration of caudal epidermal specializations in *Lygodactylus picturatus keniensis* (Gekkonidae, Lacertilia). *Journal of Morphology* 134: 467–478.

Maheritafika, H.M.R., Robsomanitrandrasana, E., Rabesihanaka, S., Rafenomanana, F., Ravaoarimalala, A., Andrianjaratina, L., Manolis, C., and Lippai, C. 2016. Preliminary assessment of human-crocodile conflict in Madagascar. *Crocodile Specialist Group Newsletter* 35(1): 19–21.

Maia, J. P., Crottini, A., and Harris, D. J. 2014. Microscopic and molecular characterization of *Hepatozoon domerguei* (Apicomplexa) and *Foleyella furcata* (Nematoda) in wild endemic reptiles from Madagascar. *Parasite* 21: 47.

Mandimbihasina, A., and Currylow, A. 2014. New data on the naturally-occurring maximum sizes attained by ploughshare tortoises (*Astrochelys yniphora*). *Herpetology Notes* 7: 685–688.

Marshall, B. M., Casewell, N. R., Vences, M., Glaw, F., Andreone, F., Rakotoarison, A., Zancolli, G., Woog, F., and Wüster, W. 2018. Widespread vulnerability of Malagasy predators to the toxins of an introduced toad. *Current Biology* 28(11): R654–R655.

Masurat, G. 2005. *Vermehrung von Chamäleons*. Offenbach: Herpeton.

Mathews, J. C., and Samonds, K. E. 2016. A juvenile subfossil crocodylian from Anjohibe Cave, northwestern Madagascar. *PeerJ* 4: e2296.

Matsubara, S., Deeming, D. C., and Wilkinson, A. 2017. Cold-blooded cognition: New directions in reptile cognition. *Current Opinion in Behavioral Sciences* 16: 126–130.

Matsumoto, R., and Evans, S. E. 2018. The first record of albanerpetontid amphibians (Amphibia: Albanerpetontidae) from East Asia. *PLoS One* 13: e0189767.

Mattioli, F., Gili, C., and Andreone, F. 2006. Economics of captive breeding applied to the conservation of selected amphibian and reptile species from Madagascar. *Natura, Rivista di Scienze Naturali* 95: 67–80.

McAllister, C. T. 2012. A new species of *Choleoeimeria* (Apicomplexa: Eimeriidae) from Oustalet's chameleon, *Furcifer oustaleti* (Sauria: Chamaeleonidae). *Folia Parasitologica* 59: 12–14.

McAllister, C. T., Bursey, C. R., and Freed, P. S. 2011. *Oochoristica chavenoni* (Cestoidea: Linstowiidae), *Abbreviata madagascariensis* (Nematoda: Physalopteridae), and *Hexametra angusticaecoides* (Nematoda: Ascarididae) in Malagasy lizards (Sauria: Chamaeleonidae: Gekkonidae). *Comparative Parasitology* 78: 208–211.

McKinney, M. L. 1997. Extinction vulnerability and selectivity: Combining ecological and paleontological views. *Annual Review of Ecology and Systematics* 28: 495–516.

Meckel, F. 1819. Beiträge zur Geschichte des Respirationssystems der Amphibien: Als Nachtrag zu Bd. 4. No. 4. S. 60. ff. *Archiv für Physiologie* 5: 213–230.

Megson, S., Mitchell, P., Köhler, J., Marsh, C., Franzen, M., Glaw, F., and D'Cruze, N. 2009a. A comprehensive survey of amphibians and reptiles in the extreme north of Madagascar. *Herpetology Notes* 2: 31–44.

Megson, S., Mitchell, P., and D'Cruze, N. 2009b. Reptilia, Serpentes, Colubridae, *Heteroliodon fohy*: Distribution extension. *Check List* 5: 692–694.

Meier, H. 1977. Beobachtungen an *Phelsuma standingi*. *Salamandra* 13: 1–12.

———. 1980. *Geckolepis*, eine besondere Gecko-Gattungs Madagaskars. *Herpetofauna* 5: 11–14.

———. 1981. Zur Ökologie, Ethologie und Taxonomie einiger Arten der Gattung *Oplurus* auf Madagaskar. *Salamandra* 17: 43–54.

Meier, H., and Böhme, W. 1996. Zum taxonomischen Status des Formenkreises von *Phelsuma abbotti* Stejneger, 1893, mit Bemerkungen über *P. masohoala* Raxworthy and Nussbaum, 1994. *Salamandra* 32: 85–98.

Meissner, A. M., Christiansen, F., Martinez, E., Pawley, M. D., Orams, M. B., and Stockin, K. A. 2015. Behavioural effects of tourism on oceanic common dolphins,

Delphinus sp., in New Zealand: The effects of Markov analysis variations and current tour operator compliance with regulations. *PLoS One* 10: e0116962.
Mercurio, V., and Andreone, F. 2005. Description of a new *Geodipsas* snake from northern Madagascar (Squamata: Colubridae). *Zootaxa* 1093: 61–68.
Meredith, R. W., Hekkala, E. R., Amato, G., and Gatesy, J. 2011. A phylogenetic hypothesis for *Crocodylus* (Crocodylia) based on mitochondrial DNA: Evidence for a trans-Atlantic voyage from Africa to the New World. *Molecular Phylogenetics and Evolution* 60: 183–191.
Mertens, R. 1955. Studien über die Reptilienfauna Madagaskars. I. Beobachtungen an einigen madagassischen Reptilien im Leben. *Zoologische Garten (Neue Folge)* 22: 57–73.
———. 1963. Studien über die Reptilienfauna Madagaskars. IV. Zwei neue Arten der Geckonengattung *Phelsuma*. *Senckenbergiana Biologica* 44: 349–356.
———. 1964. Der Eidechsenschwanz als Haftorgan. *Senckenbergiana Biologica* 45: 117–122.
———. 1972. Studien über die reptilienfauna Madagaskars. VI. Madagaskars Herpetofauna und die Kontinentaldrift. *Zoologische Mededelingen* 46: 91–98.
Metcalf, J., Bayly, N., Bisoa, M., Rabearivony, J., and Stewart-Jones, A. 2005a. *Furcifer oustaleti, Furcifer rhinoceratus* (ncn) density. *Herpetological Review* 36: 447.
———. 2005b. Edge effect from paths on two chameleon species in Madagascar. *African Journal of Herpetology* 54: 99–102.
Mezzasalma, M., Andreone, F., Branch, W. R., Glaw, F., Guarino, F. M., Nagy, Z. T., Odierna, G., and Aprea, G. 2014. Chromosome evolution in pseudoxyrhophiine snakes from Madagascar: A wide range of karyotypic variability. *Biological Journal of the Linnean Society* 112: 450–460.
Mezzasalma, M., Andreone, F., Aprea, G., Glaw, F., Odierna, G., and Guarino, F. M. 2017. Molecular phylogeny, biogeography and chromosome evolution of Malagasy dwarf geckos of the genus *Lygodactylus* (Squamata, Gekkonidae). *Zoologica Scripta* 46: 42–54.
Mezzasalma, M., Andreone, F., Glaw, F., Guarino, F. M., Odierna, G., Petraccioli, A., and Picariello, O. 2019. Changes in heterochromatin content and ancient chromosome fusion in the endemic Malagasy boid snakes *Sanzinia* and *Acrantophis* (Squamata: Serpentes). *Salamandra* 55(2): 140–144.
Mifsud, D., Stapleton, M., and Walker, R. 2017. Field observations on the natural history of the Malagasy hingeback tortoise, *Kinixys zombensis domerguei*. *Testudo* 8: 12–21.
Millennium Ecosystem Assessment. 2005. *Ecosystems and Human Well-Being: Synthesis*. Washington, DC: Island Press.
Miller, C. 2017. Morphological and roosting variation in the dwarf chameleon *Brookesia stumpffi* between primary, secondary, and degraded habitats in Nosy Be, Madagascar. *Herpetological Conservation and Biology* 12: 599–605.
Millot, J. 1951. Un lézard d'eau à Madagascar (*Scelotes astrolabi*). *Naturaliste Malgache* 3(1): 87–90.
Milner-Gulland, E., and Mace, R. 1998. *Conservation of Biological Resources*. Oxford: Blackwell Science.
Ministère de l'Environnement Malgache, ONE, ANGAP, CI, Conservation Breeding Specialist Group SSC, DGEF, DBA—Université d'Antananarivo, IUCN, Madagascar Fauna Group, and Primate Specialist Group SSC. 2001. *CAMP lémuriens, autres mammifères, reptiles et amphibiens, poissons d'eau douce et evaluation de la viabilité des populations et des habitat de* Hypogeomys antimena *(Vositse)*. Apple Valley: Conservation Specialist Breeding Group.
Miralles, A., and Vences, M. 2013. New metrics for comparison of taxonomies reveal striking discrepancies among species delimitation methods in *Madascincus* lizards. *PLoS One* 8: e68242.
Miralles, A., Köhler, J., Glaw, F., and Vences, M. 2011a. A molecular phylogeny of the *Madascincus polleni* species complex, with description of a new species of scincid lizard from the coastal dune area of northern Madagascar. *Zootaxa* 2876: 1–16.
Miralles, A., Köhler, J., Vieites, D. R., Glaw, F., and Vences, M. 2011b. Developing hypotheses on rostral shield evolution in head-first digging squamates from a molecular phylogeny and new species of the genus *Paracontias* (Scincidae). *Organisms Diversity and Evolution* 11: 135–150.
Miralles, A., Raselimanana, A. P., Rakotomalala, D., Vences, M., and Vieites, D. R. 2011c. A new large and colorful skink of the genus *Amphiglossus* from Madagascar revealed by morphology and multilocus molecular study. *Zootaxa* 2918: 47–67.
Miralles, A., Anjeriniana, M., Hipsley, C. A., Mueller, J., Glaw, F., and Vences, M. 2012. Variations on a bodyplan: Description of a new Malagasy "mermaid skink" with flipper-like forelimbs only (Scincidae: *Sirenoscincus*). *Zoosystema* 34: 701–710.
Miralles, A., Glaw, F., Ratsoavina, F. M., and Vences, M. 2015a. A likely microendemic new species of terrestrial iguana, genus *Chalarodon*, from Madagascar. *Zootaxa* 3946(2): 201–220.
Miralles, A., Hipsley, C. A., Erens, J., Gehara, M., Rakotoarison, A., Glaw, F., Müller, J., and Vences, M. 2015b. Distinct patterns of desynchronized limb regression in Malagasy scincine lizards (Squamata, Scincidae). *PLoS One* 10: e0126074.
Miralles, A., Jono, T., Mori, A., Gandola, R., Erens, J., Köhler, J., Glaw, F., and Vences, M. 2016a. A new perspective on the reduction of cephalic scales in fossorial legless skinks (Squamata, Scincidae). *Zoologica Scripta* 45: 380–393.
Miralles, A., Köhler, J., Glaw, F., and Vences, M. 2016b. Species delimitation methods put into taxonomic practice: Two new *Madascincus* species formerly allocated to historical species names (Squamata, Scincidae). *Zoosystematics and Evolution* 92(2): 257–275.
Miralles, A., Bruy, T., Crottini, A., Rakotoarison, A., Ratsoavina, F. M., Scherz, M. D., Schmidt, R., Köhler, J., Glaw, F., and Vences, M. 2021. Completing a taxonomic puzzle: Integrative review of geckos of the *Paroedura bastardi* species complex (Squamata, Gekkonidae). *Vertebrate Zoology* 71: 27–48.
Mocquard, F. 1895. Sur les reptiles recueillis à Madagascar de 1867 à 1885 par M. Grandidier. *Bulletin de la Société Philomathique de Paris*, série 8, 7: 93–111.
———. 1909. Synopsis des familles, genres et espèces des reptiles écailleux et des batraciens de Madagascar. *Nouvelles Archives du Muséum*, Paris, série 5, 1: 1–110.
Moorhouse, T. P., Dahlsjö, C. A., Baker, S. E., D'Cruze, N. C., and Macdonald, D. W. 2015. The customer isn't always right: Conservation and animal welfare implications of the increasing demand for wildlife tourism. *PLoS One* 10: e0138939.
Moorhouse, T., D'Cruze, N. C., and Macdonald, D. W. 2017. Unethical use of wildlife in tourism: What's the problem, who is responsible, and what can be done? *Journal of Sustainable Tourism* 25: 505–516.
Morgan, J., and Chng, S. 2018. Rising internet-based trade in the Critically Endangered ploughshare tortoise *Astrochelys yniphora* in Indonesia highlights need for improved enforcement of CITES. *Oryx* 52: 744–750.
Mori, A. 2002. *Leioheterodon modestus* (Madagascar brown snake) diet. *Herpetological Review* 33: 57.
Mori, A., and Mizuta, T. 2006. Envenomation by the Madagascan colubrid snake, *Ithycyphus miniatus*. *Journal of Venomous Animals and Toxins including Tropical Diseases* 12: 512–520.
Mori, A., and Randriamahazo, H.J.A.R. 2002a. Foraging mode of a Madagascan iguanian lizard, *Oplurus cuvieri cuvieri*. *African Journal of Ecology* 40: 61-64.
———. 2002b. *Leioheterodon madagascariensis* (Madagascar Menarana snake) diet. *Herpetological Review* 33: 57.
Mori, A., and Randriamboavonjy, T. M. 2010. Field observation of maternal attendance of eggs in a Madagascan snake, *Leioheterodon madagascariensis*. *Current Herpetology* 29(29): 91–95.
Morton, J. J., and Krysko, K. L. 2012. Known hosts of the nematode endoparasite (Ascarididae: *Hexametra angusticaecoides*), including the Madagascar leaf-nosed snake (Lamprophiidae: *Langaha madagascariensis*). *Management of Biological Invasions* 3: 57–59.
Münchenberg, T., Wollenberg, K. C., Glaw, F., and Vences, M. 2008. Molecular phylogeny and geographic variation of Malagasy iguanas (*Oplurus* and *Chalarodon*). *Amphibia-Reptilia* 29: 319–327.
Murphy, T. J., and Myers, A. A. 1996. The behavioural ecology of *Phelsuma astriata semicarinata* on Aride Island Nature Reserve, Seychelles. *Journal of Herpetology* 30: 117–123.
Myers, N., Mittermeier, R. A., Mittermeier, C. G., da Fonseca, A. B., and Kent, J. 2000. Biodiversity hotspots for conservation priorities. *Nature* 403: 853–858.
Nagy, Z. T., Joger, U., Wink, M., Glaw, F., and Vences, M. 2003. Multiple colonization of Madagascar and Socotra by colubrid snakes: Evidence from nuclear and mitochondrial gene phylogenies. *Proceedings of the Royal Society of London B: Biological Sciences* 270(1533): 2613–2621.
Nagy, Z. T., Glaw, F., and Vences, M. 2010. Systematics of the snake genera *Stenophis* and *Lycodryas* (Squamata, Serpentes, Pseudoxyrhophiinae) from Madagascar and the Comoros. *Zoologica Scripta* 39: 426–435.
Nagy, Z. T., Sonet, G., Glaw, F., and Vences, M. 2012. First large-scale DNA barcoding assessment of reptiles in the biodiversity hotspot of Madagascar, based on newly designed COI primers. *PLoS One* 7: e34506.
Nagy, Z., Marion, A. B., Glaw, F., Miralles, A., Nopper, J., Vences, M., and Hedges, B. 2015. Molecular systematics and undescribed diversity of Madagascan scolecophidian snakes (Squamata: Serpentes). *Zootaxa* 4040(1): 31–47.
Neaves, J., Roberts, S. H., Longosoa, T. H., Andreone, F., and Rosa, G. M. 2019. Dietary observations of the lamprophiid snake *Madagascarophis meridionalis* (Domergue, 1987) in southeastern Madagascar. *Herpetology Notes* 12: 75–78.
Nečas, P. 1999. *Chamäleons: Bunte Juwelen der Natur*. 2nd ed. Frankfurt am Main: Chimaira.

———. 2004. *Chameleons: Nature's Hidden Jewels*. Frankfurt am Main: Chimaira.

Nečas, P., and Schmidt, W. 2004. *Stummelschwanzchamäleons: Miniaturdrachen des Regenwaldes: Die Gattungen* Brookesia *und* Rhampholeon. Frankfurt am Main: Chimaira.

Nicoll, M. E., and Langrand, O. 1989. *Madagascar: Revue de la conservation et des aires protégées*. Gland: World Wide Fund for Nature.

Noonan, B. P., and Chippindale, P. T. 2006a. Dispersal and vicariance: The complex evolutionary history of boid snakes. *Molecular Phylogenetics and Evolution* 40: 347–358.

———. 2006b. Vicariant origin of Malagasy reptiles supports late Cretaceous Antarctic land bridge. *American Naturalist* 168: 730–741.

Noonan, B. P., and Sites, J. W. 2010. Tracing the origins of iguanid lizards and boine snakes in the Pacific. *American Naturalist* 175(1): 61–72.

Nopper, J., Lauströer, B., Rödel, M.-O., and Ganzhorn, J. U. 2017a. A structurally enriched agricultural landscape maintains high reptile diversity in sub-arid south-western Madagascar. *Journal of Applied Ecology* 54: 480–488.

Nopper, J., Ranaivojaona, A., Riemann, J. C., Rödel, M.-O., and Ganzhorn, J. U. 2017b. One forest is not like another: The contribution of community-based natural resource management to reptile conservation in Madagascar. *Tropical Conservation Science* 10: 1–9.

Nopper, J., Riemann, J. C., Brinkmann, K., Rödel, M.-O., and Ganzhorn, J. U. 2018. Differences in land cover-biodiversity relationships complicate the assignment of conservation values in human-used landscapes. *Ecological Indicators* 90: 112–119.

Norman, D. 1987. Man and tegu lizards in eastern Paraguay. *Biological Conservation* 41: 39–56.

Noro, M., Uejima, A., Abe, G., Manabe, M., and Tamura, K. 2009. Normal developmental stages of the Madagascar ground gecko *Paroedura pictus* with special reference to limb morphogenesis. *Developmental Dynamics* 238: 100–109.

Nussbaum, R. A., and Raxworthy, C. J. 1994a. A new rainforest gecko of the genus *Paroedura* Günther from Madagascar. *Herpetological Natural History* 2(1): 43–49.

———. 1994b. A new species of *Uroplatus* (Reptilia: Squamata: Gekkonidae) from southern Madagascar. *Herpetologica* 50: 319–325.

———. 1994c. The genus *Paragehyra* (Reptilia: Sauria: Gekkonidae) in southern Madagascar. *Journal of Zoology* 232: 37–59.

———. 1994d. A new species of *Mabuya* Fitzinger (Squamata: Scincidae) from southern Madagascar. *Herpetologica* 50: 309–319.

———. 1995a. New *Uroplatus* Duméril (Reptilia: Squamata: Gekkonidae) of the *ebenaui*-group from the Anosy Mountains of southern Madagascar. *Copeia* 1995: 118–124.

———. 1995b. Review of the scincine genus *Pseudoacontias* Barboza du Bocage (Reptilia: Squamata: Scincidae) of Madagascar. *Herpetologica* 51: 91–99.

———. 1995c. A new *Mabuya* (Reptilia: Squamata: Scincidae) of the *aureopunctata*-group from southern Madagascar. *Journal of Herpetology* 29: 28–38.

———. 1998a. Revision of the genus *Ebenavia* Boettger (Reptilia: Squamata: Gekkonidae). *Herpetologica* 54: 18–34.

———. 1998b. New long-tailed *Mabuya* Fitzinger from Lokobe Reserve, Nosy Be, Madagascar (Reptilia: Squamata: Scincidae). *Copeia* 1998: 114–119.

———. 2000a. Commentary on conservation of "Sokatra," the radiated tortoise of Madagascar. *Amphibian and Reptile Conservation* 2(1): 6–14.

———. 2000b. Systematic revision of the genus *Paroedura* Günther (Reptilia: Squamata: Gekkonidae), with the description of five new species. *Miscellaneous Publications, Museum of Zoology, University of Michigan* 189: 1–26.

Nussbaum, R. A., Raxworthy, C. J., and Pronk, O. 1998. The ghost geckos of Madagascar: A further revision of the Malagasy leaf-toed geckos (Reptilia, Squamata, Gekkonidae). *Miscellaneous Publications, Museum of Zoology, University of Michigan* 186: 1–26.

Nussbaum, R. A., Raxworthy, C. J., and Ramanamanjato, J.-B. 1999a. Additional species of *Mabuya* Fitzinger (Reptilia: Squamata: Scincidae) from western Madagascar. *Journal of Herpetology* 33: 264–280.

Nussbaum, R. A., Raxworthy, C. J., Raselimanana, A. P., and Ramanamanjato, J.-B. 1999b. Amphibians and reptiles of the Réserve Naturelle Intégrale d'Andohahela, Madagascar. In A floral and faunal inventory of the Réserve Naturelle Intégrale d'Andohahela, Madagascar: With reference to elevational variation, ed. S. M. Goodman. *Fieldiana: Zoology*, new series, 94: 155–173.

O'Brien, S., Emahalala, E. R., Beard, V., Rakotondrainy, R. M., Reid, A., Raharisoa, V., and Coulson, T. 2003. Decline of the Madagascar radiated tortoise *Geochelone radiata* due to overexploitation. *Oryx* 37: 338–343.

Odierna, G., Canapa, A., Andreone, F., Aprea, G., Barucca, M., Capriglione, T., and Olmo, E. 2002. A phylogenetic analysis of Cordyliformes (Reptilia: Squamata): Comparison of molecular and karyological data. *Molecular Phylogenetics and Evolution* 23: 37–42.

Okajima, Y., and Kumazawa, Y. 2009. Mitogenoic perspectives into iguanid phylogeny and biogeography: Gondwanan vicariance for the origin of Madagascan oplurines. *Gene* 441: 28–35.

Ormsby, A., and Mannle, K. 2006. Ecotourism benefits and the role of local guides at Masoala National Park, Madagascar. *Journal of Sustainable Tourism* 14: 271–287.

Orozco-terWengel, P., Nagy, Z. T., Vieites, D. R., Vences, M., and Louis, E., Jr. 2008. Phylogeography and phylogenetic relationships of Malagasy tree and ground boas. *Biological Journal of the Linnean Society* 95(3): 640–652.

Osadnik, G. 1984. An investigation of egg-laying in *Phelsuma* (Reptilia: Sauria: Gekkonidae). *Amphibia-Reptilia* 5: 125–134.

Ota, H., and Ineich, I. 2006. Colonization of the gold dust day gecko, *Phelsuma laticauda* (Reptilia: Gekkonidae), in Moorea of Society Archipelago, French Polynesia. *Current Herpetology* 25: 97–99.

Ota, H., Hikida, T., Matsui, M., Mori, A., and Wynn, A. H. 1991. Morphological variation, karyotype and reproduction of the parthenogenetic blind snake, *Ramphotyphlops braminus*, from the insular region of East Asia and Saipan. *Amphibia-Reptilia* 12: 181–193.

Ottley, B., Lippai, C., and Rakotondrazafy, A.M.A. 2008. Surveys of wild crocodile populations in Madagascar. Final report to Deutsche Gesellschaft für Technische Zusammenarbeit (GTZ).

Padial, J., Miralles, A., De la Riva, I., and Vences, M. 2010. Integrative future of taxonomy. *Frontiers in Zoology* 7: 16.

Pages, E. 1980. Ethoecology of *Microcebus coquereli* during the dry season. In *Nocturnal Malagasy Primates: Ecology, Physiology and Behavior*, eds. P. Charles-Dominique, H. M. Cooper, A. Hladik, C. M. Hladik, E. Pages, G. F. Pariente, A. Petter-Rousseaux, J.-J. Petter, and A. Schilling, pp. 97–116. New York: Academic Press.

Paluh, D. J., Griffing, A. H., and Bauer, A. M. 2017. Sheddable armour: Identification of osteoderms in the integument of *Geckolepis maculata* (Gekkota). *African Journal of Herpetology* 66: 12–24.

Paquette, S. R., Shore, G. D., Behncke, S. M., Lapointe, F.-J., and Louis, E. E., Jr. 2005. Characterization of polymorphic microsatellite markers for the endangered Malagasy radiated tortoise (*Geochelone radiata*). *Molecular Ecology Notes* 5: 527–530.

Parcher, S. P. 1974. Observation on the natural histories of six Malagasy Chamaeleontidae. *Zeitschrift für Tierpsychologie* 34: 500–523.

Pasteur, G. 1959. Premières observations sur les reptiles rapportés du Tsiafajavona par le Professeur Millot. *Mémoires de l'Institut Scientifique de Madagascar*, série A, 13: 149–172.

———. 1965. Recherches sur l'évolution des lygodactyles, lézards afro-malgaches actuels. *Travaux de l'Institut Scientifique Chérifien*, série *Zoologique*, 29: 1–132.

———. 1977. Quelques commentaires à propos de l'espèce chez les lygodactyles. In *Les problèmes de l'espèce dans le Règne Animal*, eds. C. Bocquet, J. Génermont, and M. Lamotte, pp. 335–358. Paris: Société Zoologique de France.

———. 1995. Biodiversité et reptiles: Diagnoses de sept nouvelles espèces fossiles et actuelles du genre de lézards *Lygodactylus* (Sauria, Gekkonidae). *Dumerilia* 2: 1–21.

Pasteur, G., and Blanc, C. P. 1991. Un lézard parthénogénétique à Madagascar? Description de *Lygodactylus pauliani* sp. nov. (Reptilia, Gekkonidae). *Bulletin du Muséum National d'Histoire Naturelle*, Paris, série 4, 13(1–2A): 209–215.

Pearson, R. G., and Raxworthy, C. J. 2009. The evolution of local endemism in Madagascar: Watershed versus climatic gradient hypotheses evaluated by null biogeographic models. *Evolution* 63: 959–967.

Pearson, R. G., Raxworthy, C. J., Nakamura, M., and Peterson, A. T. 2007. Predicting species distribution from small numbers of occurrence records: A test case using cryptic geckos in Madagascar. *Journal of Biogeography* 34: 102–117.

Pedrono, M. 2000. Gestion interactive entre les populations sauvages et captives: Stratégie de conservation de la tortue *Astrochelys yniphora* à Madagascar. PhD thesis, Université de Paris.

———. 2008. *The Tortoises and Turtles of Madagascar*. Kota Kinabalu: Natural History Publications.

———. 2011. Wasted efforts: Why captivity is not the best way to conserve species. *Madagascar Conservation and Development* 6: 57–59.

Pedrono, M., and Clausen, A. 2018. *Twilight of the Angonoka: Biology and Conservation of the World's Rarest Tortoise*. Kota Kinabalu: Natural History Publications.

Pedrono, M., and Sarovy, A. 2000. Trial release of the world's rarest tortoise *Geochelone yniphora* in Madagascar. *Biological Conservation* 95: 333–342.

Pedrono, M., Smith, L. L., Sarovy, A., Bourou R., and Tiandray, H. 2001. Reproductive ecology of the ploughshare tortoise (*Geochelone yniphora*). *Journal of Herpetology* 35: 151–156.

Pedrono, M., Smith, L. L., Clobert, J., Massot, M., and Sarrazin, F. 2004. Wild-captive metapopulation viability analysis. *Biological Conservation* 119: 463–473.

Pedrono, M., Griffiths, O. L., Clausen, A., Smith, L. L., Griffiths, C. J., Wilmé, L., and Burney, D. A. 2013. Using a surviving lineage of Madagascar's vanished megafauna for ecological restoration. *Biological Conservation* 159: 501–506.

Pedrono, M., Rambeloson, E., and Clausen, A. 2020. Giant tortoises make a comeback in Madagascar. *Nature* 587: 548.

Penny, S. G., Crottini, A., Andreone, F., Bellati, A., Rakotozafy, L.M.S., Holderied, M. W., Schwitzer, C., and Rosa, G. M. 2017. Combining old and new evidence to increase the known biodiversity value of the Sahamalaza Peninsula, northwest Madagascar. *Contributions to Zoology* 86: 273–296.

Peters, J. 1998. Sharing national park entrance fees: Forging new partnerships in Madagascar. *Society and Natural Resources* 11: 517–530.

Peters, W. 1854. Diagnosen neuer Batrachier, welche zusammen mit der früher (24 Juli u. 12 August) gegebenen Übersicht der Schlangen und Eidechsen mitgetheilt werden. *Monatsberichte der Königlichen Preuische Akademie der Wissenschaften zu Berlin* 1854: 614–628.

Petit, G. 1925. Les crocodiles Malgaches, leurs mœurs, leur chasse et leur utilisation. *Revue d'Histoire Naturelle Appliquée* 6: 236–250.

Petter, J.-J. 1978. Ecological and physiological adaptations of five sympatric nocturnal lemurs to seasonal variation in food production. In *Recent Advances in Primatology and Behaviour*, eds. D. J. Chivers and J. Herbert, pp. 211–223. London: Academic Press.

Porcel, X., Dubos, N., Rosa, G. M., Miralles, A., Nöel, J., Lava, H., Velo, J. H., Georges, Andreone, F., and Crottini A. 2021. The kiwi of all skinks: An unusual egg size in a species of *Madascincus* (Squamata: Scincidae) from eastern Madagascar. *Herpetology Notes* 14: 365–369.

Pough, F. H., Andrews, R. M., Cadle, J. E., Crump, M. L., Savitzky, A. H., and Wells, K. D. 2015. *Herpetology*. 4th ed. Sunderland: Sinauer Associates.

Preston-Mafham, K. 1991. *Madagascar: A Natural History*. Oxford: Facts on File.

Prötzel, D., Ruthensteiner, B., Scherz, M. D., and Glaw, F. 2015. Systematic revision of the Malagasy chameleons *Calumma boettgeri* and *C. linotum* (Squamata: Chamaeleonidae). *Zootaxa* 4048: 211–231.

Prötzel, D., Glaw, K., Forster, J., and Glaw, F. 2016a. Hibernation in tropical Madagascar? Unusual roosting sites of chameleons of the genus *Calumma* (Squamata, Chamaeleonidae). *Spixiana* 39: 272.

Prötzel, D., Ruthensteiner, B., and Glaw, F. 2016b. No longer single! Description of female *Calumma vatosoa* (Squamata, Chamaeleonidae) including a review of the species and its systematic position. *Zoosystematics and Evolution* 92: 13–21.

Prötzel, D., Vences, M., Scherz, M. D., Vieites, D. R., and Glaw, F. 2017. Splitting and lumping: An integrative taxonomic assessment of Malagasy chameleons in the *Calumma guibei* complex results in the new species *C. gehringi* sp. nov. *Vertebrate Zoology* 67: 231–249.

Prötzel, D., Heß, M., Scherz, M. D., Schwager, M., van't Padje, A., and Glaw, F. 2018a. Widespread bone-based fluorescence in chameleons. *Scientific Reports* 8: 698.

Prötzel, D., Lambert, S. M., Andrianasolo, G. T., Hutter, C. R., Cobb, K. A., Scherz, M. D., and Glaw, F. 2018b. The smallest "true chameleon" from Madagascar: A new, distinctly colored species of the *Calumma boettgeri* complex (Squamata, Chamaeleonidae). *Zoosystematics and Evolution* 94: 409–423.

Prötzel, D., Vences, M., Hawlitschek, O., Scherz, M. D., Ratsoavina, F. M., and Glaw, F. 2018c. Endangered beauties: Micro-CT cranial osteology, molecular genetics and external morphology reveal three new species of chameleons in the *Calumma boettgeri* complex (Squamata: Chamaeleonidae). *Zoological Journal of the Linnean Society* 184: 471–498.

Prötzel, D., Scherz, M. D., Ratsoavina, F. M., Vences, M., and Glaw, F. 2020. Untangling the trees: Revision of the *Calumma nasutum* complex (Squamata: Chamaeleonidae). *Vertebrate Zoology* 70: 23–59.

Puente, M., Thomas, M., and Vences, M. 2005. Phylogeny and biogeography of Malagasy dwarf geckos, *Lygodactylus* Gray, 1864: Preliminary data from mitochondrial DNA sequences (Squamata: Gekkonidae). In *African Biodiversity: Molecules, Organisms, Ecosystems; Proceedings of the 5th International Symposium on Tropical Biology*, eds. B. A. Huber and K. H. Lampe, pp. 229–235. Bonn: Museum Alexander Koenig.

Puente, M., Glaw, F., Vieites, D. R., and Vences, M. 2009. Review of the systematics, morphology and distribution of Malagasy dwarf geckos, genus *Lygodactylus* and *Microscalabotes* (Squamata: Gekkonidae). *Zootaxa* 2103: 1–76.

Pulliam, H. R. 1988. Sources, sinks and population regulation. *American Naturalist* 132: 652–661.

Pyron, R. A., and Burbrink, F. T. 2014. Ecological and evolutionary determinants of species richness and phylogenetic diversity for island snakes. *Global Ecology and Biogeography* 23: 848–856.

Pyron, R. A., and Wallach, V. 2014. Systematics of the blindsnakes (Serpentes: Scolecophidia: Typhlopoidea) based on molecular and morphological evidence. *Zootaxa* 3829: 1–81.

Pyron, R. A., Burbrink, F. T., and Wiens, J. J. 2013. A phylogeny and revised classification of Squamata, including 4161 species of lizards and snakes. *BMC Evolutionary Biology* 13: 93.

Pyron, R. A., Reynolds, R. G., and Burbrink, F. T. 2014. A taxonomic revision of boas (Serpentes: Boidae). *Zootaxa* 3846: 249–260.

Rabearivony, J. 1999. Contribution à l'inventaire des caméléons dans le Parc National de Ranomafana pendant l'été (Novembre 1996 au Janvier 1997) et l'hiver (Mai 1997 au Juin 1997). Mémoire de DEA, Département de Biologie Animale, Université d'Antananarivo.

Rabearivony, J., Brady, L. D., Jenkins, R.K.B., and Ravoahangimalala, O. R. 2007. Habitat use and abundance of a low-altitude chameleon assemblage in eastern Madagascar. *Herpetological Journal* 17: 247–254.

Rabemananjara, F.C.E. 1998. Contribution à l'étude de la population de *Furcifer campani* Grandidier, 1872, Chamaeleonidae endémique de Madagascar, dans la région de l'Ankaratra: Biologie et écologie. Mémoire de DEA, Département de Biologie Animale, Université d'Antananarivo.

Rabemananjara, F.C.E., Raminosoa, N. R., Ramilijaona, O. R., Rakotondravony, D., Andreone, F., et al. 2007. Malagasy poison frogs in the pet trade: A survey of levels of exploitation of species in the genus *Mantella*. In A conservation strategy for the amphibians of Madagascar, ed. F. Andreone. *Monografie del Museo Regionale di Scienze Naturali di Torino* 45: 277–300.

Radimilahy, C. 1997. Mahilaka, an eleventh- to fourteenth-century Islamic port. In *Natural Change and Human Impact in Madagascar*, eds. S. M. Goodman and B. D. Patterson, pp. 342–377. Washington, DC: Smithsonian Institution Press.

Rafeliarisoa, T. H., Walker, R.C.J., and Louis, E. E., Jr. 2013. Decline in the range and population density of radiated tortoises, *Astrochelys radiata*, in southern Madagascar. *Chelonian Research Monographs* 6: 86–92.

Rakotomalala, R. D. 1998. Caractérisation de la communauté des Chamaeleonidae (Sauria) du Parc National de Ranomafana. Mémoire de DEA, Département de Biologie Animale, Université d'Antananarivo.

———. 2002. Diversité des reptiles et amphibiens de la Réserve Spéciale de Manongarivo, Madagascar. In Inventaire floristique et faunistique de la Réserve Spéciale de Manongarivo (NW Madagascar), eds. L. Gautier and S. M. Goodman. *Boissiera* 59: 339–358.

Rakotomalala, [R.]D., and Raselimanana, A. P. 2003. Les amphibiens et les reptiles des massifs de Marojejy, d'Anjanaharibe-Sud et du couloir forestier Betaolana. In Nouveaux résultats d'inventaires biologiques faisant référence à l'altitude dans la région des massifs montagneux de Marojejy et d'Anjanaharibe-Sud, eds. S. M. Goodman and L. Wilmé. *Recherches pour le Développement, Série Sciences Biologiques* 19: 147–202.

Rakotombololona, W. F. 1998. Study of the distribution and density of the Madagascan flat-tailed tortoise *Pyxis planicauda* in dry deciduous forest of Menabe. *Dodo* 34: 172–173.

Rakotondravony, H. A. 2001. Contribution à l'étude de la dispersion des communautés de Chamaeleonidae (Reptilia—Sauria—Chamaeleonidae) à travers les corridors forestiers dans la région d'Andasibe (Madagascar). Mémoire de DEA, Département de Biologie Animale, Université d'Antananarivo.

———. 2004. Diversité des caméléons forestiers de la région d'Andasibe (Madagascar) et modèle de distribution de cette communauté selon différents types physionomiques. *Revue d'Ecologie (La Terre et la Vie)* 59: 529–544.

———. 2007. Conséquences de la variation des superficies forestières sur les communautés de reptiles et d'amphibiens dans la région Loky-Manambato, extrême nord-est de Madagascar. *Revue d'Ecologie (La Terre et la Vie)* 62: 209–227.

Rakotondravony, H. A., and Goodman, S. M. 2011. Rapid herpetofaunal surveys within five isolated forests on sedimentary rocks in western Madagascar. *Herpetological Conservation and Biology* 6: 297–311.

Rakotozafy, L.M.A. 1996. Etude de la constitution du régime alimentaire des habitants du site de Mahilaka du XIème au XIVème siècle à partir des produits de fouilles archéologiques. Thèse de Doctorat, Département de Paléontologie et d'Anthropologie Biologique, Université d'Antananarivo.

Rakotozafy, M.T.L. 2009. Biologie et estimation de la densité de la population de *Pyxis planicauda* (Grandidier, 1867) dans la forêt dense sèche et semi-caducifoliée de Menabe Antimena. Mémoire de DEA, Département de Biologie Animale, Université d'Antananarivo.

Ramanamanjato, J.-B., and Rabibisoa, N. 2002. Evaluation rapide de la diversité biologique des reptiles et amphibiens de la Réserve Naturelle Intégrale d'Ankarafantsika. In A biological assessment of the Réserve Naturelle Intégrale d'Ankarafantsika, eds. L. E. Alonso, T. Schulenberg, S. Radilofe, and O. Missa. *Bulletin RAP d'Evaluation Rapide* 23: 98–104.

Ramanamanjato, J.-B., Nussbaum, R. A., and Raxworthy, C. J. 1999a. A new species of *Mabuya* Fitzinger (Squamata: Scincidae: Lygosominae) from northern Madagascar. *Occasional Papers, Museum of Zoology, University of Michigan* 728: 1–22.

———. 1999b. A new species of *Mabuya* Fitzinger (Squamata: Scincidae) from the Onilahy River of southwest Madagascar. *Herpetological Journal* 9: 65–72.

Ramanantsoa, G. A. 1974. Connaissances des Caméléonidés communs de la province de Diégo-Suarez par la population paysanne. *Bulletin de l'Académie Malgache* 51: 147–149.

———. 1984. The Malagasy and the chameleon: A traditional view of nature. In *Key Environments: Madagascar*, eds. A. Jolly, P. Oberle, and R. Albignac, pp. 105–114. Oxford: Pergamon Press.

Ramandimbison, I., Games, I., and Lippai, C. 1998. *Madagascar Crocodiles*. Geneva: CITES.

Randriamahazo, H.J.A.R. 1998. Activity temperatures in *Oplurus cyclurus*, *Oplurus cuvieri* and *Zonosaurus laticaudatus* and resting metabolic rates in the latter two species. *Amphibia-Reptilia* 19: 215–220.

Randriamahazo, H.J.A.R., and Mori, A. 2001. Egg-laying activities and reproductive traits in females of *Oplurus cuvieri cuvieri*. *Journal of Herpetology* 35: 209–217.

———. 2005. Factors affecting the intra-populational variation in dorsal color pattern of an iguanian lizard, *Oplurus cuvieri cuvieri*. *Current Herpetology* 24: 19-26.

Randriamoria, T. M. 2019. Revue des stratégies nationales sur la biosécurité et perspectives sur la gestion des espèces exotiques envahissantes à Madagascar. *Malagasy Nature* 13: 76–87.

Randrianantoandro, J. C., Andriantsimanarilafy, R. R., Rakotovololonalimanana, H., Hantalalaina, E. F., Rakotondravony, D., Ramilijaona, O. R., Ratsimbazafy, J., Razafindrakoto, G. F., and Jenkins, R.K.B. 2007. Population assessments of chameleons from two montane sites in Madagascar. *Herpetological Conservation and Biology* 5: 23–31.

Randrianantoandro, J. C., Randrianavelona, R., Andriantsimanarilafy, R. R., Hantalalaina, E. F., Rakotondravony, D., Randrianasolo, M., Ravelomanantsoa, H. L., and Jenkins, R.K.B. 2008. Identifying important areas for the conservation of dwarf chameleons (*Brookesia* spp.) in Tsingy de Bemaraha National Park, western Madagascar. *Oryx* 42: 578–583.

Randrianantoandro, J. C., Razafimahatratra, B., Soazandry, M., Ratsimbazafy, J., and Jenkins, R.K.B. 2010. Habitat use by chameleons in a deciduous forest in western Madagascar. *Amphibia-Reptilia* 31: 27–35.

Raselimanana, A. P. 1993. Contribution à l'étude de la batrachofaune et de l'herpétofaune des zones semi-arides et des zones littorales de l'extrême sud-est de Madagascar. Mémoire de DEA, Département de Biologie Animale et Ecologie Environnementale, Université d'Antananarivo.

———. 1998. La diversité de la faune de reptiles et amphibiens. In Inventaire biologique, forêt d'Andranomay, Anjozorobe, eds. D. Rakotondravony and S. M. Goodman. *Recherches pour le Développement, Série Sciences Biologiques* 13: 43–59.

———. 1999. L'herpétofaune. In Inventaire biologique de la Réserve Spéciale du Pic d'Ivohibe et du couloir forestier qui la relie au Parc National d'Andringitra, eds. S. M. Goodman and B.P.N. Rasolonandrasana. *Recherches pour le Développement, Série Sciences Biologiques* 15: 81–97.

———. 2000. Contribution à la systématique et à l'analyse phylogénétique et biogéographique des Gerrhosauridés malgaches. Thèse de Doctorat de Troisième Cycle, Département de Biologie Animale, Université d'Antananarivo.

———. 2004. L'herpétofaune de la forêt de Mikea. In Inventaire floristique et faunistique de la forêt de Mikea: Paysage écologique et diversité biologique d'une préoccupation majeure pour la conservation, eds. A. P. Raselimanana and S. M. Goodman. *Recherches pour le Développement, Série Sciences Biologiques* 21: 37–52.

———. 2008. Herpétofaune des forêts sèches malgaches. In Les forêts sèches de Madagascar, eds. S. M. Goodman and L. Wilmé. *Malagasy Nature* 1: 46–75.

———. 2013. Faune herpétologique de la forêt de Beanka, région Melaky: Richesse biologique, intérêt biogéographique et importance dans la conservation de la biodiversité malgache. In La forêt de Beanka, région Melaky, ouest de Madagascar, eds. S. M. Goodman, L. Gautier, and M. J. Raherilalao. *Malagasy Nature* 7: 209–224.

———. 2018. Field observations of predation events in Malagasy amphibians and reptiles. *Herpetology Notes* 11: 659–662.

Raselimanana, A. P., and Goodman, S. M. 2013. Lezards ou classe des Reptilia / Lizards or the class Reptilia. In *Atlas d'une sélection de vertébrés terrestres de Madagascar / Atlas of Selected Land Vertebrates of Madagascar*, eds. S. M. Goodman and M. J. Raherilalao, pp. 35–62. Antananarivo: Association Vahatra.

Raselimanana, A. P., Rakotomalala, D., and Rakotondraparany, F. 1998. Les reptiles et amphibiens: Diversité et conservation. In Inventaire biologique de la forêt littorale de Tampolo (Fenoarivo Atsinanana), eds. J. Ratsirarson and S. M. Goodman. *Recherches pour le Développement, Série Sciences Biologiques* 14: 183–195.

Raselimanana, A. P., Raxworthy, C. J., and Nussbaum, R. A. 2000a. Herpetofaunal species diversity and elevational distribution within the Parc National de Marojejy, Madagascar. In A floral and faunal inventory of the Parc National de Marojejy, Madagascar: With reference to elevational variation, ed. S. M. Goodman. *Fieldiana: Zoology*, new series, 97: 157–174.

———. 2000b. A revision of the dwarf *Zonosaurus*, Boulenger (Reptilia: Squamata: Cordylidae) from Madagascar, including descriptions of three new species. *Scientific Papers, Natural History Museum, University of Kansas* 18: 1–16.

Raselimanana, A. P., Nussbaum, R. A., and Raxworthy, C. J. 2006. Observations and re-description of *Zonosaurus boettgeri* Steindachner 1891 and description of a second new species of long-tailed *Zonosaurus* from western Madagascar. *Occasional Papers, Museum of Zoology, University of Michigan* 739: 1–16.

Raselimanana, A. P., Noonan, B., Karanth, K. P., Gauthier, J., and Yoder, A. D. 2009. Phylogeny and evolution of Malagasy plated lizards. *Molecular Phylogenetics and Evolution* 50: 336–344.

Rasoanoro, M., Ramasindrazana, B., Goodman, S. M., Rajerison, M., and Randrianarivelojosia, M. 2019. A review of *Trypanosoma* species known from Malagasy vertebrates. *Malagasy Nature* 13: 65–75.

Rasoma, R.V.J., Raselimanana, A. P., Ratovonamana, Y. R., and Ganzhorn, J. U. 2013. Habitat use and diet of *Astrochelys radiata* in the sub-arid zone of southern Madagascar. *Chelonian Conservation and Biology* 12: 56–69.

Ratsoavina, F. M., Gehring, P.-S., Ranaivoarisoa, F. J., Rafeliarisoa, T. H., Crottini, A., Louis, E. E., Jr., and Vences, M. 2010. Molecular phylogeography of a widespread Malagasy leaf chameleon species, *Brookesia superciliaris*. *Zootaxa* 2554: 62–64.

Ratsoavina, F. M., Louis, E. E., Jr., Crottini, A., Randrianiaina, R. D., Glaw, F., and Vences, M. 2011. A new leaf tailed gecko species from northern Madagascar with a preliminary assessment of molecular and morphological variability in the *Uroplatus ebenaui* group. *Zootaxa* 3022: 39–57.

Ratsoavina, F. M., Vences, M., and Louis, E. E., Jr. 2012. Phylogeny and phylogeography of the Malagasy leaf-tailed geckos in the *Uroplatus ebenaui* group. *African Journal of Herpetology* 61: 143–158.

Ratsoavina, F. M., Raminosoa, N. R., Louis, E. E., Jr., Raselimanana, A. P., Glaw, F., and Vences, M. 2013. An overview of Madagascar's leaf tailed geckos (genus *Uroplatus*): Species boundaries, candidate species and review of geographical distribution based on molecular data. *Salamandra* 49: 115–148.

Ratsoavina, F. M., Ranjanaharisoa, F. A., Glaw, F., Raselimanana, A. P., Miralles, A., and Vences, M. 2015. A new leaf-tailed gecko of the *Uroplatus ebenaui* group (Squamata: Gekkonidae) from Madagascar's central eastern rainforests. *Zootaxa* 4006: 143–160.

Ratsoavina, F. M., Gehring, P.-S., Scherz, M. D., Vieites, D. R., Glaw, F., and Vences, M. 2017. Two new species of leaf-tailed geckos (*Uroplatus*) from the Tsaratanana mountain massif in northern Madagascar. *Zootaxa* 4347(3): 446–464.

Ratsoavina, F. M., Scherz, M. D., Tolley, K., Raselimanana, A. P., Glaw, F., and Vences, M. 2019a. Finaritra! A splendid new leaf-tailed gecko (*Uroplatus*) species from Marojejy National Park in north-eastern Madagascar. *Zootaxa* 4545: 563–577.

———. 2019b. A new species of *Uroplatus* (Gekkonidae) from Ankarana National Park, Madagascar, of remarkably high genetic divergence. *Zootaxa* 4683: 84–96.

Ratsoavina, F. M., Glaw, F., Raselimanana, A. P., Rakotoarison, A., Vieites, D. R., Hawlitschek, O., Vences, M., and Scherz, M. D. 2020. Towards completion of the species inventory of small-sized leaf-tailed geckos: Two new species of *Uroplatus* from northern Madagascar. *Zootaxa* 4895: 251–271.

Raxworthy, C. J. 1988. Reptiles, rainforest and conservation in Madagascar. *Biological Conservation* 43: 181–211.

———. 1991. Field observations on some dwarf chameleons (*Brookesia* spp.) from rainforest areas of Madagascar, with the description of a new species. *Journal of Zoology* 224: 11–25.

———. 2003. Boidae, boas. In *The Natural History of Madagascar*, eds. S. M. Goodman and J. P. Benstead, pp. 993–997. Chicago: University of Chicago Press.

———. 2008. Global warming and extinction risks for amphibians in Madagascar: A preliminary assessment of potential upslope displacement. In A conservation strategy for the amphibians of Madagascar, ed. F. Andreone. *Monografie del Museo Regionale di Scienze Naturali di Torino* 45: 67–84.

Raxworthy, C. J., and Nussbaum, R. A. 1993a. A new Madagascan *Phelsuma*, with a review of *Phelsuma trilineata* and comments on *Phelsuma cepediana* in Madagascar (Squamata: Gekkonidae). *Herpetologica* 49: 342–349.

———. 1993b. Four new species of *Amphiglossus* from Madagascar (Squamata: Scincidae). *Herpetologica* 49: 326–341.

———. 1994a. A rainforest survey of amphibians, reptiles and small mammals at Montagne d'Ambre, Madagascar. *Biological Conservation* 69: 65–74.

———. 1994b. A review of the Madagascan snake genera *Pseudoxyrhopus*, *Pararhadinaea*, and *Heteroliodon* (Squamata: Colubridae). *Miscellaneous Publications, Museum of Zoology, University of Michigan* 182: 1–37.

———. 1994c. A partial systematic revision of the day geckos, *Phelsuma* Gray, of Madagascar (Reptilia: Squamata: Gekkonidae). *Zoological Journal of the Linnean Society* 112: 321–335.

———. 1995. Systematics, speciation and biogeography of the dwarf chameleons (*Brookesia*; Reptilia, Squamata, Chamaeleontidae) of northern Madagascar. *Journal of Zoology* 235: 525–558.

———. 1996a. Amphibians and reptiles of Andringitra Massif: A study of elevational distribution and local endemicity. In A floral and faunal inventory of the eastern slopes of the Réserve Naturelle Intégrale d'Andringitra, Madagascar: With reference to elevational variation, ed. S. M. Goodman. *Fieldiana: Zoology*, new series, 85: 158–170.

———. 1996b. Montane amphibian and reptile communities in Madagascar. *Conservation Biology* 10: 750–756.

———. 1996c. Patterns of endemism for terrestrial vertebrates in eastern Madagascar. In *Biogeography of Madagascar*, ed. W. R. Lourenço, pp. 368–384. Paris: ORSTOM.

———. 1997. Biogeographic patterns of reptiles in eastern Madagascar. In *Natural Change and Human Impact in Madagascar*, eds. S. M. Goodman and B. D. Patterson, pp. 124–141. Washington, DC: Smithsonian Institution Press.

———. 2000. Extinction, and extinction vulnerability of amphibians and reptiles in Madagascar. *Amphibian and Reptile Conservation* 2: 15–23.

———. 2002. Reptile mark-recapture trial using rainforest plots at Montagne d'Ambre, Madagascar. *Phelsuma* 10: 41–48.

———. 2006. Six new species of occipital-lobed *Calumma* chameleons (Squamata: Chameleonidae) from montane regions of Madagascar, with a new description and revision of *Calumma brevicorne*. *Copeia* 2006: 711–734.

Raxworthy, C. J., Ramanamanjato, J.-B., and Raselimanana, A. P. 1994. Les reptiles et les amphibiens. In Inventaire biologique de forêt de Zombitse, eds. S. M. Goodman and O. Langrand. *Recherches pour le Développement, Série Sciences Biologiques*, No. Spécial: 41–57.

Raxworthy, C. J., Andreone, F., Nussbaum, R. A., Rabibisoa, N., and Randriamahazo, H. 1998. Amphibians and reptiles of the Anjanaharibe Massif: Elevational distributions and regional endemism. In A floral and faunal inventory of the Réserve Spéciale d'Anjanaharibe-Sud, Madagascar: With reference to elevational variation, ed. S. M. Goodman. *Fieldiana: Zoology*, new series, 90: 79–92.

Raxworthy, C. J., Forstner, M.R.J., and Nussbaum, R. A. 2002. Chameleon radiation by oceanic dispersal. *Nature* 415: 784–787.

Raxworthy, C. J., Martinez-Meyer, E., Horning, N., Nussbaum, R. A., Schneider, G. E., Ortega-Huerta, M. A., and Peterson, A. T. 2003. Predicting distributions of known and unknown reptile species in Madagascar. *Nature* 426: 837–841.

Raxworthy, C. J., Ingram, C. M., Rabibisoa, N., and Pearson, R. G. 2007. Applications of ecological niche modeling for species delimitation: A review and empirical evaluation using day geckos (*Phelsuma*) from Madagascar. *Systematic Biology* 56: 907–923.

Raxworthy, C. J., Pearson, R. G., Zimkus, B. M., Reddy, S., Deo, A. J., Nussbaum, R. A., and Ingram, C. M. 2008a. Continental speciation in the tropics: Contrasting biogeographic patterns of divergence in the *Uroplatus* leaf-tailed gecko radiation of Madagascar. *Journal of Zoology* 275: 423–440.

Raxworthy, C. J., Pearson, R. G., Rabibisoa, N., Rakotondrazafy, A. M., Ramanamanjato, J.-B., Raselimanana, A. P., Wu, S., Nussbaum, R. A., and Stone, D. 2008b. Extinction vulnerability of tropical montane endemism from warming and upslope displacement: A preliminary appraisal for the highest massif in Madagascar. *Global Change Biology* 14: 1703–1720.

Raxworthy, C. J., Ramanamanjato, J.-B., and Rakotondravony, H. 2011. *Zonosaurus maximus*. IUCN Red List of Threatened Species 2011: e.T172865A6931872. Accessed 13 Oct. 2019. http://dx.doi.org/10.2305/IUCN.UK.2011-2.RLTS.T172865A6931872.en.

Raxworthy, C. J., Ananjeva, N., and Orlov, N. L. 2012. Techniques for complete species inventories. In *Reptile Biodiversity: Standard Methods for Inventory and Monitoring*, eds. R. W. McDiarmid, M. S. Foster, C. Guyer, J. Whitfield Gibbons, and N. Chernoff, pp. 209–215. Berkeley: University of California Press.

Razafimahatratra, B., Mori, A., and Hasegawa, M. 2008. Sleeping site pattern and sleeping behavior of *Brookesia decaryi* (Chamaeleonidae) in Ampijoroa dry forest, northwestern Madagascar. *Current Herpetology* 27: 93–99.

Razafimahatratra, B., Razafimanjato, G., and Thorstrom, R. 2010. A new locality for the endangered day gecko *Phelsuma klemmeri* from western Madagascar. *Herpetology Notes* 3: 197–199.

Razafimahatratra, B., Wang, C., Mori, A., and Glaw, F. 2015. Potential envenomation by the aglyphous pseudoxyrhophiine snake *Leioheterodon madagascariensis* and description of its dentition. *Journal of Venomous Animals and Toxins including Tropical Diseases* 21: 47.

Razandrimamilafiniarivo, O. C., Reid, D., and Bekarany, E. 2000. Captive management and reproduction of the Madagascar flat-tailed tortoise *Pyxis planicauda* at the Chelonian Captive Breeding Centre, Ampijoroa, Madagascar. *Dodo* 36: 75–81.

Recknagel, H., Elmer, K. R., Noonan, B. P., Raselimanana, A. P., Meyer, A., and Vences, M. 2013. Multi-gene phylogeny of Madagascar's plated lizards, *Zonosaurus* and *Tracheloptychus* (Squamata: Gerrhosauridae). *Molecular Phylogenetics and Evolution* 69: 1215–1221.

Rendahl, H. 1918. Zwei neue Arten der Gattung *Typhlops* aus dem Kaplande. *Arkiv för Zoologi* 11: 1–6.

Renoult, J., and Raselimanana, A. P. 2009. A new species of Malagasy blind snake of the genus *Typhlops* Oppel (Serpentes: Typhlopidae). *Zootaxa* 2290: 65–68.

Republic of Madagascar. 1997. Prop. 10.2. Madagascar: Amendment proposal pursuant to ranching submitted to CoP10. Antananarivo.

Resetarits, E., and Raxworthy, C. J. 2016. Hidden in plain sight: How ventral line markings in chameleons may enhance camouflage. *American Naturalist* 187: 262–273.

Reynolds, R. G., and Henderson, R. W. 2018. Boas of the world (superfamily Booidae): A checklist with systematic, taxonomic, and conservation assessments. *Bulletin of the Museum of Comparative Zoology* 162(1): 1–58.

Reynolds, R. G., Niemiller, M. L., and Revell, L. J. 2014. Toward a tree-of-life for the boas and pythons: Multilocus species-level phylogeny with unprecedented taxon sampling. *Molecular Phylogenetics and Evolution* 71: 201–213.

Riedel, J., Böhme, W., Bleckmann, H., and Spinner, M. 2015. Microornamentation of leaf chameleons (Chamaeleonidae: *Brookesia*, *Rhampholeon*, and *Rieppeleon*)—with comments on the evolution of microstructures in the Chamaeleonidae. *Journal of Morphology* 276: 167–184.

Rieppel, O. 1987. The phylogenetic relationships within the Chamaeleonidae, with comments on some aspects of cladistic analysis. *Zoological Journal of the Linnean Society* 89: 41–62.

Rieppel, O., and Crumly, C. 1997. Paedomorphosis and skull structure in Malagasy chamaeleons (Reptilia: Chamaeleoninae). *Journal of Zoology* 243: 351–380.

Risley, T. 1997. Preliminary observations on a small population of *Chamaeleo [Calumma] parsonii parsonii* Cuvier, 1824 in eastern Madagascar. *Chameleon Information Network* 25: 25–28.

Rittenhouse, D. R., Russell, A. P., and Bauer, A. M. 1997. Laryngotracheal morphology of the *Uroplatus fimbriatus* complex (Reptilia: Gekkonidae): Yet another autapomorphic organ system in a group of highly aberrant geckos. *African Journal of Herpetology* 46: 36–48.

Robinson, J. E., Fraser, I. M., St. John, F.A.V., Randrianantoandro, J. C., Andriantsimanarilafy, R. R., Razafimanahaka, J. H., Griffiths, R. A., and Roberts, D. L. 2018a. Wildlife supply chains in Madagascar from local collection to global export. *Biological Conservation* 226: 144–152.

Robinson, J. E., Griffiths, R. A., Fraser, I. M., Raharimalala, J., Roberts, D. L., and St. John, F.A.V. 2018b. Supplying the wildlife trade as a livelihood strategy in a biodiversity hotspot. *Ecology and Society* 23: 13.

Rocha, S. 2010. Phylogeny, phylogeography and colonisation patterns of reptiles in Indian Ocean islands. PhD thesis, University of Porto.

Rocha, S., Carretero, M. A., Vences, M., Glaw, F., and Harris, D. J. 2006. Deciphering patterns of transoceanic dispersal: The evolutionary origin and biogeography of coastal lizards (*Cryptoblepharus*) in the western Indian Ocean region. *Journal of Biogeography* 33: 13–22.

Rocha, S., Ineich, I., and Harris, D. J. 2009a. Cryptic variation and recent bipolar range expansion within the stumped-toed gecko *Gehyra mutilata* across Indian and Pacific Ocean islands. *Contributions to Zoology* 78: 1–8.

Rocha, S., Vences, M., Glaw, F., Posada, D., and Harris, D. J. 2009b. Multigene phylogeny of Malagasy day geckos of the genus *Phelsuma*. *Molecular Phylogenetics and Evolution* 52: 530–537.

Rocha, S., Carretero, M. A., and Harris, J. 2010a. Genetic diversity and phylogenetic relationships of *Mabuya* spp. (Squamata: Scincidae) from western Indian Ocean islands. *Amphibia-Reptilia* 31: 375–385.

Rocha, S., Rösler, H., Gehring, P.-S., Glaw, F., Posada, D., Harris, D. J., and Vences, M. 2010b. Phylogenetic systematics of day geckos, genus *Phelsuma*, based on molecular and morphological data (Squamata: Gekkonidae). *Zootaxa* 2429: 1–28.

Röll, B., Pröhl, H., and Hoffmann, K.-P. 2010. Multigene phylogenetic analysis of *Lygodactylus* dwarf geckos (Squamata: Gekkonidae). *Molecular Phylogenetics and Evolution* 56: 327–335.

Rösler, H. 1995. *Geckos der Welt, alle Gattungen*. Leipzig: Urania-Verlag.

Rohtla, E. A., Russell, A. P., and Bauer, A. M. 2019. Sounding off: Relationships between call properties, body size, phylogeny, and laryngotracheal form of geckos. *Herpetologica* 75: 175–197.

Rosa, G. M., and Rakotozafy, S. 2013. Opportunistic but voracious: Madagascan spiny-tailed iguana, *Oplurus cuvieri* (Reptilia: Opluridae) predation upon a small mammal. *Herpetology Notes* 6: 459-461.

Rosa, G. M., Mercurio, V., Crottini, A., and Andreone, F. 2010. Predation of the snake *Leioheterodon modestus* (Günther, 1863) upon the rainbow frog *Scaphiophryne gottlebei* Busse and Böhme, 1992 at Isalo, southern Madagascar. *Herpetology Notes* 3: 259–261.

Ross, J. P. 1998. *Crocodiles: Status Survey and Conservation Action Plan*. 2nd ed. Gland: IUCN/SSC Crocodile Specialist Group.

Rovatsos, M., Altmanová, M., Pokorná, M. J., Velenský, P., Baca, A. S., and Kratochvil, L. 2017. Evolution of karyotypes in chameleons. *Genes* 8: 382.

Ruane, S., Raxworthy, C. J., Lemmon, A. R., Lemmon, E. M., and Burbrink, F. T. 2015. Comparing species tree estimation with large anchored phylogenomic and small Sanger-sequenced molecular datasets: An empirical study on Malagasy pseudoxyrhophiine snakes. *BMC Evolutionary Biology* 15: 221.

Ruane, S., Burbrink, F. T., Randriamahatantsoa, B., and Raxworthy, C. J. 2016. The cat-eyed snakes of Madagascar: Phylogeny and description of a new species of *Madagascarophis* (Serpentes: Lamprophiidae) from the Tsingy of Ankarana. *Copeia* 104: 712–721.

Ruane, S., Myers, E. A., Lo, K., Yuen, S., Welt, R. S., et al. 2018. Unrecognized species diversity and new insights into colour pattern polymorphism within the widespread Malagasy snake *Mimophis* (Serpentes: Lamprophiidae). *Systematics and Biodiversity* 16: 1–16.

Rundquist, E. M. 1994. *Day Geckos*. Neptune City: T.F.H. Publications.

Runhovde, S. R. 2018. *Illegal Online Trade in Reptiles from Madagascar*. Geneva: Global Initiative against Transnational Organized Crime.

Russell, A. P. 1986. The morphological basis of weight-bearing in the scansors of the tokay gecko (Reptilia: Sauria). *Canadian Journal of Zoology* 64: 948–955.

———. 2002. Integrative functional morphology of the gekkotan adhesive system (Reptilia: Gekkota). *Integrative and Comparative Biology* 42: 1154–1163.

Russell, A. P., and Bauer, A. M. 2008. The appendicular locomotor apparatus of *Sphenodon* and normal-limbed squamates. In *The Skull and Appendicular Locomotor Apparatus of Lepidosauria*, eds. C. Gans, A. S. Gaunt, and K. Adler, pp. 1–465. Ithaca: Society for the Study of Amphibians and Reptiles.

Russell, A. P., Hood, H. A., and Bauer, A. M. 2014. Laryngotracheal and cervical muscular anatomy in the genus *Uroplatus* (Gekkota: Gekkonidae) in relation to distress call emission. *African Journal of Herpetology* 63: 127–151.

Sakata, S., and Hikida, T. 2003a. A fossorial lizard with forelimbs only: Description of a new genus and species of Malagasy skink (Reptilia: Squamata: Scincidae). *Current Herpetology* 22: 9–15.

———. 2003b. A new fossorial scincine lizard of the genus *Pseudoacontias* (Reptilia: Squamata: Scincidae) from Nosy Be, Madagascar. *Amphibia-Reptilia* 24: 57–64.

Savitzky, A. H. 1981. Hinged teeth in snakes: An adaptation for swallowing hard-bodied prey. *Science* 212: 346–349.

Sazima, I. 1989. Feeding behavior of the snail-eating snake, *Dipsas indica*. *Journal of Herpetology* 23: 464–468.

Scantlebury, D. P. 2013. Diversification rates have declined in the Malagasy herpetofauna. *Proceedings of the Royal Society of London B: Biological Sciences* 280: 20131109.

Scherz, M. D., Daza, J. D., Köhler, J., Vences, M., and Glaw, F. 2017. Off the scale: A new species of fish-scale gecko (Squamata: Gekkonidae: *Geckolepis*) with exceptionally large scales. *PeerJ* 5: e2955.

Scherz, M. D., Glaw, F., Rakotoarison, A., Wagler, M., and Vences, M. 2018. Polymorphism and synonymy of *Brookesia antakarana* and *B. ambreensis*, leaf chameleons from Montagne d'Ambre in north Madagascar. *Salamandra* 54: 259–268.

Scherz, M. D., Köhler, J., Rakotoarison, A., Glaw, F., and Vences, M. 2019. A new dwarf chameleon, genus *Brookesia*, from the Marojejy Massif in northern Madagascar. *Zoosystematics and Evolution* 95: 95–106.

Schimmenti, G., and Jesu, R. 1996. *Brookesia exarmata* sp. nov. (Reptilia, Chamaeleonidae): A new dwarf chameleon from the limestone outcrops of western Madagascar. *Italian Journal of Zoology* 63: 193–197.

Schmidt, W. 1992. Über die erstmalig gelungene Nachzucht von *Furcifer campani* (Grandidier, 1872), sowie eine Zusammenstellung einger Eizeitigungsdaten von verschieden Chamäeleonarton in Tabellenform. *Sauria* 14: 21–23.

Schmidt, W., Tamm, K., and Wallikewitz, E. 2010. *Chamäleons: Drachen unserer Zeit*. Münster: Natur und Tier-Verlag.

Schmitz, A., Mausfeld, P., Hekkala, E., Shine, T., Nickel, H., Amato, G., and Böhme, W. 2003. Molecular evidence for species level divergence in African Nile crocodiles *Crocodylus niloticus* (Laurenti, 1786). *Comptes Rendus Palevol* 2: 703–712.

Schmitz, A., Brandley, M. C., Mausfeld, P., Vences, M., Glaw, F., Nussbaum, R. A., and Reeder, T. W. 2005. Opening the black box: Phylogenetics and morphological evolution of the Malagasy fossorial lizards of the subfamily "Scincinae." *Molecular Phylogenetics and Evolution* 34: 118–133.

Scott, D. M., Brown, D., Mahood, S., Denton, B., Silburn, A., and Rakotondraparany, F. 2006. The impacts of forest clearance on lizard, small mammal and bird communities in the arid spiny forest, southern Madagascar. *Biological Conservation* 127: 72–87.

Segura, C., Feriche, M., Pleguezuelos, J. M., and Santos, X. 2007. Specialist and generalist species in habitat use: Implications for conservation assessment in snakes. *Journal of Natural History* 41: 2765–2774.

Sentís, M., Chang, Y., Scherz, M. D., Prötzel, D., and Glaw, F. 2018. Rising from the ashes: Resurrection of the Malagasy chameleons *Furcifer monoceras* and *Furcifer voeltzkowi* (Squamata: Chamaeleonidae), based on micro-CT analyses and external morphology. *Zootaxa* 4483: 549–566.

Shea, G. M. 2021. The identity of twelve scincid generic names proposed by Cope in 1892 (Squamata: Scincidae). *Zootaxa* 5057: 577–589.

Shyamsundar, P., and Kramer, R. 1997. Biodiversity conservation: At what cost? A study of households in the vicinity of Madagascar's Mantadia National Park. *Ambio* 26: 180–184.

Siebenrock, F. 1903. Schildkröten von Madagaskar und Aldabra. *Abhandlungen der Senckenberg Naturforschenden Gesellschaft* 27: 241–259.

Sinervo, B., Mendez-de-la-Cruz, F., Miles, D. B., Heulin, B., Bastiaans, E., et al. 2010. Erosion of lizard diversity by climate change and altered thermal niches. *Science* 328: 894–899.

Smith, L. L., Bourou, R., Joby, M., and Sibo, C. 1999. Home range and microhabitat use in the angonoka tortoise (*Geochelone yniphora*) in western Madagascar. *Chelonian Conservation and Biology* 3: 393–400.

Smith, L. L., Pedrono, M., Dorazio, R. M., and Bishko, J. 2000. Morphometrics, sexual dimorphism, and growth in the angonoka tortoise (*Geochelone yniphora*) of western Madagascar. *African Journal of Herpetology* 50: 9–18.

Sommer, S. 2000. Sex-specific predation on a monogamous rat, *Hypogeomys antimena* (Muridae: Nesomyinae). *Animal Behaviour* 59: 1087–1094.

Spinner, M., Westhoff, G., and Gorb, S. N. 2013. Subdigital and subcaudal microornamentation in Chamaeleonidae: A comparative study. *Journal of Morphology* 274: 713–723.

———. 2014. Subdigital setae of chameleon feet: Friction-enhancing microstructures for a wide range of substrate roughness. *Scientific Reports* 4: 5481.

Stanley, R. C., and Raxworthy, C. J. 2016. Rediscovery of the enigmatic day gecko *Phelsuma masohoala* in northeast Madagascar. *Herpetological Conservation and Biology* 11: 4012–4017.

Stull, O. G. 1935. A check list of the family Boidae. *Proceedings of the Boston Society of Natural History* 40: 387–408.

Svatek, S., and Van Duin, S. 2002. *Plattschwanzgeckos: Die Gattung* Uroplatus. Elze: Brähmer Verlag.

Takahashi, H. 2008. Fruit feeding behavior of a chameleon *Furcifer oustaleti*: Comparison with insect foraging tactics. *Journal of Herpetology* 42: 4.

Taylor, B., and Gardner, C. 2014. Nectar feeding by the day gecko *Phelsuma mutabilis* (Squamata: Gekkonidae) on the mangrove tree *Sonneratia alba* (Lythraceae) in southwest Madagascar. *Herpetology Notes* 7: 85–87.

Tessa, G., Glaw, F., and Andreone, F. 2017. Longevity in *Calumma parsonii*, the world's largest chameleon. *Experimental Gerontology* 89: 41–44.

Teyssier, J., Saenko, S., van der Marel, D., and Milinkovitch, M. 2015. Photonic crystals cause active colour change in chameleons. *Nature Communications* 6: 6368.

Theisinger, O., and Ratianarivo, M. C. 2015. Patterns of reptile diversity loss in response to degradation in the spiny forest of southern Madagascar. *Herpetological Conservation and Biology* 10: 273–283.

Theisinger, O., Berg, W., and Dausmann, K. H. 2017. Compensation of thermal constraints along a natural environmental gradient in a Malagasy iguanid lizard (*Oplurus quadrimaculatus*). *Journal of Thermal Biology* 68: 21–26.

Thomas, L., Buckland, S., Rexstad, E. A., Laake, J. L., Strindberg, S., Hedley, S. L., Bishop, J. R., Marques, T. A., and Burnham, K. 2010. Distance software: Design and analysis of distance sampling surveys for estimating population size. *Journal of Applied Ecology* 47: 5–14.

Thorpe, R. S., and Crawford, C. M. 1979. The comparative abundance and resource partitioning of two green-gecko species (*Phelsuma*) on Praslin, Seychelles. *British Journal of Herpetology* 6: 19–24.

Tingle, J. L. 2012. Field observations on the behavioral ecology of the Madagascan leaf-nosed snake, *Langaha madagascariensis*. *Herpetological Conservation and Biology* 7(3): 442–448.

Titus, T. A., and Frost, D. R. 1996. Molecular homology assessment and phylogeny in the lizard family Opluridae (Squamata: Iguania). *Molecular Phylogenetics and Evolution* 6: 49–62.

Todd, M. 2011. *Trade in Malagasy Reptiles and Amphibians in Thailand*. Petaling Jaya, Selangor: TRAFFIC Southeast Asia.

Tolley, K. A., Townsend, T. M., and Vences, M. 2013. Large-scale phylogeny of chameleons suggests African origins and Eocene diversification. *Proceedings of the Royal Society of London B: Biological Sciences* 280: 20130184.

Townsend, T. M., Vieites, D. R., Glaw, F., and Vences, M. 2009. Testing species-level diversification hypotheses in Madagascar: The case of microendemic *Brookesia* leaf chameleons. *Systematic Biology* 58: 641–656.

Townsend, T. M., Mulcahy, D. G., Noonan, B. P., Sites, J. W., Jr., Kuczynski, C. A., Wiens, J. J., and Reeder, T. W. 2011a. Phylogeny of iguanian lizards inferred from 29 nuclear loci, and a comparison of concatenated and species-tree approaches for an ancient, rapid radiation. *Molecular Phylogenetics and Evolution* 61: 363–380.

Townsend, T. M., Tolley, K. A., Glaw, F., Böhme, W., and Vences, M. 2011b. Eastward from Africa: Palaeocurrent-mediated chameleon dispersal to the Seychelles islands. *Biology Letters* 7: 225–228.

Tronc, E., and Vuillemin, S. 1974. Contribution à l'étude de la faune endémique Malgache: Etude ostéologique de *Erymnochelys madagascariensis*. *Bulletin de l'Académie Malgache* 51: 189–224.

Uetz, P., Freed, P., and Hošek, J. 2021. The Reptile Database. Accessed 18 July 2021. http://www.reptile-database.org.

Ujvari, B., Casewell, N. R., Sunagar, K., Arbuckle, K., Wüster, W., et al. 2015. Widespread convergence in toxin resistance by predictable molecular evolution. *Proceedings of the National Academy of Sciences of the USA* 112: 11911–11916.

Vaillant, L., and Grandidier, A. 1872. Sur le crocodile fossile d'Amboulintsatre (Madagascar). *Comptes Rendus de l'Académie des Sciences* 75: 150–151.

Vaillant, L., and Grandidier, G. 1910. Histoire naturelle des reptiles, premier partie: Crocodiles et tortues. In *Histoire physique, naturelle et politique de Madagascar*, vol. 17, ed. A. Grandidier, pp. 1–86. Paris: Imprimerie Nationale.

Valido, A., and Olesen, J. M. 2019. Frugivory and seed dispersal by lizards: A global review. *Frontiers in Ecology and Evolution* 7: 49.

Vargas-Ramírez, M., Vences, M., Branch, W. R., Daniels, S. R., Glaw, F., et al. 2010. Deep genealogical lineages in the widely distributed African helmeted terrapin: Evidence from mitochondrial and nuclear DNA (Testudines: Pelomedusidae: *Pelomedusa subrufa*). *Molecular Phylogenetics and Evolution* 56: 428–440.

Velosoa, J. 2000. Contribution à l'étude de l'habitat de la distribution et la mise à jour de statut de la conservation d'*Erymnochelys madagascariensis* (Grandidier, 1867) dans la côte ouest de Madagascar. Mémoire de DEA, Facultés des Sciences, Université d'Antananarivo.

Velosoa, J., Randriamahita, and Woolaver, L. 2011. Post release monitoring of Madagascar side-necked turtles *Erymnochelys madagascariensis* in Ankarafantsika National Park 2009–2010. Unpublished report to the Turtle Conservation Fund (Grant TCF-0224) and Conservation International.

Velosoa, J., Woolaver, L., Randriamahita, Bekarany, E., Randrianarimangason, F., Mozavelo, R., García, G., and Lewis, R. E. 2013. An integrated research, management, and community conservation program for the rere (Madagascar big-headed turtle), *Erymnochelys madagascariensis*. In Turtles on the brink in Madagascar: Proceedings of two workshops on the status, conservation, and biology of Malagasy tortoises and freshwater turtles, eds. C. M. Castellano, A.G.J. Rhodin, M. Ogle, R. A. Mittermeier, H. Randriamahazo, R. Hudson, and R. E. Lewis. *Chelonian Research Monographs* 6: 171–177.

Velosoa, J., Mozavelo, R., and Woolaver, L. 2015. Community led nest monitoring and protection of rere *Erymnochelys madagascariensis* at the Lake Ambondrobe new protected area, 2013–2014. Unpublished report to the Turtle Conservation Fund (Grant TCF-0474) and Conservation International.

Velosoa, J., Volhy, A. T., and Mozavelo, R. 2019. Social and environmental management plan for the creation of the new protected area at Lake Ambondrobe for the conservation of *Erymnochelys madagascariensis*. Unpublished report to the Turtle Conservation Fund (Grant TCF-0396) and Conservation International.

Vences, M., and Glaw, F. 2003. Phylogeography, systematics and conservation status of boid snakes from Madagascar (*Sanzinia* and *Acrantophis*). *Salamandra* 39: 181–206.

Vences, M., Jung, J. M., Glaw, F., and Böhme, W. 1996. Review of the *Zonosaurus aeneus* species group, with resurrection of *Zonosaurus subunicolor* (Boettger 1881) (Reptilia: Squamata: Gerrhosauridae). *Senckenbergiana Biologica* 76(1/2): 47–59.

Vences, M., Glaw, F., and Love, W. B. 1998. Live-bearing in the snake *Stenophis citrinus* from Madagascar. *British Herpetological Society Bulletin* 64: 13–14.

Vences, M., Glaw, F., Kosuch, J., Böhme, W., and Veith, M. 2001. Phylogeny of South American and Malagasy boine snakes: Molecular evidence for the validity of *Sanzinia* and *Acrantophis* and biogeographic implications. *Copeia* 2001: 1151–1155.

Vences, M., Galán, P., Miramontes, K., and Vieites, D. R. 2004a. Weak expression of reproductive seasonality in a dwarf gecko (*Lygodactylus*) from arid south-western Madagascar. *Journal of Arid Environments* 56: 329–338.

Vences, M., Wanke, S., Vieites, D. R., Branch, W. R., Glaw, F., and Meyer, A. 2004b. Natural colonization or introduction? Phylogeographical relationships and morphological differentiation of house geckos (*Hemidactylus*) from Madagascar. *Biological Journal of the Linnean Society* 83: 115–130.

Vences, M., Wollenberg, K. C., Vieites, D. R., and Lees, D. C. 2009. Madagascar as a model region of species diversification. *Trends in Ecology and Evolution* 24: 456–465.

Vences, M., Lima, A., Miralles, A., and Glaw, F. 2014. DNA barcoding assessment of genetic variation in two widespread skinks from Madagascar, *Trachylepis elegans* and *T. gravenhorstii* (Squamata: Scincidae). *Zootaxa* 3755: 477–484.

Veress, M., Lóczy, D., Zentai, Z., Tóth, G., and Schläffer, R. 2008. The origin of the Bemaraha tsingy (Madagascar). *International Journal of Speleology* 37: 131–142.

Veress, M., Tóth, G., Zentai, Z., and Schläffer, R. 2009. The Ankarana tsingy and its development. *Carpathian Journal of Earth and Environmental Sciences* 4: 95–108.

Vidal, N., Marin, J., Morini, M., Donnellan, S., Branch, W. R., Thomas, R., Vences, M., Wynn, A., Cruaud, C., and Hedges, S. B. 2010. Blindsnake evolutionary tree reveals long history on Gondwana. *Biology Letters* 6: 558–561.

Vieites, D. R., Wollenberg, K. C., Andreone, F., Köhler, J., Glaw, F., and Vences, M. 2009. Vast underestimation of Madagascar's biodiversity evidenced by an integrative amphibian inventory. *Proceedings of the National Academy of Sciences of the USA* 106: 8267–8272.

Vieites, D. R., Ratsoavina, F. M., Randrianiaina, R.-D., Nagy, Z. T., Glaw, F., and Vences, M. 2010. A rhapsody of colours from Madagascar: Discovery of a remarkable new snake of the genus *Liophidium* and its phylogenetic relationships. *Salamandra* 46: 1–10.

Vielledent, G., Grinand, C., Rakotomalala, F. A., Ranaivosoa, R., Rakotoarijaona, J. R., Allnutt, T. F., and Achard, F. 2018. Combining global tree cover loss data with historical national forest cover maps to look at six decades of deforestation and forest fragmentation in Madagascar. *Biological Conservation* 222: 189–197.

Villeneuve, A. R. 2017. Habitat selection and population density of the world's smallest chameleon, *Brookesia micra*, on Nosy Hara, Madagascar. *Herpetological Conservation and Biology* 12: 334–341.

Voeltzkow, A. 1891. Über Eiablage und Embryonalentwicklung der Krokodile. *Sitzungsberichte der Königlich Preussischen Akademie der Wissenschaften zu Berlin* 1891: 115–120.

———. 1893. Über Biologie und Embryonalentwicklung der Krokodile. *Sitzungsberichte der Königlich Preussischen Akademie der Wissenschaften zu Berlin* 23: 347–353.

———. 1899. Beiträge zur Entwicklungsgeschichte der Reptilien: Biologie und Entwicklung der äusseren Körperform von *Crocodilus madagascariensis* Grand. *Abhandlungen der Senckenbergischen Naturforschenden Gesellschaft* 26: 3–149.

———. 1901. Die Bildung der Keimblätter von *Podocnemis madagascariensis* Grand. *Abhandlungen der Senckenberg Naturforschenden Gesellschaft* 26: 275–310.

Vogt, R. C., Cantarelli, V. H., and Guerreiro de Carvalho, A. 1994. Reproduction of the Cabeçudo, *Peltocephalus dumerilianus*, in the biological reserve of Rio Trombetas, Pará, Brazil. *Chelonian Conservation and Biology* 1: 145–148.

Vorontsova, M. S., Besnard, G., Forest, F., Malakasi, P., Moat, J., et al. 2016. Madagascar's grasses and grasslands: Anthropogenic or natural? *Proceedings of the Royal Society of London B: Biological Sciences* 283: 20152262.

Waeber, P. O., Rafanoharana, S., Rasamuel, H. A., and Wilmé, L. 2019. Parks and reserves in Madagascar: Managing biodiversity for a sustainable future. In *Protected Areas, National Parks and Sustainable Future*, eds. A. N. Bakar and M. N. Suratman, pp. 1–20. London: IntechOpen.

Wagner, P., Glaw, F., Glaw, K., and Böhme, W. 2009. Studies on African *Agama*. IV. First record of *Agama agama* (Sauria: Agamidae) from Madagascar and identity of the alien population on Grande Comore Island. *Herpetology Notes* 2: 73–77.

Walker, R.C.J. 2010. The decline of the Critically Endangered northern Madagascar spider tortoise (*Pyxis arachnoides brygooi*). *Herpetologica* 66: 411–417.

———. 2011a. The conservation issues facing the Critically Endangered Madagascar radiated tortoise (*Astrochelys radiata*). *Testudo* 7: 39–52.

———. 2011b. The internet based trade in Madagascar's Critically Endangered tortoise species: A preliminary study identifying the conservation threats. *Testudo* 7: 4.

———. 2014. The Madagascar spider tortoise *Pyxis arachnoides*. In *Western Indian Ocean Tortoises: Ecology, Diversity, Evolution, Conservation, Palaeontology*, ed. J. Gerlach, pp. 297–312. Manchester: Siri Scientific Press.

Walker, R.C.J., and Rafeliarisoa, T. H. 2012a. Status of the relict population of the Critically Endangered Madagascar spider tortoise *Pyxis arachnoides*. *Oryx* 46: 457–463.

———. 2012b. Distribution of radiated tortoise (*Astrochelys radiata*) bush meat poaching effort. *Chelonian Conservation and Biology* 11: 223–226.

Walker, R.C.J., Woods-Ballard, A. J., and Rix, C. E. 2007. Population density and seasonal activity of the threatened Madagascar spider tortoise (*Pyxis arachnoides arachnoides*) of the southern dry forests; South West Madagascar. *African Journal of Ecology* 46: 67–73.

Walker, R.C.J, Whitmore, N., Rafeliarisoa, T., and Hamylton, S. 2012. The effect of habitat degradation on the long term survival of the Critically Endangered Madagascar spider tortoise (*Pyxis arachnoides*). *Biological Conservation* 152: 152–158.

Walker, R.C.J., Gardner, C. J., Rafeliarisoa, T. H., Smith, I., Razafimanatsoa, R., and Louis, E. E., Jr., 2013. Conservation of the Madagascar spider tortoise (*Pyxis arachnoides*) amid changing land use policy: Assessing the spatial coincidence of relict populations with protected areas and mining concessions. *Chelonian Research Monographs* 6: 135–145.

Walker, R.C.J., Mifsud, D., Rakotondrainy, R., Currylow, A., Randrianjafizanaka, S., and Cummings, M. 2016. Baseline population assessment of the recently described, endemic Madagascar hinge-backed tortoise (*Kinixys zombensis domerguei*). In *Program and Abstracts of the Fourteenth Annual Symposium on the Conservation and Biology of Tortoises and Freshwater Turtles*, eds A. D. Walde, J. D. Riedle, and H. Lowe, p. 51. New Orleans: Turtle Survival Alliance.

Wallach, V. 1986. *Leioheterodon madagascariensis*, an addition to the snake fauna of the Comoro islands. *Journal of the Herpetological Association of Africa* 32: 24–25.

———. 2009. *Ramphotyphlops braminus* (Daudin): A synopsis of morphology, taxonomy, nomenclature and distribution (Serpentes: Typhlopidae). *Hamadryad* 34: 34–61.

Wallach, V., and Glaw, F. 2009. A new mid-altitude rainforest species of *Typhlops* (Serpentes: Typhlopidae) from Madagascar with notes on the taxonomic status of *T. boettgeri* Boulenger, *T. microcephalus* Werner, and *T. capensis* Rendahl. *Zootaxa* 2294: 23–38.

Wallach, V., Mercurio, V., and Andreone, F. 2007. Rediscovery of the enigmatic blind snake genus *Xenotyphlops* in northern Madagascar, with description of a new species (Serpentes: Typhlopidae). *Zootaxa* 1402: 59–68.

Watson, J.E.M., Evans, T., Venter, O., Williams, B., Tulloch, A., et al. 2018. The exceptional value of intact forest ecosystems. *Nature Ecology and Evolution* 2: 599–610.

Wegener, J., Swoboda, S., Hawlitschek, O., Franzen, M., Wallach, V., Vences, M., Nagy, Z. T., Hedges, S., Köhler, J., and Glaw, F. 2013. Morphological variation and taxonomic reassessment of the endemic Malagasy blind snake family Xenotyphlopidae (Serpentes, Scolecophidia). *Spixiana* 36: 269–282.

Weinell, J. L., Branch, W. R., Colston, T. J., Jackman, T. R., Kuhn, A., Conradie, W., and Bauer, A. M. 2019. A species-level phylogeny of *Trachylepis* (Scincidae: Mabuyinae) provides insight into their reproductive mode evolution. *Molecular Phylogenetics and Evolution* 136: 183–195.

Welt, R. S., and Raxworthy, C. J. 2022. Dispersal, not vicariance, explains the biogeographic origin of iguanas on Madagascar. *Molecular Phylogenetics and Evolution* 167: 107345.

Wermuth, H., and Fuchs, K. 1978. *Bestimmen von Krokodilen und ihrer Häute*. Stuttgart: Gustav Fischer Verlag.

Werner, F. 1912a. Eublepharidae, Uroplatuidae, Pygopodidae. *Das Tierreich* 33: 1–33.

———. 1912b. Beitrage zur Anatomie einiger seltenerer Reptilien, mit besonderer Berücksichtigung der Atmungsorgane. *Arbeiten der Zoologische Institut Wien* 19: 373–424.

Whiting, A. S., Bauer, A. M., and Sites, J. W., Jr., 2003. Phylogenetic relationships and limb loss in sub-Saharan African scincine lizards (Squamata: Scincidae). *Molecular Phylogenetics and Evolution* 29: 582–598.

Whiting, A. S., Sites, J. W., Jr., and Bauer, A. M. 2004. Molecular phylogenetics of Malagasy skinks (Squamata: Scincidae). *African Journal of Herpetology* 53: 135–146.

Wiens, J. J., Brandley, M. C., and Reeder, T. W. 2006. Why does a trait evolve multiple times within a clade? Repeated evolution of snakelike body form in squamate reptiles. *Evolution* 60: 123–141.

Williams, E. E. 1988. A new look at the Iguania. In *Proceedings of a Workshop on Neotropical Distribution Patterns*, eds. W. R. Heyer and P. E. Vanzolini, pp. 429–488. Rio de Janeiro: Academia Brasileira de Ciencias.

Wilmé, L., Goodman, S. M., and Ganzhorn, J. U. 2006. Biogeographic evolution of Madagascar's microendemic biota. *Science* 312: 1063–1065.

Wollenberg, K. C., Jenkins, R.K.B., Randrianavelona, R., Ralisata, M., Rampilamanana, R., Ramanandraibe, A., Ravoahangimalala, O. R., and Vences, M. 2010. Raising awareness of amphibian chytridiomycosis will not alienate ecotourists visiting Madagascar. *EcoHealth* 7: 248–251.

Wollenberg, K. C., Jenkins, R. K., Randrianavelona, R., Rampilamanana, R., Ralisata, M., Ramanandraibe, A., Ravoahangimalala, O. R., and Vences, M. 2011. On the shoulders of lemurs: Pinpointing the ecotouristic potential of Madagascar's unique herpetofauna. *Journal of Ecotourism* 10: 101–117.

World's Top Exports. 2019. Madagascar's Top 10 Exports. Accessed 15 Oct. 2019. http://www.worldstopexports.com/madagascars-top-10-exports/.

Wright, A. M., Lyons, K. M., Brandley, M. C., and Hillis, D. M. 2015. Which came first: The lizard or the egg? Robustness in phylogenetic reconstruction of ancestral states. *Journal of Experimental Zoology Part B: Molecular and Developmental Evolution* 324: 504–516.

Wynn, A. H., Cole, C. J., and Gardner, A. L. 1987. Apparent triploidy in the unisexual Brahminy blind snake, *Ramphotyphlops braminus*. *American Museum Novitates* 2868: 1–7.

Yoder, A. D., Olson, L. E., Hanley, C., Heckman, K. L., Rasoloarison, R., et al. 2005. A multidimensional approach for detecting species patterns in Malagasy vertebrates. *Proceedings of the National Academy of Sciences of the USA* 102: 6587–6594.

Young, R. P., Volahy, A. T., Bourou, R., Lewis, R., Durbin, J., and Fa, J. E. 2008. Estimating the population of the Endangered flat-tailed tortoise *Pyxis planicauda* in the deciduous, dry forest of western Madagascar: A monitoring baseline. *Oryx* 42: 252–258.

Zaher, H., Murphy, R. W., Arredondo, J. C., Graboski, R., Machado-Filho, P. R., et al. 2019. Large-scale molecular phylogeny, morphology, divergence-time estimation, and the fossil record of advanced caenophidian snakes (Squamata: Serpentes). *PLoS One* 14: e0216148.

Zehrer, W. 2013. *Le crocodile malgache, vu à travers des proverbes et contes*. Antananarivo: Edition Tsipika.

Zheng, Y., and Wiens, J. J. 2016. Combining phylogenomic and supermatrix approaches, and a time-calibrated phylogeny for squamate reptiles (lizards and snakes) based on 52 genes and 4162 species. *Molecular Phylogenetics and Evolution* 94: 537–547.

Ziegler, T., Vences, M., Glaw, F., and Böhme, W. 1997. Genital morphology and systematics of *Geodipsas* Boulenger, 1896 (Reptilia: Serpentes: Colubridae), with description of a new genus. *Revue Suisse de Zoologie* 104: 95–114.

CHAPTER 13

BIRDS

INTRODUCTION TO THE BIRDS

R. J. Safford, S. M. Goodman, M. J. Raherilalao, and A. F. A. Hawkins

THE MALAGASY AVIFAUNA AT A GLANCE

The bird community of Madagascar is rather species poor but extraordinarily rich in endemic forms. The total of 304 species is much lower than in continental avifaunas of comparable surface area in the tropics, but the level of endemism and great dependence on forest habitats make the Malagasy bird fauna remarkable. A complete list of Malagasy birds is presented in Table 13.1. Of these, 210 species breed on the island, nearly all as residents; the exceptions are four breeding land and freshwater species that spend the nonbreeding season in Africa (or most of their populations do so); 10 breeding seabirds likely, or known, to range more widely when not breeding; and five or six introduced species. Madagascar has fewer introduced species than many islands; only three are undisputed exotics with self-sustaining populations, although the native or introduced status of one (*Numida meleagris*, Helmeted Guineafowl) is not fully resolved (see pp. 1568); two more are rare. This leaves 94 nonbreeding visitors.

Concerning endemism, of these same 210 breeding species, 110 (52%) are endemic to Madagascar (Table 13.2). This is the highest proportion of endemic species of any relatively large country or landmass in the world. In addition to this extremely high number and proportion of endemic species, one order (the Mesitornithiformes), four families (the Mesitornithidae, Brachypteraciidae, Philepittidae, and Bernieridae), and 40 genera are endemic to Madagascar; a second order, the Leptosomiformes, containing a fifth family, the Leptosomidae, otherwise occurs only on the nearby Comoro islands, which might account for less than 1% of the order's and family's range area and population. In addition, two diverse radiations are endemic to the region: the vangas could be treated as a subfamily, the Vanginae (one out of 22 or 23 species, depending on the taxonomy adopted, having reached the Comoros), while the couas, all endemic to Madagascar, form a subfamily together with a single Asian genus, *Carpococcyx*. The presence of two orders and five families that are endemic, or virtually so, on Madagascar is particularly remarkable, and even more so when the relatively recently extinct, endemic elephant birds (order Aepyornithiformes with the single family Aepyornithidae, see pp. 1578–85) are added.

As part of the Malagasy Region, Madagascar shares another nine endemic genera and 30 species with other archipelagoes in this region: the Comoros, Seychelles, and Mascarenes (Mauritius, La Réunion, and Rodrigues), and Iles Eparses (Table 13.2). Many of these species are represented by different subspecies on the smaller islands, and with genetic analysis these might yet prove to be better treated as separate species, which would thus increase the species-level endemism on Madagascar itself. These species are members of renowned island-hopping genera like *Treron* (green-pigeons), *Hypsipetes* (bulbuls), *Terpsiphone* (paradise-flycatchers), and *Zosterops* (white-eyes), although they include some less mobile species that have managed to make the journey, such as *Leptosomus discolor* (Cuckoo-roller), *Caprimulgus madagascariensis* (Madagascar Nightjar), *Coracopsis vasa* (Greater Vasa Parrot), *C. nigra* (Lesser Vasa Parrot), *Centropus toulou* (Madagascar Coucal), and *Cisticola cherina* (Madagascar Cisticola). As might be expected, the largest number of species (21) is shared with the Comoros (the island of this archipelago closest to Madagascar is slightly less than 350 km west of Nosy Be), followed by the four atolls of the Aldabra archipelago of the far southwestern Seychelles (10).

The nonendemic component of Madagascar's avifauna is composed largely of migrant waterbirds and seabirds; the number of resident nonendemic species is low, and the number of nonbreeding migratory land-bird visitors even lower. The remainder of the avifauna is composed of vagrant species, of which the number steadily increases as experienced observers scrutinize migrants particularly at coastal sites, although several species reported still require published documentation despite having been included in recent reference books to the island.

TABLE 13.1. **Checklist of the modern bird fauna of Madagascar**

SCIENTIFIC NAME	COMMON NAME (ENGLISH)	RESIDENCY STATUS	ENDEMISM	OTHER/PAST SCIENTIFIC NAMES
ANSERIFORMES				
Anatidae	**Ducks, Geese, and Waterfowl**			
Dendrocygna viduata	White-faced Whistling-duck	R		
D. bicolor	Fulvous Whistling-duck	R		
Thalassornis leuconotus	White-backed Duck	R		
Sarkidiornis melanotos	Knob-billed Duck	R		
Nettapus auritus	African Pygmy-goose	R		
Spatula hottentota	Hottentot Teal	R		*Anas hottentota*
Anas melleri	Meller's Duck	R	*	
A. erythrorhyncha	Red-billed Duck	R		
A. bernieri	Madagascar Teal	R	*	
Aythya innotata	Madagascar Pochard	R	*	
GALLIFORMES				
Numididae	**Guineafowl**			
Numida meleagris	Helmeted Guineafowl	R (?I)[1]		*Numida mitrata*
Phasianidae	**Pheasants, Grouse, and Allies**			
Margaroperdix madagarensis	Madagascar Partridge	R	**	*Margaroperdix madagascariensis*
Coturnix coturnix	Common Quail	R		
C. delegorguei	Harlequin Quail	R		
PHOENICOPTERIFORMES				
Phoenicopteridae	**Flamingos**			
Phoenicopterus roseus	Greater Flamingo	N (R)		*Phoenicopterus ruber*
Phoeniconaias minor	Lesser Flamingo	N		*Phoenicopterus minor*
PODICIPEDIFORMES				
Podicipedidae	**Grebes**			
Tachybaptus rufolavatus	Alaotra Grebe	R[2]	*	
T. ruficollis	Little Grebe	R		
T. pelzelnii	Madagascar Grebe	R	*	
COLUMBIFORMES				
Columbidae	**Pigeons and Doves**			
Columba livia	Rock Pigeon	I		
Nesoenas picturatus	Madagascar Turtle-dove	R	##	*Streptopelia picturata*
Oena capensis	Namaqua Dove	R		
Treron australis	Madagascar Green-pigeon	R	#	

SCIENTIFIC NAME	COMMON NAME (ENGLISH)	RESIDENCY STATUS	ENDEMISM	OTHER/PAST SCIENTIFIC NAMES
Alectroenas madagascariensis	Madagascar Blue-pigeon	R	*#	
MESITORNITHIFORMES				
Mesitornithidae	**Mesites**			
Mesitornis variegatus	White-breasted Mesite	R	***	
M. unicolor	Brown Mesite	R	***	
Monias benschi	Subdesert Mesite	R	***	
PTEROCLIFORMES				
Pteroclidae	**Sandgrouse**			
Pterocles personatus	Madagascar Sandgrouse	R	*	
CUCULIFORMES				
Cuculidae	**Cuckoos**			
Coua cristata	Crested Coua	R	**	*Coua pyropyga* (treated here as a subspecies)
C. verreauxi	Verreaux's Coua	R	**	
C. caerulea	Blue Coua	R	**	
C. ruficeps	Red-capped Coua	R	**	*Coua olivaceiceps* (treated here as a subspecies)
C. reynaudii	Red-fronted Coua	R	**	
C. coquereli	Coquerel's Coua	R	**	
C. cursor	Running Coua	R	**	
C. gigas	Giant Coua	R	**	
C. serriana	Red-breasted Coua	R	**	
Centropus toulou	Madagascar Coucal	R	#	
Pachycoccyx audeberti	Thick-billed Cuckoo	R		*Cuculus audeberti*
Cuculus rochii	Madagascar Cuckoo	B (R)[3]	*	
CAPRIMULGIFORMES				
Caprimulgidae	**Nightjars and Allies**			
Gactornis enarratus	Collared Nightjar	R	**	*Caprimulgus enarratus*
Caprimulgus madagascariensis	Madagascar Nightjar	R	#	
Apodidae	**Swifts**			
Zoonavena grandidieri	Madagascar Spinetail	R	#	
Apus melba	Alpine Swift	R		*Tachymarptis melba*
A. balstoni	Madagascar Swift	R	#	*Apus barbatus*
A. affinis	Little Swift	R		
Cypsiurus gracilis	Madagascar Palm-swift	R	#	

(continued overleaf)

TABLE 13.1. ***continued***

SCIENTIFIC NAME	COMMON NAME (ENGLISH)	RESIDENCY STATUS	ENDEMISM	OTHER/PAST SCIENTIFIC NAMES
GRUIFORMES				
Sarothruridae	**Flufftails**			
Mentocrex kioloides	Madagascar Wood-rail	R	**	*Canirallus kioloides*
M. beankaensis	Tsingy Wood-rail	R	**	*Canirallus beankaensis*
Sarothrura insularis	Madagascar Flufftail	R	*	
S. watersi	Slender-billed Flufftail	R	*	*Lemurolimnas watersi*
Rallidae	**Rails, Gallinules, and Coots**			
Rallus madagascariensis	Madagascar Rail	R	*	
Dryolimnas cuvieri	White-throated Rail	R	##	
Gallinula chloropus	Eurasian Moorhen	R		
Fulica cristata	Red-knobbed Coot	R		
Porphyrio alleni	Allen's Gallinule	R		*Porphyrula alleni*
P. madagascariensis	African Swamphen	R		*Porphyrio porphyrio*
Zapornia pusilla	Baillon's Crake	R		*Porzana pusilla*
Z. olivieri	Sakalava Rail	R	*	*Amaurornis olivieri*
CHARADRIIFORMES				
Recurvirostridae	**Stilts and Avocets**			
Himantopus himantopus	Black-winged Stilt	R		
Recurvirostra avosetta	Pied Avocet	V		
Charadriidae	**Plovers and Lapwings**			
Pluvialis squatarola	Black-bellied Plover	N		
P. fulva	Pacific Golden-plover	V		
Charadrius mongolus	Lesser Sand-plover	N		
C. leschenaultii	Greater Sand-plover	N		
C. pecuarius	Kittlitz's Plover	R		
Charadrius hiaticula	Common Ringed-plover	N		
C. thoracicus	Madagascar Plover	R	*	
C. tricollaris	Three-banded Plover	R		*Charadrius bifrontatus* (treated here as a subspecies)
C. marginatus	White-fronted Plover	R		*Charadrius tenellus* (treated here as a subspecies)
Rostratulidae	**Painted-snipes**			
Rostratula benghalensis	Greater Painted-snipe	R		
Jacanidae	**Jacanas**			
Actophilornis albinucha	Madagascar Jacana	R	*	

SCIENTIFIC NAME	COMMON NAME (ENGLISH)	RESIDENCY STATUS	ENDEMISM	OTHER/PAST SCIENTIFIC NAMES
Scolopacidae	**Sandpipers and Allies**			
Numenius phaeopus	Whimbrel	N		
N. arquata	Eurasian Curlew	N		
Limosa lapponica	Bar-tailed Godwit	N		
L. limosa	Black-tailed Godwit	V		
Arenaria interpres	Ruddy Turnstone	N		
Calidris pugnax	Ruff	V		*Philomachus pugnax*
C. acuminata	Sharp-tailed Sandpiper	V		
C. ferruginea	Curlew Sandpiper	N		
C. alba	Sanderling	N		
C. minuta	Little Stint	N		
C. subruficollis	Buff-breasted Sandpiper	V		
C. melanotos	Pectoral Sandpiper	V		
Gallinago macrodactyla	Madagascar Snipe	R	*	
Xenus cinereus	Terek Sandpiper	N		*Tringa cinerea*
Phalaropus lobatus	Red-necked Phalarope	V		
Actitis hypoleucos	Common Sandpiper	N		
Tringa ochropus	Green Sandpiper	V		
T. nebularia	Common Greenshank	N		
T. stagnatilis	Marsh Sandpiper	N		
T. glareola	Wood Sandpiper	N		
Turnicidae	**Buttonquail**			
Turnix nigricollis	Madagascar Buttonquail	R	#	
Dromadidae	**Crab-plover**			
Dromas ardeola	Crab-plover	N		
Glareolidae	**Pratincoles and Coursers**			
Glareola maldivarum	Oriental Pratincole	V		
G. ocularis	Madagascar Pratincole	B	*	
Stercorariidae	**Skuas and Jaegers**			
Stercorarius maccormicki	South Polar Skua	S		
S. antarcticus	Brown Skua	S		*Catharacta antarctica*
S. pomarinus	Pomarine Jaeger	V		
S. parasiticus	Parasitic Jaeger	V		
S. longicaudus	Long-tailed Jaeger	S		

(continued overleaf)

TABLE 13.1. ***continued***

SCIENTIFIC NAME	COMMON NAME (ENGLISH)	RESIDENCY STATUS	ENDEMISM	OTHER/PAST SCIENTIFIC NAMES
Laridae[4]	**Gulls, Terns, and Skimmers**			
Chroicocephalus cirrocephalus	Gray-hooded Gull	R		*Larus cirrocephalus*
Ichthyaetus hemprichii	Sooty Gull	V		*Larus hemprichii*
Larus dominicanus	Kelp Gull	R		*Larus melisandae* (treated here as a subspecies)
Anous stolidus	Brown Noddy	B, S		
A. tenuirostris	Lesser Noddy	S		
Gygis alba	White Tern	S		
Onychoprion fuscatus	Sooty Tern	B, S		*Sterna fuscata*
O. anaethetus	Bridled Tern	B, S		*Sterna anaethetus*
Sternula saundersi	Saunders's Tern	S		*Sterna saundersi*
Gelochelidon nilotica	Gull-billed Tern	V		*Sterna nilotica*
Hydroprogne caspia	Caspian Tern	B, S		*Sterna caspia*
Chlidonias niger	Black Tern	V		
C. leucopterus	White-winged Tern	N		
C. hybrida	Whiskered Tern	R		
Sterna dougallii	Roseate Tern	B, S		
S. sumatrana	Black-naped Tern	S		
S. hirundo	Common Tern	S		
Thalasseus bergii	Great Crested Tern	B, S		*Sterna bergii*
T. sandvicensis	Sandwich Tern	V		*Sterna sandvicensis*
T. bengalensis	Lesser Crested Tern	S		*Sterna bengalensis*
PHAETHONTIFORMES				
Phaethontidae	**Tropicbirds**			
Phaethon lepturus	White-tailed Tropicbird	B, S		
P. aethereus	Red-billed Tropicbird	V		
P. rubricauda	Red-tailed Tropicbird	B, S		
SPHENISCIFORMES				
Spheniscidae	**Penguins**			
Eudyptes chrysocome/moseleyi	Rockhopper-penguin	V		
PROCELLARIIFORMES				
Diomedeidae	**Albatrosses**			
Thalassarche carteri	Indian Yellow-nosed Albatross	S		*Diomedea chlororhynchos*, *Thalassarche chlororhynchos*
T. cauta	White-capped Albatross	S		*Diomedea cauta*

SCIENTIFIC NAME	COMMON NAME (ENGLISH)	RESIDENCY STATUS	ENDEMISM	OTHER/PAST SCIENTIFIC NAMES
T. melanophris	Black-browed Albatross	S		*Diomedea melanophris*
Phoebetria fusca	Sooty Albatross	S		
Diomedea exulans	Wandering Albatross	S		
Oceanitidae	**Southern Storm-petrels**			
Oceanites oceanicus	Wilson's Storm-petrel	S		
Pelagodroma marina	White-faced Storm-petrel	S		
Fregetta grallaria	White-bellied Storm-petrel	V		
F. tropica	Black-bellied Storm-petrel	S		
Hydrobatidae	**Northern Storm-petrels**			
Oceanodroma monorhis	Swinhoe's Storm-petrel	S		
Procellariidae	**Shearwaters and Petrels**			
Macronectes giganteus	Southern Giant-petrel	S		
M. halli	Northern Giant-petrel	S		
Daption capense	Cape Petrel	S		
Pterodroma macroptera	Great-winged Petrel	V		
P. neglecta/arminjoniana/ heraldica[5]	Kermadec/Trindade/Herald Petrel	S		
P. mollis	Soft-plumaged Petrel	S		
P. baraui	Barau's Petrel	S		
Pachyptila desolata	Antarctic Prion	V		
P. belcheri	Slender-billed Prion	V		
Bulweria bulwerii	Bulwer's Petrel	S		
B. fallax	Jouanin's Petrel	S		
Pseudobulweria aterrima	Mascarene Petrel	S		
Procellaria aequinoctialis	White-chinned Petrel	S		
Calonectris leucomelas	Streaked Shearwater	V		
C. diomedea	Cory's Shearwater	S		
Ardenna carneipes	Flesh-footed Shearwater	S		*Puffinus carneipes*
A. pacifica	Wedge-tailed Shearwater	B, S		*Puffinus pacifica*
Puffinus bailloni	Tropical Shearwater	S		
CICONIIFORMES				
Ciconiidae	**Storks**			
Anastomus lamelligerus	African Openbill	R		
Mycteria ibis	Yellow-billed Stork	R		

(continued overleaf)

TABLE 13.1. *continued*

SCIENTIFIC NAME	COMMON NAME (ENGLISH)	RESIDENCY STATUS	ENDEMISM	OTHER/PAST SCIENTIFIC NAMES
SULIFORMES				
Fregatidae	**Frigatebirds**			
Fregata ariel	Lesser Frigatebird	S		
F. minor	Great Frigatebird	S		
Sulidae	**Boobies and Gannets**			
Sula dactylatra	Masked Booby	V		
S. leucogaster	Brown Booby	B, S		
S. sula	Red-footed Booby	S		
Morus capensis	Cape Gannet	V		
Anhingidae	**Anhingas**			
Anhinga rufa	African Darter	R		*Anhinga melanogaster*
Phalacrocoracidae	**Cormorants and Shags**			
Microcarbo africanus	Long-tailed Cormorant	R		*Phalacrocorax africanus, Halietor africanus*
PELECANIFORMES				
Pelecanidae	**Pelicans**			
Pelecanus rufescens	Pink-backed Pelican	V		
Scopidae	**Hamerkop**			
Scopus umbretta	Hamerkop	R		
Ardeidae	**Herons, Egrets, and Bitterns**			
Ixobrychus minutus	Little Bittern	R		
Ardea cinerea	Gray Heron	R		
A. melanocephala	Black-headed Heron	V		
A. humbloti	Madagascar Heron	R	#	
A. purpurea	Purple Heron	R		
A. goliath	Goliath Heron	V		
A. alba	Great Egret	R		*Casmerodius albus, Egretta alba*
Egretta garzetta	Little Egret	R		*Egretta dimorpha* (treated here as a subspecies), *E. gularis*
E. ardesiaca	Black Heron	R		*Hydranassa ardesiaca*
Bubulcus ibis	Cattle Egret	R		*Ardea ibis, Ardeola ibis*
Ardeola ralloides	Squacco Heron	R		
A. idae	Madagascar Pond-heron	B (R)	#	
Butorides striata	Striated Heron	R		

SCIENTIFIC NAME	COMMON NAME (ENGLISH)	RESIDENCY STATUS	ENDEMISM	OTHER/PAST SCIENTIFIC NAMES
Nycticorax nycticorax	Black-crowned Night-heron	R		
Threskiornithidae	**Ibises and Spoonbills**			
Plegadis falcinellus	Glossy Ibis	R		
Lophotibis cristata	Madagascar Crested Ibis	R	**	
Threskiornis bernieri	Madagascar Sacred Ibis	R	#	*Threskiornis aethiopicus*
Platalea alba	African Spoonbill	R		
ACCIPITRIFORMES				
Pandionidae	**Osprey**			
Pandion haliaetus	Osprey	V		
Accipitridae	**Hawks, Eagles, and Kites**			
Elanus caeruleus	Black-winged Kite	V		
Polyboroides radiatus	Madagascar Harrier-hawk	R	*	
Eutriorchis astur	Madagascar Serpent-eagle	R	**	
Aviceda madagascariensis	Madagascar Cuckoo-hawk	R	*	
Macheiramphus alcinus	Bat Hawk	R		*Machaerhamphus alcinus*
Lophaetus occipitalis	Long-crested Eagle	V		
Circus macrosceles	Madagascar Harrier	R	#	*Circus maillardi*
Accipiter francesiae	Frances's Sparrowhawk	R	#	*Accipiter francesii*
A. madagascariensis	Madagascar Sparrowhawk	R	*	
A. henstii	Henst's Goshawk	R	*	
Milvus aegyptius	Yellow-billed Kite	R		*Milvus migrans*
Haliaeetus vociferoides	Madagascar Fish-eagle	R	*	
Buteo brachypterus	Madagascar Buzzard	R	*	
STRIGIFORMES				
Tytonidae	**Barn Owls**			
Tyto alba	Barn Owl	R		
T. soumagnei	Red Owl	R	*	
Strigidae	**Owls**			
Otus rutilus	Madagascar Scops-owl	R	*	*Otus madagascariensis*
Athene superciliaris	White-browed Owl	R	*	*Ninox superciliaris*
Asio madagascariensis	Madagascar Long-eared Owl	R	*	
A. capensis	Marsh Owl	R		
LEPTOSOMIFORMES				
Leptosomidae	**Cuckoo-roller**			
Leptosomus discolor	Cuckoo-roller	R	###	

(continued overleaf)

TABLE 13.1. *continued*

SCIENTIFIC NAME	COMMON NAME (ENGLISH)	RESIDENCY STATUS	ENDEMISM	OTHER/PAST SCIENTIFIC NAMES
BUCEROTIFORMES				
Upupidae	**Hoopoes**			
Upupa marginata	Madagascar Hoopoe	R	*	*Upupa epops*
CORACIIFORMES				
Alcedinidae	**Kingfishers**			
Corythornis vintsioides	Madagascar Malachite-kingfisher	R	#	*Alcedo vintsioides*
C. madagascariensis	Madagascar Pygmy-kingfisher	R	*	*Ispidina madagascariensis, Ceyx madagascariensis*
Meropidae	**Bee-eaters**			
Merops superciliosus	Olive Bee-eater	R		
M. apiaster	European Bee-eater	V		
Coraciidae	**Rollers**			
Eurystomus glaucurus	Broad-billed Roller	B		
Brachypteraciidae	**Ground-rollers**			
Brachypteracias leptosomus	Short-legged Ground-roller	R	***	
Geobiastes squamiger	Scaly Ground-roller	R	***	*Brachypteracias squamiger*
Atelornis pittoides	Pitta-like Ground-roller	R	***	
A. crossleyi	Rufous-headed Ground-roller	R	***	
Uratelornis chimaera	Long-tailed Ground-roller	R	***	
FALCONIFORMES				
Falconidae	**Falcons and Caracaras**			
Falco newtoni	Madagascar Kestrel	R	#	
F. zoniventris	Banded Kestrel	R	*	
F. eleonorae	Eleonora's Falcon	N		
F. concolor	Sooty Falcon	N		
F. peregrinus	Peregrine Falcon	R		
PSITTACIFORMES				
Psittaculidae	**Old World Parrots**			
Coracopsis vasa	Greater Vasa Parrot	R	##	*Mascarinus vasa*
C. nigra	Lesser Vasa Parrot	R	##	*Mascarinus nigra*
Agapornis canus	Gray-headed Lovebird	R	*	
PASSERIFORMES				
Philepittidae	**Asities**			
Philepitta castanea	Velvet Asity	R	***	
P. schlegeli	Schlegel's Asity	R	***	

SCIENTIFIC NAME°	COMMON NAME (ENGLISH)	RESIDENCY STATUS	ENDEMISM	OTHER/PAST SCIENTIFIC NAMES
Neodrepanis coruscans	Common Sunbird-asity	R	***	
N. hypoxantha	Yellow-bellied Sunbird-asity	R	***	
Campephagidae	**Cuckooshrikes**			
Coracina cinerea	Madagascar Cuckooshrike	R	#	
Oriolidae	**Old World Orioles**			
Oriolus oriolus	Eurasian Golden Oriole	V		
Vangidae	**Vangas, Helmetshrikes, and Allies**			
Newtonia archboldi	Archbold's Newtonia	R	**	
N. brunneicauda	Common Newtonia	R	**	
N. amphichroa	Dark Newtonia	R	**	
N. lavarambo	Lavarambo Newtonia	R	**	*Newtonia amphichroa*
N. fanovanae	Red-tailed Newtonia	R	**	
Tylas eduardi	Tylas Vanga	R	**	
Calicalicus madagascariensis	Red-tailed Vanga	R	**	
C. rufocarpalis	Red-shouldered Vanga	R	**	
Hypositta corallirostris	Nuthatch Vanga	R	**	
Leptopterus chabert	Chabert Vanga	R	**	
Mystacornis crossleyi	Crossley's Vanga	R	**	
Cyanolanius madagascarinus	Blue Vanga	R	##	*Leptopterus madagascarinus*
Vanga curvirostris	Hook-billed Vanga	R	**	
Pseudobias wardi	Ward's Vanga	R	**	
Schetba rufa	Eastern Rufous Vanga	R	**	
S. occidentalis	Western Rufous Vanga	R	**	*Schetba rufa*
Euryceros prevostii	Helmet Vanga	R	**	
Oriolia bernieri	Bernier's Vanga	R	**	
Falculea palliata	Sickle-billed Vanga	R	**	
Artamella viridis	White-headed Vanga	R	**	*Leptopterus viridis*
Xenopirostris polleni	Pollen's Vanga	R	**	
X. xenopirostris	Lafresnaye's Vanga	R	**	
X. damii	Van Dam's Vanga	R	**	
Dicruridae	**Drongos**			
Dicrurus forficatus	Crested Drongo	R	#	
Monarchidae	**Monarch Flycatchers**			
Terpsiphone mutata	Madagascar Paradise-flycatcher	R	#	

(continued overleaf)

TABLE 13.1. ***continued***

SCIENTIFIC NAME	COMMON NAME (ENGLISH)	RESIDENCY STATUS	ENDEMISM	OTHER/PAST SCIENTIFIC NAMES
Corvidae	**Crows, Jays, and Magpies**			
Corvus splendens	House Crow	I		
C. albus	Pied Crow	R		
Alaudidae	**Larks**			
Eremopterix hova	Madagascar Lark	R	*	*Mirafra hova*
Cisticolidae	**Cisticolas and Allies**			
Neomixis tenella	Common Jery	R	**	
N. viridis	Green Jery	R	**	
N. striatigula	Stripe-throated Jery	R	**	
Cisticola cherina	Madagascar Cisticola	R	#	
Acrocephalidae	**Reed-warblers and Allies**			
Nesillas typica	Madagascar Brush-warbler	R	##	
N. lantzii	Subdesert Brush-warbler	R	*#	
Acrocephalus newtoni	Madagascar Swamp-warbler	R	*	
Locustellidae	**Grassbirds and Allies**			
Bradypterus brunneus	Brown Emutail	R	*	*Dromaeocercus brunneus*
B. seebohmi	Gray Emutail	R	*	*Dromaeocercus seebohmi, Amphilais seebohmi*
Bernieridae	**Tetrakas or Malagasy Warblers**			
Oxylabes madagascariensis	White-throated Oxylabes	R	***	
Bernieria madagascariensis	Long-billed Tetraka	R	***	*Phyllastrephus madagascariensis*
B. incelebris	Obscure Tetraka	R	***	*Phyllastrephus incelebris, P. madagascariensis*
Bernieria sp.	Tetraka "new species"	R	***	*Phyllastrephus madagascariensis*
Cryptosylvicola randrianasoloi	Cryptic Warbler	R	***	
Hartertula flavoviridis	Wedge-tailed Tetraka	R	***	*Neomixis flavoviridis*
Thamnornis chloropetoides	Thamnornis	R	***	
Xanthomixis zosterops	Spectacled Tetraka	R	***	*Bernieria zosterops, Phyllastrephus zosterops*
X. apperti	Appert's Tetraka	R	***	*Bernieria apperti, Phyllastrephus apperti*
X. cinereiceps	Gray-crowned Tetraka	R	***	*Bernieria cinereiceps, Phyllastrephus cinereiceps*
Crossleyia xanthophrys	Madagascar Yellowbrow	R	***	*Bernieria xanthophrys*

SCIENTIFIC NAME	COMMON NAME (ENGLISH)	RESIDENCY STATUS	ENDEMISM	OTHER/PAST SCIENTIFIC NAMES
C. tenebrosa	Dusky Tetraka	R	***	*Bernieria tenebrosa*, *Phyllastrephus tenebrosus*, *Xanthomixis tenebrosa*
Randia pseudozosterops	Rand's Warbler	R	***	
Hirundinidae	**Swallows**			
Riparia paludicola	Plain Martin	R		*Riparia cowani* (treated here as a subspecies)
R. riparia	Bank Swallow	V		
Phedina borbonica	Mascarene Martin	R, B	##	
Hirundo rustica	Barn Swallow	N		
Cecropis abyssinica	Lesser Striped Swallow	V		*Hirundo abyssinica*
Pycnonotidae	**Bulbuls**			
Hypsipetes madagascariensis	Madagascar Bulbul	R	#	
Zosteropidae	**White-eyes, Yuhinas, and Allies**			
Zosterops maderaspatanus	Madagascar White-eye	R	#	
Sturnidae	**Starlings**			
Creatophora cinerea	Wattled Starling	V		
Acridotheres tristis	Common Myna	I		
Hartlaubius auratus	Madagascar Starling	R	**	*Saroglossa aurata*
Muscicapidae	**Old World Flycatchers**			
Copsychus albospecularis	Madagascar Magpie-robin	R	*	
Monticola sharpei	Forest Rock-thrush	R	*	*Monticola bensoni*, *M. erythronotus*, *Pseudocossyphus bensoni*, *P. sharpei*
M. imerina	Littoral Rock-thrush	R	*	*Monticola imerinus*, *Pseudocossyphus imerinus*
Saxicola torquatus	African Stonechat	R		*Saxicola sibilla* (treated here as a subspecies)
Oenanthe oenanthe	Northern Wheatear	V		
Nectariniidae	**Sunbirds and Spiderhunters**			
Cinnyris sovimanga	Souimanga Sunbird	R	#	*Nectarinia souimanga*, *N. sovimanga*
C. notatus	Madagascar Green Sunbird	R	#	*Nectarinia notata*
Ploceidae	**Weavers and Allies**			
Nelicurvius nelicourvi	Nelicourvi Weaver	R	**	*Ploceus nelicourvi*
N. sakalava	Sakalava Weaver	R	**	*Ploceus sakalava*
Foudia madagascariensis	Madagascar Fody	R	*#	
F. omissa	Forest Fody	R	*#	

(continued overleaf)

TABLE 13.1. *continued*

SCIENTIFIC NAME	COMMON NAME (ENGLISH)	RESIDENCY STATUS	ENDEMISM	OTHER/PAST SCIENTIFIC NAMES
Estrildidae	**Waxbills and Allies**			
Estrilda astrild	Common Waxbill	I		
Lepidopygia nana	Madagascar Mannikin	R	**	*Lonchura nana*
Passeridae	**Old World Sparrows**			
Passer domesticus	House Sparrow	I		
Motacillidae	**Wagtails and Pipits**			
Motacilla flaviventris	Madagascar Wagtail	R	*	

Notes: Taxonomy, sequence, and English names follow Clements et al. (2019), modified in a relatively small number of clearly defined and referenced exceptions that reflect well-supported, more recent findings of key importance in the Malagasy context.

Status: B, breeding visitor; I, introduced; N, nonbreeding visitor; R, resident, native, breeding; S, mainly at sea; V, vagrant.

Endemism: species may be endemic to Madagascar, indicated with *; or to the Malagasy Region (including Seychelles, Comoro, and Mascarenes), indicated with #; or nonendemic (no symbol). Endemism is also indicated at family, genus, and species level; thus *Margaroperdix madagarensis* (**) is a species in a genus endemic to Madagascar, *Alectroenas madagascariensis* (*#) is a species endemic to Madagascar in a genus endemic to the Malagasy Region, and *Leptosomus discolor* (###) is a species in a genus and family endemic to the Malagasy Region.

Other/past scientific names: where a taxon has formerly been referred to under a different name in widely used literature, in particular (but not only) the first comprehensive and modern account of all the birds of Madagascar by Langrand (1990), the former name is given here. In some cases, these names are now considered to be misspellings or not consistent with more recent knowledge; the names in this column are included to help the reader relate current to former taxonomies and are not endorsed here as valid alternatives.

[1] The status of this species, either native or introduced, is uncertain.

[2] Recently extinct, probably in the 1980s.

[3] One museum specimen from Madagascar labeled *C. rochii* appears to be *C. poliocephalus* (Lesser Cuckoo) (Becking 1988), a potential vagrant to Madagascar, but further confirmation is desirable.

[4] A. Hawkins et al. (2015) include *Xema sabini* (Sabine's Gull) and *Sterna vittata* (Antarctic Tern) as vagrants, both based on single, recent records with associated photographs, in anticipation of their publication, but neither record has in fact been published.

[5] A mixed-species, hybridizing population of *Pterodroma* petrels breeds on Round Island, Mauritius, including these three species (with *P. arminjoniana* in the majority); individual birds have been tracked in Madagascar's EEZ, but placing these to species requires caution; see Le Corre et al., pp. 1637–50 (seabirds).

Compared to some other Indian Ocean islands, Madagascar has seen few extinctions within historical times; *Coua delalandei* (Snail-eating Coua) was last seen in 1836 on Ile Sainte Marie, which was (or had become) its sole range (Goodman 1993). One species, *Tachybaptus rufolavatus* (Alaotra Grebe), apparently confined to Lake Alaotra, become extinct in the late 20th century (Langrand and Wilmé 1993; A. Hawkins et al. 2000). Another *Coua* taxon, the striking *C.* (*cristata*) *maxima*, known only from near Tolagnaro and perhaps best treated as a full species, appears to have disappeared since the sole records in 1949 (Goodman 2013).

PHYLOGENETICS, PHYLOGEOGRAPHY, AND SYSTEMATICS

Over the past two to three decades, numerous studies have examined the phylogenetic relationships of Malagasy birds. In some cases, members of the island's avifauna have been included in wide-ranging systematic studies at the level of genus, family, or order; other studies have focused specifically on Malagasy species. Several of these papers address questions about the origins of the island's reputed endemic radiations and test hypotheses associated with monophyly. With the advent of molecular techniques and renewed work using classical morphological characters, these studies have brought fresh evidence to bear on these questions. Decades of study of the phylogeny of the world's major bird groups have also reached the point where the main relationships are now largely resolved (Hackett et al. 2008; Jarvis et al. 2014; Prum et al. 2015), so that the Malagasy avifauna can also be placed more confidently in its global context; this has reaffirmed its extraordinary biological significance. A newer area of inquiry in this field has been the patterns of variation within Madagascar; relatively few species have been investigated at this level, but the results where this has been done have been significant, even revealing new and cryptic species, or sometimes a converse situation of morphological differentiation apparently not matched by genetic divergence (see Reddy and Schulenberg, pp. 1621–26, for examples of both cases).

Herein we deviate from the classical higher-level classification of birds of the world that has been used for decades and is ingrained into general knowledge and reflexes, for example when trying to locate a species in a field guide. We adopt a phylogenetic approach using molecular genetic data, based on the three major studies listed above, which is intended to better reflect the real evolution of birds, rather than previous concepts of such patterns (Table 13.1).

TABLE 13.2. **Characteristics of the Malagasy avifauna: Species richness and endemism**

Total Madagascar avifauna	**304**
Breeding species	210
Breeding native residents	190[1]
Breeding visitors: land and freshwater	4
Breeding visitors: seabirds	10
Introduced species	6[2]
Nonbreeding species	94
Regular nonbreeding visitors	56
Vagrants	38
Species endemic to Madagascar	110
Species endemic to the Malagasy Region[3]	140
Shared with Comoros only	17
Shared with Seychelles only	5
Shared with Mascarenes only	1[4]
Shared with more than one other island/group	7

[1] Includes *Tachybaptus rufolavatus*, presumed recently extinct but a member of the recent avifauna.
[2] Includes *Numida meleagris*, which may, however, be native.
[3] Comprising Madagascar, Comoros, Seychelles, Mascarenes, and Iles Eparses.
[4] *Phedina borbonica* (Mascarene Martin).

At first this will be unfamiliar to certain users, but from the scientific perspective, we consider it an important advancement, and such a sequence has been adopted by all major world checklists of birds. Our default source for genus and species order is Clements et al. (2019), although at these taxonomic levels the four major world checklists currently available show few differences in their treatment of Malagasy birds. In the few cases where we depart from these, we are again adopting a phylogenetic approach to reflect evolutionary relationships as far as our knowledge permits.

In this section, we discuss the phylogenetics and systematics of each order of Madagascar's native birds, both extinct and extant, in turn. Some of the more detailed group or species accounts that follow this introduction include further details on phylogenetic studies, but even in these cases the fundamental points are provided here for completeness. Since the pioneering DNA-DNA hybridization results of Sibley and Ahlquist (1990), the constant improvement of molecular techniques has resulted in many new studies, and there are now relatively few Malagasy birds for which we entirely lack relevant molecular genetic information, although many questions remain. Therefore, we point to some of those questions worth investigating further and review other taxonomic changes proposed in the literature on the birds of the Malagasy Region. Studies continue at the population, species, and higher taxonomic levels and are certain to produce new and sometimes conflicting results.

Aepyornithiformes

The extinct Aepyornithidae, or elephant birds, were Madagascar's representatives of the palaeognaths, a group comprising the volant tinamous and the flightless ratites such as *Struthio* ostriches. However, there is considerable confusion in the definition of named genera and species, and understanding of their origins and relationships was long hindered by obstacles to molecular genetic studies of species extinct for centuries and thus with no retrievable or only highly fragmented DNA. Fortunately, the availability of improved analytical techniques has led to remarkable insights (for example, Mitchell et al. 2014; Grealy et al. 2017; Yonezawa et al. 2017; Hansford and Turvey 2018).

The palaeognaths are the sister group of all other living birds (the neognaths), and both groups underwent an explosive radiation between 69 and 52 million years ago (Mya), well after the breakup of Gondwana (see Collins et al., pp. 45–51). The Aepyornithidae contains sister taxa to the kiwis (Apterygidae) of New Zealand, and based on the age of their divergence and isolation, they are generally placed in their own order, Aepyornithiformes. The genus- and species-level relationships remain unresolved, although two genera (*Aepyornis* and *Mullerornis*) are commonly recognized. Recent morphological analysis has recovered three distinct skeletal morphotypes, two of which are associated with the type specimens of these two genera; the third was proposed as a new genus, *Vorombe*, including the heaviest of all birds, *V. titan*.

Anseriformes

Of six endemic taxa in the family Anatidae (see Young et al., pp. 1627–36, for more information on this order), two are presumed to be endemic sheldgeese (subfamily Tadorninae), now extinct: *Alopochen sirabensis* is placed in the same genus as the extant African *A. aegyptiaca* (Egyptian Goose), while *Centrornis majori* is placed in an endemic genus.

Among extant species, *Anas melleri* (Meller's Duck) has long been agreed to be part of the "Mallard (*A. platyrhynchos*) group," but molecular analysis (Johnson and Sorenson 1999; Lavretsky et al. 2014) shows it to be an early offshoot, more closely related to *A. undulata* (Yellow-billed Duck) and not merely an "island form" of *A. platyrhynchos*; behaviorally and ecologically, it is also distinct in many ways. The other endemic member of this genus, *A. bernieri* (Madagascar Teal), is the result of a different colonization, as it is a member of the otherwise largely Australasian "gray teal" group, named after the well-known *A. gracilis* of Australia and New Zealand (although another presumed member of the group, *A. theodori*, occurred on Mauritius and La Réunion but is now extinct; Cheke and Hume 2008). Both *A. melleri* and *A. bernieri* are scarce and threatened with extinction, being largely restricted to rivers and lakes in the east, and coastal wetlands in the west, respectively. Rarer still is *Aythya innotata* (Madagascar Pochard), another species with apparent Australasian origins, being most closely related to *A. australis* (Hardhead or Australian White-eye) (Sorenson and Fleischer 1996), which is morphologically similar; its dramatic rediscovery and the results of the subsequent conservation and research program are described by Rene de Roland and Young (see pp. 1650–53).

The other endemic duck taxon is currently treated as a small, dark subspecies (*insularis*) of the otherwise African *Thalassornis leuconotus* (White-backed Duck). As such, its origins are clear, but its distinctness has not been investigated with molecular techniques. The remaining six species (in five genera) of Anatidae are mainly African, but some also occur in Asia.

Galliformes

The Numididae (guineafowl) are represented only by *Numidia meleagris* (Helmeted Guineafowl), otherwise restricted to Africa; Malagasy populations are not differentiated from African ones, and its status as native or introduced is uncertain (see "Subfossil Birds," pp. 1578–87). The Phasianidae includes Madagascar's only endemic game bird (at both family and genus levels), *Margaroperdix madagarensis* (Madagascar Partridge) (Figure 13.1a). It gained its common name from its relatively large size, yet both morphological (pattern of downy young) and molecular studies show its true affinities to be with the quails: an "island giant," it is sister to the genus *Coturnix* (Frost 1975; Crowe et al. 2006; Hosner et al. 2017). Two true *Coturnix* species occur, neither of which is endemic.

Phoenicopteriformes

This order, the flamingos, has only one family (Phoenicopteridae), and the two African species both reach Madagascar, almost exclusively nowadays as nonbreeding visitors, although *Phoenicopterus major* (Greater Flamingo) occasionally breeds.

Podicipediformes

The grebes (Podicipedidae) of Madagascar comprise three species in the genus *Tachybaptus* (see Young et al., pp. 1627–36, for more information on this order), a richness not matched in this genus elsewhere in the world. No molecular study of their relationships has been carried out, but the endemic *T. pelzelnii* (Madagascar Grebe) is well differentiated from the widespread Old World *T. ruficollis* (Little Grebe), which also occurs on Madagascar, probably as a recent colonist, as the Malagasy population is not obviously different from those in Africa. The third species, *T. rufolavatus*, was only ever recorded from Lake Alaotra and its immediate surroundings; although it had some distinctive features such as a pale iris, it appears to have hybridized with *T. ruficollis*, suggesting a close relationship, but this should be investigated using molecular techniques. Tragically, such a study could now be done only with museum specimens, as the species became extinct probably in the 1980s; the reasons are discussed by Young et al. (see pp. 1627–36); see also A. Hawkins et al. (2000).

Columbiformes

Madagascar is rather poor in Columbidae (pigeons and doves) as compared, for example, to mainland Africa. If the introduced *Columba livia* (Rock Pigeon) (see "Introduced Birds," pp. 1587–90) is left aside, only four native genera occur, with one species in each; two of the genera are endemic to the Malagasy Region.

The genus *Nesoenas* is restricted to the Malagasy Region. *Nesoenas picturatus* (Madagascar Turtle-dove) is native to Madagascar, Seychelles, and the Comoros, while other species that occurred on the Mascarenes are now extinct apart from the rare *N. mayeri* (Pink Pigeon) on Mauritius. *Nesoenas* is closely related to the widespread genus *Streptopelia* and could arguably be merged with it (Johnson et al. 2001), but the morphological distinctiveness, particularly of *N. mayeri*, and the well-defined monophyletic grouping in the Malagasy Region make a case for the recognition of *Nesoenas* (Cheke 2005; Safford 2013a), with the genus *Spilopelia* recognized for the sister group comprising *S. chinensis* (Spotted Dove) and *S. senegalensis* (Laughing Dove). *Nesoenas picturatus* remains common in wooded parts of Madagascar and is primarily a terrestrial seed eater, although it is versatile, also taking other items and feeding in trees at times.

The genus *Alectroenas* is also restricted to the Malagasy Region. As well as the Madagascar-endemic *A. madagascariensis* (Madagascar Blue-pigeon) (Figure 13.1c), two other species survive on Seychelles and the Comoros, and two or three more occurred but are now extinct on the Mascarene islands (Hume 2011). With its deep blue plumage, red tail, and bare red skin around the eye, *A. madagascariensis* is a distinctive and beautiful species, common in Madagascar's moist evergreen forests. The genus has distant affinities with Indo-Pacific fruit pigeons, in particular *Drepanoptila holosericea* (Cloven-feathered Dove), of New Caledonia, with the widespread Asia-Pacific genus *Ptilinopus* representing the ancestral group (Shapiro et al. 2002; Pereira et al. 2007).

Treron australis (Madagascar Green-pigeon) (Figure 13.1b) appears to be closely related to the African *T. calvus*. A taxon on Mohéli (Mwali) in the Comoros, fairly similar to *T. australis*, may best be considered a separate species, making *T. australis* endemic to Madagascar, but no molecular study has investigated this. *Treron australis* is common in many wooded areas of Madagascar, although with its cryptic coloration it is easily overlooked in the forest canopy. The other endemic columbiform on Madagascar is the fairly distinctive *aliena* race of *Oena capensis* (Namaqua Dove), characteristic of open areas in the west and south. Species rank has never been proposed for it, but the differences from African populations may indicate lengthy isolation on Madagascar, where there has been a considerable range expansion over the past decades (Safford 2013b).

Mesitornithiformes

Birds in the Mesitornithidae (mesites) are among the most enigmatic birds of Madagascar's forests, requiring repeated molecular genetic studies to allow a consensus on their phylogenetic position, finally now agreed: rather than a family in the Gruiformes (as they were long treated), they are in fact one of Madagascar's two oldest surviving lineages (the other being the Leptosomiformes, Cuckoo-roller), sister to the Pterocliformes (sandgrouses). As such, they form a separate order, the Mesitornithiformes (Jarvis et al. 2014; Prum et al. 2015), and the group, with its three extant species, is discussed in greater detail by A. Hawkins et al. (see pp. 1653–57).

Pterocliformes

The sandgrouses include a single Old World family, Pteroclidae, of dry-country (often desert) ground birds, now known to be closely

FIGURE 13.1 **Images of an assortment of bird groups or species not illustrated elsewhere in this chapter. A) Male *Margaroperdix madagarensis* (Madagascar Partridge) at Isalo; B) *Treron australis* (Madagascar Green-pigeon) at Mangily; C) *Alectroenas madagascariensis* (Madagascar Blue-pigeon) at Mantadia; D) a group of *Pterocles personatus* (Madagascar Sandgrouse) near Zombitse-Vohibasia; E) *Coua cursor* (Running Coua) at Ifaty; and F) a pair of *Gactornis enarratus* (Collared Nightjar) at Analamazaotra.** (PHOTOS by K. Behrens.)

related to pigeons and mesites but ancient enough to be a separate order (Prum et al. 2015). Madagascar's only species, *Pterocles personatus* (Madagascar Sandgrouse) (Figure 13.1d), lives in the hot and dry lowlands of the west and south, where it is fairly common; its closest relatives are uncertain but are probably African, based on morphological similarities (Maclean 1984).

Cuculiformes

This is another order that contains a single family, the Cuculidae (cuckoos), represented on Madagascar mainly by the *Coua* radiation (nine extant species), together with three other genera with one species each. Molecular evidence suggests division of the family into five groups, treated by Sorenson and Payne (2005) as subfamilies. Two are restricted to the New World, while the other three are all represented on Madagascar, indicating three separate colonizations: the coucals (Centropodinae; one Malagasy species); the couas and Asian ground cuckoos, *Carpococcyx* (Couinae); and the "typical" cuckoos (Cuculinae; two species known from the island). Earlier suggestions of a close relationship between *Coua* and the Asian *Phaenicophaeus* (malkohas) and African *Ceuthmochares* (yellowbills) were not supported; these were instead suggested to belong in the Cuculinae. Among the Malagasy species, all but the two Cuculinae species are nest builders rather than brood parasites.

Johnson et al. (2000) examined the relationships of the genus *Coua*, using two mitochondrial genes, for six of the nine extant species, and Sorenson and Payne (2005) added the rest. This work demonstrated that these birds form a monophyletic group, and that the arboreal species (*C. cristata*, Crested Coua; *C. caerulea*, Blue Coua; and *C. verreauxi*, Verreaux's Coua) form a separate clade from the largely terrestrial species (*C. reynaudii*, Red-fronted Coua; *C. ruficeps*, Red-capped Coua; *C. cursor*, Running Coua; *C. coquereli*, Coquerel's Coua; *C. gigas*, Giant Coua; and *C. serriana*, Red-breasted Coua; the extinct *C. delalandei* was also placed in this group).

The two subspecies *Coua r. ruficeps* and *C. r. olivaceiceps*, of the west and south, respectively, have been treated by some as full species (originally by Sinclair and Langrand 1998), based on reports that the two forms occur in sympatry with differences in plumage coloration and vocalization and no sign of hybridization. However, a full justification for this taxonomic change has yet to be published, and numerous specimens from a wide area of the central west were found to be difficult to assign (Payne 2005). *Coua cristata* is another species that might merit treatment as more than one species, as the race *pyropyga* is distinctive (and was separated as a species by del Hoyo and Collar 2014), while the extinction of a potential third species, *C.* (*c.*) *maxima*, was mentioned above (Goodman 2013).

The three remaining members of the Cuculidae on Madagascar are *Centropus toulou* (Madagascar Coucal), *Pachycoccyx audeberti* (Thick-billed Cuckoo), and *Cuculus rochii* (Madagascar Cuckoo). The common and widespread *C. toulou*, found also on Aldabra, is morphologically and ecologically similar to several African and Asian members of this genus, and its closest relative has not been identified. *Pachycoccyx audeberti* is one of Madagascar's mysterious birds, observed or collected only a handful of times in forest areas, with no regular locations known; it is treated as distinct from African birds only at the subspecies level. Most of Madagascar's forest birds are endemic species, and one might expect the same of this population; a molecular study based at least in part on museum specimens would be worthwhile, preferably linked to searches for living populations. Finally, *C. rochii* looks and sounds like a typical *Cuculus* species of Africa or Eurasia but seems to be most closely related to *C. gularis* (African Cuckoo), rather than to the closely similar *C. poliocephalus* (Lesser Cuckoo) of Asia (Sorenson and Payne 2005).

Caprimulgiformes

Madagascar has two resident members of the Caprimulgidae (nightjars and allies) and five of the Apodidae (swifts). Most remarkable is *Gactornis enarratus* (Collared Nightjar) (Figure 13.1f), endemic to different mesic forest formations of the island: this species, unlike most nightjars, lays unmarked white eggs on a low shrub rather than on the ground, has pronounced facial discs, an unusual plumage pattern including a unique narrow collar on the side and rear of the neck, and apparently unusual "fly-catching" feeding behavior. A. Hawkins and Goodman (2003) recognized the need to reconsider the traditional generic placement in the typical nightjar genus *Caprimulgus*, and Han et al. (2010) duly revealed, through molecular studies, a large genetic divergence in both nuclear and mtDNA from all other genera and species of caprimulgids studied: it was found to be sister (and basal) to all apart from the eared nightjars (*Eurostopodus*), and accordingly a new genus was named for it. Puzzlingly for a not uncommon species, its voice remains undescribed.

Caprimulgus madagascariensis (Madagascar Nightjar) is common at the edge of forest zones and in nonforest areas and can even be heard in central Antananarivo. It also occurs on Aldabra. Its song, like a bouncing ping-pong ball, is remarkably similar to that of *C. asiaticus* (Indian Nightjar) (Marshall 1978), yet DNA analysis does not support a sister relationship between the two: instead, *C. madagascariensis* is suggested to be sister to a clade of African species (Han et al. 2010).

Among the Apodidae, *Zoonavena grandidieri* (Madagascar Spinetail) of woodland and forest on Madagascar and Grande Comore is a typical, small spine-tailed swift. A phylogenetic study of the spine-tailed swifts is very much needed, as this genus as currently constituted is curiously distributed with two other species, one in India and the other on São Tomé and Príncipe; unless major generic rearrangements are needed, the name of the Malagasy species may remain unchanged, as it is the type species of the genus.

Päckert et al. (2012) sampled a range of *Apus* populations in and around Africa, including *A. barbatus* (African Black Swift) samples from Madagascar and South Africa. Finding strong molecular differentiation between these latter two, they supported the recognition of the Madagascar form *balstoni* (presumably including *mayottensis* from the Comoros) as a separate species, a suggestion we tentatively follow herein. However, *A. barbatus* has a complex distribution in Africa and many populations were not sampled by Päckert et al. (2012), so further revision may be needed. *Apus* (or *Tachymarptis*) *melba* (Alpine Swift) is represented on Madagascar by the endemic race *willsi*, which is smaller and darker than its African counterparts. *Apus affinis* (Little Swift) is a recent colonist first found breeding in 1999 in Antananarivo but with scattered records elsewhere; the species occurs abundantly in Africa, the logical origin of the Malagasy population.

Recently, Mills et al. (2019) showed that the Malagasy Region forms *gracilis* (Madagascar) and *griveaudi* (Comoro islands) of *Cypsiurus parvus* (African Palm-swift) have very different vocalizations from mainland African forms; combining this difference with morphological differences, they proposed to demarcate the Malagasy forms as an endemic species, *C. gracilis*. As the above comments show, phylogenetic studies on the Apodidae on Madagascar would be of great interest, with questions to be answered for every one of the five species.

Gruiformes

Malagasy species of Gruiformes are arranged in two families, the Sarothruridae (flufftails, four endemic species) and Rallidae (rails, gallinules, and coots, eight species; two Madagascar endemic, one regionally endemic); all are reviewed by Safford (see pp. 1657–60). Highlights among recent discoveries have been the recognition of a previously undescribed species, *Mentocrex beankaensis* (Tsingy Wood-rail), in the forests on *tsingy* formations (see Bardot-Vaucoulon and Gautier, pp. 492–99) of the central west (Goodman et al. 2011: see Reddy and Schulenberg, pp. 1621–26); the recognition of the validity of the endemic genus *Mentocrex* (not a synonym of the African *Canirallus*) for this species and the commoner *M. kioloides* (Madagascar Wood-rail); and the separation of Sarothruridae as a separate family (García-R et al. 2014; Prum et al. 2015).

Charadriiformes

This large order of (mainly) waterbirds includes 62 species in 10 families on Madagascar. Many, especially in the Scolopacidae (sandpipers and allies), Stercorariidae (skuas and jaegers), and Laridae (gulls and terns), are nonbreeding migrant waterbirds and seabirds from the Palearctic, as well as from the Antarctic and sub-Antarctic, and are covered by Young et al. (see pp. 1627–36) and Le Corre et al. (see pp. 1637–50), respectively.

The migrant species of Charadriidae (also see Young et al., pp. 1627–36) occur alongside four resident species in the genus *Charadrius*. These four have been intensively studied and have become model species for a range of behavioral ecology studies, particularly concerning mating systems and parental roles, reviewed by Zefania and Székely (see pp. 1660–66). Their genetic structure has also been studied using microsatellite data and sequence-based (nuclear and mitochondrial) analyses (dos Remedios et al. 2020), with results confirming the strongest genetic differentiation from presumed ancestors in the endemic *C. thoracicus* (Madagascar Plover), and less differentiation between Malagasy and mainland populations of the three nonendemic species, *C. marginatus* (White-fronted Plover), *C. pecuarius* (Kittlitz's Plover), and, based on sequence data only, *C. tricollaris* (Three-banded Plover). Among these three, intraspecific divergence was in line with morphological differences: rather small in *C. pecuarius* (no Malagasy subspecies recognized), greater in *C. marginatus* (Malagasy endemic subspecies *tenellus* recognized, although East African populations were not studied), and greatest in *C. tricollaris*, with a subspecies (*bifrontatus*) on Madagascar morphologically distinct enough arguably to merit species ranking (as proposed by del Hoyo and Collar 2016). With suggested links between phylogeny, dispersal strategies, habitat tolerances, and mating systems, these species form a fascinating illustration of the drivers of island-mainland divergence and, as the authors note, "highlight the importance of conserving genetically unique island populations and island habitats to safeguard future evolutionary potential" (dos Remedios et al. 2020: 115).

The other endemic charadriiforms on Madagascar are *Actophilornis albinucha* (Madagascar Jacana, Jacanidae), *Gallinago macrodactyla* (Madagascar Snipe, Scolopacidae), *Turnix nigricollis* (Madagascar Buttonquail, Turnicidae), and *Glareola ocularis* (Madagascar Pratincole, Glareolidae). Of these, only *A. albinucha* has been studied in any detail, both in the field and at molecular levels, as summarized by D'Urban Jackson et al. (see pp. 1666–68); it is sister to the only similar-looking species, *A. africana* (African Jacana). The dryland genus *Turnix*, represented on Madagascar by *T. nigricollis* (Figure 13.2a), was for a long time thought to belong in the Gruiformes, but its place in the Charadriiformes is now certain; the genus is mainly Indo-Australian, but two species occur in Africa, and the origin of the Malagasy Region species (it also occurs on La Réunion, the Glorieuses Islands, and Juan de Nova in the Mozambique Channel) is not known. The two remaining Charadriiformes species that breed on Madagascar are *Himantopus himantopus* (Black-winged Stilt), a common and conspicuous wetland species, and the much shyer, but probably not uncommon *Rostratula benghalensis* (Greater Painted-snipe); neither is known to differ from continental populations, although this should be tested genetically, particularly for the apparently strictly resident *Rostratula*.

Phaethontiformes

For many years considered to belong with the Pelecaniformes or Suliformes mainly on account of their "totipalmate" feet (all four toes webbed), the single genus and family (*Phaethon* and Phaethontidae, respectively) of tropicbirds are now known to be ancient and clearly form a separate order (Prum et al. 2015). Two of the three species worldwide breed on Madagascar (see Le Corre et al., pp. 1637–50) and elsewhere in the Malagasy Region: these are *P. lepturus* and *P. rubricauda* (White-tailed and Red-tailed Tropicbird), respectively.

Sphenisciformes and Procellariiformes

These two orders include many of the of the world's seabirds, the Malagasy Region contingent of which is reviewed by Le Corre et al. (see pp. 1637–50). Members of the Spheniscidae (penguins) are of course found primarily in the sub-Antarctic and Antarctic, but one of the rockhopper-penguins (*Chrysocome*; it is not clear which) ventures north and has reached Madagascar as a vagrant. Members of the Diomedeidae (albatrosses) are scarce visitors mainly to the waters to the "deep south" of Madagascar (see Cooke et al., pp. 311–58). Both Northern and Southern Storm-petrels, now recognized as separate families, Hydrobatidae and Oceanitidae (respectively), reach Malagasy waters as nonbreeding or passage visitors, as do an impressive assortment of the Procellariidae (shearwaters and petrels), converging on Madagascar from origins in parts of all the world's oceans; of these, only one, *Ardenna pacifica* (Wedge-tailed Shearwater), breeds, and that in only small numbers compared to

FIGURE 13.2 **Images of an assortment of bird groups or species not illustrated elsewhere in this chapter. A) Female *Turnix nigricollis* (Madagascar Buttonquail) at Ifaty; B) *Lophotibis cristata* (Madagascar Crested Ibis) at Andasibe; C) *Tyto soumagnei* (Red Owl) at Montagne d'Ambre; and D) *Athene superciliaris* (White-browed Owl) at Zombitse-Vohibasia.** (PHOTOS by K. Behrens.)

the large populations of the Mascarenes and Seychelles, and elsewhere in its vast Indo-Pacific range.

Ciconiiformes, Suliformes, and Pelecaniformes

Genetic analysis has recently resolved many issues concerning the systematics of the large waterbird assemblage of tropicbirds, storks, ibises, spoonbills, pelicans, frigatebirds, boobies, cormorants, herons, and assorted unique forms. Most have remained part of a large grouping of related orders, although as noted above, the Phaethontiformes (tropicbirds) proved to be unrelated. Among the remainder, deep divergences have led to the above-named three orders being recognized (Prum et al. 2015).

The Ciconiiformes is represented on Madagascar by a single family, the Ciconiidae (storks), with two species, *Anastomus lamelligerus* (African Openbill) and *Mycteria ibis* (Yellow-billed Stork). Both breed mainly in the western wetlands. *Anastomus lamelligerus* was long ago recognized as an endemic subspecies, *A. l. madagascariensis*, although this is based mainly on some rather modest differences in bill shape (thinner, with more strongly marked longitudinal ridges); further comparisons would be worthwhile.

The Suliformes includes the Fregatidae (frigatebirds), Sulidae (boobies and gannets), Anhingidae (darters and anhingas), and Phalacrocoracidae (cormorants and shags). The first two families are seabirds, largely nonbreeding visitors although *Sula leucogaster* breeds (see Le Corre et al., pp. 1637–50), and show no endemism. In the fresh waters live one cormorant, *Microcarbo africanus* (Reed Cormorant), and one darter, *Anhinga rufa* (African Darter). The Malagasy populations of both are treated as endemic subspecies. *Anhinga r. vulsini* is morphologically distinct from, but generally closest to, African populations, which are kept separate from the Asian *A. melanogaster* (Schodde et al. 2012); it was not included in the molecular analysis of the Anhingidae by Kennedy et al. (2019). The distinctions between African (nominate) and Malagasy races (*pictilis*) of *M. africanus* are not major, concerning larger size and the detail of upper-part feather tips and juvenile underparts; they have not been tested genetically.

Pelecaniformes on Madagascar includes 20 species in four families: Pelecanidae (pelicans), Scopidae (Hamerkop), Ardeidae (herons, egrets, and bitterns), and Threskiornithidae (ibises and spoonbills). All are primarily freshwater species, reviewed by Young et al. (see pp. 1627–36); only a few show any endemism, and in most cases where this has been suggested (relating to those listed below as subspecies), the differences are rather weak. At the species level, *Ardea humbloti* (Madagascar Heron) and *Ardeola idae* (Madagascar Pond-heron) are both distinctive, regionally endemic species; most of their ranges lie on Madagascar, although both have breeding populations on Mayotte in the nearby Comoros, and *A. idae* also occurs on the atolls of Aldabra and Europa in the Malagasy Region. Four other species, *Ardea cinerea* (Gray Heron), *A. purpurea*

(Purple Heron), *Ixobrychus minutus* (Little Bittern), and *Scopus umbretta* (Hamerkop), have recognized but weakly differentiated endemic races. Finally, among the herons, the small *Egretta* species are, as elsewhere in the world, a taxonomic challenge; Malagasy and coastal East African birds are treated here as a subspecies, *Egretta garzetta dimorpha*, of the widespread Little Egret, following Kushlan and Hancock (2005); others may prefer to recognize *dimorpha* as a species, or to combine it with *E. gularis* (Western Reef Egret). As with all the species in this section, definitive, range-wide studies using a combination of molecular, morphological, and behavioral characteristics would be valuable.

The pale-eyed *Threskiornis bernieri* (Madagascar Sacred Ibis) also occurs on Aldabra; it shows several morphological differences (in addition to eye color) from the African *T. aethiopicus* and is ecologically distinct, with a narrow preference for estuarine habitats, rendering it rare and threatened. If the status of *bernieri* as a species on such bases is debatable, strong differences in the displays recently revealed by observations of captive birds (Collar 2013a; see Young et al., pp. 1627–36) strongly reinforce its separation under a Biological Species Concept. The striking, forest-living *Lophotibis cristata* (Madagascar Crested Ibis) (Figure 13.2b) does not closely resemble any other species, but a phylogenetic analysis based on morphological characters tentatively placed it basal to a diverse clade of Old World ibises including species in the genera *Bostrychia*, *Geronticus*, and *Pseudibis* (De Pietri 2013).

Accipitriformes

Molecular studies have confirmed that the falcons form a separate order, Falconiformes, from the remaining diurnal raptors, which are now the Accipitriformes, with all 11 regularly occurring Malagasy species in the family Accipitridae and the vagrant *Pandion haliaetus* (Osprey) being the only representative of the family Pandionidae. The Falconiformes of Madagascar is discussed below. The natural history of both these orders is described by Rene de Roland and Thorstrom (see pp. 1668–79).

The only extant endemic genus is the remarkable *Eutriorchis astur* (Madagascar Serpent-eagle), a classically elusive, rarely seen moist evergreen forest raptor. *Eutriorchis* is morphologically convergent in various ways with *Accipiter henstii* (Henst's Goshawk) on Madagascar and with various "snake-eagles" (Circaetinae) elsewhere, but the mitochondrial DNA studies by Lerner and Mindell (2005) placed *Eutriorchis* in a different subfamily, Gypaetinae; the same subfamily includes *Aviceda madagascariensis* (Madagascar Cuckoo-hawk) and *Polyboroides radiatus* (Madagascar Harrier-hawk).

The remaining eight Malagasy members of Accipitriformes are placed in the large subfamily Accipitrinae; no local radiations are known, meaning that each species represents a separate colonization event and subsequent differentiation. *Macheiramphus alcinus* (Bat Hawk) and *Milvus aegyptius* (Yellow-billed Kite) are presumably recent arrivals, undifferentiated from African populations. The phylogeny of the harriers, genus *Circus*, was studied by Oatley et al. (2015), and *C. macrosceles* (Madagascar Harrier) was found to be part of a group also containing *C. maillardi* of La Réunion, *C. (spilonotus) spilothorax* of New Guinea, the Indo-Malayan *C. (spilonotus) spilonotus*, and the Australasian *C. approximans*. Genetic differentiation among all these taxa is small, but plumage, morphometric, and behavioral differences may justify species treatment for most if not all. The status of the population of the *Circus* species occurring in the Comoros, generally considered *C. macrosceles*, was not addressed in this study, but if this identification is correct, the species is a Malagasy Region endemic.

The three Malagasy *Accipiter* species are the result of separate colonization events. Molecular studies support the long-held view that the powerful *A. henstii* belongs in the Old World radiation of large "accipiters" and is sister to the African *A. melanoleucus* (Black Sparrowhawk) (Kunz et al. 2019). The smaller, bird-catching *A. madagascariensis* (Madagascar Sparrowhawk) has been suggested to be sister to the African *A. ovampensis* (Ovambo Sparrowhawk), whereas the more generalist (and very often lizard-eating) *A. francesiae* (Frances's Sparrowhawk) seems to be most closely related to Asian species, in particular the now rather (geographically) distant Asian *A. soloensis* (Chinese Sparrowhawk) (Louette et al. 2011; Breman et al. 2013).

Buteo brachypterus (Madagascar Buzzard), being the smallest Old World *Buteo* species, with its short and rounded wings presumably an adaptation to living in the forest, was formerly assumed to be closely related to the somewhat similar *B. oreophilus* (Mountain Buzzard) of Africa, but DNA analysis instead placed *B. brachypterus* as basal to the Old World *Buteo* group (Kruckenhauser et al. 2004). Finally, *Haliaeetus vociferoides* (Madagascar Fish-eagle) is sister to the African *H. vocifer*, these two being sister to the tropical Asia-Pacific pair *H. leucogaster* and *H. sanfordi* (Lerner and Mindell 2005); the loss of the white head color of the Malagasy species gives it a superficially different appearance, but it shares with *H. vocifer* a unique reddish plumage and complex, melodious vocalizations.

Strigiformes

Both of the owl families, Tytonidae (barn owls) and Strigidae (typical owls), are represented on Madagascar by endemic and nonendemic species. The endemic *Tyto soumagnei* (Red Owl) (Figure 13.2c) has been found to be genetically very distinct from all other members of this genus, and sister to the entire "Common Barn Owl group" (rather than belonging with the various forest-living *Tyto* species of Australasia and insular Southeast Asia, as was previously proposed); this suggested a common ancestor "existing between Africa and Australasia" (Uva et al. 2018: 135). The cosmopolitan *T. alba* has been suggested to comprise at least three species, in which case Malagasy birds belong in the African and European group, retaining the name *T. alba*. A proposed endemic race, *hypermetra*, is not generally considered valid; Malagasy birds are similar to African ones.

Four "typical owls," Strigidae, occur on Madagascar. In the genus *Asio*, *A. capensis* (Marsh Owl), mainly of open country and wetlands, is recognized as an endemic subspecies (*A. c. hova*), smaller and with reduced plumage contrast compared to African populations, whereas the forest-living *A. madagascariensis* (Madagascar Long-eared Owl) is a distinctive endemic species; molecular studies to assess their relationships have not been carried out to our knowledge. A study of plumage, morphology, and vocalization proposed splitting the widespread *Otus rutilus* (Madagascar Scops-owl) into two species, *O. rutilus* in the east and *O. madagascariensis* in the west (Rasmussen et al. 2000). However, Fuchs et al.

(2007) questioned the validity of these characteristics for taxonomic diagnosis, as they may be ecologically linked, and carried out a genetic analysis, estimating the divergence between the two populations to be recent and considering it inappropriate to recognize two species. Recent studies have finally resolved the position of the endemic White-browed Owl (Figure 13.2d), long known as *Ninox superciliaris* but suspected to belong instead in *Athene* (Wink 2008), if not in its own genus; further genetic analysis with wider taxon sampling (Koparde et al. 2018; Salter et al. 2020) points to its attribution to *Athene*, which then becomes a cosmopolitan genus.

Leptosomiformes

Leptosomus discolor (Cuckoo-roller) (Figure 13.3a) rivals the Mesitornithiformes (mesites) among the most enigmatic forest birds of Madagascar, requiring repeated molecular genetic studies to allow a consensus to be reached on its phylogenetic position. It was long considered to be in its own family but related to either cuckoos (Cuculiformes) or rollers (Coraciiformes), although many authors pointed out its numerous morphological peculiarities (Lowe 1948; Cracraft 1971; Maurer and Raikow 1981; Burton 1984). Initial DNA studies found *Leptosomus* to be without close relatives, leaving it among the few avian taxa that could be called "living fossils" (Mayr 2008). Finally, the broadest and most comprehensive genetic reviews (Jarvis et al. 2014; Prum et al. 2015) have provided clarity and confirmation: *Leptosomus* is the single sister lineage to a large and diverse clade comprising Trogoniformes, Coraciiformes, Piciformes, and Bucerotiformes. As such, it is one of the most evolutionarily distinct bird species in the world (Jetz et al. 2014), in this regard ranking alongside, if not above, such celebrated species as *Steatornis caripensis* (Oilbird) and *Opisthocomus hoazin* (Hoatzin), both from the New World. This makes the paucity of field studies on *Leptosomus* (as pointed out by Goodman 2003; Safford 2013c) all the more extraordinary and shows a clear need for further field studies on this species.

Bucerotiformes

The Upupidae (hoopoes) are in need of a thorough taxonomic review, but the Malagasy form, *Upupa* (*epops*) *marginata*, is increasingly accepted in field guides and checklists as a distinct species from other hoopoes based on differences in size, coloration, and vocalizations (especially song: a low, cooing trill quite unlike the *hoop-hoop-hoop* known from forms elsewhere in the Old World), albeit in the absence of any molecular study. An experimental study found that the nominate *U. epops* of Europe usually does not respond to song of *U. marginata* (Turčoková et al. 2012).

Coraciiformes

This colorful order is represented on Madagascar by four families, one of them endemic. Genetic studies (Marks and Willard 2005; Moyle 2006; Moyle et al. 2007) appear to have resolved the relationships of the two species of Alcedinidae (kingfishers). The commoner species, the strictly aquatic *Corythornis vintsioides* (Madagascar Malachite-kingfisher), is sister to *C. cristatus* (African Malachite-kingfisher); this was expected based on similarity in most respects. More surprisingly, these "malachite-kingfishers" belong in a different clade from the similar-looking and widespread *Alcedo* species, supporting recognition of the African and Malagasy genus *Corythornis*. Furthermore, *C. madagascariensis* (Madagascar Pygmy-kingfisher) (Figure 13.3b) was found to be more closely related to the "malachite-kingfishers" than to the Asian or African "pygmy-kingfishers" in the genera *Ceyx* and *Ispidina*, in which it had previously been placed by different authorities, and thus belongs in the same genus as *C. vintsioides*.

The only regularly occurring member of the Meropidae is *Merops superciliosus* (Olive Bee-eater); Malagasy and East African populations are not suspected to have differentiated. The island's only true roller (Coraciidae) is the endemic, nominate race of *Eurystomus glaucurus* (Broad-billed Roller); the whole population migrates to Africa for the nonbreeding season, where three other forms (and another member of the genus) occur, but no molecular studies have investigated their relationships.

Finally, the Brachypteraciidae (ground-rollers) is another of the six endemic families now recognized, with five species in four genera; these extraordinary and highly attractive forest birds are treated in more detail, including their systematics, by Langrand (see pp. 1679–82). Here, it may suffice to say that they are confirmed as members of the order Coraciiformes, sister to the Coraciidae (true rollers), but diverged long enough ago to be treated as a separate family.

Falconiformes

The falcons and caracaras belong in a single order (Falconiformes) and family (Falconidae), shown by molecular studies to be not closely related to the other raptor orders (Accipitriformes and Cathartiformes). Five species of Falconidae occur regularly on Madagascar (see Rene de Roland and Thorstrom, pp. 1668–79), two of which are endemic species of "kestrel." *Falco newtoni* (Madagascar Kestrel) is an abundant and adaptable, typical kestrel of open country (and urban areas) with strong similarities to nine other species (such as the very widespread *F. tinnunculus*, Common or Rock Kestrel, around much of the Old World); it most likely arrived from Africa, with further expansion leading to endemic species on Mauritius and Seychelles, as well as a recent colonization of Aldabra, where an endemic subspecies occurs (Groombridge et al. 2002).

The Madagascar endemic *F. zoniventris* (Banded Kestrel) is much more distinct from other kestrels; because of its gray coloration, strong bill, and general proportions it was long assumed to be the Malagasy counterpart to the African *F. dickinsoni* and *F. ardosiaceus* (Dickinson's and Gray Kestrels). Instead, molecular study points to *F. zoniventris* as the 11th (and highly atypical) member of the same Old World kestrel clade as referred to above, but in a basal position (Fuchs et al. 2015).

The other breeding falcon is the near-cosmopolitan *F. peregrinus* (Peregrine Falcon), with the small, dark, endemic form *radama* apparently closely related to the African *minor* but not assessed genetically; the Malagasy form is widely but rather locally distributed. The Palearctic-nesting *F. eleonorae* (Eleonora's Falcon) and *F. concolor* (Sooty Falcon) are not endemic at any taxonomic level, although almost the entire Palearctic breeding population of both spends the nonbreeding season on Madagascar.

FIGURE 13.3 **Images of an assortment of bird groups or species not illustrated elsewhere in this chapter. A) *Leptosomus discolor* (Cuckoo-roller) at Anjozorobe-Angavo; B) *Corythornis madagascariensis* (Madagascar Pygmy-kingfisher) at Ranomafana; C) *Eremopterix hova* (Madagascar Lark) at Antsiranana; D) *Phedina borbonica* (Mascarene Martin) at Andasibe; E) *Hartlaubius auratus* (Madagascar Starling) at Ranomafana; F) *Cinnyris notatus* (Madagascar Green Sunbird) at Ranomafana; and G) flock of *Lepidopygia nana* (Madagascar Mannikin) near Sabotsy-Namehana.** (PHOTOS by K. Behrens.)

Psittaciformes

Recent advances in understanding of the systematics of this order have led to the splitting of the Psittaciformes (parrots) into several families, of which the three Malagasy species all belong in the Old World family Psittaculidae. The *Coracopsis* species, vasa parrots, dull in plumage but not in sexual behavior (see Ekstrom and Safford, pp. 1682–86), have no close relatives but are sister to *Psittrichas fulgidus* (Pesquet's Parrot) of New Guinea, forming a very distinct clade, even suggested by some to deserve separate family rank,

Psittrichasidae (de Kloet and de Kloet 2005; Provost et al. 2018). Two species occur on Madagascar, with other races on the Comoros (although the Comorian *C.* [*nigra*] *sibilans* may be best treated as a separate species); another, *C. barklyi*, is restricted to Seychelles.

Madagascar's third parrot is *Agapornis canus* (Gray-headed Lovebird); it is probably endemic to the island, although the status (native or introduced) of the population on the Comoros is uncertain. Molecular study suggests a long isolation on Madagascar but a systematic position within, rather than basal to, the *Agapornis* clade (Kundu et al. 2012).

Passeriformes

The remaining 78 species of extant Malagasy birds belong in the large order Passeriformes, also known as passerines, songbirds, or perching birds. Aside from five species known only as vagrants (*Oriolus oriolus*, Golden Oriole; *Riparia riparia*, Bank Swallow; *Cecropis abyssinica*, Lesser Striped Swallow; *Creatophora cinerea*, Wattled Starling; and *Oenanthe oenanthe*, Northern Wheatear), 20 families are represented. Two of these, the Philepittidae (asities, four species) and Bernieridae (tetrakas or Malagasy warblers, 13 species), are endemic families, discussed in detail by Prum and Razafindratsita (see pp. 1687–93) and Reddy and Schulenberg (see pp. 1621–26), respectively. Another characteristic Malagasy passerine group, the vangas, was for many years treated as another endemic family but was more recently found to belong with a diverse set of African and Asian passerines formerly placed in other families; this wider group now constitutes the Vangidae, with the "Malagasy vangas" considered a subfamily endemic to Madagascar, and one species occurring on the Comoros (see Schulenberg, pp. 1694–99). Molecular studies have been vital in determining which species belong in which family, revealing how many species were misplaced based on morphological criteria; indeed, the Bernieridae was recognized only about a decade ago based on such studies.

Several other passerine families include known Malagasy radiations (see Reddy and Schulenberg, pp. 1621–26). For many years the endemic genus *Neomixis* (currently three species composed of nine subspecies, with further study needed to assess these) was placed in the Timaliidae but is now known to be the basal lineage of the Cisticolidae, or cisticolas and allies (Nguembock et al. 2007; Olsson et al. 2013). A more typical member of this family is the abundant grassland and open-country *Cisticola cherina*, also found in the Aldabra archipelago (but not on Aldabra Atoll itself) and on the Glorieuses Islands; it is one of 11 tiny *Cisticola* species with streaked backs and aerial display flights, but its origins and closest relatives among these are not known. The Locustellidae (grassbirds and allies) is represented by two sister species of *Bradypterus* with distinctive "decomposed" tails, giving rise to their common name "emutails"; their closest relatives are African (Alström et al. 2018). The Ploceidae (weavers and allies) include two separate Malagasy radiations (see Craig, pp. 1712–13, pp. 1714–15, and pp. 1716–18). *Foudia* (fodies) has long been recognized as a genus endemic to the Malagasy Region, with species distributed throughout it, but two species, *F. omissa* (Forest Fody) and *F. madagascariensis* (Madagascar Fody), native to Madagascar (the latter presumably introduced elsewhere in the region by humans). Less obvious, and confirmed only by molecular analysis, is the close relationship between the two more typical weavers of Madagascar and their placement in an endemic genus, sister to the species-rich African groups (De Silva et al. 2019): these are *Nelicurvius nelicourvi* (Nelicourvi Weaver) of the moist evergreen forests and *N. sakalava* (Sakalava Weaver) of drier country.

The Malagasy *Monticola* species, known as rock-thrushes although now placed in the Muscicapidae, form another small radiation with closest relatives in Africa, containing at least two Malagasy species (*M. sharpei*, Forest Rock-thrush; and *M. imerina*, Littoral Rock-thrush), but populations in different parts of the island show various morphological and vocal distinctions (Zuccon and Ericson 2010a; Cruaud et al. 2011). In the past, two other species have been recognized based on morphology (*M. bensoni* and *M. erythronotus*), the latter having a rather striking chestnut-brown back; however, the most recent molecular studies could not confirm even subspecies-level differences, and the perplexing possibility arises that the sequenced genes evolved more slowly than those expressing external morphological characters, such as feather coloration. Two other Muscicapidae genera occur on Madagascar: *Saxicola* and *Copsychus*, both with unresolved taxonomic issues. In an analysis of mitochondrial DNA, the widespread Malagasy *sibilla* race of *S. torquatus* (African Stonechat) was found to be sister to the morphologically distinctive *S. tectes* (Réunion Stonechat), and these two were sister to birds from East Africa (*S. t. axillaris*); this would point to species status for *sibilla*, but further work and wider taxon sampling would be preferable to test this (Woog et al. 2008). Also of interest is the remarkably distinctive-looking population of stonechats on Tsaratanàna, named *S. t. tsaratananae* (Milon 1951a) but rarely mentioned since; these birds have considerably more extensive black on certain body feather tracts, resulting in some birds looking pied, entirely lacking visible rufous color. Molecular studies could usefully include such populations and examine how the distinction is maintained in the apparent absence of any mechanism of isolation from surrounding populations.

The Acrocephalidae, or reed-warblers and allies (formerly, like the Locustellidae and Cisticolidae, treated as part of the very large Old World warbler family Sylviidae), is represented by two genera on Madagascar. *Acrocephalus newtoni* (Madagascar Swamp-warbler) is a member of an Indian Ocean radiation, with other species on Rodrigues and the granitic Seychelles sister to the nonmigratory swamp-warblers of tropical Africa; the combined African and Malagasy clade is deeply divergent from other *Acrocephalus* species (Leisler and Winkler 2015). In 1995 a population of *A. newtoni* was found on the Andringitra Massif in the montane ericoid thicket just below the summit of Pic Boby (2658 m), living in a habitat very different from the marshland thought to be typical of this species (Langrand and Goodman 1997a), but a molecular analysis found no difference between this population and those living elsewhere on the island (Goodman et al. 2000a). The Malagasy Region endemic genus *Nesillas* is basal to the whole family (Fregin et al. 2009); it might, with two species on Madagascar, have been assumed to be another Madagascar radiation, but molecular analysis has shown that the two species concerned (*N. typica*, Madagascar Brush-warbler; and *N. lantzii*, Subdesert Brush-warbler) are not sister taxa (Fuchs et al. 2016): *N. lantzii* is sister to the recently extinct *N. aldabrana* (Aldabra Brush-warbler). The strikingly dark form *N. t. obscura* of the karst (*tsingy*) formations of north and west Madagascar was not found to be strongly genetically differentiated from *N. t. typica*, and its morphological distinctiveness may be the result of factors linked to recent evolution or phenotypic plasticity rather than genetic and physical isolation in geological time.

Copsychus is an Asian genus with outliers on Madagascar and Seychelles; *C. albospecularis* (Madagascar Mapgie-robin) is thus a classic example of an Asiatic lineage having reached Madagascar but not the African continent. A phylogeographic study (F. Sheldon et al. 2009) identified it as a member of a species complex encompassing three faunal regions—the Philippines, mainland and continental islands of Southeast Asia, and the Malagasy Region—with a presumably widely distributed ancestor across the Indian Ocean and South China Sea; the Philippine, then Malagasy, and other Asian populations successively became isolated. This study did not address variation within Madagascar, where three subspecies are generally recognized, but such a study would be worthwhile: the western form *pica* shows clear plumage, morphometric, and behavioral differences from the others, while the two eastern forms, the nominate and *inexspectatus*, might be considered morphs rather than subspecies (Delacour 1931; Collar 2013b).

Three more passerine families on Madagascar contain more than one taxon but are not examples of local radiations. The Campephagidae (cuckooshrikes) contains one Malagasy species, *Coracina cinerea* (Madagascar Cuckooshrike) (also with Comorian endemic races or species); the paler birds from the southwest have been named *C. t. pallida*, although this distinction has not been tested by a genetic analysis, and birds in the central west are intermediate. The species is sister to a clade of three African species (Jønsson et al. 2010); this four-species group is sufficiently deeply divergent from its Asian relatives for some authorities to recognize for it the genus *Ceblepyris* (Dickinson and Christidis 2014). The two species of Nectariniidae (sunbirds and spiderhunters)—the large *Cinnyris notatus* (Madagascar Green Sunbird) (Figure 13.3f) and the smaller *C. sovimanga* (Souimanga Sunbird)—are results of separate invasions, both apparently from Africa, each leading to a radiation across the Malagasy Region but a single species on Madagascar (Warren et al. 2003).

The same process of multiple invasions by different African ancestors accounts for the two "hirundine" (Hirundinidae) species, *Phedina borbonica* (Mascarene Martin) (Figure 13.3d) and *Riparia paludicola* (Plain Martin). *Phedina* has as its closest relatives *Phedinopsis brazzae* (Brazza's Martin) of the Congo Basin, and the widespread Afrotropical *R. cincta* (Banded Martin). Relationships within this clade were not resolved (F. Sheldon et al. 2005), but *Phedina* is retained here as a genus and species endemic to the Malagasy Region, also occurring (as another, morphologically fairly distinct subspecies) on Mauritius and La Réunion. The Malagasy race *cowani* of *R. paludicola* has recently been treated as an endemic species, the Madagascar Plain Martin, based on morphological and vocal distinctions from African birds (del Hoyo and Collar 2016). For both Malagasy hirundine species, further study using molecular techniques would be of interest. For completeness, a third species, *Hirundo rustica* (Barn Swallow), occurs on Madagascar, as a migrant probably overshooting the Mozambique Channel from Africa; its regular presence, particularly in the southwest (Gardner and Jasper 2011), reveals a remarkable exception to the usual absence of passerine migrants on the island.

We are left with nine passerine families, each with a single native species and no recognized subspecific variation within Madagascar. These include two endemic genera. *Lepidopygia nana* (Madagascar Mannikin) (Figure 13.3g) is the only native member of the Estrildidae on the island, and molecular analysis found it well removed from the Asian *Lonchura* and African *Spermestes*, although closer to the former (Payne and Sorenson 2003). Morphologically and behaviorally, it shows a medley of characters, some closer to Asian relatives, others to African ones, and it appears hard to justify placing it with either—hence recognition of a separate genus for it. *Hartlaubius auratus* (Madagascar Starling) (Figure 13.3e) is another species unjustifiably placed (for a time) in the continental genus—in this case the Asian *Saroglossa*—which it somewhat resembled; genetic analysis (Lovette and Rubenstein 2007) recognized *Hartlaubius* as a relictual lineage, possibly sister to but highly divergent from *Cinnyricinclus leucogaster* (Amethyst Starling) of Africa.

The well-streaked *Eremopterix hova* (Madagascar Lark, Alaudidae) (Figure 13.3c) looks like some African *Mirafra* species and so was long placed in that genus, until molecular analysis instead found it to be nested within the plainer-plumaged African *Eremopterix* sparrow-larks, although precise relationships, and thus the position of *E. hova*, within this group were not fully resolved (Alström et al. 2013). *Eremopterix hova* shows some geographic variation in coloration across Madagascar (Benson et al. 1976), which has not been fully assessed.

The Dicruridae is believed to have originated in Asia and then colonized Africa. A molecular analysis placed the Malagasy *Dicrurus forficatus* (Crested Drongo) in a clade containing all African and Malagasy Region species and two Asian species (*D. macrocercus*, Black Drongo; and *D. leucophaeus*, Ashy Drongo); its sister species is *D. aldabranus* from Aldabra, but their proximate origin (African or Asian) was not resolved (Pasquet et al. 2007). A phylogeographic study of Malagasy *D. forficatus* found only weak genetic structure along an east–west pattern, low genetic diversity, and extensive areas of suitable climate in both eastern and western Madagascar ever since its colonization, accounting for the lack of geographic variation across the island (Fuchs et al. 2013).

Terpsiphone mutata (Madagascar Paradise-flycatcher, Monarchidae) is discussed by Mulder and Ramiarison (see pp. 1700–1704): all Madagascar populations are now referred to a single form, *T. m. mutata*, and phylogenetic analyses suggest an Asian origin for all the Indian Ocean species in this genus, but colonization via Africa was not ruled out (Bristol et al. 2013). The many populations and taxa in the remarkably homogeneous white-eyes genus *Zosterops* (Zosteropidae) create a challenge for taxonomists. However, *Z. maderaspatanus* (Madagascar White-eye) (of Madagascar, the Comoros, Aldabra, the Glorieuses, and Europa Atoll) has by molecular assessment of numerous *Zosterops* populations in both Africa and Asia been placed in a Malagasy Region radiation (Warren et al. 2006), within a clade of otherwise African species (Moyle et al. 2009; Cox et al. 2014). Within Madagascar, variation appears to be in the form of trends in size and in the intensity of melanin in conformity with their environments (Moreau 1957; Benson et al. 1977), and no genetic differentiation consistent with subspecies recognition was found between birds from Ankaratra and the northern lowlands of Madagascar (Warren et al. 2006); accordingly, no subspecific variation is recognized on the island.

Following the removal of *Xanthomixis* and *Bernieria* to the Bernieridae (Reddy and Schulenberg, see pp. 1621–26), *Hypsipetes madagascariensis* (Madagascar Bulbul) is the sole member of the Pycnonotidae on Madagascar. The genus is, like *Copsychus* (above), Asian in origin, with an Indian Ocean radiation but no species in Africa; molecular phylogeny (Warren et al. 2005) and morphological analysis (Louette and Herremans 1985) suggest a single colonization of the Malagasy Region from Asia. The Malagasy race, *H. m. madagascariensis*, also occurs on the Comoros; another is found on the Glorieuses and Aldabra. Voelker (2002) conducted a study of the phylogenetic relationships of the wagtails (*Motacilla*) and found *M. flaviventris* (Madagascar Wagtail), Madagascar's only member of the Motacillidae, to be sister to the African "stream wagtail" clade containing *M. clara* (Mountain Wagtail) and *M. capensis* (Cape Wagtail). Finally, only one native passerine on Madagascar appears to be entirely undifferentiated from continental forms: *Corvus albus*, the Pied Crow, the only native member of the Corvidae (recently joined by the introduced *C. splendens*, House Crow; see Meier et al., pp. 1704–7).

Conclusions

Traditional views of the systematic relations between Malagasy birds and those of other parts of the world have been based on a variety of external characters. This has in many cases led to links being proposed between groups of Malagasy birds and those of Africa and Asia that have been subsequently shown, mainly through molecular studies, to be the result of convergence rather than shared recent phylogenetic history. An excellent example is the Bernieridae, which has long been regarded as part of the Timaliidae or the Pycnonotidae, with some species even placed in the same genus as the African greenbuls, *Phyllastrephus*. It is now clear that they represent a complete and separate radiation and are only distantly related to any African groups. The same can be said for many genera and species on Madagascar, and we now know that certain Malagasy groups and species represent old phylogenetic lineages, acknowledged through the recognition of two endemic orders and five endemic families.

Another popular perception is that there is a significant link with Asiatic species (Berlioz 1948; Griveaud 1967; Dorst 1972; Keith 1980). This was supported originally by the treatment of (for instance) the White-browed Owl in the Asia-Pacific genus *Ninox*, whereas it is now known to belong in *Athene*, an almost cosmopolitan genus; other examples where formerly assumed Asian affinities now seem less likely include *Hartlaubius auratus*, *Cuculus rochii*, and *Caprimulgus madagascariensis*. These join a list of species increasingly agreed to have African affinities, such as *Anas melleri*, *Pterocles personatus* (Madagascar Sandgrouse), *Treron australis*, *Sarothrura* spp., *Zapornia olivieri* (Sakalava Rail), *Rallus madagascariensis* (Madagascar Rail), *Actophilornis albinucha*, *Asio madagascariensis* (Madagascar Long-eared Owl), *Eremopterix hova*, and *Monticola* spp., alongside African species with endemic Malagasy subspecies, such as *Saxicola torquatus*, *Oena capensis*, and *Asio capensis* (Marsh Owl), and the nonendemic (at any level) *Corvus albus*; other examples could be cited. Indeed, rather few species on Madagascar do appear to retain a direct Asiatic or Australasian link (leaving aside Asian lineages that may have arrived via Africa); these include island hoppers, for instance the genera *Copsychus* and *Hypsipetes* (both genera absent in Africa), and a range of other species with varied origins such as *Anas bernieri*, *Aythya innotata*, *Alectroenas madagascariensis*, the whole genus *Coua*, *Circus macrosceles*, *Accipiter francesiae*, and *Lepidopygia nana*. Demonstrations of a true Asiatic element in Madagascar's avifauna are thus now relatively few; most of the other species with evident recent continental links seem more closely related to African taxa. However, Seychelles and the Mascarene islands, in the eastern portion of the Malagasy Region and physically closer to Asia, do seem to include a stronger Asian flavor to their avifauna (as seen in the presence of the swiftlet and parakeet genera *Aerodramus* and *Psittacula*, respectively; Warren et al. 2010) than does Madagascar, and this apparent difference deserves further investigation.

SUBFOSSIL BIRDS

Madagascar has relatively rich bird bone–bearing fossil beds dating from the Quaternary. The oldest of this material is generally no more than 20,000 years old, and a variety of different studies provide important insights into geologically recent extinctions and the potential explanatory role of climatic shifts in shaping the island's modern bird communities (Goodman and Rakotozafy 1997; Goodman 1999; Goodman and Jungers 2014). All of this material is subfossil; that is, the specimens remain more or less as the original bone. Over 90 species of birds have been identified from these subfossil remains (Table 13.3), of which 16 are extinct (Table 13.4). From Quaternary deposits a variety of bird forms have been identified. Most of this material dates from the Holocene, but radiocarbon dating shows that some is from the Late Pleistocene (Table 13.5). In the following entries we provide a brief review by order or family of some of the most noteworthy subfossil material. Over the past few decades, considerable research has been devoted to the older record of fossil birds on Madagascar, in this case real fossils with the bone replaced by mineral deposits; these are mostly from the Late Cretaceous and are discussed elsewhere (see Krause et al., pp. 59–68).

Aepyornithidae

The extinct Malagasy members of the Aepyornithidae, generally called elephant birds because of their size, are part of a group of mostly large flightless birds known as ratites, with the extant forms restricted to southern landmasses. Three genera of aepyornithids are known from the subfossil record of Madagascar (Table 13.4). On the basis of osteological characters, specifically aspects of the bony palate, they have been termed "paleognaths" and are separate from all other living birds known as "neognaths." The ratites include the extant ostriches (Struthionidae) of Africa, emus (Casuariidae) of Australia, cassowaries (Casuariidae) of Australia and New Guinea, rheas (Rheidae) of South America, and the distinctly smaller kiwis (Apterygidae) of New Zealand and tinamous (Tinamidae) of South America, as well as the recently extinct moas (Dinornithidae) of New Zealand. Ratites have been classically considered an ancient group of birds, and their modern distribution on southern landmasses was thought to be best explained by the breakup of the former Gondwana supercontinent (see Collins et al., pp. 45–51), their ancestors that gave rise to the current distribution of the group being present on different portions of Gondwana as the pieces separated via rifting.

TABLE 13.3. **Bird species recovered from subfossil sites on Madagascar**

SPECIES[1]	HABITAT[2]	CENTRAL HIGHLANDS[3]	AMPOZA[4]	ANJOHIBE AND BEANKA[5]	SOUTHWEST[6]
AEPYORNITHIFORMES					
*†*Aepyornis* spp.	T	+	+		+
*†*Mullerornis* sp.	T	+	+	+	+
*†*Vorombe titan*	T				+
ANSERIFORMES					
*†*Centrornis majori*	A	+			+
*†*Alopochen sirabensis*	A	+	+		+
Dendrocygna spp.	A		+		+
Thalassornis leuconotus	A				+
Sarkidiornis melanotos	A	+			
**Anas bernieri*	A	+	+		+
A. erythrorhyncha	A	+	+		+
**A. melleri*	A	+			?
GALLIFORMES					
‡cf. *Gallus gallus*	T				+
Numida meleagris	T	+		+	+
**Margaroperdix madagarensis*	T	+		+	
Coturnix sp.	T			+	
PHOENICOPTERIFORMES					
Phoenicopterus roseus	A		+		+
Phoeniconaias minor	A			+	+
COLUMBIFORMES					
Nesoenas picturatus	T			+	+
Oena capensis	T				+
Treron australis	T				+
MESITORNITHIFORMES					
**Monias benschi*	T				+
*†*Monias* sp.	T			+	
PTEROCLIDIFORMES					
**Pterocles personatus*	T		+		+
CUCULIFORMES					
*†*Coua berthae*[7]	T	+		+	
*†*C. primaeva*[8]	T			+	+
**C. cristata*	T			+	+

(continued overleaf)

TABLE 13.3. ***continued***

SPECIES[1]	HABITAT[2]	CENTRAL HIGHLANDS[3]	AMPOZA[4]	ANJOHIBE AND BEANKA[5]	SOUTHWEST[6]
**C. ruficeps*	T				+
**C. cursor*	T				+
**C. gigas*	T			+	+
**Coua* spp.	T			+	
**Cuculus rochii*	T			+	
Centropus toulou	T			+	
CAPRIMULGIFORMES					
Caprimulgus madagascariensis	T				+
Apus barbatus	T			+	
A. balstoni	T				+
GRUIFORMES					
**Rallus madagascariensis*	A				+
Dryolimnas cuvieri	A			+	+
Gallinula chloropus	A	+			+
Fulica cristata	A		+		+
Porphyrio madagascariensis	A	+	+	+	+
*†*Hovacrex roberti*	A	+			+
CHARADRIIFORMES					
Himantopus himantopus	A				+
Numenius phaeopus	A				+
*†*Vanellus madagascariensis*	A/T		+		+
Turnix nigricollis	T			+	+
Chroicocephalus cirrocephalus	A				+
Larus dominicanus	A				+
Larus sp.	A		+		
CICONIIFORMES					
Anastomus lamelligerus	A		+		+
Mycteria ibis	A				+
SULIFORMES					
cf. *Anhinga rufa*	A				+
†*Phalacrocorax* sp.	A	+			+
Microcarbo africanus	A	+			+
PELECANIFORMES					
Scopus umbretta	A/T				+
Ardea cinerea	A		+		

SPECIES[1]	HABITAT[2]	CENTRAL HIGHLANDS[3]	AMPOZA[4]	ANJOHIBE AND BEANKA[5]	SOUTHWEST[6]
A. humbloti	A		+		+
A. purpurea	A		+		+
A. alba	A	+			
Egretta or *Ardea* spp.	A				+
Bubulcus ibis	T			+	
Plegadis falcinellus	A				+
**Lophotibis cristata*	T	+	+	+	+
Threskiornis bernieri	A		+		+
Platalea alba	A		+		+
ACCIPITRIFORMES					
**Polyboroides radiatus*	T				+
**Accipiter madagascariensis*	T			+	+
**A. henstii*	T				+
Milvus aegyptius	T			+	+
**Haliaeetus vociferoides*	T				+
*†*Stephanoaetus mahery*	T	+			+
†*Aquila* sp. a	T	+			+
†*Aquila* sp. b	T	+			
**Buteo brachypterus*	T	+		+	+
STRIGIFORMES					
Tyto alba	T			+	+
**Otus rutilus*	T			+	+
**Athene superciliaris*	T			+	+
Asio capensis[9]	T			+	+
LEPTOSOMIFORMES					
Leptosomus discolor	T			+	+
CORACIIFORMES					
**Upupa marginata*	T				+
Corythornis vintsioides	A			+	
**Merops superciliosus*	T			+	
Eurystomus glaucurus	T			+	+
*†*Brachypteracias langrandi*	T		+		
FALCONIFORMES					
Falco newtoni	T			+	+

(continued overleaf)

TABLE 13.3. ***continued***

SPECIES[1]	HABITAT[2]	CENTRAL HIGHLANDS[3]	AMPOZA[4]	ANJOHIBE AND BEANKA[5]	SOUTHWEST[6]
PSITTACIFORMES					
Coracopsis vasa	T	+		+	+
C. nigra	T			+	
*Agapornis cana	T			+	
PASSERIFORMES					
**Newtonia brunneicauda*	T			+	
Corvus albus	T				+
**Eremopterix hova*	T			+	
Phedina borbonica	T			+	+
Hypsipetes madagascariensis	T			+	
**Nelicurvius sakalava*	T				+
**Foudia madagascariensis*	T			+	+
*cf. *Motacilla flaviventris*	T			+	

[1] Species codes: * endemic species to Madagascar; † extinct species or no longer occurring on Madagascar; ‡ introduced to Madagascar.
[2] Habitat codes: T, terrestrial; A, aquatic.
[3] Includes the sites of Ampasambazimba, those around Antsirabe, and Tsaramody and based on specimens examined by Goodman (1999) and literature citations of Andrews (1897), Lambrecht (1933), Lamberton (1934), Wiman (1935), LeNoble (1940), MacPhee et al. (1985), Goodman and Ravoavy (1993), Goodman (1994a), Goodman and Rakotozafy (1995), and Samonds et al. (2019).
[4] Based on specimens examined by Goodman (1999) and literature citations of Wiman (1935) and Goodman (1996, 2000).
[5] Based on Goodman and Ravoavy (1993) and Burney et al. (1997) for Anjohibe and Burney et al. (2019) for Beanka.
[6] Based on Goodman and Rakotozafy (1997), Goodman et al. (2013), Hansford and Turvey (2018), and H. Rasolonjatovo et al. (2021) and derived from specimens collected at Ambolisatra, Ankilitelo, Beavoha, Beloha, Belo-sur-Mer, Bemafandry, Lamboharana, Manombo (Toliara), Tsiandroina, and Tsimanampesotse.
[7] Specimens from Tsimanampesotse referred to as *C.* cf. *berthae*.
[8] Specimens from Tsimanampesotse referred to as *C.* cf. *primaeva*.
[9] Originally reported in Samonds et al. (2019) as *A. madagascariensis*, but the correct identification is *A. capensis*.

This scenario, referred to as Gondwana vicariance, has been largely supported by different molecular studies (e.g., Cloutier et al. 2019), but the critical final element in completing the evolutionary history of ratites has been DNA from the Aepyornithidae. This is now available and completely changes previous interpretations (see below).

In 1850 M. Abadie, a merchant vessel captain, obtained three giant eggs along the southwest coast of Madagascar, which formed the basis of Geoffroy Saint-Hilaire's (1851) communication to announce the discovery of the extinct elephant bird, *Aepyornis maximus*, to the Académie des Sciences de Paris. There had been previous reports of fragments of large eggshells as early as around 1830 along the southern coasts of the island, but the actual size of these birds was not appreciated at that time (Lavauden 1931). It has been estimated that *A. maximus* obtained a height of 3–4 m and a weight of over 400 kg; its eggs measured 32 × 24 cm on average and had a volume 150–170 times greater than that of a chicken egg (Cauderay 1931; Amadon 1947). Recent estimates of the genus *Vorombe* indicate that it may have reached a weight close to 650 kg (range 536–732 kg), making it the largest bird ever known (Hansford and Turvey 2018).

Etienne Flacourt (1607–1660), named commandant of Madagascar by the king of France in 1648, was based near Fort Dauphin (Tolagnaro) and was an important chronicler of the culture and biota of the region (see Andriamialisoa and Langrand, pp. 1–38). In his book *Histoire de la Grand Isle Madagascar*, published in 1658 (reprinted annotated edition in 1995), he refers in the present tense to the "Vouron-Patra," which was a forest species and with little doubt an aepyornithid.

Elephant birds were broadly distributed across the latitudinal length of the island from near Antsiranana south to Cap Sainte Marie (Goodman and Jungers 2014). The vast majority of bone remains come from sites in the west and southwest, as well as the Central Highlands. Remains of these birds have also been found in Andrahomana Cave near Ranopiso in the southeast. Few sites in the humid east have produced Holocene bone-bearing deposits, and as far as we can determine no remains of aepyornithids have been found in this region (Monnier and Lamberton 1922; Goodman and Jungers 2014).

It is clear that humans have been interacting with aepyornithids for thousands of years, and the earliest proposed evidence of human

TABLE 13.4. **Extinct Late Pleistocene and Holocene birds from Madagascar and associated synonyms**

ORDER AEPYORNITHIFORMES
Family Aepyornithidae
Aepyornis hildebrandti
  syn. *A. lentus*
  syn. *A. gracilis*
A. maximus
  syn. *A. cursor*
  syn. *A. medius*
Mullerornis modestus
  syn. *Aepyornis modestus*
  syn. *Flacourtia rudis*
  syn. *M. agilis*
  syn. *M. betsilei*
  syn. *M. rudis*
Vorombe titan
  syn. *Aepyornis ingens*
  syn. *A. titan*
Phalacrocorax sp. (undescribed?)
Centrornis majori
Alopochen sirabensis
  syn. *Chenalopex sirabensis*
Stephanoaetus mahery
Aquila sp. a (specific designation uncertain)
Aquila sp. b (specific designation uncertain)
Monias sp. (undescribed?)
Hovacrex roberti
  syn. *Tribonyx roberti*
Vanellus madagascariensis
Coua berthae
C. primaeva
Brachypteracias langrandi

Note: Taxonomy of aepyornithids follows the morphological study of Hansford and Turvey (2018), but several proposed names could not be evaluated: *Aepyornis grandidieri*—described based on eggshell remains; *A. mulleri*—no appropriate specimens referable to this species were located; and *Mullerornis grandis*—the type material was destroyed in the 1995 fire that devastated the Queen's Palace in Antananarivo.

presence on the island is from bones of *Aepyornis* with human-made cut marks dated to close to 9500 years BP based on radiocarbon analysis (Hansford et al. 2018; Table 13.5; see Wright and Rakotoarisoa, pp. 181–90). The archaeological record also contains a long history of humans exploiting these birds and their eggs for consumption, and the latter were used as a sort of jerry can to transport liquids (Dewar and Rakotovololona 1992; Goodman and Jungers 2014). Among the modern Antandroy of the Ambovombe and Marovato regions, and peoples from other areas of the island, there are still numerous oral histories about giant birds that were almost certainly aepyornithids (Lavauden 1931; Tovondrafale 1994). A modified *Aepyornis* bone found at Itampolo by Paul Martin in 1968 and radiocarbon dated to 1880 ± 70 BP shows human modifications associated with butchering or tool making (H. James in Burney 1999). There is also a report of a *Mullerornis* bone from Ampasambazimba worked into a type of hand tool (Fontoyont 1909)—however, the evidence for this is weak (Barthère 1915; MacPhee et al. 1985). Based on radiocarbon dating of elephant bird bone and eggshell remains, the most recent date for their continued existence on Madagascar is less than a millennium ago (Table 13.5).

Since the original discovery and description of *A. maximus* presented by Geoffroy Saint-Hilaire, there have been many new scientific names proposed for elephant bird egg and bone remains found in different portions of Madagascar. Given that it is notably difficult to evaluate the validity of proposed names, including which of these might be synonyms of others, or associated with holotypes of not necessarily the same bone elements, or based on eggshell remains, elephant bird systematics has until very recently been almost at a standstill. After the revision of Monnier (1913) there was little progress over the course of decades in resolving synonymies and the basic taxonomy of this family. Subsequent reviews of subfossil birds largely followed Monnier's classification (e.g., Lambrecht 1933; Wiman 1935; Brodkorb 1963). It is also important to mention that few subfossil skeletons have been found of aepyornithids with associated skeletal elements, and most of the mounted skeletons in museums are composites of different individuals and potentially different species. A recent study of leg bones of these birds in museums has resulted in important systematic advances based on morphology, including the recognition of a new genus (*Vorombe*) and a reduction in the number of recognized species (Hansford and Turvey 2018; see Table 13.4).

Given the taxonomic quandary mentioned above, which was partially resolved by Hansford and Turvey (2018) in sorting out the validity of the numerous proposed names, it was clear that molecular genetics could potentially provide the needed tool to better understand the taxonomy of these extinct birds, and in a broader sense the evolutionary history of the family, particularly if DNA could be isolated from holotype specimens. Such a research approach was notably successful for another group of extinct ratites, the New Zealand moas, based on subfossil remains (Cooper 1997). With this fascinating and tantalizing aspect in mind, several ancient DNA labs in different portions of the world tried to isolate DNA from elephant birds, but with no success. This had to do with the degraded condition of the DNA in subfossils as well as methodological complications.

Thanks to scientific advances, over the past few years several research teams were able to isolate DNA from aepyornithid bones and eggshell remains (*Aepyornis* and *Mullerornis*), and the published phylogenetic results are remarkably consistent, although the timing of events in the separation of the different ratite lineages shows some variation among the three leading studies (Mitchell et al. 2014; Grealy et al. 2017; Yonezawa et al. 2017). All three studies showed that the kiwis of New Zealand are the sister group to the aepyornithids of Madagascar. This is inconsistent with the continental drift hypothesis mentioned above, which would assume that kiwis and the extinct moas of New Zealand should be each other's closest relatives, with their common ancestor dispersing on a Gondwana plate and evolving into two very different forms of ratites. However, based on these studies, this hypothesis was not supported, and the moas are the sister group of the New World tinamous. Further, and most important to refute the Gondwana vicariance notion, the dates of the separation between kiwis and elephant birds occur distinctly after the breakup of this ancient continent.

TABLE 13.5. **Radiocarbon dates of bird bones at subfossil sites**

LOCATION	DATE	MATERIAL	SOURCE	CITATION
Ampamalora	1970 ± 90 BP	*Aepyornis* eggshell	not given	Sauer (1972)
Ampasambazimba	22,550 ± 170 BP	*Alopochen* bone	Beta-63116	Goodman (1999)
Ampoza	3381 ± 24 BP	*Vorombe* bone	OxA-34776	Hansford and Turvey (2018)
Anakao	3960 ± 150 BP	*Aepyornis* eggshell	QC-972	Dewar (1984)
	2775 ± 95 BP	*Aepyornis* eggshell	QC-970	Dewar (1984)
	2375 ± 100 BP	*Aepyornis* eggshell	QC-971	Dewar (1984)
Andrahomana	1000 ± 150 BP	*Aepyornis* eggshell	UCLA-1893	Berger et al. (1975)
Anjohibe	2380 ± 70 BP	*Mullerornis* eggshell	Beta-55094	Burney et al. (1997)
Ankazoabo-Atsimo	2470 ± 24 BP	*Vorombe* bone	OxA-33531	Hansford and Turvey (2018)
Ankilitelo	11,310 ± 40 BP	*Numida* bone	Beta-355564	Goodman et al. (2013)
	11,220 ± 50 BP	cf. *Aepyornis* eggshell	Beta-355561	Goodman et al. (2013)
	8970 ± 40 BP	*Numida* bone	Beta-355565	Goodman et al. (2013)
	8420 ± 40 BP	*Corvus* bone	Beta-355562	Goodman et al. (2013)
	6150 ± 40 BP	cf. *Aepyornis* eggshell	Beta-355559	Goodman et al. (2013)
	5550 ± 30 BP	*Stephanoaetus* bone	Beta-415922	Goodman and Muldoon (2016)
	290 ± 30 BP	*Numida* bone	Beta-355563	Goodman et al. (2013)
Antsirabe	19,250 ± 110 BP	*Alopochen* bone	Beta-63117	Goodman (1999)
	17,370 ± 90 BP	*Centrornis* bone	Beta-63119	Goodman (1999)
	17,100 ± 100 BP	*Alopochen* bone	Beta-63118	Goodman (1999)
	90 ± 60 BP	*Numida* bone	Beta-63120	Goodman (1999)
Beloha (Anavoha)	1380 ± 90 BP	*Alopochen* bone	Beta-63675	Goodman and Rakotozafy (1997)
Belo-sur-Mer (Ankilibehandry)	1830 ± 60 BP	*Aepyornis* eggshell	Beta-90099	Burney (1999)
	1280 ± 60 BP	*Mullerornis* bone	Beta-103349	Burney (1999)
Christmas River	9610 ± 60 BP	*Aepyornis* bone	Hela-1829	Muldoon et al. (2012)
	9535 ± 70 BP	*Aepyornis* bone	Hela-1774	Muldoon et al. (2012)
	9430 ± 30 BP	*Aepyornis* bone	UBA-31590	Hansford et al. (2018)
Faux Cap	>50,000 BP	*Aepyornis* eggshell	OZF 857	Clarke et al. (2006)
	4140 ± 50 BP	*Aepyornis* eggshell	OZF 856	Clarke et al. (2006)
	4060 ± 50 BP	*Aepyornis* eggshell	OZF 855	Clarke et al. (2006)
	3260 ± 50 BP	*Aepyornis* eggshell	OZF 854	Clarke et al. (2006)
	1610 ± 40 BP	*Aepyornis* eggshell	OZF 514	Clarke et al. (2006)
Irodo, Tafiampatsa	1150 ± 90 BP	*Aepyornis* eggshell	GaK[1]	Battistini (1965)
Itampolo	1880 ± 70 BP	*Aepyornis* bone[2]	Beta-67659	Burney (1999)
Manambovo	840 ± 80 BP	*Aepyornis* eggshell	not given	Battistini et al. (1963)
Maroaloke	2285 ± 40 BP	*Aepyornis* eggshell	OxA-5077	Hedges et al. (1997)
	2025 ± 40 BP	*Aepyornis* eggshell	OxA-5075	Hedges et al. (1997)

LOCATION	DATE	MATERIAL	SOURCE	CITATION
	1940 ± 45 BP	*Aepyornis* eggshell	OxA-5076	Hedges et al. (1997)
	1415 ± 40 BP	*Aepyornis* eggshell	OxA-5078	Hedges et al. (1997)
Masinandraina	4496 ± 40 BP	*Aepyornis* bone	NZA-16995	Burney et al. (2004)
	1537 ± 25 BP	*Aepyornis* bone	OxA-34758	Hansford and Turvey (2018)
Mitoho	4030 ± 70 BP	*Aepyornis* eggshell	Beta-16442	MacPhee (1986)
Toliara, "Belande"	5210 ± 140 BP	*Aepyornis* eggshell	not given	Sauer (1972)
Tsiandroina	1980 ± 60 BP	*Coua primavea*	Beta 63676	Goodman and Rakotozafy (1997)

Source: Cited publications, and partially extracted from Crowley (2010).
Note: The generic allocations from elephant bird bone published before Hansford and Turvey's (2018) revision are uncertain.
[1] No reference number given for the sample.
[2] Human-modified bone (H. James in Burney 1999).

Hence, the conclusion is that the ancestors of these different lineages were capable of sustained flight, and flightlessness and gigantism evolved on several occasions in the ratites.

Other recent technological advances have brought new insights into the ecology of aepyornithids. In one remarkable example, Torres and Clarke (2018), using digital brain reconstructions of the skulls of *A. maximus* and *A. hildebrandti* as well as other living and extinct ratites, were able to study their neuroanatomy and infer different aspects of their ecology and behavior. Two inferences are noteworthy: 1) aepyornithids had very reduced optic lobes and were presumably nocturnal; and 2) their olfactory lobes were relatively well developed, and different anatomical characters suggest that they may have lived in habitats with closed vegetation.

Anseriformes

Two forms of extinct waterbirds are known from subfossil deposits on Madagascar. These include *Centrornis majori* and *Alopochen sirabensis*. Livezey (1997) placed both of these birds in the tribe Tadornini, often called shelducks or sheldgeese. Both species were described from bone remains recovered from near Antsirabe (Andrews 1897).

Based on osteological characters, *Centrornis* was probably not a strong swimmer but rather, with its proportionately long legs, was adapted for wading and had a well-developed and elongated metacarpal spur that may have been used against intraspecific rivals, showing osteological convergence with the screamers (Anhimidae) of South America. *Centrornis* is known from deposits in the Central Highlands, the southwest, and Andrahomana Cave (Goodman and Jungers 2014). Only a single radiocarbon date is available for this bird, based on remains from Antsirabe, which yielded a date of 17,370 ± 90 BP (Table 13.5).

One of the most common birds found in subfossil deposits on Madagascar, particularly in the Central Highlands, is *A. sirabensis*; it is known from a wide variety of sites (Goodman and Rakotozafy 1997; Goodman 1999; Samonds et al. 2019). Radiocarbon analysis of bones of this species from Ampasambazimba yielded its oldest known date of 22,550 ± 170 BP, and from Beloha the youngest known of 1380 ± 90 BP (Table 13.5). Thus at least until the seventh century, this species still existed. Recent work on subfossil remains of waterbirds from La Réunion has revealed that the extinct sheldgoose *Mascarenachen kervazoi* is actually best placed in the genus *Alopochen* (Mourer-Chauviré et al. 1999), and that this form is different from *A. sirabensis* of Madagascar and *A. mauritianus* of Mauritius. Thus, there was a small radiation of shelducks on western Indian Ocean islands, all of which are now extinct, while natural populations of the African species, *A. aegyptiaca*, the only extant member of the genus, are not uncommon in portions of sub-Saharan Africa and the Nile Valley.

Two extant species of endemic dabbling ducks, *Anas melleri* and *A. bernieri*, are the subject of several modern conservation projects, as they have become distinctly rare over the past few decades (see Young et al., pp. 1627–36). Based on the localities of subfossil remains of these two birds (Table 13.3), they have experienced reductions in their geographic distributions over the past few millennia (Goodman and Rakotozafy 1997; Goodman 1999). There is no evidence of any extinct *Anas* on Madagascar. Post-17th-century bone remains on La Réunion have been tentatively identified as *Aythya innotata* (Mourer-Chauviré et al. 1999), a species that was feared to have gone extinct on Madagascar over the past couple of decades, but a small population was then discovered in the northern portion of the island (see Rene de Roland and Young, pp. 1650–53).

Numididae

Numida meleagris (Helmeted Guineafowl), long considered to be introduced to Madagascar, is widely distributed in a feral state across much of the open portions of the island, including different forms of woodlands and grasslands. Domestic guineafowl are also commonly raised in portions of the island. Bone midden remains of this species from an 11th–14th-century archaeological site near Ambanja (Rakotozafy 1996) until recently represented the oldest known evidence for it on the island.

Three radiocarbon dates are available for subfossil remains of *N. meleagris* from Ankilitelo in the southwest: the oldest yielded a date of 11,310 ± 40 BP (Goodman et al. 2013), which was well before the earliest date of human arrival on the island known at the time of that publication. Hence, these authors concluded that the presence of this species on Madagascar represented a natural colonization of the island, rather than a human introduction. Subsequently, new information on the earliest date of human presence became available, based on an elephant bird bone modified by humans that was dated to 9430 ± 30 BP and recovered from the Christmas River site (Hansford et al. 2018; Table 13.5; see Wright and Rakotoarisoa, pp. 181–90; Godfrey and Douglass, pp. 191–97), a few thousand years after the date of *Numida* material from the nearby Ankilitelo site. Hence, the possibility that these early colonizers brought this species to Madagascar cannot be excluded. Further, on linguistic grounds it can be inferred that *Numida* was introduced at some time to Madagascar, as the name of this bird in Kiswahili is *kanga* and in Malagasy *akanga*, and such loanwords are often associated with introduction (Beaujard 2003). Perhaps the best way to determine whether this species was introduced to Madagascar is through genetic studies.

Mesitornithidae

Recent excavations in the cave of Anjohibe recovered bones referable to the endemic Malagasy family Mesitornithidae. This material, referable to the genus *Monias*, is an apparently undescribed species (Burney et al. 1997). Over the past years no further work has been conducted on these remains to resolve this question.

Cuculidae

Remains of two species of large extinct couas of the genus *Coua* have been excavated from subfossil sites in the Central Highlands, and in western and southern portions of the island; both species are notably larger than extant and recently extinct (*C. delalandei*) members of the genus. *Coua primaeva* was described by Milne Edwards and Grandidier (1895) based on a tarsometatarsus recovered near Belo-sur-Mer. Subsequently, bone remains referred to this species, in some cases tentatively, have been found in deposits at Tsiandroina, Manombo (Toliara), Anjohibe, and Tsimanampesotse (Burney et al. 1997; Goodman and Rakotozafy 1997; H. Rasolonjatovo et al. 2021; Table 13.3). The bone from Tsiandroina was radiocarbon dated to 1980 ± 60 BP (Table 13.5). The second extinct subfossil species is *C. berthae*, described from Anjohibe (Goodman and Ravoavy 1993) based on a pelvis. Material identified as this species, in some cases tentatively, has been recovered from Ampasambazimba and Tsimanampesotse (Burney et al. 1997; Goodman and Rakotozafy 1997; H. Rasolonjatovo et al. 2021).

Part of the ambiguity associated with the species allocation of certain subfossil specimens is that little is known about intraspecific osteological differences within the genus *Coua*, as few full skeletons are available to quantify this aspect, and the subfossil elements are of different bones, making direct comparisons and statistical inferences difficult. Hence, until this limitation is properly addressed, it will not be possible to determine whether material named in excavation reports as *C.* cf. *berthae* and *C.* cf. *primaeva* indeed represents these species or some undescribed subfossil member(s) of the genus.

Rallidae

Andrews (1897) described *Tribonyx roberti* based on subfossil bones excavated near Antsirabe; rails of this genus, presumably members of the Rallidae, today occur only in Australia and Tasmania. Subsequently, this species has been transferred to *Hovacrex* (Brodkorb 1965), which is a monotypic genus endemic to Madagascar. *Hovacrex roberti* has also been tentatively identified from subfossil material found at Ambolisatra (Goodman and Rakotozafy 1997). To our knowledge no radiocarbon date is available for bone remains of this rail.

Charadriidae

A few bones of a lapwing, subfamily Vanellinae, were identified from deposits at Lamboharana and Ampoza and formed the basis of the description of *Vanellus madagascariensis*, an extinct Malagasy endemic (Goodman 1996). Subsequently, a carpometacarpus was identified from deposits at Tsimanampesotse (H. Rasolonjatovo et al. 2021), which is presumed to be the same species. This new element has a distinctly large spur. No radiocarbon dates are available for Malagasy subfossil *Vanellus*.

The subfamily Vanellinae is widespread across portions of the New and Old World in different habitats, ranging in the Afrotropics from at least partially disturbed wetlands to other types of open areas. This subfamily is not represented in the extant avifauna of Madagascar. From a biogeographic perspective, since the discovery of *V. madagascariensis*, the question with respect to Madagascar has shifted from why this subfamily is unknown on the island to why it no longer occurs.

Phalacrocoracidae

Bones of a large cormorant assigned to the genus *Phalacrocorax* have been found at the subfossil sites of Lamboharana and Antsirabe and are distinctly larger than bones of the only extant cormorant species known from the island (*Microcarbo africanus*). These bones represent an unidentified species, which might be an extinct cormorant endemic to the island (Goodman and Rakotozafy 1997; Goodman 1999).

Accipitridae

Three species of subfossil raptors are known from Madagascar that have disappeared from the island in geologically recent times. These include two different types of *Aquila* eagles and a large crowned-eagle, *Stephanoaetus mahery* (Goodman 1994a; Goodman and Rakotozafy 1995, 1997). Given that the genus *Aquila* contains many species in the Old and New Worlds, each of which shows sexual dimorphism in size, it was not possible to determine whether the subfossil remains recovered on Madagascar are of endemic and extinct forms or extant species occurring elsewhere in the world. All three of these raptors had relatively broad distributions on Madagascar (Table 13.3).

Brachypteraciidae

Subfossil material of this endemic Malagasy family was recovered from Ampoza and described based on a humerus as the extinct species *Brachypteracias langrandi* (Goodman 2000). Since the publication of this description, the genus *Brachypteracias* has been separated into two separate genera (*Brachypteracias* and *Geobiastes*) based on molecular characters (Kirchman et al. 2001). No osteological details are available on the separation of these genera, and the generic allocation of the subfossil is in question. Both genera occur in moist evergreen forests on Madagascar, and if this association holds for the subfossil form, the forest habitat around Ampoza, which is close to the Zombitse-Vohibasia protected area, was distinctly more mesic in the recent geological past. No radiocarbon date is available for *B. langrandi*.

Conclusion

The study of Malagasy historical archaeology and Quaternary paleontology continues, with numerous new projects and continued excavations of human occupation sites and cave and marsh deposits, generating an important amount of bird material. Further, previous collections remain to be fully worked up and identified. Based on new studies, it is almost certain that previously unrecognized species of Malagasy birds will be described, providing new insights into bird communities before and after human colonization of the island, as well as better understanding of ecological change over time since the Late Pleistocene and the reasons for these vicissitudes.

INTRODUCED BIRDS

The number of bird species introduced to Madagascar is low compared to the number on other tropical islands. We have found information for a total of five or six extant non-domesticated, non-native bird species from the island (Table 13.1), compared to 162 species in the Hawaiian archipelago, 56 on Tahiti, 38 in the Mascarene archipelago, 25 on Fiji, and 14 on Seychelles (J. Long 1981; Cheke and Hume 2008; totals include species that no longer occur).

Several domestic bird species have been introduced to Madagascar for poultry production—these include an assortment of breeds and races of chickens, guineafowl, turkeys, pigeons, ducks, geese, quails, and ostriches. The exact periods the different domestic fowl were introduced to or present on the island are not clear. Bones of pigeons (*Columba livia*), domestic ducks (cf. *Cairina moschata* and cf. *Anas platyrhynchos*), chickens (*Gallus gallus*), and guineafowl (*Numida meleagris*) have been recovered from midden deposits at Mahilaka, an 11th–14th-century CE Islamic port village near Ambanja (Rakotozafy 1996), and it is clear that by this period poultry figured in the diet of people inhabiting the area. These same domestic species are still widely consumed by the Malagasy.

A number of bird species were introduced to Madagascar for touristic attraction in the context of exchange between Malagasy and European zoos. Among these species are *Pavo cristata* (Indian Peafowl) and *Chrysolophus pictus* (Golden Pheasant), sent to the Parc Botanique et Zoologique de Tsimbazaza. Birds obtained from breeding these two species were sold to private individuals as pets (J. Ramanampamonjy, unpublished data). Another example of a local zoo that breeds introduced species in captivity is the Croc Farm near Ivato. These birds include *Musophaga rossae* (Lady Ross's Turaco), *Pteroglossus aracari* (Black-necked Aracari), *Ramphastos tucanus* (White-throated Toucan), and a few colorful species of passerines (M. J. Raherilalao, unpublished data). In these cases, biosecurity measures are crucial to prevent captive birds from escaping into the wild.

The past few years have seen studies published on the geographic origin of the form of *G. gallus* introduced to Madagascar, specifically the "rural chickens" rather than the more recent commercial "factory chickens" for large-scale production. *Gallus gallus*, also known as Red Junglefowl, is native to southeastern and southern Asia, where it was first domesticated (Miao et al. 2013; Wang et al. 2020), but numerous distinct domestic forms exist because of human selection over time. Based on the initial study of Razafindraibe et al. (2008), current evidence indicates that the haplotype group of rural chickens on Madagascar is also found in Malawi, Zimbabwe, and eastern Kenya, and this fowl was probably introduced from East Africa (Mwacharo et al. 2013).

Subsequent to the earliest (11th–14th-century) archaeological evidence of bone remains of *Gallus* on Madagascar from Mahilaka (Rakotozafy 1996; see above), remains of this species are known from a range of archaeological sites since the 17th century (Rakotozafy and Goodman 2005). *Meleagris gallopavo*, or domestic turkey, was apparently introduced to the island toward the end of the 19th century (Moussu 1933). No feral populations of *Gallus* or *Meleagris* are known from the island.

Below is an annotated list of non-native, in many cases naturalized, species introduced to Madagascar over the past 170 years or so, with information on their current status.

Galliformes

***Numida meleagris* (Helmeted Guineafowl)**: This species is discussed in some detail in the section on subfossil birds (see pp. 1578–87).

***Francolinus pictus* (Painted Francolin)**: There is a specimen of *F. pictus*, a species native to the Indian subcontinent, in the Musée Zoologique de Strasbourg that is labeled "Madagascar" and dated 1849 (Langrand and Sinclair 1994). We are unaware of any subsequent records of this species on the island.

***Francolinus pintadeanus* (Chinese Francolin)**: This Asian species was released in northeastern Madagascar from a Mauritian population (also introduced) sometime in the 18th century (Lavauden 1937). There is no modern evidence that a naturalized population remains on Madagascar; the Mauritian population has also disappeared (Cheke and Hume 2008).

Columbiformes

***Columba livia* (Rock Pigeon)**: Little is known about the history of introduction of domestic pigeons to Madagascar, but today they are broadly distributed in towns and villages across the island, and feral populations are known from certain sites, such as the cliffs of Isalo and within a few kilometers of Ranohira. These feral populations might have ecological significance in the form of competition with other ground-foraging granivores, a point of research worthy of pursuit. *Columba livia* has been identified from prey remains of *Falco peregrinus* at Lake Tritriva near Antsirabe (Razafimanjato et al. 2007).

***Geopelia striata* (Zebra Dove)**: This Asian species was introduced to Madagascar in the first portion of the 19th century. Sganzin

(1840) reported it from the Fenoarivo-Atsinanana, Mananara-Nord, and Foulpointe areas in 1831 and 1832. Reports in the 1860s agree that it was common on the island, at least in the north, although details and locations are lacking to show how widespread it truly was. According to Milne Edwards and Grandidier (1879–1885), it had been introduced "long ago" in the north of the island. Schlegel and Pollen (1868) found it abundant on Madagascar (albeit less so than on La Réunion; Schlegel 1866), often visiting villages in large flocks at particular times of day, where rice was being pounded. According to Rand (1936) it was no longer present on the island and indeed has never been reported since the 19th century. Staub (1976) noted, "This bird is now very common in the Mascarenes and Madagascar" but provided no source for his Madagascar comment, and we suggest that this completely isolated report is in error. It remains common on the Mascarene islands and several other islands in the region (Safford 2013d).

Passeriformes

Corvus splendens **(House Crow)**: This Asian species was recorded for the first time on Madagascar at Toamasina in 2014 (Linders and Langrand 2014). See Meier et al. (pp. 1704–7) for further details on this species on the island.

Zosterops borbonicus **(Réunion Gray White-eye)**: Among the birds reported by Sganzin (1840) on Ile Sainte Marie was the "petit simon de Buffon." These were widely assumed to be *Neomixis tenella* (Common Jery), but the vernacular name at the time referred to *Z. borbonicus* of La Réunion. Cheke (2009) duly confirmed that a specimen collected by Sganzin in 1931 survives in the Muséum Nationale d'Histoire Naturelle in Paris and is indeed *Z. borbonicus*; moreover, another Malagasy specimen of *Z. borbonicus* is held in the same museum, from a collection by Auguste Lantz received in 1868 and labeled "Nossi Bé" (Nosy Be). These are the only references to this species on Madagascar, suggesting that any introduction may have been short-lived and restricted to these localities with connections to La Réunion.

Acridotheres tristis **(Common Myna)**: This species was first introduced from La Réunion to the east coast of Madagascar around the first half of the 19th century with the intention that it would reduce the hordes of locusts (Milon 1951b; Decary 1962); it is native in southern and eastern Asia. A subsequent introduction took place in about 1875, also along the east coast, on the advice of Alfred Grandidier. By 1885 this species was found in the zone between Toamasina and Pointe à Larrée. Rand (1936) noted that between 1929 and 1931 *Acridotheres* was common in the environs of Toamasina and fairly common as far south as Brickaville; it also occurred north to Fenoarivo-Atsinanana. Further, he remarked that a captive individual was found at Maroantsetra and that "the natives may thus aid its spread."

Lavauden (1937) noted that the range of *Acridotheres* extended from Fenoarivo-Atsinanana south to Farafangana. About 10 years later, between 1946 and 1948 it was remarked that it was starting to advance toward the Central Highlands along the Toamasina-Antananarivo railroad; during this period it was reported inland from Brickaville near Rogez (Andekaleka) (Milon 1951b; Milon et al. 1973). By 1952 there were also records from the south-central portion of the east coast from Vatomandry south to Vohipeno (Milon et al. 1973). Milon (1951b: 70–71) noted, "Je crois qu'il serait intéressant de suivre l'expansion éventuelle de cette espèce à Madagascar. Actuellement, toute observation d'un Martin dans la plaine de l'Est au Nord de Fénérive et au Sud de Brickaville mérite d'être signalée, ainsi que toute avance en direction des Hauts-Plateaux." (I think that it will be interesting to follow the range expansion of this species on Madagascar. Currently all observations of this species along the eastern plain from Fenoarivo-Atsinanana in the north to Brickaville in the south should be reported, as well as those showing advancement in the direction of the Central Highlands.) He also proposed that the introduction and spread of this species might have adverse effects on certain endemic species, most notably tree hole–nesting birds, and it might also disperse the seeds of introduced plants.

Between 1957 and 1958 several pairs of *Acridotheres* were introduced to Ambanja, and slightly later to Nosy Be (Milon et al. 1973). These same authors mentioned that A. Peyriéras observed this species in the Berenty and Amboasary-Atsimo region near sisal plantations in 1969. Its first colonization of this zone was probably slightly earlier, as Salvan (1970) remarked that sometime after 1945 it was found 30 km west of Tolagnaro and near Amboasary-Atsimo.

By the late 1980s *Acridotheres* was found in the north and northwest near Nosy Be, Ambanja, and Vohémar, along the east coast from Sambava to Tolagnaro, and in the far south in areas of dry spiny thicket; it was also progressing across the Central Highlands, with established populations in the urban areas of Fianarantsoa, Ambalavao, and Antananarivo (Langrand 1990). In the late 1990s, with progressively more severe problems associated with locust outbreaks, several Malagasy institutions proposed releasing large numbers of *Acridotheres* as biological control agents against these pests. These plans were apparently abandoned.

As of 2020, this species has colonized virtually the complete coastal belt of the island, where it can be abundant near towns and villages, as well as isolated inland settlements and at the forest-grassland ecotone. This includes zones near moist evergreen and dry forests, as well as dry spiny thickets. Further, this species can be found across almost the entire Central Highlands at elevations up to 1985 m (Collin and Collin 1996). Across the central east, specifically from Soanierana Ivongo to Mahanoro, including Toamasina, it is common in urban and rural areas (Goodman et al. 2017a).

In cities such as Antananarivo there has been a notable increase in densities of *Acridotheres* over the past decades. Research on its population dynamics at three sites in Antananarivo between September 2015 and March 2017 found that the local population increased on average by 64% per year (Randriamiharisoa 2020). At this rate, it is not surprising that this species is one of the dominant birds in and around the capital city and is appropriately considered invasive.

Echoing the concerns of Milon (1951b) over seventy years ago, several authors have suggested that *Acridotheres* may be an important competitor with endemic bird species for food resources or nesting cavities. The impact of this starling on native birds, including those with larger bodies, has been documented in other areas of the world it has invaded, where it is highly aggressive and competitive for both nesting sites and food resources (e.g., Grarock et al. 2012); it may also be a predator of eggs, chicks, and sometimes adults of smaller birds. Negative economic impacts have also been suggested, and these could be important on a local scale, for example in small holdings, as flocks may damage a range of fruit crops (Global Invasive Species Database 2020).

Until recently little was known about the diet of this species on Madagascar. Recent observations by Randriamiharisoa and Rakotomanana (2019) and Randriamiharisoa (2020) provide detailed information for the Central Highlands around Antananarivo. Foods brought to nestlings are diverse, with slightly less than 90% being invertebrates (Orthoptera, Coleoptera, Lepidoptera, Odonata, etc.), about 9% vertebrates (chameleons, other lizards, and frogs), and the balance fruits and seeds. Further, adults consume fruits of native and introduced tress such as mulberries (*Morus*, Moraceae), figs (*Ficus*, Moraceae), *Melia* (Meliaceae), and *Cryptocarya* (Lauraceae).

One critical question, for which there are no data from Madagascar, is what diseases *Acridotheres*, as well as other non-native bird species, brought to the island. This species is known to be a reservoir of different zoonotic diseases, such as blood parasites (*Plasmodium* and *Haemoproteus* spp.) in Australia, which originally came from the Asian founding populations (Ishtiaq et al. 2006). Hence, as documented elsewhere in the world (e.g., N. Clark et al. 2015), on Madagascar, the combination of introduced birds and introduced mosquitoes (see Duchemin et al., pp. 1074–80), which act as vectors, may be responsible for the spread of non-native zoonotic diseases to endemic birds. This needs to be investigated, including possible transmission pathways. Currently, *A. tristis* is not known to enter intact closed-canopy forest on Madagascar and thus has little direct contact with forest-dependent birds, a large proportion of which are endemic to the island. However, it does invade secondary forest habitats, and this could be the interface for transmission to less habitat-sensitive endemic forest-dwelling species.

In the Malagasy Region, particularly on small islands, several programs have been put in place to eradicate introduced populations of *A. tristis*, including in parts of Seychelles (Canning 2011; Feare et al. 2017). However, given the size of Madagascar and the broad distribution and local densities of this species on the island, such programs are not feasible.

Passer domesticus **(House Sparrow)**: The previous first records of *P. domesticus* on Madagascar were from 1985 in the immediate vicinity of Toamasina harbor (Langrand and Sinclair 1994). Based on information made available by W. Zehrer (unpublished data via O. Langrand), this species arrived at Toamasina a decade earlier. In 1975 agents associated with the Service Phytosanitaire observed in the Toamasina port several individual birds, which, based on their written report, were certainly *P. domesticus* that arrived as stowaways on a cargo boat carrying rice, presumably from Pakistan. Thereafter, these birds formed the source population that established themselves in the small vegetated park next to the Club Nautique, adjacent to the port. From mid-1985 to early 1987, the estimated local population in central Toamasina was about 20 individuals (D. Halleux and O. Langrand, then unpublished data).

In 1987, Olivier Langrand, then technical adviser of WWF Madagascar, submitted a written proposal to WWF International for a program to eradicate this invasive species, which at that point was a small population in central Toamasina. WWF and the Malagasy authorities did not consider advancing the project, as at that time they did not consider it a priority in the context of conserving Malagasy biodiversity (O. Langrand, unpublished data). Subsequently the *Passer* population grew, dispersed along the coast, and expanded its geographic range. It is abundant in the greater Toamasina region, ranging from at least Soanierana Ivongo in the north to Mahanoro in the south, with the estimated number of birds as of 2016 approaching 7,700,000 in this narrow coastal strip about 350 km long (Goodman et al. 2017a). Hence, eradication of this population is outside the realm of possibility, and even population control would be notably difficult.

Based on point counts conducted during 2016 in Toamasina, specifically in the neighborhoods of Anjoma, a zone of dense human population and reduced vegetation cover, and Tahity Kely, with more dispersed houses and considerable vegetation cover, densities were 89.0 individuals per ha and 33.1 individuals per ha, respectively (Sylvestre 2018). The same exact point count system was repeated in these two areas of Toamasina in late 2019 and early 2020, and the population estimates were 108.5 individuals per ha and 63.3 individuals per ha, respectively (Raolihanintrasina 2021), an increase of 21.9% and 91.2%, respectively, in four years. These data clearly indicate important and ongoing local population increases over the course of a few years in areas where it has been long established, thus illustrating the invasive nature of this species.

After the study by Raolihanintrasina (2021), data are now available on the diet of *P. domesticus* in Toamasina. Based on a sample of the contents of 46 stomachs, more than 60% by volume contained vegetal remains, with corn (*Zea mays*) and rice (*Oryza sativa*) making up 55%. An assortment of invertebrates of seven orders, including 13 different families, was identified, which in total made up 35% by volume of the remains, dominated by coleopterans (12.5%), hymenopterans (8.6%), and dipterans (6.0%). Hence, it is clear that this species consumes a considerable quantity of grain. Based on point count surveys of *P. domesticus* in Fenoarivo-Atsinanana and Toamasina (Gauthier 2018; Sylvestre 2018), measures of density, and some other variables, it was estimated that in the greater Toamasina area (Soanierana Ivongo to Mahanoro), these birds consume 11.6 tons or rice per day, which is approaching 4100 tons per year (Goodman et al. 2017a). Hence, the prediction of Zehrer (1997) that this species might become a serious crop pest has unfortunately been realized.

The first records of *P. domesticus* in Antsiranana were in 2010, and populations increased at a quick pace. As of late 2020 this species was very common in town, with records as far south as Sakaramy and Mahavahona and east to Sakalava Bay (S. M. Goodman, unpublished data). Since 2011, it has been observed adjacent to the Mahajanga port (S. M. Goodman, unpublished data). In late 2019 and early 2020 during a survey of invasive bird species in port cities and towns of Madagascar, this species was not uncommon across much of central Mahajanga, distinctly common in Hellville and other areas of Nosy Be, and a few individuals were observed in Tolagnaro (S. M. Goodman and E. Raobson, unpublished data). Further, this species was not found at Ankify, Morondava, Toliara, Farafangana, Manakara, Maroantsetra, Antalaha, Sambava, or Vohémar (E. Raobson, unpublished data). Hence, it would appear that *P. domesticus* has been able to colonize at least five port towns on Madagascar (Antsiranana, Nosy Be, Mahajanga, Tolagnaro, and Toamasina), presumably in most cases arriving independently as stowaways on boats coming from ports outside Madagascar, but some local transfer is possible, such as on dhows moving between Mahajanga and Nosy Be.

There are also occasional records from the main rail yard in Antananarivo since 2004 (Safford 2013e), but it is unclear whether there is a breeding population in the capital. It has been proposed that this species may have reached Antananarivo from Toamasina via the train line connecting these two cities (Goodman et al. 2017a). If this is indeed the case, this species may also occur in towns and villages along the Toamasina-Antananarivo railway line. Indeed, this was recently verified by its presence near the Andasibe train station (K. Behrens, unpublished data). Train wagons not in use and parked near certain stations remain immobile for relatively long periods, and birds use these structures for nesting, with the possibility of being transported to other stations.

***Estrilda astrild* (Common Waxbill)**: This species was observed on several occasions in the 1980s on Nosy Be (Langrand and Sinclair 1994). There are subsequent reports from 1998 in the Bemarivo Special Reserve, near Besalampy (Projet ZICOMA 1998), and from 1999 near Bemaneviky (Ambanja), in the northern foothills of Manongarivo (Safford 2013f). In late November 2018, about 23 individuals were observed in the grassy area around the Nosy Be airport (L.-A. Rene de Roland, unpublished data). Hence, there is evidence that an established population of this species occurs on Nosy Be and surrounding areas of the Sambirano Region. There are no earlier reports, and Hartlaub (1877) specifically mentioned that this species was not known from Madagascar; this African species has also become established in parts of Seychelles and on the Mascarene islands (Mauritius, La Réunion, and Rodrigues), as well as on Juan de Nova in the Mozambique Channel (A. Hawkins et al. 2015).

***Hypargos margaritatus* (Pink-throated Twinspot)**: A nest of this African estrildid, housed in the Musée Zoologique de Strasbourg, is labeled "Madagascar" (Langrand and Sinclair 1994). This is the only evidence that we are aware of for this species' introduction to the island.

ZOOGEOGRAPHY

Recent Geological Times

Based on subfossil material dating from the Late Pleistocene and Holocene, it is clear that the distributions of numerous extant Malagasy birds have changed appreciably over the past few millennia. The best evidence for these distributional shifts comes from southwestern Madagascar. This area of the island, which currently receives less than 600 mm of rainfall per year on average, was distinctly wetter just a few thousand years ago. A variety of aquatic bird species have been recovered from sites in this region where they no longer occur. The most likely explanation for these changes has little to do with anthropogenic factors; rather, analysis of stable isotopes and calcite formations suggests that the changes are a consequence of natural desiccation and the resulting near-total disappearance of large areas of presumably permanent fresh water in southern Madagascar (see Godfrey and Douglass, pp. 191–97).

A review several decades ago of Holocene bird subfossils from the Central Highlands and Ampoza (southwest) found that nearly one-third of the 35 different waterbird species found in subfossil deposits are now extinct (Goodman 1999). Some additional new information has been subsequently brought to light (Samonds et al. 2019; see pp. 1578–87, "Subfossil Birds"), but these patterns still hold. When taxa of extinct birds and extant birds that no longer occur near these sites are included, 50–80% of the birds recorded in the deposits are locally extinct in the regions surrounding these sites. Thus, it is clear that over the past few millennia there have been significant changes in the distribution of birds in this portion of the island.

What effect these changes might have had on forest-dwelling species, particularly those in moist evergreen formations, is unclear; this uncertainty arises at least in part because no known site that has been the source of recovered bird subfossils is within this type of forest formation. In any case, with the contraction of certain habitats and expansion of others it is probable that the ranges of certain bird species have followed the same patterns shown for waterbirds. These factors have almost certainly had a major influence on bird community structure and genetic exchange within and between populations.

Contemporary Patterns

The major ecosystems on Madagascar that are used by birds include forests, freshwater wetlands, secondary woody vegetation, grasslands, sandy coasts, estuaries, mangroves, islands, the open sea, agricultural lands, and areas built up by humans. Terrestrial ecosystems, including fresh water, divide neatly into humid and dry habitats, the former present in the eastern third of the country. Forests reflect this division clearly, with lowland moist evergreen forests now occurring mostly along the scarp just inland from the east coast, and medium-altitude and montane forests farther inland as the land rises. In some areas, for instance around Antongil Bay, lowland forests remain along the coast, and in the northwest, a band of forest extends to the west coast in the Sambirano Region. There are also outliers of moist evergreen forests on Montagne d'Ambre and on a few isolated massifs in the Central Highlands. The moist evergreen forests are often tall, with dense understory and closed canopy. In the west, dry deciduous forests are very fragmented, with large blocks persisting largely on substrates that are unsuitable for agriculture or are protected against dry-season fires by winter mists. There are still fairly large areas of dry spiny thickets, especially on calcareous substrates, where they are naturally protected by difficult access for humans or cattle.

In general, the resident bird community of Madagascar is forest based. Endemic species are very strongly concentrated in forest habitats (Table 13.6). Only 13% of the total number of bird species are limited to open habitats. This is in marked contrast to the bird communities of adjacent African countries, where there is a diverse savanna-limited bird community. Only 11% of all Malagasy endemic land-bird species are even capable of living in open habitats, whereas 87% of forest-limited species are endemic. This, and the fact that a large proportion of endemic species depend on relatively undisturbed native forest, suggest that forest habitats, whether closed or open canopy, have been the dominant formation across much of the island.

TABLE 13.6. Distribution of Malagasy breeding bird species among ecosystems

SPECIES DISTRIBUTION	NUMBER OF SPECIES	PERCENTAGE OF TOTAL	NUMBER OF ENDEMIC SPECIES	PERCENTAGE OF ENDEMIC SPECIES	PERCENTAGE OF TOTAL ENDEMIC SPECIES
Species limited to open habitats (grassland, wooded grassland)	48	16	11	23	10
Species limited to aquatic habitats	61	20	13	21	12
Species limited to forest	104	34	86	83	77
Species limited to coastal areas	35	12	1	3	1
Species observed mainly at sea	56	18	0	0	0
Totals	304	100	111	37	100

The division of the Malagasy avifauna among the major biomes of the island is rather unequal (Table 13.7). The eastern biome holds the richest bird community; nearly half of the endemic Malagasy species are limited to the moist evergreen forest biome, and more than half of the endemic species present in the east are limited to that region. Most birds in the western biome are found in the dry deciduous forests, lakes, and marshes. The western forests are poorer in species and have fewer endemic taxa than the moist evergreen forests, and the distribution of these local endemics is very patchy, with some species absent from large areas within the biome. Several western endemics have closely related sister taxa in the east (e.g., *Xanthomixis apperti*, Appert's Tetraka, and *Schetba occidentalis*, Western Rufous Vanga, in the west; *X. cinereiceps*, Gray-crowned Tetraka, and *S. rufa*, Eastern Rufous Vanga, in the east) or south (*Xenopirostris damii*, Van Dam's Vanga, in the west, and *X. xenopirostris*, Lafresnaye's Vanga, in the south). The southern biome holds the fewest terrestrial birds, although there are more local endemic species in the dry spiny thickets, which include two of the most extraordinary species, *Uratelornis chimaera* (Long-tailed Ground-roller) and *Monias benschi* (Subdesert Mesite).

One area of Madagascar where the remarkable inter-biome bird species turnover is very evident is between the lowland moist evergreen forests (eastern biome) of parcel 1 and the dry spiny thicket (southern biome) of parcel 2 of the Andohahela protected area. Although these two sites are only a few kilometers apart they fall on opposite extremes of a rainfall gradient. There is considerably greater species turnover between these two sites than over the complete length of the moist evergreen forests of the east, approaching 1000 km (Goodman et al. 1997a).

TABLE 13.7. Distribution of Malagasy birds among florisitic biomes

	EAST	CENTER	WEST	SOUTH
Breeding species present (residents and species breeding only on Madagascar)	149	137	135	119
Species endemic to Madagascar present (percentage of total endemic species)	84 (76)	73 (66)	54 (49)	54 (49)
Species endemic to Malagasy Region present (percentage of total endemic species)	27 (24)	27 (24)	29 (26)	28 (25)
Land birds present	121	109	93	94
Endemic land birds present	77	65	46	49
Forest birds present	82	73	53	57
Forest birds endemic to Madagascar and Malagasy Region present (percentage of total forest birds)	81 (99)	71 (97)	51 (96)	53 (93)
Waterbirds present	37	33	52	29
Endemic waterbirds present	9	8	7	2
Waterbird species endemic to Malagasy Region present	3	3	4	4

Secondary woody formations and grasslands are by contrast species poor and have a lower level of local and regional endemism. Only 48 species are limited to these habitats; even in the west, where intact forest structure more resembles adjacent secondary forest, there is considerable species turnover between primary and secondary forest (A. Hawkins and Wilmé 1996).

There are considerable ecological differences between the wetland habitats of the east and those of the west, and this is reflected in their bird faunas. Western wetlands are composed largely of coastal beaches, estuaries and mangroves, salt pans, shallow coastal lakes (one each of soda and saline, and many freshwater), rivers, and marshes dominated by *Typha*, *Phragmites*, or Cyperaceae. Some sites are extensive, encompassing coastal areas to inland waters, with at least 10 areas (e.g., Mahavavy Kinkony, Ankarafantsika, Tsimembo-Manambolomaty, Ambondrobe, Menabe Antimena, Mangoky Ihotry) hosting bird communities of considerable diversity (Goodman et al. 2018). In the east, there are a few small estuaries, but most of the coast is steep sand backed with coastal lagoons, while the eastern escarpment holds in its valley bottoms small areas of marshlands dominated by *Juncus*, Cyperaceae, Poaceae, and other low, flowering plants. There are some large lakes in the east, notably Lake Alaotra, tectonic in origin and surrounded by a huge area of *Cyperus* swamp, now largely converted to rice cultivation. There are also some artificial reservoirs such as Lake Mantasoa, and many steep rivers flowing through the moist evergreen forests to the sea.

Western wetlands are richer overall in bird species than eastern ones; it is notable that one of the most species-rich wetland areas in the east, Loky Manambato, lies in the drier zone of the far northeast, with climate and wetland types more akin to the west (Goodman et al. 2018). However, western wetlands have fewer endemic species as well as a lower rate of endemism. Their communities are dominated by herons such as *Egretta* spp., *Ardea* spp., *Ardeola idae*, and *A. ralloides* (Squacco Heron), and ducks such as *Anas erythrorhyncha* (Red-billed Duck), *A. bernieri*, and *Spatula hottentota* (Hottentot Teal). There are also breeding populations of *Rostratula benghalensis*, *Himantopus himantopus*, *Dryolimnas cuvieri* (White-throated Rail), and the rare *Zapornia olivieri*. Most of these, excluding *A. bernieri* and *Z. olivieri*, also occur in the east, but less commonly. Particularly on or near the coast, this region is also characterized by large populations of nonbreeding migratory species belonging to various families such as Phoenicopteridae, Charadriidae, and Scolopacidae (see Young et al., pp. 1627–36; Rakotomavo 2017). There are few freshwater wetlands, at least today, in the southern biome, which accounts for the low number of waterbirds there (Table 13.7).

The wetlands of the east are bird rich, with several endemic species restricted to them. The east coast marshes are almost devoid of birds except the ubiquitous *Bubulcus ibis* (Cattle Egret) and a few *Ardea purpurea*, *Anas erythrorhyncha*, and *Glareola ocularis*. In the eastern marshes in and near the moist evergreen forests, by contrast, a diverse endemic community occurs, with *Rallus madagascariensis*, *Sarothrura watersi* (Slender-billed Flufftail), *Gallinago macrodactyla*, and *Bradypterus seebohmi* limited to this habitat. *Sarothrura insularis* is found here and also in somewhat drier habitats adjacent, and *A. melleri* in marshes, rivers, and lakes. The large Lake Alaotra, in the east, is (or was) the outstanding exception to the pattern of lower abundance and species richness, holding very important wetland bird diversity in both respects, but this is much declined from a few decades ago. One bird species, *Tachybaptus rufolavatus*, was apparently restricted to Lake Alaotra but is now considered extinct (A. Hawkins et al. 2000). *Aythya innotata*, one of the rarest endemic birds of Madagascar, was initially known only from Lake Alaotra, and until recently it was classified as possibly extinct. However, in 2006, a small population was rediscovered on a small shallow lake in the Bemanevika protected area, in northern Madagascar (Rene de Roland et al. 2007; see Rene de Roland and Young, pp. 1650–53). No wetland birds are entirely restricted to the limited areas of lakes and marshes of the central biome; those that do occur are mostly typical of the east.

BIRD COMMUNITIES

Trends in Species Numbers

Since the 2003 contribution of A. Hawkins and Goodman (2003), the precursor to this book, different types of research have significantly augmented the number of bird species recorded on Madagascar. These include field observations of newly recorded land bird and waterbird vagrants (e.g., Renoult 2009, among several others) and an introduced species (Linders and Langrand 2014), migrant seabirds identified through greatly increased attention to Madagascar's offshore waters, especially with new tracking technology (see Le Corre et al., pp. 1637–50), systematic revisions (e.g., Cruaud et al. 2011; Younger et al. 2019a, 2019b), and description of species new to science and other taxonomic changes (e.g., Goodman et al. 2011; Younger et al. 2018, 2019b). In addition, species richness has changed from 283 to 304 species. These changes, with a few exceptions, reflect improved knowledge more than genuine changes in Madagascar's avifauna. Given that these figures represent about a 7% augmentation in about two decades, it is likely that continued fieldwork and other forms of research will lead to further additions: we have not reached a solid, final count of the number of species on the island and in surrounding seas.

Trends also take the form of geographic variations. There are three main axes of variation in bird species numbers across forest biomes or habitats on Madagascar. The first, as described in the previous section, is inter-biome variation, from the east and center to the south and west. The second is associated with elevation in the east, and the third with latitude in the east. The western forests show regional variation in the numbers of species present, but this does not appear to follow any clear-cut pattern.

In the "Zoogeography" section above, we discussed the number of forest bird species present in eastern, western, central, and southern Madagascar (Table 13.7), showing that there are many more forest bird species in the east than elsewhere. It is also striking that of what one might regard as 58 "old" endemic species belonging to the five endemic families, one endemic subfamily, and the genus *Coua* (including the regionally endemic Leptosomidae and Vanginae), 31 are limited to the east, only five to the west, and eight to the south, with a further three species occurring in both the west and south. There are several potential explanations for this, probably all having had some effect. First, it seems likely that at least some (probably large) parts of the eastern moist evergreen forests have been present in relatively deep geological time (Wells 2003). The elevational variation within the region and associated variation in forest structure provided potential mechanisms for speciation, as cool and dry interglacial periods, when montane vegetation communities descended to lower elevations, were interspersed with warmer and wetter glacial periods, when these habitats once again became isolated at upper elevations.

Second, moist evergreen forests of any given type still contains a large panel of microhabitats (valley, slope, ridge, and vertical strata, for example) and is generally a more productive habitat than dry deciduous forests or dry spiny thickets; consequently, there are more species of plants, insects, and other biota, and thus a greater variety of food types available for birds, and more potential niches. Third, it may be that with climate fluctuations in the west and south (see Jury, pp. 91–98), fragmentation and even the complete disappearance of habitats within a region may have led to the local or complete extinction of some western or southern species. In addition, several western and southern species have very disjunct or isolated populations, being absent from large areas of apparently suitable habitat. This suggests that these species may have vanished from some areas when required habitats disappeared, and they were not able to recolonize in cases where habitat regeneration occurred. Such patchy distribution seems less a feature of the eastern forest birds.

There is a clear second center of species endemicity in southern Madagascar (Table 13.7). Even though fewer species of land birds or forest birds occur in the south compared to the west, there are more local endemics in this habitat than in the west. Of the 10 species that occur only in the south, two are monospecific genera in endemic families, and four others are members of endemic families or subfamilies. This suggests that the dry spiny thicket habitat has been present and distinct from other habitats for a long time (Wells 2003). In addition, several other species that are shared with the western biome (*Coua gigas* and *C. ruficeps*) have distributions limited to the southern part of the west, suggesting they might have originated in the south. Western dry deciduous forests show less local endemism, with two species (*Mesitornis variegatus*, White-breasted Mesite; and *Philepitta schlegeli*, Schlegel's Asity) in endemic families largely limited to the biome. *Mentocrex beankaensis* is restricted to the limestone areas of the central west lowlands (Goodman et al. 2011); another species, *Coua coquereli*, is very closely related to *C. cursor* of the south (Sorenson and Payne 2005).

A striking aspect of the biogeographic distribution of birds across Madagascar is the poverty of central Malagasy forest avifaunas. The surface area of forests left in the Central Domain (Central Highlands) is very small and highly fragmented, which perhaps accounts for this; all forest species in this portion of the island, for example at Ambohitantely, are from the moist evergreen forests and tolerate a wide range of elevations and habitat types. At the western limit of the Central Highlands, specifically in transitional and fragmented forests (for example in the Ambohijanahary protected area), there are some exceptions, and three species (*C. coquereli*, *C. gigas*, and *Falculea palliata*, Sickle-billed Vanga) found there are from the western biome (Goodman et al. 2018).

In many areas of the world there is a clear, linear decrease in bird species richness with elevation (e.g., Terborgh 1977; Diamond and LeCroy 1979). In eastern Madagascar species abundance varies with elevation, but patterns of elevational variation are slightly problematic to interpret because inventories in lowland forest (below 800 m) are few, and some species appear to have a rather patchy distribution in this habitat. However, based on current information, taxonomic diversity of Malagasy birds seems in general to peak at around 800 m (Wilmé and Goodman 2003). One exception to this pattern is the Manongarivo Massif in the northwest, where bird species diversity peaks around 1200 m (Raherilalao et al. 2002). This upward shift can be explained by the presence of a drier lowland forest formation on the massif, while on the other studied massifs of about 2000 m or higher, different forms of moist evergreen forest cover the forested slope. Across most of these massifs, there is a certain amount of species turnover between sea level and 1200 m, but the overall species number stays more or less constant (A. Hawkins 1999). After this elevation, species numbers progressively decline until the tree line (between 2000 and 2700 m), where there is an abrupt drop in bird richness.

There is less variation in bird species numbers with latitude, at least within the moist evergreen forests. Two species endemic to the eastern moist evergreen forests apparently do not occur south of the Mangoro River, for reasons that are not clear. The three species limited to the north (*Crossleyia tenebrosa*, Dusky Tetraka; *Oriolia bernieri*, Bernier's Vanga; and *Euryceros prevostii*, Helmet Vanga) are all lowland forest species; a fourth, the unnamed cryptic species in the *Bernieria madagascariensis* complex (Younger et al. 2019a), has uncertain but probably wider elevational tolerance. On the flip side, one species, *Xenopirostris polleni*, is much more common in the south, being apparently present in few localities in the north (A. Hawkins 1999). *Newtonia lavarambo* (Lavarambo Newtonia) appears to occur in the southeast from the Andringitra region south to moist evergreen forests near Tolagnaro (Younger et al. 2018), as apparently does another of the three taxa in the *Bernieria* complex (Younger et al. 2019a).

As the previous section showed, bird species richness in wetlands varies greatly among biomes. However, their distribution pattern shows no clear latitudinal or elevational gradients within a given biome. The unequal distribution of wetland species richness across the island is related to the availability and heterogeneity of suitable habitats, which is affected by long-term processes (such as climate change) but also, very strongly, by the levels of human pressure on habitats and waterbird species (Bamford et al. 2017).

Patterns in Habitat Use

The elevational variation in species number shown in Figure 13.4 conceals variation in individual species' elevational distribution in the moist evergreen forests. Only around 30% of these birds are found over the entire elevational gradient. Further, 22% are found in only one of three elevational zones: lowland (0–800 m: nine species), medium-altitude forests (800–1200 m: one species), and montane forests (1200–2800 m: nine species). Finally, 38% (30 species) occur in lowland and medium-altitude forests but not at higher elevations (A. Hawkins 1999).

Table 13.8 shows a series of variables linking elevational specialization and other characteristics associated with foraging techniques and diet. The data suggest that elevational specialists (species limited to one of the three elevational bands: lowland, medium altitude, or high altitude) are more likely to feed on substrates below the

A

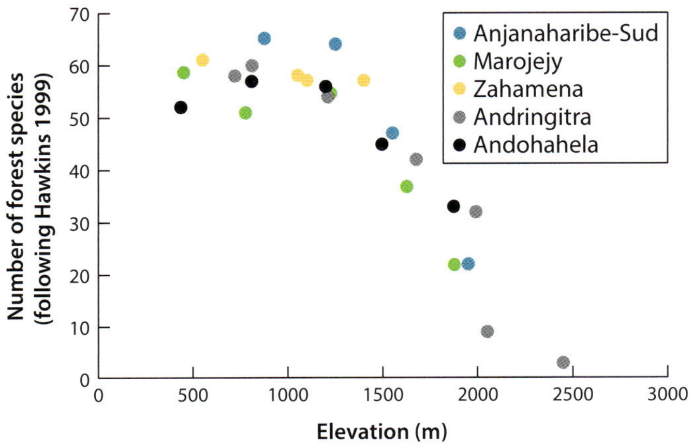

FIGURE 13.4 Variation in number of forest bird species with elevation at several sites in eastern Madagascar. The figure is based on A. Hawkins and Goodman (2003); some additional data have since been gathered, but the same general pattern holds today.

canopy (ground, understory, or bark) and to be insectivores rather than frugivores or nectarivores. For instance, lowland specialists are almost all insectivores, feeding on the ground, understory, and bark, as are high-altitude specialists, while elevational generalists are overwhelmingly canopy feeders. The fact that all the elevationally indeterminate species in Table 13.8 are ground, understory, or bark feeders suggests that they are also likely to be elevational specialists, a proposition to be tested based on more details of their natural history.

These ground-, understory-, and bark-foraging elevational specialists are more likely than canopy feeders to be endemic to moist evergreen forests (Table 13.8). This may be because they depend on a narrow range of ecological conditions in the forest understory compared to conditions in the canopy, which are more like those in other forest types. A greater tolerance by canopy species, compared to understory species, of a range of habitat types has also been noted in other tropical forests (Pearson 1975; Schemske and Brokaw 1981; A. Hawkins 1994a), perhaps because these species depend on dense masses of vegetation where insects can be found. These masses are found in secondary and degraded forest close to the ground and may be even more productive there than in primary or largely intact forest, as they have fewer secondary compounds to deter insects (Ganzhorn et al. 1990). In contrast, in non-rainforest habitats, the understory or ground-foraging niches, particularly if they depend on overhead cover or a deep litter layer, may not exist at all or be of very different ecological character.

Beside a large number of bird species with high adaptive capacity along the vertical gradient, which allows them to use all strata, casual observation has suggested that a number of species do show a stratum preference. However, knowledge of the vertical distribution patterns in lowland and medium-altitude moist evergreen forests is generally without quantification, except for the recent work of Faliarivola (2016) on the Masoala Peninsula in the northeast. She studied the vertical distribution of understory bird species as a function of forest structure and prey availability, by catching understory birds in mist nets and quantifying prey availability (arthropods) with Malaise traps. Among the bird species with sufficient individuals for analysis, five understory bird species—*Philepitta castanea* (Velvet *asity*), *Bernieria* sp., *Xanthomixis zosterops* (Spectacled Tetraka), *Terpsiphone mutata*, and *Cinnyris sovimanga*—uniformly

TABLE 13.8. Number of species displaying food and foraging location preferences within habitat groups of eastern Malagasy rainforests

HABITAT PREFERENCE	FORAGING SUBSTRATE				PRINCIPAL FOOD				TOTAL SPECIES; PERCENTAGE ENDEMICITY TO EASTERN MOIST EVERGREEN FORESTS
	G	U	C	B	I	V	F	N	
Lowland	3	2	2	2	7	1	1	0	9; 77%
Low–medium altitude	7	9	13	1	23	5	1	1	30; 22%
Medium altitude	0	0	1	0	0	0	0	1	1; 100%
High altitude	4	1	2	1	7	0	0	1	8; 87%
Generalist	6	6	14	0	16	1	7	2	26; 38%
Indeterminate	2	3	0	1	4	2	0	0	6; 66%
Total species	22	21	32	5	57	9	9	5	80
Percentage endemicity to eastern moist evergreen forests	65%	48%	19%	100%	55%	25%	10%	50%	44%

Source: Habitat preferences derived from A. Hawkins (1999), with revisions based on subsequent discoveries.
Notes: Foraging substrate: G, ground; U, understory; C, canopy; B, bark.
Food: I, invertebrates; V, vertebrates; F, fruits and seeds; N, nectar.

exploit all vertical strata of the lower understory. *Copsychus albospecularis* and *Oxylabes madagascariensis* (White-throated Oxylabes) prefer the lower portion of the understory stratum; *Accipiter francesiae*, *Schetba rufa*, and *Nelicurvius nelicourvi* prefer the middle portion of the understory stratum; and *Hypsipetes madagascariensis* occurs mainly in the upper portion of the understory stratum. Based on this study, the vertical distribution of birds among vegetation cover portions (layers or strata) is related to the vertical distribution of prey.

In the dry deciduous forests of the west and dry spiny thickets of the south, a study of vertical distribution of bird communities at three sites falling along a latitudinal gradient based mostly on forest transects found that some species are canopy specialists while others occur only in the lower strata of the forest or thicket structure (Rajaonarivelo et al. 2020). The middle stratum constitutes both a preferential vertical position for a number of species, and a contact zone for the lower and upper strata specialists where these species exploit the same feeding niches. The mid-story of dry deciduous forests contains the highest bird species richness and abundance. Nevertheless, the habitat structure of the dry spiny thickets differs from that of the dry deciduous forests, being more open and lower in stature, with the canopy having the highest species richness and the understory the highest abundance.

Wetland birds are distributed in different habitats according to their ecological requirements, ecomorphology, and biological cycles. Some species have restricted preferences, while others demonstrate broader adaptations and frequent different types of habitats or microhabitats. Migratory shorebirds such as members of the families Charadriidae and Scolopacidae, for example, exploit in particular tidal mudflats, muddy estuaries, mangroves, and sandbanks, all in coastal areas (Safford and Hawkins 2013; Rakotomavo 2017), while the majority of the Ardeidae, Anatidae, and Jacanidae, except for a relatively small portion of these families in mangroves and along the edges of mudflats in coastal areas, exploit mainly lakes, marshes, and degraded or modified wetlands such as rice fields (Safford and Hawkins 2013). Rahobilalaina (2017) found in the northwest that species diversity of the Ardeidae is higher in lakes than in the other wetland habitats of this area.

Community Structure and Foraging Guilds

Birds play important roles in ecosystem functioning, both as prey and as predators. Malagasy birds, especially passerines at different stages of their development cycle from egg to adult, are taken by a considerable diversity of predators. At least three endemic carnivorans of the family Eupleridae—*Cryptoprocta ferox* (see Gerber and Hawkins, pp. 1978–83), *Galidia elegans* (see Farris and Goodman, pp. 1989–92), and *Mungotictis decemlineata* (see Kappeler et al., pp. 1996–98)—are known to prey on birds (Goodman 2012). For example, birds constitute more than 32% of the diet of *C. ferox* in the upper sections of the Andringitra Massif (Goodman et al. 1997b). Snakes, including terrestrial and arboreal species, such as *Sanzinia madagascariensis* (family Sanziniidae) and *Madagascarophis colubrinus* (family Pseudoxyrophiidae), hunt sleeping birds (A. P. Raselimanana, unpublished data), and eggs in nests (M. J. Raherilalao, unpublished data). Raptors like *Haliaeetus vociferoides*, *Accipiter* spp., and *Buteo brachypterus* attack birds (among other prey) generally weighing less than their own body weight (see Rene de Roland and Thorstrom, pp. 1668–79), with different hunting techniques according to life-history traits (aerial, catching on branches or on the ground).

Given the rather small number of bird species on the island, it is perhaps not surprising that there is a certain unevenness in the distribution of species among foraging guilds as compared to other Old World tropical areas. In all Malagasy forest habitats, the dominant food source is insects, and there are very few frugivores. For instance, in moist evergreen forests, there are only 15 species among the 90 or so basically forest-dwelling species that have been recorded eating fruit, and only seven of these species appear to be essentially frugivorous. Few studies have investigated the roles of Malagasy frugivorous birds as dispersers or predators (see Razafindratsima et al., pp. 142–52). Two such birds are parrots (*Coracopsis* spp.), which eat a wide range of fruit; they are regarded as seed predators more than dispersers (they were excluded from a recent analysis of seed dispersal on Madagascar presumably for this reason; Albert-Daviaud et al. 2018), but they may disperse seeds of certain species (Böhning-Gaese et al. 1999; see Ekstrom and Safford, pp. 1682–86). Two others, *Alectroenas madagascariensis* and *Treron australis*, are pigeons, and again their roles as seed dispersers or seed predators (so-called fruit-pigeons worldwide may be either or both) are not well known. Limited evidence suggests that *Alectroenas* may be a more typical disperser, with a thin-walled gizzard as in *Ptilinopus* (Cowles and Goodwin 1959), the gut of which often allows seeds to pass intact (Cadow 1933). Field data are scanty but in one study, *A. madagascariensis* dispersed the seeds of most species it ate (Bollen et al. 2004a, 2004b). *Treron australis* appears to be, like its congeners elsewhere, a *Ficus* (fig) specialist; other *Treron* species have highly muscular gizzards and digest *Ficus* seeds as well as the pulp (Cowles and Goodwin 1959), suggesting a seed-predator role in the Malagasy species.

The three frugivorous members of the Passeriformes are seed dispersers. Two understory frugivores belonging to the genus *Philepitta* feed largely on Aphloiaceae, Myrsinaceae, Euphorbiaceae, Piperaceae, Melastomataceae, and Rubiaceae. Prum and Razafindratsita (pp. 1687–93) suggest a unique niche and critical role for *P. castanea* in seed dispersal and regeneration of plants in the forest understory; the same could be true of the poorly studied *P. schlegeli*. The third frugivore is *Hypsipetes madagascariensis*, a common forest and open-country bulbul feeding on a wide range of unrelated small fruit (including Arecaceae, Moraceae, Phytolaccaceae, Rubiaceae, Solanaceae, and Verbenaceae) (M. J. Raherilalao, unpublished data). However, there are more "occasional" frugivores: species generally considered insectivorous or granivorous that also feed occasionally on fruits; these include at least four species of Vangidae (see Schulenberg, pp. 1694–99), *Coracina cinerea* and *Zosterops maderaspatanus* (Goodman and Putnam 1996; Goodman et al. 1997a), and *Coua* species (below). Recent observation by the authors adds *Eremopterix hova* and *Saxicola torquatus*, two species of open habitats that consume fruits of *Phytolacca dodecandra* (Phytolaccaceae) around Ankazomivady in the Central Highlands, and two species of *Neomixis* that eat ripe fruits of *Commiphora simplicifolia* (Burseraceae) in the dry spiny thickets of Tsimanampesotse (M. J. Raherilalao, unpublished data). Finally, anecdotal observation of the common yet unstudied *Hartlaubius auratus* suggests a more important component of fruit in its diet (Rand 1936; Langrand 1990). However, there is no evidence regarding the ecological significance of frugivory by these species; in future studies, dispersal of non-native (such as *Psidium cattleianum*, *Lantana camara*, and *Clidemia hirta*, all often used by birds) as well as native plants needs to be considered.

Within Malagasy forests, even fewer species specialize on seeds. In total five species fall into this class, and only four (*Monias benschi*, *Mesitornis variegatus*, *Nesoenas picturatus*, and *Foudia omissa*) apparently consume seeds with any regularity. The second species seems to concentrate more on seeds in the cool dry austral winter, when fewer invertebrates are around (A. Hawkins 1994a).

There are few nectar specialists, chiefly two species of *Cinnyris* sunbirds and two species of *Neodrepanis* sunbird-asities, the latter remarkable in their convergence with the former: both genera have long, decurved bills and bright plumage, as well as brush tongues, but the two genera belong to different families. Unlike the sunbirds, the sunbird-asities are limited to moist evergreen forests (A. Hawkins et al. 1997).

Among the insectivorous species are the small leaf-gleaning genera, each with one to three species (as in *Neomixis* and *Newtonia*) in any forest habitat, and occurring essentially in the canopy or subcanopy. They show a marked convergence in body and beak morphology with Old World Sylviidae warblers. The tetrakas (Bernieridae) show a range of adaptations to different portions of this habitat (see Reddy et al., pp. 1707–11). *Bernieria* is a specialist on dense leaf clumps and insects hidden in shallow holes; *Xanthomixis zosterops* perches on narrow side stems of understory shrubs and takes small insects from overhanging leaves; *Crossleyia tenebrosa* and *X. apperti* are essentially terrestrial; and *X. cinereiceps* clings to moss covering trunks and stems with its long claws and finds invertebrates within it. *Oxylabes madagascariensis*, *C. xanthophrys*, and *Mystacornis crossleyi*, all relatively small insectivorous birds of the understory, are also terrestrial or nearly so.

There is a range of medium-size insectivores in the canopy and subcanopy in all Malagasy forests. They are mostly sally gleaners or gleaners, although they practice a range of variations on this theme. *Euryceros prevostii* and *Schetba rufa* are passive searchers, using prey movement as the primary detection cue while resting on perches (A. Hawkins 1994b), while a number of other species (e.g., *Coracina cinerea*, *Vanga curvirostris*, *Leptopterus viridis* [Chabert Vanga], *Calicalicus madagascariensis*, *C. rufocarpalis*, *Cyanolanius madagascarinus*, and *Tylas eduardi*) hunt for more or less concealed prey such as caterpillars and beetles. A number of marked specializations in the vangas make them an excellent example of adaptive radiation. *Falculea palliata* hunts for prey in deep crevices and under clumps of detritus, while *Hypositta corallirostris* (and *Randia pseudozosterops*, a member of the Bernieridae) hunt for bark-living invertebrates while creeping up or along bark. *Oriolia bernieri* and the three *Xenopirostris* species forage for concealed insects by tearing off loose bark or moss, snapping off the ends of dead twigs, and excavating detritus in epiphytic plants, tree ferns, and *Pandanus* trees (Yamagishi and Eguchi 1996). *Hartertula flavoviridis* and *Nelicurvius nelicourvi* use a modification of this technique to hunt for smaller prey. The former species specializes in opening up clumps of dead leaves in spider webs at the ends of thin branches, where its long claws, triangular bill, and long tail (for balance) help extract prey. A further set of foragers catches insects on the wing. This includes *Pseudobias wardi* (Ward's Vanga) and *Terpsiphone mutata*—the former a flycatcher-like vangid species and the latter a real paradise-flycatcher (Monarchidae)—and *Dicrurus forficatus* (Crested Drongo).

The raptors form a guild of their own, not particularly species rich and fairly typical of other tropical regions of the world (see Rene de Roland and Thorstrom, pp. 1668–79, for specific details on the diets of most species). *Haliaeetus vociferoides*, the largest extant bird of prey on Madagascar, feeds mainly on freshwater and coastal fish. There are three species of *Accipiter* on Madagascar: *A. henstii*, a very large goshawk that feeds on lemurs and a variety of bird species, most of moderate body size; *A. madagascariensis*, a medium-size bird specialist with long legs and extremely long middle toes; and *A. francesiae*, a small bird that specializes on reptiles and to some extent insects. *Buteo brachypterus* also appears to hunt birds frequently, while the enigmatic *Eutriorchis astur* takes many large reptiles, particularly chameleons. *Aviceda madagascariensis*, like other members of this genus, is partly crepuscular and feeds on frogs, lizards, and large insects. The nocturnal owls include a small *Otus* and *Athene superciliaris*, both essentially insectivorous, and three species that feed mainly on vertebrates, varying their diet according to availability of vertebrate prey. However, patterns emerge from diet studies: *Tyto soumagnei* appears to feed extensively on native small mammals (Goodman and Thorstrom 1998), while the African race of *T. alba* may largely consume introduced rats (Goodman et al. 1993a) but is notably adaptable; for example, the fruit bat *Rousettus madagascariensis* accounted for about 80% by number and biomass of total prey at a cave site near Antonibe, in western Madagascar (Goodman and Griffiths 2009). *Asio madagascariensis* eats whatever small mammals are available (Goodman et al. 1993b).

In the adaptive radiation of *Coua* species, the now extinct *C. delalandei* was apparently a snail specialist to the extent of using stones within its territory as anvils on which to smash the shells of these mollusks (Goodman and Wilmé 2003; Goodman 2013). The nine extant couas divide neatly into three species in the arboreal group and six in the terrestrial group. The former includes *C. cristata*, *C. caerulea*, and *C. verreauxi*, specialists on medium-size arboreal invertebrates and small vertebrates; they also consume fruit and even tree resin on occasion (Charles-Dominique 1976). Their adaptations to arboreality and agility in the trees are strongly reminiscent of African turacos. However, the diet of turacos contains a large percentage of fruit. Among the terrestrial *Coua* species, four are limited to the west and south, including the closely related *C. cursor* and *C. coquereli*. *Coua ruficeps*, a long-legged form, is often common in degraded western forest. *Coua gigas* is usually limited to dense, relatively intact vegetation, often in sympatry with *C. cursor* and *C. coquereli*, but feeding on distinctly larger prey (Urano et al. 1994). In the east, *C. reynaudii* tends to be more common at higher elevations and in dense vegetation, occasionally climbing in vegetation, while *C. serriana* is limited to lowlands and is strictly terrestrial.

SEASONAL PATTERNS

Breeding and Molting Seasons in Land Birds

Data regarding the breeding seasons of the birds of Madagascar refer to geographically separate localities and are dispersed throughout the vast body of published literature. Safford and Hawkins (2013) have compiled available information species by species, but these data have never been analyzed for the whole country. For species with less-clear breeding seasons, a compilation of countrywide data may seem to suggest year-round breeding, when closer study at a given location will reveal seasonal patterns.

In the light of these pitfalls, the study and analysis undertaken by Appert (2011) is unique, bringing together his decades of information on the lower Mangoky region of the southwest, for 98 breeding bird species (almost half the national total). Predominantly insectivorous forest and grassland birds, those that also took small reptiles such as chameleons (including *Leptosomus* and *Vanga curvirostris*), and raptors usually bred in the summer rains, when the availability of insects, and hence presumably other resources, was greatest. Granivores and grassland birds often bred somewhat later (December to March) than insectivorous forest birds, as grass regrew. Terrestrial nonforest species had extended or irregular breeding seasons, while waterbirds often bred toward the end of southern summer and the beginning of southern winter, when the wet-season vegetation provided optimal feeding conditions.

A simple overview of other data supports the idea that for most forest birds, the breeding season coincides with the start of summer rains, when food resources, particularly insects, start to increase in abundance. This means that song and display usually start in September or October, reaching a peak in mid-November, and many birds have nests and young in December. This pattern may be disrupted by prolonged early rain in the moist evergreen forests, causing a reduction particularly in song in October and November. That said, the actual breeding season for many birds is very long, and nesting attempts for many species go on until May, possibly associated with multiple broods per breeding season or nest predation. Some birds start their breeding season unusually early; for instance, *Oxylabes madagascariensis* may have nests and eggs in August (Safford and Duckworth 1990), while others are habitually late; the peak period for *Bernieria madagascariensis* song may be in January, and juveniles are rarely seen before March.

Foudia madagascariensis, having a wide distribution and a conspicuous reddish breeding plumage in the male, provides an easily observed case of variable timing of breeding. In Antananarivo, most birds start to acquire breeding colors by the end of October. Near the coast and in the north, males start going red later, in January or February, and nests may be observed in May. In the west, around wetlands such as Lake Bemamba, birds have been observed in breeding plumage in August. By contrast, *F. omissa* seems to be more regular in its timing, acquiring breeding plumage in September or October and nesting in November or December (A. Hawkins and Goodman 1999).

For other birds the breeding season is surprisingly variable. The open-country insectivore *Cisticola cherina* appears to breed year-round, with no peak evident; however, in Appert's (2011) study in the Mangoky River valley, most bred between December and March, coinciding with fresh grass growth. There is some evidence that *Monias benschi* does not have a fixed breeding season but responds to rain at whatever time of year it falls; nests and young have been found in nearly every month (Seddon 2001). Wetland birds, particularly colonially nesting ardeids, often breed from October to June, with a peak for many species (for instance *Ardea cinerea* and *A. humbloti*) toward the end of the rainy season in March.

For most Malagasy species, a complete molt follows the breeding season (i.e., a prebasic molt), so by April or May most adults are replacing flight and tail feathers. There is little information on species-specific molt patterns, as few netting studies have been conducted at the appropriate time of year. A notable exception is male *Philepitta castanea*, which entirely lacks the pre-breeding (or pre-alternate) molt (Salomonsen 1965; Prum and Razafindratsita 1997; also see Prum and Razafindratsita, pp. 1687–93) and gains its pure black breeding plumage by loss through abrasion of the yellow tips of the body feathers. The other three species of Philepittidae have the more normal molt pattern including the partial pre-breeding (or pre-alternate) molt. These, and a few other species such as *Foudia* and *Cinnyris sovimanga*, have a different, duller body plumage after the prebasic molt, sometimes referred to as "eclipse" plumage.

In some species, such as the vangids *Schetba rufa* and *Xenopirostris polleni*, and the Philepittidae, males show delayed plumage maturation, involving an intermediate phase between the female-like juvenile plumage and the male adult plumage. In *Schetba* at least, the intermediate plumage is associated with cooperative breeding, being limited to helper males (Yamagishi et al. 1995). For *Terpsiphone mutata*, definitive adult plumage in males is not acquired until at least three years of age, and four different "transitional" phases can be recognized among younger males (see Mulder and Ramiarison, pp. 1700–1704). Delayed plumage maturation is not necessarily a consequence of developmental constraints and is more likely a strategy to maximize reproductive success in circumstances where young adults cannot effectively compete with older adults for limited resources, particularly breeding opportunities (G. Hawkins et al. 2012).

The female *Coracopsis vasa* has a bizarre "molt" of the head feathers during the breeding season—virtually all the feathers fall out and the skin turns orange. This is apparently associated with a form of subcutaneous vascularization (Wilkinson and Birkhead 1995) and coincides with the female's song period after egg laying, which may function to attract provisioning males as part of this species' unique breeding behavior (see Ekstrom and Safford, pp. 1682–86).

Seasonal Movements and Migrations

A few species migrate to Madagascar to breed. *Eurystomus glaucurus*, *Cuculus rochii*, *Glareola ocularis*, and *Ardeola idae* arrive on Madagascar in September or October to commence reproduction and leave in April or May when this has been completed. Of the four, *Eurystomus glaucurus* is the earliest, with individuals sometimes turning up in August. Not all *Cuculus* individuals leave Madagascar—some have been seen regularly in western Madagascar in May and June, and singing individuals have been recorded in eastern Madagascar in July. An unknown but perhaps considerable number of *A. idae* do not leave Madagascar (Ó Marcaigh et al. 2020; Rabarisoa et al. 2020), with presence in the colder months in the west perhaps masked until recently by the similarity of the commoner resident *A. ralloides*. *Glareola ocularis* usually breeds in eastern Madagascar in November to January and moves across the Central Highlands, assembling in large groups on western rivers after the breeding season (ZICOMA 1999) before departing for Africa. *Phedina borbonica* also migrates to Africa but seems to be rare there, and birds are present on Madagascar year-round (internal migrations on Madagascar are also suspected); the proportion that migrate and the strategy behind this are not understood.

Some species appear to move elevationally, usually descending in the cool season. *Neodrepanis hypoxantha* (Yellow-bellied Sunbird-asity) often appears somewhat below its usual high-elevation range in the cool season (A. Hawkins et al. 1997), although it is not clear whether this relates to post-fledging dispersal of juveniles or a genuine elevational movement. It is also possible that the seasonal presence and absence of *Mesitornis unicolor* and *Atelornis pittoides* is linked to elevational movements. The former has been suggested to be absent from some low-lying areas of moist evergreen forests in the warm season, while it is present or at least more visible in the same areas in April and May (Evans et al. 1996). *Atelornis pittoides* may even make larger-scale movements, as it has been recorded in several places apparently as a vagrant: in Antananarivo in the last century (Dee 1986) and at Nosy Mangabe (where it does not normally occur) in 1988 (Safford and Duckworth 1990). In addition, it occurs in isolated forest fragments in the Ambohitantely protected area (Langrand and Wilmé 1997), and in the isolated moist evergreen forest on Montagne d'Ambre, which it might have colonized through dispersive movements.

Leptosomus discolor appears to make seasonal movements, if its sporadic presence in Antananarivo (generally in April and October) is any indication. However, the direction of movement is unclear, and perhaps this species wanders erratically. *Merops superciliosus* certainly makes seasonal movements, sometimes in significant numbers, but whether individuals cross the Mozambique Channel is unclear, although large groups of this species, up to 1000, spend the cool months (June to August) in mangroves in western Madagascar. The apparent sporadic presence of *Neodrepanis coruscans* in Ambohitantely (Andrianarimisa 1995), 200 km from the nearest source populations, suggests that even this tiny species is capable of significant dispersal.

The number of extralimitally breeding species that regularly spend their nonbreeding season on Madagascar is surprisingly low. They can be divided into land birds, waterbirds (of inland waters and coasts), and seabirds; in each of these three categories, there are also vagrants, or species of irregular occurrence that are often far off course from their intended routes.

The near absence of migratory land-bird visitors is a remarkable feature of Madagascar's avifauna, in relation to the large-scale movements and thus large numbers of migrant visitors throughout other continental areas of the New and Old Worlds. Whereas over 100 species of migratory land birds are known from Mozambique, Madagascar's nearest neighboring country on the African mainland (BirdLife International 2020a), there are only two regular nonbreeding terrestrial visitors to Madagascar: *Falco concolor* and *F. eleonorae* (Sooty and Eleonora's Falcons). The former breeds in northeast Africa and the Middle East, the latter on islands in the Mediterranean Sea and Atlantic Ocean off northwest Africa. Almost the entire world population of both species spends the boreal winter on Madagascar. *Falco concolor* is most common during the warm season on Madagascar in the west and south, where it is best known around Morondava and a few favored locations in Antananarivo; it sometimes forms flocks, formerly of over 100, now rather fewer (see Rene de Roland and Thorstrom, pp. 1668–79). A third nonbreeding terrestrial visitor is *Hirundo rustica* (Barn Swallow), although it is still rare and perhaps best considered a relatively frequent vagrant.

Nonbreeding waterbirds are dominated by shorebirds or "waders," including fairly large concentrations (in approximate order of abundance) of some northern Palearctic shorebirds such as *Charadrius leschenaultii*, *C. hiaticula*, *Numenius phaeopus*, *Arenaria interpres*, *Calidris ferruginea*, *C. alba*, *Xenus cinereus*, *Actitis hypoleucos*, and *Tringa nebularia*. Other species such as *Limosa lapponica*, *Charadrius mongolus*, *Calidris minuta*, and *T. stagnatilis* are more sporadic. All occur most commonly on the west coast, where their preferred intertidal habitat is extensive, particularly in areas such as the bays of Ambavanankarana, Mahajamba, and Bombetoka and the estuaries of the Mahavavy, Tsiribihina, and Mangoky Rivers (Safford and Hawkins 2013; see Young et al., pp. 1627–36). For most of these Palearctic species, the Malagasy wintering population seems to be a small percentage of that in the African-Eurasian flyway, although numbers of *Calidris ferruginea* may be significant (Dodman et al. 1998). Coastal species such as *Dromas ardeola* (Crab-plover, Dromadidae) and *Thalasseus bengalensis* (Lesser Crested Tern, Laridae), which breed along the eastern coast of Africa and in the Red Sea and Arabian Gulf regions, occur in internationally significant numbers: groups of 500+ *D. ardeola* at many sites during the warm season, and flocks of 5000+ *T. bengalensis* at several sites, notably near upwellings around Cap Saint André and Nosy Be (ZICOMA 1999).

Pelagic (occurring in the open sea) seabirds have received relatively little attention around Madagascar, but recent research combining increased field observation with satellite tracking technology has added a range of species originating from all the world's oceans, with the waters south of Madagascar found to be most important; these, including presumed vagrants, are reviewed by Le Corre et al. (see pp. 1637–50).

With increasing observer effort, there have been some recent records of both passerine and nonpasserine land-bird and waterbird vagrants from both Africa and the Palearctic, as well as seabirds from all quarters, and new species continue to be added; these are indicated as vagrants in Table 13.1. It is certain, given the frequency with which other Palearctic species occur in Seychelles (Skerrett and Disley 2011), that further migratory species will be recorded as vagrants.

BREEDING SOCIAL ORGANIZATION

Malagasy birds show a wide array of social systems, especially related to breeding, many of which are far from clear. Perhaps most land birds show at least outward signs of monogamy, if the lack of plumage color differences between the sexes (sexual dichromatism) is anything to go by; conversely, polygamy may be associated with the competitive sex (often male) being larger and more ornate than its mate, although there are numerous exceptions, and sexual dimorphism in the form of strong dichromatism rather than size difference may be more associated with extra-bond paternity (Owens and Hartley 1998). Monogamy has been confirmed in enough Malagasy bird species, by direct observation at nests, to be seen as the "default" breeding system, but a wide range of exceptions exists. Few species have been examined for extra-bond paternity, but in the well-studied monogamous *Terpsiphone mutata*, extra-pair fertilizations may occur at high frequency at Bealoka in the extreme southeast, concerning nearly 50% of all nestlings (n = 686) and affecting two-thirds of broods (n = 271) (see Mulder and Ramiarison, pp. 1700–1704).

In the Malagasy vangids, sexes are similar in some species, but there is slight to strong sexual dichromatism in others, and again, most are socially monogamous. *Mystacornis* males are fiercely territorial, to the extent of attacking tape recorders replaying song, so it would be reasonable to assume that competition between males occurs. The gregarious *Falculea palliata* is polyandrous: the female copulates with more than one male, and males have a dominance hierarchy, as several participate in nest construction, incubation, and nestling care, but the socially dominant male contributes the most (Nakamura et al. 2001a). At least three species—*Leptopterus chabert*, *Artamella viridis* (White-headed Vanga), and *Schetba occidentalis*—often breed cooperatively, and *Oriolia bernieri* may do so too. The best studied of these is *S. occidentalis*, although detailed information on it comes from a single site, Ampijoroa (Yamagishi et al. 1995; Eguchi et al. 2002, 2009; Yamagishi 2005; publications refer to *S. rufa*, pre-dating the treatment, adopted here, of the western *Schetba* birds as a separate species from the eastern). At this site, the average group size is 2.6, and breeding units may consist of a pair only or include one or two helpers, usually the sons of the breeding pair they are helping. Most young females disperse from their natal territory, whereas males are philopatric and do not breed in the first year after hatching; most remain as helpers on natal or (less often) non-natal territories. Helpers contribute to antipredator and territorial defense, nest building, incubation, and provisioning of nestlings, but the benefits are not simple: overall, helping is not considered to enhance reproductive success (Eguchi et al. 2009). There may be other direct benefits to male helpers, even if the male does not actively "help": a young male remaining in his natal territory may avoid harassment by other territorial individuals, increase his probability of territory acquisition and of copulation with unrelated breeding females, and gain indirect fitness benefits by lightening his mother's labor.

Many other common Malagasy birds exhibit marked sexual dichromatism (e.g., *Leptosomus discolor*, *Monticola* spp., *Nelicurvius* spp., *Foudia* spp.), which is compatible with a range of breeding strategies in addition to simple monogamous pairs, including polyandry, polygyny, and cooperative breeding. *Foudia madagascariensis* is usually considered monogamous but may also be polygynous, one male pairing with up to five females in a season (Rasamison and Andrianarimisa 2013); the same may be true of *F. omissa* and *Nelicurvius sakalava* (see Craig, pp. 1714–15). Field and genetic research on other sexually dichromatic species, in particular the most distinctive endemic species such as *L. discolor*, might produce some very interesting surprises.

Sexual monochromatism does not necessarily imply monogamous pairs without helpers. Multiple *Xanthomixis cinereiceps* adults, with no known sexual dimorphism, have been recorded at an active nest, suggestive of cooperative breeding (A. Hawkins et al. 1998), and the wetland-living *Haliaeetus vociferoides* is basically monogamous but often has the help of one or two extra-pair adults or juvenile birds in breeding activities; this species is sexually monochromatic but dimorphic in size (female is larger) (see Rene de Roland and Thorstrom, pp. 1668–79). *Centropus toulou*, also sexually monochromatic but with larger females, probably displays polyandrous behavior if the example of the related *C. grillii* is anything to go by (Andersson 1995; Slotow 1996).

Philepitta castanea, uniquely among Malagasy birds based on current information, has a polygynous lek breeding system (see Prum and Razafindratsita, pp. 1687–93): males occupy non-resource-based "lek" territories defended from other males, where they perform elaborate secondary sexual displays to attract females; these display territories lack the food and nest site resources necessary for reproduction. This was observed at Ranomafana, yet elsewhere males were seen participating in nest construction, an unexpected although not incompatible behavior in a lek species, so there may be plasticity in the breeding system, and such a possibility could apply in other species and their respective breeding systems.

Three Malagasy species, each in a separate family in the Charadriiformes, *Turnix nigricollis*, *Rostratula benghalensis*, and *Actophilornis albinucha*, show reversed gender roles in which the female is most concerned with competing for mates and may lead territorial and courtship activities, while the male incubates and cares for the offspring. For the first two species, the female is strikingly more strongly patterned and brighter than the male, as well as somewhat larger. *Turnix nigricollis* was the subject of some of the first studies on the breeding of the Turnicidae, carried out in captivity and helping to reveal details of the gender role reversal for which the family is now well known (summarized in Safford 2013g): in line with her brighter plumage, the female leads territorial, courtship, and most nesting activities, and the breeding system may be serially polyandrous. A similar situation exists in the widespread, nonendemic *R. benghalensis*, although it has not been studied on Madagascar; for *A. albinucha*, dimorphism is most notable in the larger size of the female (see D'Urban Jackson et al., pp. 1666–68).

Sexual roles are further stretched beyond birds' usual limits in the polygynandrous breeding system of *Coracopsis vasa* (see Ekstrom and Safford, pp. 1682–86): females copulate with at least five different males, and most or all broods are of mixed paternity with up to three fathers. Males do not visit nests but may feed some females (which come off their eggs or chicks) in between copulating with others. Females defend a territory around the nest from conspecific females and sing to attract males to feed them, suggesting strong female-female competition for food.

Monias benschi shows a social system of surpassing interest, as it lives in groups of up to 10 individuals, dominated by a heavy female (see Hawkins et al., pp. 1653–57). The group sings in a chorus, to which the contribution of a given individual seems to be linked to the individual's status in the group and its potential sexual interest in members of adjacent groups. It is known that more than one female may lay in the same nest, and more than one male tends the young. The other mesite species appear to have a less unusual breeding system; at least, *Mesitornis variegatus* does not breed cooperatively although juveniles stay with adults for extended periods (up to 13 months) after fledging and are cared for by both adults, which in almost all cases are the parents (Gamero et al. 2013).

A range of hypotheses concerning breeding systems have been tested on the Malagasy breeding species of *Charadrius* plovers: Zefania and Székely (see pp. 1660–66) have shown how subtle differences in morphology may hide very significant variation in breeding systems, from low mate fidelity, uniparental care, and a flexible breeding system (i.e., often polygamy) in *C. pecuarius*, to high mate fidelity, biparental care, and social monogamy in *C. thoracicus* and *C. marginatus*.

Finally, a very different breeding strategy in Malagasy birds is interspecific brood parasitism, in which the female (the parasite) lays her eggs in the nest of another species and so passes the cost of rearing her offspring on to another individual (the host). This is known in several clades of birds worldwide, but the only Malagasy brood parasites are the two cuckoos, the common *Cuculus rochii* with a wide range of small passerine hosts, and the rare *Pachycoccyx audeberti*, the hosts of which are unknown but may be Vangidae; the other members of the Cuculidae are nest builders (Safford 2013h).

Many species maintain what appear to be family groups during the post-breeding season. This behavior is particularly marked in forest birds. *Mesitornis variegatus* lives in near-exclusive family territories during the nonbreeding season (A. Hawkins 1994a), with the young from the last breeding season. In mixed-species flocks, birds that appear to move in family groups include species of *Neomixis*, *Bernieria*, and *Xanthomixis*, and several different Vangidae species. Some of these species (e.g., *Calicalicus madagascariensis*) appear to maintain nonbreeding territories but join mixed-species flocks when they pass through their territory.

Very few other Malagasy birds have been studied sufficiently for detailed conclusions about breeding systems to be drawn. Assumptions may prove incorrect: *Anas melleri*, long incorrectly considered an island form of *A. platyrhynchos* (Mallard), has now been shown to be a species with long pair bonds and strong territoriality (Young 1995; see "Phylogenetics, Phylogeography, and Systematics" section above). While the breeding systems of Malagasy birds and their consequences or associated traits are increasingly well described, the selective pressures favoring them are generally still unclear. As Ekstrom et al. (2007: 313) pointed out for *Coracopsis vasa*, which is perhaps the strangest of them all, "some sort of ecological constraint, such as food availability, may be important," but the ultimate drivers remain largely unknown.

CONSERVATION OF MALAGASY BIRDS

Given the heavy reliance of much of the Malagasy avifauna on forest habitats and the rapid recent decline in primary forest (Vieilledent et al. 2018), it is not surprising that many species are considered threatened. The 2020 revision of the IUCN Red List for birds by BirdLife International (2020a), summarized in Table 13.9, shows that 38 species on Madagascar are considered threatened with global extinction, with two species Critically Endangered, 17 Endangered, and 19 Vulnerable; another 13 are in the Near Threatened category, suggesting that if threats continue at present rates, those species too will soon become threatened. Two species were recently removed from the list of threatened species: *Tachybaptus rufolavatus* is now accepted as Extinct, while the formerly Vulnerable *Crossleyia tenebrosa* is now treated as Data Deficient; this does not mean its status has improved, rather that it has been appreciated that the quantitative Red List criteria cannot be applied because of the lack of reliable information.

Nine of 51 threatened and near-threatened species are nonbreeding visitors, including four species of seabirds using Malagasy waters (see Le Corre et al., pp. 1637–50), and four waterbirds using the coastal wetlands (see Young et al., pp. 1627–36). The conservation importance of Madagascar is usually (and reasonably) framed in terms of resident endemic species, but this shows the importance of the island's coastal and marine zones for other species; their conservation is discussed in the respective contributions to this chapter. The ninth threatened nonbreeding species is *Falco concolor*, of which most of the world population spends part of the year on Madagascar (see Rene de Roland and Thorstrom, pp. 1668–79).

Although forest loss certainly contributes greatly to the threat of extinction of Malagasy birds (discussed below), it is striking that both of the species considered Critically Endangered and 10 of the 17 Endangered species are waterbirds. In addition, all four of Madagascar's endemic shorebird species are Vulnerable. *Aythya innotata* is one of the world's rarest birds, although this is an improvement over its Possibly Extinct status before its rediscovery in 2006 (see Rene de Roland and Young, pp. 1650–53); *Haliaeetus vociferoides* is one of the world's rarest raptors (see Rene de Roland and Thorstrom, pp. 1668–79). *Anas bernieri*, *Zapornia olivieri*, and *Threskiornis bernieri* may have extremely low population levels, and other wetland species have exhibited very marked recent population declines. The overarching reason for the high threat categories of waterbirds is the destruction and "profound and pervasive" degradation of wetlands, especially freshwater (Bamford et al. 2017; see Young et al., pp. 1627–36). This is exacerbated for many bird species by unconstrained and increasing exploitation for food by people; in the east, especially at Lake Alaotra, use of fine-mesh nylon nets, which trap and drown diving waterbirds, delivered probably the final blow to *Tachybaptus rufolavatus* (A. Hawkins et al. 2000) but also affects other species. Conversion of wetlands into agricultural areas for growing rice and other crops is extensive throughout the island wherever this habitat occurs.

Rather in contrast, forest birds in the higher threat categories are those that are present in threatened forest types. The most threatened moist forest type is lowland forest, and species that are limited to this habitat are thus considered the most likely to be threatened, particularly if they are also restricted to certain portions of the rainforest belt, or are present at low population densities. Such is the case for *Euryceros prevostii* and *Oriolia bernieri*; both are Endangered, as is *Eutriorchis astur*, found over a relatively wide area from Tsaratanàna in the north to at least Ranomafana in the south, but probably very thinly distributed, resulting in what must be a small population. This group of species seems particularly at risk in the longer term from the prospect of climate change entirely removing their habitat. Several other moist forest species with some limitation on range or population, such as *Brachypteracias leptosomus* (Short-legged Ground-roller), *Geobiastes squamiger* (Scaly Ground-roller), *Neodrepanis hypoxantha*, and *Newtonia fanovanae* (Red-tailed Newtonia), are fairly common in some areas but are considered threatened.

Several species of the western dry forests and dry spiny thickets are also threatened by habitat loss, including the effects of fire. The rarest, and the only one currently treated as Endangered, is *Xenopirostris damii*, known from only a few sites; it is a specialist on insects in dead wood and its densities even in intact forest appear quite low.

Several species were entirely missing from the national protected area system before its recent expansion, and wetland species

TABLE 13.9. **Threatened Malagasy birds**

CRITICALLY ENDANGERED
Aythya innotata, Madagascar Pochard
Haliaeetus vociferoides, Madagascar Fish-eagle
ENDANGERED
Anas melleri, Meller's Duck
A. bernieri, Madagascar Teal
Tachybaptus pelzelnii, Madagascar Grebe
Sarothrura watersi, Slender-billed Flufftail
Zapornia olivieri, Sakalava Rail
Thalassarche carteri, Indian Yellow-nosed Albatross
Pterodroma baraui, Barau's Petrel
Threskiornis bernieri, Madagascar Sacred Ibis
Ardeola idae, Madagascar Pond-heron
Ardea humbloti, Madagascar Heron
Actophilornis albinucha, Madagascar Jacana
Eutriorchis astur, Madagascar Serpent-eagle
Circus macrosceles, Madagascar Harrier
Euryceros prevostii, Helmet Vanga
Xenopirostris damii, Van Dam's Vanga
Oriolia bernieri, Bernier's Vanga
Monticola erythronotus, Amber Mountain Rock-thrush[1]
VULNERABLE
Mesitornis variegatus, White-breasted Mesite
M. unicolor, Brown Mesite
Monias benschi, Subdesert Mesite
Rallus madagascariensis, Madagascar Rail
Diomedea exulans, Wandering Albatross
Procellaria aequinoctialis, White-chinned Petrel
Charadrius thoracicus, Madagascar Plover
Gallinago macrodactyla, Madagascar Snipe
Glareola ocularis, Madagascar Pratincole
Tyto soumagnei, Red Owl
Accipiter henstii, Henst's Goshawk
VULNERABLE
Brachypteracias leptosomus, Short-legged Ground-roller
Geobiastes squamiger, Scaly Ground-roller
Uratelornis chimaera, Long-tailed Ground-roller
Falco concolor, Sooty Falcon
Neodrepanis hypoxantha, Yellow-bellied Sunbird-asity
Newtonia fanovanae, Red-tailed Newtonia
Calicalicus rufocarpalis, Red-shouldered Vanga
Xanthomixis apperti, Appert's Tetraka
NEAR THREATENED
Phoeniconaias minor, Lesser Flamingo
Mentocrex beankaensis, Tsingy Wood-rail
Lophotibis cristata, Madagascar Crested Ibis
Numenius arquata, Eurasian Curlew
Limosa lapponica, Bar-tailed Godwit
Calidris ferruginea, Curlew Sandpiper
Accipiter madagascariensis, Madagascar Sparrowhawk
Atelornis crossleyi, Rufous-headed Ground-roller
Philepitta schlegeli, Schlegel's Asity
Xenopirostris polleni, Pollen's Vanga
Hartertula flavoviridis, Wedge-tailed Tetraka
Xanthomixis cinereiceps, Gray-crowned Tetraka
Crossleyia xanthophrys, Madagascar Yellowbrow
DATA DEFICIENT[2]
Crossleyia tenebrosa Dusky Tetraka

Source: See BirdLife International (2020a) for definitions of threat categories.
Note: English names have been modified in line with those used elsewhere in this volume.
[1] See text and Reddy et al. (p. 1707–11) regarding the uncertain taxonomic status of this form.
[2] Data Deficient is not a true threat category, as it admits to the possibility that the taxon may prove not to be threatened.

(not only of birds) were formerly very poorly represented. Several phases of fieldwork and desk study to identify and prioritize sites for conservation included the identification of Important Bird and Biodiversity Areas (ZICOMA 1999, 2001); with integration of information on other taxa of fauna and flora, a wider prioritization exercise led to a remarkable expansion of the protected area network (Goodman et al. 2018). Among the many new areas and habitats now included are Mikea and Ranobe PK32 in the southwestern dry spiny thickets, and some remarkable landscapes containing wetlands, forests, coasts, and other habitats as well as human populations in Mahavavy Kinkony, Menabe Antimena, and Mangoky Ihotry (Goodman et al. 2018). The recent protection of some truly large moist forest blocks, such as COMATSA Nord and Sud, Makira, Ankeniheny-Zahamena, and Ambositra-Vondrozo, adding to the longer-established protected areas such as Masoala, Marojejy, Zahamena, Andringitra, and Andohahela, is notable; several of these sites are contiguous, an important factor in ensuring persistence of populations of birds and other species.

While some important sites remain unprotected and need protection, the main challenge to the conservation of Malagasy birds is arguably the sustainable management and conservation of these sites and the species they support. These topics are discussed elsewhere (see Jones et al., pp. 2130–40). However, even if habitat protection can be achieved, direct threats are causing mortality or reduced productivity in birds, and this particularly affects waterbirds (although forest birds are hunted too; Campera et al. 2019). None of the threatened waterbird species are known to have stable, fully protected, self-sustaining populations; for these species, locally appropriate habitat management schemes that protect their nesting and feeding habitats are vital. This has been shown to be possible, with clear successes for the two Critically Endangered species—but not to the extent that their status has been "downlisted" to a lower threat category. If such measures are not greatly expanded and replicated soon, then several of these species look set to follow *T. rufolavatus* to extinction in the next few decades.

For birds and other plant and animal species, conservation is not about only threatened organisms; common species need to remain in a healthy environment. For many people on Madagascar and elsewhere in the world, it is generally birds that they see, and as such, birds are the most frequent reminder of the beauty and wonder of the natural world. Birds also have enormous ecological value in the ecosystems they inhabit, including aspects important to people. Birds are more widespread than most animal groups on Madagascar; a rich selection can be found even in and around cities such as Antananarivo, and they provide opportunities to advocate and promote nature conservation to all. These too can be—alongside the rare and spectacular—flagships for Madagascar's threatened biodiversity.

FINAL REMARKS

Remarkable progress has been made in the past 20 or so years since the publication of A. Hawkins and Goodman (2003), in the precursor of this book, regarding information on the natural history of Malagasy birds. Thanks to a range of phylogenetic, phylogeographic, and systematic studies, the uniqueness and extraordinary biological importance of the birds of Madagascar have become not just clearer but also far better understood. Renewed research by national and foreign ornithologists has made considerable strides in understanding the natural history of the island's birds (Figure 13.5). Answers to questions concerning the effects of forest loss and fragmentation, and the ecology, phylogeny, origin, and phylogeography of the Malagasy avifauna are progressing at a remarkable pace, and it is certain that some details presented in this introduction and the subsequent contributions in this chapter will be obsolete before or soon after this book is published.

Subject editors: Roger J. Safford and Steven M. Goodman

FIGURE 13.5 **The past couple of decades have seen the emergence of numerous Malagasy ornithologists who are actively involved in field research and different forms of bird monitoring. A) Field agents of Asity Madagascar studying *Sarothrura watersi* (Slender-billed Flufftail) in the Torotorofotsy Marsh; B) Rivo Rabarisoa handling *Gallinago macrodactyla* (Madagascar Snipe) in the Torotorofotsy Marsh; C) group conducting ecological monitoring of the waterbirds of the Mahavavy Kinkony protected area; from left to right, Noelson Tsaradia, Jeÿnne Evah Rahariniaina Mirana (largely hidden), and Marie Jeanne Raherilalao; and D) Noelson Tsaradia and Rivo Rabarisoa measuring eggs for a study of nesting shorebirds in the Namakia sugarcane area near Lake Kinkony.** (PHOTOS A and C by R. Rabarisoa, B by Bruno Raveloson, and D by P. Laurit.)

THE IMPACT OF HABITAT CHANGE ON MADAGASCAR'S BIRDS

C. J. Gardner

Madagascar is a top global priority for the conservation of birds, largely because of its high levels of endemism at the species and, in particular, higher taxonomic levels (Jetz et al. 2014). Approximately 41% of regularly occurring species are found nowhere else in the world, and two orders (Mesitornithiformes and Leptosomiformes, each containing a single family), three further endemic families (Bernieridae, Brachypteraciidae, and Philepittidae), and 32 genera are also restricted to the Malagasy Region, most to Madagascar itself (see Safford et al., pp. 1553–602).

Ensuring the conservation of this unique avifauna requires an understanding of species sensitivity to habitat change, for three main reasons: 1) habitat loss is the greatest driver of biodiversity declines across the country (Vieilledent et al. 2018), and the majority of endemic species are habitat specialists dependent on native forests or wetlands (Safford and Hawkins 2013); 2) further habitat change will occur even within sites set aside for conservation, because many of the country's new generation of protected areas are designated as multiple-use sites in which resource extraction activities are permitted and capacity to enforce regulations is low (Gardner 2009; Gardner et al. 2018; Goodman et al. 2018); and 3) habitat change disproportionately impacts the most valuable components of the bird fauna, because the sensitivity of forest birds to habitat modifications is thought to be related to their level of taxonomic endemism: in other words, endemic species are in general more sensitive to habitat change than nonendemics, but members of endemic genera and families are more sensitive still (Wilmé 1996).

However, while some important research on this topic has been conducted over the last two decades and since the review by Goodman and Raherilalao (2003), the available information lacks synthesis. Here, I review the available evidence on bird responses to habitat change, focusing primarily on forest habitats (in which most research has been concentrated), and then on wetland transformation. For further information on the impacts of forest fragmentation on other vertebrate groups on the island, see Riemann et al. (pp. 1336–41) for amphibians, Crottini et al. (pp. 1446–52) for reptiles, and Steffens et al. (pp. 1812–17) for mammals.

DEFORESTATION AND FOREST DEGRADATION

Although the extent of original forest cover is debated (see Lehmann et al., pp. 152–68), Madagascar's forests and thickets have been cleared for agricultural expansion over centuries and now cover less than 15% of the island (Vieilledent et al. 2018). In addition to the reduction in forest area, deforestation results in the fragmentation of remaining forests, which can reduce the viability of the remaining biodiversity by reducing the area of habitat patches, increasing their isolation, and increasing edge effects (Haddad et al. 2015). As a result, many forest fragments are too small to meet the ecological requirements of some of their former constituent species, and the isolation and limited dispersal ability of the remaining species prevent genetic interchange between populations. Edge effects occur when differences in abiotic or other conditions render forest edges less suitable for sensitive species; such effects can be expected to be a particular problem on Madagascar, where 46% of remaining forest is within 100 m of the forest edge (Vieilledent et al. 2018). Beyond the problem of deforestation, many remaining forests are used for economic activities such as selective logging, charcoal production, livestock foraging, and the collection of nontimber forest products (Fritz-Vietta et al. 2011), which may alter the structure and composition of the vegetation. I term such impacts "forest degradation."

IMPACTS OF DEFORESTATION: FOREST AND OPEN-AREA INTERFACE

The impact of deforestation on bird communities depends largely on the fate of deforested landscapes. In some regions, recently deforested areas near deforestation fronts may comprise a mosaic of smallholder agricultural zones with isolated trees, regenerating scrubland, and secondary forest (e.g., Martin et al. 2009; Gardner et al. 2016). However, repeated clearance or burning drastically reduces vegetation complexity, so most deforested areas comprise species-poor grasslands or thickets of non-native plants.

Little was known on Madagascar about the impacts of deforestation until recently because biodiversity survey work in terrestrial areas was rarely carried out away from forests (Martin et al. 2012), at least in part because grassland areas were previously considered to be entirely anthropogenic habitats (see Lehmann et al., pp. 152–68). Indeed, on Madagascar there have been few robust bird inventories published of nonaquatic grassland sites (or other equally transformed habitats, such as secondary or exotic thickets, agricultural areas, or cities). However, grasslands of any form far from forests have low species richness; for example, during 10 visits to grasslands of Tampoketsa d'Ankazobe (110 km north of Antananarivo, elevational range 1450–1600 m), Salvan (1972) recorded only 12 species, of which seven are endemic to Madagascar or the Malagasy Region (*Polyboroides radiatus*, Madagascar Harrier-hawk; *Falco newtoni*, Madagascar Kestrel; *Margaroperdix madagarensis*, Madagascar Partridge; *Turnix nigricollis*, Madagascar Buttonquail; *Eremopterix hova*, Madagascar Lark; *Cisticola cherina*, Madagascar Cisticola; and *Foudia madagascariensis*, Madagascar Fody).

Several surveys comparing the bird communities of relatively intact forests with those of the recently deforested landscapes surrounding them provide insight into the species able to persist near intact forests if isolated trees and small patches of regenerating scrub or secondary forest remain in the landscape. However, note that in many cases the forest surveys failed to record some of the

FIGURE 13.6 **Sequence of habitat change in dry spiny thicket of Ranobe PK32, southwest Madagascar. A) largely intact thicket but with largest hardwood trees absent. B) moderately degraded thicket with all hardwood trees absent and large areas opened up by charcoal production. C) thicket cleared for shifting cultivation and subsequently abandoned.** (PHOTOS by L. Jasper.)

rarer forest species known from the region, so forest species richness is likely to be underestimated.

On the edge of the Ambositra-Vondrozo forest corridor in the moist evergreen forests of eastern Madagascar (elevational range 1100–1250 m), the species richness of nonwetland birds was similar in the mature forest corridor (35 species) and the agricultural mosaic that bordered it (34 species) (Martin et al. 2012). However, this was driven by the range of different habitats within the mosaic (which included secondary forest patches, old fallows, *Eucalyptus* plantations, and croplands), and the richness of each separate habitat was only one-third to one-half that of the forest corridor. Of the 52 species recorded across the landscape, 28 were classified as forest dependent: of these, 11 were observed only in the forest corridor, seven were significantly more abundant in the forest corridor, and 10 were frequently observed in the agricultural mosaic (*Accipiter henstii*, Henst's Goshawk; *Sarothrura insularis*, Madagascar Flufftail; *Nesoenas picturatus*, Madagascar Turtle-dove; *Coracina cinerea*, Madagascar Cuckooshrike; *Hypsipetes madagascariensis*, Madagascar Bulbul; *Neomixis tenella*, Common Jery; *N. viridis*, Green Jery; *Cinnyris notatus*, Madagascar Green Sunbird; *Zosterops maderaspatanus*, Madagascar White-eye; and *Leptopterus chabert*, Chabert Vanga) (Martin et al. 2012). The presence of isolated trees (generally *Ficus* spp.) was particularly important in driving this set of forest birds outside the forest corridor; richness and abundance of forest birds were significantly higher in isolated trees than in open areas, and overall bird richness was higher in areas containing trees than in areas lacking them (Martin et al. 2009).

These results contrast with those of Rocha et al. (2015), who found species richness to be significantly higher (52 species) in moist evergreen forest areas at 1010 m mean elevation than in the surrounding agricultural matrix around Ranomafana National Park at 840 m mean elevation (34 species). Of the 63 species recorded, 24 occurred only in forests and six only in agricultural areas; however, over half (52.9%) of the 51 species classified as forest dependent were also recorded in the agricultural matrix.

Elsewhere in eastern moist evergreen forests, bird species richness at Maromizaha, (elevational range 800–1200 m) was highest at a site at the forest edge (49 species), intermediate at two sites within the forest interior (both 43 species), and lowest at two sites in the agricultural matrix outside the forest (34 and 37 species). Of the 77 species recorded across the landscape, 22 were observed only in the forest and eight only in the agricultural matrix (Woog et al. 2006).

In the dry spiny thickets of Ranobe PK32 in southwest Madagascar (elevational range 20–50 m), Gardner et al. (2016) found that the estimated richness of birds in a mosaic of agricultural fields, regenerating scrub, small thicket patches (Figure 13.6), and isolated trees (about 40 species) did not differ significantly from that in the adjacent relatively intact thicket (about 42 species). Of the 53 species recorded across the landscape, 17 occurred only in the dry spiny thickets, and seven occurred only in the agricultural mosaic. Importantly, numerous forest-dependent species (including *Monias benschi*, Subdesert Mesite; *Coua cursor*, Running Coua; *Nesillas lantzii*, Subdesert Brush-warbler; *Newtonia archboldi*, Archbold's Newtonia; and *Xenopirostris xenopirostris*, Lafresnaye's Vanga) were able to persist in the agricultural mosaic outside the intact thicket, though generally at lower abundances than within the thicket.

Elsewhere in the dry spiny thickets, in Behara Commune in the Androy Region (elevational range 0–100 m), D. M. Scott et al. (2006) likewise found no significant difference in species richness between relatively intact thickets and cleared areas. Of the 43 bird species recorded, 11 occurred only in forest areas and eight only in cleared areas.

In the dry deciduous forests of Ankarafantsika in western Madagascar (elevation 75 m), deforestation can be caused by fire. However, the initial passage of fire tends to trigger an increase in the regrowth of understory vegetation, with repeated burning leading to the development of grassland formations. Bird surveys across the habitat gradient found that mean species richness, abundance, and diversity were highest in once-burnt forest (38 species), intermediate in unburnt forest (31 species), and lowest in anthropogenic grasslands (21 species) (Pons and Wendenberg 2005). Once-burnt forest retained most forest specialist species (all except *Coua ruficeps*, Red-capped Coua; *Vanga curvirostris*, Hook-billed Vanga; and *Cyanolanius madagascarinus*, Blue Vanga) but was also used by open-area birds that did not enter intact forest (such as *Turnix nigricollis*; *Merops superciliosus*, Olive Bee-eater; and *Falco newtoni*), resulting in higher species richness.

IMPACTS OF FOREST DEGRADATION

In contrast to deforestation, fewer researchers have investigated the impacts of forest degradation on bird communities and species. In the dry deciduous forest of Kirindy Forest CNFEREF (Centre National de Formation, d'Etudes et de Recherche en Environnement et Foresterie) (Menabe Antimena) in western Madagascar (elevation 50 m), there was no significant difference between the bird communities of selectively logged and unlogged forests (A. Hawkins and Wilmé 1996). However, in this same vegetation type at Ankarafantsika, forests opened up by degradation had higher species richness than intact forests (Andrianarimisa 1992). A similar pattern is repeated in the dry spiny thickets, where Gardner et al. (2016) found estimated species richness to be higher in thicket opened up by charcoal production (about 47 species) than in relatively intact thicket (about 42 species) or the agricultural mosaic outside the thicket (about 40 species). Although these differences were not significant, the higher richness in degraded areas is explained by the retention of forest species (though generally at lower abundance than in intact thicket) and the additional influx of species more typical of open areas.

There has been little research on the impact of degradation on individual bird species. The exception is couas (*Coua* spp.), and the results suggest that impacts may vary depending on the species and the type of degradation involved. In selectively logged dry deciduous forests of Menabe, density of *C. coquereli* (Coquerel's Coua) increases and density of *C. gigas* (Giant Coua) decreases compared to the densities in unlogged forests (Chouteau 2004). However, in the dry deciduous forests of Ankarafantsika, *C. coquereli* has lower abundance in once-burnt forests than in unburnt forests, while *C. ruficeps* shows the opposite pattern (Chouteau et al. 2004; Chouteau 2007). Other terrestrial insectivores also display idiosyncratic responses to degradation. For example, *Mesitornis variegatus* (White-breasted Mesite) densities are slightly higher in selectively logged dry deciduous forests of Menabe than in unlogged forests (A. Hawkins 1994a); however, the related *Monias benschi* avoids more degraded dry spiny thicket habitats (Seddon et al. 2003; Seddon and Tobias 2007). *Uratelornis chimaera* (Long-tailed Ground-roller) nesting density is higher in degraded thicket habitats, and the species will preferentially nest alongside a road or track if one is available (Seddon and Tobias 2007).

IMPACTS OF FOREST FRAGMENTATION

Research on fragmentation effects on Madagascar has been carried out in four largely deforested landscapes whose remaining forests are highly fragmented; one is in the Central Highlands and three are in the eastern portion of the island. On Madagascar and elsewhere in the tropics, forest fragmentation tends to favor habitat generalists over forest specialists, leading to high turnover in bird communities (Langrand 1994, 1995; Ferraz et al. 2007; Matthews et al. 2014).

In the Central Highlands, the Ambohitantely protected area provided a focus for research in the 1990s because at the time it comprised over 500 fragments of medium-altitude moist evergreen forest (elevation 1500 m) separated by anthropogenic grassland (Langrand and Wilmé 1997; see Figure 13.7). In a study of eight fragments ranging in size from 0.64 ha to 1250 ha, there was a strong correlation between fragment size and species richness, and a decline from 51 species in the largest fragment to 14 species in the smallest. The extinction of species from fragments of increasingly smaller size was nonrandom and showed a high degree of nestedness (Langrand and Wilmé 1997, 2000). Forest-dependent species were found to disappear first from fragments of decreasing size, and generalists made up an increasingly larger proportion of the bird species in smaller fragment sizes (from <70% at 1250 ha to 100% at 0.64 ha; Langrand and Wilmé 1997).

However, while numerous bird species were unable to survive in the smallest fragments, fragmentation appeared to have no effect on the genetic structure of populations that did persist in smaller forest blocks. Andrianarimisa et al. (2000) examined the genetic variation of four species across the range of fragment sizes (0.64–1250 ha); neither the forest-dwelling species (*Monticola sharpei*, Forest Rock-thrush; *Terpsiphone mutata*, Madagascar Paradise-flycatcher; and *Foudia omissa*, Forest Fody) nor the open-area specialist (*F. madagascariensis*) showed any effect of fragmentation on genetic variability. These results may arise because the populations continue to exchange genetic material despite fragmentation, or because time lag effects mean that any fragmentation effects have not yet manifested in the genetic structure of the subpopulations. Further, the analyses are based on small sample sizes and on genetic markers that today would not be considered the most appropriate.

Data from Ambohitantely should be interpreted with caution because the largest block of 1250 ha is itself a fragment and is therefore not representative of an intact forest bird community (Goodman and Raherilalao 2003). Many species that are not known from Ambohitantely are present in the nearest large forest of Andranomay-Anjozorobe, about 90 km to the east, which until recently (at the scale of a century or so) was presumed to be contiguous with the main moist evergreen forest block. This suggests that these species were probably formerly present at Ambohitantely, and therefore that an isolated fragment of 1250 ha is insufficiently large to maintain populations of these species in the long term.

The littoral forests of southeast Madagascar occur on a narrow coastal band of sand and alluvium and are highly fragmented, separated by a matrix of ericaceous vegetation and grassland. An analysis of the bird communities of 30 forest patches, ranging in size from less than 1 ha to over 40 ha, found that total species richness and richness of forest-dependent species were both significantly correlated with fragment size, but not isolation (J. Watson et al. 2004a). The minimal area requirements for forest species ranged from 15 to 150 ha, with most species occurring only in patches larger than 30 ha. However, as at Ambohitantely, nothing is known about the original bird community of the littoral forests prior to fragmentation, and it is possible that the most fragmentation-sensitive species may already be locally extinct (J. Watson et al. 2004a).

Further research in the two largest fragments of littoral forest (>172 ha) in the same area in the southeast suggests that the loss of species from smaller blocks may be driven primarily by edge effects

FIGURE 13.7 **The forests of Ambohitantely in the Central Highlands are highly fragmented, with forest blocks separated by a nonforest matrix that is inhospitable to many bird species.** (PHOTO by L. Jasper.)

resulting from changes in forest structure and complexity (J. Watson et al. 2004b). Sites in the forest core (>300 m from the edge) had significantly greater species richness than sites at the forest edge or in the matrix (core, 62 species; edge, 44 species; matrix, 29 species), and 31 (68%) forest-dependent species were found to be edge sensitive. Indeed, 24 species were recorded only in forest core habitats.

In the moist evergreen forest belt at Ranomafana National Park (elevational range 700–1200 m), bird communities were assessed in a control block of approximately 13,750 ha and six fragments ranging from 0.45 to 8.93 ha (Raherilalao 2001). Species richness and the richness of forest-dependent species were significantly affected by fragment area. The largest fragment contained 66.7% of the 54 species recorded in the control site and 44.8% of the 29 forest-dependent species, while the smallest fragment contained only five species, of which none were forest dependent.

Elsewhere in the lowland moist evergreen forests, the bird communities of seven forest fragments adjacent to the Mantadia-Zahamena forest corridor (size range 510–6680 ha, elevational range 60–630 m) were compared to those of three reference sites within the corridor (elevational range 450–895 m) (Andriamasimanana et al. 2001; Rakotoarisoa and Capparella 2013). The mean species richness of forest-dependent birds decreased from 29.3 in reference sites (n = 3) to 19.5 in large fragments (4170–6680 ha, n = 2), 11.0 in medium fragments (2086–2313 ha, n = 2), and 5.7 in small fragments (510–669 ha, n = 3). Of the 38 forest bird species recorded across the landscape, 11 were not recorded in any forest fragment, suggesting that in this region a minimal fragment size of at least 6680 ha is required to permit the survival of *Eutriorchis astur* (Madagascar Serpent-eagle), *Accipiter madagascariensis* (Madagascar Sparrowhawk), *Mesitornis unicolor* (Brown Mesite), *Neodrepanis coruscans* (Common Sunbird-asity), *Crossleyia tenebrosa* (Dusky Tetraka), *Newtonia fanovanae* (Red-tailed Newtonia), *Pseudobias wardi* (Ward's Vanga), *Oriolia bernieri* (Bernier's Vanga), *Euryceros prevostii* (Helmet Vanga), and *Hypositta corallirostris* (Nuthatch Vanga).

IMPACTS OF HABITAT CHANGE ON BIRD FORAGING GUILDS

Habitat changes do not impact all birds equally, and the responses of different foraging guilds tend to be rather uniform across habitat types and forms of degradation. In particular, on Madagascar the richness of granivores and aerial feeders is consistently highest outside intact forests (Andrianarimisa 1992; J. Watson et al. 2004b; Pons and Wendenberg 2005; D. M. Scott et al. 2006; Martin et al. 2012; Rocha et al. 2015), while carnivores and sallying insectivores also tend to increase in richness as forests are opened up (J. Watson et al. 2004b; Pons and Wendenberg 2005; Martin et al. 2012).

Frugivores and canopy insectivores tend to be more species rich in forests than in matrix habitats (Martin et al. 2012; Rocha et al. 2015) and prefer core forest areas to forest edges (J. Watson et al. 2004b). As a result, they are highly sensitive to forest fragmentation (J. Watson et al. 2004a). However, the responses of terrestrial insectivores are less clear: these occur at lower abundance in degraded compared to intact dry deciduous forests (Andrianarimisa 1992) but are richer in the agricultural matrix adjacent to moist evergreen forest areas than within the mature forest corridor (Martin et al. 2012).

IMPACTS OF WETLAND CONVERSION AND DEGRADATION

Freshwater wetlands on Madagascar provide habitat for a number of endemic bird species but are highly threatened by conversion to rice cultivation, clearing of reedbeds, invasive aquatic plant species, and changes to hydrology related to forest clearance (Bamford et al. 2017; Young et al., pp. 1627–36). I am not aware of published research on the impacts of wetland conversion or degradation for birds, but the general pattern appears to follow the pattern for forests, with a turnover from a strong element of endemic species within intact wetlands, to largely nonendemic species in converted wetlands (e.g., Ardeidae, Anatidae; Safford and Hawkins 2013; C. J. Gardner, unpublished data). Such is the impact and level of conversion of these habitats that wetland species are among Madagascar's most threatened birds; both of the Critically Endangered species and 10 of the 17 Endangered species currently listed are wetland species (see Safford et al., pp. 1553–602).

OVERVIEW AND CONCLUSION

Research from Madagascar's forests shows that intermediate levels of habitat change may have a positive effect on species richness, driven by an increase in habitat complexity and heterogeneity (Andrianarimisa 1992; Pons and Wendenberg 2005; Gardner et al. 2016). This is compatible with the intermediate disturbance hypothesis of Connell (1978) and arises because degraded forests retain (at least in the short term) many of the forest specialists present in intact forests but additionally attract habitat generalists and open-area specialists (Pons and Wendenberg 2005; Gardner et al. 2016). However, a focus on richness alone masks a high degree of community turnover, from communities comprising mainly endemic forest specialists in intact habitats, to communities dominated by generalists and open-area specialists. This is a serious concern for conservation because habitat specialists sensitive to habitat change are more likely to be endemic at species and higher taxonomic levels (Wilmé 1996). Thus, habitat degradation and fragmentation appear to disproportionately affect the species of greatest conservation value, Madagascar's endemics (Gardner 2009), although none of the studies reviewed here explicitly addressed this question.

Nevertheless, research to date shows that while endemic species as a whole are highly sensitive to habitat change, many can survive in highly degraded environments, at least in the short term, as long as they are close to contiguous forest and the landscape retains some vegetation complexity (in particular, native trees) (Martin et al. 2009, 2012; Rocha et al. 2015; Gardner et al. 2016). However, the presence of forest species within degraded landscapes does not necessarily imply that they exist as viable populations, because the population may be maintained only through source-sink dynamics from nearby forests (Gilroy and Edwards 2017). Alternatively, there may be time lags between forest degradation and the manifestation of impacts on the bird community, with the result that some degraded or fragmented areas may be carrying an "extinction debt" (Kuussaari et al. 2009).

Although the reviewed research investigated the responses of bird communities to habitat change, it is important to note that the observed impacts are not necessarily the direct result of vegetation change or associated abiotic changes. This is because birds may also be affected by anthropogenic impacts that occur in parallel with those that drive habitat change, such as bushmeat hunting and the intrusion of introduced or feral carnivoran mammals. Human forest users such as charcoal producers, livestock herders, and forest product collectors typically hunt birds opportunistically (Garcia and Goodman 2003; Gardner and Davies 2014; Randriamiharisoa et al. 2015). Hence, many species can be expected to suffer heavier hunting pressure in degraded rather than intact forests or even in relatively intact forests close to human populations. In Tsimanampesotse National Park, for example, Randriamiharisoa et al. (2015) found lower bird abundance (but not richness) along routes of cattle transhumance compared to intact dry spiny thicket habitats away from paths; however, the difference was attributed to hunting by herders, rather than to trampling and grazing by livestock.

In addition to hunting, anthropogenic forest degradation provides opportunities for introduced carnivorans, including feral dogs and cats and the Small Indian Civet (*Viverricula indica*; see Murphy and Farris, pp. 2001–3), to penetrate forests along paths. Their presence can have a significant negative impact on ground-dwelling forest specialists, as was found for *Mentocrex kioloides* (Madagascar Wood-rail), *Coua serriana* (Red-breasted Coua), *Geobiastes squamiger* (Scaly Ground-roller), and *Copsychus albospecularis* (Madagascar Magpie-robin) in Masoala National Park (Murphy et al. 2019).

The suggestion that habitat modification disproportionately affects endemic species and drives a turnover from endemic to nonendemic species, though not explicitly tested by the reviewed studies, has important implications for conservation, particularly given that Madagascar has seen a policy shift from strict protected areas to multiple-use protected areas in which certain destructive livelihood activities are permitted (Gardner et al. 2018; Goodman et al. 2018). In particular, it suggests that strict protected areas in which large expanses of intact forest are effectively protected from extractive use are irreplaceable and must be maintained if the full complement of endemic birds is to be conserved (Gardner 2009); similarly, the strict protection zones or *noyaux durs* of multiple-use protected areas must remain unaltered. Further, it may suggest that the country's first generation of strict protected areas may be of greater value for the conservation of endemic birds than the new generation of multiple-use sites: however, this assertion requires testing.

Further priority research should focus on the identification of thresholds of patch size and levels of degradation beyond which endemic species are unable to persist, in different forest formations. The latter is particularly important for multiple-use protected areas in which human activities persist, but it is hampered by the generally qualitative (rather than quantitative) descriptions of degradation in most existing research. Further, more work with appropriate markers of the genetic impacts of forest-dependent bird species associated with habitat isolation and reduction needs to be conducted. Given that degradation and fragmentation are dynamic processes, resurveying previously studied landscapes will also generate insights into the temporal aspects of changes in bird communities and strengthen a body of knowledge that consists only of "snapshots" thus far.

Subject editors: Roger J. Safford and Steven M. Goodman

BIRD WEIGHTS

M. L. Faliarivola, M. J. Raherilalao, L. Wilmé, A. Benjara, L.-A. Rene de Roland, and S. M. Goodman

Over the past couple of decades, considerable fieldwork has been conducted on Madagascar and new data are available on bird weights. Building on a similar contribution to this one in the precursor of this book (Ravokatra et al. 2003), we combine here the previous and new data associated with captured and weighed birds (Table 13.10). Some data come from published sources, which were summarized by Safford and Hawkins (2013) for publications up to around 2012; published sources since then are quoted separately. A number of endemic birds species lack weight data, and filling in this information should be kept in mind by field workers.

Data presented here concern only adult individuals. Based on the normal curve of the combined data separated by sex, extreme measurements have been removed where they might be erroneous, related to different factors such as faulty manipulation of scales, error in age and sex identification, and females about to lay eggs. Species known to be sexually dimorphic, based on body size measurements presented in Safford and Hawkins (2013), herein have their respective weights given separately, while for those with small sample sizes and that are not dimorphic, the sexes are combined. To allow researchers to access the mean body weights for a given species, for example when analyzing raptor pellet remains, and to derive different statistics, we have added a line of combined values. Subspecies are combined for a given species unless they have been the subject of genetic analyses that support the separation and clearly define the geographic ranges of the different forms. Weights of 1–50 g are in general taken to a precision of 0.1 g and reported as such in Table 13.10, while those of >50–100 g have a precision of 0.5 g, and generally those greater than 100 g have a precision to the nearest gram. Details on the standard deviation of measurements are added only for samples of three individuals or more.

Subject editor: Roger J. Safford

TABLE 13.10. **Weights and associated descriptive statistics of selected Malagasy bird species**

SPECIES	SEX	WEIGHT (g)			
		MEAN ± S.D.	MIN.	MAX.	n
ANSERIFORMES					
Anatidae					
Dendrocygna viduata	U	500 ± 99.6	440	615	3
D. bicolor	U	320	–	–	1
Spatula hottentota	C	237.5 ± 10.40	225	250	4
*Anas melleri**	U	1050	–	–	1
	F	911 ± 66.6	831.5	1140	21
	M	1010 ± 99.8	883	1240	19
A. erythrorhyncha	M	522	–	–	1
*A. bernieri**	U	376 ± 39.0	320	405	5
	F	368 ± 34.0	300	450	64
	M	378 ± 36.0	290	490	119
Aythya innotata	U	685	–	–	1
GALLIFORMES					
Numididae					
Numida meleagris	F	1350	–	–	1
Phasianidae					
Margaroperdix madagarensis	U	240	–	–	1
	F	250	–	–	1
PODICIPEDIFORMES					
Podicipedidae					
Tachybaptus pelzelnii	U	197	–	–	1
COLUMBIFORMES					
Columbidae					
Nesoenas picturatus	U	179 ± 22.0	153	210	9
	F	185.5 ± 15.17	157	200	12
	M	187.5 ± 7.17	176	195	8
	C	184 ± 15.9	153	210	29
Oena capensis	U	38.7 ± 3.06	36.0	42.0	3
	F	35.8 ± 2.02	34.0	38.0	3
	M	38.4 ± 2.51	36.0	42.0	5
	C	37.7 ± 2.60	34.0	42.0	11
Treron australis	C	229 ± 23.7	215	256	3
Alectroenas madagascariensis	C	173 ± 52.4	113	210	3

(continued overleaf)

TABLE 13.10. ***continued***

SPECIES	SEX	WEIGHT (g)			
		MEAN ± S.D.	MIN.	MAX.	n
MESITORNITHIFORMES					
Mesitornithidae					
Mesitornis unicolor	F	–	110	148	2
PTEROCLIFORMES					
Pteroclidae					
Pterocles personatus	F	–	360	360	2
	M	410	–	–	1
	C	377 ± 28.9	360	410	3
CUCULIFORMES					
Cuculidae					
Coua cristata	C	144.5 ± 7.53	133	152	10
C. caerulea	C	255 ± 19.0	225	270	7
C. ruficeps	U	168	–	–	1
C. reynaudii	C	153 ± 17.5	128	175	5
C. cursor	C	111 ± 7.7	103	124	7
C. gigas	C	422 ± 25.7	400	450	3
C. serriana	C	280 ± 24.2	252	298	3
Centropus toulou	C	174 ± 34.6	130	220	7
Cuculus rochii	M	59	–	–	1
CAPRIMULGIFORMES					
Caprimulgidae					
Gactornis enarratus	C	53 ± 6.1	43	60	10
Caprimulgus madagascariensis	U	40.0 ± 3.25	36.0	46.5	9
	F	48 ± 2.5	45	51	4
	M	40 ± 2.2	37	43	8
	C	41.5 ± 4.08	36.0	51.0	21
Apodidae					
Apus melba	M	43.5	–	–	1
A. balstoni	U	–	36	40	2
GRUIFORMES					
Sarothruridae					
Mentocrex beankaensis	M	189	–	–	1
M. kioloides	M	172	–	–	1
Sarothrura insularis	U	23.5	–	–	1

SPECIES	SEX	WEIGHT (g)			
		MEAN ± S.D.	MIN.	MAX.	n
S. watersi	F	24 ± 1.0	23	25	3
	M	27 ± 2.2	25	30	4
	C	25.7 ± 2.29	23.0	30.0	7
Rallidae					
Rallus madagascariensis	U	–	88	105	2
Dryolimnas cuvieri	C	240 ± 33.9	215	290	4
Gallinula chloropus	M	238	–	–	1
Porphyrio madagascariensis	M	805	–	–	1
Zapornia olivieri	F	–	96	100	2
	M	–	80	90	2
	C	91.5 ± 8.70	80.0	100.0	4
CHARADRIIFORMES					
Rostratulidae					
Rostratula benghalensis	F	142	–	–	1
Turnicidae					
Turnix nigricollis	U	60	–	–	1
	F	69.5 ± 8.81	59.0	80.0	4
	M	58.0 ± 3.19	54.0	61.5	5
	C	64 ± 8.5	45	80	10
PHAETHONIFORMES					
Phaethontidae					
Phaethon lepturus	F	365	–	–	1
SULIFORMES					
Phalacrocoracidae					
Microcarbo africanus	M	850	–	–	1
PELECANIFORMES					
Ardeidae					
Egretta garzetta	C	422 ± 7.6	415	430	3
E. ardesiaca	C	352 ± 10.8	340	365	6
Bubulcus ibis	U	391	–	–	1
Butorides striata	F	194.5 ± 9.2	189	205	3
ACCIPITRIFORMES					
Accipitridae					
Eutriorchis astur	F	–	850	851	2
	M	770	–	–	1

(continued overleaf)

TABLE 13.10. ***continued***

SPECIES	SEX	WEIGHT (g)			
		MEAN ± S.D.	MIN.	MAX.	n
	C	823.7 ± 46.48	770	851	3
Aviceda madagascariensis	F	400	–	–	1
	M	–	350	390	2
	C	380 ± 26.5	350	400	3
Macheiramphus alcinus	M	555	–	–	1
Accipiter francesiae	U	117 ± 8.7	110	128	4
	F	138 ± 14.1	123	151	3
	M	115.5 ± 8.88	104	138	13
	C	119.2 ± 12.04	104	151	20
A. madagascariensis	F	–	277	348	2
	M	–	108	109	2
	C	210.5 ± 121.29	108	348	4
A. henstii	F	–	960	1140	2
	M	–	600	618	2
	C	829.5 ± 265.11	600	1140	4
Milvus migrans	F	–	580	700	2
	M	–	624	650	2
	C	638.5 ± 50.16	580	700	4
Haliaeetus vociferoides	F	3032.5 ± 170.84	2750	3300	8
	M	2405 ± 214.5	2000	2700	14
	C	2633.2 ± 365.61	2000	3300	22
Buteo brachypterus	F	645 ± 45.5	600	730	3
STRIGIFORMES					
Tytonidae					
Tyto soumagnei	F	337.5 ± 10.40	325	350	4
	M	298 ± 5.7	292	305	4
	C	317.8 ± 22.49	292	350	8
Strigidae					
Otus rutilus	C	100.5 ± 9.46	85	121	34
Athene superciliaris	M	217	–	–	1
Asio madagascariensis	U	410	–	–	1
	F	770	–	–	1
	M	395	–	–	1
	C	525 ± 212.3	395	770	3

SPECIES	SEX	WEIGHT (g) MEAN ± S.D.	MIN.	MAX.	n
BUCEROTIFORMES					
Upupidae					
Upupa marginata	U	76	–	–	1
	F	75.0 ± 12.94	58.5	93.0	9
	M	77.5 ± 14.31	62.0	90.5	4
	C	75.5 ± 12.33	58.5	93.0	14
CORACIIFORMES					
Alcedinidae					
Corythornis vintsioides	C	17.5 ± 1.61	14.5	20.0	22
C. madagascariensis	U	19.3 ± 1.82	16.0	21.5	14
	F	19.3 ± 2.95	16.0	23.5	11
	M	17.9 ± 0.97	16.0	20.0	18
	C	18.7 ± 1.98	16.0	23.5	43
Meropidae					
Merops superciliosus	C	42 ± 4.4	37	48	5
Coraciidae					
Eurystomus glaucurus	C	148.5 ± 21.3	129	180	5
Brachypteraciidae					
Brachypteracias leptosomus	U	–	186	217	2
	F	154	–	–	1
	M	182.7 ± 3.51	179	186	3
	C	184.2 ± 20.11	154	217	6
Geobiastes squamiger	U	147 ± 16.5	128	158	3
	F	–	135	140	2
	M	–	145	165	2
	C	146.6 ± 13.33	128	165	7
Atelornis pittoides	C	90 ± 8.4	76	107	16
A. crossleyi	C	75.5 ± 6.25	69	85	11
Uratelornis chimaera	U	70	–	–	1
FALCONIFORMES					
Falconidae					
Falco newtoni	U	98	–	–	1
	M	85	–	–	1
F. zoniventris	F	180	–	–	1
	M	145	–	–	1

(continued overleaf)

TABLE 13.10. ***continued***

SPECIES	SEX	WEIGHT (g)			
		MEAN ± S.D.	MIN.	MAX.	n
PSITTACIFORMES					
Psittaculidae					
Coracopsis vasa	F	560	–	–	1
C. nigra	C	246.5 ± 36.36	215	293	4
Agapornis canus	C	30.9 ± 2.51	27.0	34.5	7
PASSERIFORMES					
Philepittidae					
Philepitta castanea	U	35.2 ± 4.26	30.0	44.5	14
	F	36.2 ± 3.05	30.0	43.5	50
	M	34.4 ± 2.48	30.5	40.0	60
	C	35.2 ± 3.05	30.0	44.5	124
P. schlegeli	F	–	26	29	2
	M	23.9 ± 1.74	21.0	25.0	5
	C	24.9 ± 2.42	21.0	29.0	7
Neodrepanis coruscans	U	6.4 ± 0.34	6.0	7.0	10
	F	6.4 ± 0.73	6.0	8.5	16
	M	6.5 ± 0.60	5.8	9.0	33
	C	6.5 ± 0.59	5.8	9.0	59
N. hypoxantha	U	7.2 ± 0.42	7.0	8.0	5
	F	7.5 ± 0.36	7.0	8.0	5
	M	7.3 ± 0.65	6.4	8.1	11
	C	7.4 ± 0.53	6.4	8.1	21
Campephagidae					
Coracina cinerea	U	44.7 ± 2.75	41.5	46.5	3
	F	44.0 ± 5.96	35.5	49.0	4
	M	44.9 ± 6.79	35.0	55.5	8
	C	44.6 ± 5.65	35.0	55.5	15
Vangidae					
Newtonia archboldi	C	7.3 ± 0.86	6.0	9.0	12
N. brunneicauda	C	10.1 ± 1.61	8.0	14.5	134
N. amphichroa	C	12.2 ± 1.44	10.0	16.5	63
N. lavarambo	C	11.6 ± 0.78	10.2	12.5	8
N. fanovanae	M	12.5	–	–	1
Tylas eduardi	U	45.9 ± 5.14	37.5	53.0	10
	F	48.7 ± 3.79	42.0	54.0	8

SPECIES	SEX	WEIGHT (g) MEAN ± S.D.	MIN.	MAX.	n
	M	–	43.1	43.5	2
	C	46.8 ± 4.59	37.5	54.0	20
Calicalicus madagascariensis	U	18	–	–	1
	F	17.7 ± 1.66	15.5	20.0	9
	M	16.7 ± 1.81	15.0	18.6	3
	C	17.5 ± 1.61	15.0	20.0	13
C. rufocarpalis	M	16	–	–	1
Hypositta corallirostris	U	–	13.0	15.5	2
	F	13.0 ± 1.26	11.0	14.2	6
	M	–	12.0	13.5	2
	C	13.2 ± 1.29	11.0	15.5	10
Leptopterus chabert	C	18.6 ± 1.89	15.0	22.5	15
Mystacornis crossleyi	U	23.9 ± 2.49	20.5	27.5	10
	F	22.8 ± 2.51	20.0	26.5	5
	M	24.5 ± 1.50	23.0	28.5	11
	C	23.9 ± 2.13	20.0	28.5	26
Cyanolanius madagascarinus	U	22.5	–	–	1
	F	24.5	–	–	1
	M	21.8 ± 0.76	21.0	22.5	3
	C	22.5 ± 1.27	21.0	24.5	5
Vanga curvirostris	U	66.5 ± 4.47	62.0	72.5	8
	F	68 ± 2.6	65	71	5
	M	69.5 ± 4.14	61.0	75.0	10
	C	68 ± 4.0	61	75	23
Pseudobias wardi	C	12.7 ± 0.67	12.0	13.3	3
Schetba rufa	U	34.4 ± 3.47	30.5	40.0	5
	F	38.3 ± 3.73	32.0	42.0	9
	M	36.6 ± 3.09	31.0	40.0	9
	C	36.8 ± 3.61	30.5	42.0	23
S. occidentalis	F	36.1 ± 1.97	33.0	39.0	11
	M	38.1 ± 1.91	35.0	42.0	11
	C	37.1 ± 2.15	33.0	42.0	22
Euryceros prevostii	C	98 ± 11.0	84	114	10
Oriolia bernieri	F	52	–	–	1
	M	52	–	–	1

(continued overleaf)

TABLE 13.10. ***continued***

SPECIES	SEX	WEIGHT (g)			
		MEAN ± S.D.	MIN.	MAX.	n
Falculea palliata	C	107 ± 7.3	96	122.5	10
Artamella viridis	F	44.1 ± 4.01	41.0	50.0	4
	M	41	–	–	1
	C	43.5 ± 3.74	41.0	50.0	5
Xenopirostris damii†	M	51	–	–	
X. polleni	U	61.5	–	–	1
X. xenopirostris	F	48.2 ± 5.67	40.0	54.0	5
	M	57 ± 6.9	50	68	6
	C	53 ± 7.5	40	68	11
Dicruridae					
Dicrurus forficatus	U	46.1 ± 4.28	38.0	53.0	11
	F	41.8 ± 4.36	35.0	46.5	3
	M	43.2 ± 5.04	36.0	52 .5	20
	C	43.4 ± 4.83	35.0	53.0	47
Monarchidae					
Terpsiphone mutata‡	U	13.8 ± 1.27	10.0	16.5	46
	F	13 ± 1.5	10	17	79
	M	13.5 ± 1.35	10.5	17.0	93
	C	13.4 ± 1.41	10.0	17.0	218
Corvidae					
Corvus albus	F	580	–	–	1
Alaudidae					
Eremopterix hova	C	18.3 ± 1.03	17.0	20.5	13
Cisticolidae					
Neomixis tenella‡	C	6.8 ± 0.88	5.0	9.0	30
N. viridis‡	U	7	–	–	1
N. striatigula‡	U	9.0 ± 0.78	8.2	9.8	4
	F	8.8 ± 2.28	5.5	11.5	8
	M	7.1 ± 1.87	5.0	11.0	12
	C	8.0 ± 2.03	5.0	11.5	24
Cisticola cherina	U	10.5	–	–	1
	F	7	–	–	1
Acrocephelidae					
Nesillas typica	U	17.9 ± 1.47	15.0	21.5	50
	F	16.9 ± 1.09	15.6	18.5	10

SPECIES	SEX	WEIGHT (g)			
		MEAN ± S.D.	MIN.	MAX.	n
	M	18.1 ± 1.53	15.0	21.5	49
	C	17.9 ± 1.49	15.0	21.5	109
N. lantzii	U	16.5 ± 2.21	13.5	18.5	4
	F	17 ± 1.0	16	18	3
	M	16.9 ± 2.14	14.5	20.0	7
	C	16.8 ± 1.83	13.5	20.0	14
Acrocephalus newtoni	C	18.6 ± 1.91	16.0	21.0	7
Locustellidae					
Bradypterus brunneus	C	14.2 ± 0.29	14.0	14.5	3
Bernieridae					
Oxylabes madagascariensis	U	24.3 ± 2.05	21.0	28.5	25
	F	23.1 ± 2.13	20.0	28.5	22
	M	23.5 ± 1.95	20.0	27.5	32
	C	23.6 ± 2.08	20.0	28.5	79
Bernieria madagascariensis	U	30.4 ± 4.35	21.0	35.0	14
	F	25.7 ± 3.95	20.5	35.5	17
	M	31.5 ± 3.99	25.0	39.0	27
	C	29.5 ± 4.47	20.5	39.0	58
B. incelebris	U	27.9 ± 3.98	20.0	35.5	35
	F	23.6 ± 2.78	20.0	32.0	53
	M	28.1 ± 3.73	20.0	35.0	69
	C	26.5 ± 4.07	20.0	35.5	157
Bernieria sp.	F	22.0	–	–	1
	M	27.5 ± 5.20	22.0	33.5	5
	C	26.5 ± 5.15	22.0	33.5	6
Cryptosylvicola randrianasoloi	U	8.7 ± 0.46	8.2	9.0	3
	F	8.3	–	–	1
	M	8.1 ± 1.02	7.1	9.8	7
	C	8.3 ± 0.86	7.1	9.8	11
Hartertula flavoviridis	U	9.0 ± 0.78	8.0	10.5	9
	F	–	8.5	8.8	2
	M	9.7 ± 1.54	8.0	11.5	5
	C	9.2 ± 1.05	8.0	11.5	16
Thamnornis chloropetoides	U	14	–	–	1
	F	14 ± 1.0	13	15	3

(continued overleaf)

TABLE 13.10. ***continued***

SPECIES	SEX	WEIGHT (g)			
		MEAN ± S.D.	MIN.	MAX.	n
	M	14.2 ± 1.11	12.0	15.5	10
	C	14.1 ± 1.01	12.0	15.5	14
Xanthomixis zosterops	U	17.2 ± 2.74	11.5	24.5	84
	F	16.4 ± 2.52	11.5	21.5	45
	M	19.1 ± 1.38	13.0	25.0	82
	C	17.8 ± 2.78	11.5	25.0	211
X. apperti	U	14.8 ± 1.37	11.5	16.5	14
	F	14.5	–	–	1
	M	14.3 ± 1.76	12.5	16.0	4
	C	14.7 ± 1.37	11.5	16.5	19
X. cinereiceps	U	17.5 ± 1.39	15.0	20.5	22
	F	17.6 ± 1.68	16.1	20.6	8
	M	18.5 ± 1.88	15.0	20.5	20
	C	17.9 ± 1.63	15.0	23.0	50
Crossleyia xanthophrys	U	20.0 ± 1.61	18.5	22 .5	6
	M	21.1 ± 1.25	19.5	22 .5	4
	C	20.5 ± 1.51	18.5	22.5	10
C. tenebrosa	U	21.4	–	–	1
Randia pseudozosterops	U	12	–	–	1
Hirundinidae					
Riparia paludicola	U	9.3 ± 1.00	8.5	10.5	3
Phedina borbonica	U	20.0 ± 0.35	19.5	21.0	4
	F	–	20.0	22.5	2
	M	22.2 ± 1.04	21.0	23.5	5
	C	21.2 ± 1.40	19.5	23.5	11
Pycnonotidae					
Hypsipetes madagascariensis	U	45.6 ± 3.49	40.0	51.0	24
	F	47.4 ± 3.46	42.0	53.0	17
	M	45.1 ± 3.17	40.0	52.0	36
	C	45.7 ± 3.41	40.0	53.0	77
Zosteropidae					
Zosterops maderaspatanus	U	12.3 ± 1.50	10.0	15.0	33
	F	10.4 ± 1.17	8.4	13.0	22
	M	10.4 ± 1.26	8.0	13.5	20
	C	11.3 ± 1.64	8.0	15.0	75

SPECIES	SEX	WEIGHT (g)			
		MEAN ± S.D.	MIN.	MAX.	n
Sturnidae					
Acridotheres tristis[§]	M	132 ± 16.4	117.5	150	3
Hartlaubius auratus	F	41.5	–	–	1
Muscicapidae					
Copsychus albospecularis	U	23.4 ± 2.68	19.0	29.0	31
	F	22.6 ± 2.69	17.0	29.5	95
	M	22.8 ± 2.51	18.0	28.5	152
	C	22.8 ± 2.60	17.0	29.5	278
Monticola sharpei	U	26.0 ± 1.97	24.5	29.0	5
	F	25.9 ± 1.54	23.0	28.5	16
	M	25.3 ± 1.38	23.0	29.5	23
	C	25.6 ± 1.50	23.0	29.5	44
Saxicola torquatus	U	–	15	15	2
	F	15.4 ± 1.11	14.0	16.5	4
	M	14.9 ± 1.02	14.0	16.5	5
	C	15.1 ± 0.91	14.0	16.5	11
Nectariniidae					
Cinnyris sovimanga[‡]	U	6.5 ± 0.63	5.7	7.6	16
	F	6.7 ± 0.62	5.3	8.0	47
	M	7.5 ± 0.95	5.5	10.5	77
	C	7.1 ± 0.92	5.3	10.5	140
C. notatus[‡]	U	13.6 ± 1.65	11.5	15.5	4
	F	12.7 ± 1.15	11.0	15.0	9
	M	15.8 ± 1.72	13.8	19.0	8
	C	14.1 ± 2.00	11.0	19.0	21
Ploceidae					
Nelicurvius nelicourvi	U	23.6 ± 1.64	21.0	26.5	15
	F	22.9 ± 1.49	20.0	25.5	22
	M	24.7 ± 2.31	20.5	28.5	39
	C	23.9 ± 2.10	20.0	28.5	76
N. sakalava[‡]	U	24.4 ± 2.16	21.0	26.5	5
	F	22.6 ± 2.50	18.0	28.5	29
	M	24.3 ± 2.33	18.0	28.0	26
	C	23.5 ± 2.51	18.0	28.5	60

(continued overleaf)

TABLE 13.10. ***continued***

SPECIES	SEX	WEIGHT (g)			
		MEAN ± S.D.	MIN.	MAX.	n
Foudia madagascariensis	U	16.3 ± 1.71	14.0	19.5	16
	F	16.1 ± 1.24	14.0	18.0	34
	M	16.9 ± 1.61	14.0	20.0	47
	C	16.2 ± 1.53	14.0	20.0	97
F. omissa	U	19.8 ± 1.73	17.5	24.5	13
	F	17.7 ± 1.26	15.0	20.0	26
	M	19.3 ± 1.88	15.0	24.5	64
	C	19.9 ± 1.86	15.0	24.5	103
Passer domesticus[§]	F	22.5 ± 1.75	19.6	26.6	15
	M	21.6 ± 1.49	19.3	25.7	19
	C	22.0 ± 1.65	19.3	26.6	34
Estrildidae					
Lepidopygia nana	C	8.2 ± 0.80	7.4	9.0	3
Motacillidae					
Motacilla flaviventris	U		22.0	22.5	2
	F	24.8 ± 1.57	23.0	25.9	3
	M	23.5 ± 0.87	22.0	24.5	6
	C	23.6 ± 1.29	22.0	25.9	11

Notes: Only data for adults are presented. C, sexes combined; F, female; M, male; U, sex unknown. For details on the systematic order adopted here, see Safford et al. (p. 1553–602) and Table 13.1.

[*] Data from Razafindrajao et al. (2012).

[†] Data from Rasamison et al. (2018).

[‡] Considerable variation in this species is presumably associated with the combination of subspecies that show clinal variation in body size.

[§] Introduced to Madagascar.

THE AVIAN RADIATIONS OF MADAGASCAR

S. Reddy and T. S. Schulenberg

Given the isolation and size of Madagascar, its endemic avifauna is a result of both chance colonizations and in situ diversification. The approximately 114 endemic bird species comprise at least 55 independent lineages that have colonized Madagascar at various times and include representatives from across the avian evolutionary tree (Figure 13.8). Of these, about 12 lineages are known to have subsequently diversified in situ on the island. The last two decades have led to remarkable changes in our understanding of bird evolution in general and on Madagascar in particular. A considerable number of genetic studies have clarified the evolutionary relationships of these lineages and have shed new light on the membership of these endemic groups.

The 12 Malagasy radiating lineages, which vary widely in terms of species richness and phenotypic diversity, are drawn widely from the avian tree of life (Figure 13.8, Table 13.11). Most prominent among these is the extraordinary radiation of Malagasy vangas (see Schulenberg, pp. 1694–99), which have diversified into at least 23 species and include a spectacular range of trophic adaptations (Jønsson et al. 2012; Reddy et al. 2012). The second most diverse clade, the Bernieridae, was only recently discovered using genetic data that showed that 13 species previously placed in three different families are a monophyletic endemic assemblage (Cibois et al. 2001, 2010; Younger et al. 2019a). Recent studies have also pointed out the presence of cryptic or hidden species, where deep evolutionary divergence is distinguishable in genes but outward appearances have not changed substantially (Block 2012; Block et al. 2015; Younger et al. 2018, 2019a), and the true diversity of Malagasy birds may not be apparent until we complete a systematic review based on molecular genetics of all species with wide geographic ranges.

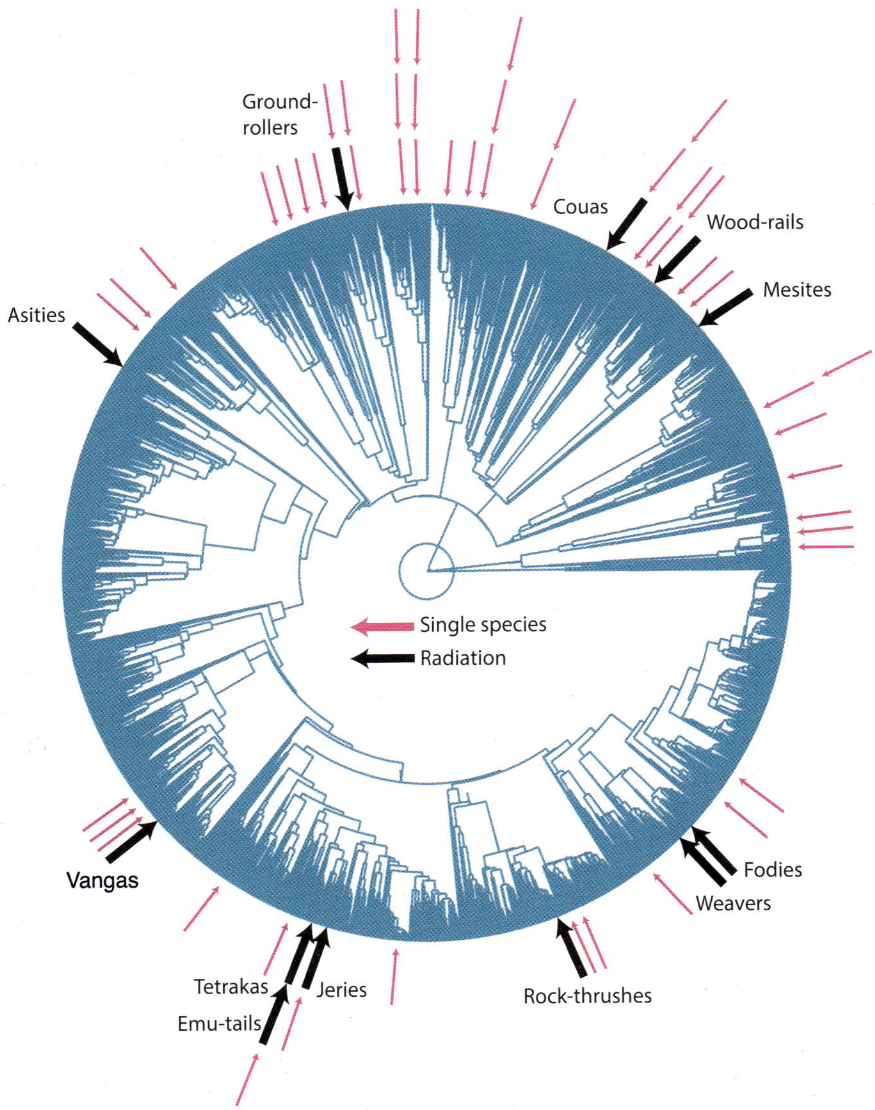

FIGURE 13.8 The bird tree of life. Arrows point to Malagasy lineages, with black indicating radiations (in situ diversifications) and pink showing single-species endemics. (SOURCE: redrawn from Jetz et al. 2012.)

TABLE 13.11. **Endemic avian radiations of Madagascar following classical taxonomic order**

MALAGASY LINEAGE	NUMBER OF SPECIES	FAMILY	REFERENCES
Mesitornithidae	3	Mesitornithidae	Prum et al. (2015); Reddy et al. (2017)
Mentocrex	2	Sarothruridae	Goodman et al. (2011); Boast et al. (2019)
Coua	10	Cuculidae	Sorenson and Payne (2005)
Brachypteraciidae	5	Brachypteraciidae	Kirchman et al. (2001); McCullough et al. (2019)
Philepittidae	4	Philepittidae	Prum (1993); Moyle et al. (2006)
Vanginae	23	Vangidae	Reddy et al. (2012); Jønsson et al. (2012)
Bradypterus	2	Locustellidae	Alström et al. (2011, 2018)
Bernieridae	13	Bernieridae	Cibois et al. (2010); Younger et al. (2019a)
Neomixis	3	Cisticolidae	Olsson et al. (2013); Nguembock et al. (2007)
Monticola	2	Muscicapidae	Zuccon and Ericson (2010a); Cruaud et al. (2011)
Nelicurvius	2	Ploceidae	De Silva et al. (2017, 2019)
Foudia	2	Ploceidae	Warren et al. (2003), De Silva et al. (2019)

The extant endemic avifauna of Madagascar can be divided rather neatly into two categories, depending on their pattern of endemism; for our purposes here, an "endemic" species or genus may be either restricted only to Madagascar, or, more generally, found only on Madagascar and adjacent small islands, such as the Comoro archipelago. The two categories of Malagasy birds then consist of lineages representing single endemic species (43 species) that clearly belong to widespread genera (i.e., genera that also are found in Asia, Africa, or both), and endemic species (71 species) that belong to the 12 endemic lineages that have radiated (undergone in situ speciation) on Madagascar.

In almost all cases, the evolutionary history of Malagasy endemics has proved to be most enigmatic. Recent studies that focused on the phylogenies of a broad array of Malagasy birds with substantial amounts of genetic data and wide taxonomic sampling to include many potential representatives have contributed a great deal of insight into the origins and membership of these radiations. These data provide, in many cases for the first time, explicit hypotheses regarding the affinities of the Malagasy taxa and permit the identification of the sister group to the Malagasy radiations.

Given Madagascar's size and habitat diversity, perhaps it is not surprising that no single passerine radiation is dominant on the island, in contrast to the Darwin's finches (Geospizinae) on the Galápagos Islands or the Hawaiian honeycreepers (Drepanidinae) on the Hawaiian Islands. Yet perhaps more unexpected is the finding that the number of ancient colonizing events on Madagascar may be much smaller than was originally thought given its relative proximity to Africa. We now know that the underlying wind and ocean currents made dispersals from Africa unlikely for much of the Cenozoic era and might instead have favored movements from eastern landmasses across the Indian Ocean (Ali and Huber 2010; see Samonds et al., pp. 73–78). This is supported by a number of Malagasy lineages showing Asian affinities as well as geological evidence of landmasses in the western Indian Ocean that were likely subaerial during periods of lower sea level and may have acted as "stepping stones" to dispersal (Warren et al. 2010).

In this contribution, we discuss the 12 Malagasy radiating lineages in light of the latest phylogenetic studies. Here we will deviate from traditional ordering based on taxonomic classifications and instead discuss these groups in order of decreasing diversity. In this manner, we highlight studies that have led to remarkable new discoveries about the uniqueness of the Malagasy avifauna.

THE VANGAS (VANGINAE)

The vangas (Vanginae or Vangidae) of Madagascar have been proposed to be an adaptive radiation similar to classic examples like Darwin's finches and Hawaiian honeycreepers. Although ornithologists have long recognized an endemic Malagasy radiation of shrike-like birds, the composition of the Vangidae and confirmation of its monophyly were unclear until recently. Currently circumscribed as a group of 23 species, the vangas are the largest avian radiation on Madagascar and exhibit a great range of morphological, behavioral, and ecological diversity (see Schulenberg, pp. 1694–99). The composition of the group has long been a source of uncertainty, with recent studies suggesting additional members and some questioning its monophyly (Schulenberg 1995; Yamagishi et al. 2001; Johansson et al. 2008; Manegold 2008; Jønsson et al. 2012; Reddy et al. 2012). The first comprehensive phylogenetic study of vangas using substantial amounts of genetic data supported monophyly of the group with their close relatives in both Asia and Africa (Reddy et al. 2012). Malagasy vangas are now referred to as the subfamily Vanginae, while their continental relatives, a group of aberrant genera from Africa and Asia (i.e., *Philentoma*, *Hemipus*, *Tephrodornis*, *Bias*, *Megabyas*, *Prionops*), are ascribed to the subfamily Prionopinae, the two groups together constituting the family Vangidae (Reddy et al. 2012; Dickinson and Christidis 2014).

An interesting aspect of the vanga radiation is that it appears to be even larger than previously realized. In addition to the 15 species of "known" vangas based largely on morphology (e.g., as set out in Langrand 1990), the molecular data suggest that several additional endemic Malagasy genera belong to this radiation. One of these is *Mystacornis crossleyi* (previously called Crossley's Babbler and placed in the Timaliidae, now Crossley's Vanga), which is indeed a vangid (Johansson et al. 2008; Reddy et al. 2012). *Mystacornis* represents more than the mere addition of another species to the vanga radiation, as this species is ground dwelling and therefore also represents a previously unrecognized foraging strategy among the Vangidae. Another new member is *Pseudobias wardi* (previously called Ward's Flycatcher, formerly considered part of the Monarchidae, now Ward's Vanga). Again, the addition of *Pseudobias* represents a novel foraging strategy within the Vangidae. *Pseudobias* is a "flycatcher" that sallies to capture flying prey and is one of very few passerines on Madagascar that rely on this foraging technique. Finally, the genus *Newtonia*, composed of four recognized species and once thought to be part of the Sylviidae (warblers), is part of the vanga radiation (Yamagishi et al. 2001; Reddy et al. 2012).

The incredible diversity of forms encompassed in the vangas of Madagascar arose as an in situ radiation and exhibits a pattern consistent with the ecological opportunity model of adaptive diversification (Jønsson et al. 2012; Reddy et al. 2012). Upon colonization of Madagascar, the speciation rate of the early lineages was high but then declined dramatically over time, presumably owing to the occupation and saturation of niches. Vangas exhibit a great diversity in bill size and shape and show evidence of niche divergence into novel foraging strategies that are correlated with phylogeny. For example, some species probe bark for insects with their bills, an unusual behavior in passerine birds and similar to woodpeckers, which are absent on Madagascar (Yamagishi and Eguchi 1996). Vangas, therefore, fit the model of an adaptive radiation, surpassing Darwin's finches in the number of species and rivaling Hawaiian honeycreepers in ecomorphological disparity (Reddy et al. 2012). In fact, the extent of the disparity in terms of bill shape and size across vangas is equivalent to the range exhibited by all passerines (Jønsson et al. 2012).

THE TETRAKAS, MALAGASY "WARBLERS" (BERNIERIDAE)

One of the most surprising discoveries about Malagasy birds in the past two decades is that several species previously thought to represent widespread Old World lineages—warblers (Sylviidae), babblers (Timaliidae), and bulbuls (Pycnonotidae)—are actually part of an endemic radiation (Cibois et al. 1999, 2001, 2010; Younger et al. 2019a; see Reddy et al., pp. 1707–11). This taxonomic revelation was discovered only with molecular systematics, although earlier ornithologists had proposed similar groupings (Salomonsen 1934a). In 2010 this monophyletic assemblage was designated as an endemic family, Bernieridae (Cibois et al. 2010), referred to as the tetrakas. Bernieridae comprises 13 species of songbirds, including most of the former Malagasy "bulbuls" ("*Phyllastrephus*," now *Xanthomixis* and *Bernieria*); several (but not all) representatives of the taxa previously assigned to babblers (*Oxylabes madagascariensis*, White-throated Oxylabes; *Hartertula flavoviridis*, Wedge-tailed Tetraka; *Crossleyia xanthophrys*, Madagascar Yellowbrow); and a few species previously placed among the warblers (*Thamnornis chloropetoides*, Thamnornis; *Cryptosylvicola randrianasoloi*, Cryptic Warbler).

The tetrakas exhibit a considerable variety of bill shapes, wing and tail proportions, and tarsus lengths. This morphological diversity may have concealed the monophyly of this endemic clade from ornithologists in the past, since much of the traditional classification of birds is based on similarity of morphological features. Additionally, it is notable that most tetrakas are syntopic, with up to nine species co-occurring in moist evergreen forests of Madagascar. Although there are some patterns of latitudinal and elevational zonation, up to six of these species may be found in the same mixed-species foraging flock. Only a few taxa are found in the relatively species-poor dry deciduous forests and dry spiny thickets of the southwest (e.g., *X. apperti*, Appert's Tetraka; *T. chloropetoides*). All tetrakas are largely insectivorous, with mainly generalist diets (A. Hawkins and Sartain 2013; Faliarivola et al. 2020).

The tetrakas are part of the Sylviida radiation of the Passeriformes, which has undergone several taxonomic rearrangements in the past two decades (Barker et al. 2004; Alström et al. 2006; Oliveros et al. 2019). The closest relatives are the Locustellidae, a speciose family widespread in Africa and Asia, and the monotypic *Donacobius* (Black-capped Donacobius, Donacobiidae) in the Neotropics (Beresford et al. 2005; Alström et al. 2011; Younger et al. 2019a). These evolutionary relationships have intriguing implications for biogeography, as well as ecology. The Locustellidae contains primarily grassland birds, *Donacobius* inhabits wetlands, and the Bernieridae is exclusively forest dwelling. The closest outgroup to the clade of Bernieridae+*Donacobius*+Locustellidae is the typically marsh- and bush-living Acrocephalidae; this implies a shift to forested habitats in the Malagasy lineage. The Bernieridae is now the second most diverse avian radiation on Madagascar and has been alluded to as an adaptive radiation. Only with a more concerted understanding of the similarities and distinct characteristics of these species can we fully comprehend the extent of their adaptive diversification.

THE COUAS (*COUA*: CUCULIDAE)

The third largest radiation on Madagascar is the genus *Coua*, which includes some of the most striking birds on the island. These relatively large birds have prominently colored, largely naked skin ranging from intense bluish to purplish tones, surrounding the eyes and on portions of the head, and some are stunningly colorful, like *C. caerulea* (Blue Coua) (Figure 13.9a). There are nine living and three extinct species known so far, but there is some evidence for hidden diversity in phenotypically variable species such as *C. cristata* (Crested Coua). However, more studies are needed to clarify this and the phylogenetic relationships within this genus. Only two genetic studies have focused on *Coua* evolution (Johnson et al. 2000; Sorenson and Payne 2005). These studies confirm that the extant couas are split into two clades that show a separation in their habits: the arboreal (three species) and the ground-dwelling clades (six species).

FIGURE 13.9 **Some representatives of endemic birds of Madagascar not illustrated elsewhere in this book. A) *Coua caerulea* (Blue Coua) at Andasibe, subfamily Couinae. B) *Neomixis tenella* (Common Jery) along the Mandrare River near Berenty, family Cisticolidae; based on distribution and plumage coloration this individual would be *N. t. debilis*. C) *Monticola sharpei* (Forest Rock-thrush) at Montagne d'Ambre National Park, family Muscicapidae; the population at this site was previously considered a separate species, *M. erythronotus*. D) *Bradypterus seebohmi* (Gray Emutail) at Ranomafana National Park, family Locustellidae. E) *Nesillas lantzii* (Subdesert Brush-warbler) along the Mandrare River near Berenty, family Acrocephalidae.** (PHOTOS by K. Behrens.)

In contrast to African cuckoos, the Malagasy couas exhibit behaviors typical of terrestrial birds, with even the arboreal species "walking" along branches (Goodman 2013). The closest relatives of the couas are thought to be members of the genus *Carpococcyx*, a group of ground-dwelling cuckoos found in the humid forests of Asia (Sorenson and Payne 2005). The genera *Coua* and *Carpococcyx* (sometimes including *Centropus*) form the subfamily Couinae within the single family, Cuculidae, of the order Cuculiformes. Given their shared ancestry, it is likely that the couas are ancestrally terrestrial and arboreality is novel on Madagascar in this subfamily. Limited phylogenetic studies of the Cuculiformes make it difficult to propose many conclusive statements about the evolution of the Malagasy endemics. Since few tissue samples exist for many Asian species, and none for the recently extinct taxa, this issue may be difficult to resolve without historical museum and subfossil samples.

THE GROUND-ROLLERS (BRACHYPTERACIIDAE)

The ground-rollers of Madagascar are a very distinctive family of five species in four genera—*Atelornis* (two species), *Brachypteracias*, *Geobiastes*, and *Uratelornis* (see Langrand, pp. 1679–82). Most species occur in the moist evergreen forests, while *Uratelornis* is the lone taxon to inhabit the dry spiny thickets. At one point, *G. squamiger* (Scaly Ground-roller) was congeneric with *B. leptosomus* (Short-legged Ground-roller), but genetic data show that these do not form a monophyletic group (Kirchman et al. 2001; McCullough et al. 2019). The phylogenetic placement of *U. chimaera* (Long-tailed Ground-roller) is still somewhat unstable because of problems with sequencing from old specimens; the latest phylogeny places it as sister to *Atelornis* (McCullough et al. 2019). Genetic and morphological data corroborate a sister relationship between the Malagasy ground-rollers and the Coraciidae, generically known as rollers and found mainly in tropical Africa and Asia (Hackett et al. 2008). Dispersal from Africa to Madagascar likely occurred around 41 Mya (McCullough et al. 2019). Despite its name and some similarities, the Cuckoo-roller (*Leptosomus discolor*), also occurring in the Comoros, is not closely related to ground-rollers or rollers; it is not even in the order Coraciiformes as once hypothesized but is placed in its own order (Leptosomiformes) because its phylogenetic relationships are still unstable (Prum et al. 2015; Reddy et al. 2017). Evidence for population differentiation in *Leptosomus* on different islands in the Comoro archipelago needs further assessment with more detailed genetic and ecological information.

THE ASITIES (PHILEPITTIDAE)

It has long been recognized that the four suboscine species of Madagascar constitute a single radiation, traditionally recognized as the endemic family Philepittidae containing two genera, asities *Philepitta* and sunbird-asities *Neodrepanis*, with two species each (see Prum and Razafindratsita, pp. 1687–93). These two genera are quite divergent from one another in size and many morphological features, with *Philepitta* being relatively small and plump and having small bills and short tails, and *Neodrepanis* being even smaller and having long, decurved bills reminiscent of sunbirds and once earning them the moniker "false-sunbirds." Males of all species have colorful wattles or bare skin (caruncles) during breeding plumage, and the females are much drabber overall. While there is little to unite these genera apart from a few plumage features, shared behaviors, and the characteristic syrinx structure typical of suboscines, the asities definitively form a monophyletic clade and represent an endemic radiation (Prum 1993; Irestedt et al. 2006; Moyle et al. 2006). Phylogenetic studies show that asities are nested within the Old World radiation of broadbills (Eurylaimides) and are sister to a clade of Asian broadbills plus the African *Pseudocalyptomena*, which are now considered to form the Eurylaimidae *sensu stricto* (Moyle et al. 2006). Given their phylogenetic relationships, the most likely biogeographic reconstruction indicates that ancestral asities originated via dispersal from Asia rather than Africa as previously thought. The divergence of suboscines postdates Gondwanan breakup, but dispersal to Madagascar was likely still an ancient event (around 41 Mya) at a time when island fragments from the Indian subcontinent's path toward Asia might have formed a stepping-stone pathway facilitating movements between these landmasses (Warren et al. 2010).

THE MESITES (MESITORNITHIDAE)

Possibly the most enigmatic birds on Madagascar are the mesites of the family Mesitornithidae, whose evolutionary relationships have long baffled ornithologists (see A. Hawkins et al., pp. 1653–57). In 20th-century classifications based on morphological similarity, they were placed with rails and bustards in the Gruiformes, an order whose membership is now drastically altered with evidence from large-scale genomic data (Hackett et al. 2008). We now have strong evidence to support a sister relationship to sandgrouse (Pterocliformes), a discovery that is found across several phylogenomic studies (Hackett et al. 2008; Prum et al. 2015; Reddy et al. 2017). The clade of mesites and sandgrouse together is sister to the Columbiformes, comprising the pigeons and doves. Mesites, currently classified in their own order, Mesitornithiformes, include two genera—*Mesitornis* and *Monias*—with three extant species in total. These birds are generally cryptic ground dwellers that inhabit the understories of Malagasy forests.

THE JERIES (*NEOMIXIS*: CISTICOLIDAE)

The jeries are small, warbler-like birds (Figure 13.9b) whose phylogenetic relationships were muddled for many years. After the movement of one species (*Hartertula flavoviridis*) to the Bernieridae, the remaining three species of *Neomixis* have been shown to be monophyletic and part of the family Cisticolidae, known as African warblers (Nguembock et al. 2007; Olsson et al. 2013). Interestingly, the *Neomixis* clade is deeply divergent and sister to all remaining cisticolids, indicating that the Malagasy lineage of this family is older than previously hypothesized (Olsson et al. 2013). More analyses, especially genetic, are needed to understand their biogeography and diversification given that several subspecies have been described in recognition of substantial morphological variation within these species.

THE EMUTAILS (*BRADYPTERUS*: LOCUSTELLIDAE)

The two species of Malagasy emutails were at one point placed in their own genus, *Dromaeocercus*, and thought to be warblers in the family Sylviidae. Genetic evidence showed that *D. brunneus* (Brown Emutail) was embedded within the genus *Bradypterus* (Locustellidae), known as bush warblers, and was part of the many taxonomic changes in this genus and family (Alström et al. 2011). A subsequent study supported this and also found that *Amphilais seebohmi* (Gray Emutail) (Figure 13.9d) is also a *Bradypterus* and sister to the other emutail species, confirming again that this is an endemic radiation of locustellid warblers on Madagascar (Alström et al. 2018). The ancestor to emutails likely colonized from Africa more than 6 Mya. The family-level phylogenetic study also discovered remarkably high divergence between two samples of *B. brunneus* from different populations, indicating the possibility of cryptic diversification, which needs further study.

THE WOOD-RAILS (*MENTOCREX*: SAROTHRURIDAE)

Despite their worldwide distribution, rails have been notoriously understudied in terms of phylogenetics. A second species of *Mentocrex* was described recently (Goodman et al. 2011), making this genus a Malagasy endemic radiation. These forest-dwelling birds were previously considered congeneric with *Canirallus oculeus*, an African species, but recent studies show that *Mentocrex* species are not true rails in the family Rallidae but part of the related

Sarothruridae, or flufftails (García-R et al. 2014; Boast et al. 2019; see Safford, pp. 1657–60). A new study points to a biogeographically anomalous yet intriguing relationship with an extinct flightless group from New Zealand called adzebills (Boast et al. 2019).

THE MALAGASY WEAVERS (*NELICURVIUS*: PLOCEIDAE)

Two weaver species endemic to Madagascar were traditionally placed in the large genus *Ploceus*, including species from across Africa and Asia, and belonging to the family Ploceidae (see Craig, pp. 1712–13 and pp. 1714–15). Recent family-level analyses uncovered that the traditional genus *Ploceus* is not monophyletic and comprises multiple clades circumscribed by geographic region, such that the Asian weavers are a separate clade from the African and Malagasy species (De Silva et al. 2017, 2019). Even more remarkable is that the Malagasy weavers are deeply divergent and form a sister relationship to the entire clade of African weavers (renamed *Malimbus*). The two species of Malagasy weavers, now in a separate genus, *Nelicurvius*, descended from a lineage that likely dispersed from Africa around 5–7 Mya (De Silva et al. 2017).

THE FODIES (*FOUDIA*: PLOCEIDAE)

Another Malagasy group in the weaver family, Ploceidae, is the fodies (see Craig, pp. 1716–18). It remains unclear whether the two species on Madagascar, *Foudia madagascariensis* (Madagascar Fody) and *F. omissa* (Forest Fody), are each other's sisters, as this genus comprises multiple lineages that seem to readily disperse among western Indian Ocean islands (Warren et al. 2012; De Silva et al. 2019). More data are needed to clarify this issue as well as whether the fodies on Madagascar represent two distinct species (Warren et al. 2012; S. Reddy et al., unpublished data).

THE ROCK-THRUSHES (*MONTICOLA*: MUSCICAPIDAE)

In the past, the Malagasy rock-thrushes were placed in the genus *Pseudocossyphus*, but this is no longer recognized and they are now placed in the widespread Old World genus *Monticola* (Goodman and Weigt 2002; Zuccon and Ericson 2010b; Cruaud et al. 2011). The number of recognized species on Madagascar is in flux, with current genetic support for only two distinct species, *M. imerina* (Littoral Rock-thrush) in the southwest and *M. sharpei* (Forest Rock-thrush) including populations in different portions of the island, which may show some morphological distinctions (Figure 13.9c).

DOUBLE INVASIONS OF CONGENERS

A number of congeneric species on Madagascar are the result of independent colonizations to the island. Members of these seven genera are intriguing, as they are closely related and colonized in close succession, but these separate species often occupy different habitats. In some cases, these groups are apparently able to easily disperse between western Indian Ocean islands and may be the result of multiple colonizations in and/or out of Madagascar. Examples of these include *Coracopsis* parrots (Psittaculidae), *Nesillas* brush-warblers (Acrocephalidae) (Figure 13.9e), and *Cinnyris* sunbirds (Nectariniidae) (Warren et al. 2003; Kundu et al. 2012; Fuchs et al. 2016). Other cases, such as *Corythornis* kingfishers (Alcedinidae), represent multiple invasions from Africa (Andersen et al. 2017). The last category includes genera that are globally widespread and have multiple independent Malagasy lineages—such as *Accipiter* sparrowhawks (Accipitridae), *Anas* ducks (Anatidae), *Sarothrura* flufftails (Sarothruridae), and *Charadrius* plovers (Charadriidae).

FINAL COMMENTS

Regardless of emerging new details, the general pattern remains the same among endemic lineages—a predominance of very small genera, a scarcity of speciose ones, and a low level of congeneric sympatry (the only examples of which are *Xanthomixis*, *Newtonia*, *Neomixis*, and *Coua*). Furthermore, among both the vangas and the tetrakas, we see a pattern of large genetic distances between related or sister taxa. This suggests that the Malagasy avifauna retains the imprint of very ancient radiations, but it begs the question as to why more of these lineages have not speciated. Was there only a low rate of speciation after the first, ancient radiation that followed each colonizing event, and if so, why? Or does this pattern again indicate a high rate of recent extinctions on Madagascar (see Moreau 1966)?

This is an exciting period in research on the Malagasy avifauna. In addition to the recently published studies cited above, a great deal of ongoing research continues to increase our understanding of the phylogeny and biogeographic histories of the different Malagasy bird lineages. Another issue that remains is how many species are cryptic in widespread species and remain to be recognized. There is some evidence for this in recent works (Goodman et al. 1997c, 2011; Younger et al. 2018, 2019a, 2019b), and a more complete investigation will help decipher microendemism patterns on the island. We can also hope that the information now being gathered will lead to a more general understanding of the history of avian differentiation on Madagascar and will provide insights into some of the remaining mysteries, such as the general impoverishment of the avifauna and its (seemingly) low rates of speciation.

Subject editors: Roger J. Safford and Steven M. Goodman

SYSTEMATIC ACCOUNTS

WATERBIRDS

H. G. Young, R. E. Lewis, F. Razafindrajao, and A. I. Bin Aboudou

The diversity of waterbird species on Madagascar is low, with around 81 nonpasserine species including one kingfisher, compared with, for example, East Africa, where Kenya has around 180 nonpasserine waterbirds including kingfishers, as well as a wider range of wetland-living passerines (Lepage 2020). However, there is some endemism at the species (but not genus) level, and endemic subspecies have been recognized for some taxa, although several of these are based on subtle morphological differences and to date have not been examined using molecular tools. Many wetland species on the island are shared with the Afrotropical region. Others have a wider Old World or even global distribution, such as flamingos (family Phoenicopteridae), some wading birds (families Rostratulidae, Charadriidae, and Scolopacidae), and gulls and terns (family Laridae). The origins, as distinct from wider distribution, of Madagascar's wetland avifauna, as far as we know, are also varied, with a strong Afrotropical component (Keith 1980) but also Asian and even Australasian elements (Young 1996a; Young and Kear 2006); see the family accounts below.

A significant number of waterbird species are migrants, a few visiting to breed on Madagascar, but most arriving as nonbreeders. Twenty-four of the 29 species in the families Charadriidae and Scolopacidae recorded on Madagascar are nonbreeding migrants from the Palearctic (Table 13.12). Movements of other wetland birds between Madagascar and other areas of the world are poorly understood: *Ardeola idae* (Madagascar Pond-heron) (Figure 13.10d) and *Glareola ocularis* (Madagascar Pratincole) (Figure 13.10f) migrate to East Africa after breeding, and other species may be at least partial migrants, moving between Africa and Madagascar (e.g., Phoenicopteridae and Anatidae) (see Dodman and Diagana 2007).

Many other Malagasy bird species visit freshwater habitats to drink and bathe, and others may forage in wetlands of different kinds. It is therefore not unusual to find open-country birds such as sandgrouse (*Pterocles personatus*, Madagascar Sandgrouse) or parrots (*Coracopsis* spp. and *Agapornis canus*, Gray-headed Lovebird) at lake edges, or a variety of other species (e.g., *Falco newtoni*, Madagascar Kestrel; *Centropus toulou*, Madagascar Coucal; *Merops superciliosus*, Olive Bee-eater; *Foudia madagascariensis*, Madagascar Fody; as well as members of the families Apodidae and Hirundinidae) foraging over open water, or deep in among reedbeds or on "floating" islands a long way from the lakeshore. Several predatory birds such as *Asio capensis* (Marsh Owl), while regularly found in wetlands, may also occur in a variety of other habitats. However, within several other bird families some species are considered partially or largely dependent on wetland habitats (Table 13.13).

There have been very few studies of waterbird assemblages on Madagascar, with most studies from the Menabe and Melaky Regions in central western Madagascar (Young et al. 2006a, 2014; Roux and Bejoma 2009). In the following sections we review aspects of waterbirds based on taxonomic grouping. Several wetland birds have been well studied, and accordingly *Aythya innotata* (Madagascar Pochard) (see Rene de Roland and Young, pp. 1650–53), *Haliaeetus vociferoides* (Madagascar Fish-eagle) (see Rene de Roland and Thorstrom, pp. 1668–79), *Actophilornis albinucha* (Madagascar Jacana) (see D'Urban Jackson et al., pp. 1666–68), plovers in the genus *Charadrius* (see Zefania and Székely, pp. 1660–66), and rails (Rallidae and Sarothruridae) (see Safford, pp. 1657–60), also included in Table 13.13, are discussed in further detail elsewhere in this volume. While we focus on fresh water, including some inland lakes with high dissolved mineral (not only salt) concentrations, we also include in this chapter species associated primarily with coastal, and therefore brackish or saline, wetlands, particularly tidal mudflats, because nearly all these species also use freshwater or inland wetlands. We do not intend to discuss vagrants or irregular visitors such as *Pandion haliaetus* (Osprey) and *Recurvirostra avosetta* (Pied Avocet) (although vagrant waterbirds are included in Table 13.13), or seabirds (see Le Corre et al., pp. 1637–50).

HABITATS OF WETLAND BIRDS AND THE THREATS THEY FACE

Of particular interest to wetland birds are Madagascar's many lakes, which are often large and shallow, associated extensive sedge (Cyperaceae, including *Cyperus* [papyrus]; see Larridon et al., pp. 580–85) and *Phragmites* (reed) marshes, rivers, streams, large river estuaries, and mangroves (see Manjato et al., pp. 470–92 for a description of wetland plants and Cooke et al., pp. 311–58 for estuary and mangrove habitats).

A high proportion of native wetland birds are threatened with extinction (BirdLife International 2020a). This is mainly because most wetland habitats have suffered badly since human colonization of the island and are among the most degraded of all the country's ecosystems (Langrand and Wilmé 1993; Langrand and Goodman 1995; Young 1996b; Bamford et al. 2017). Siltation following extensive deforestation, pollution, introduced plants and animals (notably fish), and aridification and conversion of wetlands to rice paddies have all contributed to an overall decline in bird numbers. Extensive rice cultivation has not only modified many wetlands unfavorably for birds but has also brought many species into direct, generally detrimental, conflict with agriculturists, resulting in their persecution as pests.

A further threat comes from direct persecution of wetland birds for subsistence and "sport" hunting, which is somewhat widespread, often indiscriminate, and poorly regulated. Large waterbirds, especially herons (Ardeidae) but also storks (Ciconiidae), ibises (Threskiornithidae), and relatives, are found throughout Madagascar and are a familiar sight in any wetland area.

TABLE 13.12. **Bird families represented on Madagascar and the number of waterbird species considered to be dependent on freshwater or coastal habitat**

FAMILY	NUMBER OF SPECIES ON MADAGASCAR	NUMBER OF WATERBIRD SPECIES	NUMBER OF ENDEMIC WATERBIRD TAXA	
			SPECIES	SUBSPECIES
Anatidae	10	10	3	1
Numididae	1	0	0	0
Phasianidae	3	0	0	0
Phoenicopteridae	2	2	0	0
Podicipedidae	3	3	2	0
Columbidae	5	0	0	0
Mesitornithidae	3	0	0	0
Pteroclidae	1	0	0	0
Cuculidae	12	0	0	0
Caprimulgidae	2	0	0	0
Apodidae	5	0	0	0
Sarothruridae	4	2	2	0
Rallidae	8	10	3	2
Recurvirostridae	2	2	0	0
Charadriidae	9	5	2	1
Rostratulidae	1	1	0	0
Jacanidae	1	1	1	0
Scolopacidae	20	12	0	0
Turnicidae	1	0	0	0
Dromadidae	1	0	0	0
Glareolidae	2	2	1	0
Stercorariidae	5	0	0	0
Laridae	20	5	0	0
Ciconiidae	2	2	0	1
Anhingidae	1	1	0	0
Phalacrocoracidae	1	1	0	1
Pelecanidae	1	1	0	0
Scopidae	1	1	0	1
Ardeidae	14	14	2	4
Threskiornithidae	4	3	1	0
Pandionidae	1	1	0	0
Accipitridae	13	1	1	0
Tytonidae	2	0	0	0
Strigidae	4	0	0	0

FAMILY	NUMBER OF SPECIES ON MADAGASCAR	NUMBER OF WATERBIRD SPECIES	NUMBER OF ENDEMIC WATERBIRD TAXA	
			SPECIES	SUBSPECIES
Leptosomidae	1	0	0	0
Upupidae	1	0	0	0
Alcedinidae	2	1	1	0
Meropidae	2	0	0	0
Coraciidae	1	0	0	0
Brachypteraciidae	5	0	0	0
Falconidae	5	0	0	0
Psittaculidae	3	0	0	0
Philepittidae	4	0	0	0
Campephagidae	1	0	0	0
Oriolidae	1	0	0	0
Vangidae	23	0	0	0
Dicruridae	1	0	0	0
Monarchidae	1	0	0	0
Corvidae	2	0	0	0
Alaudidae	1	0	0	0
Cisticolidae	4	0	0	0
Acrocephalidae	3	1	1	0
Locustellidae	2	1	1	0
Bernieridae	13	0	0	0
Hirundinidae	5	0	0	0
Pycnonotidae	1	0	0	0
Zosteropidae	1	0	0	0
Sturnidae	3	0	0	0
Muscicapidae	5	0	0	0
Nectariniidae	2	0	0	0
Ploceidae	4	0	0	0
Estrildidae	2	0	0	0
Passeridae	1	0	0	0
Motacillidae	1	1	1	0

Note: Seabird families that typically do not occur in fresh water (Phaethontidae, Spheniscidae, Diomedeidae, Oceanitidae, Hydrobatidae, Procellariidae, Fregatidae, and Sulidae) are omitted.

Unfortunately, many species are persecuted, and because they often nest colonially, they are vulnerable to disturbance and nest robbing by local people, who take the eggs and young for food. Several species, particularly those with localized distribution, are threatened with extinction as a result.

ANSERIFORMES: ANATIDAE (WILDFOWL)

Unlike many other nonpasserine bird families, the Anatidae is well represented on Madagascar. Twelve recent resident species are known, compared to 14 in Kenya (Lewis and Pomeroy 1989) and

FIGURE 13.10 **A selection of characteristic waterbirds of Madagascar. A) *Ardea humbloti* (Madagascar Heron) along the sea cliffs at Saint Augustin, B) *Ardea purpurea* (Purple Heron) near Andasibe, C) *Mycteria ibis* (Yellow-billed Stork) in the Betsiboka Delta, D) *Ardeola idae* (Madagascar Pond-heron) near Oronjia, E) *Gallinago macrodactyla* (Madagascar Snipe) near Ranomafana, F) *Glareola ocularis* (Madagascar Pratincole) at Bemanevika, G) *Plegadis falcinellus* (Glossy Ibis) at Ankarafantsika, and H) *Charadrius tricollaris* (Three-banded Plover) along the road between Toliara and Ifaty.** (PHOTOS by K. Behrens.)

10 on the Indian subcontinent (Grimmett et al. 1998). However, unlike these other areas, Madagascar has no regular migratory species or nonbreeding visitors. The Palearctic-nesting *Anas querquedula* (Garganey) winters in Africa and Asia and has been recorded within the Malagasy Region—including Seychelles (Skerrett 1996), La Réunion (Barré and Barau 1982), the Comoros (Clément et al. 2008), and Rodrigues (Staub 1976)—but to our knowledge not yet on Madagascar.

The 12 wildfowl species show a wide range of origins (Young 1996a; Young and Kear 2006). Three are pantropical, seven show obvious African affinities (including two extinct sheldgoose species, subfamily Tadornini [see below], and surviving endemics *Thalassornis leuconotus* [White-backed Duck] and *A. melleri* [Meller's Duck]), and two (endemics *A. bernieri*, Madagascar Teal; and *Aythya innotata*) are closely related to Australasian species. Six of these wildfowl taxa are endemic.

Seasonal intra-island movements of Madagascar's wildfowl are poorly known. The breeding season of all species most likely depends on rainfall and may show a high degree of variation across Madagascar. For example, *Anas bernieri* shows marked local movements, with nonbreeding birds collecting in shallow wetlands during the dry season and molting flocks developing in more secluded sites (Young 2006).

Nonendemic Wildfowl

Two pantropical ducks, *Dendrocygna viduata* (White-faced Whistling-duck) (Figure 13.11a) and *D. bicolor* (Fulvous Whistling-duck), are widespread across Madagascar except in arid areas. While *D. bicolor* is often a quiet and unassuming duck of marshland, *D. viduata* is more regularly seen and is even found in central Antananarivo. Both whistling-duck species are still relatively common but are widely hunted throughout the year in most of their range.

Two African dabbling ducks, *Anas erythrorhyncha* (Red-billed Duck) and *Spatula hottentota* (Hottentot Teal) (Figure 13.11a), are common and widespread. Until 2000, breeding records of *A. erythrorhyncha* were rare, and it had been considered that this species

TABLE 13.13. **Wading birds (shorebirds) recorded on Madagascar**

SPECIES	RESIDENCY STATUS	HABITAT
Himantopus himantopus, Black-winged Stilt	Resident	4
Recurvirostra avosetta, Eurasian Avocet	Vagrant	3
Pluvialis squatarola, Gray Plover	Nonbreeder	3
P. fulva, Pacific Golden-plover	Nonbreeder	3
Charadrius mongolus, Lesser Sand-plover	Nonbreeder	3
C. leschenaultii, Greater Sand-plover	Nonbreeder	3
C. pecuarius, Kittlitz's Plover	Resident	4
C. hiaticula, Common Ringed-plover	Nonbreeder	3
C. thoracicus, Madagascar Plover	Resident endemic	2
C. tricollaris, Three-banded Plover	Resident	1
C. marginatus, White-fronted Plover	Resident	2
Rostratula benghalensis, Greater Painted-snipe	Resident	1
Actophilornis albinucha, Madagascar Jacana	Resident endemic	1
Numenius phaeopus, Whimbrel	Nonbreeder	2
N. arquata, Eurasian Curlew	Nonbreeder	3
Limosa lapponica, Bar-tailed Godwit	Nonbreeder	3
L. limosa, Black-tailed Godwit	Nonbreeder	4
Arenaria interpres, Ruddy Turnstone	Nonbreeder	3
Calidris pugnax, Ruff	Vagrant	1
C. acuminata, Sharp-tailed Sandpiper	Vagrant	1
C. ferruginea, Curlew Sandpiper	Nonbreeder	4
C. alba, Sanderling	Nonbreeder	3
C. minuta, Little Stint	Nonbreeder	2
C. subruficollis, Buff-breasted Sandpiper*	Vagrant	1
C. melanotos, Pectoral Sandpiper	Vagrant	1
Gallinago macrodactyla, Madagascar Snipe	Resident endemic	1
Xenus cinereus, Terek Sandpiper	Nonbreeder	3
Phalaropus lobatus, Red-necked Phalarope*	Vagrant	2
Actitis hypoleucos, Common Sandpiper	Nonbreeder	4
Tringa ochropus, Green Sandpiper	Vagrant	1
T. nebularia, Common Greenshank	Nonbreeder	4
T. stagnatilis, Marsh Sandpiper	Nonbreeder	1
T. glareola, Wood Sandpiper	Nonbreeder	1
Dromas ardeola, Crab-plover	Nonbreeder	3
Glareola maldivarum, Oriental Pratincole	Vagrant	1
G. ocularis, Madagascar Pratincole	Breeding endemic	1

Source: Status and habitat details are from Safford and Hawkins (2013).
Notes: Habitat: 1, predominantly fresh water; 2, predominantly coastal but may be recorded in fresh water; 3, coastal; and 4, possible in any suitable wetland.
*Added by Rush and Hoddinott (2014).

might be a migrant from tropical Africa (Langrand 1990). In 2000 several broods of ducklings and territorial pairs were found at Lake Alaotra and in nearby rivers. It is likely that this species breeds unobtrusively throughout Madagascar where conditions are suitable. *Spatula hottentota* is often a secretive duck, staying deep inside quiet, well-vegetated marshes. This diminutive species may, however, become more active at dusk and often feeds in agricultural areas and where cattle have disturbed lake edges.

Nettapus auritus (African Pygmy-goose) (Figure 13.11g) and *Sarkidiornis melanotos* (Knob-billed Duck) (Figure 13.11e) are tropical African ducks that are still found in reasonable numbers on Madagascar, particularly in the west. The latter species is also found in Asia. Both are most readily found in well-vegetated, quiet wetlands and are predominantly tree-hole nesters. Although *Sarkidiornis* may leave secluded areas to feed on agricultural land at dusk or to roost, *Nettapus* is only rarely found away from its main food,

FIGURE 13.11 **A selection of characteristic freshwater ducks and grebes of Madagascar. A) assorted ducks, from left: *Anas erythrorhyncha* (Red-billed Duck), two *Spatula hottentota* (Hottentot Teal), nine *Dendrocygna viduata* (White-faced Whistling-duck), with *Egretta ardesiaca* (Black Heron) in foreground, at Lake Tsarasaotra in Antananarivo; B) *Anas melleri* (Meller's Duck) at Lake Tsarasaotra in Antananarivo; C) *Anas bernieri* (Madagascar Teal) in the Betsiboka Delta; D) *Tachybaptus pelzelnii* (Madagascar Grebe) at Bemanevika; E) *Sarkidiornis melanotos* (Knob-billed Duck) at Lake Tsarasaotra in Antananarivo; F) *Gallinula chloropus* (Eurasian Moorhen) at Lake Tsarasaotra in Antananarivo; and G) *Nettapus auritus* (African Pygmy-goose) at Andranofasika, close to Ankarafantsika.** (PHOTOS by K. Behrens.)

Nymphaea (water lilies). *Sarkidiornis* is dramatically dimorphic: males are much larger than females, and this is easily seen as these ducks fly in long lines at dusk.

Endemic Wildfowl

The origins and conservation of Madagascar's endemic wildfowl species have been reviewed at the group level (Young 1996b; Young and Kear 2006; Young et al. 2013; Razafindrajao et al. 2017). Two species of presumed endemic Tadorninae, at least one of which is considered a close relative of *Alopochen aegyptiaca* (Egyptian Goose), are known only from subfossil remains (see Safford et al., pp. 1553–602). The exact former distribution on Madagascar of these species, *A. sirabensis* and *Centrornis majori*, is unknown, but based on excavated remains, both were once common in the southwest and the Central Highlands.

Aythya innotata was once common at Lake Alaotra (Webb 1936; Delacour 1966), and its rapid decline at this site may have directly followed the introduction into Lake Alaotra of herbivorous fish such as *Tilapia*, which have dramatically changed the floral composition of the lake and its associated marsh (see Young and Smith 1989; Wilmé 1994). *Aythya innotata*, despite several extensive searches at Lake Alaotra in the 1980s and 1990s, and the capture of a living bird there in 1991, was not positively observed in nature from 1960 until rediscovery near Bemanevika in 2006. This species is covered in more detail herein (see Rene de Roland and Young, pp. 1650–53).

The tropical *Thalassornis leuconotus* is represented on Madagascar by a smaller, darker subspecies, *T. l. insularis*. This unassuming little duck prefers quiet, thickly vegetated lakes and pools, often within forested areas. It is vegetarian, diving for the seeds and vegetative parts of *Nymphaea*, and is often found in association with *Nettapus*, both species blending with the emergent vegetation. Occasionally flocking in open water but normally quite reluctant to fly, it is seminomadic, moving to new areas in accordance with water and salinity levels (salinity increases in west coast lakes as they dry out in the dry season and *Nymphaea* dies back, regenerating following rainfall). This duck is apparently easy to catch and is extensively hunted—its proportionately large eggs are also a much sought-after food source (Young et al. 2006b).

Anas bernieri is restricted to a narrow coastal strip along the west coast of Madagascar, and until recently this small, uniformly soft brown duck was probably the least known of the country's wildfowl (Figure 13.11c). Seen only rarely during the years of European exploration, *A. bernieri* was considered rediscovered in 1969 (Andriamampianina 1976), when small numbers were found at Bemamba south of Antsalova (Salvan 1970). No more than 120 birds were on Lake Bemamba in 1973 (D. Scott and Lubbock 1974); however, no nests were recorded, and indeed the exact nesting season and preferred habitat were unknown. This species is the westernmost representative of the principally Australasian gray teal group, which includes five species of often highly dispersive small ducks, such as the abundant and well-known *A. gracilis* (Gray Teal) of Australia and New Zealand (Young et al. 1998).

Survey work and an extensive program of field research, initially centered on Lake Bemamba, since the early 1990s has begun to answer many of the questions surrounding *A. bernieri*. This duck nests in tree holes in west coast mangrove trees (*Avicennia*), following the onset of the wet season, during December–March (Young et al. 2001). After the young have fledged, groups often move to open, shallow wetlands such as drying lakes or estuaries and exposed sandbars. Flocks of adults may migrate annually to the same safe and often thickly vegetated wetlands before molting wing feathers and entering a short flightless period (Young 2006; Razafindrajao et al. 2012).

Anas bernieri has been found in small numbers at many locations from Lokia Bay in the north to Lake Tsimanampesotse in the south; the only concentrations recorded have been at Lake Antsamaka, near Bemamba, and in the estuaries of the Betsiboka, Mahavavy, and Tsiribihina Rivers (Young 2013). Teal are being forced out of many suitable areas as marsh reclamation for rice paddies increases in the western portion of the island. Adults are hunted during molt and nests are often systematically robbed of eggs. Suitable nest sites may also be in short supply.

Anas melleri is principally a duck of the extensive drainage system of the eastern portion of the Central Highlands (Figure 13.11b). It can be found breeding in the numerous narrow streams and their adjoining marshes that meander through the forested uplands (some pairs may remain in this habitat all year, but this has not been confirmed). The species has been recorded from sea level to 2500 m, including sites such as along the Pangalanes Canal and in rivers and small ponds at Andringitra and Kalambatritra (ZICOMA 1999). There have been occasional sporadic records from western Madagascar, probably resulting from post-breeding dispersal. This duck was undoubtedly once more widespread in the now highly degraded Central Highlands. Breeding occurs principally after the rains (November–January), although adults may be present on some rivers throughout the year. Numbers congregate to feed and roost on open water in large lakes (Young and Smith 1989). Lake Alaotra has often been considered the stronghold; however, while small numbers do breed in the narrow channels and pools within the marsh, the large numbers that have been recorded here may include many nonbreeders.

Anas melleri has strong pair bonds when breeding, is highly territorial when nesting, and may be very aggressive to conspecifics—all habits suited to river nesting (Young 1995). *Anas melleri* is part of the mallard group of dabbling ducks but is not an island form of *A. platyrhynchos* (contra Lorenz 1941 and others; see Young and Rhymer 1998; Lavretsky et al. 2014). The large, distinctive, narrow bill of *A. melleri* is that of a generalist and is possibly useful for feeding on aquatic mollusks. The exact diet of wild individuals, however, is not known. *Anas melleri* is shy when on territory and is easily disturbed by human presence. Large-scale habitat modification, particularly deforestation and the conversion of riverside marsh to rice cultivation, as well as relentless hunting in many places, has seriously reduced numbers of this duck.

The four surviving endemic taxa are all threatened with extinction: the IUCN Red List includes *Aythya innotata* as Critically Endangered, and *Anas bernieri* and *A. melleri* as Endangered, while *Thalassornis l. insularis* is considered Endangered at the subspecies level.

PODICIPEDIFORMES: PODICIPEDIDAE (GREBES)

The plight of Madagascar's two endemic grebes has been reasonably well documented (Voous and Payne 1965; A. Hawkins et al. 2000; Safford 2013i). The largest of these small waterbirds, the heavy-billed, fish-eating *Tachybaptus rufolavatus* (Alaotra Grebe) was short winged and may have been close to flightless. This endemic species was apparently restricted to Lake Alaotra, where intense habitat modification, alteration of the fish fauna following the widespread introduction of non-native fish, and modern fishing techniques pushed it toward extinction. It is also possible that hybridization with the smaller *T. ruficollis* (Little Grebe), a species recorded in increasing numbers on Madagascar since the 19th century, helped lead to the demise of *T. rufolavatus*, which may have been last seen in 1988 (A. Hawkins et al. 2000). The Alaotra Grebe was declared Extinct in 2010. *Tachybaptus ruficollis* today is widespread and, able to best exploit the many non-native fish species on Madagascar's wetlands, is the most common species of grebe on the island, but it too is subject to trapping in nets—few if any grebes of any species have been recorded at Lake Alaotra in recent years.

The endemic *T. pelzelnii* (Madagascar Grebe) (Figure 13.11d) is more widespread than *T. rufolavatus* was and it is unlikely that hybridization with *T. ruficollis* has been a problem with this species. *Tachybaptus pelzelnii* inhabits quiet, well-vegetated pools and is regularly found in rivers, even deep into forest; its more insect- and crustacean-based diet compared to the fish-eating *T. ruficollis* and *T. rufolavatus* reduces competition, allowing this grebe to thrive in areas without fish. All grebes, however, are vulnerable to habitat modification, accidental capture in monofilament fishing nets, and pollution. Numbers are generally low and in decline, so the species is considered Endangered.

PHOENICOPTERIFORMES: PHOENICOPTERIDAE (FLAMINGOS)

Phoenicopterus roseus (Greater Flamingo) and *Phoeniconaias minor* (Lesser Flamingo) occur very sporadically in western and southern Madagascar. Flocks of varying size, from a few to hundreds of individuals, are often encountered in shallow freshwater areas as well as in more saline environments. Some lakes, like Antsamaka, become saline as water levels drop during the dry season, becoming suitable for flamingos only after aquatic vegetation dies back. The name Antsamaka is derived from *samaky*, the Malagasy name for flamingo. Other sites, like Lake Bemamba, may have been more hospitable to flamingos in the past—a reduction in salinity following an undated change of inflow from Soahiny River between the 1970s and early 1990s allowed increased rice cultivation and restricted the necessary habitat for flamingos.

Both flamingo species are nomadic on the island, often flying at night. The ecology and movements of flamingos on Madagascar are poorly understood and in need of intensive study; *Phoeniconaias minor* has not been recorded nesting on Madagascar and is presumably represented by birds migrating from Africa. Movement from Africa was first proven in 2016 when a satellite-tracked bird flew from South Africa to Madagascar. This bird returned to Mozambique in 2018 (Endangered Wildlife Trust 2018). *Phoenicopterus ruber* has been known to nest on salt lakes (e.g., Lake Tsimanampesotse and Lake Ihotry) but seemingly had not done so since the 1970s (Safford 2013j), until nests with eggs and juveniles were found at Tsimanampesotse in December 2007 (S. Zefania, unpublished data); no subsequent reports of breeding are known. Both flamingo species are hunted, and it is unlikely that they will nest successfully with any regularity unless afforded full protection on their breeding grounds.

GRUIFORMES: SAROTHRURIDAE (FLUFFTAILS AND WOOD-RAILS) AND RALLIDAE (RAILS)

Madagascar's freshwater marshes, swamps, and lakes offer prime habitats for several rail species, which are considered to belong in two families, the exclusively African and Malagasy Sarothruridae and the globally distributed Rallidae. The Sarothruridae includes two species of *Sarothrura* flufftails, and two of *Mentocrex* wood-rails; all are endemic but the latter are forest rather than wetland birds. The eight species of Rallidae are arranged in six genera, all dependent on wetlands; two species are endemic to Madagascar, another to the Malagasy Region, and others such as *Gallinula chloropus* (Common Gallinule) (Figure 13.11f) are widespread throughout parts of the Old World. All are described in more detail elsewhere in this volume (see Safford, pp. 1657–60).

CHARADRIIFORMES: RECURVIROSTRIDAE, CHARADRIIDAE, ROSTRATULIDAE, JACANIDAE, SCOLOPACIDAE, DROMADIDAE, GLAREOLIDAE (WADING BIRDS, SHOREBIRDS), AND LARIDAE (GULLS AND TERNS)

Most wading bird species recorded in Malagasy wetlands are nonbreeding migrants from the Palearctic, and of these several have been recorded only as vagrants (Table 13.13). Some migrant waders are more frequently found on the seashore or in saline habitats such as salt pans or estuarine mudflats (see Young et al. 2006a, 2014; Roux and Bejoma 2009) but may move to fresh water; *Tringa nebularia* (Common Greenshank), *Calidris ferruginea* (Curlew Sandpiper), and *Actitis hypoleucos* (Common Sandpiper) are the most common examples. Nonbreeding birds, particularly immatures, may stay on Madagascar during the northern summer months.

The widely distributed *Himantopus himantopus* (Black-winged Stilt) is resident in suitable wetland habitat throughout Madagascar. Deep in marshes, *Rostratula benghalensis* (Greater Painted-snipe) is still reasonably common in certain areas, whereas the endemic *Gallinago macrodactyla* (Madagascar Snipe) (Figure 13.10e), found mostly in the north and east, has declined with loss of marshes in the Central Highlands. *Gallinago macrodactyla* is considered Vulnerable on the Red List. The endemic *Glareola ocularis* (Madagascar Pratincole) (Figure 13.10f), also considered Vulnerable, nests on and among rocks in rivers and, less commonly, elsewhere. Flocks often gather to feed in grassland or at lake edges. The pratincole breeds more commonly in eastern Madagascar, from September to April. Records from the west involve principally birds migrating to or from Africa, although some breeding occurs in the northwest (Safford 2013k). This species was not uncommon along certain rivers in eastern Madagascar until a few decades ago, but in recent years it seems to be reduced in numbers.

Seven small plovers, genus *Charadrius*, are recorded on Madagascar. The nonbreeding *C. hiaticula* (Common Ringed-plover), and *C. leschenaultii* (Greater Sand-plover) and *C. mongolus* (Lesser Sand-plover) are typically found on the coast (Safford 2013l). Four other species are resident: *C. thoracicus* (Madagascar Plover) is restricted to the west and southwest coasts (P. Long et al. 2008; Zefania et al. 2008) and is found alongside two more widespread close relatives, *C. pecuarius* (Kittlitz's Plover) and *C. marginatus* (White-fronted Plover; Madagascar race *C. m. tenellus*). *Charadrius thoracicus* is most often associated with saline habitats and coastal short grassland. However, it has been regularly recorded in small numbers at the edges of shallow freshwater lakes (e.g., Lake Bemamba). *Charadrius thoracicus* is considered Vulnerable. The more widespread *C. tricollaris* (Three-banded Plover) (Figure 13.10h) on Madagascar is morphologically and genetically distinct from its African counterparts (dos Remedios et al. 2020); although usually treated as an endemic subspecies (*C. t. bifrontatus*), it may deserve species status. This plover is often found along stream edges and in rice fields. More details on members of this genus are presented herein (see Zefania and Székely, pp. 1660–66).

The endemic *Actophilornis albinucha* is found throughout the island in well-vegetated waters and is considered Near Threatened. However, in view of recent declines it may need to be treated as a threatened species (D'Urban Jackson et al. 2019; see D'Urban Jackson et al., pp. 1666–68).

While many tern species are recorded on Madagascar (see Safford and Hawkins 2013), only *Chlidonias hybrida* (Whiskered Tern) is regularly found in freshwater habitats, where it also nests. This species is widespread and may gather in large flocks (individuals may migrate to Africa), often feeding over marsh, open water, or dry ground. *Hydroprogne caspia* (Caspian Tern) is more a coastal bird; however, small numbers regularly fly from the coast to roost, wash, and feed in freshwater lakes, (e.g., Lake Bemamba). Two gull species are resident on Madagascar, and of these, only *Chroicocephalus cirrocephalus* (Gray-hooded Gull) is regularly found on fresh water—small flocks are often found on Central Highland lakes and on the west coast. *Larus dominicanus* (Kelp Gull) is restricted to the south and southwest coasts; this large coastal species may fly short distances inland along rivers or to reach lakes such as Tsimanampesotse (see Le Corre et al., pp. 1637–50).

Two further families in the Charadriiformes, Turnicidae (buttonquails) and Stercorariidae (skuas), are represented on Madagascar but do not occur in freshwater habitats (see Safford et al., pp. 1553–602, and Le Corre et al., pp. 1637–50, respectively, for more details).

CICONIIFORMES: CICONIIDAE (STORKS AND OPENBILLS)

Mycteria ibis (Yellow-billed Stork) (Figure 13.10c) and *Anastomus lamelligerus* (African Openbill) are found predominantly in western Madagascar, the latter represented by the endemic subspecies *A. l. madagascariensis*. Both species have undoubtedly declined in numbers.

SULIFORMES: ANHINGIDAE (ANHINGAS) AND PHALACROCORACIDAE (CORMORANTS)

Microcarbo africanus (Reed Cormorant) and *Anhinga rufa* (African Darter) are common African species, represented on Madagascar by the endemic subspecies *M. a. pictilis* and *A. r. vulsini*, respectively. Both are relatively widespread on the island, although more common in the north and west, and are hunted or accidentally captured with monofilament fishing nets. Both were formerly present on Lake Alaotra but in recent years appear to have been absent from this site; they may be found in nearby less developed areas. Darters are often found in forest lakes and may roost in trees, on exposed sandbars, and on short grass, while cormorants prefer marsh and reed-fringed, quiet waters. Both species nest colonially, cormorants often with herons.

Two further suliform families, Fregatidae (frigatebirds) and Sulidae (boobies), are represented in Madagascar waters but are restricted to marine rather than freshwater habitats (see Le Corre et al., pp. 1637–50).

PELECANIFORMES: PELECANIDAE (PELICANS), SCOPIDAE (HAMERKOP), ARDEIDAE (HERONS, EGRETS, AND BITTERNS), AND THRESKIORNITHIDAE (IBISES AND SPOONBILLS)

Pelecanus rufescens (Pink-backed Pelican), now a rare visitor from Africa to western Madagascar, formerly bred in the Antsalova region during the 1950s and 1960s, but because it was relatively tame and confiding, it was probably exterminated by villagers (Milon et al. 1973). One or two individuals of *P. rufescens* were seen at Lake Bedo in western Madagascar in 2003 and 2004 (Mwema and Razafindrajao 2006); there have been no further sightings of this species at the site despite regular visits, which presumably indicates that today it is a vagrant to Madagascar.

Scopus umbretta (Hamerkop) is represented on Madagascar by the endemic subspecies *S. u. tenuirostris* and remains reasonably common, more so in the Central Highlands, where declines in recent decades have been noted (S. M. Goodman, unpublished data), and in the west. Its large stick-and-grass domed nest, up to 1.8 m in diameter and 5–10 m above the ground in a tree fork, is often very obvious. Hamerkops feed on animal prey in areas of rice cultivation and may be protected in some areas by local customs (Sartain and Hawkins 2013a).

Among the herons, white egrets are usually the most conspicuous species: *Ardea alba* (Great Egret), *Egretta garzetta* (Little Egret), and *Bubulcus ibis* (Cattle Egret) are found in all freshwater habitats and are often common in areas of rice cultivation and alongside human activity. There are large colonies even in Antananarivo, but only at protected sites where nests are more difficult to rob. The taxonomy of *E. garzetta* is interesting and still unresolved: this bird, under the name *dimorpha*, has been considered a full species ("Dimorphic Egret") or a subspecies of *E. garzetta* or *E. gularis*, which are sometimes themselves considered conspecific (see Kushlan and Hancock 2005; Turner 2010; del Hoyo et al. 2020). Two color morphs occur on Madagascar: the white form predominates inland and in freshwater habitats, while the dark form is more common in coastal areas. *Egretta garzetta dimorpha* also breeds on the Aldabra Atoll (Seychelles) and in East Africa (Kushlan and Hancock 2005; Sartain and Hawkins 2013b). *Egretta ardesiaca* (Black Egret) is locally common (Figure 13.11a), particularly in the west. However, marked declines have been noted (Martínez-Vilalta et al. 2020).

Ardeola ralloides (Squacco Heron) is very common, with no evidence of significant decline (Sartain and Hawkins 2013c). Often more shy than egrets, it has adapted well to human-modified environments. The endemic *A. idae* (Madagascar Pond-heron) (Figure 13.10d) is very similar in most plumages (except adult breeding) to *A. ralloides* but is more restricted in its choice of habitat and is less likely to occur on agricultural land. *Ardeola idae* breeds mainly on Madagascar, with smaller populations on Mayotte (Comoro archipelago), Europa (southern Mozambique Channel), and Aldabra Atoll (Seychelles archipelago), and migrates to East Africa for the nonbreeding season. It is recorded on Madagascar mainly from October to May, but some appear to remain year-round (Rabarisoa et al. 2020), and it is more common in the west. This heron still nests in very small numbers in Antananarivo but is recognized as globally Endangered and has possibly declined through competition with *A. ralloides*, the latter species being so much more successful in modified habitats (Kushlan and Hafner 2000). An international action plan for the conservation of *A. idae* was published in 2008 (Ndang'ang'a and Sande 2008). The population in 2016 was estimated at around 1100 breeding birds globally, of which around 800 were on Madagascar and the rest mainly on Mayotte; at colonies with long-term monitoring, the population had declined by around half since 1993 (Rabarisoa et al. 2020). Studies to track movements began in 2020.

Nycticorax nycticorax (Black-crowned Night-heron), which is distinctly crepuscular and nocturnal, and *Butorides striata* (Striated Heron), which is diurnal, are found throughout the country in suitable habitat, even extremely modified wetlands, and are reasonably common. The latter species is represented by the endemic subspecies *B. s. rutenbergi*. Both herons can be seen at Lake Anosy and other wetlands in Antananarivo. *Ixobrychus minutus* (Little Bittern), represented by the endemic subspecies *I. m. podiceps*, is found in reedbeds and dense marsh vegetation at many locations on the island. Nowhere is it particularly common. It has been suspected that the Eurasian subspecies, *I. m. minutus*, may occasionally winter on Madagascar.

Ardea cinerea (Gray Heron) and *A. purpurea* (Purple Heron) (Figure 13.10b) are represented on the island by the regionally endemic subspecies *A. c. firasa* and *A. p. madagascariensis*. *Ardea purpurea*, possibly by virtue of its more retiring habits and often solitary nesting, is more common and widespread. The large *A. humbloti* (Madagascar Heron) (Figure 13.10a) is found principally in the west; it is almost confined to Madagascar, but small numbers also breed on Mayotte (Jeanne et al. 2015). This impressive bird is occasionally seen in rice fields, as well as in shallow lakes and rivers; it is Endangered by habitat loss and persecution. Two other large herons, *A. goliath* (Goliath Heron) and *A. melanocephala* (Black-headed Heron), have been recorded as vagrants to western Madagascar (Safford and Hawkins 2013).

Three ibis species occur on the island, of which two are endemic. However, one, the Near Threatened *Lophotibis cristata* (Madagascar Crested Ibis), is predominantly a forest bird. *Threskiornis bernieri* (Madagascar Sacred Ibis) is a localized wetland bird of the west coast (and Aldabra Atoll, which holds a different subspecies, *T. b. abbotti*). This rare bird, occasionally seen in fresh water, is more at home in estuaries and mangroves and is considered Endangered. It was until recently considered conspecific with *T. aethiopicus* (African Sacred Ibis), from which it differs in structure, pale eye color, plumage, and displays; the latter are unique in the genus, both in the position and use of the inflatable neck sac and in the accompanying postures (Collar 2013a). *Plegadis falcinellus* (Glossy Ibis) (Figure 13.10g) is found in Africa, Europe, Asia, North and South America, and Australasia, and on Madagascar it is relatively common, particularly in the western portion of the island. This is one of the few Malagasy waterbirds that have recently increased in numbers (Rabarisoa 2019), and it may be found in a variety of wetland habitats, including cultivated areas. *Platalea alba* (African Spoonbill) is found mostly in the west but has markedly declined in numbers.

OTHER BIRD ORDERS ASSOCIATED WITH WETLANDS

Two kingfisher species (Coraciiformes: Alcedinidae) are endemic to Madagascar. *Corythornis madagascariensis* (Madagascar Pygmy-kingfisher) is restricted to forest, while *C. vintsioides* (Madagascar Malachite-kingfisher) is common throughout most of the country in almost all wetlands, of any size, and regularly lives close to humans.

Many passerine species (Passeriformes) are found in suitable wetland habitat. However, a small number are generally considered to be dependent on freshwater habitats. The endemic *Motacilla flaviventris* (Madagascar Wagtail, family Motacillidae), *Acrocephalus newtoni* (Madagascar Swamp-warbler, family Acrocephalidae), and *Bradypterus seebohmi* (Gray Emutail, family Locustellidae) are found principally in association with marshes, streams, or the water's edge. *Bradypterus seebohmi* is restricted to relatively high-elevation (above 700 m) marshlands in the eastern moist evergreen forests, while the other two species are much more widespread. The wagtail is often found in towns, including central Antananarivo, in places living seemingly independently of wetlands.

CONCLUSION

Wetlands contain unique aspects of the flora and fauna of Madagascar and, by way of their importance for rice paddies, are also integral to the way of life of most of the island's human population. A long history of human modification and destruction of these habitats, especially freshwater wetlands, is pushing marsh-dwelling birds toward extinction. Wetlands were initially neglected in Madagascar's reserve network, and wetland birds were afforded little effective legal protection. However, this has been substantially rectified with the creation of several large and small wetland protected areas; those with substantial freshwater areas or other inland wetland types include Bemanevika, Lake Alaotra, Torotorofotsy, Bombetoka Beloboka, Mahavavy Kinkony, Mandrozo, Tsimembo-Manambolomaty, Ambondrobe, Mangoky Ihotry, Amoron'i Onilahy, and Tsimanampesotse (Goodman et al. 2018); many other sites, dominated by other habitats, include some freshwater wetlands.

Conservation projects, often species based, have been and continue to be implemented, with education awareness programs increasingly focusing on wetlands and their inhabitants, and community-based wetland conservation and restoration programs at many freshwater sites including several of those mentioned above and also Lake Sofia (Rene de Roland and Young, pp. 1650–53; Goodman et al. 2018); mangrove restoration is also taking place at various sites. Madagascar became a contracting party to the Ramsar Convention on Wetlands in 1998 and to date has designated and committed to effectively manage 20 Ramsar sites (Wetlands of International Importance), most including significant areas of freshwater wetlands. It can only be hoped that the diversity, value, and spectacle of the country's wetlands will continue throughout the 21st century (e.g., Young et al. 2013).

Subject editors: Roger J. Safford and Steven M. Goodman

SEABIRDS

M. Le Corre, E. Bemanaja, A. Mbelomanana, A. Jaeger, R. Rabarisoa, L. Andriatahina, and T. E. Davies

As well as nearly 5000 km of coastline, Madagascar has 270 offshore islands and islets that could be suitable for breeding seabirds, suggesting the potential for a rich breeding seabird fauna. However, the current abundance and diversity of breeding seabirds are lower than on other islands in the western Indian Ocean, which is, for the purposes of this contribution, defined as the area between the east coast of Africa and 75°E, and between 27°S and 15°N (see map in Danckwerts et al. 2014). Eleven seabird species are known to breed on Madagascar (including its islets), out of 30 that breed in the western Indian Ocean. The total number of breeding seabirds is around 78,000 pairs, representing fewer than 3% of the total number of breeding pairs in the western Indian Ocean (Danckwerts et al. 2014; M. Le Corre, unpublished data). These figures may be overestimates in the absence of recent and complete censuses at some islands that were known to hold seabird colonies in the past. Many of these islands have not been visited for many years, and populations may have declined or disappeared as a result of hunting and egg harvest, which continue to be a conservation problem on Madagascar. A few islets are now well protected and consequently seabird colonies are recovering rapidly, which demonstrates Madagascar's great potential for seabird conservation through the reduction or abatement of human pressures on seabirds.

As a very large island, Madagascar also has a correspondingly large Exclusive Economic Zone (EEZ), defined as a band extending 200 nautical miles (370 km) from the shore; typically, any point within an overlapping area with another state defaults to the nearest state. Madagascar's EEZ covers around 1.2 million km² and extends from tropical waters at around 10°S to subtropical waters (with a series of seamounts of potential interest to foraging seabirds) as far as 29°S. Such an area would be expected to attract seabirds from tropical and southern regions of the Indian Ocean and beyond. However, the nonbreeding seabird communities of Madagascar, or specifically its EEZ, have been poorly documented up to now.

In this contribution we first present the main seabird colonies known from Madagascar, including the breeding species, population trends, threats, and conservation measures. We then review the nonbreeding species that can be observed within the EEZ of Madagascar. Finally, we review the status and ecology of the main breeding and nonbreeding species with a focus on certain case studies and on marine Important Bird and Biodiversity Areas. The information and data presented herein are derived from the literature, unpublished field trip reports and data sets, and unpublished university higher degree studies.

MAIN SEABIRD BREEDING COLONIES

The nine main regions of Madagascar known to host significant seabird colonies are discussed below (Tables 13.14 and 13.15) and illustrated in Figure 13.12. Most of these are around the northern tip of the country or along the west coast, with only one breeding site known along the east coast (with breeding seabirds now possibly extinct), and two islets in the south. For seabird breeding sites included in marine or coastal protected areas, we use the place names and legal status presented in Goodman et al. (2018) and in the Marine Protection Atlas (2020).

1. Islets off Toamasina (Nosy Fonga, N. Faho, N. Dombala)—East Coast

A small multispecies colony of terns was found on Nosy Dombala in 1971 (Salvan 1971) totaling 5500 pairs of *Onychoprion fuscatus* (Sooty Tern), 200 pairs of *Anous stolidus* (Brown Noddy), 100 pairs of *Sterna dougallii* (Roseate Tern), 60 pairs of *Thalasseus bergii* (Great Crested Tern), and 20 pairs of *Hydroprogne caspia* (Caspian Tern). This multispecies colony was previously mentioned by Milon (1950). However, the islets are only 5–6 km from the mainland and are easily accessible, and consequently the colony has been heavily poached (Milon 1950; Salvan 1971). A visit to the islets by BirdLife International in June 1998 (ZICOMA 1999, 2001), the start of the expected breeding season, did not find any breeding seabirds, suggesting that the colony may now be extinct. However, the absence of breeding seabirds may also be a result of seasonal or interannual changes in breeding activities. We are not aware of any more recent ornithological surveys of these islets.

2. East Coast of Antsiranana—Northern Tip

This vast region includes the islets of Mer d'Emeraude, the islets of Sakalava Bay, the Ambodivahibe Marine Protected Area (just south of Antrema, south of Antsiranana Bay), and Nosy Manampaho, an islet of the Nosy Ankao archipelago (80 km south of the Antsiranana Bay) and falling within the Loky Manambato protected area.

Mer d'Emeraude: this is a wide lagoon protected by a coral reef in the north of Antsiranana Bay. It includes 11 uninhabited rocky islands and islets covered by dense bushes. Milon (1946) found only 12 to 15 nests of *Phaethon lepturus* (White-tailed Tropicbird) on one of these islets (Nosy Diégo). He also noticed that the species was heavily poached by local people. Nosy Antali Be, the main islet of the Mer d'Emeraude, was visited in July 2008 (Le Corre and Bemanaja 2009), and only one pair of *P. lepturus* was found breeding. Introduced *Rattus rattus* (Black Rat), a known predator of many seabird species, is abundant on all islets of the area. The current status of *P. lepturus* in Mer d'Emeraude is unknown.

Oronjia, Sakalava Bay, and Ambodivahibe: this area is just to the south of Antsiranana Bay. It includes the peninsula of Oronjia (Orangéa), which is a protected area, along with the cliffs of Cap Miné, five rocky islets off Sakalava Bay, and eight islets of the Ambodivahibe

TABLE 13.14. Seabird species, populations, trends, and threats at the nine main seabird colonies or groups of colonies in Madagascar

AREA NAME	BREEDING SPECIES	NUMBER OF BREEDING PAIRS	YEAR OF LAST SURVEY (AND FIRST AUTHOR)	TREND	THREAT	CONSERVATION STATUS	STATE OF KNOWLEDGE
1) Islets off Toamasina (Nosy Fonga, Nosy Faho, Nosy Dombala)	*A. stolidus*	200	1971 (Salvan)	Possibly extinct	Egg harvest and hunting	Unprotected	Very poor (no census since 1971)
	O. fuscatus	5500	No birds found in 1998				
	H. caspia	20					
	S. dougallii	100					
	T. bergii	60					
2) East coast of Antsiranana	*O. fuscatus*	48,600	1947 (Nosy Tsara, Milon) 2012 (Nosy Bataiza, Rabarisoa)	Increasing	Invasive *Rattus rattus*	Ambodivahibe Marine Protected Area (Bataiza) and National Park of the Loky Manambato (Manampaho)	Good. Nosy Bataiza requires resurvey (last census in 2012). Current status of large colony of *H. caspia* found by Milon in 1947 at Nosy Tsara is unknown.
	H. caspia	? 65	2018 (Nosy Manampaho, Le Corre)				
	S. dougallii	250					
	T. bergii	3360					
	P. lepturus	? A few pairs					
3) Nosy Hara Marine National Park and Tanjon' Androntany (Cap Saint Sébastien)	*O. fuscatus*	2000	2013 (Bemanaja)	Unknown, possibly increasing in the protected area	Invasive *Rattus rattus* and *Mus musculus*; egg harvest	Nosy Hara Marine National Park	Good for a few islands, poor for the rest, especially the most remote
	O. anaethetus	30					
	H. caspia	24					
	T. bergii	10,800					
	P. lepturus	15					
4) Nosy Mitsio and surroundings	*P. lepturus*	? A few pairs	No census	Unknown	Unknown	Ankarea Marine Protected Area	Poor (no census)
	Fregata spp. (roost)	?					
	Su. leucogaster	250					
5) Nosy Be and the islets between Nosy Be and Analava	*P. lepturus*	15	No census	Unknown	Unknown	Ankivonjy Marine Protected Area	Poor (no census)
	Su. leucogaster	"a few dozen"					
6) Iles Barren	*O. fuscatus*	25	2008 (Bemanaja)	Decreasing	Egg harvest and hunting	Future Nosy Barren Marine Protected Area	Medium (no census since 2007)
	O. anaethetus	500					
	S. dougallii	1750					

AREA NAME	BREEDING SPECIES	NUMBER OF BREEDING PAIRS	YEAR OF LAST SURVEY (AND FIRST AUTHOR)	TREND	THREAT	CONSERVATION STATUS	STATE OF KNOWLEDGE
7) Islets off Morombe and Andavadaoka	*Ar. pacifica*	125	1965 (Appert); 2008 (Bemanaja, partial census)	Decreasing	Hunting	Locally managed Velondriake marine area	Poor (no complete census since 1965, partial census in 2007)
8) Nosy Vé	*L. dominicanus*	"a few"	2018 (Le Corre)	Increasing	None	Community-based protection	Very good
9) Nosy Manitra and Nosimborona	*O. fuscatus*	100	1948 (Milon), 2008 (Bemanaja, no census)	Decreasing	Egg harvest and hunting	Unprotected	Poor (no census since 1948)
	O. anaethetus	100					
	H. caspia	25					
	S. dougallii	4000					
	P. rubricauda	800					

Notes: See Figure 13.12. The genera of breeding species are *A.* (*Anous*), *Ar.* (*Ardenna*), *H.* (*Hydroprogne*), *L.* (*Larus*), *O.* (*Onychoprion*), *P.* (*Phaethon*), *S.* (*Sterna*), *Su.* (*Sula*), *T.* (*Thalasseus*).

Marine Protected Area. Milon (1946) found breeding *Phaethon lepturus* on the cliffs of Cap Miné and on all islets of Sakalava Bay and reported that these birds were hunted by local people. The current status of the colony is unknown. Milon (1950) also mentioned a colony of 65 pairs of *Hydroprogne caspia* and 165 pairs of *Thalasseus bergii* breeding between March and June 1947. The current status of this colony is also unknown; if it still exists as it was in 1947 it would be the largest *H. caspia* colony in the western Indian Ocean. Rivo Rabarisoa and colleagues visited the eight islets of Ambodivahibe in June 2012 (Rabarisoa 2018). They found an active colony of 2836 pairs of *T. bergii* on Nosy Bataiza, a small islet 800 m off the coast, and a few pairs of *H. caspia* nesting on the islets. Most pairs were incubating and others had chicks of various ages. They also saw numerous *Rattus rattus*, presumed predators of eggs and chicks. Rabarisoa suggested that the inclusion of these islets within the Ambodivahibe protected area has greatly reduced poaching and was probably beneficial for the local conservation of these species. We are not aware of any further surveys on these islands. The observations made by Milon in 1950 and Rabarisoa in 2012 suggest that March to June is the main breeding season for terns at Ambodivahibe.

Nosy Manampaho: Nosy Manampaho (Nosy Ankao archipelago), of 29 ha (Goodman et al. 2017b), is a well-known *Onychoprion fuscatus* colony, although egg harvest has been recorded here in the past (ZICOMA 2001). Le Corre and Bemanaja surveyed the colony in July 2008; Bemanaja visited again several times in 2012 and 2013, and Le Corre and collaborators in 2018. In July 2008 the only breeding seabird on the island was *Onychoprion fuscatus*, with 21,800 breeding pairs. *Sterna dougallii* (135 birds), *Anous stolidus* and *A. tenuirostris* (Lesser Noddy) (five birds for each species), *Thalasseus bergii* (three birds), and *Hydroprogne caspia* (two birds) were also observed, but no evidence of breeding was found (Le Corre and Bemanaja 2009). At that time the *O. fuscatus* colony was heavily exploited (800–5000 eggs per day during the breeding season; Figures 13.13a and c), but there was some regulation from local villagers: one-third of the surface of the colony was not harvested and the adults were not poached on the entire island. Egg harvest stopped in 2011 and the island is now privately managed and fully protected, although some illegal egg harvest may still occur. In July 2018 (Le Corre et al. 2018), three seabird species were breeding on Nosy Manampaho, including 48,600 pairs of *O. fuscatus*, 500 pairs of *T. bergii*, and 250 pairs of *S. dougallii*. One pair of *H. caspia* was also observed on Nosy Lavahely (a tiny islet just 50 m from Nosy Manampaho). A *Phaethon lepturus* individual was also observed flying above the island, suggesting that the species may be breeding somewhere in the Nosy Ankao archipelago. S. M. Goodman and colleagues (unpublished data) found one pair of *P. lepturus* on Nosy Ratsy, a small islet included in the Nosy Ankao archipelago, in February 2016. The two species of *Anous* use the island as a roosting site, numbering a few hundred individuals of each species (M. Le Corre, unpublished data).

The fact that the *O. fuscatus* colony size doubled in just 10 years and that two other species now breed in numbers on the island is clearly the consequence of conservation actions, with a total ban of egg harvesting. Based on the size of the island and the area of available breeding habitats, the colony would be expected to continue to grow in the future. However, *R. rattus* is present (Goodman et al. 2017b) and likely preys on eggs and chicks, which may impact the

TABLE 13.15. **Breeding seabirds of Madagascar, including most recent estimates of population size and state of knowledge**

SPECIES	NUMBER OF PAIRS	COMMENT	STATE OF KNOWLEDGE
L. dominicanus	"a few"	Very few data, most breeding sites unknown	Low
A. stolidus	200	Possibly extinct	Low
O. fuscatus	56,225	One large colony increasing, otherwise unknown	Good for one large colony
O. anaethetus	630	Some colonies may be reduced or extinct	Low
H. caspia	134	Possibly more	Low
S. dougallii	6100	Some colonies may be reduced or extinct	Low
T. bergii	14,220	Possibly increasing	Good
P. lepturus	30	Several breeding places in the north, none well censused	Low
P. rubricauda	800	Increasing	Very good
Ar. pacifica	125	Probably declining	Low
Fregata spp.	?	Breeding status unknown	Low
Su. leucogaster	250	Possibly increasing	Low
TOTAL	78,649		

Notes: See text for dates. See Table 13.14 for codes to genera.

colony. Despite this threat, Nosy Manampaho currently has the largest breeding seabird populations in Madagascar. All tern species that breed do so in the austral winter. In July–August 2018 the first field course in Madagascar for seabird monitoring was organized on Nosy Manampaho (Figure 13.13i).

3. Nosy Hara Marine National Park and Tanjon' Androntany (Cap Saint Sébastien)

This vast region includes all the islands and islets of the Nosy Hara Marine National Park area and the islets off Cap Androntany, farther west (34 islands and islets in total). Only a few of them have been surveyed for seabird colonies, so the information here is almost certainly incomplete. In particular we know nothing about seabird colonies on the islands and islets off Cap Androntany, although some have been known to host tern colonies in the past. In July 1997 on Nosy Fasy about 600 pairs of *Thalasseus bergii* and 2000 pairs of *Onychoprion fuscatus* were recorded, while on Nosy Foty there were 1500 pairs of *T. bergii*, 30 pairs of *O. fuscatus*, and 50 pairs of *Hydroprogne caspia* (ZICOMA 1999, 2001). Le Corre and Bemanaja surveyed three of the islets of the Nosy Hara protected area in July 2008. They found 10,800 pairs of *T. bergii* actively breeding on Nosy Foty (Figure 13.13g), together with 22 pairs of *H. caspia* and three pairs of *Phaethon lepturus*. Ten pairs of *P. lepturus* and one pair of *H. caspia* were found on Nosy Vaha, and two pairs of *P. lepturus* and one pair of *H. caspia* on Nosy Bamaho (Le Corre and Bemanaja 2009).

As far as we know, no other islands of this area have recently been surveyed for seabird colonies. Most of the islands of the Nosy Hara archipelago and the islets off Tonjon' Androntany are uninhabited, and some are notably distant from the coast (especially Nosy Faty, at around 25 km), which ensures some protection against poaching and egg harvest. The numbers found in 2008 made the *T. bergii* colony on Nosy Foty the largest in the entire Indian Ocean (Le Corre and Bemanaja 2009) (Figure 13.13g). Although there was historically large-scale egg harvest throughout the archipelago, it seems that this stopped after the creation of the Nosy Hara Marine National Park in 2001. Bemanaja visited Nosy Foty in 2012 and 2013 and found *T. bergii* (4140 pairs in 2012, 300 pairs in 2013), *H. caspia* (six pairs), and *P. lepturus* (four pairs), as well as a small colony of 30 pairs of *O. anaethetus* (Bridled Tern) in 2013 (Bemanaja 2013). He suggested that the interannual variation in numbers of *T. bergii* may be caused by terns changing their breeding sites within the Nosy Hara protected area from one year to another; in 2013, most of the terns were on Nosy Vaha, according to the protected area staff. *Rattus rattus* is very abundant on all visited islands and likely has a negative impact on eggs and chicks. As for other tern colonies, the main breeding season for *T. bergii* on Nosy Hara is austral winter.

4. Nosy Mitsio and Surroundings

This archipelago includes a large, inhabited island and several small islands and islets, some of which are uninhabited. Among these, the Quatre Frères are four small dome-shaped rocky islets (Figures 13.14a and b). The Quatre Frères hold the larger of the two breeding colonies of *Sula leucogaster* (Brown Booby) in Madagascar (Figure 13.14c). Polunin (1979) found 250 breeding pairs in the 1970s, and the population was thought to have increased by 1997 (ZICOMA 2001), although no complete census has been conducted recently. The Quatre Frères also host a large nonbreeding roost of *Fregata minor* (Great Frigatebird) and *F. ariel* (Lesser Frigatebird) (Langrand 1990). It has been suggested that 50 to 100 pairs of frigatebirds may breed on one of the Quatre Frères islets (ZICOMA

FIGURE 13.12 **Location of the nine main seabird breeding colonies (discussed in detail in the text), and Important Bird and Biodiversity Areas (IBAs) relevant to this contribution (i.e., marine IBA, seabird IBA, or IBA located near main seabird breeding colony). See Table 13.14 for further species details.**

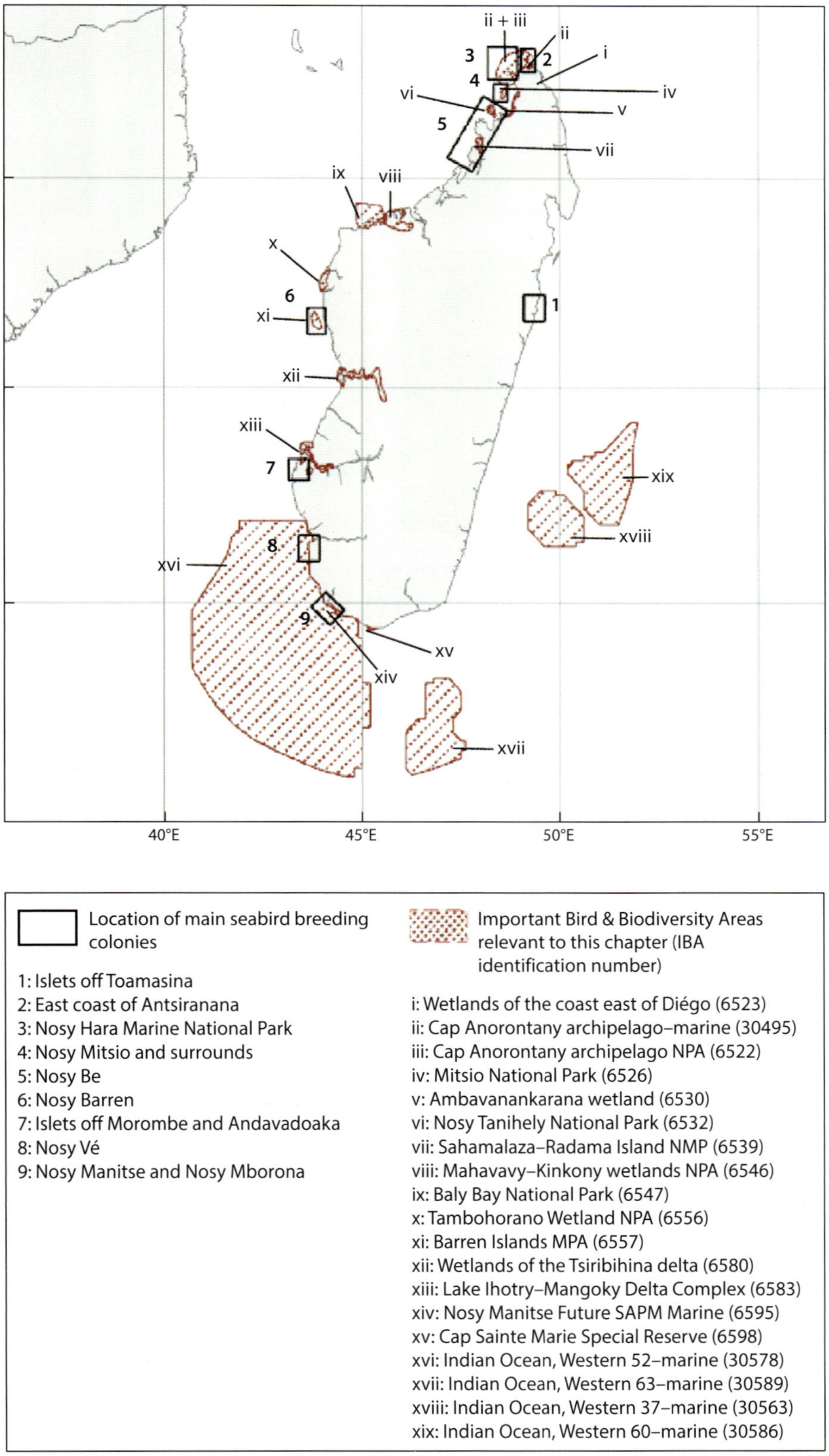

2001), but no clear evidence of breeding has been found, and recent tracking studies have shown that the *F. minor* roosting in the Nosy Mitsio archipelago breed on Europa Atoll, 1345 km farther south in the Mozambique Channel (Weimerskirch et al. 2017). Boobies and frigatebirds are still regularly observed in large numbers by sailors visiting the archipelago (Figures 13.14e and f), but no survey has recently been carried out and the number of breeding seabirds is unknown. The archipelago also holds breeding *Phaethon lepturus* (ZICOMA 2001).

The Quatre Frères are naturally protected by their cliffs, which drop vertically into the sea and make access difficult. Most of the nests, particularly those of the boobies, are located on the cliffs.

FIGURE 13.13 Different aspects of seabirds in Malagasy waters. A) Egg harvest on Nosy Manampaho, July 2008. B) *Onychoprion fuscatus* (Sooty Tern) hunted at Nosimborona, September 2006. C) Egg harvest at Nosy Manampaho, July 2008; each stack of eggs represents a day's harvest. D) Hunters of *Ardenna pacifica* (Wedge-tailed Shearwater) preparing their snares at Nosy Anjamanjiky Bé, April 2008. E) An adult *A. pacifica* walking near a series of snares, Nosy Anjamanjiky Bé, April 2008. F) A woman selling a trapped *A. pacifica* in a market near Morombe, April 2008. G) *Thalasseus bergii* (Great Crested Tern) colony at Nosy Foty, Nosy Hara protected area, July 2008. H) A displaying adult *Phaethon rubricauda* (Red-tailed Tropicbird), Nosy Vé, July 2011. I) Training course on seabird monitoring at Nosy Manampaho, July 2018. J) Ecotourists visiting Nosy Vé, July 2011. K) "Circuit paille en queue" (Tropicbird Trail) on Nosy Vé, July 2011. (PHOTOS A, H, and J by F. Henze; B and D–F by E. Bemanaja; C, G, and K by M. Le Corre; and I by C. Caumes.)